**SYMBIOSIS**

THE PEARSON CUSTOM LIBRARY FOR THE
# BIOLOGICAL SCIENCES

**PEARSON**

*Cover Art:* Courtesy of Michael R. Martin, Darryl Johnson, Photodisk, DK Images, Photodisc/Getty Images, and Prentice-Hall, Inc. "TEM of Gardnerella vaginalis bacteria" courtesy of Alloy Photography/Veer; "Bacterium background" Courtesy of Fedorov Oleksiy/Shutterstock; "Silhouette of a lizard on a leaf back lit by sunlight" courtesy of Santhosh Kumar/Veer; "Frog on leaf" courtesy of Kerstin Klaassen/iStockphoto; "Baby feet" courtesy of igabriela/Veer; "Mother Giraffe and Youngster" courtesy of Peter Malsbury/iStockphoto.

This special edition published in cooperation with Pearson Learning Solutions.

Please visit our website at *www.pearsonlearningsolutions.com*.

Attention bookstores: For permission to return unused stock, contact us at *pe-uscustomreturns@pearson.com*.

Pearson Learning Solutions, 501 Boylston Street, Suite 900, Boston, MA 02116
A Pearson Education Company
www.pearsoned.com

Printed in the United States of America.
V0UD

ISBN 10: 0-558-54167-4
ISBN 13: 978-0-558-54167-5

# Laboratory Safety:
# General Guidelines

1. Notify your instructor immediately if you are pregnant, color blind, allergic to any insects or chemicals, taking immunosuppressive drugs, or have any other medical condition (such as diabetes, immunologic defect) that may require special precautionary measures in the laboratory.

2. Upon entering the laboratory, place all books, coats, purses, backpacks, etc. in designated areas, not on the bench tops.

3. Locate and, when appropriate, learn to use exits, fire extinguisher, fire blanket, chemical shower, eyewash, first aid kit, broken glass container, and cleanup materials for spills.

4. In case of fire, evacuate the room and assemble outside the building.

5. Do not eat, drink, smoke, or apply cosmetics in the laboratory.

6. Confine long hair, loose clothing, and dangling jewelry.

7. Wear shoes at all times in the laboratory.

8. Cover any cuts or scrapes with a sterile, waterproof bandage before attending lab.

9. Wear eye protection when working with chemicals.

10. Never pipet by mouth. Use mechanical pipeting devices.

11. Wash skin immediately and thoroughly if contaminated by chemicals or microorganisms.

12. Do not perform unauthorized experiments.

13. Do not use equipment without instruction.

14. Report all spills and accidents to your instructor immediately.

15. Never leave heat sources unattended.

16. When using hot plates, note that there is no visible sign that they are hot (such as a red glow). Always assume that hot plates are hot.

17. Use an appropriate apparatus when handling hot glassware.

18. Keep chemicals away from direct heat or sunlight.

19. Keep containers of alcohol, acetone, and other flammable liquids away from flames.

20. Do not allow any liquid to come into contact with electrical cords. Handle electrical connectors with dry hands. Do not attempt to disconnect electrical equipment that crackles, snaps, or smokes.

21. Upon completion of laboratory exercises, place all materials in the disposal areas designated by your instructor.

22. Do not pick up broken glassware with your hands. Use a broom and dustpan and discard the glass in designated glass waste containers; never discard with paper waste.

23. Wear disposable gloves when working with blood, other body fluids, or mucous membranes. Change gloves after possible contamination and wash hands immediately after gloves are removed.

24. The disposal symbol indicates that items that may have come in contact with body fluids should be placed in your lab's designated container. It also refers to liquid wastes that should not be poured down the drain into the sewage system.

25. Leave the laboratory clean and organized for the next student.

26. Wash your hands with liquid or powdered soap prior to leaving the laboratory.

27. The biohazard symbol indicates procedures that may pose health concerns.

The caution symbol points out instruments, substances, and procedures that require special attention to safety. These symbols appear throughout this manual.

# Measurement Conversions

| Metric to American Standard | American Standard to Metric |
|---|---|

## Length

| | |
|---|---|
| 1 mm = 0.039 inches | 1 inch = 2.54 cm |
| 1 cm = 0.394 inches | 1 foot = 0.305 m |
| 1 m = 3.28 feet | 1 yard = 0.914 m |
| 1 m = 1.09 yards | 1 mile = 1.61 km |

## Volume

| | |
|---|---|
| 1 mL = 0.0338 fluid ounces | 1 fluid ounce = 29.6 mL |
| 1 L = 4.23 cups | 1 cup = 237 mL |
| 1 L = 2.11 pints | 1 pint = 0.474 L |
| 1 L = 1.06 quarts | 1 quart = 0.947 L |
| 1 L = 0.264 gallons | 1 gallon = 3.79 L |

## Mass

| | |
|---|---|
| 1 mg = 0.0000353 ounces | 1 ounce = 28.3 g |
| 1 g = 0.0353 ounces | 1 pound = 0.454 kg |
| 1 kg = 2.21 pounds | |

## Temperature

To convert temperature:

$$°C = \frac{5}{9}(F - 32) \qquad °F = \frac{9}{5} + 32$$

# Table of Contents

# Cell Structure and Function

From Chapter 3 of *Microbiology with Diseases by Taxonomy*, Third Edition. Robert W. Bauman. Copyright © 2011 by Pearson Education, Inc. Published by Benjamin Cummings, Inc. All rights reserved.

# Cell Structure and Function

Can a microbe be a magnet? The answer is yes, if it is a **magnetobacterium**.

Magnetobacteria are microorganisms with an unusual feature: cellular structures called *magnetosomes*. Magnetosomes are stored deposits (also called **inclusions**) of the mineral magnetite. These deposits align magnetobacteria with the lines of the Earth's magnetic field, much like a compass. In the Southern Hemisphere, magnetobacteria exist as south-seeking varieties; in the Northern Hemisphere, they exist as **north-seeking** varieties.

How do these bacteria benefit from magnetosomes? Magnetobacteria prefer environments with little or no oxygen, such as those that exist below the surfaces of land and sea. The magnetosomes point toward the **underground** magnetic poles, helping magnetobacteria move toward regions with optimal oxygen content.

 Take the pre-test for this chapter online. Visit the Study Area at www.masteringmicrobiology.com.

Haixin Sui and Kenneth Downing/Lawrence Berkeley National Laboratory

▲ *Aquaspirillum magnetotacticum*, a spiral-shaped magnetobacterium, contains a clearly visible magnetosome composed of tiny square inclusions of magnetite.

All living things—including our bodies and the bacterial, protozoan, and fungal pathogens that attack us—are composed of living cells. If we want to understand disease and its treatment, therefore, we must first understand the life of cells. How pathogens attack our cells, how our bodies defend themselves, how current medical treatments assist our bodies in recovering—all of these activities have their basis in the biology of our, and our pathogens', cells.

In this chapter, we will examine cells and the structures within cells. We will discuss similarities and differences between the three major kinds of cells—bacterial, archaeal, and eukaryotic. The differences are particularly important because they allow researchers to develop treatments that inhibit or kill pathogens without adversely affecting a patient's own cells. We will also learn about cellular structures that allow pathogens to evade the body's defenses and cause disease.

# Processes of Life

## Learning Objective

✓ Describe four major processes of living cells.

Microbiology is the study of particularly small living things. What we have not yet discussed is the question of how we define life. Scientists once thought that living things were composed of special organic chemicals, such as glucose and amino acids, that carried a "life force" found only in living organisms. These organic chemicals were thought to be formed only by living things and to be very different from the inorganic chemicals of nonliving things.

The idea that organic chemicals could come only from living organisms had to be abandoned in 1828, when Friedrich Wöhler (1800–1882) synthesized urea, an organic molecule, using only inorganic reactants in his laboratory. Today we know that all living things contain both organic and inorganic chemicals, and that many organic chemicals can be made from inorganic chemicals by laboratory processes. If organic chemicals can be made even in the absence of life, what is the difference between a living thing and a nonliving thing? What is life?

At first this may seem a simple question. After all, you can usually tell when something is alive. However, defining "life" itself is difficult, so biologists generally avoid setting a definition, preferring instead to describe characteristics common to all living things. Biologists agree that all living things share at least four processes of life: growth, reproduction, responsiveness, and metabolism.

- **Growth.** Living things can grow; that is, they can increase in size.
- **Reproduction.** Organisms normally have the ability to reproduce themselves. Reproduction means that they increase in number, producing more organisms organized like themselves. Reproduction may be accomplished asexually (alone) or sexually with gametes (sex cells). Note that reproduction is an increase in number, whereas growth is an increase in size. Growth and reproduction often occur simultaneously.
- **Responsiveness.** All living things respond to their environment. They have the ability to change internal and/or external properties in reaction to changing conditions around or within them. Many organisms also have the ability to move toward or away from environmental stimuli—a response called *taxis*.
- **Metabolism.** Metabolism can be defined as the ability of organisms to take in nutrients from outside themselves and use the nutrients in a series of controlled chemical reactions to provide the energy and structures needed to grow, reproduce, and be responsive. Metabolism is a unique process of living things; nonliving things cannot metabolize. Cells store metabolic energy in the chemical bonds of *adenosine triphosphate* (ă-den'ō-sēn trī-fos'fāt), or *ATP*.

Table 1 shows how these characteristics, along with cell structure, relate to various kinds of microbes.

Organisms may not exhibit these processes at all times. For instance, in some organisms, reproduction may be postponed or curtailed by age or disease, or in humans at least, by choice.

**TABLE 1**

## Characteristics of Life and Their Distribution in Microbes

| Characteristic | Bacteria, Archaea, Eukaryotes | Viruses |
|---|---|---|
| **Growth:** increase in size | Occurs in all | Does not occur |
| **Reproduction:** increase in number | Occurs in all | Host cell replicates the virus |
| **Responsiveness:** ability to react to environmental stimuli | Occurs in all | Reaction to host cells seen in some viruses |
| **Metabolism:** controlled chemical reactions of organisms | Occurs in all | Uses host cell's metabolism |
| **Cellular structure:** membrane-bound structure capable of all of the above functions | Present in all | Lacks cytoplasmic membrane or cellular structure |

## IT'S ALIVE!? . . . MAYBE.

An ongoing discussion in microbiology concerns the nature of viruses. Are they alive?

Viruses are noncellular; that is, they lack cell membranes, cell walls, and most other cellular components. However, they do contain genetic material in the form of either DNA or RNA. (Few viruses have both DNA and RNA.) While many viruses use DNA molecules for their genes, others such as HIV and poliovirus use RNA for genes

instead of DNA. No cells use RNA molecules for their genes.

However, viruses have some characteristics of living cells. For instance, some demonstrate responsiveness to their environment, as when they inject their genetic material into susceptible host cells. Nevertheless, viruses lack most characteristics of life: they are unable to grow, reproduce, or metabolize outside of a host cell, although once they enter a cell they take control of the cell's

▲ *Influenzaviruses.* TEM  |——| 100 nm

metabolism and cause it to make more viruses. This takeover typically leads to the death of the cell and results in disease in an organism.

Likewise, the rate of metabolism may be reduced, as occurs in a seed, a hibernating animal, or a bacterial endospore,[1] and growth often stops when an animal reaches a certain size. However, microorganisms typically grow, reproduce, respond, and metabolize as long as conditions are suitable.

A group of pathogens essential to the debate regarding "What constitutes life?" are the viruses. **Highlight: It's Alive!? . . . Maybe** discusses whether viruses should be considered living things.

## Prokaryotic and Eukaryotic Cells: An Overview

### Learning Objective

✓ Compare and contrast prokaryotic and eukaryotic cells.

In the 1800s, two German biologists, Theodor Schwann (1810–1882) and Matthias Schleiden (1804–1881) developed the theory that all living things are composed of cells. *Cells* are living entities, surrounded by a membrane, that are capable of growing, reproducing, responding, and metabolizing. The smallest living things are single-celled microorganisms.

There are many different kinds of cells (Figure 1). Some cells are free-living, independent organisms; others live together in colonies or form the bodies of multicellular organisms. Cells also exist in various sizes, from the smallest bacteria to bird eggs, which are the largest of cells. All cells may be described as either *prokaryotes* (prō-kar'ē-ōts) or *eukaryotes* (yū-kar'ē-ōts).

Scientists categorize organisms based on shared characteristics into groups called *taxa*. "Prokaryotic" is a characteristic of organisms in two taxa—*Domain Archaea* and *Domain Bacteria*—but "prokaryote" itself is not a taxon. The distinctive feature of **prokaryotes** is that they can make proteins simultaneously to

reading the genetic code because the typical prokaryote does not have a membrane surrounding its genetic material (DNA). In other words, a typical prokaryote does not have a nucleus (Figure 2). (Researchers have discovered a few prokaryotes with internal membranes that look like nuclei, but further investigation is needed to determine what these structures are.) The word *prokaryote* comes from Greek words meaning "before nucleus." Moreover, electron microscopy has revealed that prokaryotes typically lack various types of internal structures bound with phospholipid membranes that are present in eukaryotic cells.

Bacteria and archaea differ fundamentally in such ways as the type of lipids in their cytoplasmic membranes, and in the chemistry of their cell walls. In many ways, archaea are more like eukaryotes than they are like bacteria.

**Eukaryotes** have a membrane surrounding their DNA, forming a nucleus (Figure 3), which sets eukaryotes in *Domain Eukarya*. Indeed, the term *eukaryote* comes from Greek words meaning "true nucleus." Besides the nuclear membrane, eukaryotes have numerous other internal membranes that compartmentalize cellular functions. These compartments are membrane-bound **organelles**—specialized structures that act like tiny organs to carry on the various functions of the cell. Organelles and their functions are discussed later in this chapter. The cells of algae, protozoa, fungi, animals, and plants are eukaryotic. Eukaryotes are usually larger and more complex than prokaryotes, which are typically 1.0 μm in diameter or smaller, as compared to 10–100 μm for eukaryotic cells (Figure 4). (See **Highlight: Giant Bacteria** for some interesting exceptions concerning the size of prokaryotes.)

Although there are many kinds of cells, they all share the characteristic processes of life as previously described, as well as certain physical features. In this chapter, we will distinguish between bacterial, archaeal, and eukaryotic "versions" of physical features common to cells, including (1) external structures, (2) the cell wall, (3) the cytoplasmic membrane, and (4) the cytoplasm. We will also discuss features unique to each type.

Next, we explore characteristics of bacterial cells beginning with external features and working into the cell.

---

[1]Endospores are resting stages, produced by some bacteria, that are tolerant of environmental extremes.

▶ **Figure 1** **Examples of types of cells.** **(a)** *Escherichia coli* bacterial cells. **(b)** A neutrophil, a defensive white blood cell, amidst human red blood cells. **(c)** *Paramecium*, a single-celled eukaryote. **(d)** *Volvox*, a colonial, photosynthetic eukaryote composed of numerous small cells and daughter colonies. Note the differences in magnification.

Gopal Murti/Photo Researchers

Michael Ross/Photo Researchers

Neutrophil

Red blood cell

**(a)** SEM  2 µm

**(b)** LM  10 µm

Steve Gschmeissner/Photo Researchers, Inc.

Stephen Durr

**(c)** SEM  50 µm

**(d)** LM  2 mm

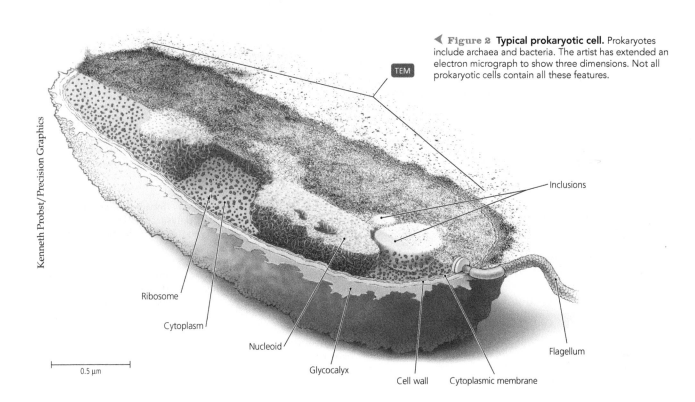

Kenneth Probst/Precision Graphics

◀ **Figure 2** **Typical prokaryotic cell.** Prokaryotes include archaea and bacteria. The artist has extended an electron micrograph to show three dimensions. Not all prokaryotic cells contain all these features.

TEM

Inclusions

Ribosome

Cytoplasm

Nucleoid

Glycocalyx

Cell wall

Cytoplasmic membrane

Flagellum

0.5 µm

5

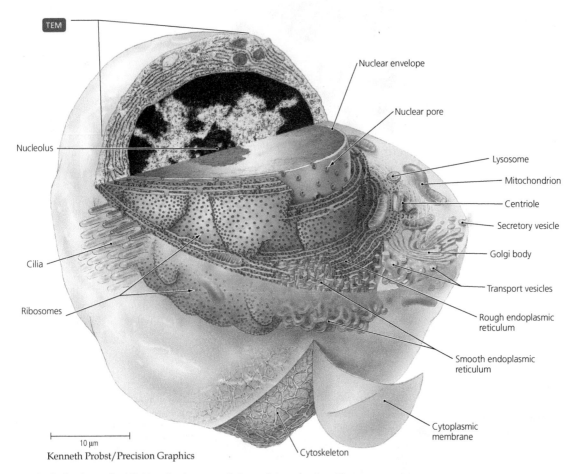

**▲ Figure 3 Typical eukaryotic cell.** Not all eukaryotic cells have all these features. The artist has extended the electron micrograph to show three dimensions. Note the difference in magnification between this cell and the prokaryotic cell in the previous figure. *Besides size, what major difference between prokaryotes and eukaryotes was visible to early microscopists?*

*Figure 3 Eukaryotic cells contain nuclei, which are visible with light microscopes, whereas prokaryotes lack nuclei.*

# External Structures of Bacterial Cells

Many cells have special external features that enable them to respond to other cells and their environment. In bacteria, these features include glycocalyces, flagella, fimbriae, and pili.

## Glycocalyces

### Learning Objective

✓ Describe the composition, function, and relevance to human health of glycocalyces.

✓ Distinguish between capsules and slime layers.

Some cells have a gelatinous, sticky substance that surrounds the outside of the cell. This substance is known as a **glycocalyx** (plural: *glycocalyces*), which literally means "sugar cup." The glycocalyx may be composed of polysaccharides, polypeptides, or both. These chemicals are produced inside the cell and extruded onto the cell's surface.

When the glycocalyx of a bacterium is composed of organized repeating units of organic chemicals firmly attached to the cell surface, the glycocalyx is called a **capsule** (Figure 5a). A loose, water-soluble glycocalyx is called a **slime layer** (Figure 5b). Capsules and slime layers protect cells from desiccation (drying).

The presence of a glycocalyx is a feature of numerous pathogenic bacteria. Their glycocalyces play an important role in the ability of these cells both to survive and to cause disease. Slime layers are often *viscous* (sticky), providing one means by which bacteria attach to surfaces. For example, they enable oral bacteria to colonize the teeth, where they produce acid and cause

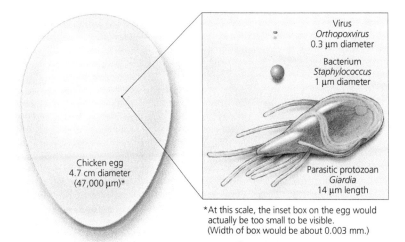

Virus
*Orthopoxvirus*
0.3 μm diameter

Bacterium
*Staphylococcus*
1 μm diameter

Chicken egg
4.7 cm diameter
(47,000 μm)*

Parasitic protozoan
*Giardia*
14 μm length

*At this scale, the inset box on the egg would actually be too small to be visible. (Width of box would be about 0.003 mm.)

Darwen Hennings/Kenneth Probst/Precision Graphics

decay. Since the chemicals in many capsules are similar to those normally found in the body, they may prevent bacteria from being recognized or devoured by defensive cells of the host. For example, the capsules of *Streptococcus pneumoniae* (strep-tō-kok'ūs nū-mō'nē-ī) and *Klebsiella pneumoniae* (kleb-sē-el'ă nū-mō'nē-ī) enable these prokaryotes to avoid destruction by defensive cells in the respiratory tract and cause pneumonia. Unencapsulated strains of these same bacterial species do not cause disease because the body's defensive cells destroy them.

## Flagella

### Learning Objectives

✓ Discuss the structure and function of bacterial flagella.

✓ List and describe four bacterial flagellar arrangements.

A cell's motility may enable it to flee from a harmful environment or move toward a favorable environment such as one where food or light is available. The most notable structures responsible for such bacterial movement are flagella. **Flagella** (singular: *flagellum*) are long structures that extend beyond the surface of a cell and its glycocalyx and propel the cell through its environment. Not all bacteria have flagella, but for those that do, the flagella are very similar in composition, structure, and development. **ANIMATIONS:** *Motility*

### Structure

Bacterial flagella are composed of three parts: a long, thin *filament*, a *hook*, and a *basal body* (Figure 6). The hollow filament is a long hollow shaft, about 20 nm in diameter, that extends out

**Figure 5 Glycocalyces. (a)** Micrograph of *Streptococcus pneumoniae*, the common cause of pneumonia, showing a prominent capsule. **(b)** *Bacteroides*, a common fecal bacterium, has a slime layer surrounding the cell. *What advantage does a glycocalyx provide a cell?*

*Figure 5 A glycocalyx provides protection from drying and from being devoured; it may also help attach cells to one another and to surfaces in the environment.*

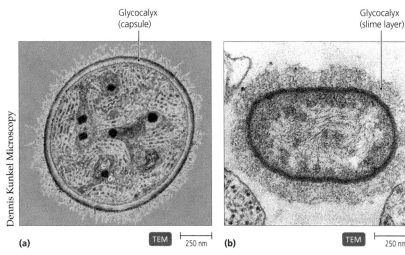

Glycocalyx
(capsule)

Glycocalyx
(slime layer)

Dennis Kunkel Microscopy

Bergey's Manual Trust, Michigan State University

**(a)** TEM 250 nm **(b)** TEM 250 nm

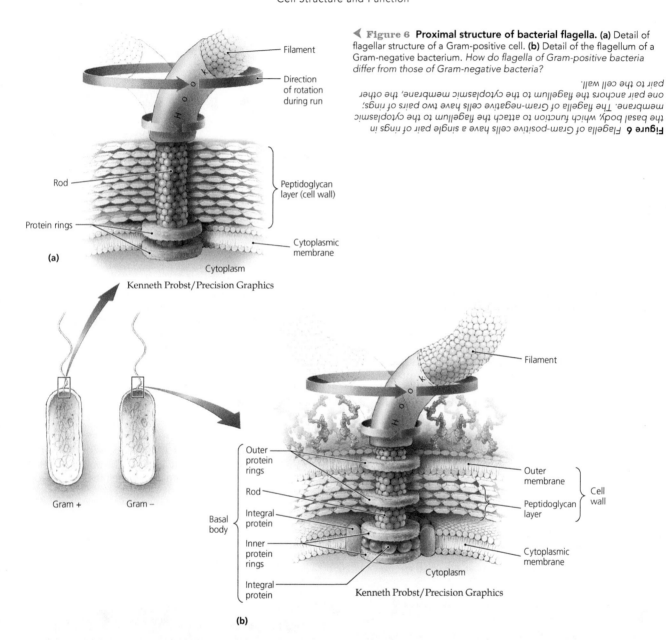

**◀ Figure 6 Proximal structure of bacterial flagella. (a)** Detail of flagellar structure of a Gram-positive cell. **(b)** Detail of the flagellum of a Gram-negative bacterium. *How do flagella of Gram-positive bacteria differ from those of Gram-negative bacteria?*

*Figure 6 Flagella of Gram-positive cells have a single pair of rings in the basal body, which function to attach the flagellum to the cytoplasmic membrane. The flagella of Gram-negative cells have two pairs of rings; one pair anchors the flagellum to the cytoplasmic membrane, the other pair to the cell wall.*

Labels in figure (a): Filament; Direction of rotation during run; Rod; Peptidoglycan layer (cell wall); Protein rings; Cytoplasmic membrane; Cytoplasm; (a); Kenneth Probst/Precision Graphics; HOOK

Labels in figure (b): Gram +; Gram –; Filament; Outer protein rings; Rod; Integral protein; Inner protein rings; Integral protein; Basal body; Outer membrane; Peptidoglycan layer; Cell wall; Cytoplasmic membrane; Cytoplasm; Kenneth Probst/Precision Graphics; (b); HOOK

into the cell's environment. It is composed of many identical globular molecules of a protein called *flagellin.* The cell extrudes molecules of flagellin through the hollow core of the flagellum to be deposited in a clockwise helix at the lengthening tip. Bacterial flagella sense external wetness, inhibiting their own growth in dry habitats.

No membrane covers the filament of bacterial flagella. At its base a filament inserts into a curved structure, the hook, which is composed of a different protein. The basal body, which is composed of still different proteins, anchors the filament and hook to the cell wall and cytoplasmic membrane by means of a rod and a series of either two or four rings of integral proteins. Together the hook, rod, and rings allow the filament to rotate 360°. Differences in the proteins associated with bacterial flagella vary enough to allow classification of species into groups (strains) called *serovars.* **ANIMATIONS:** *Flagella: Structure*

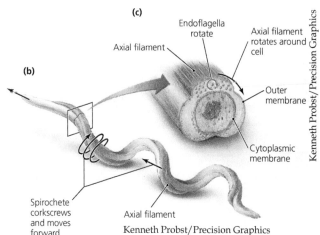

**(a)** SEM 1 μm

**(b)** SEM 0.7 μm

**(c)** SEM 0.5 μm

A. Barry Dowsett/Photo Researchers

Dennis Kunkel Microscopy

The American Phytopathological Society

▲ **Figure 7 Micrographs of basic arrangements of bacterial flagella. (a)** Peritrichous. **(b)** Single polar flagellum. **(c)** Tuft of polar flagella.

## Arrangement

Bacteria may have one of several flagellar arrangements (Figure 7). Flagella that cover the surface of the cell are termed **peritrichous;**[2] in contrast, **polar** flagella are only at the ends. Some cells have tufts of polar flagella.

Some spiral-shaped bacteria, called *spirochetes* (spī'rō-kēts),[3] have flagella at both ends that spiral tightly around the cell instead of protruding into the surrounding medium. These flagella, called **endoflagella,** form an **axial filament** that wraps around the cell between its cytoplasmic membrane and an outer membrane (Figure 8). Rotation of endoflagella evidently causes the axial filament to rotate around the cell, causing the spirochete to

[2]From Greek *peri*, meaning around, and *trichos*, meaning a hair.
[3]From Greek *speira*, meaning coil, and *chaeta*, meaning hair.

Bill Schwartz, CDC

**(a)** SEM 5 μm

Kenneth Probst/Precision Graphics

**(c)**

Endoflagella rotate

Axial filament

Axial filament rotates around cell

Outer membrane

Cytoplasmic membrane

**(b)**

Spirochete corkscrews and moves forward

Axial filament

Kenneth Probst/Precision Graphics

▲ **Figure 8 Axial filament. (a)** Scanning electron micrograph of spirochetes, *Treponema pallidum*. **(b)** Diagram of axial filament wrapped around a spirochete. **(c)** Cross section of the spirochete, which reveals that the axial filament is composed of endoflagella.

"corkscrew" through its medium. *Treponema pallidum* (trep-ō-nē'mă pal'li-dŭm), the agent of syphilis, and *Borrelia burgdorferi* (bō-rē'lē-ă burg-dōr'fer-ē), the cause of Lyme disease, are notable spirochetes. Some scientists think the corkscrew motility of these pathogens allows them to invade human tissues. **ANIMATIONS:** *Flagella: Arrangement; Spirochetes*

## Function

Although the precise mechanism by which bacterial flagella move is not completely understood, we do know that they rotate 360° like boat propellers rather than whipping from side to side. The flow of hydrogen ions ($H^+$) or of sodium ions ($Na^+$) through the cytoplasmic membrane near the basal body powers the rotation, propelling the bacterium through the environment at about 60 cell lengths per second—equivalent to a car traveling at 670 miles per hour! Flagella rotate at more than 100,000 rpm and can change direction from counterclockwise to clockwise.

Bacteria move with a series of "runs" punctuated by "tumbles." Counterclockwise flagellar rotation produces runs, which are movements of a cell in a single direction for some time. If more than one flagellum is present, the flagella align and rotate

## GIANT BACTERIA

Most prokaryotes are small compared to eukaryotes. The dimensions of a typical bacterial cell—for example, a cell of *Escherichia coli*—are 1.0 μm × 2.0 μm. Typical eukaryotic cells are often tens of micrometers in diameter.

For many years biologists thought that the small size of prokaryotes was a necessary result of the nature of their cells. Without internal compartments, prokaryotes that were as large as eukaryotes could not isolate and control the metabolic reactions of life; nor could they efficiently distribute nutrients and eliminate wastes.

However, scientists have located a new unicellular organism from the intestines of a surgeonfish. Its cells are 0.6 mm (600 μm) long, a size visible to the unaided eye. Microscopic examination reveals the presence of a fine covering of what appear to be cilia, which are a feature of eukaryotic cells

only. The new organism is named *Epulopiscium fishelsoni*,[a] but a surprise came when these cells were examined with an electron microscope. They contained no nuclei or other eukaryotic organelles, and the "cilia" more closely resembled short bacterial flagella. *Epulopiscium*, as it turned out, is indeed a giant prokaryote. (Compare the size of *Epulopiscium* with that of *Paramecium*, a eukaryote, in the box photo.)

It is not, however, the largest prokaryote. In 1997, a German microbiologist discovered an even larger bacterium, named *Thiomargarita namibiensis*,[b] which lives in chains of 2–50 cells in ocean sediments off the coast of Namibia, Africa. The spherical cells of *Thiomargarita* can grow to 750 μm in diameter, or about the size of the period at the end of this sentence. Such large cells have volumes over 66 times those of the largest *Epulopiscium*.

*Paramecium   Epulopiscium fishelsoni*

Esther R. Angert

LM   100 μm

If a single cell of *Thiomargarita* were the size of an African elephant, then *Epulopiscium* would be the size of a cow, *Paramecium* would be the size of an adult Labrador retriever, and *Escherichia* would be the size of an ant.

_____

[a]*Epulopiscium* in Latin means "guest at a banquet of fish."
[b]This name means "sulfur pearl of Namibia," because granules of sulfur stored in the cytoplasm cause the cells to glisten white, like a string of pearls.

---

together as a bundle. Tumbles are abrupt, random changes in direction resulting from clockwise flagellar rotation where each flagellum rotates independently. Both runs and tumbles occur in response to stimuli.

Receptors for light or chemicals on the surface of the cell send signals to the flagella, which then adjust their speed and direction of rotation. A bacterium can position itself in a more favorable environment by varying the number and duration of runs and tumbles. The presence of favorable stimuli increases

the number of runs and decreases the number of tumbles; as a result, the cell tends to move toward an attractant (Figure 9). Unfavorable stimuli increase the number of tumbles, which increases the likelihood that it will move randomly in another direction, away from a repellant.

Movement in response to a stimulus is termed **taxis**. The stimulus may be either light (**phototaxis**) or a chemical (**chemotaxis**). Movement toward a favorable stimulus is *positive taxis*, whereas movement away from an unfavorable stimulus is

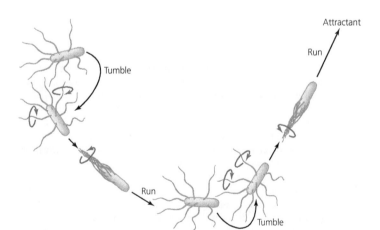

Tumble

Run

Tumble

Precision Graphics

Attractant

Run

◀ **Figure 9  Motion of a peritrichous bacterium.** In peritrichous bacteria, runs occur when all of the flagella rotate counterclockwise and become bundled. Tumbles occur when the flagella rotate clockwise, become unbundled, and the cell spins randomly. In positive chemotaxis (shown), runs last longer than tumbles, resulting in motion toward the chemical attractant. *What triggers a bacterial flagellum to rotate counterclockwise, producing a run?*

**Figure 9** *Favorable environmental conditions induce runs.*

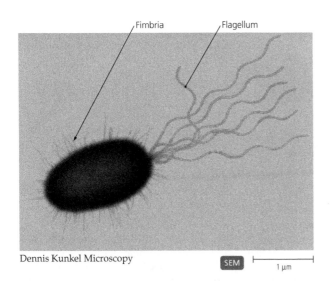

Dennis Kunkel Microscopy

SEM ⊢——⊣ 1 μm

▲ **Figure 10 Fimbriae.** *Pseudomonas aeruginosa* has fimbriae and flagella.

Linda Stannard, UCT/Photo Researchers

TEM ⊢——⊣ 0.5 μm

▲ **Figure 11 Pili.** Several *Escherichia coli* cells are connected by conjugation pili. *How are pili different from bacterial flagella?*

Figure 11 *Bacterial flagella are flexible structures that rotate to propel the cell; pili are hollow tubes that mediate transfer of DNA from one cell to another.*

*negative taxis.* For example, movement toward a nutrient would be *positive chemotaxis.* **ANIMATIONS:** *Flagella: Movement*

## Fimbriae and Pili

### Learning Objective

✓ Compare and contrast the structures and functions of fimbriae, pili, and flagella.

Some bacteria have rodlike proteinaceous extensions called fimbriae and pili. Bacteria use **fimbriae** (fim′brē-ē)—sticky, bristle-like projections—to adhere to one another and to substances in the environment. There may be hundreds of fimbriae per cell, and they are usually shorter than flagella (Figure 10). An example of a bacterium with fimbriae is *Neisseria gonorrhoeae* (nī-se′rē-ă go-nor-rē′ī), which causes gonorrhea. Such pathogens must be able to adhere to their hosts if they are to survive and cause disease. This bacterium is able to colonize the mucous membrane of the reproductive tract by attaching with fimbriae. *Neisseria* cells that lack fimbriae are nonpathogenic.

Bacteria may use fimbriae to move across a substrate or toward another bacterium via a process similar to pulling an object with a rope. The bacterium extrudes a fimbria, which attaches to the substrate or to another bacterium; then the bacterium retracts the fimbria, pulling itself toward the attachment point.

Fimbriae also serve an important function in **biofilms,** slimy masses of microbes adhering to a substrate by means of fimbriae and glycocalyces. Some fimbriae act as electrical wires, conducting electrical signals among cells in a biofilm. It has been estimated that at least 99% of bacteria in nature exist in biofilms. Researchers are interested in biofilms because of the roles they play in human diseases and in industry. (See **Highlight: Biofilms: Slime Matters.**)

**Pili** (pī′lī; singular: *pilus*), which are also called *conjugation pili,* are tubules composed of a protein called *pilin.* Pili are longer than fimbriae, but usually shorter than flagella. Typically only one to a few pili are present per cell in bacteria that have them. Conjugation pili mediate the transfer of DNA from one cell to the other via a process termed *conjugation* (Figure 11).

## Bacterial Cell Walls

### Learning Objectives

✓ Describe common shapes and arrangements of bacterial cells.

✓ Describe the sugar and peptide portions of peptidoglycan.

✓ Compare and contrast the cell walls of Gram-positive and Gram-negative bacteria in terms of structure and Gram staining.

The cells of most prokaryotes are surrounded by a **cell wall** that provides structure and shape to the cell and protects it from osmotic forces. In addition, a cell wall assists some cells in attaching to other cells or in resisting antimicrobial drugs. Note that animal cells do not have walls, a difference that plays a key role in treatment of many bacterial diseases with certain types of antibiotics. For example, penicillin attacks the cell wall of bacteria but is harmless to human cells, which lack walls.

(a)　　　　　(b)

◀ **Figure 12 Bacterial shapes and arrangements.**
**(a)** Spherical cocci may be in arrangements such as single, chains (streptococci), clusters (staphylococci), and cuboidal packets.
**(b)** Rod-shaped bacilli may also be single or in arrangements such as chains.

Cell walls give bacterial cells characteristic shapes. Spherical cells, called cocci (kok'sī), may appear in various arrangements, including singly or in chains (streptococci), clusters (staphylococci), or cuboidal packets (sarcinae, sar'si-nī) (Figure 12) depending on the planes of cell division. Rod-shaped cells, called bacilli (bă-sil'ī), typically appear singly or in chains.

Bacterial cell walls are composed of **peptidoglycan,** a complex polysaccharide. Peptidoglycan in turn is composed of two types of regularly alternating sugar molecules, called N-*acetylglucosamine (NAG)* and N-*acetylmuramic acid (NAM)*, which are structurally similar to glucose (Figure 13). Millions of NAG and NAM molecules are covalently linked in chains in which NAG alternates with NAM. These chains are the "glycan" portions of peptidoglycan.

Chains of NAG and NAM are attached to other chains by crossbridges of four amino acids (tetrapeptides). Figure 14 illustrates one possible configuration. These peptide crossbridges are the "peptido" portion of peptidoglycan. Depending on the bacterium, tetrapeptide bridges are either covalently bonded to one another or are held together by *short connecting* chains of other amino acids as shown in Figure 14. Peptidoglycan covers the entire surface of a cell, which must insert millions of new subunits if it is to grow and divide.

Scientists describe two basic types of bacterial cell walls as *Gram-positive* cell walls or *Gram-negative* cell walls. They distinguish Gram-positive and Gram-negative cells by the use of the Gram staining procedure, which was invented long before the structure and chemical nature of bacterial cell walls were known.

## Gram-Positive Bacterial Cell Walls

### Learning Objective

✓ Compare and contrast the cell walls of acid-fast bacteria with typical Gram-positive cell walls.

**Gram-positive** bacterial cell walls have a relatively thick layer of peptidoglycan that also contains unique chemicals called *teichoic* (tī-kō'ik)[4] *acids.* Some teichoic acids are covalently linked to lipids, forming *lipoteichoic acids* that anchor the peptidoglycan to the cytoplasmic membrane (Figure 15a). Teichoic acids have negative electrical charges, which help give the surface of a Gram-positive bacterium a negative charge and may play a role in the passage of ions through the wall. The thick cell wall of a Gram-positive bacterium retains the crystal violet dye used in the Gram staining procedure, so the stained cells appear purple under magnification.

Some additional chemicals are associated with the walls of some Gram-positive bacteria. For example, species of *Mycobacterium* (mī'kō-bak-tēr'ē-ŭm), which include the causative

[4]From Greek *teichos*, meaning wall.

Glucose　　　　　*N*-acetylglucosamine　*N*-acetylmuramic acid
　　　　　　　　　　NAG　　　　　　　NAM

(a)　　　　　(b)

▲ **Figure 13 Comparison of the structures of glucose, NAG, and NAM. (a)** Glucose. **(b)** N-acetylglucosamine (NAG) and N-acetylmuramic acid (NAM) molecules linked as in peptidoglycan. Blue shading indicates the differences between glucose and the other two sugars. Orange boxes highlight the difference between NAG and NAM.

Sugar backbone

Tetrapeptide (amino acid) crossbridge

Connecting chains of amino acids

▲ **Figure 14 One possible structure of peptidoglycan.** Peptidoglycan is composed of chains of NAG and NAM linked by tetrapeptide crossbridges and, in some cases, connecting chains of amino acids to form a tough yet flexible structure. The amino acids of the crossbridges differ among bacterial species.

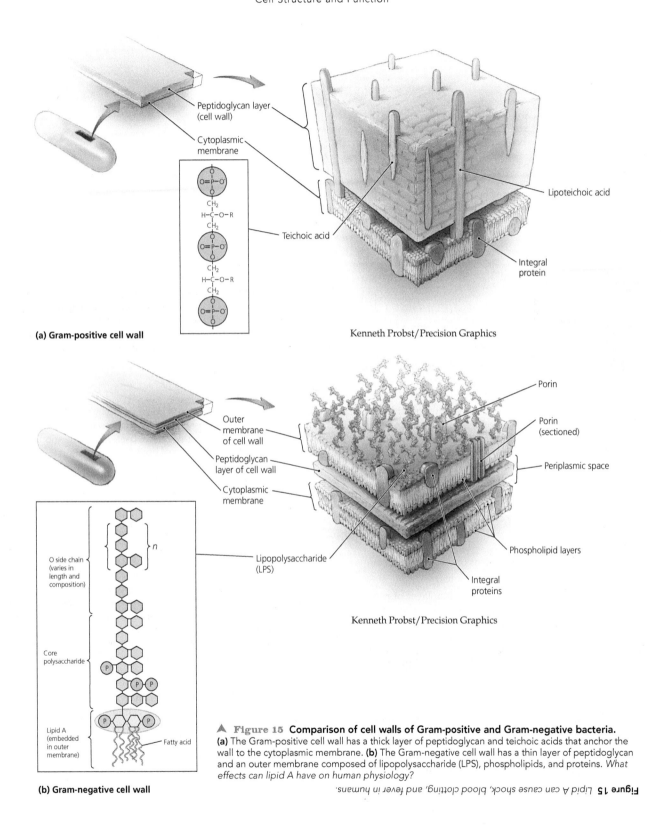

(a) Gram-positive cell wall

Peptidoglycan layer (cell wall)

Cytoplasmic membrane

Teichoic acid

Lipoteichoic acid

Integral protein

Kenneth Probst/Precision Graphics

Outer membrane of cell wall

Peptidoglycan layer of cell wall

Cytoplasmic membrane

Lipopolysaccharide (LPS)

Porin

Porin (sectioned)

Periplasmic space

Phospholipid layers

Integral proteins

Kenneth Probst/Precision Graphics

O side chain (varies in length and composition)

Core polysaccharide

Lipid A (embedded in outer membrane)

Fatty acid

(b) Gram-negative cell wall

▲ **Figure 15** **Comparison of cell walls of Gram-positive and Gram-negative bacteria.** **(a)** The Gram-positive cell wall has a thick layer of peptidoglycan and teichoic acids that anchor the wall to the cytoplasmic membrane. **(b)** The Gram-negative cell wall has a thin layer of peptidoglycan and an outer membrane composed of lipopolysaccharide (LPS), phospholipids, and proteins. *What effects can lipid A have on human physiology?*

**Figure 15** *Lipid A can cause shock, blood clotting, and fever in humans.*

## HIGHLIGHT

### BIOFILMS: SLIME MATTERS

They form plaque on teeth; they are the slime on rocks in rivers and streams; and they can cause disease, clog drains, or aid in hazardous-waste cleanup. They are biofilms—organized, layered systems of bacteria and other microbes attached to a surface. Understanding biofilms holds the key to many important clinical and industrial applications.

Bacteria in biofilms behave in significantly different ways from individual, free-floating bacteria. For example, as a free-floating cell, the soil bacterium *Pseudomonas putida* propels itself through water with its flagella; however, once it becomes part of a biofilm, it turns off the genes for flagellar proteins and starts synthesizing pili instead. In addition, the genes for antibiotic resistance in *P. putida* are more active within cells in a biofilm than within a free-floating cell.

Bacteria in a biofilm also communicate via chemical and electrical signals that help them organize and form three-dimensional structures. The architecture of a biofilm provides protection that free-floating bacteria lack. For example, the lower concentrations of oxygen found in the interior of biofilms thwart the effectiveness of some antibiotics. Moreover, the presence of multiple bacterial species in most biofilms increases the likelihood that some bacteria within the biofilm community will remain resistant to a given antibiotic.

The more we understand biofilms, the more readily we can reduce their harmful effects or put them to good use. Biofilms account for two-thirds of bacterial infections in humans, including gum disease and the serious lung infections suffered by cystic fibrosis

▲ **Biofilm on medical tubing.** SEM | 4 μm

patients. Biofilms are also the culprits in many industrial problems, including corroded pipes and clogged water filters, which cause millions of dollars of damage each year. Fortunately, not all biofilms are detrimental; some show potential as aids in preventing and controlling certain kinds of industrial pollution.

From: Critical Role of Bcr1-Dependent Adhesins in C. albicans Biofilm Formation In Vitro and In Vivo. C. J. Nobile, D. R. Andes, J. E. Nett, F. J. Smith Jr., F. Yue, et al. *PLoS Pathog.* 2006; 2(7):e63, Fig.8c

agents of tuberculosis and leprosy, have walls with up to 60% mycolic acid, a waxy lipid. Mycolic acid helps these cells survive desiccation and makes them difficult to stain with regular water-based dyes. Researchers have developed a special staining procedure called the *acid-fast stain* to stain these Gram-positive cells that contain large amounts of waxy lipids. Such cells are called *acid-fast bacteria*.

## Gram-Negative Bacterial Cell Walls

### Learning Objective

✓ Describe the clinical implications of the structure of the Gram-negative cell wall.

**Gram-negative** cell walls have only a thin layer of peptidoglycan (Figure 15b), but outside this layer is an asymmetric bilayer membrane. The inner leaflet of the outer membrane is composed of phospholipids and proteins, while the outer leaflet is made of **lipopolysaccharide (LPS)**. Integral proteins called *porins* form channels through both leaflets of the outer membrane, allowing for the movement of glucose and other monosaccharides across the membrane. The outer membrane is protective, allowing Gram-negative bacteria such as *Escherichia coli* (esh-ĕ-rik′ē-ă kō′lē) to better survive in harsh environments.

LPS is a union of lipid with sugar. The lipid portion of LPS is known as **lipid A.** The erroneous idea that lipid A is *inside* Gram-negative cells led to the use of the term *endotoxin*[5] for this chemical. A dead cell releases lipid A when the outer membrane

disintegrates, and lipid A may trigger fever, vasodilation, inflammation, shock, and blood clotting in humans. Because killing large numbers of Gram-negative bacteria with antimicrobial drugs releases large amounts of lipid A, which might threaten the patient more than the live bacteria, any internal infection by Gram-negative bacteria is cause for concern.

The Gram-negative outer membrane can also be an impediment to the treatment of disease. For example, the outer membrane may prevent the movement of penicillin to the underlying peptidoglycan, thus rendering the drug ineffectual against many Gram-negative pathogens.

Between the cytoplasmic membrane and the outer membrane of Gram-negative bacteria is a **periplasmic space** (see Figure 15b). The periplasmic space contains the peptidoglycan and *periplasm,* the name given to the gel between the membranes of these Gram-negative cells. Periplasm contains water, nutrients, and substances secreted by the cell, such as digestive enzymes and proteins involved in specific transport. The enzymes function to catabolize large nutrient molecules into smaller molecules that can be absorbed or transported into the cell.

Because the cell walls of Gram-positive and Gram-negative bacteria differ, the Gram stain is an important diagnostic tool. After the Gram staining procedure, Gram-negative cells appear pink, and Gram-positive cells appear purple.

## Bacteria Without Cell Walls

A few bacteria, such as *Mycoplasma pneumoniae* (mī′kō-plaz-mă nū-mō′nē-ī), lack cell walls entirely. In the past, these bacteria were often mistaken for viruses because of their small size and

[5]From Greek *endo*, meaning inside, and *toxikon*, meaning poison.

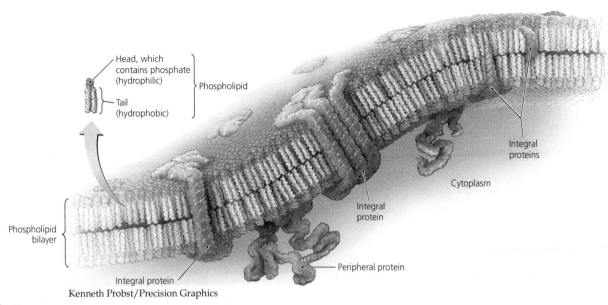

Head, which contains phosphate (hydrophilic)

Tail (hydrophobic)

Phospholipid

Phospholipid bilayer

Integral proteins

Cytoplasm

Integral protein

Peripheral protein

Integral protein

Kenneth Probst/Precision Graphics

▲ **Figure 16**
**The structure of a prokaryotic cytoplasmic membrane: a phospholipid bilayer.**

lack of walls. However, they do have other features of prokaryotic cells, such as prokaryotic ribosomes (discussed later in the chapter).

### CRITICAL **THINKING**

After a man infected with the bacterium *Escherichia coli* was treated with the correct antibiotic for this pathogen, the bacterium was no longer found in the man's blood, but his symptoms of fever and inflammation worsened. What caused the man's response to the treatment? Why was his condition worsened by the treatment?

## Bacterial Cytoplasmic Membranes

Beneath the glycocalyx and the cell wall is a **cytoplasmic membrane.** The cytoplasmic membrane may also be referred to as *the cell membrane* or a *plasma membrane.*

### Structure

#### Learning Objective

✓ Diagram a phospholipid bilayer, and explain its significance in reference to a cytoplasmic membrane.

✓ Explain the fluid mosaic model of membrane structure.

Cytoplasmic membranes are about 8 nm thick and composed of phospholipids and associated proteins. Some bacterial membranes also contain sterol-like molecules, called *hopanoids,* that help stabilize the membrane.

The structure of a cytoplasmic membrane is referred to as a **phospholipid bilayer** (Figure 16). A phospholipid molecule is bipolar; that is, the two ends of the molecule are different. The phosphate-containing heads of each phospholipid molecule are *hydrophilic,*[6] that is, they are attracted to water at the two surfaces of the membrane. The hydrocarbon tails of each phospholipid molecule are *hydrophobic*[7] and huddle together with other tails in the interior of the membrane, away from water. Phospholipids placed in a watery environment naturally form a bilayer because of their bipolar nature.

About half of a bacterial cytoplasmic membrane is composed of *integral proteins* inserted amidst the phospholipids. Some integral proteins penetrate the entire bilayer; others are found in only half the bilayer. In contrast, *peripheral proteins* are loosely attached to the membrane on one side or the other. Proteins of cell membranes may act as recognition proteins, enzymes, receptors, carriers, or channels.

The **fluid mosaic model** describes our current understanding of membrane structure. The term *mosaic* indicates that the membrane proteins are arranged in a way that resembles the tiles in a mosaic, and *fluid* indicates that the proteins and lipids are free to flow laterally within a membrane. ANIMATIONS: *Membrane Structure*

---

[6]From Greek *hydro,* meaning water, and *philos,* meaning love.
[7]From Greek *hydro,* meaning water, and *phobos,* meaning fear.

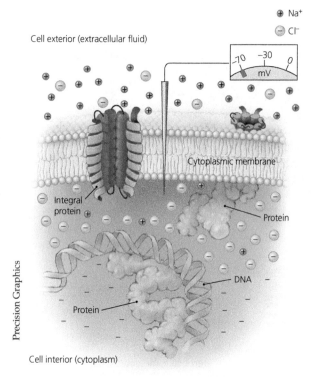

⊕ Na⁺

⊖ Cl⁻

Cell exterior (extracellular fluid)

Cytoplasmic membrane

Integral protein

Protein

DNA

Protein

Cell interior (cytoplasm)

Precision Graphics

▲ **Figure 17 Electrical potential of a cytoplasmic membrane.** The electrical potential exists across a membrane because there are more negative charges inside the cell than outside it.

## Function

### Learning Objectives

✓ Describe the functions of a cytoplasmic membrane as they relate to permeability.

✓ Compare and contrast the passive and active processes by which materials cross a cytoplasmic membrane.

✓ Define *osmosis*, and distinguish among isotonic, hypertonic, and hypotonic solutions.

A cytoplasmic membrane does more than separate the contents of the cell from the outside environment. The cytoplasmic membrane controls the passage of substances into and out of the cell. Nutrients are brought into the cell and wastes are removed. The membrane also functions in production of molecules for energy storage, and to harvest light energy in photosynthetic bacteria.

In its function of controlling the contents of the cell, the cytoplasmic membrane is **selectively permeable;** that is, it allows some substances to cross it while preventing the crossing of others. How does a membrane exert control over the contents of the cell, and the substances that move across it? **ANIMATIONS:** *Membrane Permeability*

A phospholipid bilayer is naturally impermeable to most substances. Large molecules cannot cross through it; ions and molecules with an electrical charge are repelled by it; and hydrophilic substances cannot easily cross its hydrophobic interior. However, cytoplasmic membranes, unlike plain phospholipid bilayers in a scientist's test tube, contain proteins, and these proteins allow substances to cross the membrane by functioning as pores, channels, or carriers.

Movement across the cytoplasmic membrane occurs either by passive or active processes. Passive processes do not require the expenditure of a cell's ATP energy store, whereas active processes require the expenditure of ATP, either directly or indirectly. Active and passive processes will be discussed shortly, but first you must understand another feature of selectively permeable cytoplasmic membranes: their ability to maintain a *concentration gradient.*

Membranes enable a cell to concentrate chemicals on one side of the membrane or the other. The difference in concentration of a chemical on the two sides of a membrane is its **concentration gradient** (also known as a *chemical gradient*).

Because many of the substances that have concentration gradients across cell membranes are electrically charged chemicals, a corresponding **electrical gradient,** or voltage, also exists across the membrane (Figure 17). For example, a greater concentration of negatively charged proteins exists inside the membrane, and positively charged sodium ions are more concentrated outside the membrane. One result of the segregation of electrical charges by a membrane is that the interior of a cell is usually electrically negative compared to the exterior. This tends to repel negatively charged chemicals and attract positively charged substances into the cell. **ANIMATIONS:** *Passive Transport: Principles of Diffusion*

### Passive Processes

In passive processes, the electrochemical gradient provides a source of energy; the cell does not expend its ATP energy reserve. Passive processes include diffusion, facilitated diffusion, and osmosis.

**Diffusion** Diffusion is the net movement of a chemical down its concentration gradient—that is, from an area of higher concentration to an area of lower concentration. It requires no energy output by the cell, a common feature of all passive processes. In fact, diffusion occurs even in the absence of cells or their membranes. In the case of diffusion into or out of cells, only chemicals that are small or lipid soluble can diffuse through the lipid portion of the membrane (Figure 18a). For example, oxygen, carbon dioxide, alcohol, and fatty acids can freely diffuse through the cytoplasmic membrane, but molecules such as glucose and proteins cannot.

**Facilitated Diffusion** The phospholipid bilayer blocks the movement of large or electrically charged molecules, so they do not cross the membrane unless there is a pathway for diffusion. As we have seen, cytoplasmic membranes contain integral proteins. Some of these proteins act as channels or carriers to allow certain molecules to diffuse into or out of the cell. This process is called **facilitated diffusion** because the proteins facilitate the

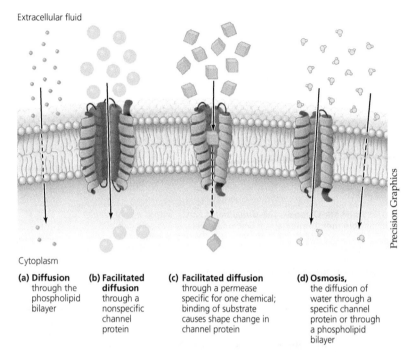

> **Figure 18** **Passive processes of movement across a cytoplasmic membrane.** Passive processes always involve movement down an electrochemical gradient. **(a)** Diffusion. **(b)** Facilitated diffusion through a nonspecific channel protein. **(c)** Facilitated diffusion through a specific channel protein. **(d)** Osmosis through a nonspecific channel protein or through a phospholipid bilayer.

Extracellular fluid

Cytoplasm

**(a) Diffusion** through the phospholipid bilayer

**(b) Facilitated diffusion** through a nonspecific channel protein

**(c) Facilitated diffusion** through a permease specific for one chemical; binding of substrate causes shape change in channel protein

**(d) Osmosis,** the diffusion of water through a specific channel protein or through a phospholipid bilayer

process by providing a pathway for diffusion. The cell expends no energy in facilitated diffusion; the electrochemical gradient provides all of the energy necessary.

Some channel proteins allow the passage of a range of chemicals that have the right size or electrical charge (Figure 18b). Other channel proteins, known as *permeases,* are more specific, carrying only certain substrates (Figure 18c). A permease has a binding site that is selective for one substance.

## CRITICAL **THINKING**

A scientist who is studying passive movement of chemicals across the cytoplasmic membrane of *Salmonella enterica* serotype Typhi measures the rate at which two chemicals diffuse into a cell as a function of external concentration. The results are shown in the following figure. Chemical A diffuses into the cell more rapidly than does B at lower external concentrations, but the rate levels off as the external concentration increases. The rate of diffusion of chemical B continues to increase as the external concentration increases.

1. How can you explain the differences in the diffusion rates of chemicals A and B?

2. Why does the diffusion rate of chemical A taper off?

3. How could the cell increase the diffusion rate of chemical A?

4. How could the cell increase the diffusion rate of chemical B?

**Osmosis** When discussing simple and facilitated diffusion, we considered a solution in terms of the solutes (dissolved materials) it contains, because it is those solutes that move in and out of the cell. In contrast, with osmosis it is useful to consider the concentration of the solvent, which in organisms is always water. **Osmosis** is the special name given to the diffusion of water across a selectively permeable membrane—that is, across a membrane that is permeable to water molecules, but not to all solutes that are present, such as proteins, amino acids, salts, or glucose (Figure 18d). Because these solutes cannot freely penetrate the membrane, they cannot diffuse no matter how unequal their concentrations on either side of the membrane may be. Instead, what diffuses is the water, which crosses from the side of the membrane that contains a higher concentration of water (lower concentration of solute) to the side that contains a lower concentration of water (higher concentration of solute). Osmosis continues until equilibrium is reached, or until the pressure of water is equal to the force of osmosis (Figure 19).

We commonly classify solutions according to their concentrations of solutes. When solutions on either side of a selectively permeable membrane have the same concentration of solutes, the two solutions are said to be **isotonic.**[8] In an isotonic situation, neither side of a selectively permeable membrane will experience a net loss or gain of water (Figure 20a).

When the concentrations of solutions are unequal, the solution with the higher concentration of solutes is said to be **hypertonic**[9] to the other. The solution with a lower concentration

[8]From Greek *isos,* meaning equal, and *tonos,* meaning tone.
[9]From Greek *hyper,* meaning more or over.

Precision Graphics

J.B. Woolsey Associates, LLC

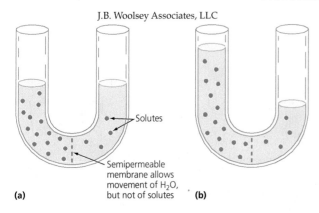

**(a)** **(b)**

▲ **Figure 19 Osmosis, the diffusion of water across a selectively permeable membrane. (a)** A membrane separates two solutions of different concentrations in a U-shaped tube. The membrane is permeable to water, but not to the solute. **(b)** After time has passed, water has moved down its concentration gradient until water pressure prevented the osmosis of any additional water. *Which side of the tube more closely represents a living cell?*

*Figure 19 The left-hand side represents the cell, because cells are typically hypertonic to their environment.*

of solutes is **hypotonic**[10] in comparison. Note that the terms *hypertonic* and *hypotonic* refer to the concentration of solute, even though osmosis refers to the movement of the *solvent*, which, in cells, is water. The terms *isotonic, hypertonic,* and *hypotonic* are relative. For example, a glass of tap water is isotonic to another glass of the same water, but it is hypertonic compared to distilled water, and hypotonic when compared to seawater. In biology, the three terms are traditionally used relative to the interior of cells.

[10]From Greek *hypo*, meaning less or under.

Obviously, a higher concentration of solutes necessarily means a lower concentration of water; that is, a hypertonic solution has a lower concentration of water than does a hypotonic solution. Like other chemicals, water moves down its concentration gradient from a hypotonic solution into a hypertonic solution. A cell placed in a hypertonic solution will therefore lose water and shrivel (Figure 20b).

On the other hand, water will diffuse into a cell placed in a hypotonic solution because the cell has a higher solutes-to-water concentration. As water moves into the cell, water pressure against its cytoplasmic membrane increases, and the cell expands (Figure 20c). One function of a cell wall, such as the peptidoglycan of bacteria, is to resist further osmosis and prevent cells from bursting.

It is useful to compare solutions to the concentration of solutes in a patient's blood cells. Isotonic saline solutions administered to a patient have the same percent dissolved solute (in this case, salt) as do the patient's blood cells. Thus, the patient's intracellular and extracellular environments remain in equilibrium when an isotonic saline solution is administered. However, if the patient is infused with a hypertonic solution, water will move out of the patient's cells, and the cells will shrivel, a condition called *crenation*. Conversely, if a patient is infused with a hypotonic solution, water will move into the patient's cells, which will swell and possibly burst. **ANIMATIONS:** *Passive Transport: Special Types of Diffusion*

## CRITICAL **THINKING**

Solutions hypertonic to bacteria and fungi are used for food preservation. For instance, jams and jellies are hypertonic with sugar, and pickles are hypertonic with salt. How do hypertonic solutions kill bacteria and fungi that would otherwise spoil these foods?

Precision Graphics

Cells without a wall (e.g., mycoplasmas, animal cells)

Cells with a wall (e.g., plants, fungal and bacterial cells)

Cell wall

Cell wall

Cell membrane

Cell membrane

**(a)** Isotonic solution

**(b)** Hypertonic solution

**(c)** Hypotonic solution

◀ **Figure 20 Effects of isotonic, hypertonic, and hypotonic solutions on cells. (a)** Cells in isotonic solutions experience no net movement of water. **(b)** Cells in hypertonic solutions shrink due to the net movement of water out of the cell. **(c)** Cells in hypotonic solutions undergo a net gain of water. Animal cells burst because they lack a cell wall; in cells with a cell wall, the pressure of water pushing against the interior of the wall eventually stops the movement of water into the cell.

▶ **Figure 21 Mechanisms of active transport. (a)** Via a uniport. **(b)** Via an antiport. **(c)** Via a uniport coupled with a symport. In this example, the membrane uses ATP energy to pump one substance out through a uniport. As this substance flows back into the cell it brings another substance with it through the symport. *What is the usual source of energy for active transport?*

*Figure 21 ATP is the usual source of energy for active transport processes.*

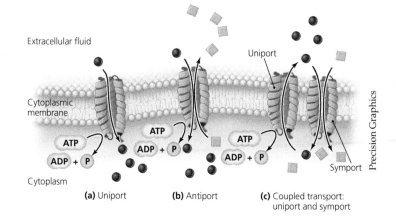

Extracellular fluid

Uniport

Cytoplasmic membrane

ATP

ATP

ATP

ADP + P

ADP + P

ADP + P

Symport

Cytoplasm

**(a)** Uniport       **(b)** Antiport       **(c)** Coupled transport: uniport and symport

Precision Graphics

## Active Processes

As stated previously, active processes require the cell to expend energy stored in ATP molecules to move materials across the cytoplasmic membrane against their electrochemical gradient. This is analogous to moving water uphill. As we will see, ATP may be utilized directly during transport, or indirectly at some other site and at some other time. Active processes in bacteria include *active transport* by means of carrier proteins and a special process termed *group translocation*. **ANIMATIONS:** *Active Transport: Overview*

**Active Transport** Like facilitated diffusion, **active transport** utilizes transmembrane permease proteins; however, the functioning of active transport proteins requires the cell to expend ATP to transport molecules across the membrane. Some such proteins are referred to as *gated channels* or *ports* because they are controlled. When the cell is in need of a substance, the protein becomes functional (the gate "opens"). At other times the gate is "closed."

If only one substance is transported at a time, the permease is called a *uniport* (Figure 21a). In contrast, *antiports* simultaneously transport two chemicals, but in opposite directions; that is, one substance is transported into the cell at the same time that a second substance is transferred out of the cell (Figure 21b). In other types of active transport, two substances move together in the same direction across the membrane by means of a single carrier protein. Such proteins are known as *symports* (Figure 21c).

In all cases, active transport moves substances against their electrochemical gradient. Typically, the protein acts as an ATPase—an enzyme that breaks down ATP into ADP and inorganic phosphate during transport, releasing energy that is used to move the chemical against its electrochemical gradient across the membrane.

With symports and antiports, one chemical's electrochemical gradient may provide the energy needed to transport the second chemical, a mechanism called *coupled transport* (Figure 21c). For example, $H^+$ moving into a cell down its electrochemical gradient by facilitated diffusion provides energy to carry glucose into the cell, against the glucose gradient. The two

processes are linked by a symport. However, ATP may still be utilized for transport because the $H^+$ gradient can be previously established by the active pumping of $H^+$ to the outside of the cell by an ATP-dependent $H^+$ uniport. The use of ATP is thus separated in time and space from the active transport of glucose, but ATP was still expended. **ANIMATIONS:** *Active Transport: Types*

**Group Translocation** **Group translocation** is an active process that occurs only in some bacteria. In group translocation, the substance being actively transported across the membrane is chemically changed during transport (Figure 22). The membrane is impermeable to the altered substance, trapping it inside the cell. Group translocation is very efficient at bringing substances into a cell. It can operate efficiently even if the external concentration of the chemical being transported is as low as 1 part per million (ppm).

One well-studied example of group translocation is the accumulation of glucose inside a bacterial cell. As glucose is transported across the bacterial cell membrane, it is phosphorylated;

Glucose

$CH_2OH$

Extracellular fluid

$PO_4$

Cytoplasm

$CH_2OPO_4$

Glucose 6-$PO_4$

Precision Graphics

▲ **Figure 22 Group translocation.** This process involves a chemical change in a substance as it is being transported. This figure depicts glucose being transported into a bacterial cell via group translocation.

that is, a phosphate group is added to the glucose. The glucose is changed into glucose 6-phosphate, a sugar that cannot cross back out, but can be utilized in the ATP-producing metabolism of the cell. Other carbohydrates, fatty acids, purines, and pyrimidines are also brought into bacterial cells by group translocation. A summary of bacterial transport processes is shown in Table 2.

# Cytoplasm of Bacteria

## Learning Objectives

✓ Describe bacterial cytoplasm and its basic contents.

✓ Define *inclusion* and give two examples.

✓ Describe the formation and function of endospores.

**Cytoplasm** is the general term used to describe the gelatinous material inside a cell. Cytoplasm is semitransparent, fluid, elastic, and aqueous. It is composed of cytosol, inclusions, ribosomes, and in many cells, a cytoskeleton. Some bacterial cells produce internal, resistant, dormant forms called endospores.

## Cytosol

The liquid portion of the cytoplasm is called **cytosol.** It is mostly water, but it also contains dissolved and suspended substances, including ions, carbohydrates, proteins (mostly enzymes), lipids, and wastes. The cytosol of prokaryotes also contains the cell's DNA in a region called the **nucleoid.** Recall that a distinctive feature of prokaryotes is lack of a phospholipid membrane surrounding this DNA.

Most bacteria have a single, circular DNA molecule organized as a chromosome. Some bacteria, such as *Vibrio cholerae* (vib′rē-ō kol′er-ī), the bacterium that causes cholera, are unusual in that they have two chromosomes.

The cytosol is the site of some chemical reactions. For example, enzymes within the cytosol function to produce amino acids and degrade sugar.

Polyhydroxybutyrate

From: Influence of phenylacetic acid on poly-β-hydroxybutyrate (PHB) polymerization and cell elongation in Azotobacter chroococcum Beij. M. P. Nuti, M. De Bertoldi, A. A. Lepidi. *Canadian Journal of Microbiology.* 1972 Aug;18(8):1257–61

TEM | 250 nm

▲ **Figure 23  Granules of PHB in the bacterium** *Azotobacter chroococcum.*

## Inclusions

Deposits, called **inclusions,** are often found within bacterial cytosol. Rarely, a cell surrounds its inclusions with a polypeptide membrane. Inclusions may include reserve deposits of lipids, starch, or compounds containing nitrogen, phosphate, or sulfur. Such chemicals may be taken in and stored in the cytosol when nutrients are in abundance and then utilized when nutrients are scarce. The presence of specific inclusions is diagnostic for several pathogenic bacteria.

Many bacteria store carbon and energy in molecules of glycogen, which is a polymer of glucose molecules, or as a lipid polymer called *polyhydroxybutyrate (PHB)* (Figure 23). Long

**TABLE 2**

## Transport Processes Across Bacterial Cytoplasmic Membranes

| | Description | Examples of Transported Substances |
|---|---|---|
| **Passive transport processes** | Processes require no use of energy by the cell; the electrochemical gradient provides energy. | |
| Diffusion | Molecules move down their electrochemical gradient through the phospholipid bilayer of the membrane. | Oxygen, carbon dioxide, lipid-soluble chemicals |
| Facilitated diffusion | Molecules move down their electrochemical gradient through channels or carrier proteins. | Glucose, fructose, urea, some vitamins |
| Osmosis | Water molecules move down their concentration gradient across a selectively permeable membrane. | Water |
| **Active transport processes** | Cell expends energy in the form of ATP to move a substance against its electrochemical gradient. | |
| Active transport | ATP-dependent carrier proteins bring substances into cell. | Na$^+$, K$^+$, Ca$^{2+}$, H$^+$, Cl$^-$ |
| Group translocation | The substance is chemically altered during transport; found only in some bacteria. | Glucose, mannose, fructose |

chains of PHB accumulate as inclusion granules in the cytoplasm. Slight chemical modification of PHB produces a plastic that can be used for packaging and other applications (see **Beneficial Microbes: Plastics Made Perfect?**). PHB plastics are biodegradable, breaking down in a landfill in a few weeks rather than persisting for years as petroleum-based plastics do.

Many aquatic cyanobacteria (blue-green photosynthetic bacteria) contain inclusions called *gas vesicles* that store gases in protein sacs. The gases buoy the cells to the surface and into the light needed for photosynthesis. Other interesting inclusions are the small crystals of magnetite stored by *magnetobacteria*, featured at the beginning of this chapter. Invaginations of the cytoplasmic membrane surround the magnetite to form membrane-bound sacs.

## Endospores

Some bacteria, notably *Bacillus* (ba-sil'ūs) and *Clostridium* (klos-trid'ē-ŭm), are characterized by the ability to produce unique structures called **endospores,** which are important for several reasons, including their durability and potential pathogenicity. Though some people refer to endospores simply as "spores," endospores should not be confused with the reproductive spores of actinobacteria, algae, and fungi. A single bacterial cell, called a *vegetative* cell to distinguish it from an endospore, transforms into only one endospore, which then germinates to grow into only one vegetative cell; therefore, endospores are not reproductive structures. Instead, endospores constitute a defensive strategy against hostile or unfavorable conditions.

A vegetative cell normally transforms itself into an endospore only when one or more nutrients (such as carbon or nitrogen) are in limited supply. The process of endospore formation, called *sporulation*, requires 8 to 10 hours and proceeds in seven steps (Figure 24). During the process, two membranes, a thick layer of peptidoglycan, and a spore coat form around a copy of the cell's DNA and a small portion of cytoplasm. The cell deposits large quantities of dipicolinic acid, calcium, and DNA-binding proteins within the endospore while removing most of the water. Depending on the species, a cell forms an endospore either *centrally, subterminally* (near one end), or *terminally* (at one end). Sometimes an endospore is so large it swells the vegetative cell.

Endospores are extremely resistant to drying, heat, radiation, and lethal chemicals. For example, they remain alive in boiling water for several hours; are unharmed by alcohol, peroxide, bleach, and other toxic chemicals; and can tolerate over 400 rad of radiation, which is more than five times the dose that is lethal to most humans. Endospores are stable resting stages that barely metabolize—they are essentially in a state of suspended animation—and they germinate only when conditions improve. Scientists do not know how endospores are able to resist harsh conditions, but it appears that the double membrane, spore coats, dipicolinic acid, calcium, and DNA-binding proteins serve to stabilize DNA and enzymes, protecting them from adverse conditions.

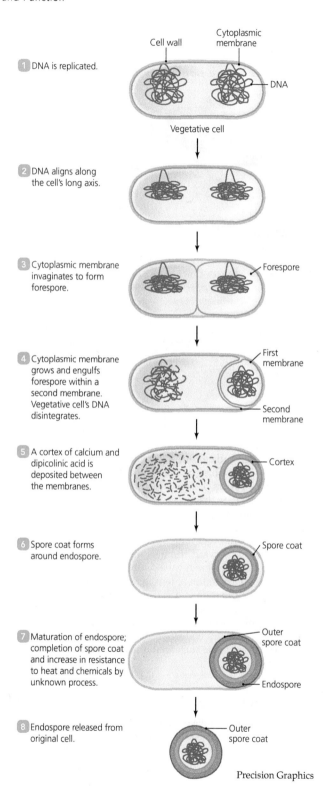

1  DNA is replicated.

Cell wall · Cytoplasmic membrane · DNA

Vegetative cell

2  DNA aligns along the cell's long axis.

3  Cytoplasmic membrane invaginates to form forespore.

Forespore

4  Cytoplasmic membrane grows and engulfs forespore within a second membrane. Vegetative cell's DNA disintegrates.

First membrane · Second membrane

5  A cortex of calcium and dipicolinic acid is deposited between the membranes.

Cortex

6  Spore coat forms around endospore.

Spore coat

7  Maturation of endospore; completion of spore coat and increase in resistance to heat and chemicals by unknown process.

Outer spore coat · Endospore

8  Endospore released from original cell.

Outer spore coat

Precision Graphics

▲ **Figure 24 The formation of an endospore.** The steps depicted occur over a period of 8–10 hours.

## BENEFICIAL MICROBES

### PLASTICS MADE PERFECT?

▲ *PHB bottle caps. One partially biodegraded in 60 days.*

Josh Reynolds/ AP Images

Petroleum-based plastics play a considerable role in modern life, appearing in packaging, bottles, appliances, furniture, automobiles, disposable diapers, and many other synthetic goods. Despite the good that plastic brings to our lives, there are problems with this artificial polymer.

Manufacturers make plastic from oil, exacerbating the dependence of the U.S. on foreign supplies of crude oil. Consumers discard plastic, filling landfills with more than 15 million tons of plastic every year in the United States. Because plastic is artificial, microorganisms do not break it down effectively, and discarded plastic will remain in landfills for decades or centuries. What is needed is a functional "green" plastic—a plastic that is strong and light and that can be shaped and colored as needed, yet a plastic that is naturally biodegradable.

Enter the bacteria. Many bacterial cells, particularly Gram-negative bacteria, use polyhydroxybutyrate (PHB) as a storage molecule and energy source much as humans use fat. PHB and similar storage molecules turn out to be rather versatile plastics that are produced when bacteria metabolizing certain types of sugar are simultaneously deprived of an essential element such as nitrogen, phosphorus, or potassium. The bacteria, faced with such a nutritionally stressed environment, convert the sugar to PHB, which they store as intracellular inclusions. Scientists harvest these biologically created molecules by breaking the cells open and treating the cytoplasm with chemicals to isolate the plastics and remove dangerous endotoxin.

Purified PHB possesses many of the properties of petrochemically derived plastic—its melting point, crystal structure, molecular weight, and strength are very similar. Further, PHB has a singular, overwhelming advantage compared to artificial plastic: PHB is naturally and completely biodegradable—bacteria catabolize PHB into carbon dioxide and water. The positive effect this would have on our overtaxed landfills would be tremendous, and replacing just half of the oil-based plastic used in the United States with PHB could reduce oil imports by more than 250 million barrels per year, improving our foreign trade balance and reducing our dependence on overseas oil suppliers.

---

The ability to survive harsh conditions makes endospores the most resistant and enduring cells. In one case, scientists were able to revive endospores of *Clostridium* that had been sealed in a test tube for 34 years. This record pales, however, beside other researchers' claim to have revived *Bacillus* endospores from inside 250-million-year-old salt crystals retrieved from an underground site near Carlsbad, New Mexico. Some scientists question this claim, suggesting that the bacteria might be recent contaminants that entered through invisible cracks in the salt crystals. In any case, there is little doubt that endospores can remain viable for a minimum of tens, if not thousands, of years.

Endospore formation is a serious concern to food processors, health care professionals, and governments because endospores are resistant to treatments that inhibit other microbes, and because endospore-forming bacteria produce deadly toxins that cause such fatal diseases as anthrax, tetanus, and gangrene.

### CRITICAL THINKING

Following the bioterrorist anthrax attacks in the fall of 2001, a news commentator suggested that people steam their mail for 30 seconds before opening it. Would the technique protect people from anthrax infections? Why or why not?

## Nonmembranous Organelles

### Learning Objective

✓ Describe the structure and function of ribosomes and the cytoskeleton.

As previously noted, prokaryotes do not usually have membranes surrounding their organelles. However, two types of *nonmembranous organelles* are found in direct contact with the cytosol in bacterial cytoplasm. Some investigators do not consider them to be true organelles because they lack a membrane, but other scientists consider them organelles. Nonmembranous organelles in bacteria include ribosomes and the cytoskeleton.

### Ribosomes

**Ribosomes** are the sites of protein synthesis in cells. Bacterial cells have thousands of ribosomes in their cytoplasm, which gives cytoplasm a grainy appearance (see Figure 2). The approximate size of ribosomes—and indeed other cellular structures—is expressed in Svedbergs (S),[11] and is determined by their sedimentation rate—the rate at which they move to the bottom of a test tube during centrifugation. As you might expect, large, compact, heavy particles sediment faster than small,

---

[11]Svedberg units are named for Theodor Svedberg, a Nobel Prize winner and the inventor of the ultracentrifuge.

Rut Carballido-López

[LM] ├────┤ 2 μm

▲ **Figure 25 A simple helical cytoskeleton.** The rod-shaped bacterium *Bacillus subtilis* has a cytoskeleton composed of only a single protein, which has been stained with a fluorescent dye.

loosely packed, or light ones, and are assigned a higher number. Prokaryotic ribosomes are 70S; in contrast, the larger ribosomes of eukaryotes are 80S.

All ribosomes are composed of two subunits, each of which is composed of polypeptides and molecules of RNA called **ribosomal RNA (rRNA).** The subunits of prokaryotic 70S ribosomes are a smaller 30S subunit and a larger 50S subunit; the 30S subunit contains polypeptides and a single rRNA molecule, whereas the 50S subunit has polypeptides and two rRNA molecules. Because sedimentation rates are dependent not only on mass and size but also on shape, the sedimentation rates of subunits do not add up to the sedimentation rate of a whole ribosome.

Many antibacterial drugs act on bacterial 70S ribosomes or their subunits without deleterious effects on the larger 80S ribosomes of eukaryotic cells. This is why such drugs can stop protein synthesis in bacteria without affecting protein synthesis in a patient.

### Cytoskeleton

Most cells contain an internal network of fibers called a **cytoskeleton** that plays a role in forming a cell's basic shape. Additionally, the contractile cytoskeleton of the nonflagellated bacterium *Spiroplasma* (spē-ro-plaz'mă) allows the cell to swim through its environment. Bacteria were long thought to lack cytoskeletons, but research has revealed that bacteria have simple ones (Figure 25).

We have considered bacterial cells. Next we turn our attention to archaea—the other prokaryotic cells—and compare them to bacterial cells.

# External Structures of Archaea

Archaeal cells have external structures similar to those seen in bacteria. These include glycocalyces, flagella, and fimbriae. Some archaea have another kind of proteinaceous appendage

called a *hamus*. We consider each of these in order beginning with the outermost structures—glycocalyces.

## Glycocalyces

### Learning Objective

✓ Compare the structure and chemistry of archaeal and bacterial glycocalyces.

Like those of bacteria, archaeal glycocalyces are gelatinous, sticky, extracellular structures composed of polysaccharides, polypeptides, or both. Scientists have not studied archaeal glycocalyces as much as those of bacteria, but archaeal glycocalyces function at a minimum in the formation of biofilms—adhering cells to one another, to other types of cells, and to inanimate surfaces in the environment. Organized glycocalyces (capsules) of bacteria and bacterial biofilms are often associated with disease, but researchers have not demonstrated such a link between archaeal capsules or biofilms and disease. Though some research has demonstrated the presence of archaea in some biofilms associated with oral gum disease, no archaeon has been shown conclusively to be pathogenic.

## Flagella

### Learning Objectives

✓ Describe the structure and formation of archaeal flagella.

✓ Compare and contrast archaeal flagella with bacterial flagella.

Archaea use flagella to move through their environments, though at a slower speed than bacteria. An archaeal flagellum is superficially similar to a bacterial flagellum, consisting of a basal body, hook, and filament, each composed of protein. The flagellum extends outside the cell and is not covered by a membrane. The basal body anchors the flagellum in the cell wall and cytoplasmic membrane. As with bacterial flagella, archaeal flagella rotate like propellers.

However, scientists have discovered many differences between archaeal and bacterial flagella:

- Archaeal flagella are 10–14 nm in diameter, which is about half the thickness of bacterial flagella, and lack a central channel.

- Therefore, archaeal flagella grow with the addition of subunits at the base of the filament.

- The proteins making up archaeal flagella share common amino acid sequences across archaeal species. These are very different from the amino acid sequences common to bacterial flagella.

- Sugar molecules are attached to the filaments of many archaeal flagella, a condition which is rare in bacteria.

- Archaeal flagella are powered with energy stored in molecules of ATP, whereas the flow of hydrogen ions across the membrane powers bacterial flagella.

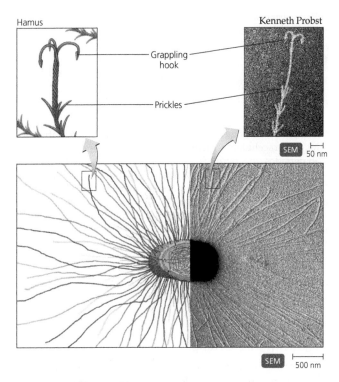

Hamus
Kenneth Probst
Grappling hook
Prickles
SEM · 50 nm
SEM · 500 nm

▲ **Figure 26 Archaeal hami.** Archaea use hami, which are shaped like grappling hooks on barbed wire, to attach themselves to structures in the environment.
From: The unique structure of archaeal 'hami', highly complex cell appendages with nano-grappling hooks. C. Moissl, R. Rachel, A. Briegel, H. Engelhardt, R. Huber, *Mol. Microbiol.* 2005 Apr; 56(2):361–70; Fig. 1 and 2

- Archaeal flagella rotate together as a bundle both when they rotate clockwise and counterclockwise. In contrast, bacterial flagella operate independently when rotating clockwise.

These differences indicate that archaeal flagella arose independently of bacterial flagella; they are *analogous* structures—having similar structure without having a common ancestor.

## Fimbriae and Hami

Learning Objectives

✓ Compare the structure and function of archaeal and bacterial fimbriae.

✓ Describe the structure and function of hami.

Many archaea have fimbriae—nonmotile, rodlike, sticky projections. As with bacteria, archaeal fimbriae are composed of protein and anchor the cells to one another and to environmental surfaces.

Some archaea make unique proteinaceous, fimbriae-like structures called **hami**[12] (singular: *hamus*). More than 100 hami may radiate from the surface of a single archaeon (Figure 26).

[12]From Latin *hamus*, meaning prickle, claw, hook, or barb.

Each hamus is a helical filament with tiny prickles sticking out at regular intervals much like barbed wire. The end of the hamus is frayed into three distinct arms, each of which has a thickened end and bends back toward the cell to make the entire structure look like a grappling hook. Indeed, hami function to securely attach archaea to biological and inanimate surfaces.

## Archaeal Cell Walls and Cytoplasmic Membranes

Learning Objectives

✓ Contrast types of archaeal cell walls with each other and with bacterial cell walls.

✓ Contrast the archaeal cytoplasmic membrane with that of bacteria.

Most archaea, like most bacteria, have cell walls. All archaea have cytoplasmic membranes. However, there are distinct differences between archaeal and bacterial walls and membranes, further emphasizing the uniqueness of archaea.

Archaeal cell walls are composed of specialized proteins or polysaccharides. In some species, the outermost protein molecules form an array that coats the cell like chain mail. All archaeal walls lack peptidoglycan, which is common to all bacterial cell walls.

Gram-negative archaeal cells have an outer layer of protein rather than an outer lipid bilayer as seen in Gram-negative bacteria. Gram-negative archaea still appear pink when Gram stained. Gram-positive archaea have a thick cell wall and Gram stain purple, like Gram-positive bacteria.

Archaeal cells are typically spherical or rod shaped, though irregularly shaped, needle-like, rectangular, and flattened square archaea exist (Figure 27).

Archaeal cytoplasmic membranes are composed of lipids that lack phosphate groups and have branched hydrocarbons linked to glycerol by ether linkages rather than the ester linkages seen in bacterial membranes. Ether linkages are stronger in many ways than ester linkages, allowing archaea to live in extreme environments such as near boiling water and in hypersaline lakes. Some archaea—particularly those that thrive in very hot water—have a single layer of lipid composed of two glycerol groups covalently linked with branched hydrocarbon chains.

The archaeal cytoplasmic membrane maintains electrical and chemical gradients in the cell. It also functions to control the import and export of substances from the cell using membrane proteins as ports and pumps, just as proteins are used in bacterial cytoplasmic membranes.

## Cytoplasm of Archaea

Learning Objective

✓ Compare and contrast the cytoplasm of archaea with that of bacteria.

From: An archaeal bi-species biofilm formed by Pyrococcus furiosus and Methanopyrus kandleri. S. Schopf, G. Wanner, R. Rachel, R. Wirth. *Arch. Microbiol.* 2008 Sep: 190(3):371–7; Epub 2008 Apr 26

William Hixon and Dennis G. Searcy

SEM | 0.5 µm
SEM | 1 µm
LM | 5 µm

Mike Dyall-Smith (www.haloarchaea.com)

▲ **Figure 27 Representative shapes of archaea. (a)** Cocci, *Pyrococcus furiosus*, attached to rod-shaped *Methanopyrus kandleri*. **(b)** Irregularly shaped archaeon, *Thermoplasma acidophilum*. **(c)** Square archaeon, *Haloquadra walsbyi*.

Cytoplasm is the gel-like substance found in all cells, including archaea. Like bacteria, archaeal cells have 70S ribosomes, a fibrous cytoskeleton, and circular DNA suspended in a liquid cytosol. Also, like bacteria, they do not have membranous organelles.

However, archaeal cytoplasm differs from that of bacteria in several ways. For example, the ribosomes of archaea have different proteins than do the ribosomes of bacteria; indeed, archaeal ribosomal proteins are more like those of eukaryotes. Scientists further distinguish archaea from bacteria in that archaea use different metabolic enzymes to make RNA and use a genetic code more similar to the code used by eukaryotes. Table 3 contrasts features of archaea and bacteria.

To this point, we have discussed basic features of bacterial and archaeal prokaryotic cells. Next we turn our attention to eukaryotic cells.

# External Structure of Eukaryotic Cells

Some eukaryotic cells have glycocalyces, which are similar to those of prokaryotes.

## Glycocalyces

### Learning Objective

✓ Describe the composition, function, and importance of eukaryotic glycocalyces.

Animal and most protozoan cells lack cell walls, but they have sticky carbohydrate glycocalyces that are anchored to their cytoplasmic membranes via covalent bonds to membrane proteins and lipids. The functions of eukaryotic glycocalyces, which are never as structurally organized as prokaryotic capsules, include helping to anchor animal cells to each other, strengthening the cell surface, providing some protection

## TABLE 3

### Some Structural Characteristics of Prokaryotes

| Feature | Archaea | Bacteria |
|---|---|---|
| Glycocalyx | Polypeptide or polysaccharide | Polypeptide or polysaccharide |
| Flagella | Present in some, 10–14 nm in diameter, grow at base, rotate both counterclockwise and clockwise as a bundle | Present in some, about 20 nm in diameter, grow at the tip, rotate independently clockwise to create tumbles |
| Fimbriae | Proteinaceous, used for attachment and in formation of biofilms | Proteinaceous, used for attachment, gliding motility, and in formation of biofilms |
| Pili | None discovered | Present in some, proteinaceous, used in bacterial exchange of DNA |
| Hami | Present in some, used for attachment | Absent |
| Cell walls | Present in most, composed of polysaccharides (not peptidoglycan) or proteins | Present in most, composed of peptidoglycan—a polysaccharide |
| Cytoplasmic membrane | Present in all, membrane lipids made with ether linkages, some have single lipid layer | Present in all, phospholipids made with ester linkages in bilayer |
| Cytoplasm | Cytosol contains circular DNA molecule and 70S ribosomes, ribosomal proteins similar to eukaryotic ribosomal proteins | Cytosol contains at least a circular DNA molecule and 70S ribosomes with bacterial proteins |

against dehydration, and functioning in cell-to-cell recognition and communication. Glycocalyces are absent in eukaryotes that have cell walls such as plants and fungi.

# Eukaryotic Cell Walls and Cytoplasmic Membranes

## Learning Objectives

✓ Compare and contrast prokaryotic and eukaryotic cell walls and cytoplasmic membranes.

✓ Contrast exocytosis and endocytosis.

✓ Describe the role of pseudopodia in eukaryotic cells.

The eukaryotic cells of fungi, algae, plants, and some protozoa have cell walls. Recall that glycocalyces are absent from eukaryotes with cell walls; instead, the cell wall takes on one of the functions of a glycocalyx by providing protection from the environment. The wall also provides shape and support against osmotic pressure. Most eukaryotic cell walls are composed of various polysaccharides, but not the peptidoglycan seen in the walls of bacteria.

The walls of plant cells are composed of *cellulose*, a polysaccharide that is familiar to you as paper and dietary fiber. Fungi also have walls of polysaccharides, including cellulose, *chitin*, and/or *glucomannan*. The walls of algae (Figure 28) are composed of a variety of polysaccharides or other chemicals, depending on the type of alga. These chemicals include cellulose,

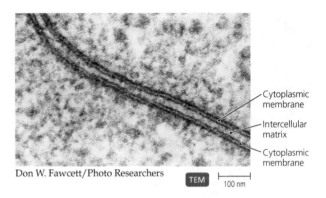
Don W. Fawcett/Photo Researchers · TEM · 100 nm

▲ **Figure 29 Eukaryotic cytoplasmic membrane.** Note that this micrograph depicts the cytoplasmic membranes of two adjoining cells.

[labels: Cytoplasmic membrane; Intercellular matrix; Cytoplasmic membrane]

proteins, *agar, carrageenan, silicates, algin, calcium carbonate,* or a combination of these substances.

All eukaryotic cells have cytoplasmic membranes (Figure 29). (Botanists call the cytoplasmic membrane of an algal or plant cell a *plasmalemma.*) A eukaryotic cytoplasmic membrane, like those of bacteria, is a fluid mosaic of phospholipids and proteins, which act as recognition molecules, enzymes, receptors, carriers, or channels. Channel proteins for facilitated diffusion are more common in eukaryotes than in prokaryotes. Additionally, within multicellular organisms some membrane proteins serve to anchor cells to each other.

Eukaryotic cytoplasmic membranes may differ from prokaryotic membranes in several ways. Eukaryotic membranes contain steroid lipids *(sterols),* such as cholesterol in animal cells, that help maintain membrane fluidity. Paradoxically, at high temperatures sterols stabilize a phospholipid bilayer by making it less fluid, but at low temperatures sterols have the opposite effect—they prevent phospholipid packing, making the membrane more fluid.

Eukaryotic cytoplasmic membranes may contain small, distinctive assemblages of lipids and proteins that remain together as a functional group and do not flow independently amidst other membrane components. Such distinct regions are called **membrane rafts.** Eukaryotic cells appear to use membrane rafts to compartmentalize cellular processes including signaling the inside of the cell, protein sorting, and some kinds of cell movement. Some viruses, including those of AIDS, Ebola, measles, and flu, use membrane rafts to enter human cells or during viral replication and propagation. Researchers hope that blocking molecules in membrane rafts will provide a way to limit the spread of these viruses.

Eukaryotic cells frequently attach chains of sugar molecules to the outer surfaces of lipids and proteins in their cytoplasmic membranes; prokaryotes rarely do this. Sugar molecules may act in intercellular signaling, cellular attachment, and in other roles.

[labels: Cell wall; Cytoplasmic membrane]
Robert Bauman · TEM · 1 µm

▲ **Figure 28 A eukaryotic cell wall.** The cell wall of the red alga *Gelidium* is composed of layers of the polysaccharide called agar. *What is the function of a cell wall?*

**Figure 28** *The cell wall provides support, protection, and resistance to osmotic forces.*

➤ **Figure 30** **Endocytosis.** Pseudopodia extend to surround solid and/or liquid nutrients, which become incorporated into a food vesicle inside the cytoplasm. *What is the difference between phagocytosis and pinocytosis?*

**Figure 30** *Phagocytosis is endocytosis of a solid; pinocytosis is endocytosis of a liquid.*

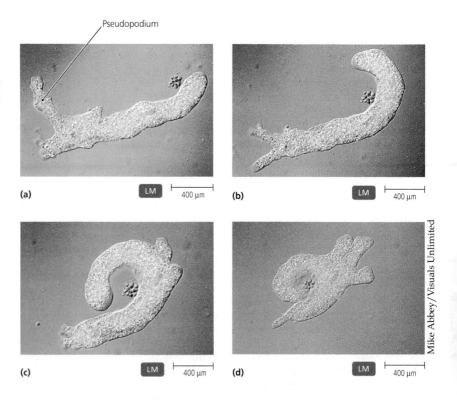

Pseudopodium

(a)  LM  400 µm

(b)  LM  400 µm

(c)  LM  400 µm

(d)  LM  400 µm

Mike Abbey/Visuals Unlimited

Like its prokaryotic counterpart, a eukaryotic cytoplasmic membrane controls the movement of materials into and out of a cell. Eukaryotic cytoplasmic membranes use both passive processes (diffusion, facilitated diffusion, and osmosis; see Figure 18) and active transport (see Figure 21). Eukaryotic membranes do not perform group translocation, which occurs only in some prokaryotes, but many perform another type of active transport—**endocytosis** (Figure 30), which involves physical manipulation of the cytoplasmic membrane around the cytoskeleton. Endocytosis occurs when the membrane distends to form **pseudopodia** (false feet) that surround a substance, bringing it into the cell. Endocytosis is termed **phagocytosis** if a solid is brought into the cell, and **pinocytosis**

if only liquid is brought into the cell. Nutrients brought into a cell by endocytosis are then enclosed in a *food vesicle.* Vesicles and digestion of the nutrients they contain are discussed in more detail shortly.

Some eukaryotes also use pseudopodia as a means of locomotion. The cell extends a pseudopod and then the cytoplasm streams into it, a process called *amoeboid action.*

**Exocytosis,** another solely eukaryotic process, is the reverse of endocytosis in that it enables substances to be exported from the cell. Not all eukaryotic cells can perform endocytosis or exocytosis.

Table 4 lists some of the features of endocytosis and exocytosis.

**TABLE 4**

## Active Transport Processes Found Only in Eukaryotes: Endocytosis and Exocytosis

| | Description | Examples of Transported Substances |
|---|---|---|
| Endocytosis: phagocytosis and pinocytosis | Substances are surrounded by pseudopodia and brought into the cell. Phagocytosis involves solid substances; pinocytosis involves liquids. | Bacteria, viruses, aged and dead cells; liquid nutrients in extracellular solutions |
| Exocytosis | Vesicles containing substances are fused with cytoplasmic membrane, dumping their contents to the outside. | Wastes, secretions |

# Cytoplasm of Eukaryotes

## Learning Objectives

✓ Compare and contrast the cytoplasm of prokaryotes and eukaryotes.

✓ Identify nonmembranous and membranous organelles.

The cytoplasm of eukaryotic cells is more complex than that of either bacteria or archaea. The most distinctive difference is the presence of numerous membranous organelles in eukaryotes. However, before we discuss these membranous organelles, we will consider organelles of locomotion and other nonmembranous organelles in eukaryotes.

## Flagella

### Learning Objective

✓ Compare and contrast the structure and function of prokaryotic and eukaryotic flagella.

### Structure and Arrangement

Some eukaryotic cells are flagellated. Flagella of eukaryotes (Figure 31a) differ structurally and functionally from flagella of prokaryotes. First, eukaryotic flagella are within the cytoplasmic membrane; they are internal structures that push the cytoplasmic membrane out around them. Their basal bodies are in the cytoplasm. Second, the shaft of a eukaryotic flagellum is composed of molecules of a globular protein called *tubulin* arranged in chains to form hollow *microtubules* (Figure 31b). Nine pairs of microtubules surround two microtubules in the center. This "9 + 2" arrangement of microtubules is common to all flagellated eukaryotic cells, whether they are found in protozoa, algae, animals, or plants. The filaments of eukaryotic flagella are anchored in the cytoplasm by a basal body, but no hook connects the two parts, as in prokaryotes. The basal body has *triplets* of microtubules instead of pairs, and there are no microtubules in the center, so scientists say it has a "9 + 0" arrangement of microtubules. Eukaryotic flagella may be single or multiple and are generally found at one pole of the cell.

### Function

The flagella of eukaryotes also move differently from those of prokaryotes. Rather than rotating like prokaryotic flagella, those of eukaryotes undulate rhythmically (Figure 32a). Some eukaryotic flagella push the cell through the medium (as occurs in animal sperm), whereas others pull the cell through the medium (as occurs in many protozoa). Positive and negative phototaxis and chemotaxis are seen in eukaryotic cells, but such cells do not move in runs and tumbles.

## Cilia

### Learning Objectives

✓ Describe the structure and function of cilia.

✓ Compare and contrast eukaryotic cilia and flagella.

Other eukaryotic cells move by means of internal hairlike structures called **cilia,** which extend the surface of the cell and are shorter and more numerous than flagella (Figure 31c). No prokaryotic cells have cilia. Like flagella, cilia are composed primarily of tubulin microtubules, which are arranged in a "9 + 2" arrangement of pairs in their shafts and a "9 + 0" arrangement of triplets in their basal bodies (Figure 31b).

A single cell may have hundreds or even thousands of cilia. Cilia beat rhythmically, much like a swimmer doing a butterfly stroke (Figure 32b). Coordinated beating of cilia propels single-celled eukaryotes through their environment. Cilia are also used within multicellular eukaryotes to move substances in the local environment past the surface of the cell. For example, such movement of cilia helps cleanse the human respiratory tract of dust and microorganisms.

## Other Nonmembranous Organelles

### Learning Objectives

✓ Describe the structure and function of ribosomes, cytoskeletons, and centrioles.

✓ Compare and contrast the ribosomes of prokaryotes and eukaryotes.

✓ List and describe the three filaments of a eukaryotic cytoskeleton.

Here we discuss three nonmembranous organelles found in eukaryotes: ribosomes and cytoskeleton (both of which are also present in prokaryotes), and centrioles (which are present only in certain kinds of eukaryotic cells).

### Ribosomes

The cytosol of eukaryotes, like that of prokaryotes, is a semitransparent fluid composed primarily of water containing dissolved and suspended proteins, ions, carbohydrates, lipids, and wastes. Within the cytosol of eukaryotic cells are ribosomes that are larger than prokaryotic ribosomes; instead of 70S ribosomes, eukaryotic ribosomes are 80S and are composed of 60S and 40S subunits. In addition to the 80S ribosomes found within the cytosol, many eukaryotic ribosomes are attached to the membranes of the endoplasmic reticulum (discussed shortly).

### Cytoskeleton

Eukaryotic cells contain an extensive cytoskeleton composed of an internal network of fibers and tubules. The eukaryotic

> **Figure 31 Eukaryotic flagella and cilia. (a)** Micrograph of *Euglena*, which possesses a single flagellum. **(b)** Details of the arrangement of microtubules of eukaryotic flagella and cilia. Both flagella and cilia have the same internal structure. **(c)** Light micrograph of a protozoan *Blepharisma*, which has numerous cilia. *How do eukaryotic flagella differ from cilia?*

**Figure 31** *Flagella are longer and less numerous than cilia.*

Flagellum

SPL/Photo Researchers

(a)  SEM  15 µm

Cilia

Steve Gschmeissner/Photo Researchers

(c)  SEM  10 µm

TEM  200 nm

(b)

Kenneth Probst/Precision Graphics

Cytoplasmic membrane
Cytosol
Central pair microtubules
Microtubules (doublet)
"9 + 2" arrangement
Cytoplasmic membrane
Portion cut away to show transition area from doublets to triplets and the end of central microtubules
Basal body
Microtubules (triplet)
"9 + 0" arrangement

Omnikron/Science Library/Photo Researchers

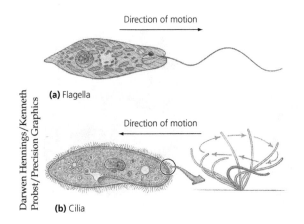

**(a)** Flagella

Direction of motion

Direction of motion

**(b)** Cilia

Darwen Hennings/Kenneth Probst/Precision Graphics

▲ **Figure 32 Movement of eukaryotic flagella and cilia.**
**(a)** Eukaryotic flagella undulate in waves that begin at one end and traverse the length of the flagellum. **(b)** Cilia move with a power stroke followed by a return stroke. In the power stroke a cilium is stiff; it relaxes during the return stroke. *How is the movement of eukaryotic flagella different from that of prokaryotic flagella?*

**Figure 32** *Eukaryotic flagella undulate in a wave that moves down the flagellum; the flagella of prokaryotes rotate about the basal body.*

cytoskeleton acts to anchor organelles and functions in cytoplasmic streaming and in movement of organelles within the cytosol. Cytoskeletons in some cells enable the cell to contract, move the cytoplasmic membrane during endocytosis and amoeboid action, and produce the basic shapes of the cells.

The eukaryotic cytoskeleton is made up of *tubulin microtubules* (also found in flagella and cilia), thinner *microfilaments* composed of *actin,* and *intermediate filaments* composed of various proteins (Figure 33).

## Centrioles and Centrosome

Animal cells and some fungal cells contain two **centrioles,** which lie at right angles to each other near the nucleus, in a region of the cytoplasm called the **centrosome** (Figure 34). Plants, algae, and most fungi (and prokaryotes) lack centrioles but usually have a region of cytoplasm corresponding to a centrosome. Centrioles are composed of nine *triplets* of tubulin microtubules arranged in a way that resembles the "9 + 0" arrangement seen at the base of eukaryotic flagella and cilia.

Centrosomes play a role in *mitosis* (nuclear division), *cytokinesis* (cell division), and the formation of flagella and cilia. However, because many eukaryotic cells that lack centrioles, such as brown algal sperm and numerous one-celled algae, are still able to form flagella and undergo mitosis and cytokinesis, the function of centrioles is the subject of ongoing research.

# Membranous Organelles

### Learning Objectives

✓ Discuss the function of each of the following membranous organelles: nucleus, ER, Golgi body, lysosome, peroxisome, vesicle, vacuole, mitochondrion, and chloroplast.

✓ Label the structures associated with each of the membranous organelles.

Eukaryotic cells contain a variety of organelles that are surrounded by phospholipid bilayer membranes similar to the cytoplasmic membrane. These membranous organelles include the nucleus, endoplasmic reticulum, Golgi body, lysosomes, peroxisomes, vacuoles, vesicles, mitochondria, and chloroplasts. Prokaryotic cells lack these structures.

Precision Graphics

Tubulin

25 nm

Microtubule

Actin subunit

7 nm

Microfilament

Protein subunits

10 nm

Intermediate filament

**(a)**

**(b)**

LM   5 µm

Jennifer Waters

▲ **Figure 33 Eukaryotic cytoskeleton.** The cytoskeleton of eukaryotic cells serves to anchor organelles, provides a "track" for the movement of organelles throughout the cell, and provides shape to animal cells. Eukaryotic cytoskeletons are composed of microtubules, microfilaments, and intermediate filaments. **(a)** Artist's rendition of cytoskeleton filaments. **(b)** Various elements of the cytoskeleton shown here have been stained with different fluorescent dyes.

Centrioles

Centrosome

TEM | 200 nm

(a)

(b)

Microtubules

Triplet

Kenneth Probst/Precision Graphics

David M. Phillips/Visuals Unlimited

Precision Graphics

▲ **Figure 34** **Centrosome.** A centrosome is a region of cytoplasm that in animal cells contains two centrioles at right angles to one another; each centriole has nine triplets of microtubules. **(a)** Transmission electron micrograph of centrosome and centrioles. **(b)** Artist's rendition of a centrosome. *How do centrioles compare with the basal body and shafts of eukaryotic flagella and cilia (see Figure 31b)?*

*Figure 34 Centrioles have the same "9 + 0" arrangement of microtubules that is found in the basal bodies of eukaryotic cilia and flagella.*

## Nucleus

The **nucleus** is usually spherical to ovoid and is often the largest organelle in a cell[13] (Figure 35). Some cells have a single nucleus; others are multinucleate, while still others lose their nuclei. The nucleus is often referred to as "the control center of the cell" because it contains most of the cell's genetic instructions in the form of DNA. Cells that lose their nuclei, such as mammalian red blood cells, can survive for only a few months.

Just as the semiliquid portion of the cell is called cytoplasm, the semiliquid matrix of the nucleus is called **nucleoplasm.** Within the nucleoplasm may be one or more **nucleoli** (noo-klē'ō-lī; singular: *nucleolus*), which are specialized regions where RNA is synthesized. The nucleoplasm also contains **chromatin,** which is a threadlike mass of DNA associated with special proteins called *histones* that play a role in packaging nuclear DNA. During mitosis (nuclear division) chromatin becomes visible as *chromosomes.*

Surrounding the nucleus is a double membrane called the **nuclear envelope,** which is composed of two phospholipid bilayers, for a total of four phospholipid layers. The nuclear envelope contains **nuclear pores** (see Figure 35) that function to control the import and export of substances through the envelope.

## Endoplasmic Reticulum

Continuous with the outer membrane of the nuclear envelope is a netlike arrangement of flattened hollow tubules called **endoplasmic reticulum (ER)** (Figure 36). The ER traverses the cytoplasm of eukaryotic cells. Endoplasmic reticulum functions as a transport system and is found in two forms: **smooth endoplasmic reticulum (SER)** and **rough endoplasmic reticulum (RER).** SER plays a role in lipid synthesis as well as transport. Rough endoplasmic reticulum is rough because ribosomes adhere to its outer surface. Proteins produced by ribosomes on the RER are inserted into the lumen (central canal) of the RER and transported throughout the cell.

## Golgi Body

A **Golgi**[14] **body** is like the shipping department of a cell: it receives, processes, and packages large molecules for export from the cell (Figure 37). The Golgi body packages secretions in sacs called **secretory vesicles,** which then fuse with the cytoplasmic membrane before dumping their contents outside the cell via exocytosis. Golgi bodies are composed of a series of flattened hollow sacs that are circumscribed by a phospholipid bilayer. Not all eukaryotic cells contain Golgi bodies.

## Lysosomes, Peroxisomes, Vacuoles, and Vesicles

Lysosomes, peroxisomes, vacuoles, and vesicles are membranous sacs that function to store and transfer chemicals within

[13]Historically, the nucleus was not considered an organelle because it is large and not considered part of the cytoplasm.
[14]Camillo Golgi was an Italian histologist who first described the organelle in 1898. This organelle is also known as a Golgi complex or Golgi apparatus and in plants and algae as a dictyosome.

Precision Graphics

◄ **Figure 35 Eukaryotic nucleus.**
Micrograph and artist's conception of a nucleus showing chromatin, a nucleolus, and the nuclear envelope. Nuclear pores punctuate the two membranes of the nuclear envelope.

TEM

Nucleolus

Nucleoplasm

Chromatin

Nuclear envelope

Two phospholipid bilayers

Nuclear pores

Rough ER

D. W. Fawcett/Photo Researchers

Rough ER

Kenneth Probst/Precision Graphics

TEM   250 nm

eukaryotic cells. Both **vesicle** and **vacuole** are general terms for such sacs. Large vacuoles are found in plant and algal cells that store starch, lipids, and other substances in the center of the cell. Often a central vacuole is so large that the rest of the cytoplasm is pressed against the cell wall in a thin layer (Figure 38).

**Lysosomes,** which are found in animal cells, contain catabolic enzymes that damage the cell if they are released from their packaging into the cytosol. The enzymes are used during the self-destruction of old, damaged, and diseased cells, and to digest nutrients that have been phagocytized. For example, the digestive enzymes in lysosomes are utilized by white blood cells to destroy phagocytized pathogens (Figure 39).

**Peroxisomes** are vesicles derived from ER. They contain *oxidase* and *catalase,* which are enzymes that degrade poisonous metabolic wastes (such as free radicals and hydrogen peroxide) resulting from some oxygen-dependent reactions. Peroxisomes

are found in all types of eukaryotic cells but are especially prominent in the kidney and liver cells of mammals.

## Mitochondria

**Mitochondria** are spherical to elongated structures found in most eukaryotic cells (Figure 40). Like nuclei, they have two membranes, each composed of a phospholipid bilayer. The inner membrane is folded into numerous *cristae* that increase the inner membrane's surface area. Mitochondria are often called the "powerhouses of the cell" because their cristae produce most of the ATP in many eukaryotic cells.

The interior matrix of a mitochondrion contains ("prokaryotic") 70S ribosomes and a circular molecule of DNA. This DNA contains genes for some RNA molecules and for a few mitochondrial polypeptides that are manufactured

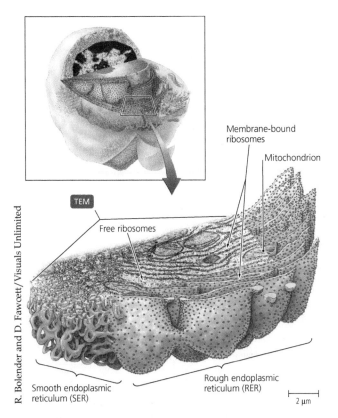

TEM

Membrane-bound ribosomes

Mitochondrion

Free ribosomes

Smooth endoplasmic reticulum (SER)

Rough endoplasmic reticulum (RER)

2 μm

▲ **Figure 36 Endoplasmic reticulum.** ER functions in transport throughout the cell. Ribosomes are on the surface of rough ER; smooth ER lacks ribosomes.

Kenneth Probst/Precision Graphics

by mitochondrial ribosomes; however, most mitochondrial proteins are coded by nuclear DNA and synthesized by cytoplasmic ribosomes.

## Chloroplasts

**Chloroplasts** are light-harvesting structures found in photosynthetic eukaryotes (Figure 41). Like mitochondria and the nucleus, chloroplasts have two phospholipid bilayer membranes and DNA. Further, like mitochondria, chloroplasts can synthesize a few polypeptides with their own 70S ribosomes. The pigments of chloroplasts gather light energy to produce ATP and form sugar from carbon dioxide. Numerous membranous sacs called *thylakoids* form an extensive surface area for the biochemical and photochemical reactions of chloroplasts. The fluid between the thylakoids and the inner membrane is called the *stroma*. The space enclosed by the thylakoids is called the thylakoid space.

Photosynthetic prokaryotes lack chloroplasts and instead have infoldings of their cytoplasmic membranes called *photosynthetic lamellae*.

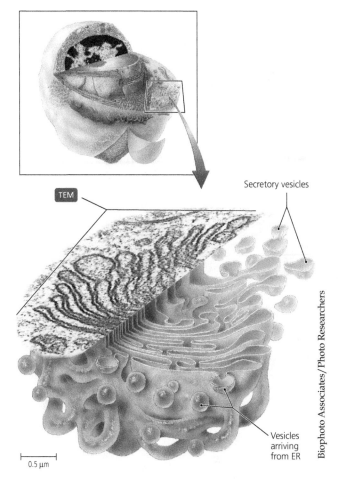

TEM

Secretory vesicles

Vesicles arriving from ER

0.5 μm

▲ **Figure 37 Golgi body.** A Golgi body is composed of flattened sacs. Proteins synthesized by ribosomes on RER are transported via vesicles to a Golgi body. The Golgi body then modifies the proteins and sends them via secretory vesicles to the cytoplasmic membrane, where they can be secreted from the cell by exocytosis.

Kenneth Probst/Precision Graphics

The functions of the nonmembranous and membranous organelles, and their distribution among prokaryotic and eukaryotic cells, are summarized in Table 5.

## Endosymbiotic Theory

### Learning Objectives

✓ Describe the endosymbiotic theory of the origin of mitochondria, chloroplasts, and eukaryotic cells.

✓ List evidence for the endosymbiotic theory.

Mitochondria and chloroplasts are semiautonomous; that is, they divide independently of the cell but remain dependent on the cell for most of their proteins. As we have seen, both

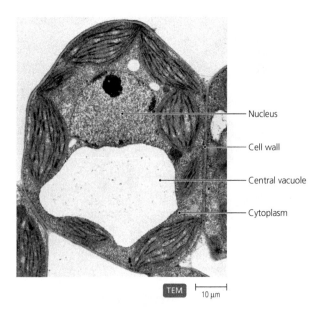

TEM | 10 μm

▲ **Figure 38 Vacuole.** The large central vacuole of a plant cell, which constitutes a storehouse for the cell, presses the cytoplasm against the cell wall.

From: *Plant Cell Vacuoles: An Introduction.* D. N. De. (2000) CSIRO Publishing, Melbourne, Australia. Reproduced with permission from CSIRO. Photo by Celia Miller, CSIRO Plant Industry, Canberra, Australia

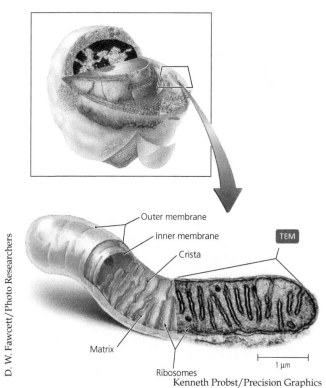

D. W. Fawcett/Photo Researchers

Outer membrane
Inner membrane
Crista
TEM
Matrix
Ribosomes
Kenneth Probst/Precision Graphics

1 μm

▲ **Figure 40 Mitochondrion.** Note the double membrane. The inner membrane is folded into cristae that increase its surface area. *What is the importance of the increased surface area of the inner membrane that results from having cristae?*

**Figure 40** *The chemicals involved in aerobic ATP production are located on the inner membranes of mitochondria. Increased surface area provides more space for more chemicals.*

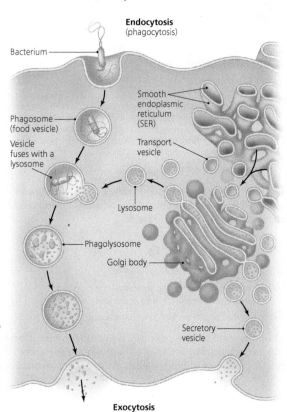

Darwen Hennings

**Endocytosis**
(phagocytosis)

Bacterium

Phagosome
(food vesicle)

Vesicle
fuses with a
lysosome

Smooth
endoplasmic
reticulum
(SER)

Transport
vesicle

Lysosome

Phagolysosome

Golgi body

Secretory
vesicle

**Exocytosis**
(elimination, secretion)

◀ **Figure 39 The roles of vesicles in the destruction of a phagocytized pathogen within a white blood cell.** Before endocytosis, vesicles from the SER deliver digestive enzymes to the Golgi body, which then packages them into lysosomes. During endocytosis, phagocytized particles (in this case, a bacterium) are enclosed within a vesicle called a phagosome (food vesicle), which then fuses with a lysosome to form a phagolysosome. Once digestion within the phagolysosome is complete, the resulting wastes can be expelled from the cell via exocytosis.

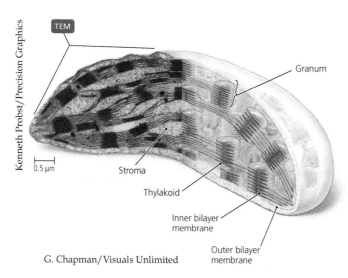

Kenneth Probst/Precision Graphics

TEM

0.5 µm

Granum

Stroma

Thylakoid

Inner bilayer membrane

Outer bilayer membrane

G. Chapman/Visuals Unlimited

▲ **Figure 41 Chloroplast.** Chloroplasts have an ornate internal structure designed to harvest light energy for photosynthesis.

mitochondria and chloroplasts contain a small amount of DNA and 70S ribosomes, and each can produce a few polypeptides with its own ribosomes. The presence of circular DNA, 70S ribosomes, and two bilipid membranes in these semiautonomous organelles led scientist Lynn Margulis (1938–) to popularize the **endosymbiotic**[15] **theory** for the formation of eukaryotic cells. This theory suggests that eukaryotes formed from the union of small aerobic[16] prokaryotes with larger anaerobic prokaryotes. The smaller prokaryotes were not destroyed by the larger cells, but instead became internal parasites that remained surrounded by a vesicular membrane of the host.

According to the theory, the parasites eventually lost the ability to exist independently, but they retained a portion of their DNA, some ribosomes, and their cytoplasmic membranes. During the same time, the larger cell became dependent on the parasites for aerobic ATP production. According to the theory, the aerobic prokaryotes eventually evolved into mitochondria, and their cytoplasmic membranes became cristae. Margulis

[15]From Greek *endo*, meaning inside, and *symbiosis*, meaning to live with.
[16]*Aerobic* means requiring oxygen; *anaerobic* is the opposite.

## 5

## TABLE

## Nonmembranous and Membranous Organelles of Cells

| | General Function | Prokaryotes | Eukaryotes |
|---|---|---|---|
| **Nonmembranous organelles** | | | |
| Ribosomes | Protein synthesis | Present in all | Present in all |
| Cytoskeleton | Shape in prokaryotes; support, cytoplasmic streaming, and endocytosis in eukaryotes | Present in some | Present in all |
| Centrosome | Appears to play a role in mitosis, cytokinesis, and flagella and cilia formation in animal cells | Absent in all | Present in animals |
| **Membranous organelles** | Sequester chemical reactions within the cell | | |
| Nucleus | "Control center" of the cell | Absent in all | Present in all |
| Endoplasmic reticulum | Transport within the cell, lipid synthesis | Absent in all | Present in all |
| Golgi bodies | Exocytosis, secretion | Absent in all | Present in some |
| Lysosomes | Breakdown of nutrients, self-destruction of damaged or aged cells | Absent in all | Present in some |
| Peroxisomes | Neutralization of toxins | Absent in all | Present in some |
| Vacuoles | Storage | Absent in all | Present in some |
| Vesicles | Storage, digestion, transport | Absent in all | Present in all |
| Mitochondria | Aerobic ATP production | Absent in all | Present in most |
| Chloroplasts | Photosynthesis | Absent in all, though infoldings of cytoplasmic membrane called photosynthetic lamellae have same function in photosynthetic prokaryotes | Present in plants, algae, and some protozoa |

## 6 Comparison of Archaeal, Bacterial, and Eukaryotic Cells

| Characteristic | Archaea | Bacteria | Eukaryotes |
|---|---|---|---|
| Nucleus | Absent in all | Absent | Present in all |
| Free organelles bound with phospholipid membranes | Absent in all | Present in few | Present; include ER, Golgi bodies, lysosomes, mitochondria, and chloroplasts |
| Glycocalyx | Present | Present as organized capsule or unorganized slime layer | Present, surrounding some animal cells |
| Motility | Present in some | Present in some | Some have complex undulating flagella and cilia composed of a "9 + 2" arrangement of microtubules; others move with amoeboid action using pseudopodia |
| Flagella | Some have flagella, each composed of basal body, hook, and filament; flagella rotate | Some have flagella, each composed of basal body, hook, and filament; flagella rotate | Present in some |
| Cilia | Absent in all | Absent in all | Present in some |
| Fimbriae or pili | Present in some | Present in some | Absent in all |
| Hami | Present in some | Absent in all | Absent in all |
| Cell wall | Present in most, lacking peptidoglycan | Present in most; composed of peptidoglycan | Present in plants, algae, and fungi |
| Cytoplasmic membrane | Present in all | Present in all | Present in all |
| Cytosol | Present in all | Present in all | Present in all |
| Inclusions | Present in most | Present in most | Present in some |
| Endospores | Absent in all | Present in some | Absent in all |
| Ribosomes | Small (70S) | Small (70S) | Large (80S) in cytosol and on ER, smaller (70S) in mitochondria and chloroplasts |
| Chromosomes | Commonly single and circular | Commonly single and circular | Linear and more than one chromosome per cell |

described a similar scenario for the origin of chloroplasts from phagocytized photosynthetic prokaryotes. The theory provides an explanation for the presence of 70S ribosomes and circular DNA within mitochondria and chloroplasts, and it accounts for the presence of their two membranes.

The endosymbiotic theory is widely but not universally accepted, however, partly because it does not explain all of the facts. For example, the theory provides no explanation for the two membranes of the nuclear envelope; nor does it explain why only a few polypeptides of mitochondria and chloroplasts are made in the organelles while the bulk of their proteins come from nuclear DNA and cytoplasmic ribosomes.

Table 6 summarizes features of prokaryotic and eukaryotic cells.

### CRITICAL THINKING

Eukaryotic cells are almost always larger than prokaryotic cells. What structures might allow for their larger size?

# Chapter Summary

### Processes of Life

1. All living things have some common features, including **growth,** an increase in size; **reproduction,** an increase in number; **responsiveness,** reactions to environmental stimuli; **metabolism,** controlled chemical reactions in an organism; and cellular structure.

2. Viruses are acellular and do not grow, self-reproduce, or metabolize.

## Prokaryotic and Eukaryotic Cells: An Overview

1. All cells can be described as either **prokaryotic** or **eukaryotic.** These descriptive terms help scientists categorize organisms in groups called taxa. Generally, prokaryotic cells make proteins simultaneously to reading the genetic code, and lack a nucleus and organelles surrounded by phospholipid membranes. Domain Bacteria and Domain Archaea are prokaryotic taxa.

2. Eukaryotes (Domain Eukarya) have internal, membrane-bound **organelles,** including nuclei. Animals, plants, algae, fungi, and protozoa are eukaryotic.

3. Cells share common structural features. These include external structures, cell walls, cytoplasmic membranes, and cytoplasm.

## External Structures of Bacterial Cells

1. The external structures of bacterial cells include glycocalyces, flagella, fimbriae, and pili.

2. **Glycocalyces** are sticky external sheaths of cells. They may be loosely attached **slime layers** or firmly attached **capsules.** Glycocalyces prevent cells from drying out. Capsules protect cells from phagocytosis by other cells, and slime layers enable cells to stick to each other and to surfaces in their environment.

3. A prokaryotic **flagellum** is a long, whiplike protrusion of some cells composed of a basal body, hook, and filament. Flagella allow cells to move toward favorable conditions such as nutrients or light, or move away from unfavorable stimuli such as poisons.
**ANIMATIONS:** *Motility; Flagella: Structure*

4. Bacterial flagella may be **polar** (single or tufts), or cover the cell (**peritrichous**). **Endoflagella,** which are special flagella of a spirochete, form an **axial filament,** located in the periplasmic space.
**ANIMATIONS:** *Arrangement, Spirochetes*

5. **Taxis** is movement that may be either a positive response or a negative response to light (**phototaxis**) or chemicals (**chemotaxis**).
**ANIMATIONS:** *Flagella: Movement*

6. **Fimbriae** are extensions of some bacterial cells that function along with glycocalyces to adhere cells to one another and to environmental surfaces. A mass of such bacteria on a surface is termed a **biofilm.** Cells may also use fimbriae to pull themselves across a surface.

7. **Pili,** also known as conjugation pili, are hollow, nonmotile tubes of protein that allow bacteria to pull themselves forward and mediate the movement of DNA from one cell to another. Not all bacteria have fimbriae or pili.

## Bacterial Cell Walls

1. Most prokaryotic cells have **cell walls** that provide shape and support against osmotic pressure. Cell walls are composed primarily of polysaccharide chains.

2. Cell walls of bacteria are composed of a large, interconnected molecule of **peptidoglycan.** Peptidoglycan is composed of alternating sugar molecules called *N*-acetylglucosamine (NAG) and *N*-acetylmuramic acid (NAM).

3. A **Gram-positive** bacterial cell has a thick layer of peptidoglycan.

4. A **Gram-negative** bacterial cell has a thin layer of peptidoglycan and an external wall membrane with a **periplasmic space** between. This wall membrane contains **lipopolysaccharide (LPS),** which contains **lipid A.** During an infection with Gram-negative bacteria, lipid A can accumulate in the blood, causing shock, fever, and blood clotting.

5. Acid-fast bacteria have waxy lipids in their cell walls.

## Bacterial Cytoplasmic Membranes

1. A **cytoplasmic membrane** is typically composed of phospholipid molecules arranged in a double layer configuration called a **phospholipid bilayer.** Proteins associated with the membrane vary in location and function and are able to flow laterally within the membrane. The **fluid mosaic model** is descriptive of the current understanding of membrane structure.
**ANIMATIONS:** *Membrane Structure*

2. The **selectively permeable** cytoplasmic membrane prevents the passage of some substances while allowing other substances to pass through protein pores or channels, sometimes requiring carrier molecules.
**ANIMATIONS:** *Membrane Permeability*

3. The relative concentrations inside and outside the cell of a chemical create a **concentration gradient.** Differences of electrical charges on the two sides of a membrane create an **electrical gradient** across the membrane. The gradients have a predictable effect on the passage of substances through the membrane.
**ANIMATIONS:** *Passive Transport: Principles of Diffusion*

4. Passive processes that move chemicals across the cytoplasmic membrane require no energy expenditure by the cell. Molecular size and concentration gradients determine the rate of simple **diffusion. Facilitated diffusion** depends on the electrochemical gradient and carriers within the membrane that allow certain substances to pass through the membrane. **Osmosis** specifically refers to the diffusion of water molecules across a selectively permeable membrane.

5. The concentrations of solutions can be compared. **Hypertonic** solutions have a higher concentration of solutes than **hypotonic** solutions, which have a lower concentration of solutes. Two **isotonic solutions** have the same concentrations of solutes. In biology, comparisons are usually made with the cytoplasm of cells.
**ANIMATIONS:** *Passive Transport: Special Types of Diffusion*

6. Active transport processes require cell energy from ATP. **Active transport** moves a substance against its electrochemical gradient via carrier proteins. These carriers may move two substances in the same direction at once (symports) or move substances in opposite directions (antiports). **Group translocation** occurs in prokaryotes, during which the substance being transported is chemically altered in transit.
**ANIMATIONS:** *Active Transport: Overview, Types*

## Cytoplasm of Bacteria

1. **Cytoplasm** is composed of the liquid **cytosol** inside a cell plus nonmembranous organelles and inclusions. **Inclusions** in the cytosol are deposits of various substances.

2. Both prokaryotic and eukaryotic cells contain nonmembranous organelles.

3. The **nucleoid** is the nuclear region in prokaryotic cytosol. It has no membrane and usually contains a single circular molecule of DNA.

4. Inclusions include reserve deposits of lipids, starch, or compounds containing nitrogen, phosphate, or sulfur. Inclusions called gas vesicles store gases.

5. Some bacteria produce dormant resistant **endospores** within vegetative cells.

6. **Ribosomes,** composed of protein and **ribosomal RNA (rRNA),** are nonmembranous organelles, found in both prokaryotes and eukaryotes, that function to make proteins. The 70S ribosomes of prokaryotes are smaller than the 80S ribosomes of eukaryotes.

7. The **cytoskeleton** is a network of fibrils that appears to help maintain the basic shape of prokaryotes.

## External Structures of Archaea

1. Archaea form polysaccharide and polypeptide glycocalyces that function in attachment and biofilm formation but are evidently not associated with diseases.

2. Archaeal flagella differ from bacterial flagella. For example, archaeal flagella are thinner than bacterial flagella.

3. Archaeal flagella rotate together as a bundle in both directions and are powered by molecules of ATP.

4. Archaea may have fimbriae and grappling-hook-like **hami** that serve to anchor the cells to environmental surfaces.

## Archaeal Cell Walls and Cytoplasmic Membranes

1. Archaeal cell walls are composed of protein or polysaccharides but not peptidoglycan.

2. Phospholipids in archaeal cytoplasmic membranes are built with ether linkages rather than ester linkages, which are seen in bacterial membranes.

## Cytoplasm of Archaea

1. Gel-like archaeal cytoplasm is similar to the cytoplasm of bacteria, having DNA, ribosomes, and a fibrous cytoskeleton, all suspended in the liquid cytosol.

2. 70S ribosomes of archaea have proteins more similar to those of eukaryotic ribosomes than to bacterial ribosomes.

## External Structure of Eukaryotic Cells

1. Eukaryotic animal and some protozoan cells lack cell walls but have glycocalyces that prevent desiccation, provide support, and enable cells to stick together.

2. Wall-less eukaryotic cells have glycocalyces, which are not found with eukaryotic cells that have walls.

## Eukaryotic Cell Walls and Cytoplasmic Membranes

1. Fungal, plant, algal, and some protozoan cells have cell walls composed of polysaccharides or other chemicals. Cell walls provide support, shape, and protection from osmotic forces.

2. Fungal cell walls are composed of chitin or other polysaccharides. Plant cell walls are composed of cellulose. Algal cell walls contain agar, carrageenan, algin, cellulose, or other chemicals.

3. Eukaryotic cytoplasmic membranes contain sterols such as cholesterol, which act to strengthen and solidify the membranes when temperatures rise and provide fluidity when temperatures fall.

4. **Membrane rafts** are distinct assemblages of certain lipids and proteins that remain together in the cytoplasmic membrane. Some viruses use lipid rafts during their infections of cells.

5. Some eukaryotic cells transport substances into the cytoplasm via **endocytosis,** which is an active process requiring the expenditure of energy from ATP. In endocytosis, **pseudopodia**—movable extensions of the cytoplasm and membrane of the cell—surround a substance and move it into the cell. When solids are brought into the cell, endocytosis is called **phagocytosis;** the incorporation of liquids by endocytosis is called **pinocytosis.**

6. **Exocytosis** is the active export of substances out of a cell.

## Cytoplasm of Eukaryotes

1. Eukaryotic cytoplasm is characterized by membranous organelles, particularly a nucleus. It also contains nonmembranous organelles and cytosol.

2. Some eukaryotic cells have long, whiplike flagella that differ from the flagella of prokaryotes. They have no hook, and the basal bodies and shafts are arrangements of microtubules. Further, eukaryotic flagella are internal to the cytoplasmic membrane.

3. Some eukaryotic cells have **cilia,** which have the same structure as eukaryotic flagella but are much shorter and more numerous. Cilia are internal to the cytoplasmic membrane.

4. The 80S ribosomes of eukaryotic cells are composed of 60S and 40S subunits. They are found free in the cytosol and attached to endoplasmic reticulum. The ribosomes within mitochondria and chloroplasts are 70S.

5. The eukaryotic cytoskeleton is composed of microtubules, intermediate filaments, and microfilaments. It provides an infrastructure and aids in movement of cytoplasm and organelles.

6. **Centrioles,** which are nonmembranous organelles in animal and some fungal cells only, are found in a region of the cytoplasm called the **centrosome** and are composed of triplets of microtubules in a "9 + 0" arrangement. Centrosomes function in the formation of flagella and cilia and in cell division.

7. The **nucleus,** a membranous structure in eukaryotic cells, contains **nucleoplasm** in which are found one or more **nucleoli** and **chromatin.** Chromatin consists of the multiple strands of DNA and associated histone proteins that become obvious as chromosomes during mitosis. **Nuclear pores** penetrate the four phospholipid layers of the **nuclear envelope** (membrane).

8. The **endoplasmic reticulum** functions as a transport system. It can be **rough ER (RER),** which has ribosomes on its surface, or **smooth ER (SER),** which lacks ribosomes.

9. A **Golgi body** is a series of flattened hollow sacs surrounded by phospholipid bilayers. It packages large molecules destined for export from the cell in **secretory vesicles,** which release these molecules from the cell via exocytosis.

10. **Vesicles** and **vacuoles** are general terms for membranous sacs that store or carry substances. More specifically, **lysosomes** of animal cells contain digestive enzymes, and **peroxisomes** contain enzymes that neutralize poisonous free radicals and hydrogen peroxide.

11. Four phospholipid layers surround **mitochondria,** site of production of ATP in a eukaryotic cell. The inner bilayer is folded into cristae, which greatly increase the surface area available for chemicals that generate ATP.

12. Photosynthetic eukaryotes possess **chloroplasts,** which are organelles containing membranous thylakoids that provide increased surface area for photosynthetic reactions.

13. The **endosymbiotic theory** has been suggested to explain why mitochondria and chloroplasts have 70S ribosomes, circular DNA, and two membranes. The theory states that the ancestors of these organelles were prokaryotic cells that were internalized by other prokaryotes and then lost the ability to exist outside their host—thus forming early eukaryotes.

# Questions for Review

*Answers to the Questions for Review (except Short Answer Questions) appear at the end of this chapter.*

## Multiple Choice

1. A cell may allow a large or charged chemical to move across the cytoplasmic membrane, down the chemical's electrical and chemical gradients, in a process called
   a. active transport.
   b. facilitated diffusion.
   c. endocytosis.
   d. pinocytosis.

2. Which of the following statements concerning growth and reproduction is *not* true?
   a. Growth and reproduction may occur simultaneously in living organisms.
   b. A living organism must reproduce to be considered alive.
   c. Living things may stop growing and reproducing, yet still be alive.
   d. Normally, living organisms have the ability to grow and reproduce themselves.

3. A "9 + 2" arrangement of microtubules is seen in
   a. archaeal flagella.
   b. bacterial flagella.
   c. eukaryotic flagella.
   d. all prokaryotic flagella.

4. Which of the following is most associated with diffusion?
   a. symports
   b. antiports
   c. carrier proteins
   d. endocytosis

5. Which of the following is *not* associated with prokaryotic organisms?
   a. nucleoid
   b. glycocalyx
   c. cilia
   d. circular DNA

6. Which of the following is true of Svedbergs?
   a. They are not exact but are useful for comparisons.
   b. They are abbreviated "sv."
   c. They are prokaryotic in nature but exhibit some eukaryotic characteristics.
   d. They are an expression of sedimentation rate during high-speed centrifugation.

7. Which of the following statements is true?
   a. The cell walls of bacteria are composed of peptidoglycan.
   b. Peptidoglycan is a fatty acid.
   c. Gram-positive bacterial walls have a relatively thin layer of peptidoglycan anchored to the cytoplasmic membrane by teichoic acids.
   d. Peptidoglycan is found mainly in the cell walls of fungi, algae, and plants.

8. Which of the following is *not* a function of a glycocalyx?
   a. It forms pseudopodia for faster mobility of an organism.
   b. It can protect a bacterial cell from drying out.
   c. It hides a bacterial cell from other cells.
   d. It allows a bacterium to stick to a host.

9. Bacterial flagella
   a. are anchored to the cell by a basal body.
   b. are composed of hami.
   c. are surrounded by an extension of the cytoplasmic membrane.
   d. are composed of tubulin in hollow microtubules in a "9 + 2" arrangement.

10. Which cellular structure is important in classifying a bacterial species as Gram-positive or Gram-negative?
    a. flagella
    b. cell wall
    c. cilia
    d. glycocalyx

11. A Gram-negative cell is moving uric acid across the cytoplasmic membrane against its chemical gradient. Which of the following statements is true?
    a. The exterior of the cell is probably electrically negative compared to the interior of the cell.
    b. The acid probably moves by a passive means such as facilitated diffusion.
    c. The acid moves by an active process such as active transport.
    d. The movement of the acid requires phagocytosis.

12. Gram-positive bacteria
    a. have a thick cell wall, which retains crystal violet dye.
    b. contain teichoic acids in their cell walls.
    c. appear purple after Gram staining.
    d. all of the above

13. Endospores
    a. are reproductive structures of some bacteria.
    b. occur in some archaea.
    c. can cause shock, fever, and inflammation.
    d. are dormant, resistant cells.

14. Inclusions have been found to contain
    a. DNA.
    b. sulfur globules.
    c. dipicolinic acid.
    d. tubulin.

15. Dipicolinic acid is an important component of
    a. Gram-positive archaeal walls.
    b. cytoplasmic membranes in eukaryotes.
    c. endospores.
    d. Golgi bodies.

## Matching

1. Match the structures on the left with the descriptions on the right. A letter may be used more than once or not at all, and more than one letter may be correct for each blank.

____ Glycocalyx     A. Bristlelike projections found in quantities of 100 or more

____ Flagella

____ Axial filaments     B. Long whip

____ Cilia     C. Responsible for conjugation

____ Fimbriae     D. "Sugar cup" composed of polysaccharides and/or polypeptides

____ Pili

____ Hami     E. Short, numerous, nonmotile projections

     F. Responsible for motility of spirochetes

     G. Extensions not used for cell motility

     H. Made of tubulin in eukaryotes

     I. Made of flagellin in bacteria

2. Match the term on the left with its description on the right. Only one description is intended for each term.

____ Ribosome     A. Site of protein synthesis

____ Cytoskeleton     B. Contains enzymes to neutralize hydrogen peroxide

____ Centriole

____ Nucleus     C. Functions as the transport system within a eukaryotic cell

____ Mitochondrion     D. Allows contraction of the cell

____ Chloroplast     E. Site of most DNA in eukaryotes

____ ER     F. Contains microtubules in "9 + 0" arrangement

____ Golgi body

____ Peroxisome     G. Light-harvesting organelle

     H. Packages large molecules for export from the cell

     I. Its internal membranes are sites for ATP production

## Short Answer

1. Describe (or draw) an example of diffusion down a concentration gradient.

2. Sketch, name, and describe three flagellar arrangements in bacteria.

3. Define *cytosol*.

4. The term *fluid mosaic* has been used in describing the cytoplasmic membrane. How does each word of that phrase accurately describe our current understanding of a cell membrane?

5. A local newspaper writer has contacted you, an educated microbiology student from a respected college. He wants to obtain scientific information for an article he is writing about "life" and poses the following query: "What is the difference between a living thing and a nonliving thing?" Knowing that he will edit your material to fit the article, give an intelligent, scientific response.

6. What is the difference between growth and reproduction?

7. Compare bacterial cells and algal cells, giving at least four similarities and four differences.

8. Contrast a cell of *Streptococcus pyogenes* (a bacterium) with the unicellular protozoan *Entamoeba histolytica*, listing at least eight differences.

9. Differentiate among pili, fimbriae, and cilia using sketches and descriptive labels.

10. Can nonliving things metabolize? Explain your answer.

11. How do archaeal flagella differ from bacterial flagella and eukaryotic flagella?

12. Contrast bacterial and eukaryotic cells by filling in the following table.

| Characteristic | Bacteria | Eukaryotes |
| --- | --- | --- |
| Size | | |
| Presence of nucleus | | |
| Presence of membrane-bound organelles | | |
| Structure of flagella | | |
| Chemicals in cell walls | | |
| Type of ribosomes | | |
| Structure of chromosomes | | |

13. What is the function of glycocalyces and fimbriae in forming a biofilm?

14. What factors may prevent a molecule from moving across a cell membrane?

15. Compare and contrast three types of passive transport across a cell membrane.

16. Contrast the following active processes for transporting materials into or out of a cell: active transport, group translocation, endocytosis, exocytosis.

17. Contrast symports and antiports.

18. Describe the endosymbiotic theory. What evidence supports the theory? Which features of eukaryotic cells are not explained by the theory?

19. Label the structures of the following prokaryotic and eukaryotic cells. With a single word or short phrase, explain the function of each structure.

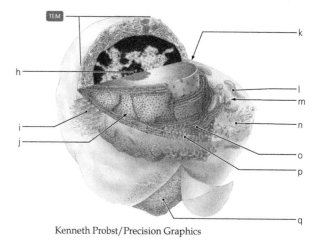

Kenneth Probst/Precision Graphics

Kenneth Probst/Precision Graphics

 Concept Mapping

Using the following terms, fill in the following concept map that describes the bacterial cell wall. In coming chapters, you'll be asked to draw your own maps to link concepts in a logical way to help you study processes and relationships of microbiological terms. Use this map as a guide, but know that all maps will be different because there are many ways to draw them. You also have the option to complete this and other concept maps online by going to the Study Area at www.masteringmicrobiology.com.

Glycan chains
Gram-negative cell wall
Gram-positive cell wall

Lipid A
Lipopolysaccharide (LPS)
*N*-acetylglucosamine

Peptidoglycan
Periplasm

Porins
Teichoic acids

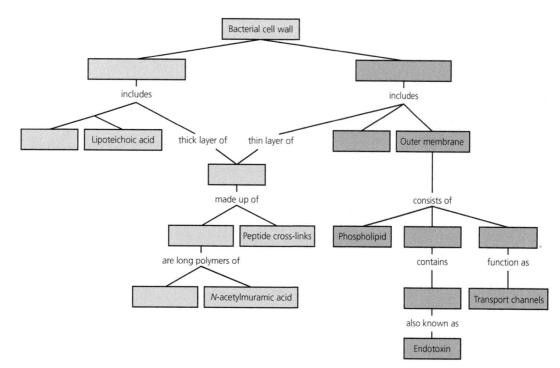

# Critical Thinking

1. A scientist develops a chemical that prevents Golgi bodies from functioning. Contrast the specific effects the chemical would have on human cells versus bacterial cells.

2. Methylene blue binds to DNA. What structures in a yeast cell would be stained by this dye?

3. A new chemotherapeutic drug kills bacteria, but not humans. Discuss the possible ways the drug may act selectively on bacterial cells.

4. Some bacterial toxins cause cells lining the digestive tract to secrete ions, making the contents of the tract hypertonic. What effect does this have on a patient's water balance?

5. A researcher carefully inserts an electrode into a plant cell. He determines that the electrical charge across the cytoplasmic membrane is −70 millivolts. Then he slips the electrode deeper into the cell across another membrane and measures an electrical charge of −90 millivolts compared to the outside. What relatively large organelle is surrounded by the second membrane? Explain your answer.

6. Does Figure 2 best represent a Gram-positive or a Gram-negative cell? Defend your answer.

7. An electron micrograph of a newly discovered cell shows long projections with a basal body in the cell wall. What kind of projections are these? Is the cell prokaryotic or eukaryotic? How might this cell behave in its environment because of the presence of this structure?

8. An entry in a recent scientific journal reports positive phototaxis in a newly described species. What condition could you create in the lab to encourage the growth of these organisms?

9. A medical microbiological lab report indicates that a sample contained a biofilm, and that one species in the biofilm was identified as *Neisseria gonorrhoeae.* Is this strain of *Neisseria* likely to be pathogenic? Why or why not?

10. A researcher treats a cell to block the function of SER only. Describe the initial effects this would have on the cell.

Access more review material online in the Study Area at **www.masteringmicrobiology.com.** There, you'll find

- **Animations**
- **BioFlix**
- **Videos**
- **MP3 Tutor Sessions**
- **Concept Mapping Activities**
- **Flashcards**
- **Quizzes**

and more to help you succeed.

# Answers

Answers to multiple-choice, fill-in-blank, labeling, matching, and true/false questions are listed here. Answers for Short Answer and Critical Thinking questions are available for instructors only in the Instructor's Manual that accompanies this text.

**Multiple Choice**
1. b; 2. b; 3. c; 4. c; 5. c; 6. d; 7. a; 8. a; 9. a; 10. b; 11. c; 12. d; 13. d; 14. b; 15. c

**Matching**
1. D Glycocalyx; B,H,I Flagella; F Axial filaments; H Cilia; A,E Fimbriae; C,G Pili; A,E,G Hami; 2. A Ribosome; D Cytoskeleton; F Centriole; E Nucleus; I Mitochondrion; G Chloroplast; C Endoplasmic reticulum; H Golgi body; B Peroxisome

# Microbial Metabolism

From Chapter 5 of *Microbiology with Diseases by Taxonomy*, Third Edition. Robert W. Bauman. Copyright © 2011 by Pearson Education, Inc. Published by Benjamin Cummings, Inc. All rights reserved.

# Microbial Metabolism

The next time you bite into a delicious piece of chocolate, consider this: microbial metabolism played a key role in how that chocolate became delicious.

Chocolate comes from cacao seeds, found inside the pods of *Theobroma cacao* trees. After the pods are split open, the seeds and the surrounding pulp are scooped out and placed in heaps on top of plantain or banana leaves. The heaps are then covered and left to ferment for two to seven days. Fermentation occurs as microorganisms—including yeast and several kinds of bacteria—grow on the fleshy, sugary pulp. Bathed in fermenting pulp, the cacao seeds (which start off tasting bitter) begin to develop the flavors and colors that we associate with chocolate. After fermentation, the seeds are dried, roasted, and then processed further by chocolate manufacturers before becoming one of our favorite desserts.

In this chapter we will learn about many metabolic processes of microorganisms, including fermentation.

 **Take the pre-test for this chapter online. Visit the Study Area at www.masteringmicrobiology.com.**

This chapter has *MicroFlix* . Go to **www.masteringmicrobiology.com** to view movie-quality animations for metabolism.

bobo/Alamy

Microorganisms will ferment these sun-dried cacao seeds to begin the transformation of cacao into chocolate.

How do pathogens acquire energy and nutrients at the expense of a patient's health? How does grape juice turn into wine, and how does yeast cause bread to rise? How do disinfectants, antiseptics, and antimicrobial drugs work? When laboratory personnel perform biochemical tests to identify unknown microorganisms and help diagnose disease, what exactly are they doing?

The answers to all of these questions require an understanding of microbial **metabolism,**[1] the collection of controlled biochemical reactions that takes place within the microbe. While it is true that metabolism in its entirety is complex, consisting of thousands of chemical reactions and control mechanisms, the reactions are nevertheless elegantly logical and can be understood in a simplified form. In this chapter we will concern ourselves only with central metabolic pathways and energy metabolism.

Your study of metabolism will be manageable if you keep in mind that the ultimate function of an organism's metabolism is to reproduce the organism, and that metabolic processes are guided by the following eight elementary statements:

- Every cell acquires *nutrients,* which are the chemicals necessary for metabolism.
- Metabolism requires energy from light or from the *catabolism* (kă-tab'ō-lizm; breakdown) of acquired nutrients.
- Energy is stored in the chemical bonds of *adenosine triphosphate (ATP).*
- Using *enzymes,* cells catabolize nutrient molecules to form elementary building blocks called *precursor metabolites.*
- Using these precursor metabolites, energy from ATP, and other enzymes, cells construct larger building blocks in *anabolic* (an-ă-bol'ik; biosynthetic) reactions.
- Cells use enzymes and additional energy from ATP to anabolically link building blocks together to form macromolecules in *polymerization* reactions.
- Cells grow by assembling macromolecules into cellular structures such as ribosomes, membranes, and cell walls.
- Cells typically reproduce once they have doubled in size.

We will discuss each aspect of metabolism in the chapters that most directly apply. In this chapter we examine the importance of enzymes in catabolic and anabolic reactions, study the three ways that ATP molecules are synthesized, and show that catabolic and anabolic reactions are linked. We also examine the catabolism of nutrient molecules; the anabolic reactions involved in the synthesis of carbohydrates, lipids, amino acids, and nucleotides; and a few ways that cells control their metabolic activities.

[1] From Greek *metabole,* meaning change.

# Basic Chemical Reactions Underlying Metabolism

In the following sections we will examine the basic concepts of catabolism, anabolism, and a special class of reactions called *oxidation-reduction reactions.* The latter involve the transfer of electrons between molecules. Then we will turn our attention briefly to the synthesis of ATP and energy storage before we discuss the organic catalysts called *enzymes,* which make metabolism possible. **ANIMATIONS:** *Metabolism: Overview*

## Catabolism and Anabolism

### Learning Objective

✓ Distinguish among metabolism, anabolism, and catabolism.

Metabolism, which is all of the chemical reactions in an organism, can be divided into two major classes of reactions: **catabolism** and **anabolism** (Figure 1). A series of such reactions is called a *pathway.* Cells have *catabolic pathways,* which break larger molecules into smaller products, and *anabolic pathways,* which synthesize large molecules from the smaller products of catabolism. Even though catabolic and anabolic pathways are intimately linked in cells, it is often useful to study the two types of pathways as if they were separate.

When catabolic pathways break down large molecules, they release energy; that is, catabolic pathways are *exergonic* (ek-ser-gon'ik). Cells store some of this released energy in the bonds of ATP, though much of the energy is lost as heat. Another result of the breakdown of large molecules by catabolic pathways is the production of numerous smaller molecules, some of which are **precursor metabolites** of anabolism. Some organisms, such as *Escherichia coli* (esh-ĕ-rik'ē-ă kō'lē), can synthesize everything in their cells just from precursor metabolites; other organisms must acquire some anabolic building blocks from outside their cells as nutrients. Catabolic *pathways,* but not necessarily *individual* catabolic *reactions,* produce ATP, or metabolites, or both. An example of a catabolic pathway is the breakdown of lipids into glycerol and fatty acids.

Anabolic pathways are functionally the opposite of catabolic pathways in that they synthesize macromolecules and cellular structures. Because building anything requires energy, anabolic pathways are *endergonic* (en-der-gon'ik); that is, they require more energy than they release. The energy required for anabolic pathways usually comes from ATP molecules produced during catabolism. An example of an anabolic pathway is the synthesis of lipids for cell membranes from glycerol and fatty acids.

To summarize, a cell's metabolism involves both catabolic pathways that break down macromolecules to supply molecular building blocks and energy in the form of ATP, and anabolic pathways that use the building blocks and ATP to synthesize macromolecules needed for growth and reproduction.

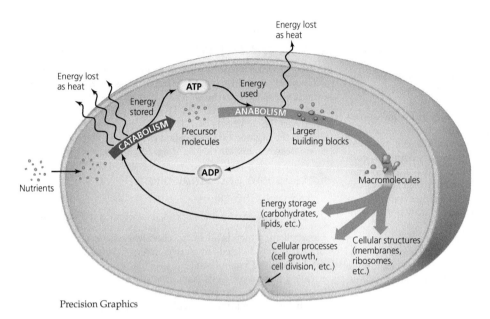

Energy lost as heat

Energy lost as heat

ATP

Energy stored

Energy used

ANABOLISM

CATABOLISM

Precursor molecules

Larger building blocks

ADP

Nutrients

Macromolecules

Energy storage (carbohydrates, lipids, etc.)

Cellular processes (cell growth, cell division, etc.)

Cellular structures (membranes, ribosomes, etc.)

Precision Graphics

◄ **Figure 1 Metabolism is composed of catabolic and anabolic reactions.** Some energy released in catabolism is stored in ATP molecules, but most is lost as heat. Anabolic reactions require energy, typically provided by ATP. There is some heat loss in anabolism as well. The products of catabolism provide many of the building blocks for anabolic reactions. These reactions produce macromolecules and cellular structures, leading to cell growth and division.

## Oxidation and Reduction Reactions

### Learning Objective

✓ Contrast reduction and oxidation reactions.

Many metabolic reactions involve the transfer of electrons from an *electron donor* (a molecule that donates an electron) to an *electron acceptor* (a molecule that accepts an electron). Such electron transfers are called **oxidation-reduction reactions,** or **redox reactions** (Figure 2). An electron acceptor is said to be *reduced.* This may seem backward, but electron acceptors are reduced because their gain in electrons reduces their overall electrical charge (that is, they are more negatively charged). Molecules that lose electrons are said to be *oxidized* because frequently

their electrons are donated to oxygen atoms. An acronym to help you remember these concepts is OIL RIG: oxidation involves loss; reduction involves gain.

Reduction and oxidation reactions always happen simultaneously because every electron donated by one chemical is accepted by another chemical. A chemical may be reduced by gaining either a simple electron or an electron that is part of a hydrogen atom—which is composed of one proton and one electron. **Beneficial Microbes: Gold-Mining Microbes** describes an interesting example of how some prokaryotes are able to reduce gold dissolved in solution.

In contrast, a molecule may be oxidized in one of three ways: by losing a simple electron, by losing a hydrogen atom, or by gaining an oxygen atom. Biological oxidations often involve the loss of

---

**BENEFICIAL MICROBES**

### GOLD-MINING MICROBES

▲ *Solid gold is gold in its reduced form.*

Gold, as found in nature, exists in two forms: gold-ore deposits, which are gold in its reduced form, usually found near the Earth's crust, and gold dissolved in solution, as found in thermal springs and in seawater. Dissolved gold, which is gold in its oxidized forms, is largely useless to humans; it cannot be converted inexpensively into solid gold. Even though gold in either form is toxic when

ingested by most living things, scientists have discovered that certain bacteria, such as *Ralstonia metallidurans*, can metabolize oxidized gold. When placed in a solution containing oxidized gold, these microorganisms reduce the gold and encase themselves in solid gold, which is their metabolic waste.

Entrepreneurial minds may wonder whether *Ralstonia* could be potentially profitable. While it is true that a great deal of dissolved gold is found in thermal springs and oceans, the gold is very dilute—only minute amounts are present in very large volumes of water. Moreover, were someone to perfect a way of using microorganisms to convert dissolved gold to great quantities of solid gold, they would be wise to keep it to themselves: so much solid gold could become available that its market value would plunge dramatically.

Precision Graphics

▲ **Figure 2 Oxidation-reduction, or redox, reactions.** When electrons are transferred from donor molecules to acceptor molecules, donors become oxidized and acceptors become reduced. *Why are acceptor molecules said to be reduced when they are gaining electrons?*

**Figure 2** *"Reduction" refers to the overall electrical charge on a molecule. Because electrons have a negative charge, the gain of an electron reduces the molecule's overall charge.*

hydrogen atoms; such reactions are also called *dehydrogenation* (dē-hī′drō-jen-ā′shŭn) *reactions.*

Electrons rarely exist freely in cytoplasm; instead, they orbit atomic nuclei. Therefore, cells use electron carrier molecules to carry electrons (often in hydrogen atoms) from one location in a cell to another. Three important electron carrier molecules, which are derived from vitamins, are **nicotinamide adenine dinucleotide ($NAD^+$), nicotinamide adenine dinucleotide phosphate ($NADP^+$), and flavin adenine dinucleotide (FAD).** Cells use each of these molecules in specific metabolic pathways to carry pairs of electrons. One of the electrons carried by either $NAD^+$ or $NADP^+$ is part of a hydrogen atom, forming NADH or NADPH. FAD carries two electrons as hydrogen atoms ($FADH_2$). Many metabolic pathways, including those that synthesize ATP, require such electron carrier molecules. **ANIMATIONS:** *Oxidation-Reduction Reactions*

### CRITICAL **THINKING**

Arsenic is a poison that exists in two states in the environment—arsenite ($H_2AsO_3^-$) and arsenate ($H_2AsO_4^-$). Arsenite dissolves in water, making the water dangerous to drink. Arsenate is less soluble and binds to minerals, making this form of arsenic less toxic in the environment. Some strains of the bacterium *Thermus* oxidize arsenic in an aerobic environment but reduce arsenic under anaerobic conditions. In case of arsenic contamination of water, how could scientists use *Thermus* to remediate the problem?

## ATP Production and Energy Storage

### Learning Objective

✓ Compare and contrast the three types of ATP phosphorylation.

Nutrients contain energy, but that energy is spread throughout their chemical bonds and generally is not concentrated enough for use in anabolic reactions. During catabolism, organisms release energy from nutrients that can then be concentrated and stored in high-energy phosphate bonds of molecules such as

ATP. This happens by a general process called *phosphorylation* (fos′fōr-i-lā′shŭn), in which inorganic phosphate ($PO_4^{3-}$) is added to a substrate. For example, cells phosphorylate adenosine diphosphate (ADP), which has two phosphate groups, to form adenosine triphosphate (ATP), which has three phosphate groups.

As we will examine in the following sections, cells phosphorylate ADP to form ATP in three specific ways:

- *Substrate-level phosphorylation,* which involves the transfer of phosphate to ADP from another phosphor-ylated organic compound
- *Oxidative phosphorylation,* in which energy from redox reactions of respiration (described shortly) is used to attach inorganic phosphate to ADP
- *Photophosphorylation,* in which light energy is used to phosphorylate ADP with inorganic phosphate

We will investigate each of these in more detail as we proceed through the chapter.

After ADP is phosphorylated to produce ATP, anabolic pathways use some energy of ATP by breaking a phosphate bond (which re-forms ADP). Thus the cyclical interconversion of ADP and ATP functions somewhat like rechargeable batteries: ATP molecules store energy from light (in photosynthetic organisms) and from catabolic reactions and then release stored energy to drive cellular processes (including anabolic reactions, active transport, and movement). ADP molecules can be "recharged" to ATP again and again.

## The Roles of Enzymes in Metabolism

### Learning Objectives

✓ Make a table listing the six basic types of enzymes, their activities, and an example of each.

✓ Describe the components of a holoenzyme and contrast protein and RNA enzymes.

✓ Define *activation energy, enzyme, apoenzyme, cofactor, coenzyme, active site,* and *substrate,* and describe their roles in enzyme activity.

✓ Describe how temperature, pH, substrate concentration, and competitive and noncompetitive inhibition affect enzyme activity.

Reactions occur when chemical bonds are broken or formed between atoms. In catabolic reactions, a bond must be destabilized before it will break, whereas in anabolic reactions reactants collide with sufficient energy for bonds to form between them. In anabolism, increasing either the concentrations of reactants or ambient temperatures increases the number of collisions and produces more chemical reactions; however, in living organisms, neither reactant concentration nor temperature is usually high enough to ensure that bonds will form. Therefore, the chemical reactions of life depend upon *catalysts,* which are chemicals that increase the likelihood of a reaction but are not permanently changed in the process. Organic catalysts are known as **enzymes.** **ANIMATIONS:** *Enzymes: Overview*

## TABLE 1 Enzyme Classification Based on Reaction Types

| Class | Type of Reaction Catalyzed | Example |
|---|---|---|
| Hydrolase | Hydrolysis (catabolic) | Lipase—breaks down lipid molecules |
| Isomerase | Rearrangement of atoms within a molecule (neither catabolic nor anabolic) | Phosphoglucoisomerase—converts glucose 6-phosphate into fructose 6-phosphate during glycolysis |
| Ligase or polymerase | Joining two or more chemicals together (anabolic) | Acetyl-CoA synthetase—combines acetate and coenzyme A to form acetyl-CoA for the Krebs cycle |
| Lyase | Splitting a chemical into smaller parts without using water (catabolic) | Fructose-1,6-bisphosphate aldolase—splits fructose 1,6-bisphosphate into G3P and DHAP |
| Oxidoreductase | Transfer of electrons or hydrogen atoms from one molecule to another | Lactic acid dehydrogenase—oxidizes lactic acid to form pyruvic acid during fermentation |
| Transferase | Moving a functional group from one molecule to another (may be anabolic) | Hexokinase—transfers phosphate from ATP to glucose in the first step of glycolysis |

## Naming and Classifying Enzymes

The names of enzymes usually end with the suffix "-ase," and the name of each enzyme often incorporates the name of that enzyme's **substrate,** which is the molecule the enzyme acts upon. Based on their mode of action, enzymes can be grouped into six basic categories:

- *Hydrolases* catabolize molecules by adding water in a decomposition process known as *hydrolysis*. Hydrolases are used primarily in the depolymerization of macromolecules.
- *Isomerases*[2] rearrange the atoms within a molecule but do not add or remove anything (so they are neither catabolic nor anabolic).
- *Ligases,* or *polymerases,* join two molecules together (and are thus anabolic). They often use energy supplied by ATP.
- *Lyases* split large molecules (and are thus catabolic) without using water in the process.
- *Oxidoreductases* remove electrons from (oxidize) or add electrons to (reduce) various substrates. They are used in both catabolic and anabolic pathways.
- *Transferases* transfer functional groups, such as an amino group ($NH_2$), a phosphate group, or a two-carbon (acetyl) group, between molecules. Transferases can be anabolic.

Table 1 summarizes these types of enzymes and gives examples of each.

## The Makeup of Enzymes

Many protein enzymes are complete in themselves, but others are composed of both protein and nonprotein portions. The proteins, called **apoenzymes** (ap'ō-en-zīms), are inactive if they are not bound to one or more of the nonprotein substances called **cofactors.** Cofactors are either inorganic ions (such as iron, magnesium, zinc, or copper ions) or certain organic molecules called coenzymes. All **coenzymes** (ko-en'zīms) are either vitamins or

contain vitamins, which are organic molecules that are required for metabolism but cannot be synthesized by certain organisms (especially mammals). Some apoenzymes bind with inorganic cofactors, some bind with coenzymes, and some bind with both. The binding of an apoenzyme and its cofactor(s) forms an active enzyme, called a **holoenzyme** (hol-ō-en'zīm; Figure 3).

Table 2 lists several examples of inorganic cofactors and organic cofactors (coenzymes). Note that three important coenzymes are the electron carriers $NAD^+$, $NADP^+$, and FAD, which, as we have seen, carry electrons in hydrogen atoms from place to place within cells. We will examine more closely the roles of these coenzymes in the generation of ATP later in the chapter.

Not all enzymes are proteinaceous; some are RNA molecules called **ribozymes.** In eukaryotes, ribozymes process other RNA molecules by removing sections of RNA and splicing the remaining pieces together. Recently, researchers have discovered that the functional core of a ribosome is a ribozyme; therefore, given that ribosomes make all proteins, ribosomal enzymes make protein enzymes.

Precision Graphics

▲ **Figure 3 Makeup of a protein enzyme.** The combination of a proteinaceous apoenzyme with one or more cofactors forms a holoenzyme, which is the active form of an enzyme. A cofactor is either an inorganic ion or a coenzyme, which is an organic cofactor derived from a vitamin. The apoenzyme is inactive unless it is bound to its cofactors. *Name four metal ions that can act as cofactors.*

**Figure 3** *Iron, magnesium, zinc, and copper ions can act as cofactors.*

---

[2]An isomer is a compound with the same molecular formula as another molecule, but with a different arrangement of atoms.

## TABLE 2 Representative Cofactors of Enzymes

| Cofactors | Examples of Use in Enzymatic Activity | Substance Transferred in Enzymatic Activity | Vitamin Source (of Coenzyme) |
|---|---|---|---|
| **Inorganic (Metal Ion)** | | | |
| Magnesium ($Mg^{2+}$) | Forms bond with ADP during phosphorylation | Phosphate | None |
| **Organic (Coenzymes)** | | | |
| Nicotinamide adenine dinucleotide ($NAD^+$) | Carrier of reducing power | Two electrons and a hydrogen ion | Niacin |
| Nicotinamide adenine dinucleotide phosphate ($NADP^+$) | Carrier of reducing power | Two electrons and a hydrogen ion | Niacin |
| Flavin adenine dinucleotide (FAD) | Carrier of reducing power | Two hydrogen atoms | Riboflavin |
| Tetrahydrofolate | Used in synthesis of nucleotides and some amino acids | One-carbon molecule | Folic acid |
| Coenzyme A | Formation of acetyl-CoA in Krebs cycle and beta-oxidation | Two-carbon molecule | Pantothenic acid |
| Pyridoxal phosphate | Transaminations in the synthesis of amino acids | Amine group | Pyridoxine |
| Thiamine pyrophosphate | Decarboxylation of pyruvic acid | Aldehyde group (CHO) | Thiamine |

## Enzyme Activity

Within cells, enzymes catalyze reactions by lowering the **activation energy,** which is the amount of energy needed to trigger a chemical reaction (Figure 4). Whereas heat can provide energy to trigger reactions, the temperatures needed to reach activation energy for most metabolic reactions are often too high to allow cells to survive, so enzymes are needed if metabo-

lism is to occur. This is true regardless of whether the enzyme is a protein or RNA, or whether the chemical reaction is anabolic or catabolic.

The activity of enzymes depends on the closeness of fit between the functional sites of an enzyme and its substrate. The shape of an enzyme's functional site, called its **active site,** is complementary to the shape of the substrate. Generally, the shapes and locations of only a few amino acids or nucleotides determines the shape of an enzyme's active site. A change in a single component—for instance, through mutation—can render an enzyme less effective or even completely nonfunctional.

*Enzyme-substrate specificity,* which is critical to enzyme activity, has been likened to the fit between a lock and key. This analogy is not completely apt because enzymes change shape slightly when they bind to their substrate, almost as if a lock could grasp its key once it had been inserted. This latter description of enzyme-substrate specificity is called the **induced-fit model** (Figure 5).

In some cases, several different enzymes possess active sites that are complementary to various portions of a single substrate molecule. For example, an important precursor metabolite called phosphoenolpyruvic acid (PEP) is the substrate for at least five enzymes; depending on the enzyme involved, various products are produced from PEP. In one catabolic pathway PEP is converted to pyruvic acid, whereas in a particular anabolic pathway PEP is converted to the amino acid phenylalanine.

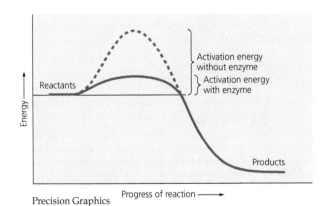

Precision Graphics

▲ **Figure 4 The effect of enzymes on chemical reactions.** Enzymes catalyze reactions by lowering the activation energy—that is, the energy needed to trigger the reaction.

Precision Graphics

**(a)** Active sites · Substrate · Enzyme · Enzyme-substrate complex

**(b)** Active site · Substrate · Enzyme · Enzyme-substrate complex

Ken Eward, Biografx.com

▲ **Figure 5 Enzymes fitted to substrates. (a)** The induced-fit model of enzyme-substrate interaction. An enzyme's active site is generally complementary to the shape of its substrate, but a perfect fit between them does not occur until the substrate and enzyme bind to form a complex. **(b)** Space-filling models of an enzyme that changes shape to bind its substrate more tightly.

Although the exact ways that enzymes lower activation energy are not known, it appears that several mechanisms are involved. Some enzymes appear to bring reactants into sufficiently close proximity to enable a bond to form, whereas other enzymes change the shape of a reactant, inducing a bond to be broken. In any case, enzymes increase the likelihood that bonds will form or break.

The activity of enzymes is believed to follow the process illustrated in Figure 6, which depicts the catabolic lysis of a molecule called fructose 1,6-bisphosphate:

1. An enzyme associates with a specific substrate molecule having a shape that is complementary to that enzyme's active site.

2. The enzyme and its substrate bind to form a temporary intermediate compound called an enzyme-substrate complex. The binding of the substrate induces the enzyme to fit the shape of the substrate even more closely.

3. Bonds within the substrate are broken, forming two (and in some other reactions, more than two) products. (This is a catabolic reaction; in anabolic reactions, reactants are linked together to form products.)

4. The enzyme dissociates from the newly formed molecules, which diffuse away from the site of the reaction, and the enzyme resumes its original configuration and is ready to associate with another substrate molecule.

Many factors influence the rate of enzymatic reactions, including temperature, pH, enzyme and substrate concentrations, and the presence of inhibitors. **ANIMATIONS:** *Enzymes: Steps in a Reaction*

**Temperature** As mentioned, higher temperatures tend to increase the rate of most chemical reactions because molecules are moving faster and collide more frequently, which encourages bonds to form or break. However, this is not entirely true of enzymatic reactions, because the active sites of enzymes change shape as temperature changes. If the temperature rises too high or falls too low, an enzyme is often no longer able to achieve a fit with its substrate.

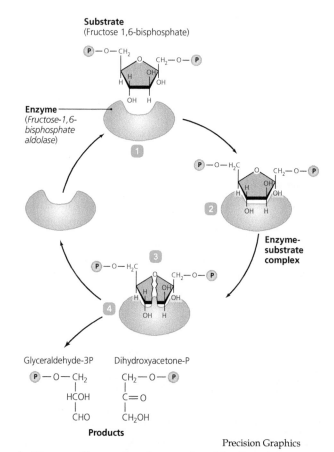

**Substrate** (Fructose 1,6-bisphosphate)

**Enzyme** (*Fructose-1,6-bisphosphate aldolase*)

Enzyme-substrate complex

Glyceraldehyde-3P

Dihydroxyacetone-P

**Products**

Precision Graphics

▲ **Figure 6 The process of enzymatic activity.** Shown here is the lysis of fructose 1,6-bisphosphate by the enzyme fructose-1,6-bisphosphate aldolase (a catabolic reaction). After the enzyme associates with the substrate (1), the two molecules bind to form an enzyme-substrate complex. (2), As a result of binding, the enzyme's active site is induced to fit the substrate even more closely. Next, bonds within the substrate are broken (3), after which the enzyme dissociates from the two new products (4). The enzyme resumes its initial configuration and is then ready to associate with another substrate molecule. This entire process occurs 14 times per second at 37°C.

**(a) Temperature**

Precision Graphics

**(b) pH**

Precision Graphics

**(c) Substrate concentration**

Precision Graphics

▲ **Figure 7 Representative effects of temperature, pH, and substrate concentration on enzyme activity.** Effects on each enzyme will vary. **(a)** Rising temperature enhances enzymatic activity to a point, but above some optimal temperature an enzyme denatures and loses function. **(b)** Enzymes typically have some optimal pH, at which point enzymatic activity reaches a maximum. **(c)** At lower substrate concentrations, enzyme activity increases as the substrate concentration increases and as more and more active sites are utilized. At the substrate concentration at which all active sites are utilized, termed the saturation point, enzymatic activity reaches a maximum, and any additional increase in substrate concentration has no effect on enzyme activity. *What is the optimal pH of the enzyme shown in part (b)?*

Figure 7 *The enzyme's optimal pH is approximately 7.2.*

Functional protein       Denatured protein

Precision Graphics

▲ **Figure 8 Denaturation of protein enzymes.** Breakage of noncovalent bonds (such as hydrogen bonds) causes the protein to lose its secondary and tertiary structure and become denatured; as a result, the enzyme is no longer functional.

Each enzyme has an optimal temperature for its activity (Figure 7a). The optimum temperature for the enzymes in the human body is 37°C, which is normal body temperature. Part of the reason certain pathogens can cause disease in humans is that the optimal temperature for the enzymes in those microorganisms is also 37°C. The enzymes of some other microorganisms, however, function best at much higher temperatures; this is the case for *hyperthermophiles,* organisms that grow best at temperatures above 80°C.

If temperature rises beyond a certain critical point, the noncovalent bonds within an enzyme (such as the hydrogen bonds between amino acids) will break, and the enzyme will **denature** (Figure 8). Denatured enzymes lose their specific three-dimensional structure, so they are no longer functional. Denaturation is said to be *permanent* when an enzyme cannot regain its original three-dimensional structure once conditions return to normal, much like the irreversible solidification of the protein albumin when egg whites are cooked and then cooled. In other cases denaturation is *reversible*—the denatured enzyme's noncovalent bonds reform upon the return of normal conditions.

## CRITICAL **THINKING**

Explain why hyperthermophiles do not cause disease in humans.

**pH** Extremes of pH also denature enzymes when ions released from acids and bases interfere with hydrogen bonding and distort and disrupt an enzyme's secondary and tertiary structures. Therefore, each enzyme has an optimal pH (Figure 7b).

Changing the pH provides a way to control the growth of unwanted microorganisms by denaturing their proteins. For example, vinegar (acetic acid, pH 3.0) acts as a preservative in dill pickles, and ammonia (pH 11.5) can be used as a disinfectant.

## CRITICAL **THINKING**

In addition to extremes in temperature and pH, other chemical and physical agents denature proteins. These agents include ionizing radiation, alcohol, enzymes, and heavy-metal ions. For example, the first antimicrobial drug, arsphenamine, contained the heavy metal arsenic and was used to inhibit the enzymes of the bacterium *Treponema pallidum*, the causative agent of syphilis.

Given that both human and bacterial enzymes are denatured by heavy metals, how was arsphenamine used to treat syphilis without poisoning the patient? Why is syphilis no longer treated with arsenic-containing compounds?

**Enzyme and Substrate Concentration** Another factor that determines the rate of enzymatic activity within cells is the concentration of substrate present (Figure 7c). As substrate concentration increases, enzymatic activity increases as more and more enzyme active sites bind more and more substrate molecules. Eventually, when all enzyme active sites have bound substrate, the enzymes have reached their saturation point, and the addition of more substrate will not increase the rate of enzymatic activity.

Obviously, the rate of enzymatic activity is also affected by the concentration of enzyme within cells. In fact, one way that organisms regulate their metabolism is by controlling the quantity and timing of enzyme synthesis. In other words, many enzymes are produced in the amounts and at the times they are needed to maintain metabolic activity. Additionally, eukaryotic cells control some enzymatic activities by compartmentalizing enzymes inside membranes so that certain metabolic reactions proceed physically separated from the rest of the cell. For example, white blood cells catabolize phagocytized pathogens using enzymes packaged within lysosomes.

**Inhibitors** Enzymatic activity can be influenced by a variety of inhibitory substances that block an enzyme's active site. Enzymatic inhibitors, which may be either competitive or noncompetitive, do not denature enzymes.

**Competitive inhibitors** are shaped such that they fit into an enzyme's active site and thus prevent the normal substrate from binding (Figure 9a). However, such inhibitors do not undergo a chemical reaction to form products. Competitive inhibitors can bind permanently or reversibly to an active site. Permanent binding results in permanent loss of enzymatic activity; reversible competition can be overcome by an increase in the concentration of substrate molecules, which increases the likelihood that active sites will be filled with substrate instead of inhibitor (Figure 9b). ANIMATIONS: *Enzymes: Competitive Inhibition*

An example of competitive inhibition is the action of sulfanilamide, which has a shape similar to that of para-aminobenzoic acid (PABA).

Sulfanilamide has great affinity for the active site of an enzyme required in the conversion of PABA into folic acid, which

**(a)**
Precision Graphics

**(b)**
Precision Graphics

▲ **Figure 9 Competitive inhibition of enzyme activity.**
**(a)** Inhibitory molecules, which are similar in shape to substrate molecules, compete for and block active sites. **(b)** Reversible inhibition can be overcome by an increase in substrate concentration.

is essential for DNA synthesis. Once sulfanilamide is bound to the enzyme, it stays bound. As a result, it prevents synthesis of folic acid. Sulfanilamide effectively inhibits bacteria that make folic acid. Humans do not synthesize folic acid—we must acquire it as a vitamin in our diets—so sulfanilamide does not affect us in this way.

Sulfanilamide          PABA
Precision Graphics

**Noncompetitive inhibitors** do not bind to the active site but instead prevent enzymatic activity by binding to an *allosteric* (al-ō-stār′ik) *site* located elsewhere on the enzyme. Binding at an allosteric site alters the shape of the active site so that substrate cannot be bound. Allosteric control of enzyme activity can take two forms: inhibitory and excitatory. *Allosteric (noncompetitive) inhibition* halts enzymatic activity in the manner just described (Figure 10a). In *excitatory allosteric control*, the binding of certain activator molecules (such as a heavy-metal ion cofactor) to an allosteric site causes a change in shape of the active site, which activates an otherwise inactive enzyme (Figure 10b). Some enzymes have several allosteric sites, both inhibitory and excitatory, which allows their function to be closely regulated. ANIMATIONS: *Enzyme-Substrate Interaction: Noncompetitive Inhibition*

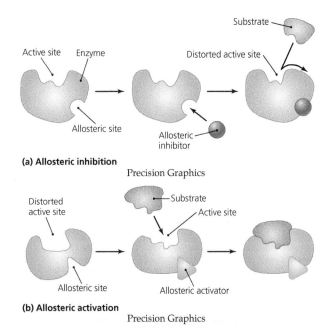

Precision Graphics

**(a) Allosteric inhibition**

Precision Graphics

**(b) Allosteric activation**

Precision Graphics

▲ **Figure 10 Allosteric control of enzyme activity. (a)** Allosteric (noncompetitive) inhibition results from a change in the shape of the active site when an inhibitor binds to an allosteric site. **(b)** Allosteric activation results when the binding of an activator molecule to an allosteric site causes a change in the active site that makes it capable of binding substrate.

Cells often control the action of enzymes through **feedback inhibition** (also called *negative feedback* or *end-product inhibition*). Allosteric feedback inhibition functions in much the way a thermostat controls a heater. As the room gets warmer, a sensor inside the thermostat changes shape and sends an electrical signal that turns off the heater. Similarly, in metabolic feedback inhibition, the end-product of a series of reactions is an allosteric inhibitor of an enzyme in an earlier part of the pathway (**Figure 11a**). Because the product of each reaction in the pathway is the substrate for the next reaction, inhibition of the first enzyme in the series inhibits the entire pathway, thereby saving the cell energy. For example, in *Escherichia coli,* the presence of the amino acid isoleucine allosterically inhibits the first enzyme in the anabolic pathway that produces isoleucine. In this manner, the bacterium prevents the synthesis of isoleucine when the amino acid is already available. When isoleucine is depleted, the enzyme is no longer inhibited, and isoleucine production resumes.

Feedback inhibition can occur in even more complex ways. For instance, even though the first step in the synthesis of the amino acids tyrosine, phenylalanine, and tryptophan is the same—the linkage of phosphoenolpyruvic acid (PEP) and erythrose 4-phosphate to form 3-deoxy-arabino-heptulosonic acid 7-phosphate (DAHAP)—three different synthetase enzymes are

involved (**Figure 11b**). In other words, enzymatic reactions convert DAHAP into the three amino acids via three different pathways. As shown, each of the end-product amino acids inhibits only one of the three synthetase enzymes. Therefore, an excess of all three amino acids is needed to completely hinder synthesis of DAHAP and thereby stop the production of these amino acids.

To this point we have viewed the concept of metabolism as a collection of chemical reactions (pathways) that can be categorized as either catabolic (breaking down) or anabolic (building up). Because enzymes are required to lower the activation energy of these reactions, we examined these catalysts in some detail.

Energy is also critical to metabolism, so we examined redox reactions as a means of transferring energy within cells. We saw, for example, that redox reactions and carrier molecules are used to transfer energy from catabolic pathways to ATP, a molecule that stores energy in cells.

We will now consider how cells acquire and utilize metabolites, which are used to synthesize the macromolecules necessary for growth and, eventually, reproduction—the ultimate goal of metabolism. We will also consider in more detail the phosphorylation of ADP to make ATP.

# Carbohydrate Catabolism

## Learning Objective

✓ In general terms, describe the three stages of aerobic glucose catabolism (glycolysis, the Krebs cycle, and the electron transport chain), including their substrates, products, and net energy production.

Many organisms oxidize carbohydrates as their primary energy source for anabolic reactions. They use glucose most commonly, though other sugars, amino acids, and fats are also utilized, often by first converting them into glucose. Glucose is catabolized via one of two processes: either via *cellular respiration*[3]—a process that results in the complete breakdown of glucose to carbon dioxide and water—or via *fermentation,* which results in organic waste products.

As shown in **Figure 12**, both cellular respiration and fermentation begin with *glycolysis* (glī-kol′i-sis), a process that catabolizes a single molecule of glucose to two molecules of pyruvic acid (also called pyruvate) and results in a small amount of ATP production. Respiration then continues via the *Krebs cycle* and the *electron transport chain,* which results in a significant amount of ATP production. Fermentation involves the conversion of pyruvic acid into other organic compounds. Because it lacks the Krebs cycle and electron transport chain, fermentation results in the production of much less ATP than does respiration.

[3]Cellular respiration is often referred to simply as *respiration,* which should not be confused with breathing, also called respiration.

**(a)**

Precision Graphics

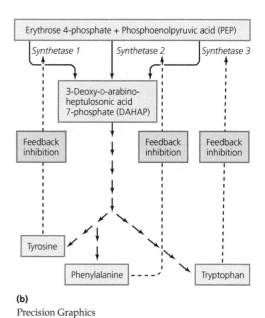

**(b)**

Precision Graphics

◄ **Figure 11 Feedback inhibition. (a)** The end-product of a metabolic pathway allosterically inhibits the initial step, shutting down the pathway. **(b)** In this example, each of the three end-products (tyrosine, phenylalanine, and trypotophan) inhibits a different synthetase enzyme. An excess of all three end-products is needed to completely hinder the synthesis of 3-deoxy-arabino-heptulosonic acid 7-phosphate. Each arrow indicates an individual metabolic step.

The following is a simplified discussion of glucose catabolism. To help understand the basic reactions in each of the pathways of glucose catabolism, pay special attention to three things: the number of carbon atoms in each of the intermediate products, the relative numbers of ATP molecules produced in each pathway, and the changes in the coenzymes $NAD^+$ and FAD as they are reduced and then oxidized back to their original forms.

## Glycolysis

**Glycolysis,**[4] also called the *Embden-Meyerhof pathway* after the scientists who discovered it, is the first step in the catabolism of glucose via both respiration and fermentation. Glycolysis occurs in most cells. In general, as its name implies, glycolysis involves

the splitting of a six-carbon glucose molecule into two three-carbon sugar molecules. When these three-carbon molecules are oxidized to pyruvic acid, some of the energy released is stored in molecules of ATP. **ANIMATIONS:** *Glycolysis: Overview*

Glycolysis, which occurs in the cytosol, can be divided into three stages involving a total of 10 steps (Figure 13), each of which is catalyzed by its own enzyme. The three stages of glycolysis are:

1. *Energy-investment stage* (steps **1**–**3**). As with money, one must invest before a profit can be made. In this case, the energy in two molecules of ATP is invested to phosphorylate a six-carbon glucose molecule and rearrange its atoms to form fructose 1,6-bisphosphate.

2. *Lysis stage* (steps **4** and **5**). Fructose 1,6-bisphosphate is cleaved into glyceraldehyde 3-phosphate (G3P)[5] and dihydroxyacetone phosphate (DHAP). Each of these compounds contains three carbon atoms and is freely convertible into the other.

3. *Energy-conserving stage* (steps **6**–**10**). G3P is oxidized to pyruvic acid, yielding two ATP molecules. DHAP is converted to G3P and also oxidized to pyruvic acid, yielding another two ATP molecules, for a total of four ATP molecules.

---

[4]From Greek *glukus*, meaning sweet, and *lusis*, meaning to loosen.
[5]G3P is also known as phosphoglyceraldehyde or PGAL.

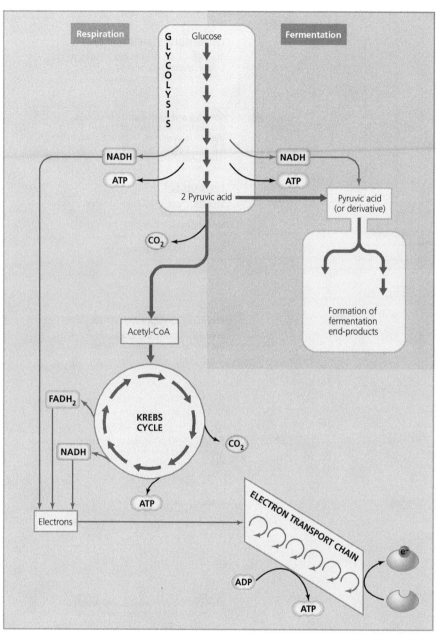

▶ **Figure 12 Summary of glucose catabolism.** Glucose catabolism begins with glycolysis, which forms pyruvic acid and two molecules of both ATP and NADH. Two pathways branch from pyruvic acid: respiration and fermentation. In aerobic respiration (shown here), the Krebs cycle and the electron transport chain completely oxidize pyruvic acid to $CO_2$ and $H_2O$, in the process synthesizing many molecules of ATP. Fermentation results in the incomplete oxidation of pyruvic acid to form organic fermentation products.

(MM)™ To see a 3-D animation on metabolism, go to the Study Area at **www.masteringmicrobiology.com** and watch the *MicroFlix*.

Precision Graphics

**ANIMATIONS:** *Glycolysis: Steps*

Our study of glycolysis provides our first opportunity to study *substrate-level phosphorylation* (see steps ①, ③, ⑦, and ⑩). Let's examine this important process more closely by considering the 10th and final step of glycolysis.

Each of the two phosphoenolpyruvic acid (PEP) molecules produced in step ⑨ of glycolysis is a three-carbon compound containing a high-energy phosphate bond. In the presence of a specific holoenzyme (which requires a $Mg^{2+}$ cofactor), the high-energy phosphate in PEP (one substrate) is transferred to an ADP molecule (a second substrate) to form ATP (step ⑩ and **Figure 14**); the direct transfer of the phosphate between the two substrates is the reason the process is called **substrate-level phosphorylation.** A variety of substrate-level phosphorylations occur in metabolism. As you might expect, each type has its own enzyme that recognizes both its substrate molecule and ADP.

### ENERGY-INVESTMENT STAGE

**Step 1.** Glucose is phosphorylated by ATP to form glucose 6-phosphate.

**Steps 2 and 3.** The atoms of glucose 6-phosphate are rearranged to form fructose 6-phosphate. Fructose 6-phosphate is phosphorylated by ATP to form fructose 1,6-bisphosphate.

### LYSIS STAGE

**Step 4.** Fructose 1,6-bisphosphate is cleaved to form glyceraldehyde 3-phosphate (G3P) and dihydroxyacetone phosphate (DHAP).

**Step 5.** DHAP is rearranged to form another G3P.

### ENERGY-CONSERVING STAGE

**Step 6.** Inorganic phosphates are added to the two G3P, and two NAD⁺ are reduced.

**Step 7.** Two ADP are phosphorylated by substrate-level phosphorylation to form two ATP.

**Steps 8 and 9.** The remaining phosphates are moved to the middle carbons. A water molecule is removed from each substrate.

**Step 10.** Two ADP are phosphorylated by substrate-level phosphorylation to form two ATP. Two pyruvic acid are formed.

Precision Graphics

▲ **Figure 13 Glycolysis.** Glucose is cleaved and ultimately transformed into two molecules of pyruvic acid in this process (also known as the Embden-Meyerhof pathway). Four ATPs are formed and two ATPs are used, so a net gain of two ATPs results. Two molecules of NAD⁺ are reduced to NADH.

Precision Graphics

▲ **Figure 14 Substrate-level phosphorylation.** High-energy phosphate bonds are transferred from one substrate to another in this process. *What role does $Mg^{2+}$ play in this reaction?*

**Figure 14** *$Mg^{2+}$ is a cofactor of the enzyme.*

In glycolysis, two ATP molecules are invested by substrate-level phosphorylation to prime glucose for lysis, and four molecules of ATP are produced by substrate-level phosphorylation. Therefore, a net gain of two ATP molecules occurs for each molecule of glucose that is oxidized to pyruvic acid. Glycolysis also yields two molecules of NADH.

## Cellular Respiration

### Learning Objectives

✓ Discuss the roles of acetyl-CoA, the Krebs cycle, and electron transport in carbohydrate catabolism.

✓ Contrast electron transport in aerobic and anaerobic respiration.

✓ Identify four classes of carriers in electron transport chains.

✓ Describe the role of chemiosmosis in oxidative phosphorylation of ATP.

After glucose has been oxidized via glycolysis or one of the alternate pathways considered shortly, a cell uses the resultant pyruvic acid molecules to complete either cellular respiration or fermentation (which we will discuss in a later section). Our topic here—**cellular respiration**—is a metabolic process that involves the complete oxidation of substrate molecules and then production of ATP by a series of redox reactions. The three stages of cellular respiration are: (1) synthesis of acetyl-CoA, (2) the Krebs cycle, and (3) a final series of redox reactions, called an electron transport chain, that passes electrons to a chemical not derived from the cell's metabolism.

### Synthesis of Acetyl-CoA

Before pyruvic acid (generated by glycolysis or an alternate pathway) can enter the Krebs cycle for respiration, it must first be converted to *acetyl-coenzyme A* or **acetyl-CoA** (as'e-til kō-ā';). Enzymes remove one carbon from pyruvic acid as $CO_2$ and join the remaining two-carbon acetate to *coenzyme A*

Precision Graphics

▲ **Figure 15 Formation of acetyl-CoA.** The responsible enzyme acts in a stepwise manner to ① remove $CO_2$ from pyruvic acid, ② attach the remaining two-carbon acetate to coenzyme A, and ③ reduce a molecule of $NAD^+$ to NADH.

with a high-energy bond (Figure 15). The removal of $CO_2$, called *decarboxylation,* requires a coenzyme derived from the vitamin thiamine. One molecule of NADH is also produced during this reaction.

Recall that two molecules of pyruvic acid were derived from each molecule of glucose. Therefore, at this stage, two molecules of acetyl-CoA, two molecules of $CO_2$, and two molecules of NADH are produced.

### The Krebs Cycle

At this point in the catabolism of a molecule of glucose, a great amount of energy remains in the bonds of acetyl-CoA. The **Krebs cycle**[6] is a series of eight enzymatically catalyzed reactions that transfer much of this stored energy to the coenzymes $NAD^+$ and FAD. The two carbon atoms in acetate are oxidized, and the coenzymes are reduced. The Krebs cycle, which occurs in the cytosol of prokaryotes and in the matrix of mitochondria in eukaryotes, is diagrammed in Figure 16. It is also known as the *tricarboxylic acid (TCA) cycle,* because many of its compounds have three carboxyl (—COOH) groups, and as the *citric acid cycle,* for the first compound formed in the cycle.

---

[6]Named for biochemist Hans Krebs, who elucidated its reactions in the 1940s.

Precision Graphics

▲ **Figure 16 The Krebs cycle.** 1 Acetyl-CoA enters the Krebs cycle by joining with oxaloacetic acid to form citric acid and coenzyme A. 2 – 4 Two oxidations and decarboxylations and the addition of coenzyme A yield succinyl-CoA. 5 Substrate-level phosphorylation produces ATP and regenerates coenzyme A. 6 – 8 Further oxidations and rearrangements regenerate oxaloacetic acid, and the cyle can begin anew.

There are six types of reactions in the Krebs cycle:

- Anabolism of citric acid (step **1**)
- Isomerization reaction (step **2**)
- Redox reactions (steps **3**, **4**, **6**, and **8**)
- Decarboxylations (steps **3** and **4**)
- Substrate-level phosphorylation (step **5**)
- Hydration reaction (step **7**)

In the first step of the Krebs cycle, the splitting of the high-energy bond between acetate and coenzyme A releases enough energy to enable the binding of the freed two-carbon acetate to a four-carbon compound called oxaloacetic acid, forming the six-carbon compound citric acid.

As you study Figure 16, notice that after isomerization (step **2**), the decarboxylations of the Krebs cycle release two molecules of $CO_2$ for each acetyl-CoA that enters (steps **3** and **4**). Thus, for every two carbon atoms that enter the cycle, two are lost to the environment. At this juncture in the respiration of a molecule of glucose, all six carbon atoms have been lost to the environment: two as $CO_2$ molecules produced in decarboxylation of two molecules of pyruvic acid to form two acetyl-CoA molecules, and four in $CO_2$ molecules produced in decarboxylations in the *two* turns through the Krebs cycle. (One molecule of acetyl-CoA enters the cycle at a time.)

A small amount of ATP is also produced in the Krebs cycle. For every two molecules of acetyl-CoA that pass through the Krebs cycle, two molecules of ATP are generated by substrate-level phosphorylation (step **5**). A molecule of guanosine triphosphate (GTP), which is similar to ATP, can serve as an intermediary in this process.

Redox reactions reduce FAD to $FADH_2$ (step **6**) and $NAD^+$ to NADH (steps **3**, **4**, and **8**), so that for every two molecules of acetyl-CoA that move through the cycle, six molecules of NADH and two of $FADH_2$ are formed. In the Krebs cycle, little energy is captured directly in high-energy phosphate bonds, but much energy is transferred via electrons to NADH and $FADH_2$. These coenzymes are the most important molecules of respiration because they carry a large amount of energy that is subsequently used to phosphorylate ADP to ATP. **ANIMATIONS:** *Krebs Cycle: Overview, Steps*

## Electron Transport

Some scientists estimate that each day an average human synthesizes his or her own weight in ATP molecules and uses them for metabolism, responsiveness, growth, and cell reproduction. ATP turnover in prokaryotes is relatively as copious. The most significant production of ATP does not occur through glycolysis or the Krebs cycle, but rather through the stepwise release of energy from a series of redox reactions known as an **electron transport chain** (Figure 17). **ANIMATIONS:** *Electron Transport Chain: Overview*

An electron transport chain consists of a series of membrane-bound carrier molecules that pass electrons from one to another and ultimately to a *final electron acceptor.* Typically, as we have seen, electrons come from the catabolism of an organic molecule such as glucose; however, microorganisms called *lithotrophs* (lith′ō-trōfs) acquire electrons from inorganic sources such as $H_2$, $NO^{2-}$, or $Fe^{2+}$. In any case, carrier molecules pass electrons down the chain to the final acceptor like firefighters of old passed buckets of water from one to another until the last one threw the water on a fire. As with a bucket brigade, the final step of electron transport is irreversible. Energy from the electrons is used to actively transport (pump) protons ($H^+$) across the membrane, establishing a *proton gradient* that generates ATP via a process called *chemiosmosis,* which we will discuss shortly.

To avoid getting lost in the details of electron transport, keep the following critical concepts in mind:

- Electrons pass sequentially from one membrane-bound carrier molecule to another and eventually to a final acceptor molecule.
- The electrons' energy is used to pump protons across the membrane.

Electron transport chains are located in the inner mitochondrial membranes (cristae) of eukaryotes and in the cytoplasmic membrane of prokaryotes (Figure 18). Though NADH and $FADH_2$ donate electrons as hydrogen atoms (electrons and protons), many carrier molecules pass only the electrons down the chain. There are four categories of carrier molecules in electron transport chains. They are:

- *Flavoproteins* are integral membrane proteins, many of which contain flavin, a coenzyme derived from riboflavin (vitamin $B_2$). One form of flavin is flavin mononucleotide (FMN), which is the initial carrier molecule of electron transport chains of mitochondria. The familiar FAD is a coenzyme for other flavoproteins. Like all carrier molecules in the electron transport chain, flavoproteins alternate between the reduced and oxidized states.

- *Ubiquinones* (yū-bik′wi-nōns) are lipid-soluble, nonprotein carriers that are so named because they are ubiquitous in all cells. Ubiquinones are derived from vitamin K. In mitochondria, the ubiquinone is called *coenzyme Q.*

- *Metal-containing proteins* are a mixed group of integral proteins with a wide-ranging number of iron, sulfur, and copper atoms that can alternate between the reduced and oxidized states. Iron-sulfur proteins occur in various places in electron transport chains of various organisms. Copper proteins are found only in electron transport chains involved in photosynthesis (discussed shortly).

- *Cytochromes* (sī′tō-krōms) are integral proteins associated with *heme,* which is the same iron-containing, nonprotein, pigmented molecule found in the hemoglobin of blood. Iron can alternate between a reduced ($Fe^{2+}$) state and an oxidized ($Fe^{3+}$) state. Cytochromes are identified by letters and numbers based on the order in which they were identified, so their sequence in electron transport chains does not always seem logical. **ANIMATIONS:** *Electron Transport Chain: The Process*

The carrier molecules in electron transport chains are diverse—bacteria typically have different carrier molecules arranged in different sequences than do archaea or the

▲ **Figure 17 An electron transport chain.** ATP production is indicated at the approximate point in the chain that energy is captured as electrons move down the chain, but the molecules of the chain do not actually synthesize ATP. Red arrows indicate the path of electrons down the chain.

Precision Graphics

mitochondria of eukaryotes. Even among bacteria, the makeup of carrier molecules can vary. For example, the pathogens *Neisseria* (nī-se′rē-ă) and *Pseudomonas* (soo-dō-mō′nas) contain two cytochromes, *a* and $a_3$—together called *cytochrome oxidase*—that oxidize cytochrome *c;* such bacteria are said to be *oxidase positive.* In contrast, other bacterial pathogens, such as *Escherichia, Salmonella* (sal′mŏ-nel′ă), and *Proteus* (prō′tē-ŭs), lack cytochrome oxidase and are thus considered to be *oxidase negative.* Some bacteria including *E. coli* can even vary their carrier molecules under different environmental conditions.

Electrons carried by NADH enter the transport chain at a flavoprotein, and those carried by $FADH_2$ are introduced via a ubiquinone. This explains why more molecules of ATP are generated from NADH than from $FADH_2$. Researchers do not agree on which carrier molecules are the actual proton pumps, nor on the number of protons that are pumped. Figure 18 shows one possibility.

In some organisms, the final electron acceptors are oxygen atoms, which, with the addition of hydrogen ions, generate $H_2O$; these organisms conduct **aerobic**[7] **respiration** and are called *aerobes.* **Highlight: Glowing Bacteria** describes an unusual aerobic bacterial electron transport system that produces light instead of ATP.

Other organisms, called *anaerobes,*[8] use other inorganic molecules (or rarely an organic molecule) instead of oxygen as the final electron acceptor and perform **anaerobic respiration.** The anaerobic bacterium *Desulfovibrio* (dē′sul-fō-vib-rē-ō), for example, reduces sulfate ($SO_4^{2-}$) to hydrogen sulfide gas ($H_2S$), whereas other anaerobes in the genera *Bacillus* (ba-sil′ŭs) and *Pseudomonas* utilize nitrate ($NO_3^-$) to produce nitrite ions ($NO_2^-$), nitrous oxide ($N_2O$), or nitrogen gas ($N_2$). Some prokaryotes—particularly archaea called methanogens—reduce carbonate

[7]From Greek *aer*, meaning air (that is, oxygen), and *bios*, meaning life.
[8]The Greek prefix *an* means not.

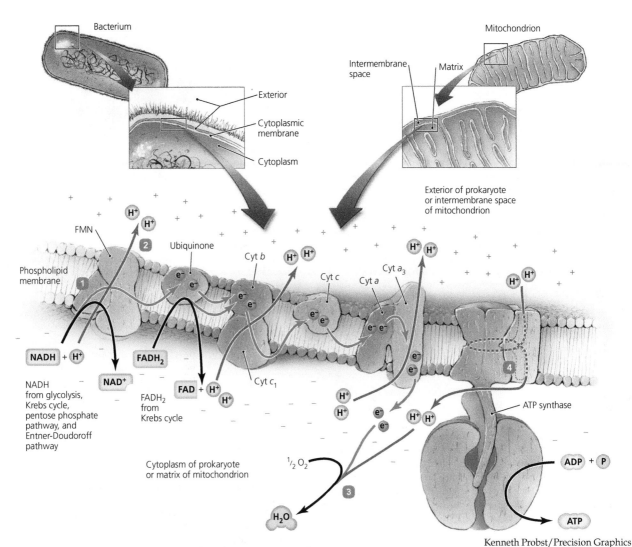

Bacterium

Mitochondrion

Intermembrane space

Matrix

Exterior

Cytoplasmic membrane

Cytoplasm

Exterior of prokaryote or intermembrane space of mitochondrion

FMN

Phospholipid membrane

Ubiquinone

Cyt b

Cyt c

Cyt a

Cyt $a_3$

NADH + H⁺

NAD⁺

FADH₂

FAD + H⁺

Cyt $c_1$

NADH from glycolysis, Krebs cycle, pentose phosphate pathway, and Entner-Doudoroff pathway

FADH₂ from Krebs cycle

Cytoplasm of prokaryote or matrix of mitochondrion

$\frac{1}{2}$ O₂

H₂O

ATP synthase

ADP + P

ATP

Kenneth Probst/Precision Graphics

▲ **Figure 18 One possible arrangement of an electron transport chain.** Electron transport chains are located in the cytoplasmic membranes of prokaryotes and in the inner membranes of mitochondria in eukaryotes. The exact types and sequences of carrier molecules in electron transport chains vary among organisms. As electrons move down the chain (red arrows) (**1**), their energy is used to pump protons (H⁺) across the membrane (**2**). Eventually the electrons pass to a final acceptor, in this case oxygen (**3**). The protons then flow through ATP synthase (ATPase), which synthesizes ATP (**4**). Approximately one molecule of ATP is generated for every two protons that cross the membrane. *Why is it essential that electron carriers of an electron transport chain be membrane bound?*

**Figure 18** *The carrier molecules of electron transport chains are membrane bound for at least two reasons: (1) Carrier molecules need to be in fairly close proximity so they can pass electrons between each other; (2) The goal of the chain is the pumping of H⁺ across a membrane to create a proton gradient; without a membrane, there could be no gradient.*

## HIGHLIGHT

### GLOWING BACTERIA

Bacteria in the genus *Photobacterium* possess an interesting electron tansport chain that generates light instead of ATP. These organisms can switch the flow of electrons from a standard electron transport chain (composed of cytochromes, proton pumps, and $O_2$ as the final electron acceptor) to an alternate chain. Whereas the standard chain establishes a proton gradient that is used to synthesize ATP, the alternate chain uncouples electron transport from ATP synthesis: instead of transferring electrons to proton pumps, the alternate chain shunts the electrons to the coenzyme flavin mononucleotide (FMN). Then, in the presence of an enzyme

called luciferase and a long-chain hydrocarbon, the alternate chain emits light as it transfers electrons to $O_2$ (see the diagram). The exact mechanism of bioluminescence is not known, but both FMN and the hydrocarbon are oxidized as oxygen is reduced.

Interestingly, free-living *Photobacterium* are usually not bioluminescent. It is primarily when these bacteria colonize the tissues of marine animals such as squid and fish that they use their light-generating pathway. The animals gain from the association because the light produced serves as an attractant for mates and a warning against predators. One species,

the "flashlight fish" (*Kryptophanaron alfredi*), has a special organ near its mouth that is specially adapted for the growth of luminescent bacteria. Enough light is generated from millions of bacteria that the fish can navigate over coral reefs at night and attract prey to their light. The light organ even has a membrane that descends like an eyelid to control the amount of light emitted.

It is not clear what the bacteria gain from this association. Presumably, the protection and nutrients the bacteria gain from the fish make up for the enormous metabolic cost the bacteria incur in the form of lost ATP synthesis.

▲ *Kryptophanaron alfredi.* |— 2 cm

Frederick R. McConnaughey / Photo Researchers

Precision Graphics

---

$(CO_3{}^{2-})$ to methane gas $(CH_4)$. Laboratory technologists test for products of anaerobic respiration, such as nitrite, to aid in identification of some species of bacteria. Anaerobic respiration is also critical for the recycling of nitrogen and sulfur in nature. **ANIMATIONS:** *Electron Transport Chain: Factors Affecting ATP Yield*

### CRITICAL **THINKING**

Figure 18 illustrates events in aerobic respiration where oxygen acts as the final electron acceptor to yield water. How would the figure be changed to reflect anaerobic respiration?

In summary, a number of redox reactions in glycolysis or alternate pathways and in the Krebs cycle strip electrons, which carry energy, from glucose molecules and transfer them to molecules of NADH and $FADH_2$. In turn, NADH and $FADH_2$ pass the electrons to an electron transport chain. As the electrons move down the electron transport chain, proton pumps use the electrons' energy to actively transport protons $(H^+)$ across the membrane, creating a proton concentration gradient.

Recall, however, that the significance of electron transport is not merely that it pumps protons across a membrane, but that it ultimately results in the synthesis of ATP. We turn now to the process by which cells synthesize ATP using the proton gradient.

### Chemiosmosis

**Chemiosmosis** is a general term for the use of ion gradients to generate ATP; that is, ATP is synthesized utilizing energy released by the flow of ions down their electrochemical gradient across a membrane. The term should not be confused with osmosis of water.

Recall that chemicals diffuse from areas of high concentration to areas of low concentration, and toward an electrical charge opposite their own. We call the composite of differences in concentration and charge an *electrochemical gradient.* Chemicals diffuse down their electrochemical gradients. Recall as well that membranes of cells and organelles are impermeable to most chemicals unless a specific protein channel allows their passage across the membrane. A membrane maintains an electrochemical gradient by keeping one or more chemicals in a higher concentration on one side. The blockage of diffusion creates potential energy, like water behind a dam.

Chemiosmosis uses the potential energy of an electrochemical gradient to phosphorylate ADP into ATP. Even though chemiosmosis is a general principle with relevance to both *oxidative phosphorylation* and *photophosphorylation,* here we consider it as it relates to oxidative phosphorylation.

As we have seen, cells use the energy released in the redox reactions of electron transport chains to actively transport

**3**

## Summary of Ideal Prokaryotic Aerobic Respiration of One Molecule of Glucose

| Pathway | ATP Produced | ATP Used | NADH Produced | FADH$_2$ Produced |
|---|---|---|---|---|
| Glycolysis | 4 | 2 | 2 | 0 |
| Synthesis of acetyl-CoA and Krebs cycle | 2 | 0 | 8 | 2 |
| Electron transport chain | 34 | 0 | 0 | 0 |
| Total | 40 | 2 | | |
| Net total | 38 | | | |

protons (H$^+$) across a membrane. Theoretically, an electron transport chain pumps three pairs of protons for each pair of electrons contributed by NADH, and pumps two pairs of protons for each electron pair delivered by FADH$_2$. This difference results from the fact that FADH$_2$ delivers electrons farther down the chain than does NADH; therefore, energy carried by FADH$_2$ is used to transport one-third fewer protons (see Figure 17). Because lipid bilayers are impermeable to protons, the transport of protons to one side of the membrane creates an electrochemical gradient known as a **proton gradient,** which has potential energy known as a *proton motive force.*

Protons, propelled by the proton motive force, flow down their electrochemical gradient through protein channels, called **ATP synthases (ATPases),** that phosphorylate molecules of ADP to ATP (see Figure 18 ❹). Such phosphorylation is called **oxidative phosphorylation** because the proton gradient is created by the oxidation of components of an electron transport chain.

In the past, scientists attempted to calculate the exact number of ATP molecules synthesized per pair of electrons that travel down an electron transport chain. However, it is now apparent that phosphorylation and oxidation are not directly coupled. In other words, chemiosmosis does not require exact constant relationships among the number of molecules of NADH and FADH$_2$ reduced, the number of electrons that move down an electron transport chain, and the number of molecules of ATP that are synthesized. Additionally, cells use proton gradients for other cellular processes, including active transport and bacterial flagellar motion, so not every transported electron results in ATP production.

Nevertheless, about 34 molecules of ADP per molecule of glucose are oxidatively phosphorylated to ATP via chemiosmosis: three from each of the 10 molecules of NADH generated from glycolysis, the synthesis of acetyl-CoA, and the Krebs cycle, and two from each of the two molecules of FADH$_2$ generated in the Krebs cycle. Given that glycolysis produces a net two molecules of ATP by substrate-level phosphorylation, and that the Krebs cycle produces two more, the complete aerobic oxidation of one molecule of glucose by a prokaryote can theoretically yield a net total of 38 molecules of ATP (Table 3). The theoretical net maximum for eukaryotic cells is generally given as 36 molecules of ATP because the energy from two ATP molecules is required to transport NADH generated by glycolysis in the cytoplasm into the mitochondria.

## CRITICAL **THINKING**

Suppose you could insert a tiny pH probe into the space between mitochondrial membranes. Would the pH be above or below 7.0? Why?

## Alternatives to Glycolysis

### Learning Objective

✓ Compare the pentose phosphate pathway and the Entner-Doudoroff pathway with glycolysis in terms of energy production and products.

The initial part of the catabolism of glucose can also proceed via two alternate pathways: the pentose phosphate pathway and the Entner-Doudoroff pathway. Though they yield fewer molecules of ATP than glycolysis, these alternate pathways reduce coenzymes and yield substrate metabolites that are needed in anabolic pathways. Next we briefly examine each of these alternate pathways.

### Pentose Phosphate Pathway

The **pentose phosphate pathway** (sometimes called the *phosphogluconate pathway*) is named for the phosphorylated pentose (five-carbon) sugars—ribulose, xylulose, and ribose—that are formed from glucose 6-phosphate by enzymes in the pathway (Figure 19). The pentose phosphate pathway is primarily used for the production of precursor metabolites used in anabolic reactions, including the synthesis of nucleotides for nucleic acids, of certain amino acids, and of glucose by *photosynthesis* (described in a later section). The pathway reduces two molecules of NADP$^+$ to NADPH and nets a single molecule of ATP from each molecule of glucose. NADPH is a necessary coenzyme for anabolic enzymes that synthesize DNA nucleotides, steroids, and fatty acids.

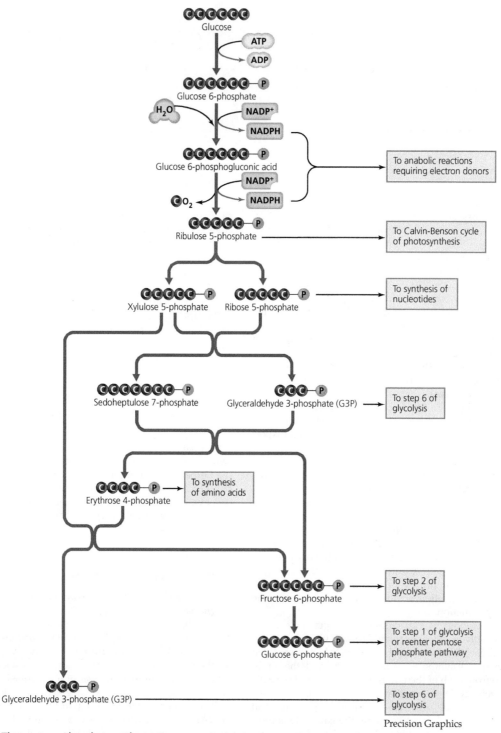

▲ **Figure 19 The pentose phosphate pathway.** Energy captured during the pentose phosphate pathway is less than that from glycolysis, but the pathway produces ribose 5-phosphate and erythrose 4-phosphate, two metabolites necessary for synthesis of nucleotides and certain amino acids, respectively. Ribulose 5-phosphate, necessary for glucose synthesis in photosynthetic organisms, and NADPH, an electron carrier for anabolic reactions, are also produced.

Precision Graphics

CRITICAL **THINKING**

Examine the biosynthetic pathway for the production of the amino acids tryptophan, tyrosine, and phenylalanine in Figure 11b. Where do the initial reactants (erythrose 4-phosphate and PEP) originate?

### Entner-Doudoroff Pathway

Many bacteria use glycolysis and the pentose phosphate pathway, but a few substitute the **Entner-Doudoroff pathway** (Figure 20) for glycolysis. This pathway, named for its discoverers, is a series of reactions that catabolize glucose to pyruvic acid using different enzymes from those used in either glycolysis or the pentose phosphate pathway.

Among organisms, only a very few bacteria use the Entner-Doudoroff pathway. These include the Gram-negative bacterium *Pseudomonas aeruginosa* and the Gram-positive bacterium *Enterococcus faecalis* (en-ter-ō-kok′ŭs fē-kă′lis). Like the pentose phosphate pathway, the Entner-Doudoroff pathway nets only a single molecule of ATP for each molecule of glucose, but it does yield precursor metabolites and NADPH. The latter is unavailable from glycolysis.

CRITICAL **THINKING**

Even though *Pseudomonas aeruginosa* and *Enterococcus faecalis* usually grow harmlessly, they can cause disease. Because these bacteria use the Entner-Doudoroff pathway instead of glycolysis to catabolize glucose, investigators can use clinical tests that provide evidence of the Entner-Doudoroff pathway to identify the presence of these potential pathogens.

Suppose you were able to identify the presence of any specific organic compound. Name a substrate molecule you would find in *Pseudomonas* and *Enterococcus* cells, but not in human cells.

## Fermentation

### Learning Objectives

✓ Describe fermentation, and contrast it with respiration.

✓ Identify three useful end-products of fermentation, and explain how fermentation reactions are used in the identification of bacteria.

✓ Discuss the use of biochemical tests for metabolic enzymes and products in the identification of bacteria.

Sometimes cells cannot completely oxidize glucose by cellular respiration. For instance, they may lack sufficient final electron acceptors, as is the case, for example, for an aerobic bacterium in the anaerobic environment of the colon. Electrons cannot flow down an electron transport chain unless oxidized carrier molecules are available to receive them. Our bucket brigade analogy can help clarify this point.

Suppose the last person in the brigade did not throw the water, but instead held onto two full buckets. What would happen? The entire brigade would soon consist of firefighters

▲ **Figure 20 Entner-Doudoroff pathway.** A few bacteria use this alternate pathway for the oxidation of glucose to pyruvic acid. *What potential pathogens use this pathway?*

Figure 20 *Pseudomonas aeruginosa* and *Enterococcus faecalis* use the Entner-Doudoroff pathway.

holding full buckets of water. The analogous situation occurs in an electron transport chain: All the carrier molecules are forced to remain in their reduced states when there is not a final electron acceptor. Without the movement of electrons down the chain, protons cannot be transported, the proton motive force is lost, and oxidative phosphorylation of ADP to ATP ceases. Without sufficient ATP, a cell is unable to anabolize, grow, or divide.

ATP could be synthesized in glycolysis and the Krebs cycle by substrate-level phosphorylation. After all, together these pathways produce four molecules of ATP per molecule of glucose. However, careful consideration reveals that glycolysis and the Krebs cycle require a continual supply of oxidized $NAD^+$ molecules (see Figures 13 and 16). Electron transport produces the required $NAD^+$ in respiration, but without a final electron acceptor, this source of $NAD^+$ ceases to be available. A cell in such a predicament must use an alternate source of $NAD^+$ provided by alternative metabolic pathways, called *fermentation pathways*.

In the vernacular, fermentation refers to the production of alcohol from sugar, but in microbiology, fermentation has an expanded meaning. **Fermentation** is the partial oxidation of sugar (or other metabolites) to release energy using an organic molecule from within the cell as the final electron acceptor. In other words, fermentation pathways are metabolic reactions that oxidize NADH to $NAD^+$ while reducing cellular organic molecules. In contrast, respiration reduces externally acquired substances—oxygen in aerobic respiration, and in anaerobic respiration, some other inorganic chemical such as sulfate and nitrate or (rarely) an organic molecule. **Figure 21** illustrates two common fermentation pathways that reduce pyruvic acid to lactic acid and ethanol, oxidizing NADH in the process.

The essential function of fermentation is the regeneration of $NAD^+$ for glycolysis, so that ADP molecules can be phosphorylated to ATP. Even though fermentation pathways are not as energetically efficient as respiration because much of the potential energy stored in glucose remains in the bonds of fermentation products, the major benefit of fermentation is that it allows ATP production to continue in the absence of cellular respiration. Table 4 compares fermentation to aerobic and anaerobic respiration with respect to four crucial aspects of these processes.

Microorganisms produce a variety of fermentation products depending on the enzymes and substrates available to each. Though fermentation products are wastes to the cells that make them, many are useful to humans, including ethanol (drinking alcohol) and lactic acid (used in the production of cheese, sauerkraut, and pickles) (Figure 22).

Other fermentation products are harmful to human health and industry. For example, fermentation products of the bacterium *Clostridium perfringens* (klos-trid′ē-um per-frin′jens) are involved in the necrosis (death) of muscle tissue associated with gangrene. Also, Pasteur discovered that bacterial contaminants in grape juice fermented the sugar into unwanted products such as acetic acid and lactic acid, which spoiled the wine.

Precision Graphics

▲ **Figure 21 Fermentation.** In the simplest fermentation reaction, NADH reduces pyruvic acid to form lactic acid. Another simple fermentation pathway involves a decarboxylation reaction and reduction to form ethanol.

Laboratory personnel routinely use the detection of fermentation products in the identification of microbes. For example, *Proteus* ferments glucose but not lactose, whereas *Escherichia* and *Enterobacter* ferment both. Further, glucose fermentation by *Escherichia* produces mixed acids (acetic, lactic, succinic, and formic), whereas *Enterobacter* produces 2,3-butanediol. Common fermentation tests contain a carbohydrate and a pH indicator, which is a molecule that changes color as the pH changes. An organism that utilizes the carbohydrate causes a change in pH, causing the pH indicator to change color. **ANIMATIONS:** *Fermentation*

In this section on carbohydrate catabolism, we have spent some time examining glycolysis, alternatives to glycolysis, the Krebs cycle, and electron transport because these pathways are central to metabolism. They generate all of the precursor metabolites and most of the ATP needed for anabolism. We have seen that

▲ **Figure 22 Representative fermentation products and the organisms that produce them.** All of the organisms are bacteria except *Saccharomyces* and *Aspergillus*, which are yeasts. *Why does Swiss cheese have holes, but cheddar does not?*

Precision Graphics

**Figure 22** *Swiss cheese is a product of Propionibacterium, which ferments pyruvic acid to produce CO₂; bubbles of this gas cause the holes in the cheese. Cheddar is a product of Lactobacillus, which does not produce gas.*

some ATP is generated in respiration by substrate-level phosphorylation (in both glycolysis and the Krebs cycle), but that most ATP is generated by oxidative phosphorylation via chemiosmosis utilizing the reducing power of NADH and FADH$_2$. We also saw that some microorganisms use fermentation to provide an alternate source of NAD$^+$.

Thus far we have concentrated on the catabolism of glucose as a representative carbohydrate, but microorganisms can also use other molecules as energy sources. In the next section we will examine catabolic pathways that utilize lipids and proteins.

**TABLE 4**

## Comparison of Aerobic Respiration, Anaerobic Respiration, and Fermentation

| | Aerobic Respiration | Anaerobic Respiration | Fermentation |
|---|---|---|---|
| **Oxygen required** | Yes | No | No |
| **Type of phosphorylation** | Substrate-level and oxidative | Substrate-level and oxidative | Substrate-level |
| **Final electron (hydrogen) acceptor** | Oxygen | $NO_3^-$, $SO_4^{2-}$, $CO_3^{2-}$, or externally acquired organic molecules | Cellular organic molecules |
| **Potential molecules of ATP produced per molecule of glucose** | 38 in prokaryotes, 36 in eukaryotes | 2–36 | 2 |

# Other Catabolic Pathways

Lipid and protein molecules contain abundant energy in their chemical bonds and can also be converted into precursor metabolites. These molecules are first catabolized to produce their constituent monomers, which serve as substrates in glycolysis and the Krebs cycle.

## Lipid Catabolism

### Learning Objective

✓ Explain how lipids are catabolized for energy and metabolite production.

The most common lipids involved in ATP and metabolite production are fats, which consist of glycerol and fatty acids. In the first step of fat catabolism, enzymes called *lipases* hydrolyze the bonds attaching the glycerol to the fatty acid chains (Figure 23a).

Subsequent reactions further catabolize the glycerol and fatty acid molecules. Glycerol is converted to DHAP, which as one of the substrates of glycolysis is oxidized to pyruvic acid (see Figure 13 ④). The fatty acids are degraded in a catabolic process known as **beta-oxidation**[9] (Figure 23b). In this process, enzymes repeatedly split off pairs of the hydrogenated carbon atoms that make up a fatty acid and join each pair to coenzyme A to form acetyl-CoA, until the entire fatty acid has been converted to molecules of acetyl-CoA. Beta-oxidation also generates NADH and $FADH_2$, and more of these molecules are generated when the acetyl-CoA is utilized in the Krebs cycle to generate ATP (see Figure 16). As is the case for the Krebs cycle, the enzymes involved in beta-oxidation are located in the cytosol of prokaryotes and in the mitochondria of eukaryotes.

## CRITICAL **THINKING**

How and where do cells use the molecules of NADH and $FADH_2$ produced during beta-oxidation?

## Protein Catabolism

### Learning Objective

✓ Explain how proteins are catabolized for energy and metabolite production.

Some microorganisms, notably food-spoilage bacteria, pathogenic bacteria, and fungi, normally catabolize proteins as an important source of energy and metabolites. Most cells catabolize proteins and their constituent amino acids only when carbon sources such as glucose and fat are not available.

Generally, proteins are too large to cross cytoplasmic membranes, so prokaryotes typically conduct the first step in the process of protein catabolism outside the cell by secreting

[9]"Beta" is part of the name of this process because enzymes break the bond at the second carbon atom from the end of a fatty acid, and beta is the second letter in the Greek alphabet.

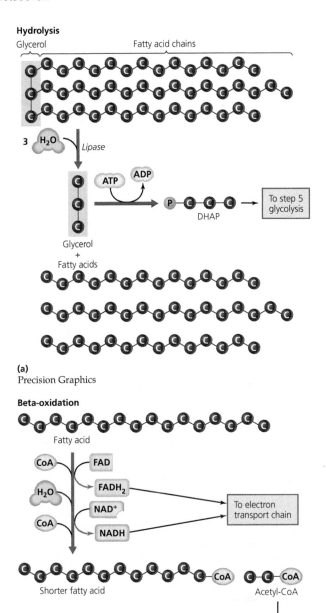

**(a)**
Precision Graphics

**(b)**
Precision Graphics

▲ **Figure 23** **Catabolism of a fat molecule.** (a) Lipase breaks fats into glycerol and three fatty acids by hydrolysis. Glycerol is converted to DHAP, which can be catabolized via glycolysis and the Krebs cycle. (b) Fatty acids are catabolized via beta-oxidation reactions that produce molecules of acetyl-CoA and reduced coenzymes (NADH and $FADH_2$).

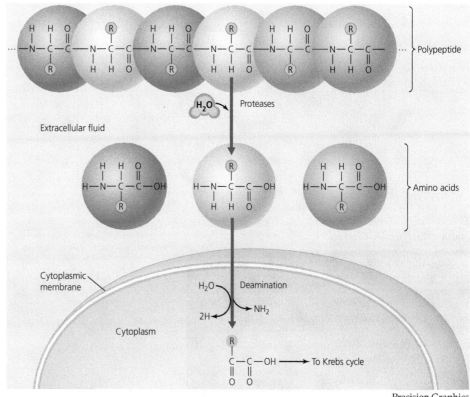

▶ **Figure 24 Protein catabolism.** Secreted proteases hydrolyze proteins, releasing amino acids, which are deaminated after uptake to produce molecules used as substrates in the Krebs cycle. R indicates the side group, which varies among amino acids.

Precision Graphics

**proteases** (prō'tē-ās-ez)—enzymes that split proteins into their constituent amino acids (Figure 24). Once released by the action of proteases, amino acids are transported into the cell, where special enzymes split off amino groups in a reaction called **deamination.** The resulting altered molecules enter the Krebs cycle, and the amino groups are either recycled to synthesize other amino acids or excreted as nitrogenous wastes such as ammonia ($NH_3$), ammonium ion ($NH_4^+$), or trimethylamine oxide (which has the chemical formula $(CH_3)_3NO$ and is abbreviated TMAO). As **Highlight: What's That Fishy Smell?** describes, TMAO plays an interesting role in the production of the odor we describe as "fishy."

Thus far, we have examined the catabolism of carbohydrates, lipids, and proteins. Now we turn our attention to the synthesis of these molecules, beginning with the anabolic reactions of photosynthesis.

# Photosynthesis

## Learning Objective

✓ Define *photosynthesis.*

Many organisms use only organic molecules as a source of energy and metabolites, but where do they acquire organic molecules? Ultimately every food chain begins with anabolic pathways in organisms that synthesize their own organic

ImageSource/age fotostock

**HIGHLIGHT**

### WHAT'S THAT FISHY SMELL?

Ever wonder why fish at the supermarket sometimes have that "fishy" smell? The reason relates to bacterial metabolism.

Trimethylamine oxide (TMAO) is an odorless, nitrogenous waste product of fish metabolism used to dispose of excess nitrogen (as amine groups) produced in the catabolism of amino acids. TMAO does not affect the smell, appearance, or taste of fresh fish; however, some bacteria use TMAO as a final electron acceptor in anaerobic respiration, reducing TMAO to trimethyl amine (TMA), a compound with a very definite—and, for most people, unpleasant— "fishy" odor. Thus, the "fishy" odor is really the odor of contaminating bacteria. A human nose is able to detect even a few molecules of TMA. Because bacterial degradation of fish begins as soon as a fish is dead, a fish that smells fresh probably is fresh, or was frozen while still fresh.

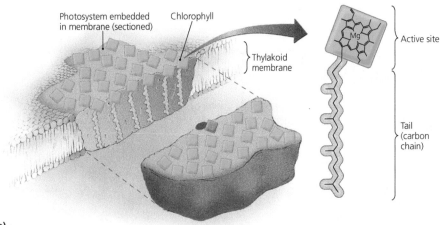

**(a)**
Kenneth Probst/Precision Graphics

Photosystem embedded in membrane (sectioned)

Chlorophyll

Thylakoid membrane

Active site

Mg

Tail (carbon chain)

Thylakoid

**(b)**
Eye of Science/Photo Researchers

TEM    0.2 µm

◀ **Figure 25 Photosynthetic structures in a prokaryote.**
**(a)** Chlorophyll molecules are grouped together in thylakoid membranes to form photosystems. Chlorophyll contains a light-absorbing active site that is connected to a long hydrocarbon tail. The chlorophyll shown here is bacteriochlorophyll *a*; other chlorophyll types differ in the side chains protruding from the central ring. **(b)** Prokaryotic thylakoids are infoldings of the cytoplasmic membrane, here in a cyanobacterium.

molecules from inorganic carbon dioxide. Most of these organisms capture light energy from the sun and use it to drive the synthesis of carbohydrates from $CO_2$ and $H_2O$ by a process called **photosynthesis.** Cyanobacteria, purple sulfur bacteria, green sulfur bacteria, green nonsulfur bacteria, purple nonsulfur bacteria, algae, green plants, and a few protozoa are photosynthetic. **ANIMATIONS:** *Photosynthesis: Overview*

### CRITICAL **THINKING**

Photosynthetic organisms are rarely pathogenic. Why?

## Chemicals and Structures

### Learning Objective

✓ Compare and contrast the basic chemicals and structures involved in photosynthesis in prokaryotes and eukaryotes.

Photosynthetic organisms capture light energy with pigment molecules, the most important of which are **chlorophylls.** Chlorophyll molecules are composed of a hydrocarbon tail attached to a light-absorbing *active site* centered around a magnesium ion ($Mg^{2+}$) (Figure 25a). The active sites are structurally similar to the cytochrome molecules found in electron transport chains, except chlorophylls use $Mg^{2+}$ rather than $Fe^{2+}$. Chlorophylls, typically designated with letters—for example, chlorophyll *a*, chlorophyll *b*, and bacteriochlorophyll *a*—vary slightly in the lengths and structures of their hydrocarbon tails and in the atoms that extend from their active sites. Green plants, algae, photosynthetic protozoa, and cyanobacteria principally use chlorophyll *a*, whereas green and purple bacteria use bacteriochlorophylls.

The slight structural differences among chlorophylls cause them to absorb light of different wavelengths. For example, chlorophyll *a* from algae best absorbs light with wavelengths of about 425 nm and 660 nm (violet and red), whereas bacteriochlorophyll *a* from purple bacteria best absorbs light with wavelengths of about 350 nm and 880 nm (ultraviolet and infrared). Because they best use light with differing wavelengths, algae and purple bacteria successfully occupy different ecological niches.

Cells arrange numerous molecules of chlorophyll and other pigments within a protein matrix to form light-harvesting matrices called **photosystems** that are embedded in cellular membranes called **thylakoids.** Thylakoids of photosynthetic prokaryotes are invaginations of their cytoplasmic membranes (Figure 25b). The thylakoids of eukaryotes appear to be formed from infoldings of the inner membranes of chloroplasts, though thylakoid membranes and the inner membranes are not connected in mature chloroplasts. Thylakoids of chloroplasts are arranged in stacks called *grana.* An outer chloroplast membrane surrounds the grana, and the space between the outer membrane and the thylakoid membrane is known as the *stroma.* The thylakoids enclose a narrow, convoluted cavity called the *thylakoid space.*

There are two types of photosystems, named photosystem I (PS I) and photosystem II (PS II), in the order of their discovery. Photosystems absorb light energy and use redox reactions to store this energy in molecules of ATP and NADPH. Because they depend upon light energy, these reactions of photosynthesis are classified as **light-dependent reactions.** Photosynthesis also involves **light-independent reactions** that actually synthesize glucose from carbon dioxide and water. Historically, these reactions were called *light* and *dark reactions,* but this older terminology implies that light-independent reactions occur only in the dark, which is not the case. We first consider the light-dependent reactions of the two photosystems.

## Light-Dependent Reactions

### Learning Objectives

✓ Describe the components and function of the two photosystems, PS I and PS II.

✓ Contrast cyclic and noncyclic photophosphorylation.

The pigments of photosystem I absorb light energy and transfer it to a neighboring molecule within the photosystem until the energy eventually arrives at a special chlorophyll molecule called the **reaction center chlorophyll** (Figure 26). Light energy from hundreds of such transfers excites electrons in the reaction center chlorophyll, which passes its excited electrons to the reaction center's electron acceptor, which is the initial carrier of an electron transport chain. As electrons move down the chain, their energy is used to pump protons across the membrane, creating a proton motive force. In prokaryotes, protons are pumped out of the cell; in eukaryotes they are pumped from the stroma into the interior of the thylakoids.

The proton motive force is used in chemiosmosis, in which, you should recall, protons flow down their electrochemical gradient through ATPases, which generate ATP. In photosynthesis, this process is called *photophosphorylation,* which can be either cyclic or noncyclic.

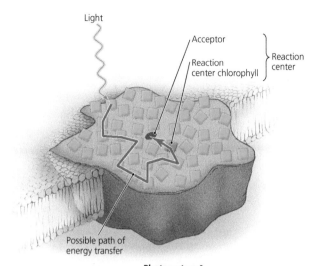

**Photosystem I**
Kenneth Probst/Precision Graphics

▲ **Figure 26  Reaction center of a photosystem.** Light energy absorbed by pigments anywhere in the photosystem is transferred to the reaction center chlorophyll, where it is used to excite electrons for delivery to the reaction center's electron acceptor.

## Cyclic Photophosphorylation

Electrons moving from one carrier molecule to another in a thylakoid must eventually pass to a final electron acceptor. In **cyclic photophosphorylation,** which occurs in all photosynthetic organisms, the final electron acceptor is the original reaction center chlorophyll that donated the electrons (Figure 27a). In other words, when light energy excites electrons in PS I, they pass down an electron transport chain and return to PS I. The energy from the electrons is used to establish a proton gradient that drives the phosphorylation of ADP to ATP by chemiosmosis. **ANIMATIONS:** *Photosynthesis: Light Reaction: Cyclic Photophosphorylation*

## Noncyclic Photophosphorylation

Some photosynthetic bacteria and all plants, algae, and photosynthetic protozoa utilize **noncyclic photophosphorylation** as well. (Exceptions are green and purple sulfur bacteria.) Noncyclic photophosphorylation, which requires both PS I and PS II, not only generates molecules of ATP but also reduces molecules of coenzyme $NADP^+$ to NADPH (Figure 27b).

When light energy excites electrons of PS II, they are passed to PS I through an electron transport chain. (Note that photosystem II occurs first in the pathway, and photosystem I second, a result of the fact that the photosystems were named for the order in which they were discovered, not the order in which they operate.) PS I further energizes the electrons with additional light energy and transfers them through an electron transport chain to $NADP^+$, which is thereby reduced to NADPH. The hydrogen ions added to NADPH come from the stroma or cytosol. NADPH subsequently participates in the synthesis of glucose in the light-independent reactions, which we will examine in the next section.

**(a) Cyclic photophosphorylation**

Kenneth Probst/Precision Graphics

**(b) Noncyclic photophosphorylation**

▲ **Figure 27** **The light-dependent reactions of photosynthesis: Cyclic and noncyclic photophosphorylation. (a)** In cyclic photophosphorylation, electrons excited by light striking photosystem I travel down an electron transport chain (red arrows), and then return to the reaction center. **(b)** In noncyclic photophosphorylation, light striking photosystem II excites electrons that are passed to photosystem I, simultaneously establishing a proton gradient. Light energy collected by photosystem I further excites the electrons, which are used to reduce $NADP^+$ to NADPH via an electron transport chain. In oxygenic organisms, new electrons are provided by the lysis of $H_2O$ (bottom left). In both types of photophosphorylation, the proton gradient drives the phosphorylation of ADP by ATP synthase (chemiosmosis).

**5**

## A Comparison of the Three Types of Phosphorylation

| | Source of Phosphate | Source of Energy | Location in Eukaryotic Cell | Location in Prokaryotic Cell |
|---|---|---|---|---|
| Substrate-level phosphorylation | Organic molecule | High-energy phosphate bond of donor | Cytosol and mitochondrial matrix | Cytosol |
| Oxidative phosphorylation | Inorganic phosphate ($PO_4^{3-}$) | Proton motive force | Inner membrane of mitochondrion | Cytoplasmic membrane |
| Photophosphorylation | Inorganic phosphate ($PO_4^{3-}$) | Proton motive force | Thylakoid of chloroplast | Thylakoid of cytoplasmic membrane |

In noncyclic photophosphorylation, a cell must constantly replenish electrons to the reaction center of photosystem II. *Oxygenic* (oxygen-producing) organisms, such as algae, green plants, and cyanobacteria, derive electrons from the dissociation of $H_2O$ (see Figure 27b). In these organisms, two molecules of water give up their electrons, producing molecular oxygen ($O_2$) as a waste product during photosynthesis. *Anoxygenic* photosynthetic bacteria get electrons from inorganic compounds such as $H_2S$, which results in a nonoxygen waste such as sulfur.

Table 5 compares photophosphorylation to substrate-level and oxidative phosphorylation.

### CRITICAL **THINKING**

We have seen that of the two ways ATP is generated via chemiosmosis—photophosphorylation and oxidative phosphorylation—the former can be cyclical, but the latter is never cyclical. Why can't oxidative phosphorylation be cyclical; that is, why aren't electrons passed back to the molecules that donated them?

To this point, we have examined the use of photosynthetic pigments and thylakoid structure to harvest light energy to produce both ATP and reducing power in the form of NADPH. Next we examine the light-independent reactions of photosynthesis. **ANIMATIONS:** *Photosynthesis: Light Reaction: Noncyclic Photophosphorylation*

## Light-Independent Reactions

### Learning Objectives

✓ Contrast the light-dependent and light-independent reactions of photosynthesis.

✓ Describe the reactants and products of the Calvin-Benson cycle.

Light-independent reactions of photosynthesis do not require light directly; instead, they use ATP and NADPH generated by the light-dependent reactions. The key reaction of the light-independent pathway of photosynthesis is **carbon fixation** by the **Calvin-Benson cycle,**[10] which involves the attachment of molecules of $CO_2$ to molecules of a five-carbon organic compound called ribulose 1,5-bisphosphate (RuBP). RuBP is derived initially from phosphorylation of a precursor metabolite produced by the pentose phosphate pathway (see Figure 19).

The Calvin-Benson cycle is reminiscent of the Krebs cycle in that the substrates of the cycle are regenerated. It is helpful to notice the number of carbon atoms during each part of the three steps of the Calvin-Benson cycle (Figure 28):

1. *Fixation of $CO_2$.* An enzyme attaches three molecules of carbon dioxide (3 carbon atoms) to three molecules of RuBP (15 carbon atoms), which are then split to form six molecules of 3-phosphoglyceric acid (18 carbon atoms).

2. *Reduction.* Molecules of NADPH reduce the six molecules of 3-phosphoglyceric acid to form six molecules of glyceraldehyde 3-phosphate (G3P) (18 carbon atoms). These reactions require six molecules each of ATP and NADPH generated by the light-dependent reactions.

3. *Regeneration of RuBP.* The cell regenerates three molecules of RuBP (15 carbon atoms) from five molecules of G3P (15 carbon atoms). It uses the remaining molecule of glyceraldehyde 3-phosphate to synthesize glucose by reversing the reactions of glycolysis.

In summary, ATP and NADPH from the light-dependent reactions drive the synthesis of glucose from $CO_2$ in the light-independent reactions of the Calvin-Benson cycle. For every three molecules of $CO_2$ that enter the Calvin-Benson cycle, a molecule of glyceraldehyde 3-phosphate (G3P) leaves. Glycolysis is subsequently reversed to anabolically combine two molecules of G3P to synthesize glucose 6-phosphate. **ANIMATIONS:** *Photosynthesis: Light-Independent Reaction*

The processes of oxygenic photosynthesis and aerobic respiration complement one another to complete both a carbon cycle and an oxygen cycle. During the synthesis of glucose in oxygenic photosynthesis, water and carbon dioxide are used, and oxygen is released as a waste product; in aerobic respiration, oxygen serves as the final electron acceptor in the oxidation of glucose to carbon dioxide and water.

In this section we examined an essential anabolic pathway for life on Earth—photosynthesis, which produces glucose. Next we will consider anabolic pathways involved in the synthesis of other organic molecules.

---

[10]Named for the men who elucidated its pathways.

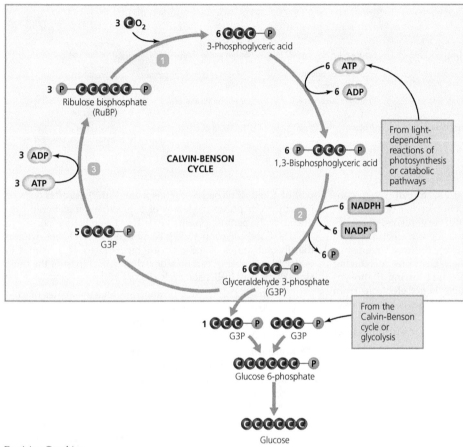

**Figure 28 Simplified diagram of the Calvin-Benson cycle.** 1 Fixation of $CO_2$. Three molecules of RuBP combine with three molecules of $CO_2$. 2 Reduction. The resulting molecules are reduced to form six molecules of G3P. 3 Generation of RuBP. Five molecules of G3P are converted to three molecules of RuBP, which completes the cycle. Two turns of the cycle also yield two molecules of G3P, which are polymerized to synthesize glucose 6-phosphate.

Precision Graphics

# Other Anabolic Pathways

## Learning Objective

✓ Define *amphibolic reaction*.

Anabolic reactions are synthesis reactions. As such, they require energy and a source of metabolites. Energy for anabolism is provided by ATP generated in the catabolic reactions of aerobic respiration, anaerobic respiration, and fermentation, and by the initial redox reactions of photosynthesis. Glycolysis, the Krebs cycle, and the pentose phosphate pathway provide 12 basic precursor metabolites from which all macromolecules and cellular structures can be made (Table 6). Some microorganisms, such as *E. coli*, can synthesize all 12 precursors, while other organisms, such as humans, must acquire some precursors in their diets.

Many anabolic pathways are the reversal of the catabolic pathways we have discussed; therefore, much of the material that follows has *in a sense* been discussed in the sections on catabolism. Reactions that can proceed in either direction—toward catabolism or toward anabolism—are said to be **amphibolic.** The following sections discuss the synthesis of carbohydrates, lipids, amino acids, and nucleotides.

## Carbohydrate Biosynthesis

### Learning Objective

✓ Describe the biosynthesis of carbohydrates.

As we have seen, anabolism begins in photosynthetic organisms with carbon fixation by the enzymes of the Calvin-Benson cycle to form molecules of G3P. Enzymes use G3P as the starting point for synthesizing sugars, complex polysaccharides such as starch, cellulose for cell walls in algae, and peptidoglycan for cell walls of bacteria. Animals and protozoa synthesize the storage molecule glycogen.

Some cells are able to synthesize sugars from noncarbohydrate precursors such as amino acids, glycerol, and fatty acids by

TABLE 6

## The Twelve Precursor Metabolites

| | Pathway That Generates the Metabolite | Examples of Macromolecule Synthesized from Metabolite[a] | Examples of Functional Use |
|---|---|---|---|
| Glucose 6-phosphate | Glycolysis | Lipopolysaccharide | Outer membrane of cell wall |
| Fructose 6-phosphate | Glycolysis | Peptidoglycan | Cell wall |
| Glyceraldehyde 3-phosphate (G3P) | Glycolysis | Glycerol portion of lipids | Fats—energy storage |
| Phosphoglyceric acid | Glycolysis | Amino acids: cysteine, selenocysteine, glycine, and serine | Enzymes |
| Phosphoenolpyruvic acid (PEP) | Glycolysis | Amino acids: phenylalanine, tryptophan, and tyrosine | Enzymes |
| Pyruvic acid | Glycolysis | Amino acids: alanine, leucine, and valine | Enzymes |
| Ribose 5-phosphate | Pentose phosphate pathway | DNA, RNA, amino acid, and histidine | Genome, enzymes |
| Erythrose 4-phosphate | Pentose phosphate pathway | Amino acids: phenylalanine, tryptophan, and tyrosine | Enzymes |
| Acetyl-CoA | Krebs cycle | Fatty acid portion of lipids | Cytoplasmic membrane |
| α-Ketoglutaric acid | Krebs cycle | Amino acids: arginine, glutamic acid, glutamine, and proline | Enzymes |
| Succinyl-CoA | Krebs cycle | Heme | Cytochrome electron carrier |
| Oxaloacetate | Krebs cycle | Amino acids: aspartic acid, asparagine, isoleucine, lysine, methionine, and threonine | Enzymes |

[a]Examples given apply to the bacterium *E. coli.*

pathways collectively called *gluconeogenesis*[11] (glū'kō-nē-ō-jen'ĕ-sis; Figure 29). Most of the reactions of gluconeogenesis are amphibolic, using enzymes of glycolysis in reverse, but four of the reactions require unique enzymes. Gluconeogenesis is highly endergonic and can proceed only if there is an adequate supply of energy.

### CRITICAL THINKING

A scientist moves a green plant grown in sunlight to a room with 24 hours of artificial green light. Will this increase or decrease the plant's rate of photosynthesis? Why?

## Lipid Biosynthesis

### Learning Objective

✓ Describe the biosynthesis of lipids.

Lipids are a diverse group of organic molecules that function as energy-storage compounds and as components of membranes. *Carotenoids,* which are reddish pigments found in many bacterial and plant photosystems, are also lipids.

[11]From Greek *glukus*, meaning sweet, *neo*, meaning new, and *genesis*, meaning generate.

Because of their variety, it is not surprising that lipids are synthesized by a variety of routes. For example, fats are synthesized in anabolic reactions that are the reverse of their catabolism—cells polymerize glycerol and three fatty acids (Figure 30). Glycerol is derived from G3P generated by the Calvin-Benson cycle and glycolysis; the fatty acids are produced by the linkage of two-carbon acetyl-CoA molecules to one another by a sequence of endergonic reactions that effectively reverse the catabolic reactions of beta-oxidation. Other lipids, such as steroids, are synthesized in complex pathways involving polymerizations and isomerizations of sugar and amino acid metabolites.

*Mycobacterium tuberculosis* (mī'kō-bak-tēr'ē-ŭm too-ber-kyū-lō'sis), the pathogen that causes tuberculosis, makes copious amounts of a waxy lipid called *mycolic acid,* which is incorporated into its cell wall. The arduous, energy-intensive process of making long lipid chains explains why this organism grows slowly, and why tuberculosis requires a long course of treatment with antimicrobial drugs.

## Amino Acid Biosynthesis

### Learning Objective

✓ Describe the biosynthesis of amino acids.

Cells synthesize amino acids from precursor metabolites derived from glycolysis, the Krebs cycle, and the pentose phosphate pathway, and from other amino acids. Some organisms (such as

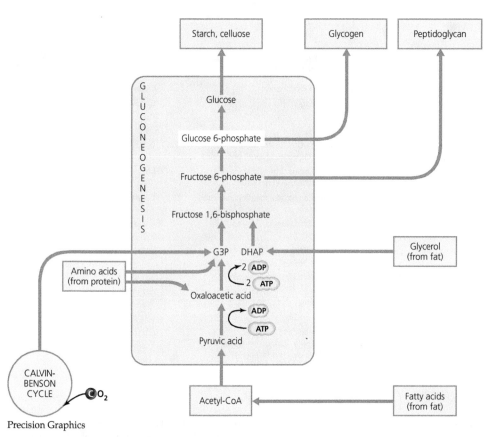

◀ **Figure 29 The role of gluconeogenesis in the biosynthesis of complex carbohydrates.** Complex carbohydrates are synthesized from simple sugar molecules such as glucose, glucose 6-phosphate, and fructose 6-phosphate. Starch and cellulose are found in algae; glycogen is found in animals and protozoa; and peptidoglycan is found in bacteria.

Precision Graphics

*E. coli,* and most plants and algae) synthesize all their amino acids from precursor metabolites. Other organisms, including humans, cannot synthesize certain amino acids, called *essential amino acids;* they must be acquired in the diet. One extreme example is *Lactobacillus* (lak'-tō-bǎ-sil'ŭs), a bacterium that ferments milk and produces some cheeses. This microorganism cannot synthesize any amino acids; it acquires all of them by catabolizing proteins in its environment.

Precursor metabolites are converted to amino acids by the addition of an amine group. This process is called **amination** when the amine group comes from ammonia ($NH_3$); an example

is the formation of aspartic acid from $NH_3$ and the Krebs cycle intermediate oxaloacetic acid **(Figure 31a)**. Amination reactions are the reverse of the catabolic deamination reactions we discussed previously. More commonly, however, a cell moves the amine group from one amino acid and adds it to a metabolite, producing a different amino acid. This process is called **transamination** because the amine group is transferred from one amino acid to another **(Figure 31b)**. All transamination enzymes use a coenzyme, *pyridoxal phosphate,* which is derived from vitamin $B_6$.

◀ **Figure 30 Biosynthesis of fat, a lipid.** A fat molecule is synthesized from glycerol and three molecules of fatty acid, the precursors of which are produced in glycolysis.

Precision Graphics

Precision Graphics

▲ **Figure 31** **Examples of the synthesis of amino acids via amination and transamination.**
**(a)** In amination, an amine group from ammonia is added to a precursor metabolite. In this example, oxaloacetic acid is converted into the amino acid aspartic acid. **(b)** In transamination, the amine group is derived from an existing amino acid. In the example shown here, the amino acid glutamic acid donates its amine group to oxaloacetic acid, which is converted into aspartic acid. Note that transamination is a reversible reaction.

Ribozymes of ribosomes polymerize amino acids into proteins.

## CRITICAL **THINKING**

What class of enzyme is involved in amination reactions? What class of enzyme catalyzes transaminations?

## Nucleotide Biosynthesis

### Learning Objective

✓ Describe the biosynthesis of nucleotides.

The building blocks of nucleic acids are nucleotides, each of which consists of a five-carbon sugar, a phosphate group, and a purine or pyrimidine base. Nucleotides are produced from precursor metabolites of glycolysis and the Krebs cycle (Figure 32):

➤ **Figure 32**
**The biosynthesis of nucleotides.**

Precision Graphics

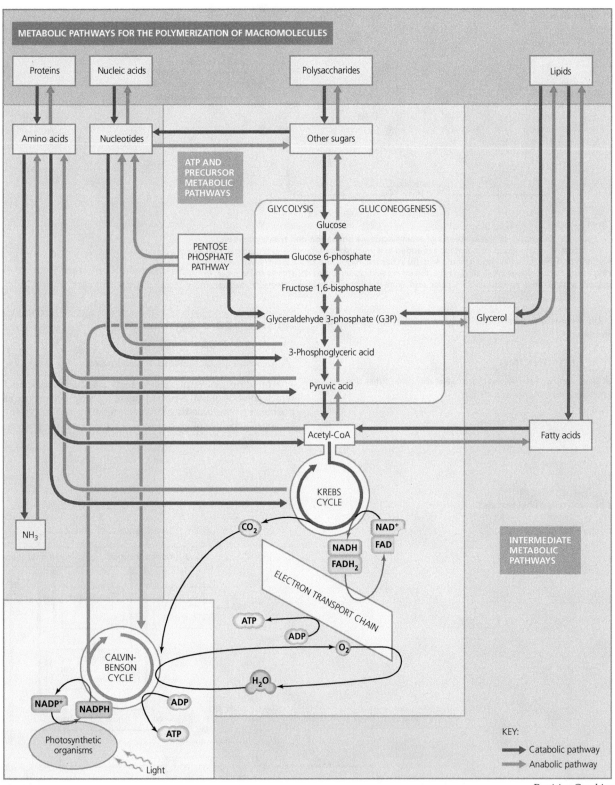

◀ **Figure 33 Integration of cellular metabolism (shown in an aerobic organism).** Cells possess three major categories of metabolic pathways: pathways for the polymerization of macromolecules (proteins, nucleic acids, polysaccharides, and lipids), intermediate pathways, and ATP and precursor pathways (glycolysis, Krebs cycle, the pentose phosphate pathway, and the Entner-Doudoroff pathway [not shown]). Cells of photosynthetic organisms also have the Calvin-Benson cycle.

- The five-carbon sugars—ribose in RNA and deoxyribose in DNA—are derived from ribose 5-phosphate from the pentose phosphate pathway.
- The phosphate group is derived ultimately from ATP.
- Purines and pyrimidines are synthesized in a series of ATP-requiring reactions from the amino acids glutamine and aspartic acid derived from Krebs cycle intermediates, ribose 5-phosphate, and *folic acid*. (The latter is synthesized by many bacteria and protozoa but is a vitamin for humans.)

# Integration and Regulation of Metabolic Functions

## Learning Objectives

✓ Describe interrelationships between catabolism and anabolism in terms of ATP and substrates.

✓ Discuss regulation of metabolic activity.

As we have seen, catabolic and anabolic reactions interact with one another in several ways. First, ATP molecules produced by catabolism are used to drive anabolic reactions. Second, catabolic pathways produce precursor metabolites to use as substrates for anabolic reactions. Additionally, most metabolic pathways are amphibolic; they function as part of either catabolism or anabolism as needed.

Cells regulate metabolism in a variety of ways to maximize efficiency in growth and reproductive rate. Among the mechanisms involved are the following:

- Cells synthesize or degrade channel and transport proteins to increase or decrease the concentration of chemicals in the cytosol or organelles.
- Cells often synthesize the enzymes needed to catabolize a particular substrate only when that substrate is available. For instance, the enzymes of beta-oxidation are not produced when there are no fatty acids to catabolize.
- If two energy sources are available, cells catabolize the more energy efficient of the two. For example, a bacterium growing in the presence of both glucose and lactose will produce enzymes only for the transport and catabolism of glucose. Once the supply of glucose is depleted, lactose-utilizing proteins are produced.
- Cells synthesize the metabolites they need, but they typically cease synthesis if a metabolite is available as a nutrient. For instance, bacteria grown with an excess of aspartic acid will cease the amination of oxaloacetic acid (see Figure 31).
- Eukaryotic cells keep metabolic processes from interfering with each other by isolating particular enzymes within membrane-bounded organelles. For example, proteases sequestered within lysosomes digest phagocytized proteins without destroying vital proteins in the cytosol.
- Cells use inhibitory and excitatory allosteric sites on enzymes to control the activity of enzymes (see Figure 10).
- Feedback inhibition slows or stops anabolic pathways when the product is in abundance (see Figure 11).
- Cells regulate catabolic and anabolic pathways that use the same substrate molecules by requiring different coenzymes for each. For instance, NADH is used almost exclusively with catabolic enzymes, whereas NADPH is typically used for anabolism.

Note that these regulatory mechanisms are generally of two types: *control of gene expression*, in which cells control the amount and timing of protein (enzyme) production, and *control of metabolic expression*, in which cells control the activity of proteins (enzymes) once they have been produced.

Figure 33 schematically diagrams some of the numerous interrelationships among the metabolic pathways discussed in this chapter. **ANIMATIONS:** *Metabolism: The Big Picture*

# Chapter Summary

 This chapter has *MicroFlix*. Go to the Study Area at **www.masteringmicrobiology.com** to view movie-quality animations for metabolism.

## Basic Chemical Reactions Underlying Metabolism

1. **Metabolism** is the sum of biochemical reactions within the cells of an organism, including **catabolism,** which breaks down molecules and releases energy, and **anabolism,** which synthesizes molecules and uses energy. **ANIMATIONS:** *Metabolism: Overview*

2. **Precursor metabolites,** often produced in catabolic reactions, are used to synthesize all other organic compounds.

3. **Reduction** reactions are those in which electrons are added. The molecule that donates an electron is **oxidized.** If the electron is

part of a hydrogen atom, an oxidation reaction is also called dehydrogenation. Oxidation and reduction reactions always occur in pairs called **oxidation-reduction (redox) reactions.**
**ANIMATIONS:** *Oxidation-Reduction Reactions*

4. Three important electron carrier molecules are **nicotinamide adenine dinucleotide (NAD⁺), nicotinamide adenine dinucleotide phosphate (NADP⁺), and flavin adenine dinucleotide (FAD).**

5. Phosphorylation is the addition of phosphate to a molecule. Three types of phosphorylation form ATP: **Substrate-level phosphorylation** involves the transfer of phosphate from a phosphorylated organic compound to ADP. In **oxidative phosphorylation,** energy from redox reactions of respiration is used to attach inorganic phosphate ($PO_4^{3-}$) to ADP. **Photophosphorylation** is the phosphorylation of ADP with inorganic phosphate using energy from light.

6. Catalysts increase the rates of chemical reactions and are not permanently changed in the process. **Enzymes,** which are organic catalysts, are often named for their **substrates**—the molecules upon which they act. Enzymes can be classified as hydrolases, isomerases, ligases (polymerases), lyases, oxidoreductases, or transferases, reflecting their mode of action.
**ANIMATIONS:** *Enzymes: Overview*

7. **Apoenzymes** are the portions of enzymes that may require one or more **cofactors** such as inorganic ions or organic cofactors (also called **coenzymes**). The combination of both apoenzyme and its cofactors is a **holoenzyme.** RNA molecules functioning as enzymes are called **ribozymes.**

8. **Activation energy** is the amount of energy required to initiate a chemical reaction.

9. Substrates fit into the specifically shaped **active sites** of the enzymes that catalyze their reactions.
**ANIMATIONS:** *Enzymes: Steps in a Reaction*

10. Enzymes may be **denatured** by physical and chemical factors such as heat and pH. Denaturation may be reversible or permanent.

11. Enzyme activity proceeds at a rate proportional to the concentration of substrate molecules until all the active sites are filled.

12. **Competitive inhibitors** block active sites and thereby block enzyme activity. **Noncompetitive inhibitors** attach to an allosteric site on an enzyme, altering the active site so that it is no longer functional.
**ANIMATIONS:** *Enzymes: Competitive Inhibition, Noncompetitive Inhibition*

13. **Feedback inhibition** (negative feedback) occurs when the final product of a series of reactions is an allosteric inhibitor of some previous step in the series. Thus, accumulation of the end-product "feeds back" into the series a signal that stops the process.

## Carbohydrate Catabolism

1. **Glycolysis** involves the splitting of a glucose molecule in a three-stage, 10-step process that ultimately results in two molecules of pyruvic acid and a net gain of two ATP and two NADH molecules.
**ANIMATIONS:** *Glycolysis: Overview, Steps*

2. The **pentose phosphate** and **Entner-Doudoroff pathways** are alternative means for the catabolism of glucose that yield fewer ATP

molecules than does glycolysis. However, they produce precursor metabolites not produced in glycolysis.

3. **Cellular respiration** is a metabolic process that involves the complete oxidation of substrate molecules and the production of ATP following a series of redox reactions.

4. Two carbons from pyruvic acid join coenzyme A to form acetyl-coenzyme A (**acetyl-CoA**), which then enters the **Krebs cycle,** a series of eight enzymatic steps that transfer electrons from acetyl-CoA to coenzymes NAD⁺ and FAD.
**ANIMATIONS:** *Krebs Cycle: Overview, Steps*

5. An **electron transport chain** is a series of redox reactions that pass electrons from one membrane-bound carrier to another, and then to a final electron acceptor. The energy from these electrons is used to pump protons across the membrane.
**ANIMATIONS:** *Electron Transport Chain: Overview*

6. The four classes of carrier molecules in electron transport systems are flavoproteins, ubiquinones, metal-containing proteins, and cytochromes.
**ANIMATIONS:** *Electron Transport Chain: The Process*

7. Aerobes use oxygen atoms as final electron acceptors in their electron transport chains in a process known as **aerobic respiration,** whereas anaerobes use other inorganic molecules (such as $NO_3^-$, $SO_4^{2-}$, and $CO_3^{2-}$, or rarely an externally acquired organic molecule) as the final electron acceptor in **anaerobic respiration.**
**ANIMATIONS:** *Electron Transport Chain: Factors Affecting ATP Yield*

8. In **chemiosmosis,** ions flow down their electrochemical gradient across a membrane through **ATP synthase (ATPase)** to synthesize ATP.

9. A **proton gradient** is an electrochemical gradient of hydrogen ions across a membrane. It has potential energy known as a proton motive force.

10. Oxidative phosphorylation and photophosphorylation use chemiosmosis.

11. **Fermentation** is the partial oxidation of sugar to release energy using a cellular organic molecule rather than an electron transport chain as the final electron acceptor. End-products of fermentation, which are often useful to humans and aid in identification of microbes in the laboratory, include acids, alcohols, and gases.
**ANIMATIONS:** *Fermentation*

## Other Catabolic Pathways

1. Lipids and proteins can be catabolized into smaller molecules, which can be used as substrates for glycolysis and the Krebs cycle.

2. **Beta-oxidation** is a catabolic process in which enzymes split pairs of hydrogenated carbon atoms from a fatty acid and join them to coenzyme A to form acetyl-CoA.

3. **Proteases** secreted by microorganisms digest proteins outside the microbes' cell walls. The resulting amino acids are moved into the cell and used in anabolism, or **deaminated** and catabolized for energy.

## Photosynthesis

1. **Photosynthesis** is a process in which light energy is captured by pigment molecules called **chlorophylls** (bacteriochlorophylls in

some bacteria) and transferred to ATP and metabolites. **Photosystems** are networks of light-absorbing chlorophyll molecules and other pigments held within a protein matrix on membranes called **thylakoids.**
ANIMATIONS: *Photosynthesis: Overview*

2. The redox reactions of photosynthesis are classified as **light-dependent reactions** and **light-independent reactions.**

3. A **reaction center chlorophyll** is a special chlorophyll molecule in a photosystem in which electrons are excited by light energy and passed to an acceptor molecule of an electron transport chain.

4. In **cyclic photophosphorylation,** the electrons return to the original reaction center after passing down the electron transport chain.
ANIMATIONS: *Photosynthesis: Light Reaction: Cyclic Photophosphorylation*

5. In **noncyclic photophosphorylation,** photosystem II works with photosystem I, and the electrons are used to reduce $NADP^+$ to NADPH. In oxygenic photosynthesis, cyanobacteria, algae, and green plants replenish electrons to the reaction center by dissociation of $H_2O$ molecules, resulting in the release of $O_2$ molecules. Anoxygenic bacteria derive electrons from inorganic compounds such as $H_2S$, producing waste such as sulfur.
ANIMATIONS: *Photosynthesis: Light Reaction: Noncyclic Photophosphorylation*

6. In the light-independent pathway of photosynthesis, **carbon fixation** occurs in the **Calvin-Benson cycle,** in which $CO_2$ is reduced to produce glucose.
ANIMATIONS: *Photosynthesis: Light-Independent Reaction*

## Other Anabolic Pathways

1. **Amphibolic reactions** are metabolic reactions that are reversible—they can operate catabolically or anabolically.

2. Some cells are able to synthesize glucose from amino acids, glycerol, and fatty acids via a process called gluconeogenesis.

3. **Amination** reactions involve adding an amine group from ammonia to a metabolite to make an amino acid. **Transamination** occurs when an amine group is transferred from one amino acid to another.

4. Nucleotides are synthesized from precursor metabolites produced by glycolysis, the Krebs cycle, and the pentose phosphate pathway.

## Integration and Regulation of Metabolic Functions

1. Cells regulate metabolism by control of gene expression or metabolic expression. They control the latter in a variety of ways, including synthesizing or degrading channel proteins and enzymes, sequestering reactions in membrane-bounded organelles (seen only in eukaryotes), and feedback inhibition.
ANIMATIONS: *Metabolism: The Big Picture*

# Questions for Review
Answers to the Questions for Review (except Short Answer questions) appear at the end of this chapter.

## Multiple Choice

For each of the phrases in questions 1–7, indicate the type of metabolism referred to, using the following choices:
    a. anabolism only
    b. both anabolism and catabolism (amphibolic)
    c. catabolism only

1. Breaks a large molecule into smaller ones

2. Includes dehydration synthesis reactions

3. Is exergonic

4. Is endergonic

5. Involves the production of cell membrane constituents

6. Includes hydrolytic reactions

7. Includes metabolism

8. Redox reactions
    a. transfer energy.
    b. transfer electrons.
    c. involve oxidation and reduction.
    d. are involved in all of the above.

9. A reduced molecule
    a. has gained electrons.
    b. has become more positive in charge.
    c. has lost electrons.
    d. is an electron donor.

10. Activation energy
    a. is the amount of energy required during an activity such as flagellar motion.
    b. requires the addition of nutrients in the presence of water.
    c. is lowered by the action of organic catalysts.
    d. results from the movement of molecules.

11. Coenzymes
    a. are types of apoenzymes.
    b. are proteins.
    c. are inorganic cofactors.
    d. are organic cofactors.

12. Which of the following statements best describes ribozymes?
    a. Ribozymes are proteins that aid in the production of ribosomes.
    b. Ribozymes are nucleic acids that produce ribose sugars.
    c. Ribozymes store enzymes in ribosomes.
    d. Ribozymes process RNA molecules in eukaryotes.

13. Which of the following does *not* affect the function of enzymes?
    a. ubiquinone
    b. substrate concentration
    c. temperature
    d. competitive inhibitors

14. Most oxidation reactions in bacteria involve the
    a. removal of hydrogen ions and electrons.
    b. removal of oxygen.
    c. addition of hydrogen ions and electrons.
    d. addition of hydrogen ions.

15. Under ideal conditions, the fermentation of one glucose molecule by a bacterium allows a net gain of how many ATP molecules?
    a. 2      b. 4      c. 38      d. 0

16. Under ideal conditions, the complete aerobic oxidation of one molecule of glucose by a bacterium allows a net gain of how many ATP molecules?
    a. 2      b. 4      c. 38      d. 0

17. Which of the following statements is *not* true of the Entner-Doudoroff pathway?
    a. It is a series of reactions that synthesizes glucose.
    b. Its products are sometimes used to determine the presence of *Pseudomonas*.
    c. It is a pathway of chemical reactions that catabolizes glucose.
    d. It is an alternative pathway to glycolysis.

18. Reactions involved in the light-independent reactions of photosynthesis constitute the
    a. Krebs cycle.
    b. Entner-Doudoroff pathway.
    c. Calvin-Benson cycle.
    d. pentose phosphate pathway.

19. The glycolysis pathway is basically
    a. catabolic.           c. anabolic.
    b. amphibolic.          d. cyclical.

20. A major difference between anaerobic respiration and anaerobic fermentation is
    a. in the use of oxygen.
    b. that the former requires breathing.
    c. the latter uses organic molecules within the cell as final electron acceptors.
    d. fermentation only produces alcohol.

## Matching

1. ____ Occurs when energy from a compound containing phosphate reacts with ADP to form ATP

2. ____ Involves formation of ATP via reduction of coenzymes in the electron transport chain

3. ____ Begins with glycolysis

4. ____ Occurs when all active sites on substrate molecules are filled

A. Saturation

B. Oxidative phosphorylation

C. Substrate-level phosphorylation

D. Photophosphorylation

E. Carbohydrate catabolism

## Fill in the Blanks

1. The final electron acceptor in cyclic photophosphorylation is _____.

2. Two ATP molecules are used to initiate glycolysis. Enzymes generate molecules of ATP for each molecule of glucose that undergoes glycolysis. Thus a net gain of _____ molecules of ATP is produced in glycolysis.

3. The initial catabolism of glucose occurs by glycolysis and/or the _____ and _____ pathways.

4. _____ is a cyclic series of eight reactions involved in the catabolism of acetyl-CoA that yields eight molecules of NADH and two molecules of $FADH_2$.

5. The final electron acceptor in aerobic respiration is _____ .

6. Three common inorganic electron acceptors in anaerobic respiration are _____, _____, and _____.

7. Chemolithotrophs *acquire* electrons from (organic/inorganic) _____ compounds.

8. Complete the following chart:

| Category of Enzymes | Description |
| --- | --- |
|  | Catabolizes substrate by adding water |
| Isomerase |  |
| Ligase/polymerase |  |
|  | Moves functional groups such as an acetyl group |
|  | Adds or removes electrons |
| Lyase |  |

9. The use of a proton motive force to generate ATP is _____.

10. The main coenzymes that carry electrons in catabolic pathways are _____ and _____.

## Short Answer

1. Why are enzymes necessary for anabolic reactions to occur in living organisms?

2. How do organisms control the rate of metabolic activities in their cells?

3. How does a noncompetitive inhibitor at a single allosteric site affect a whole pathway of enzymatic reactions?

4. Explain the mechanism of negative feedback with respect to enzyme action.

5. Facultative anaerobes can live under either aerobic or anaerobic conditions. What metabolic pathways allow these organisms to continue to harvest energy from sugar molecules in the absence of oxygen?

6. How does oxidation of a molecule occur without oxygen?

7. List at least four groups of microorganisms that are photosynthetic.

8. Why do we breathe oxygen and give off carbon dioxide?

9. Why do cyanobacteria and algae take in carbon dioxide and give off oxygen?

10. What happens to the carbon atoms in sugar catabolized by *Escherichia coli*?

11. How do yeast cells make alcohol and cause bread to rise?

12. Where specifically does the most significant production of ATP occur in prokaryotic and eukaryotic cells?

13. Why are vitamins essential metabolic factors for microbial metabolism?

14. A laboratory scientist notices that a certain bacterium does not utilize lactose when glucose is available in its environment. Describe a cellular regulatory mechanism that would explain this observation.

15. How does amination differ from transamination?

16. Label the diagram on the right to indicate acetyl-CoA, electron transport chain, FADH₂, fermentation, glycolysis, Krebs cycle, NADH, and respiration. Indicate the net number of molecules of ATP that could be synthesized at each stage during bacterial respiration of one molecule of glucose.

Precision Graphics

#  Concept Mapping

Using the following terms, draw a concept map that describes aerobic respiration. Or, complete this concept map online by going to the Study Area at www.masteringmicrobiology.com.

| | | | |
|---|---|---|---|
| 2 ATP **(2)** | Electron transport chain | Oxidative | Substrate-level |
| 34 ATP | Glycolysis | phosphorylation | phosphorylation **(2)** |
| Chemiosmosis | Krebs cycle | | Synthesis of acetyl-CoA |

# Critical Thinking

1. Why might an organism that uses glycolysis and the Krebs cycle also need the pentose phosphate pathway?

2. Describe how bacterial fermentation causes milk to sour.

3. *Giardia intestinalis* and *Entamoeba histolytica* are protozoa that live in the colons of mammals and can cause life-threatening diarrhea. Interestingly, these microbes lack mitochondria. What kind of pathway must they have for carbohydrate catabolism?

4. Two cultures of a facultative anaerobe are grown in the same type of medium, but one is exposed to air and the other is maintained under anaerobic conditions. Which of the two cultures will contain more cells at the end of a week? Why?

5. What is the maximum number of molecules of ATP that can be generated by a bacterium after the complete aerobic oxidation of a fat molecule containing three 12-carbon chains? (Assume that all the available energy released during catabolism goes to ATP production.)

6. In terms of its effects on metabolism, why is a fever over 40°C often life threatening?

7. Cyanide is a potent poison because it irreversibly blocks cytochrome $a_3$. What effect would its action have on the rest of the electron transport chain? What would be the redox state (reduced or oxidized) of ubiquinone in the presence of cyanide?

8. How are photophosphorylation and oxidative phosphorylation similar? How are they different?

9. Members of the pathogenic bacterial genus *Haemophilus* require $NAD^+$ and heme from their environment. For what purpose does *Haemophilus* use these growth factors?

10. Compare and contrast aerobic respiration, anaerobic respiration, and fermentation.

11. Scientists estimate that up to one-third of Earth's biomass is composed of methanogenic prokaryotes in ocean sediments (*Science* 295:2067–2070). Describe the metabolism of these organisms.

12. A young student was troubled by the idea that a bacterium is able to control its diverse and complex metabolic activities, even though it lacks a brain. How would you explain its metabolic control?

13. If a bacterium uses beta-oxidation to catabolize a molecule of the fatty acid arachidic acid, which contains 20 carbon atoms, how many acetyl-CoA molecules will be generated?

14. Some desert rodents rarely have water to drink. How do they get enough water for their cells without drinking it?

15. Why do fatty acids typically contain an even number of carbon atoms?

16. We have examined the total ATP, NADH, and $FADH_2$ production in the Krebs cycle for each molecule of glucose coming through Embden-Meyerhof glycolysis. How many of each of these molecules would be produced if the Entner-Doudoroff pathway were used instead of Embden-Meyerhof glycolysis?

Access more review material online in the Study Area at **www.masteringmicrobiology.com.** There, you'll find
- **Animations**
- **Microflix**
- **MP3 Tutor Sessions**
- **Concept Mapping Activities**
- **Flashcards**
- **Quizzes**

and more to help you succeed.

# Answers

Answers to multiple-choice, fill-in-blank, labeling, matching, and true/false questions are listed here. Answers for Short Answer and Critical Thinking questions are available for instructors only in the Instructor's Manual that accompanies this text.

**Multiple Choice**
1. c; 2. a; 3. c; 4. a; 5. c; 6. c; 7. b; 8. d; 9. a; 10. c; 11. d; 12. d; 13. a; 14. a; 15. a; 16. c; 17. a; 18. c; 19. a; 20. c

**Matching**
1. C; 2. B; 3. E; 4. A

**Fill in the Blanks**
1. the original reaction center, chlorophyll; 2. 2; 3. pentose phosphate, Entner-Doudoroff; 4. The Krebs cycle; 5. $O_2$; 6. $NO_3^-$, $SO_4^{2-}$, $CO_3^{2-}$; 7. inorganic

8.

| Category of Enzyme | Description |
|---|---|
| Hydrolase | Catabolizes substrate by adding water |
| Isomerase | Rearranges atoms |
| Ligase/polymerase | Joins 2 molecules together |
| Transferase | Moves functional groups |
| Oxidoreductase | Adds or removes electrons |
| Lyase | Splits large molecules |

9. chemiosmosis; 10. $NAD^+$, FAD

# Controlling Microbial Growth in the Body: Antimicrobial Drugs

From Chapter 10 of *Microbiology with Diseases by Taxonomy*, Third Edition. Robert W. Bauman. Copyright © 2011 by Pearson Education, Inc. Published by Benjamin Cummings, Inc. All rights reserved.

# Controlling Microbial Growth in the Body: Antimicrobial Drugs

Meet *Staphylococcus aureus*, a common bacterium that is the number one cause of hospital-acquired infections in the United States. The particular strain of *S. aureus* shown here, however, is remarkable in some very important and alarming ways. It is not only resistant to methicillin, the antimicrobial that is traditionally used to treat staphylococcal infections; it is also resistant to vancomycin, a drug that was long considered the last line of defense against methicillin-resistant *S. aureus*. Although other drugs may be used to fight it, this "superbug" strain of *S. aureus* leaves patients few options for defense—and indeed it can cause death.

How do antimicrobial drugs work? Why do they work on some microorganisms and not on others? What can be done about the increasing problem of superbugs that resist a wide variety of existing drugs? This chapter focuses on the chemical control of pathogens in the body.

 Take the pre-test for this chapter online. Visit the Study Area at www.masteringmicrobiology.com.

CDC/Science Source/Photo Researchers

▲ Some strains of *Staphylococcus aureus*, such as the cells shown here, are resistant to multiple drugs, including methicillin and vancomycin.

Chemicals that affect physiology in any manner, such as caffeine, alcohol, and tobacco, are called *drugs*. Drugs that act against diseases are called *chemotherapeutic agents*. Examples include insulin, anticancer drugs, and drugs for treating infections—called **antimicrobial agents (antimicrobials),** the subject of this chapter.

In the pages that follow we'll examine the mechanisms by which antimicrobial agents act, the factors that must be considered in the use of antimicrobials, and several issues surrounding resistance to antimicrobial agents among microorganisms. First, however, we begin with a brief history of antimicrobial chemotherapy.

# The History of Antimicrobial Agents

## Learning Objectives

✓ Describe the contributions of Paul Ehrlich, Alexander Fleming, and Gerhard Domagk in the development of antimicrobials.

✓ Explain how semisynthetic and synthetic antimicrobials differ from antibiotics.

The little girl lay struggling to breathe as her parents stood mutely by, willing the doctor to do something—anything—to relieve the symptoms that had so quickly consumed their four-year-old daughter's vitality. Sadly, there was little the doctor could do. The thick "pseudomembrane" of diphtheria, composed of bacteria, mucus, blood-clotting factors, and white blood cells, adhered tenaciously to her pharynx, tonsils, and vocal cords. He knew that trying to remove it could rip open the underlying mucous membrane, resulting in bleeding, possibly additional infections, and death. In 1902, there was little medical

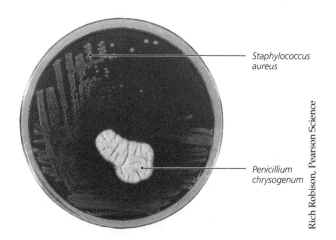

**▲ Figure 1 Antibiotic effect of the mold *Penicillium chrysogenum*.** Alexander Fleming observed that this mold secretes penicillin, which inhibits the growth of bacteria, as is apparent with *Staphylococcus aureus* growing on this blood agar plate.

*Staphylococcus aureus*

*Penicillium chrysogenum*

Rich Robison, Pearson Science

science could offer for the treatment of diphtheria; all physicians could do was wait and hope.

At the beginning of the 20th century, much of medicine involved diagnosing illness, describing its expected course, and telling family members either how long a patient might be sick or when they might expect her to die. Even though physicians and scientists had recently accepted the germ theory of disease and knew the causes of many diseases, very little could be done to inhibit pathogens, including *Corynebacterium diphtheriae* (kŏ-rī'nē-bak-tēr'ē-ŭm dif-thi'rē-ī), and alter the course of infections. In fact, one-third of children born in the early 1900s died from infectious diseases before the age of five.

It was at this time that Paul Ehrlich (1854–1915), a visionary German scientist, proposed the term *chemotherapy* to describe the use of chemicals that would selectively kill pathogens while having little or no effect on a patient. He wrote of "magic bullets" that would bind to receptors on germs to bring about their death while ignoring host cells, which lacked the receptor molecules.

Ehrlich's search for antimicrobial agents resulted in the discovery of one arsenic compound that killed trypanosome parasites and another that worked against the bacterial agent of syphilis. A few years later, in 1929, the British bacteriologist Alexander Fleming (1881–1955) reported the antibacterial action of penicillin released from *Penicillium* (pen-i-sil'ē-ŭm) mold **(Figure 1)**.

Though arsenic compounds and penicillin were discovered first, they were not the first antimicrobials in widespread use: Ehrlich's arsenic compounds are toxic to humans, and penicillin was not available in large enough quantities to be useful until the late 1940s. Instead, *sulfanilamide,* discovered in 1932 by the German chemist Gerhard Domagk (1895–1964), was the first practical antimicrobial agent efficacious in treating a wide array of bacterial infections.

Selman Waksman (1888–1973) discovered other microorganisms that are sources of useful antimicrobials, most notably

## CLINICAL CASE STUDY

### Antibiotic Overkill

A young woman was taking antibiotic pills for a urinary infection. Several days into her course of medication, she began to experience peculiar symptoms. At first they were hardly noticeable. Very quickly, however, they worsened and became embarrassing and unbearable.

She noticed a white coating on her tongue, bad breath, and an awful taste in her mouth. Despite persistent brushing and mouthwash applications, she was unable to completely remove the film. Furthermore, she had excessive vaginal discharges consisting of a cheeselike white substance. When she began to have vaginal itching, she finally decided it was time to seek help.

Reluctantly she revisited her personal physician and described the symptoms. Her doctor explained the symptoms and provided additional prescriptions to alleviate her distress.

1. What happened to the young woman in this situation?

2. How had her body's defenses been violated?

3. How can she avoid a repeat of this situation?

## TABLE 1

### Sources of Some Common Antibiotics and Semisynthetics

| Microorganism | Antimicrobial |
|---|---|
| **Fungi** | |
| *Penicillium chrysogenum* | Penicillin |
| *Penicillium griseofulvum* | Griseofulvin |
| *Cephalosporium* spp.[a] | Cephalothin |
| **Bacteria** | |
| *Amycolatopsis orientalis* | Vancomycin |
| *Amycolatopsis rifamycinica* | Rifampin |
| *Bacillus licheniformis* | Bacitracin |
| *Bacillus polymyxa* | Polymyxin |
| *Micromonospora purpurea* | Gentamicin |
| *Pseudomonas fluorescens* | Mupirocin |
| *Streptomyces griseus* | Streptomycin |
| *Streptomyces fradiae* | Neomycin |
| *Streptomyces aureofaciens* | Tetracycline |
| *Streptomyces venezuelae* | Chloramphenicol |
| *Streptomyces erythraeus* | Erythromycin |
| *Streptomyces nodosus* | Amphotericin B |
| *Streptomyces avermitilis* | Ivermectin |

[a]spp. is the abbreviation for multiple species of a genus.

species of soil-dwelling bacteria in the genus *Streptomyces* (strep-tō-mī′sēz). Waksman coined the term **antibiotics** to describe antimicrobial agents that are produced naturally by an organism **(Highlight: Microbe Altruism: Why Do They Do It?).** In common usage today "antibiotic" means "an antibacterial agent," including synthetic compounds and excluding agents with antiviral and antifungal activity.

Other scientists produced **semisynthetics**—chemically altered antibiotics—that are more effective, longer lasting, or easier to administer than naturally occurring antibiotics. Antimicrobials that are completely synthesized in a laboratory are called **synthetics.** Most antimicrobials are either natural or semisynthetic.

Table 1 provides a partial list of common antibiotics and semisynthetics and their sources.

## CRITICAL **THINKING**

Why aren't antibiotics effective against the common cold?

# Mechanisms of Antimicrobial Action

### Learning Objectives

✓ Explain the principle of selective toxicity.

✓ List five mechanisms by which antimicrobial drugs affect the growth of pathogens.

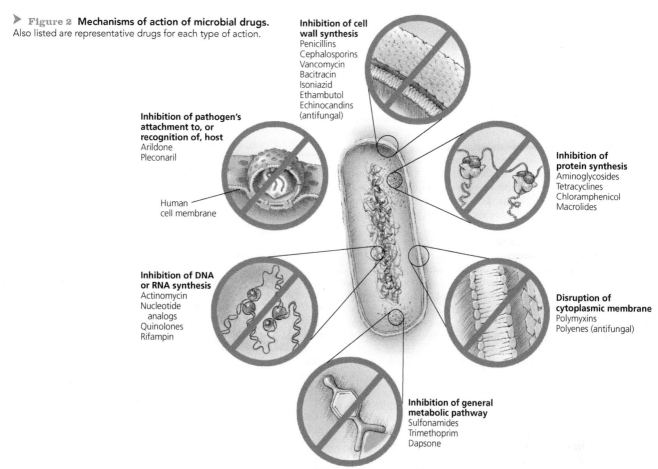

▶ **Figure 2** **Mechanisms of action of microbial drugs.**
Also listed are representative drugs for each type of action.

**Inhibition of cell wall synthesis**
Penicillins
Cephalosporins
Vancomycin
Bacitracin
Isoniazid
Ethambutol
Echinocandins (antifungal)

**Inhibition of pathogen's attachment to, or recognition of, host**
Arildone
Pleconaril

Human cell membrane

**Inhibition of protein synthesis**
Aminoglycosides
Tetracyclines
Chloramphenicol
Macrolides

**Inhibition of DNA or RNA synthesis**
Actinomycin
Nucleotide analogs
Quinolones
Rifampin

**Disruption of cytoplasmic membrane**
Polymyxins
Polyenes (antifungal)

**Inhibition of general metabolic pathway**
Sulfonamides
Trimethoprim
Dapsone

Kenneth Probst/Precision Graphics

As Ehrlich foresaw, the key to successful chemotherapy against microbes is **selective toxicity;** that is, an effective antimicrobial agent must be more toxic to a pathogen than to the pathogen's host. Selective toxicity is possible because of differences in structure or metabolism between the pathogen and its host. Typically, the more differences, the easier it is to discover or create an effective antimicrobial agent.

Because there are many differences between the structure and metabolism of pathogenic bacteria and their eukaryotic hosts, antibacterial drugs constitute the greatest number and diversity of antimicrobial agents. Fewer antifungal, antiprotozoan, and anthelmintic drugs are available because fungi, protozoa, and helminths—like their animal and human hosts—are eukaryotic and thus share many common features. The number of effective antiviral drugs is also limited, despite major differences in structure, because viruses utilize their host cells' enzymes and ribosomes to metabolize and replicate. Therefore, drugs that are effective against viral replication are likely toxic to the host as well.

Although they can have a variety of effects on pathogens, antimicrobial drugs can be categorized into several general groups according to their mechanisms of action (Figure 2):

- Drugs that inhibit cell wall synthesis. These drugs are selectively toxic to certain fungal or bacterial cells, which have cell walls, but not to animals, which lack cell walls.
- Drugs that inhibit protein synthesis (translation) by targeting the differences between prokaryotic and eukaryotic ribosomes.
- Drugs that disrupt unique components of the cytoplasmic membrane.
- Drugs that inhibit general metabolic pathways not used by humans.
- Drugs that inhibit nucleic acid synthesis.
- Drugs that block a pathogen's recognition of or attachment to its host.

In the following sections we examine these mechanisms in turn.
**ANIMATIONS:** *Chemotherapeutic Agents: Modes of Action*

## Inhibition of Cell Wall Synthesis

### Learning Objective

✓ Describe the actions and give examples of drugs that affect the cell walls of bacteria and fungi.

A cell wall protects a cell from the effects of osmotic pressure. Both pathogenic bacteria and fungi have cell walls, which animals and humans lack. First, we examine drugs that act against bacterial cell walls.

### Inhibition of Synthesis of Bacterial Walls

The major structural component of a bacterial cell wall is its peptidoglycan layer. Peptidoglycan is a huge macromolecule composed of polysaccharide chains of alternating N-acetylglucosamine (NAG) and N-acetylmuramic acid (NAM) molecules that are cross-linked by short peptide chains extending between NAM subunits. To enlarge or divide, a cell must synthesize more peptidoglycan by adding new NAG and NAM subunits to existing NAG-NAM chains, and the new NAM subunits must then be bonded to neighboring NAM subunits (Figure 3a and b).

The most common antibacterial agents act by preventing the cross-linkage of NAM subunits. Most prominent among these drugs are **beta-lactams,** such as penicillins and cephalosporins, which are antimicrobials whose functional portions are called *beta-lactam (β-lactam) rings* (Figure 3c). Beta-lactams inhibit peptidoglycan formation by irreversibly binding to the enzymes that cross-link NAM subunits (Figure 3d). In the absence of correctly formed peptidoglycan, growing bacterial cells have weakened cell walls that are less resistant to the effects of osmotic pressure. The underlying cytoplasmic membrane bulges through the weakened portions of cell wall as water moves into the cell, and eventually the cell lyses (Figure 3e).

Chemists have made alterations to natural beta-lactams, such as penicillin G, to create semisynthetic derivatives such as methicillin and cephalothin (see Figure 3c), which are more stable in the acidic environment of the stomach, more readily absorbed in the intestinal tract, less susceptible to deactivation by bacterial enzymes, or more active against more types of bacteria. The simplest beta-lactams are *monobactams,* which are seldom used because they are effective only against aerobic Gram-negative bacteria.

Other antimicrobials such as **vancomycin** (van-kō-mī'sin), which is obtained from *Amycolatopsis orientalis* (am-ē-kō′la-top-sis o-rē-en-tal′is), and **cycloserine,** a semisynthetic, disrupt cell wall formation in a different manner. They directly interfere with particular alanine-alanine bridges that link the NAM subunits in many Gram-positive bacteria. Those bacteria that lack alanine-alanine crossbridges are naturally resistant to these drugs. Still another drug that prevents cell wall formation, **bacitracin** (bas-i-trā′sin), blocks the transport of NAG and NAM from the cytoplasm out to the wall. Like beta-lactams, vancomycin, cycloserine, and bacitracin result in cell lysis due to the effects of osmotic pressure.

Since all these drugs prevent bacteria from *increasing* the amount of cell wall material but have no effect on existing peptidoglycan, they are effective only on bacterial cells that are growing or reproducing; dormant cells are unaffected.

Bacteria of the genus *Mycobacterium* (mī′kō-bak-tēr′ē-ŭm), notably the agents of leprosy and tuberculosis, are characterized by unique, complex cell walls that have a layer of arabinogalactan-mycolic acid in addition to the usual peptidoglycan of prokaryotic cells. **Isoniazid** (ī-sō-nī′ă-zid), or **INH,**[1] and **ethambutol** (eth-am′boo-tol) disrupt the formation of this extra layer. Mycobacteria typically only reproduce every 12–24 hours, in part because of the complexity of their cell walls, so antimicrobial agents that act against mycobacteria must be administered for months or even years to be effective. It is often difficult to ensure that patients continue such a long regimen of treatment.

### Inhibition of Synthesis of Fungal Walls

Fungal cell walls are composed of various polysaccharides containing a sugar, 1,3-D-glucan, that is not found in mammalian cells. A new class of antifungal drugs called **echinocandins** such as *caspofungin,* inhibit the enzyme that synthesizes glucan, and without glucan fungal cells cannot make cell walls, leading to osmotic rupture.

## Inhibition of Protein Synthesis

Cells use proteins for structure and regulation, as enzymes in metabolism, and as channels and pumps to move materials across cell membranes. Thus, a consistent supply of proteins is vital for the active life of a cell. Given that all cells, including human cells, use ribosomes to translate proteins using information from messenger RNA templates, it is not immediately obvious that drugs could selectively target differences related to protein synthesis. Recall, however, that prokaryotic ribosomes differ from eukaryotic ribosomes in structure and size: prokaryotic ribosomes are 70S and composed of 30S and 50S subunits, whereas eukaryotic ribosomes are 80S with 60S and 40S subunits.

Many antimicrobial agents take advantage of the differences between ribosomes to selectively target bacterial protein translation without significantly affecting eukaryotes. Note, however, that because some of these drugs affect eukaryotic mitochondria, which also contain 70S ribosomes like those of prokaryotes, such drugs may be harmful to animals and humans, especially the very active cells of the liver and bone marrow.

Understanding the actions of antimicrobials that inhibit protein synthesis requires an understanding of the process of translation, because various parts of ribosomes are the targets of antimicrobial drugs. Both the 30S and 50S subunits of a prokaryotic ribosome play a role in the initiation of protein synthesis, in codon recognition, and in the docking of tRNA–amino acid complexes, and that the 50S subunit contains the enzymatic portion that actually forms peptide bonds.

Among the antimicrobials that target the 30S ribosomal subunit are aminoglycosides and tetracyclines. **Aminoglycosides** (am′i-nō-glī′kō-sīds), such as *streptomycin* and *gentamicin,* change the shape of the 30S subunit, making it impossible for the ribosome to read the codons of mRNA correctly (Figure 4a). Other aminoglycosides and **tetracyclines** (tet-ră-sī′klēns) block the tRNA docking site (A site), which then prevents the incorporation of additional amino acids into a growing polypeptide (Figure 4b).

---

[1]From *isonicotinic acid hydrazide*, the correct chemical name for isoniazid.

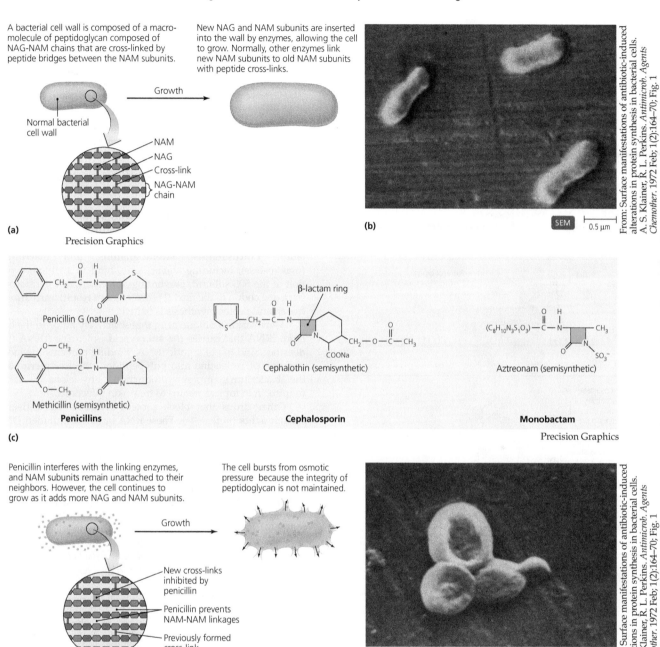

A bacterial cell wall is composed of a macromolecule of peptidoglycan composed of NAG-NAM chains that are cross-linked by peptide bridges between the NAM subunits.

New NAG and NAM subunits are inserted into the wall by enzymes, allowing the cell to grow. Normally, other enzymes link new NAM subunits to old NAM subunits with peptide cross-links.

Growth

Normal bacterial cell wall

NAM
NAG
Cross-link
NAG-NAM chain

(a) Precision Graphics

(b)

SEM | 0.5 μm

From: Surface manifestations of antibiotic-induced alterations in protein synthesis in bacterial cells. A. S. Klainer, R. L. Perkins. *Antimicrob. Agents Chemother.* 1972 Feb; 1(2):164–70; Fig. 1

Penicillin G (natural)

Methicillin (semisynthetic)

**Penicillins**

β-lactam ring

COONa

Cephalothin (semisynthetic)

**Cephalosporin**

$(C_8H_{10}N_3S_1O_3)$

$CH_3$

$SO_3^-$

Aztreonam (semisynthetic)

**Monobactam**

(c)

Precision Graphics

Penicillin interferes with the linking enzymes, and NAM subunits remain unattached to their neighbors. However, the cell continues to grow as it adds more NAG and NAM subunits.

The cell bursts from osmotic pressure because the integrity of peptidoglycan is not maintained.

Growth

New cross-links inhibited by penicillin

Penicillin prevents NAM-NAM linkages

Previously formed cross-link

(d) Precision Graphics

(e)

SEM | 0.5 μm

From: Surface manifestations of antibiotic-induced alterations in protein synthesis in bacterial cells. A. S. Klainer, R. L. Perkins. *Antimicrob. Agents Chemother.* 1972 Feb; 1(2):164–70; Fig. 1

▲ **Figure 3 Bacterial cell wall synthesis, and the inhibitory effects of beta-lactams on it. (a)** A schematic depiction of a normal peptidoglycan cell wall showing NAG-NAM chains and cross-linked NAM subunits. **(b)** Bacterial cells with normal cell walls. **(c)** Structural formulas of some beta-lactam drugs. Their functional portion is the beta-lactam ring. **(d)** A schematic depiction of the effect of penicillin on peptidoglycan in preventing NAM-NAM cross-links. **(e)** Bacterial lysis due to the effects of penicillin. *After a beta-lactam weakens a peptidoglycan molecule by preventing NAM-NAM cross-linkages, what force actually kills an affected bacterial cell?*

**Figure 3** *Cells lyse because of osmotic movement of water into the cell.*

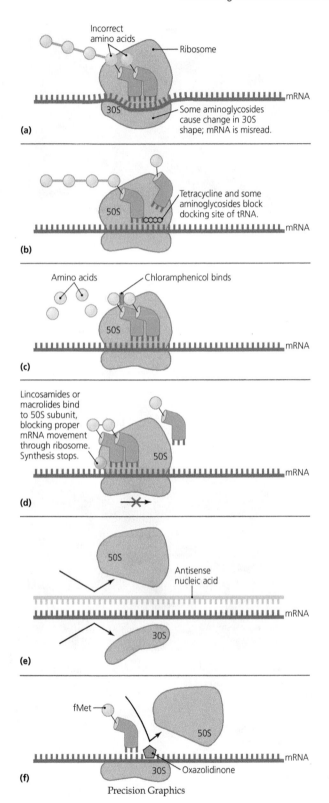

(a) Incorrect amino acids — Ribosome — 30S — mRNA — Some aminoglycosides cause change in 30S shape; mRNA is misread.

(b) 50S — Tetracycline and some aminoglycosides block docking site of tRNA. — mRNA

(c) Amino acids — Chloramphenicol binds — 50S — mRNA

(d) Lincosamides or macrolides bind to 50S subunit, blocking proper mRNA movement through ribosome. Synthesis stops. — 50S — mRNA

(e) 50S — Antisense nucleic acid — mRNA — 30S

(f) fMet — 50S — mRNA — 30S — Oxazolidinone

Precision Graphics

◀ **Figure 4 The mechanisms by which antimicrobials inhibit protein synthesis by targeting prokaryotic ribosomes.** (a) Aminoglycosides change the shape of the 30S subunit, causing incorrect pairing of tRNA anticodons with mRNA codons. (b) Tetracyclines block the tRNA docking site (A site) on the 30S subunit, preventing protein elongation. (c) Chloramphenicol blocks enzymatic activity of the 50S subunit, preventing the formation of peptide bonds between amino acids. (d) Lincosamides or macrolides bind to the 50S subunit, preventing movement of the ribosome along the mRNA. (e) Antisense nucleic acids bind to mRNA, blocking ribosomal subunits. (f) Oxazolidinones inhibit initiation of translation. *Which tRNA anticodon should align with the codon CUG?*

**Figure 4** *Anticodon GAC is the correct complement for the codon CUG.*

Other antimicrobials interfere with the function of the 50S subunit. **Chloramphenicol** and similar drugs block the enzymatic site of the 50S subunit (Figure 4c), which prevents translation. **Lincosamides**, **streptogramins**, and **macrolides** (mak′rō-līds), including *erythromycin*, bind to a different portion of the 50S subunit, preventing movement of the ribosome from one codon to the next (Figure 4d); as a result, translation is frozen and protein synthesis is halted.

*Mupirocin* is a unique drug that selectively binds to the bacterial tRNA that carries the amino acid isoleucine (tRNA^Ile). It does not bind to eukaryotic tRNA. Binding prevents the incorporation of isoleucine into polypeptides, effectively crippling the bacterium's protein production. Physicians prescribe mupirocin in topical creams to treat skin infections.

Other drugs that block protein synthesis are **antisense nucleic acids** (Figure 4e). These RNA or single-stranded DNA molecules are designed to be complementary to specific mRNA molecules of pathogens. They block ribosomal subunits from attaching to that mRNA with no effect on human mRNA. *Fomiversen* is the first of this class of drugs to be approved. It inactivates cytomegalovirus and is used to treat eye infections.

**Oxazolidinones** are antimicrobial drugs that work to stop protein synthesis by blocking initiation of translation. Oxazolidinones are used as a last resort in treating infections of Gram-positive bacteria resistant to other antimicrobials, including vancomycin and methicillin-resistant *Staphylococcus aureus* (staf′i-lō-kok′ŭs o′rē-ŭs) mentioned in the chapter opener.

## Disruption of Cytoplasmic Membranes

Some antibacterial drugs, such as the short polypeptide *gramicidin*, disrupt the cytoplasmic membrane of a targeted cell, often by forming a channel through the membrane, damaging its integrity. This is also the mechanism of action of a group of antifungal drugs called **polyenes** (pol-ē-ēns′). The polyenes *nystatin* and *amphotericin B* (Figure 5a) are fungicidal because they attach to *ergosterol*, a lipid constituent of fungal membranes (Figure 5b), in the process disrupting the membrane and causing lysis of the cell. The cytoplasmic membranes of humans are somewhat susceptible to amphotericin B because they contain cholesterol, which is similar to ergosterol, though cholesterol does not bind amphotericin B as well as does ergosterol.

**Azoles,** such as *fluconazole,* and **allylamines,** such as *terbinafine,* are two other classes of antifungal drugs that disrupt cytoplasmic membranes. They act by inhibiting the synthesis of ergosterol; without ergosterol, the cell's membrane does not remain intact, and the fungal cell dies. Azoles and allylamines are generally harmless to humans, because human cells do not manufacture ergosterol.

Most bacterial membranes lack sterols, so these bacteria are naturally resistant to polyenes, azoles, and allylamines; however, there are other agents that disrupt bacterial membranes. An example of these antibacterial agents is *polymyxin,* produced by *Bacillus polymyxa* (ba-sil'ŭs po-lē-miks'a). Polymyxin is effective against Gram-negative bacteria, particularly *Pseudomonas* (soo-dō-mō'nas), but because it is toxic to human kidneys it is usually reserved for use against external pathogens that are resistant to other antibacterial drugs.

*Pyrazinamide* disrupts transport across the cytoplasmic membrane of *M. tuberculosis* (too-ber-kyū-lō'sis). The pathogen uniquely activates and accumulates the drug. Unlike many other antimicrobials, pyrazinamide is most effective against intracellular, nonreplicating bacterial cells.

Some antiparasitic drugs also act against cytoplasmic membranes. For example, *praziquantel* and *ivermectin* change the permeability of cell membranes of several types of parasitic worms.

## Inhibition of Metabolic Pathways

Metabolism can be defined simply as the sum of all chemical reactions that take place within an organism. Whereas most living things share certain metabolic reactions—for example, glycolysis—other chemical reactions are unique to certain organisms. Whenever differences exist between the metabolic processes of a pathogen and its host, *antimetabolic agents* can be effective.

Various kinds of antimetabolic agents are available, including *atovaquone,* which interferes with electron transport in protozoa and fungi; heavy metals (such as arsenic, mercury, and antimony), which inactivate enzymes; agents that disrupt tubulin polymerization and glucose uptake by many protozoa and parasitic worms; drugs that block the activation of viruses; and metabolic antagonists such as sulfanilamide, the first commercially available antimicrobial agent.

Sulfanilamide and similar compounds, collectively called **sulfonamides,** act as antimetabolic drugs because they are **structural analogs** of—that is, are chemically very similar to—*para-aminobenzoic acid (PABA; Figure 6a).* PABA is crucial in the synthesis of nucleotides required for DNA and RNA synthesis. Many organisms, including some pathogens, enzymatically convert PABA into dihydrofolic acid, and then dihydrofolic acid into tetrahydrofolic acid (THF), a form of folic acid that is used as a coenzyme in the synthesis of purine and pyrimidine nucleotides (Figure 6b). As analogs of PABA, sulfonamides compete with PABA molecules for the active site of the enzyme involved in the production of dihydrofolic acid (Figure 6c). This competition leads to a decrease in the production of THF, and thus of DNA and RNA. The end result of sulfonamide

Amphotericin B

**(a)**

**(b)**

▲ **Figure 5 Disruption of the cytoplasmic membrane by the antifungal amphotericin B. (a)** The structure of amphotericin B. **(b)** The proposed action of amphotericin B. The drug binds to molecules of ergosterol, which then congregate, forming a pore.

competition with PABA is the cessation of cell metabolism, which leads to cell death.

Note that humans do not synthesize THF from PABA; instead, we take simple folic acids found in our diets and convert them into THF. As a result, human metabolism is unaffected by sulfonamides.

Another antimetabolic agent, *trimethoprim,* also interferes with nucleic acid synthesis. However, instead of binding to the enzyme that converts PABA to dihydrofolic acid, trimethoprim binds to the enzyme involved in the conversion of dihydrofolic acid to THF, the second step in this metabolic pathway.

Some antiviral agents target the unique aspects of the metabolism of viruses. After attachment to a host cell, viruses must penetrate the cell's membrane and be uncoated to release viral genetic instructions and assume control of the cell's metabolic machinery. Some viruses of eukaryotes are uncoated as a result

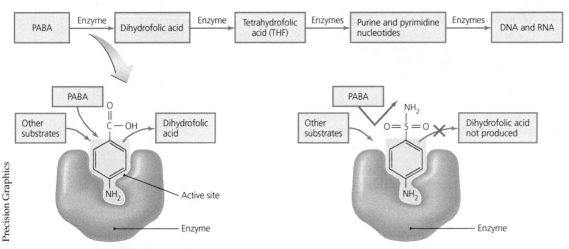

(a) Para-aminobenzoic acid (PABA) and its structural analogs, the sulfonamides

(b) Role of PABA in folic acid synthesis in bacteria and protozoa

(c) Inhibition of folic acid synthesis by sulfonamide

Precision Graphics

▲ **Figure 6** **The antimetabolic action of sulfonamides in inhibiting nucleic acid synthesis.**
(a) Para-aminobenzoic acid (PABA) and representative members of its structural analogs, the sulfonamides. The analogous portions of the compounds are shaded. (b) The metabolic pathway in bacteria and protozoa by which folic acid is synthesized from PABA. (c) The inhibition of folic acid synthesis by the presence of a sulfonamide, which deactivates the enzyme by binding irreversibly to the enzyme's active site.

of the acidic environment within phagolysosomes. *Amantadine, rimantadine,* and weak organic bases can neutralize the acid of phagolysosomes and thereby prevent viral uncoating; thus, these are antiviral drugs. Amantadine is used exclusively to prevent infections by influenza type A virus.

*Protease inhibitors* interfere with the action of protease—an enzyme that HIV needs near the end of its replication cycle. These drugs, when used as part of a "cocktail" of drugs including reverse transcriptase inhibitors (discussed shortly), have revolutionized treatment of AIDS patients in industrialized countries. Researchers have reduced the number of pills in the daily cocktail to just a few that contain all the drugs formerly found in 35 or more daily pills.

### CRITICAL **THINKING**

It would be impractical and expensive for every American to take amantadine during the entire flu season to prevent influenza infections. For what group of people might amantadine prophylaxis be cost effective?

## Inhibition of Nucleic Acid Synthesis

The nucleic acids DNA and RNA are built from purine and pyrimidine nucleotides and are critical to the survival of cells. Several drugs function by blocking either the replication of DNA or its transcription into RNA.

Because only slight differences exist between the DNA of prokaryotes and eukaryotes, drugs that affect DNA replication often act against both types of cells. For example, *actinomycin* binds to DNA and effectively blocks DNA synthesis and RNA transcription not only in bacterial pathogens but in their hosts as well. Generally, drugs of this kind are not used to treat infections, though they are used in research of DNA replication and may be used judiciously to slow replication of cancer cells.

Other compounds that can act as antimicrobials by interfering with the function of nucleic acids are called **nucleotide analogs** because of the compounds' structural similarities to the normal nucleotide building blocks of nucleic acids (Figure 7). The structures of certain nucleotide analogs enable them to be incorporated into the DNA or RNA of pathogens, where they

NUCLEOSIDES

◀ **Figure 7 Nucleosides and some of their antimicrobial analogs.** The arrows indicate synthesis pathways. (For simplicity, the nucleotides and analogs are shown without phosphate groups, i.e., as nucleosides.) *How do nucleotide analogs interfere with DNA replication and RNA transcription?*

**Figure 7** *Because of the distortions they cause in nucleic acids, nucleotide analogs do not form proper base pairs with normal nucleotides. This increases the number of mismatches in the transcription of RNA and replication of DNA.*

Precision Graphics

distort the shapes of the nucleic acid molecules and prevent further replication, transcription, or translation. Nucleotide analogs are most often used against viruses because viral DNA polymerases are tens to hundreds of times more likely to incorporate nonfunctional nucleotides into nucleic acids than is human DNA polymerase. Additionally, complete viral nucleic acid synthesis is more rapid than cellular nucleic acid synthesis. These characteristics make viruses more susceptible to nucleotide analogs than their hosts are, though nucleotide analogs are also effective against rapidly dividing cancer cells.

The synthetic drugs called *quinolones* and *fluoroquinolones* are unusual because they are active against prokaryotic DNA specifically. These antibacterial agents inhibit *DNA gyrase,* an enzyme necessary for correct coiling and uncoiling of replicating bacterial DNA; they typically have little effect on eukaryotes or viruses.

Other antimicrobial agents function by binding to and inhibiting the action of RNA polymerases during the synthesis of RNA from a DNA template. Several drugs, including *rifampin* (rif′am-pin), bind more readily to prokaryotic RNA polymerase than to eukaryotic RNA polymerase; as a result, rifampin is more toxic to prokaryotes than to eukaryotes. Rifampin is used primarily against *M. tuberculosis* and other pathogens that metabolize slowly and thus are less susceptible to antimicrobials targeting active metabolic processes.

*Clofazimine* binds to the DNA of *Mycobacterium leprae* (lep′rī), the causative agent of leprosy, and prevents normal replication and transcription. It is also used to treat tuberculosis and other mycobacterial infections. *Pentamidine* and *propamidine isethionate* bind to protozoan DNA, inhibiting the pathogen's reproduction and development.

**The Spectrum of Activity of Selected Antimicrobial Drugs**

| Prokaryotes | | | | Eukaryotes | | | Viruses |
|---|---|---|---|---|---|---|---|
| Mycobacteria | Gram-negative bacteria | Gram-positive bacteria | Chlamydias, rickettsias | Protozoa | Fungi | Helminths | |
| Isoniazid ⟶ | | | | | | Niclosamide | Arildone |
| | Polymyxin | | | | Azoles | | Ribavirin |
| | | Penicillin | | | | Praziquantel | Acyclovir |
| Streptomycin | | | | | | | |
| | Erythromycin | | | | | | |
| | Tetracycline | | | | | | |
| | | Sulfonamides | | | | | |

*Precision Graphics*

▲ **Figure 8 Spectrum of action for selected antimicrobial agents.** The more kinds of pathogens a drug affects, the broader its spectrum of action.

*Reverse transcriptase inhibitors,* which are part of AIDS cocktails, act against reverse transcriptase, which is an enzyme HIV uses early in its replication cycle to make DNA copies of its RNA genome (reverse transcription). Since people lack reverse transcriptase, the inhibitor does not harm patients.

## Prevention of Virus Attachment

Many pathogens, particularly viruses, must attach to their host's cells via the chemical interaction between attachment proteins on the pathogen and complementary receptor proteins on a host cell. Attachment of viruses can be blocked by peptide and sugar analogs of either attachment or receptor proteins. When these sites are blocked by analogs, viruses can neither attach to nor enter their hosts' cells. The use of such substances, called *attachment antagonists,* is an exciting new area of antimicrobial drug development. *Arildone* and *pleconaril* are antagonists of the receptor of polioviruses and some cold viruses. They block attachment of these viruses and deter infections.

# Clinical Considerations in Prescribing Antimicrobial Drugs

Even though antibiotics are produced commonly by many fungi and bacteria, most of these chemicals are not effective for treating diseases because they are toxic to humans and animals, are too expensive, are produced in minute quantities, or lack adequate potency. The ideal antimicrobial agent to treat an infection or disease would be one that is:

- Readily available
- Inexpensive
- Chemically stable (so that it can be transported easily and stored for long periods of time)
- Easily administered

- Nontoxic and nonallergenic
- Selectively toxic against a wide range of pathogens

No agent has all of these qualities, so doctors and medical laboratory technicians must evaluate antimicrobials with respect to several characteristics: the range of pathogens against which they are effective; their efficacy, including the dosages required to be effective; the routes by which they can be administered; their overall safety; and any side effects they produce. We consider each of these characteristics of antimicrobials in the following sections.

## Spectrum of Action

### Learning Objective

✓ Distinguish between narrow-spectrum drugs and broad-spectrum drugs in terms of their targets and side effects.

The number of different kinds of pathogens a drug acts against is known as its **spectrum of action** (Figure 8); drugs that work against only a few kinds of pathogens are **narrow-spectrum drugs,** whereas those that are effective against many different kinds of pathogens are **broad-spectrum drugs.** For instance, because tetracycline acts against many different kinds of bacteria, including Gram-negative, Gram-positive, chlamydias, and rickettsias, it is considered a broad-spectrum antibiotic. In contrast, penicillin cannot easily penetrate the outer membrane of a Gram-negative bacterium to reach and prevent the formation of peptidoglycan, so its efficacy is largely limited to Gram-positive bacteria. Thus penicillin has a narrower spectrum of action than erythromycin, which acts against protein synthesis in numerous bacteria.

The use of broad-spectrum antimicrobials is not always as desirable as it might seem. Broad-spectrum antimicrobials can also open the door to serious secondary infections by transient pathogens or *superinfections* by members of the normal microbiota unaffected by the antimicrobial. This results because the killing of normal microbiota reduces *microbial antagonism,* the competition between normal microbes and pathogens for nutrients and space. Microbial antagonism reinforces the body's defense by limiting the ability of pathogens to colonize the skin and mucous membranes. Thus a woman using erythromycin to treat strep throat (a bacterial disease) could develop vaginitis resulting from the excessive growth of *Candida albicans* (kan'did-ă al'bi-kanz), a yeast that is unaffected by erythromycin and is freed from microbial antagonism when the antibiotic kills normal bacteria in the vagina.

## Efficacy

### Learning Objective

✓ Compare and contrast Kirby-Bauer, Etest, MIC, and MBC tests.

To effectively treat infectious diseases, physicians must know which antimicrobial agent is most effective against a particular pathogen. To ascertain the efficacy of antimicrobials, microbiologists conduct a variety of tests, including diffusion susceptibility tests, the minimum inhibitory concentration test, and the minimum bactericidal concentration test.

### Diffusion Susceptibility Test

**Diffusion susceptibility tests,** also known as *Kirby-Bauer* tests, involve uniformly inoculating a Petri plate with a standardized amount of the pathogen in question. Then small disks of paper containing standard concentrations of the drugs to be tested are firmly arranged on the surface of the plate. The plate is incubated, and the bacteria grow and reproduce to form a "lawn" everywhere but the areas where effective antimicrobial drugs diffuse through the agar. After incubation, the plates are examined for the presence of a **zone of inhibition**—that is, a clear area where bacteria do not grow (Figure 9). A zone of inhibition is measured as the diameter (to the closest millimeter) of the clear region.

If all drugs were equal, then the larger the zone of inhibition, the more effective that drug is; however, the size of a zone depends on the rate of diffusion of the antimicrobial; for example, drugs with lower molecular weights generally diffuse more quickly than those with higher molecular weights. The size of a zone of inhibition must be compared to a standard table for that particular drug before accurate comparisons can be made. Diffusion susceptibility tests enable scientists to classify pathogens as *susceptible, intermediate,* or *resistant* to each drug.

### CRITICAL **THINKING**

Sometimes it is not possible to conduct a susceptibility test, either because of a lack of time or an inability to access the bacteria (from an inner-ear infection, for instance). How could a physician select an appropriate therapeutic agent in such cases?

### Minimum Inhibitory Concentration (MIC) Test

Once scientists identify an effective antimicrobial agent, they quantitatively express its potency as a **minimum inhibitory concentration (MIC).** As the name suggests, the MIC is the smallest amount of the drug that will *inhibit* growth and reproduction of the pathogen. The MIC can be determined via a **broth dilution test,** in which a standardized amount of bacteria is

Bacterial lawn          Zone of inhibition

L. Brent Selinger, Pearson Science

▲ **Figure 9 Zones of inhibition in a diffusion susceptibility (Kirby-Bauer) test.** In general, the larger the zone of inhibition around disks, which are impregnated with an antimicrobial agent, the more effective that antimicrobial is against the organism growing on the plate. The organism is classified as either susceptible, intermediate, or resistant to the antimicrobials tested based on the sizes of the zones of inhibition. *If all of these antimicrobial agents diffuse at the same rate and are equally safe and easily administered, which one would be the drug of choice for killing this pathogen?*

**Figure 9** *The drug ENO, a fluoroquinolone found in the uppermost disk, is most effective.*

added to serial dilutions of antimicrobial agents in tubes or wells containing broth. After incubation, turbidity (cloudiness) indicates bacterial growth; lack of turbidity indicates that the bacteria were either inhibited or killed by the antimicrobial agent (Figure 10). Dilution tests can be conducted simultaneously in wells, and the entire process can be automated, with turbidity measured by special scanners connected to computers.

Another test that determines minimum inhibitory concentration combines aspects of an MIC test and a diffusion susceptibility test. This test, called an **Etest,**[2] involves placing a plastic strip containing a gradient of the antimicrobial agent being tested on a plate uniformly inoculated with the organism of interest (Figure 11). After incubation, an elliptical zone of inhibition indicates antimicrobial activity, and the minimum inhibitory concentration can be noted where the zone of inhibition intersects a scale printed on the strip.

### Minimum Bactericidal Concentration (MBC) Test

Similar to the MIC test is a **minimum bactericidal concentration (MBC) test,** though an MBC test determines the amount of drug required to kill the microbe rather than just the amount to inhibit it, as the MIC does. In an MBC test, samples taken from clear MIC tubes (or alternatively, from zones of inhibition from a series of diffusion susceptibility tests) are transferred to plates containing a drug-free growth medium (Figure 12). The appearance of bacterial growth in these subcultures after appropriate incubation

---

[2]The name *Etest* has no specific origin.

Turbid tubes      Clear tubes

Increasing concentration of drug

◀ **Figure 10** **Minimum inhibitory concentration (MIC) test in test tubes.** *What is the MIC for the drug acting against this bacterium?*

**Figure 10** *The MIC is 1.6 mcg (mg) per ml.*

indicates that at least some bacterial cells survived that concentration of the antimicrobial drug and were able to grow and multiply once placed in a drug-free medium. Any drug concentration at which growth occurs in subculture is *bacteriostatic,* not *bactericidal,* for that bacterium. The lowest concentration of drug for which no growth occurs in the subcultures is the minimum bactericidal concentration (MBC).

## Routes of Administration

### Learning Objective

✓ Discuss the advantages and disadvantages of the different routes of administration of antimicrobial drugs.

An adequate amount of an antimicrobial agent must reach a site of infection if it is to be effective. For external infections such as athlete's foot, drugs can be applied directly. This is known as *topical* or *local* administration. For internal infections, drugs can be administered *orally, intramuscularly (IM),* or *intravenously (IV).* Each route has advantages and disadvantages.

Even though the oral route is simplest (it requires no needles and is self-administered), the drug concentrations achieved in the body are lower than occur via other routes of administration

▲ **Figure 11** **An Etest, which combines aspects of Kirby-Bauer and MIC tests.** The plastic strip contains a gradient of the antimicrobial agent of interest. The MIC is estimated to be the concentration printed on the strip where the zone of inhibition intersects the strip. In this example, the MIC is 0.75 µg/ml.

Concentration of antibacterial drug (µg/ml)

Clear MIC tube

8      16      25

Bacterial colonies      No colonies      No colonies

Drug-free media

▲ **Figure 12** **A minimum bactericidal concentration (MBC) test.** In this test, plates containing a drug-free growth medium are inoculated with samples taken from zones of inhibition or from clear MIC tubes. After incubation, growth of bacterial colonies on a plate indicates that the concentration of antimicrobial drug (in this case, 8 µg/ml) is bacteriostatic. The lowest concentration for which no bacterial growth occurs on the plate is the minimum bactericidal concentration; in this case, the MBC is 16 µg/ml.

98

(Figure 13). Further, because patients administer the drug themselves, they do not always follow prescribed timetables.

IM administration via a hypodermic needle allows a drug to diffuse slowly into the many blood vessels within muscle tissue, but the concentration of the drug in the blood is never as high as that achieved by IV administration, which delivers the drug directly into the bloodstream through either a needle or a catheter (a plastic or rubber tube). Even though the amount of the drug in the blood is initially very high for the IV route, the concentration can rapidly diminish as the liver and kidneys remove the drug from the circulation, unless the drug is continuously administered.

In addition to considering the route of administration, physicians must consider how antimicrobial agents are distributed to infected tissues by the blood. For example, an agent removed rapidly from the blood by the kidneys might be the drug of choice for a bladder infection but would not be chosen to treat an infection of the heart. Finally, given that blood vessels in the brain, spinal cord, and eye are almost impermeable to many antimicrobial agents (because the tight structure of capillary walls in these structures creates the blood-brain barrier), infections there are often difficult to treat.

## Safety and Side Effects

### Learning Objective

✓ Identify three main categories of side effects of antimicrobial therapy.

Another aspect of chemotherapy that physicians must consider is the possibility of adverse side effects. These fall into three main categories—toxicity, allergies, and disruption of normal microbiota.

### Toxicity

Though antimicrobial drugs are ideally selectively toxic against microbes and harmless to humans, many in fact have toxic side effects. The exact cause of many adverse reactions is poorly understood, but drugs may be toxic to the kidneys, the liver, or nerves. For example, polymyxin and aminoglycosides can have fatally toxic effects on kidneys. Not all toxic side effects are so serious. *Metronidazole (Flagyl)*, an antiprotozoan drug, may cause a harmless temporary condition called "black hairy tongue," which results when the breakdown products of hemoglobin accumulate in the papillae of the tongue (Figure 14a).

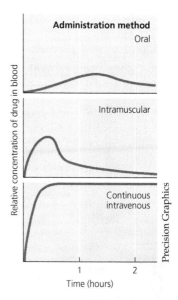

▲ **Figure 13 The effect of route of administration on blood levels of a chemotherapeutic agent.** Although intravenous (IV) and intramuscular (IM) administration achieve higher drug concentrations in the blood, oral administration has the advantage of simplicity.

Doctors must be especially careful when prescribing drugs for pregnant women, as many drugs that are safe for adults can have adverse affects when absorbed by a fetus. For instance, tetracyclines form complexes with calcium that can become incorporated into bones and developing teeth, causing malformation of the skull and stained, weakened tooth enamel (Figure 14b).

### Allergies

In addition to toxicity, some drugs trigger allergic immune responses in sensitive patients. Although relatively rare, such reactions may be life threatening, especially in an immediate, violent reaction called *anaphylactic shock*. For example, about 0.1% of Americans have an anaphylactic reaction to penicillin, resulting in approximately 300 deaths per year. However, not every allergy to an antimicrobial agent is so serious. Recent studies indicate that patients with mild allergies to penicillin frequently lose their sensitivity to it over time. Thus, an initial mild reaction to penicillin need not preclude its use in treating future infections.

▶ **Figure 14 Some side effects resulting from toxicity of antimicrobial agents. (a)** "Black hairy tongue," caused by the antiprotozoan drug metronidazole (Flagyl). **(b)** Discoloration and damage to tooth enamel caused by tetracycline. *Who should avoid taking tetracycline?*

**Figure 14** *Pregnant women and children should not use tetracycline.*

(a)                    (b)

99

## EMERGING DISEASES

### COMMUNITY-ASSOCIATED MRSA

Julie was proud and excited about her new tattoo; it was crunk! Jason, her boyfriend, had bought it as a gift for her 18th birthday, and she loved the way it covered her arm. A week later something else covered her arm . . . and his leg.

Julie and Jason had fallen victim to an emerging disease—community-associated, methicillin-resistant *Staphylococcus aureus* (CA-MRSA) infection. Julie's arm was covered with red, swollen, painful, pus-containing lesions, and she had a fever.

Jason thought he had a spider bite on Wednesday, but by Thursday morning a bright red line extended from his ankle to his groin. He could barely

walk, and then his condition worsened. By the weekend, he was hospitalized, and his fever hit 107°F during his 10 days

Precision Graphics

there. MRSA had entered his blood (bacteremia) and infected his bones (osteomyelitis). Jason's pain was so severe that he wondered only when he might die to be free of the agony.

For years health care workers have battled nosocomial MRSA, which commonly afflicts patients in hospitals. Now, researchers are concerned that victims who have never been in a hospital are succumbing; MRSA has escaped hospitals and now travels in the community, including among athletes, students in middle schools, and customers of unsafe tattooists. The bacterium can be spread between individuals who share fomites—towels, razors, clothing, or sheets.

Physicians drained Julie's lesions and prescribed oral antimicrobials, including trimethoprim, sulfamethoxazole, levofloxacin, and clindamycin. Jason received intravenous vancomycin. Both eventually recovered, but her tattoo is now a reminder of a terrible experience and not a happy birthday.

**(MM)** Track community-associated MRSA online by going to the Study Area at www.masteringmicrobiology.com.

*Toledo-Lucas County Health Department*

### Disruption of Normal Microbiota

As we have seen, drugs that disrupt normal microbiota and their microbial antagonism of opportunistic pathogens may result in secondary infections. In instances when a member of the normal microbiota is not affected by a drug, it can overgrow, causing a superinfection. For example, long-term use of broad-spectrum antibacterials often results in explosions in the growth rate of *Candida albicans* in the vagina (vaginitis) or mouth (thrush) and the multiplication of *Clostridium difficile* (klos-trid'ē-ŭm di-fi'sil-ē) in the colon, causing a potentially fatal condition called *pseudomembranous colitis*. Such superinfections are of greatest concern for hospitalized patients, who are often not only debilitated but also more likely to be exposed to pathogens with resistance to antimicrobial drugs—the topic of the next section.

**Beneficial Microbes: Probiotics: The New Sheriff in Town** focuses on how normal microbiota can help keep pathogens in check.

# Resistance to Antimicrobial Drugs

Among the major challenges facing microbiologists today are the problems presented by pathogens that are resistant to antimicrobial agents (see **Emerging Diseases: Community–Associated**

**MRSA**). In the sections that follow we examine the development of resistant populations of pathogens, the mechanisms by which pathogens are resistant to antimicrobials, and some ways that resistance can be retarded.

## The Development of Resistance in Populations

### Learning Objectives

✓ Describe how populations of resistant microbes can arise.

✓ Describe the relationship between R-plasmids and resistant cells.

Not all pathogens are equally sensitive to a given therapeutic agent; a population may contain a few organisms that are naturally either partially or completely resistant. Among bacteria, individual cells can acquire such resistance in two ways: through new mutations of chromosomal genes or by acquiring resistance genes on extrachromosomal pieces of DNA called **R-plasmids** (or *R-factors*) via the processes of horizontal gene transfer—transformation, transduction, or conjugation. We focus here on resistance in populations of bacteria, but resistance is known to occur among protozoa and viruses.

The process by which a resistant strain of bacteria develops is depicted in **Figure 15**. In the absence of an antimicrobial drug, resistant cells are usually less efficient than their normal neighbors

Precision Graphics

Drug-sensitive cell | Drug-resistant mutant

Exposure to drug

Remaining population grows over time

**(a)** Population of microbial cells | **(b)** Sensitive cells inhibited by exposure to drug | **(c)** Most cells now resistant

▲ **Figure 15 The development of a resistant strain of bacteria. (a)** A bacterial population contains both drug-sensitive and drug-resistant cells, although sensitive cells constitute the vast majority of the population. **(b)** Exposure to an antimicrobial drug inhibits the sensitive cells; so long as the drug is present, reduced competition from sensitive cells facilitates the multiplication of resistant cells. **(c)** Eventually resistant cells constitute the majority of the population. *Why do resistant strains of bacteria more often develop in hospitals and nursing homes than in college dormitories?*

**Figure 15** *Resistant strains are more likely to develop in hospitals and other health care facilities because the extensive use of antimicrobial agents in those places inhibits the growth of sensitive strains and selects for the growth of resistant strains.*

because they must expend extra energy to maintain resistance genes and proteins. Under these circumstances, resistant cells remain the minority in a population because they reproduce more slowly. However, when an antimicrobial agent is present, the majority of cells (which are sensitive to the antimicrobial) are inhibited or die while the resistant cells continue to grow and multiply, often more rapidly because they then face less competition. The result is that resistant cells soon replace the sensitive cells as the majority in the population. The bacterium has evolved resistance. It should be noted that the presence of the antimicrobial agent does not *produce* resistance but instead selects for the replication of resistant cells that were already present in the population. **ANIMATIONS:** *Antibiotic Resistance: Origins of Resistance*

## CRITICAL **THINKING**

*Enterococcus faecium* is frequently resistant to vancomycin. Why might this be of concern in a hospital setting in terms of developing resistant strains of *other* genera of bacteria?

## Mechanisms of Resistance

### Learning Objective

✓ List six ways by which microorganisms can be resistant to antimicrobial drugs.

The problem of resistance to antimicrobial drugs is a major health threat to our world. An "alphabet soup" of resistant pathogens and diseases plague health care professionals: MRSA,[3] VRSA,[4] VISA,[5] VRE,[6] and MDR-TB[7] are just some of these.

How do microbes gain resistance to antimicrobial drugs? Consider the path a typical antimicrobial drug must take to affect a microbe: The drug must cross the cell's wall, then cross the cytoplasmic membrane to enter the cell; there the antimicrobial

[3]Methicillin-resistant *S. aureus*
[4]Vancomycin-resistant *S. aureus*
[5]*S. aureus* with intermediate level of resistance to vancomycin
[6]Vancomycin-resistant enterococci
[7]Multi-drug-resistant tuberculosis

**BENEFICIAL** MICROBES

### PROBIOTICS: THE NEW SHERIFF IN TOWN

SciMAT/Photo Researchers

▲ *Lactobacillus reuteri.*  SEM | 1 μm

As overuse of antimicrobials has allowed more bacteria that are drug resistant to thrive, scientists are investigating alternative methods of combating microbial infections. One growing field of interest is *probiotics*, the use of microorganisms for health benefits.

Probiotics include bacteria such as *Lactobacillus*, which may help reduce symptoms of diarrhea in children, relieve milk allergies, and alleviate certain respiratory infections. One of the central ideas behind probiotics is that "good" bacteria, such as *Lactobacillus* (which lives naturally and harmlessly in our intestines and other parts of the body), compete with harmful microorganisms for resources, keeping pathogenic microbes in check. Some evidence suggests that *Lactobacillus* also induces the expression of certain proteins that protect the intestines against harmful bacteria and viruses. Much more research remains to be done, but the preliminary findings are encouraging.

binds to its target (receptor) molecule. Only then can it inhibit or kill the microbe. Microbes gain resistance by blocking some point in this pathway. There are at least six mechanisms of resistance:

- Resistant cells may produce an enzyme that destroys or deactivates the drug. This common mode of resistance is exemplified by **beta-(χ) lactamases** (penicillinases), which are enzymes that break the beta-lactam rings of penicillin and similar molecules, rendering them inactive (Figure 16). Many MRSA strains have evolved resistance to penicillin-derived antimicrobials in this manner. Over 200 different lactamases have been identified. Frequently their genes are located on R-plasmids.

- Resistant microbes may slow or prevent the entry of the drug into the cell. This mechanism typically involves changes in the structure or electrical charge of the cytoplasmic membrane proteins that constitute channels or pores. Such proteins in the outer membranes of Gram-negative bacteria are called *porins*. Altered pore proteins result from mutations in chromosomal genes. Resistance against tetracycline and penicillin are known to occur via this mechanism.

- Resistant cells may alter the target of the drug so that the drug either cannot attach to it or binds it less effectively. This form of resistance is often seen against antimetabolites (such as sulfonamides) and against drugs that thwart protein translation (such as erythromycin).

- Resistant cells may alter their metabolic chemistry, or they may abandon the sensitive metabolic step altogether. For example, a cell may become resistant to a drug by producing more enzyme molecules for the affected metabolic pathway, effectively reducing the power of the drug. Alternatively, cells become resistant to sulfonamides by abandoning the synthesis of folic acid, absorbing it from the environment instead.

- Resistant cells may pump the antimicrobial out of the cell before the drug can act. So-called *resistance pumps*, which are typically powered by ATP, are often able to pump more than one type of antimicrobial from a cell. Some microbes become multi-drug resistant (perhaps to as many as 10 or more drugs) by utilizing resistance pumps.

- Some resistant strains of the bacterium *Mycobacterium tuberculosis* have a novel method of resistance against fluoroquinolone drugs that bind to DNA gyrase. These strains synthesize an unusual protein that forms a negatively charged, rodlike helix about the width of a DNA molecule. This protein, called *MfpA protein*, binds to DNA gyrase in place of DNA, depriving fluoroquinolone of its target site. This is the first method of antibiotic resistance that involves protecting the target of an antimicrobial drug rather than, say, changing the target or deactivating the drug. MfpA protein probably slows down cellular division of *M. tuberculosis*, but that is better for the bacterium than being killed. **ANIMATIONS:** *Antibiotic Resistance: Forms of Resistance*

## Multiple Resistance and Cross Resistance

### Learning Objective

✓ Define *cross resistance*, and distinguish it from multiple resistance.

A given pathogen can acquire resistance to more than one drug at a time, especially when resistance is conferred by R-plasmids, which are exchanged readily among bacterial cells. Such multiresistant strains of bacteria frequently develop in hospitals and nursing homes, where the constant use of many kinds of antimicrobial agents eliminates sensitive cells and encourages the development of resistant strains.

**Multiple-drug-resistant pathogens** (commonly called *superbugs*) are resistant to three or more types of antimicrobial agents. Multiple-drug-resistant strains of *Staphylococcus, Streptococcus* (strep-tō-kok'ŭs), *Enterococcus* (en'ter-ō-kok'ŭs), *Pseudomonas, Mycobacterium tuberculosis,* and *Plasmodium* (plaz-mō'dē-ŭm) (the protozoan that causes malaria) pose unique problems for health care professionals, who must treat infected patients without effective antimicrobials while taking extra care to protect themselves and other patients from infection.

Resistance to one antimicrobial agent may confer resistance to similar drugs, a phenomenon called **cross resistance.** Cross resistance typically occurs when drugs are similar in structure. For example, resistance to one aminoglycoside drug, such as streptomycin, may confer resistance to similar aminoglycoside drugs.

## Retarding Resistance

### Learning Objective

✓ Describe four ways that development of resistance can be retarded.

The development of resistant populations of pathogens can be averted in at least four ways. First, sufficiently high concentrations of the drug can be maintained in a patient's body for a long enough time to kill all sensitive cells and inhibit others long enough for the body's defenses to defeat them. Discontinuing a drug before all of the pathogens have been neutralized promotes the development of resistant strains. For this reason, it is important that patients finish their entire antimicrobial prescription and resist the temptation to "save some for another day."

## CLINICAL CASE STUDY

### To Treat or Not to Treat?

A young Hispanic mother brought her frail infant to a South Texas emergency room. While she waited, her infant began to have seizures. The staff stabilized the baby, while the mother explained that the child had been ill for many days. Feverish at times, the infant had lost weight because she was too short of breath to nurse. Other family members were ill with bad coughs.

The baby girl was later diagnosed with a dangerous form of tuberculosis (TB) that affected her brain. She was hospitalized and placed in isolation. Health department officials investigated and discovered that the infant had been exposed to TB from two individuals: an infected uncle and her TB-infected father whom the mother had visited in a Mexican jail. Inmates from the jail carried a potent strain of TB that was resistant to several standard anti-tuberculosis drugs. It would take many weeks to determine which of the two strains was affecting her brain.

Doctors had to make a tough decision: Should they immediately begin treating the infant for the multi-drug-resistant strain (MDR-TB), which involves using five to seven different drugs with multiple and painful side effects for many months, or treat her for the more normal form of TB using a more typical and less stressful drug regimen for an equal length of time?

1. What issues must be considered in order to determine the drug therapy for the infant?

2. What treatment would you guess was used for the infant?

Reference: Adapted from *MMWR* 40:373–375. 1991.

Disk with semisynthetic amoxicillin-clavulanic acid

Disk with semisynthetic aztreonam

E. Vercauteren, Dept. of Microbiology, University Hospital, Antwerp, Belgium

▲ **Figure 17 An example of synergism between two antimicrobial agents.** The portion of the zone of inhibition outlined in green represents the synergistic enhancement of antimicrobial activity beyond the activities of the individual drugs (outlined in white). *What does clavulanic acid do?*

**Figure 17** *Clavulanic acid deactivates β-lactamase, allowing penicillins to work.*

A second way to avert resistance is to use antimicrobial agents in combination so that pathogens resistant to one drug will be killed by other drugs, and vice versa. Additionally, one drug sometimes enhances the effect of a second drug in a process called **synergism** (sin'er-jizm) (Figure 17). In one example of a synergistic drug combination, the inhibition of cell wall formation by penicillin makes it easier for streptomycin molecules to enter bacteria and interfere with protein synthesis. Synergism can also result from combining an antimicrobial drug and a chemical, as occurs when *clavulanic acid* enhances the effect of penicillin by deactivating β-lactamase. (Not all drugs act synergistically; some combinations of drugs can be *antagonistic*—interfering with each other. For example, drugs that slow bacterial growth are antagonistic to the action of penicillin, which acts only against growing and dividing cells.)

A third way to reduce the development of resistance is to limit the use of antimicrobials to necessary cases. Unfortunately, many antimicrobial agents are used indiscriminately, both in developed countries and in less developed regions where many are available without a physician's prescription. In the United States, an estimated 50% of prescriptions for antibacterial agents to treat sore throats, and 30% of prescriptions for ear infections, are inappropriate because the diseases are viral,

not bacterial. Likewise, because antibacterial drugs have no effect on cold and flu viruses, 100% of antibacterial prescriptions for treating these diseases are superfluous. As discussed previously, the use of antimicrobial agents encourages the reproduction of resistant bacteria by limiting the growth of sensitive cells; therefore, inappropriate use of such drugs increases the likelihood that resistant strains of bacteria will multiply.

Finally, scientists can combat resistant strains by developing new variations of existing drugs, in some cases by adding novel side chains to the original molecule. In this way, scientists develop semisynthetic *second-generation* drugs. If resistance develops to these drugs, *third-generation* drugs may be developed to replace them.

Alternatively, scientists are searching for new antibiotics, semisynthetics, and synthetics. Researchers are exploring diverse habitats such as peat bogs, ocean sediments, marine organisms, garden soil, and people's mouths for organisms that produce novel antibiotics. For example, a compound produced by parasitic hookworms that interferes with blood coagulation may mitigate the deadly effects of Ebola. Some researchers see potential in *bacteriocins*—antibacterial proteins coded by bacterial plasmids. Bacteria use bacteriocins to inhibit other bacterial strains; perhaps we can do the same. Tinkering with these and other antibiotics should yield promising new semisynthetics.

With the advent of genome sequencing and enhanced understanding of protein folding, some scientists predict that we are moving into a new golden era of antimicrobial drug discovery and development. They point out that researchers who know the exact shapes of microbial proteins should be able to design drugs complementary to those shapes—drugs that will inhibit microbial proteins without affecting humans. Currently scientists are examining ways to inhibit the following: secretion systems; peptide formylase, the critical enzyme used by bacteria to remove fMet from its initial position in polypeptides; parts of the 50S ribosomal subunit; attachment molecules and their receptors; biofilm signaling molecules; bacterial cell division; and unique metabolic pathways of bacteria.

Despite researchers' best efforts, other health care professionals and scientists are concerned about how long drug developers can stay ahead of the development of resistance by pathogens.

Selected antimicrobial agents, their modes of action, clinical considerations, and other features are summarized in Tables 2–6.

## TABLE 2
## Antibacterial Drugs

| Drug | Description and Mode of Action | Clinical Considerations | Method of Resistance |
|---|---|---|---|
| **Antibacterial Drugs That Inhibit Cell Wall Synthesis** | | | |
| **Bacitracin** | Isolated from *Bacillus licheniformis* growing on a patient named Tracy; appears to have three modes of action:<br><br>• Interference with the movement of peptidoglycan precursors through the bacterial cell membrane to the cell wall<br><br>• Inhibition of RNA transcription<br><br>• Damage to the bacterial cytoplasmic membrane<br><br>The latter two modes of action have not been proven definitely | **Spectrum of action:** Gram-positive (G+) bacteria<br><br>**Route of administration:** Topical<br><br>**Adverse effects:** Toxic to kidneys | Resistance most often involves changes in bacterial cell membranes that prevent bacitracin from entering the cell |
| **Beta-lactams**<br><br>Representative natural penicillins:<br>  Penicillin G<br>  Penicillin V<br><br>Representative semisynthetic penicillin:<br>  Ampicillin<br>  Methicillin<br>  Dicloxacillin<br><br>Representative natural cephalosporin:<br>  Cephalothin<br><br>Representative semisynthetic cephalosporins:<br>  Cefixime<br>  Ceftriaxone<br>  Cefuroxime<br><br>Representative semisynthetic monobactam:<br>  Aztreonam | Large number of natural and semisynthetic derivatives from *Penicillium* (penicillins) and *Cephalosporium* (cephalosporins); bind to and deactivate the enzyme that cross-links the NAM subunits of peptidoglycan<br><br>Monobactams have only a single ring instead of the two rings seen in other beta-lactams | **Spectrum of action:** Natural drugs have limited action against most Gram-negative (G−) bacteria because they do not readily cross the outer membrane; semisynthetics have broader spectra of action<br><br>Monobactams have a limited spectrum of action, affecting only aerobic, G− bacteria<br><br>**Route of administration:** Penicillin V, a few cephalosporins (e.g., cephalexin), and monobactams: oral; penicillin G, and many semisynthetics (e.g., methicillin, ampicillin, carbenicillin, cephalothin): IM or IV<br><br>**Adverse effects:** Allergic reactions against beta-lactams in some adults; monobactams are least allergenic | Develops in three ways in G− bacteria:<br><br>• Change their outer membrane structure to prevent entrance of the drug<br><br>• Modify the enzyme so that the drug no longer binds<br><br>• Synthesize beta-lactamases that cleave the functional lactam ring of the drug; genes for lactamases are often carried on R-plasmids |
| **Cycloserine** | Analog of alanine that interferes with the formation of alanine-alanine bridges between NAM subunits | **Spectrum of action:** Some G+ bacteria, mycobacteria<br><br>**Route of administration:** Oral<br><br>**Adverse effects:** Toxic to nervous system, producing depression, aggression, confusion, and headache | Some G+ bacteria enzymatically deactivate the drug |
| **Ethambutol** | Prevents the formation of mycolic acid; used in combination with other antimycobacterial drugs | **Spectrum of action:** Mycobacteria, including *M. tuberculosis* and *M. leprae*<br><br>**Route of administration:** Oral<br><br>**Adverse effects:** None | Resistance is due to random mutations of bacterial chromosomes that result in alteration of target site |

**TABLE 2** *(continued)*

| Drug | Description and Mode of Action | Clinical Considerations | Method of Resistance |
|---|---|---|---|
| **Antibacterial Drugs That Inhibit Cell Wall Synthesis** | | | |
| **Isoniazid** (isonicotinic acid hydrazide, INH) | Blocks the gene for an enzyme that forms mycolic acid; analog of the vitamins nicotinamide and pyridoxine | **Spectrum of action:** Mycobacteria, including *M. tuberculosis* and *M. leprae* **Route of administration:** Oral **Adverse effects:** May be toxic to liver | Resistance is due to random mutations of bacterial chromosomes that result in alteration of target site or overproduction of target molecules |
| **Vancomycin** | Produced by *Amycolatopsis orientalis*; directly interferes with the formation of alanine-alanine bridges between NAM subunits | **Spectrum of action:** Effective against most G+ bacteria but generally reserved for use against strains resistant to other drugs such as methicillin-resistant *Staphylococcus aureus* (MRSA) **Route of administration:** IV **Adverse effects:** Damage to ears and kidneys, allergic reactions | G– bacteria are naturally resistant because the drug is too large to pass through the outer membrane; some G+ bacteria (e.g., *Lactobacillus*) are naturally resistant because they do not form alanine-alanine bonds between NAM subunits |
| **Antibacterial Drugs That Inhibit Protein Synthesis** | | | |
| **Aminoglycosides** Representatives: Gentamicin Kanamycin Neomycin Paromomycin Spiramycin Streptomycin | Compounds in which two or more amino sugars are linked with glycosidic bonds; were originally isolated from species of the bacterial genera *Streptomyces* and *Micromonospora*. Inhibit protein synthesis by irreversibly binding to the 30S subunit of prokaryotic ribosomes, this either causing the ribosome to mistranslate mRNA, producing aberrant proteins, or causing premature release of the ribosome from mRNA, which stops synthesis. Also bactericidal by destroying outer membranes of G– bacteria | **Spectrum of action:** Broad: effective against both G+ and G– bacteria **Route of administration:** IV; do not traverse blood-brain barrier **Adverse effects:** May be toxic to kidneys or auditory nerves, causing deafness | Uptake of these drugs is energy dependent, so anaerobic bacteria with less ATP available are less susceptible; aerobic bacteria alter membrane pores to prevent uptake, or synthesize enzymes that alter or degrade the drug once it enters; rarely, bacteria alter the binding site on the ribosome; some bacteria make biofilms when exposed to the drugs |
| **Chloramphenicol** | Rarely used drug that prevents prokaryotic ribosomes from moving along mRNA by binding to their 50S subunits | **Spectrum of action:** Broad, but rarely used except in treatment of typhoid fever **Route of administration:** Oral; traverses blood-brain barrier **Adverse effects:** In 1 of 24,000 patients, causes aplastic anemia, a potentially fatal condition in which blood cells fail to form; can also cause neurological damage | Develops via gene carried on an R-plasmid that codes for an enzyme that deactivates drug |
| **Lincosamides** Representative: Clindamycin | Binds to 50S ribosomal subunit and stops protein elongation | **Spectrum of action:** Effective against G+ and anaerobic G– bacteria **Route of administration:** Oral or IV; does not traverse blood-brain barrier **Adverse effects:** Gastrointestinal distress, including nausea, diarrhea, vomiting, and pain | Develops via changes in ribosomal structure that prevent drug from binding; resistance genes are same as those of aminoglycosides |
| **Macrolides** Representatives: Azithromycin Erythromycin Telithromycin | Group of antimicrobials typified by a macrocyclic lactone ring; the most prescribed is erythromycin, which is produced by *Streptomyces erythraeus*; act by binding to the 50S subunit of prokaryotic ribosomes and preventing the elongation of the nascent protein | **Spectrum of action:** Effective against G+ and a few G– bacteria **Route of administration:** Oral; do not traverse blood-brain barrier **Adverse effects:** Nausea, mild gastro-intestinal pain, vomiting; erythromycin increases risk of cardiac arrest | Develops via changes in ribosomal RNA that prevent drugs from binding, or via R-plasmid genes coding for the production of macrolide-digesting enzymes; resistance genes are same as those of lincosamides |

continued ▶

## 2 Antibacterial Drugs *(continued)*

| Drug | Description and Mode of Action | Clinical Considerations | Method of Resistance |
|---|---|---|---|
| **Antibacterial Drugs That Inhibit Protein Synthesis** | | | |
| **Mupirocin** | Produced by *Pseudomonas fluorescens*; binds to bacterial tRNA$^{\text{Ile}}$, which prevents delivery of isoleucine to ribosomes, blocking polypeptide synthesis | **Spectrum of action:** Primarily effective against G+ bacteria<br>**Route of administration:** Topical cream<br>**Adverse effects:** None reported | Resistance develops from mutations that change the shape of tRNA$^{\text{Ile}}$ |
| **Oxazolidinones**<br>Representative:<br>Linezolid | Synthetic; inhibits initiation of polypeptide synthesis | **Spectrum of action:** G+ bacteria<br>**Route of administration:** Oral, IV<br>**Adverse effects:** Rash, diarrhea, loss of appetite, constipation, fever | Method of resistance not known |
| **Streptogramin**<br>Representatives:<br>Quinupristin<br>Dalfopristin | Binds to 50S ribosomal subunit, stops protein synthesis; the synergistic drugs quinupristin and dalfopristin are taken together | **Spectrum of action:** Broad but reserved for use against multiple-drug-resistant strains<br>**Route of administration:** IV<br>**Adverse effects:** Muscle and joint pain | Not known |
| **Tetracyclines**<br>Representatives:<br>Doxycycline<br>Tetracycline | Composed of four hexagonal rings with various side groups; prevent tRNA molecules, which carry amino acids, from binding to ribosomes at the 30S subunit's docking site | **Spectrum of action:** Most are broad: effective against many G+ and G− bacteria as well as against bacteria that lack cell walls, such as *Mycoplasma*<br>**Route of administration:** Oral, cross poorly into brain<br>**Adverse effects:** Nausea, diarrhea, sensitivity to light; forms complexes with calcium, which stains developing teeth and adversely affects the strength and shape of bones | Develops in three ways; bacteria may:<br>• Alter gene for pores in outer membrane; new pore prevents drug from entering cell<br>• Alter binding site on the ribosome to allow tRNA to bind even in presence of drug<br>• Actively pump drug from cell |
| **Antibacterial Drugs That Alter Cytoplasmic Membranes** | | | |
| **Gramicidin** | Short polypeptide that forms pore across cytoplasmic membrane, allowing single-charged cations to cross freely | **Spectrum of action:** G+ bacteria<br>**Route of administration:** Topical<br>**Adverse effects:** Toxic (also forms pores in eukaryotic membranes) | Not known |
| **Polymyxin** | Produced by *Bacillus polymyxa*; destroys cytoplasmic membranes of susceptible cells | **Spectrum of action:** Effective against G+ bacteria, particularly *Pseudomonas*, and some amoebae<br>**Route of administration:** Topical<br>**Adverse effects:** Toxic to kidneys | Results from changes in cell membrane that prohibit entrance of the drug |
| **Pyrazinamide** | Disrupts membrane transport | **Spectrum of action:** *Mycobacterium tuberculosis*<br>**Route of administration:** Oral<br>**Adverse effects:** Malaise, nausea, diarrhea | Results from point mutations in bacterial gene for enzyme necessary to activate drug |

**TABLE 2** *(continued)*

| Drug | Description and Mode of Action | Clinical Considerations | Method of Resistance |
|---|---|---|---|
| **Antibacterial Drugs That Are Antimetabolites** | | | |
| **Dapsone** | Interferes with synthesis of folic acid | **Spectrum of action:** *M. leprae, M. tuberculosis*<br>**Route of administration:** Oral<br>**Adverse effects:** Insomnia, headache, nausea, vomiting, increased heart rate | Not known |
| **Sulfonamides**<br>Representatives:<br>Sulfadiazine<br>Sulfadoxine<br>Sulfanilamide | Synthetic drugs; first produced as a dye; analogs of PABA that bind irreversibly to enzyme that produces dihydrofolic acid; synergistic with trimethoprim | **Spectrum of action:** Broad: effective against G+ and G− bacteria and some protozoa and fungi; however, resistance is widespread<br>**Route of administration:** Oral<br>**Adverse effects:** Rare: allergic reactions, anemia, jaundice, mental retardation of fetus if administered in last trimester of pregnancy | *Pseudomonas* is naturally resistant due to permeability barriers; cells that require folic acid as a vitamin are also naturally resistant; chromosomal mutations result in lowered affinity for the drugs |
| **Trimethoprim** | Blocks second metabolic step in the formation of folic acid from PABA; synergistic with sulfonamides | **Spectrum of action:** Broad: effective against G+ and G− bacteria and some protozoa and fungi; however, resistance is widespread<br>**Route of administration:** Oral<br>**Adverse effects:** Allergic reactions or liver damage in some patients | *Pseudomonas* is naturally resistant due to permeability barriers; cells that require folic acid as a vitamin are also naturally resistant; chromosomal mutations result in lowered affinity for the drug |
| **Antibacterial Drugs That Inhibit Nucleic Acid Synthesis** | | | |
| **Clofazimine** | Binds to DNA, preventing replication and transcription | **Spectrum of action:** Mycobacteria, especially *M. tuberculosis*, *M. leprae*, and *M. ulcerans*<br>**Route of administration:** Oral<br>**Adverse effects:** Diarrhea, discoloration of skin and eyes | Not known |
| **Fluoroquinolones**<br>Representatives:<br>Ciprofloxacin<br>Moxifloxacin<br>Ofloxacin | Synthetic agents that inhibit DNA gyrase, which is needed to correctly replicate bacterial DNA; penetrate cytoplasm of cells | **Spectrum of action:** Broad: G+ and G− bacteria are affected<br>**Route of administration:** Oral<br>**Adverse effects:** Tendonitis, tendon rupture | Results from chromosomal mutations that lower affinity for drug, reduce its uptake, or protect gyrase from drug |
| **Nitroimidazoles**<br>Representative:<br>Metronidazole | Anaerobic conditions reduce the molecule, which then damages DNA and prevents its correct replication | **Spectrum of action:** Obligate anaerobic bacteria | Not known |
| **Rifamycin**<br>Representatives:<br>Rifampin<br>Rifaximin | Natural and semisynthetic derivatives from *Amycolatopsis rifamycinica* that bind to bacterial RNA polymerase, preventing transcription of RNA; used with other antimicrobial bacterial drugs | **Spectrum of action:** Bacteriostatic against aerobic G+ bacteria; bactericidal against mycobacteria<br>**Route of administration:** Oral<br>**Adverse effects:** None of major significance | Results from chromosomal mutation that alters binding site on enzyme; G− bacteria are naturally resistant due to poor uptake |

## Antiviral Drugs

| Drug | Description and Mode of Action | Clinical Considerations | Method of Resistance |
|---|---|---|---|
| **Attachment Antagonists** | | | |
| Arildone Pleconaril | Blocks attachment molecule on host cell or pathogen | **Spectrum of action:** Picornaviruses (e.g., poliovirus, some cold viruses) **Route of administration:** Oral **Adverse effects:** None | Not known |
| Neuraminidase inhibitors Representatives: Oseltamivir Zanamivir | Prevent influenzaviruses from attaching to or exiting from cells | **Spectrum of action:** Influenzavirus **Route of administration:** Oral (oseltamivir) or aerosol (zanamivir) **Adverse effects:** None | Not known |
| **Antiviral Drugs That Inhibit Viral Uncoating** | | | |
| Amantadine | Neutralizes acid environment within phagolysosomes that is necessary for viral uncoating | **Spectrum of action:** Influenza A virus **Route of administration:** Oral **Adverse effects:** Toxuc to central nervous system; results in nervousness, irritability, insomnia, and blurred vision | Mutation resulting in a single amino acid change in a membrane ion channel leads to viral resistance |
| Rimantadine | Neutralizes phagolysosomal acid, preventing viral uncoating | **Spectrum of action:** Influenza A virus **Route of administration:** Oral, adults only **Adverse effects:** Toxic to central nervous system; results in nervousness, irritability, insomnia, and blurred vision | Mutation resulting in a single amino acid change in a membrane ion channel leads to viral resistance |
| **Antiviral Drugs That Inhibit Nucleic Acid Synthesis** | | | |
| Acyclovir (ACV) Representative: Ganciclovir | Phosphorylation by virally coded kinase enzyme activates the drug; inhibits DNA and RNA synthesis | **Spectrum of action:** Viruses that code for kinase enzymes: herpes, Epstein-Barr, cytomegalovirus, varicella viruses **Route of administration:** Oral **Adverse effects:** None | Mutations in genes for kinase enzymes may render them ineffective at drug activation |
| Adenosine arabinoside | Phosphorylation by cell-coded kinase enzyme activates the drug: inhibits DNA synthesis; viral DNA polymerase more likely to incorporate the drugs than human DNA polymerase | **Spectrum of action:** Herpesvirus **Route of administration:** IV **Adverse effects:** Fatal to host cells that incorporate the drug into cellular DNA; anemia | Results from mutation of viral DNA polymerase |
| Nucleotide analogs Representatives (see also Figure 7): Adefovir Azidothymidine (AZT) Entecavir Lamivudine Tenofovir Valaciclovir | Phosphorylation by cell-coded kinase enzyme activates these drugs: inhibits DNA synthesis; viral reverse transcriptase more likely to incorporate these drugs; used in conjunction with protease inhibitor to treat HIV | **Spectrum of action:** HIV, hepatitis B virus **Route of administration:** Oral **Adverse effects:** Nausea, bone marrow toxicity | Results from mutation of viral reverse transcriptase |
| Ribavirin | Phosphorylation by virally coded kinase enzyme activates the drug; inhibits DNA and RNA synthesis; viral DNA polymerase more likely to incorporate the drugs | **Spectrum of action:** Respiratory syncytial, hepatitis C, influenza A, measles, some hemorrhagic fever viruses **Route of administration:** Oral, aerosol, IV **Adverse effects:** Perhaps harmful to developing fetus | Not known |

## TABLE 3 *(continued)*

| Drug | Description and Mode of Action | Clinical Considerations | Method of Resistance |
|---|---|---|---|
| **Antiviral Drugs That Inhibit Protein Synthesis** | | | |
| **Antisense nucleic acids**<br>Representative:<br>  Fomiversen | Complementary to mRNA; binding prevents protein synthesis by blocking ribosomes | **Spectrum of action:** Specific to species with complementary mRNA; fomiversen specific against cytomegalovirus<br>**Route of administration:** Fomiversen injected weekly into eyes<br>**Adverse effects:** Possible glaucoma | Not known |
| **Antiviral Drugs That Inhibit Viral Proteins** | | | |
| **Protease inhibitors** | Computer-assisted modeling of protease enzyme, which is unique to HIV, allowed the creation of drugs that block the active site; used in conjunction with drugs active against nucleic acid synthesis | **Spectrum of action:** HIV<br>**Route of administration:** Oral<br>**Adverse effects:** None | Result from mutation in protease gene |

## TABLE 4 Antimicrobials Against Eukaryotes: Antifungal Drugs

| Drug | Description and Mode of Action | Clinical Considerations | Method of Resistance |
|---|---|---|---|
| **Antifungal Drugs That Inhibit Cell Membranes** | | | |
| **Allylamines**<br>Representative:<br>  Terbinafine | Antifungal action due to inhibition of ergosterol synthesis | **Spectrum of action:** Fungi<br>**Route of administration:** Oral, IV<br>**Adverse effects:** Headache, nausea, vomiting, diarrhea, liver damage, rash | Not known |
| **Azoles**<br>Representatives:<br>  Fluconazole<br>  Itraconazole<br>  Ketoconazole<br>  Voriconazole | Antifungal action due to inhibition of synthesis of ergosterol, an essential component of fungal cytoplasmic membranes | **Spectrum of action:** Fungi and protozoa<br>**Route of administration:** Topical, IV<br>**Adverse effects:** Possibly causes cancer in humans | Mutation in gene for target enzyme |
| **Polyenes**<br>Representatives:<br>  Amphotericin B<br>  Nystatin | Associate with molecules of ergosterol, forming a pore through the fungal membrane, which leads to leakage of essential ions from the cell; amphotericin B is produced by *Streptomyces nodosus* | **Spectrum of action:** Fungi, some amoebae<br>**Route of administration:** Amphotericin B: IV; nystatin: topical<br>**Adverse effects:** Chills, vomiting, fever | Rare; decrease in amount or change in chemistry of ergosterol |
| **Other Antifungal Drugs** | | | |
| **Echinocandins**<br>Representative:<br>  Caspofungin | Inhibits synthesis of glucan subunit of fungal cell walls | **Specimen of action:** *Candida, Aspergillus*<br>**Route of administration:** IV<br>**Adverse effects:** Rash, facial swelling, respiratory spasms, gastrointestinal distress | Result from mutation in glucan synthase gene |
| **5-Fluorocytosine** | Fungi, but not mammals, have an enzyme that converts this drug into 5-fluorouracil, an analog of uracil that inhibits RNA function | **Spectrum of action:** *Candida, Cryptococcus, Aspergillus*<br>**Route of administration:** Oral<br>**Adverse effects:** None | Develops from mutations in the genes for enzymes necessary for utilization of uracil |
| **Griseofulvin** | Isolated from *Penicillium griseofulvum*; deactivates tubulin, preventing cytokinesis and segregation of chromosomes during mitosis | **Spectrum of action:** Molds of ringworm (tinea)<br>**Route of administration:** Topical, oral<br>**Adverse effects:** None | Not known |

## 5

### Antimicrobials Against Eukaryotes: Anthelmintic Drugs

| Drug | Description and Mode of Action | Clinical Considerations | Method of Resistance |
|---|---|---|---|
| **Anthelmintic Drugs That Are Antimetabolites** | | | |
| **Benzimidazole derivatives** Representatives: Albendazole Mebendazole Thiabendazole Triclabendazole | Inhibit microtubule formation and glucose uptake | **Spectrum of action:** Helminths, protozoa  **Route of administration:** Oral  **Adverse effects:** Possible diarrhea | Not known |
| **Iodoquinol** | Halogenated (iodine-containing), possibly works by sequestering iron ions required by protozoan | **Spectrum of action:** *Entamoeba*  **Route of administration:** Oral  **Adverse effects:** Neuropathy and blindness with prolonged use | Not known |
| **Ivermectin Metrifonate** | Produce flaccid paralysis by blocking neurotransmitters | **Spectrum of action:** Helminths  **Route of administration:** Oral  **Adverse effects:** Allergic reactions may result from antigens of dead helminths | Not known |
| **Niclosamide** | Inhibits oxidative phosphorylation of ATP by mitochondria | **Spectrum of action:** Cestodes  **Route of administration:** Oral  **Adverse effects:** Abdominal pain, nausea, diarrhea | Not known |
| **Praziquantel** | Changes membrane permeability to calcium ions, which are required for muscular contraction; induces complete muscular contraction in helminths | **Spectrum of action:** Cestodes, trematodes  **Route of administration:** Oral  **Adverse effects:** None | Not known |
| **Pyrantel pamoate Diethylcarbamazine** | Bind to neurotransmitter receptors, causing complete muscular contraction of helminths | **Spectrum of action:** Nematodes  **Route of administration:** Oral  **Adverse effects:** None | Not known |
| **Anthelmintic Drugs That Inhibit Nucleic Acid Synthesis** | | | |
| **Niridazole** | When partially catabolized by schistosome enzymes, binds to DNA, preventing replication | **Spectrum of action:** *Schistosoma* | Not known |
| **Oltipraz** | Possibly acts by reducing the supply of deoxyribonucleotides | **Spectrum of action:** *Schistosoma* | Not known |
| **Oxamniquine** | Schistosome enzyme activates drug, which then inhibits DNA synthesis | **Spectrum of action:** *Schistosoma* | Not known |

## 6

### Antimicrobials Against Eukaryotes: Antiprotozoan Drugs

| Drug | Description and Mode of Action | Clinical Considerations | Method of Resistance |
|---|---|---|---|
| **Antiprotozoan Drugs That Are Antimetabolites** | | | |
| **Artemisinin** | Derived from Chinese wormwood shrub; interferes with heme detoxification and with $Ca^{2+}$ transport | **Spectrum of action:** *Plasmodium*  **Route of administration:** Oral  **Adverse effects:** Nausea, vomiting, itching, dizziness | Mutation in $Ca^{2+}$ transporter gene |
| **Atovaquone** | Analog of coenzyme Q or cytochrome *b* of several protozoa and of *Pneumocystis*; interrupts electron transport | **Spectrum of action:** Protozoa, *Pneumocystis*  **Route of administration:** Oral  **Adverse effects:** Possible rash, diarrhea, headache | Cells modify the structure of their electron transport chain proteins |

**TABLE 6 (continued)**

| Drug | Description and Mode of Action | Clinical Considerations | Method of Resistance |
|---|---|---|---|
| **Antiprotozoan Drugs That Are Antimetabolites** | | | |
| **Benzimidazole derivatives**<br>Representative:<br>  Mebendazole | Inhibit microtubule formation and glucose uptake | **Spectrum of action:** Helminths, protozoa<br>**Route of administration:** Oral<br>**Adverse effects:** Possible diarrhea | Not known |
| **Furazolidone** | Appear to block a number of metabolic pathways, including carbohydrate metabolism and initiation of translation | **Spectrum of action:** Protozoa, Gram+, Gram− bacteria<br>**Route of administration:** Oral<br>**Adverse effects:** Possible nausea and vomiting | Not known |
| **Heavy metals (e.g., Hg, As, Cr, Sb)**<br>Representatives:<br>  Meglumine antimonate<br>  Melarsoprol<br>  Salvarsan (contains As)<br>  Sodium stibogluconate (contains Sb) | Deactivate enzymes by breaking hydrogen bonds necessary for effective tertiary structure; drugs containing arsenic were the first recognized selectively toxic chemotherapeutic agents | **Spectrum of action:** Metabolically active cells<br>**Route of administration:** Topical, oral<br>**Adverse effects:** Toxic to active cells, such as those of the brain, kidney, liver, and bone marrow | Not known |
| **Iodoquinol** | Mode of action unknown | **Spectrum of action:** Intestinal amoebae<br>**Route of administration:** Oral<br>**Adverse effects:** Fever, chills, rash | Not known |
| **Nifurtimox** | Interferes with electron transport | **Spectrum of action:** *Trypanosoma*<br>**Route of administration:** Oral<br>**Adverse effects:** Abdominal pain, nausea | Not known |
| **Proguanil Pyrimethamine** | Block second metabolic step in the formation of folic acid from PABA; synergistic with sulfonamides | **Spectrum of action:** Broad: effective against G+ and G− bacteria and some protozoa and fungi; however, resistance is widespread<br>**Route of administration:** Oral<br>**Adverse effects:** Allergic reactions in some patients | Cells that require folic acid as a vitamin are also naturally resistant; chromosomal mutations result in lowered affinity for the drugs |
| **Sulfonamides**<br>Representatives:<br>  Sulfadiazine<br>  Sulfadoxine<br>  Sulfanilamide | Synthetic drugs; first produced as a dye; analogs of PABA that bind irreversibly to enzyme that produces dihydrofolic acid; synergistic with trimethoprim | **Spectrum of action:** Broad: effective against G+ and G− bacteria and some protozoa and fungi; however, resistance is widespread<br>**Route of administration:** Oral<br>**Adverse effects:** Rare: Allergic reactions, anemia, jaundice, mental retardation of fetus if administered in last trimester of pregnancy | Cells that require folic acid as a vitamin are also naturally resistant; chromosomal mutations result in lowered affinity for the drugs |
| **Suramin** | Inhibits specific enzymes in some protozoa | **Spectrum of action:** *Trypanosoma*<br>**Routine of administration:** Oral<br>**Adverse effects:** None | Not known |
| **Trimethoprim** | Block second metabolic step in the formation of folic acid from PABA; synergistic with sulfonamides | **Spectrum of action:** Broad: effective against some protozoa, fungi, and some G+ and G− bacteria; however, resistance is widespread<br>**Route of administration:** Oral<br>**Adverse effects:** Allergic reactions in some patients | Cells that require folic acid as a vitamin are also naturally resistant; chromosomal mutations result in lowered affinity for the drugs |

continued ▶

**6**

## Antimicrobials Against Eukaryotes: Antiprotozoan Drugs (continued)

| Drug | Description and Mode of Action | Clinical Considerations | Method of Resistance |
|---|---|---|---|
| **Antiprotozoan Drugs That Inhibit DNA Synthesis** | | | |
| **Eflornithine** | Inhibits synthesis of precursors of nucleic acids | **Spectrum of action:** Primarily *Trypanosoma brucei*<br><br>**Route of administration:** Oral<br><br>**Adverse effects:** Anemia, inhibition of blood clotting, nausea, vomiting | Not known |
| **Nitroimidazoles**<br><br>Representatives:<br>Benznidazole<br>Metronidazole | Anaerobic conditions reduce the drug, which then damages DNA, preventing correct replication and transcription | **Spectrum of action:** Protozoa<br><br>**Route of administration:** Oral<br><br>**Adverse effects:** Metronidazole causes cancer in laboratory rodents | Not known |
| **Pentamidine** | Binds to nucleic acids, inhibiting replication, transcription, and translation | **Spectrum of action:** Protozoa and *Pneumocystis* (fungus)<br><br>**Route of administration:** IM, IV<br><br>**Adverse effects:** Rash, low blood pressure, irregular heartbeat, kidney and liver failure | Not known |
| **Quinolones**<br><br>Representatives:<br>Natural quinine<br>Semisynthetic quinines:<br>Chloroquine<br>Mefloquine<br>Primaquine | Natural and semisynthetic drugs derived from the bark of cinchona tree; inhibit metabolism of malaria parasites by one or more unknown methods | **Spectrum of action:** *Plasmodium*<br><br>**Route of administration:** Oral<br><br>**Adverse effects:** Allergic reactions, visual disturbances | Results from the presence of quinoline pumps that remove the drugs from parasite's cells |

# Chapter Summary

## The History of Antimicrobial Agents

1. Chemotherapeutic agents are chemicals used to treat diseases. Among them are **antimicrobial agents (antimicrobials),** which include **antibiotics** (biologically produced agents), **semisynthetics** (chemically modified antibiotics), and **synthetic** agents.

## Mechanisms of Antimicrobial Action

1. Successful chemotherapy against microbes is based on **selective toxicity;** that is, using antimicrobial agents that are more toxic to pathogens than to the patient.

2. Antimicrobial drugs affect pathogens by inhibiting cell wall synthesis, inhibiting the translation of proteins, disrupting cytoplasmic membranes, inhibiting general metabolic pathways, inhibiting the replication of DNA, blocking the attachment of viruses to their hosts, or by blocking a pathogen's recognition of its host. **ANIMATIONS:** *Chemotherapeutic Agents: Modes of Action*

3. **Beta-lactams**—penicillins, cephalosporins, and monobactams—have a functional lactam ring. They prevent bacteria from cross-linking NAM subunits of peptidoglycan in the bacterial cell wall during growth. **Vancomycin** and **cycloserine** also disrupt cell wall formation in many Gram-positive bacteria. **Bacitracin** blocks NAG and NAM transport from the cytoplasm. **Isoniazid (INH)** and **ethambutol** block mycolic acid synthesis in the walls of mycobacteria. **Echinocandins** block synthesis of fungal cell walls.

4. Antimicrobial agents that inhibit protein synthesis include **aminoglycosides** and **tetracyclines,** which inhibit functions of the 30S ribosomal subunit, and **chloramphenicol, lincosamides, streptogramins,** and **macrolides,** which inhibit 50S subunits. Mupirocin stops polypeptide synthesis by binding to tRNA molecules that carry isoleucine. **Oxazolidinones** block initiation of translation. **Antisense nucleic acid** molecules also inhibit protein synthesis.

5. **Polyenes, azoles,** and **allylamines** disrupt the cytoplasmic membranes of fungi. Polymyxin acts against the membranes of Gram-negative bacteria.

6. **Sulfonamides** are **structural analogs** of para-aminobenzoic acid (PABA), a chemical needed by some microorganisms but not by humans. The substitution of sulfonamides in the metabolic pathway leading to nucleic acid synthesis kills those organisms. Trimethoprim also blocks this pathway.

7. Drugs that inhibit nucleic acid replication in pathogens include actinomycin, **nucleotide analogs,** fluoroquinolones, quinolones, and rifampin.

## Clinical Considerations in Prescribing Antimicrobial Drugs

1. Chemotherapeutic agents have a **spectrum of action** and may be classed as either **narrow-spectrum drugs or broad-spectrum drugs** depending on how many kinds of pathogens they affect.

2. **Diffusion susceptibility tests,** such as the Kirby-Bauer test, reveal which drug is most effective against a particular pathogen; in general, the larger the **zone of inhibition** around a drug-soaked disk on a Petri plate, the more effective the drug.

3. The **minimum inhibitory concentration (MIC),** usually determined by either a **broth dilution test** or an **Etest,** is the smallest amount of a drug that will inhibit a pathogen.

4. A **minimum bactericidal concentration (MBC) test** ascertains whether a drug is bacteriostatic and the lowest concentration of a drug that is bactericidal.

5. In choosing antimicrobials, physicians must consider how a drug is best administered—orally, intramuscularly, or intravenously—and possible side effects, including toxicity and allergic responses.

## Resistance to Antimicrobial Drugs

1. Some members of a pathogenic population may develop resistance to a drug due to extra DNA pieces called **R-plasmids** or to the mutation of genes. Microorganisms may resist a drug by producing enzymes such as **χ-lactamase** that deactivate the drug, by inducing changes in the cell membrane that prevent entry of the drug, by altering the drug's target to prevent its binding, by altering the cell's metabolic pathways, by pumping the drug out of the cell, or by protecting the drug's target by binding another molecule to it.
   **ANIMATIONS:** *Antibiotic Resistance: Origins of Resistance, Forms of Resistance*

2. **Cross resistance** occurs when resistance to one chemotherapeutic agent confers resistance to similar drugs. **Multiple-drug-resistant pathogens** are resistant to three or more types of antimicrobial drugs.

3. **Synergism** describes the interplay between drugs that results in efficacy that exceeds the efficacy of either drug alone. Some drug combinations are antagonistic.

# Questions for Review
*Answers to the Questions for Review (except Short Answer questions) appear at the end of this chapter.*

## Multiple Choice

1. Diffusion and dilution tests that expose pathogens to antimicrobials are designed to
   a. determine the spectrum of action of a drug.
   b. determine which drug is most effective against a particular pathogen.
   c. determine the amount of a drug to use against a particular pathogen.
   d. both b and c

2. In a Kirby-Bauer susceptibility test, the presence of a zone of inhibition around disks containing antimicrobial agents indicates
   a. that the microbe does not grow in the presence of the agents.
   b. that the microbe grows well in the presence of the agents.
   c. the smallest amount of the agent that will inhibit the growth of the microbe.
   d. the minimum amount of an agent that kills the microbe in question.

3. The key to successful chemotherapy is
   a. selective toxicity.
   b. a diffusion test.
   c. the minimum inhibitory concentration test.
   d. the spectrum of action.

4. Which of the following statements is relevant in explaining why sulfonamides are effective?
   a. Sulfonamides attach to sterol lipids in the pathogen, disrupt the membranes, and lyse the cells.
   b. Sulfonamides prevent the incorporation of amino acids into polypeptide chains.
   c. Humans and microbes use folic acid and PABA differently in their metabolism.
   d. Sulfonamides inhibit DNA replication in both pathogens and human cells.

5. Cross resistance is
   a. the deactivation of an antimicrobial agent by a bacterial enzyme.
   b. alteration of the resistant cells so that an antimicrobial agent cannot attach.
   c. the mutation of genes that affect the cell membrane channels so that antimicrobial agents cannot cross into the cell's interior.
   d. resistance to one antimicrobial agent because of its similarity to another antimicrobial agent.

6. Multiple-drug-resistant microbes
   a. are resistant to all antimicrobial agents.
   b. respond to new antimicrobials by developing resistance.
   c. frequently develop in hospitals.
   d. all of the above

7. Which of the following is most closely associated with a beta-lactam ring?
   a. penicillin          c. bacitracin
   b. vancomycin          d. isoniazid

8. Drugs that act against protein synthesis include
   a. beta-lactams.          c. polymyxin.
   b. trimethoprim.          d. aminoglycosides.

9. Which of the following statements is *false* concerning antiviral drugs?
   a. Macrolide drugs block attachment sites on the host cell wall and prevent viruses from entering.
   b. Drugs that neutralize the acidity of phagolysosomes prevent viral uncoating.
   c. Nucleotide analogs in antiviral drugs can be used to stop viral replication.
   d. Drugs containing protease inhibitors retard viral growth by blocking the production of essential viral proteins.

10. PABA is
   a. a substrate used in the production of penicillin.
   b. a type of β-lactamase.
   c. molecularly similar to cephalosporins.
   d. used to synthesize folic acid.

## Labeling

Label each figure below to indicate the class of drug that is stopping polypeptide translation.

1. _____
   blocks initiation.

Incorrect amino acids

2. _____
   changes 30S subunit.

3. _____
   blocks ribosome attachment.

Amino acids    Peptide bonding

4. _____
   inhibits peptide bonding.

5. _____
   blocks ribosome movement.

6. _____
   blocks tRNA docking.

Precision Graphics

## Short Answer

1. What characteristics would an ideal chemotherapeutic agent have? Which drug has these qualities?

2. Contrast narrow-spectrum and broad-spectrum drugs. Which are more effective?

3. Why is the fact that drug Z destroys the NAM portions of a cell's wall structure an important factor in considering the drug for chemotherapy?

4. Given that both human cells and pathogens synthesize proteins at ribosomal sites, how can antimicrobial agents that target this process be safe to use in humans?

5. Support or refute the following statement: antimicrobial agents produce resistant cells.

6. Given that resistant strains of pathogens are a concern to the general health of a population, what can be done to prevent their development?

7. Why are antiviral drugs difficult to develop?

8. A man has been given a broad-spectrum antibiotic for his stomach ulcer. What unintended consequences could arise from this therapy?

9. Compare and contrast the actions of polyenes, azoles, allylamines, and polymyxin.

10. What is the difference in drug action of synergists contrasted with that of antagonists?

 # Concept Mapping

Using the following terms, draw a concept map that describes antimicrobial resistance. Or, complete this concept map online by going to the Study Area at www.masteringmicrobiology.com.

| | | | |
|---|---|---|---|
| Altered pore proteins | Beta lactamase | Entry of antibiotic into bacterial cell | Pumping antimicrobial out of the cell |
| Altered target | Binding of antibiotic | | |
| Antibiotics | Cell division | Mutation | Resistance pumps |
| Bacterial enzymes | Conjugation | Penicillin | Transduction |

# Critical Thinking

1. AIDS is treated with a "cocktail" of several antiviral agents at once. Why is the cocktail more effective than a single agent? What is a physician trying to prevent by prescribing several drugs at once?

2. How does *Penicillium* escape the effects of the penicillin it secretes?

3. How might a colony of *Bacillus licheniformis* escape the effects of its own bacitracin?

4. Fewer than 1% of known antibiotics have any practical value in treatment of disease. Why is this so?

5. In the summer issue of *News of the Lepidopterists' Society* in 2000, a recommendation was made to moth and butterfly collectors to use antimicrobials to combat disease in the young of these insects. What are the possible ramifications for human health of such usage of antimicrobials?

6. Even though aminoglycosides such as gentamicin can cause deafness, there are still times when they are the best choice for treating some infections. What laboratory test would a clinical scientist use to show that gentamicin is the best choice to treat a particular *Pseudomonas* infection?

7. Your pregnant neighbor has a sore throat and tells you that she is taking some tetracycline she had left over from a previous infection. Give two reasons why her decision is a poor one.

8. Acyclovir has replaced adenosine arabinoside as treatment for herpes infections. Compare the ways these drugs are activated (see Table 3). Why is acyclovir a better choice?

9. Why might amphotericin B affect the kidneys more than other human organs?

10. Antiparasitic drugs in the benzimidazole family inhibit the polymerization of tubulin. What effect might these drugs have on mitosis and flagella?

Access more review material online in the Study Area at
**www.masteringmicrobiology.com**. There, you'll find
- **Animations**
- **MP3 Tutor Sessions**
- **Concept Mapping Activities**
- **Flashcards**
- **Quizzes**

and more to help you succeed.

# Answers

Answers to multiple-choice, fill-in-blank, labeling, matching, and true/false questions are listed here. Answers for Short Answer and Critical Thinking questions are available for instructors only in the Instructor's Manual that accompanies this text.

**Multiple Choice**
1. d; 2. a; 3. a; 4. c; 5. d; 6. c; 7. a; 8. d; 9. a; 10. d

**Labeling**
See Figure 4.

# Infection, Infectious Diseases, and Epidemiology

Gopal Murti/Visuals Unlimited/Getty Images

Severe acute respiratory syndrome (SARS) virus traveled halfway around the world in just weeks, providing health care workers and governments with unique opportunities to monitor and contain an epidemic.

A new **mysterious** illness began appearing in China's Guangdong province in the winter of 2002–2003. Characterized by fever, shortness of breath, and atypical pneumonia, the highly infectious illness spread rapidly, particularly among food handlers and hospital workers tending to the already stricken. Initially confined to China, the disease is believed to have begun its worldwide **spread** in February 2003, when a physician who had contracted the disease in Guangdong traveled to Hong Kong. During his stay in a Hong Kong hotel, the physician passed the disease on to at least 12 other hotel guests, including travelers who continued on to Canada, Singapore, and Vietnam, unknowingly advancing the disease's spread to these countries. By March 2003, the **disease** had a name—severe acute respiratory syndrome (SARS)—and the World Health Organization (WHO) issued a global **alert**, triggering quarantines, travel cancellations, and other measures intended to curb the spread of this new, sometimes-fatal disease.

How do microorganisms **infect** and cause disease in people? And how do experts investigate the transmission and spread of infectious diseases in populations? Read on.

 Take the pre-test for this chapter online. Visit the Study Area at www.masteringmicrobiology.com.

From Chapter 14 of *Microbiology with Diseases by Taxonomy*, Third Edition. Robert W. Bauman.

We have discussed characteristics of microorganisms and their metabolism. We examined ways microbes can be controlled, viewed, identified, and used for our benefit. Now it is time to examine how microbes directly affect our bodies. In this discussion, continually bear in mind that most microorganisms are neither harmful nor expressly beneficial to humans—they live their lives, and we live ours. Relatively few microbes either directly benefit us or harm us.

In this chapter we first examine the general types of relationships that microbes can have with the bodies of their hosts. Then we discuss sources of infectious diseases of humans; how microbes enter and attach to their hosts; the nature of infectious diseases; and how microbes leave hosts to become available to enter new hosts. Next we explore the ways that infectious diseases are spread among hosts. Finally, we consider *epidemiology*, the study of the occurrence and spread of diseases within groups of humans, and the methods by which we can limit the spread of pathogens within society.

# Symbiotic Relationships Between Microbes and Their Hosts

**Symbiosis** (sim-bī-o′sis) means "to live together." Each of us has symbiotic relationships with countless microorganisms, although often we are completely unaware of them. The 10 trillion or so cells in your body provide homes for more than 100 trillion bacteria and fungi and even more viruses. We begin this section by considering the types of relationships between microbes and their hosts.

## Types of Symbiosis

### Learning Objectives

✓ Distinguish among the types of symbiosis, listing them in order from most beneficial to most harmful for the host.

✓ Describe the relationships among the terms *parasite*, *host*, and *pathogen*.

Biologists see symbiotic relationships as a continuum from cases that are beneficial to both members of a pair to situations in which one member lives at a damaging expense to the other. In the following sections, we examine three conditions along the continuum: mutualism, commensalism, and parasitism.

### Mutualism

In **mutualism** (mū′tū-ăl-izm), both members benefit from their interaction. For example, bacteria in your colon receive a warm, moist, nutrient-rich environment in which to thrive, while you absorb vitamin precursors and other nutrients released from the bacteria. In this example, the relationship is beneficial to microbe and human alike but is not required by either. Many of the bacteria could live elsewhere, and you could get vitamins from your diet.

Some mutualistic relationships provide such important benefits that one or both of the parties cannot live without the other. For instance, termites, which cannot digest the cellulose

▲ **Figure 1 Mutualism.** Wood-eating termites in the genus *Reticulitermes* cannot digest the cellulose in wood, but the protozoan *Trichonympha*, which lives in their intestines, can digest cellulose with the help of bacteria. The three organisms maintain a mutualistic relationship that is crucial for the life of the termite. *What benefits accrue to each of the symbionts in this mutalistic relationship?*

**Figure 1** *The termite gets digested cellulose from the protozoa, which get a constant supply of wood pulp to digest, so the bacteria get a food source as well.*

in wood by themselves, would die without a mutualistic relationship with colonies of wood-digesting protozoa and bacteria living in their intestines (Figure 1). The termites provide wood pulp and a home to the protozoa, while the protozoa break down the wood within the termite intestines using enzymes from the bacteria, which live on the protozoa. The microbes share the nutrients released with the termites. **Beneficial Microbes: A Bioterrorist Worm** describes another mutualistic relationship.

### Commensalism

In **commensalism** (kŏ-men′săl-izm), a second type of symbiosis, one member of the relationship benefits without significantly affecting the other. For example, *Staphylococcus epidermidis* (staf′i-lō-kok′us ep-i-der-mid′is) growing on the skin typically causes no measurable harm to a person. An absolute example of commensalism is difficult to prove because the host may experience unobserved benefits. In this example, *Staphylococcus* may inhibit pathogenic microbes from colonizing the skin.

### Parasitism

Of concern to health care professionals is a third type of symbiosis called **parasitism**[1] (par′ă-si-tizm). A **parasite** derives benefit from its **host** while harming it, though some hosts sustain only slight damage. In the most severe cases, a parasite kills its host, in the process destroying its own home, which is not

---

[1]From Greek *parasitos*, meaning one who eats at the table of another.

## TABLE 1
## The Three Types of Symbiotic Relationships

| | Organism 1 | Organism 2 | Example |
|---|---|---|---|
| Mutualism | Benefits | Benefits | Bacteria in human colon |
| Commensalism | Benefits | Neither benefits nor is harmed | *Staphylococcus* on skin |
| Parasitism | Benefits | Is harmed | Tuberculosis bacteria in human lung |

beneficial for the parasite. Therefore, parasites that allow their hosts to survive are more likely to spread. Similarly, hosts that tolerate a parasite are more likely to reproduce. The result over time will be *coevolution* toward commensalism or mutualism. Any parasite that causes disease is called a **pathogen** (path′ō-jen).

A variety of protozoa, fungi, and bacteria are microscopic parasites of humans. Larger parasites of humans include parasitic worms and biting arthropods,[2] including mites (chiggers), ticks, mosquitoes, fleas, and bloodsucking flies.

You should realize that microbes that are parasitic may become mutualistic or vice versa; that is, the relationships between and among organisms can change over time. Table 1 summarizes three types of symbiosis.

### CRITICAL **THINKING**

Corals are colonial marine animals that feed by filtering small microbes from seawater in tropical oceans worldwide. Biologists have discovered that the cells of most corals are hosts to microscopic algae called zooxanthellae. Design an experiment to ascertain whether corals and zooxanthellae coexist in a mutual, commensal, or parasitic relationship.

## Normal Microbiota in Hosts
### Learning Objective

✓ Describe the normal microbiota, including resident and transient members.

Even though many parts of your body are *axenic*[3] (ā-zen′ik) environments—that is, sites that are free of any microbes—other parts of your body shelter millions of mutualistic and commensal symbionts. Each square centimeter of your skin, for example, contains about 3 million bacteria, and your large intestine contains 400 to 1000 kinds of bacteria outnumbering your own cells many times. The microbes that colonize the surfaces of the body without normally causing disease constitute the body's **normal microbiota** (Figure 2), also sometimes called the *normal flora*[4]

---

[2]From Greek *arthros*, meaning jointed, and *pod*, meaning foot.
[3]From Greek *a*, meaning no, and *xenos*, meaning foreigner.
[4]This usage of the term *flora*, which literally means plants, derives from the fact that bacteria and fungi were considered plants in early taxonomic schemes. *Microbiota* is preferable because it properly applies to all microbes (whether eukaryotic or prokaryotic) and to viruses.

---

## BENEFICIAL MICROBES

### A BIOTERRORIST WORM

Killed insect    *Steinernema*

Ralph E. Berry

LM  4 mm

▲ The worm *Steinernema* (white) kills by infecting insects with lethal *Xenorhabdus* bacteria.

Bioterrorism has been defined as the deliberate release of viruses, bacteria, or other germs to cause illness or death. A nematode worm, *Steinernema*, is by that definition a bioterrorist, releasing its mutualistic bacterial symbiont, *Xenorhabdus*.

Nematodes are microscopic, unsegmented, round worms that live in soil worldwide. *Steinernema* preys on insects, including ants, termites, and the immature stages of various beetles, weevils, worms,

fleas, ticks, and gnats. The bioterrorist worms crawl into an insect's mouth or anus and then cross the intestinal walls to enter the insect's blood. The nematodes then release their symbiotic *Xenorhabdus*. This bacterium inactivates the insect's defensive systems; generates antibacterial compounds, which eliminate other bacteria; produces insecticidal toxins to kill the insect; and secretes digestive enzymes. The bacterial enzymes turn the insect's body into a slimy porridge of nutrients within 48 hours. Meanwhile, *Steinernema* nematodes mature, mate, and reproduce within the insect's liquefying body. The nematodes' offspring feed on the gooey fluid until they are old enough to emerge from the insect's skeleton, but not before taking up a supply of bacteria for their own future bioterroist raids on new insect hosts.

This is a true mutualistic symbiosis: The nematode depends upon the bacterium to kill and digest the insect host, while the bacterium depends on the nematode to deliver it to new hosts. Both benefit. Farmers too can benefit. They can use *Steinernema* and its bacterium to control insect pests without damaging their crops, animals, or people.

Tony Brain/Photo Researchers

▲ **Figure 2  An example of normal microbiota.** Bacteria (pink) colonize the human nasal cavity.

or the *indigenous microbiota*. The normal microbiota are of two main types: resident microbiota and transient microbiota.

### Resident Microbiota

*Resident microbiota* remain a part of the normal microbiota of a person throughout life. These organisms are found on the skin and on the mucous membranes of the digestive tract, upper respiratory tract, distal[5] portion of the urethra,[6] and vagina. Table 2 illustrates these environments and lists some of the resident bacteria, fungi, and protozoa that live there. Most of the resident microbiota are commensal; that is, they feed on excreted cellular wastes and dead cells without causing harm.

### Transient Microbiota

*Transient microbiota* remain in the body for only a few hours, days, or months before disappearing. They are found in the same locations as the resident members of the normal microbiota but cannot persist because of competition from other microorganisms, elimination by the body's defense cells, or chemical and physical changes in the body that dislodge them.

### Acquisition of Normal Microbiota

You developed in your mother's womb without a normal microbiota because you had surrounded yourself with an amniotic membrane and fluid, which generally kept microorganisms at bay, and because your mother's uterus was essentially an axenic environment.

---

[5]*Distal* refers to the end of some structure, as opposed to *proximal*, which refers to the beginning of a structure.
[6]The tube that empties the bladder.

Your normal microbiota began to develop when your surrounding amniotic membrane ruptured and microorganisms came in contact with you during birth. Microbes entered your mouth and nose as you passed through the birth canal, and your first breath was loaded with microorganisms that quickly established themselves in your upper respiratory tract. Your first meals provided the progenitors of resident microbiota for your colon, while *Staphylococcus* and other microbes transferred from the skin of both the medical staff and your parents began to colonize your skin. Although you continue to add to your transient microbiota, most of the resident microbiota was initially established during your first months of life.

## How Normal Microbiota Become Opportunistic Pathogens

### Learning Objective

✓ Describe three conditions that create opportunities for normal microbiota to cause disease.

Under ordinary circumstances, normal microbiota do not cause disease. However, these same microbes may become harmful if an opportunity to do so arises. In this case, normal microbiota (or other normally harmless microbes from the environment) become **opportunistic pathogens** or *opportunists*. Conditions that create opportunities for pathogens include the following:

- *Introduction of a member of the normal microbiota into an unusual site in the body.* As we have seen, normal microbiota are present only in certain body sites, and each site has only certain species of microbiota. If a member of the normal microbiota in one site is introduced into a site it normally does not inhabit, the organism may become an opportunistic pathogen. In the colon, for example, *Escherichia coli* (esh-ĕ-rik'ē-ăkō'lē) is mutualistic, but should it enter the urethra it becomes an opportunist that can produce disease.

- *Immune suppression.* Anything that suppresses the body's immune system—including disease, malnutrition, emotional or physical stress, extremes of age (either very young or very old), the use of radiation or chemotherapy to combat cancer, or the use of immunosuppressive drugs in transplant patients—can enable opportunistic pathogens. AIDS patients often die from opportunistic infections that are typically controlled by a healthy immune system, because HIV infection suppresses immune system function.

- *Changes in the normal microbiota.* Normal microbiota use nutrients, take up space, and release toxic waste products, all of which make it less likely that arriving pathogens can compete well enough to become established and produce disease. This situation is known as **microbial antagonism** or **microbial competition.** However, changes in the relative abundance of normal microbiota, for whatever reason, may allow a member of the normal microbiota to become an opportunistic pathogen and thrive. For example, when a woman must undergo long-term antimicrobial treatment for a bacterial blood infection, the antimicrobial may also

## 2

## Some Resident Microbiota[a]

### Upper Respiratory Tract

| Genera | Notes |
|---|---|
| *Fusobacterium, Haemophilus, Lactobacillus, Moraxella, Staphylococcus, Streptococcus, Veillonella, Candida* (fungus) | The nose is cooler than the rest of the respiratory system and has some unique microbiota. The trachea and bronchi have a sparse microbiota compared to the nose and mouth. The alveoli of the lungs, which are too small to depict in this illustration, have no natural microbiota—they are axenic. |

*Labels: Trachea, Bronchi, Nose, Mouth, Epiglottis*

### Upper Digestive Tract

| Genera | Notes |
|---|---|
| *Actinomyces, Bacteroides, Corynebacterium, Haemophilus, Lactobacillus, Neisseria, Staphylococcus, Treponema, Entamoeba* (protozoan), *Trichomonas* (protozoan) | Microbes colonize surfaces of teeth, gingiva, lining of cheeks, and pharynx, and are found in saliva in large numbers. Dozens of species have never been identified. |

*Labels: Epiglottis, Esophagus, Liver, Pancreas, Gallbladder, Small intestine (section removed), Rectum, Mouth, Stomach, Colon*

### Lower Digestive Tract

| Genera | Notes |
|---|---|
| *Bacteroides, Bifidobacterium, Clostridium, Enterococcus, Escherichia, Fusobacterium, Lactobacillus, Proteus, Shigella, Candida* (fungus), *Entamoeba* (protozoan), *Trichomonas* (protozoan) | The bacteria are mostly strict anaerobes, though some facultative anaerobes are also resident. |

### Female Urinary and Reproductive Systems

| Genera | Notes |
|---|---|
| *Bacteroides, Clostridium, Lactobacillus, Staphylococcus, Streptococcus, Candida* (fungus), *Trichomonas* (protozoan) | Microbiota change as acidity in the vagina changes during menstrual cycle. The flow of urine prevents extensive colonization of the urinary bladder or urethra. |

*Labels: Cervix, Rectum, Vagina, Ovary, Uterus, Bladder, Urethra*

### Male Urinary and Reproductive Systems

| Genera | Notes |
|---|---|
| *Bacteroides, Fusobacterium, Lactobacillus, Mycobacterium, Peptostreptococcus, Staphylococcus, Streptococcus* | The flow of urine prevents extensive colonization of the urinary bladder or urethra. |

*Labels: Rectum, Seminal vesicle, Prostate gland, Testis, Bladder, Ductus (vas) deferens*

### Eyes and Skin

| Genera | Notes |
|---|---|
| Skin: *Corynebacterium, Micrococcus, Propionibacterium, Staphylococcus, Candida* (fungus), *Malassezia* (fungus)<br><br>Conjunctiva: *Staphylococcus* | Microbiota live on the outer, dead layers of the skin and in hair follicles and pores of glands. The deeper layers (dermis and hypodermis) are axenic.<br><br>Tears wash most microbiota from the eyes, so there are few compared to the skin. |

*Labels: Epidermis, Dermis, Hypodermis, Orbicularis oculi muscle, Skin section, Conjunctiva*

[a]Genera are bacteria unless noted.

Kenneth Probst/Precision Graphics

kill normal bacterial microbiota in the vagina. In the absence of competition from bacteria, *Candida albicans* (kan′did-ă al′bi-kanz), a yeast and also a member of the normal vaginal microbiota, grows prolifically, producing an opportunistic vaginal yeast infection. Other conditions that can disrupt the normal microbiota are hormonal changes, stress, changes in diet, and exposure to overwhelming numbers of pathogens.

Now that we have considered the relationships of the normal microbiota to their hosts, we turn our attention to the

**TABLE**

**3**

## Some Common Zoonoses

| Disease | Causative Agent | Animal Reservoir | Mode of Transmission |
|---------|-----------------|------------------|----------------------|
| **Helminthic** | | | |
| Tapeworm infestation | *Dipylidium caninum* | Dogs | Ingestion of larvae transmitted in dog saliva |
| *Fasciola* infestation | *Fasciola hepatica* | Sheep, cattle | In gestion of contaminated vegetation |
| **Protozoan** | | | |
| Malaria | *Plasmodium* spp. | Monkeys | Bite of *Anopheles* mosquito |
| Toxoplasmosis | *Toxoplasma gondii* | Cats and other animals | Ingestion of contaminated meat, inhalation of pathogen, direct contact with infected tissues |
| **Fungal** | | | |
| Ringworm | *Trichophyton* sp. | Domestic animals | Direct contact |
| | *Microsporum* sp. | | |
| | *Epidermophyton* sp. | | |
| **Bacterial** | | | |
| Anthrax | *Bacillus anthracis* | Domestic livestock | Direct contact with infected animals, inhalation |
| Bubonic plague | *Yersinia pestis* | Rodents | Flea bites |
| Lyme disease | *Borrelia burgdorferi* | Deer | Tick bites |
| Salmonellosis | *Salmonella* spp. | Birds, rodents, reptiles | Ingestion of fecally contaminated water or food |
| Typhus | *Rickettsia prowazekii* | Rodents | Louse bites |
| **Viral** | | | |
| Rabies | *Lyssavirus* sp. | Bats, skunks, foxes, dogs | Bite of infected animal |
| *Hantavirus* pulmonary syndrome | *Hantavirus* sp. | Deer mice | Inhalation of viruses in dried feces and urine |
| Yellow fever | *Flavivirus* sp. | Monkeys | Bite of *Aedes* mosquito |

movement of microbes into new hosts by considering aspects of human diseases.

# Reservoirs of Infectious Diseases of Humans

## Learning Objective

✓ Describe three types of reservoirs of infection in humans.

Most pathogens of humans cannot survive for long in the relatively harsh conditions they encounter outside their hosts. Thus if these pathogens are to enter new hosts, they must survive in some site from which they can infect new hosts. Sites where pathogens are maintained as a source of infection are called **reservoirs of infection.** In this section we discuss three types of reservoirs: animal reservoirs, human carriers, and nonliving reservoirs.

## Animal Reservoirs

Many pathogens that normally infect either domesticated or sylvatic[7] (wild) animals can also affect humans. The more

[7]From Latin *sylva*, meaning woodland.

similar an animal's physiology is to human physiology, the more likely its pathogens are to affect human health. Diseases that spread naturally from their usual animal hosts to humans are called **zoonoses** (zō-ō-nō′sēz). Over 150 zoonoses have been identified throughout the world. Well-known examples include yellow fever, anthrax, bubonic plague, and rabies.

Humans may acquire zoonoses from animal reservoirs via a number of routes, including various types of direct contact with animals and their wastes, by eating animals, or via blood-sucking arthropods. Human infections with zoonoses are difficult to eradicate because extensive animal reservoirs are often involved. The larger the animal reservoir (that is, the greater the number and types of infected animals) and the greater the contact between humans and the animals, the more difficult and costly it is to control the spread of the disease to humans. This is especially true when the animal reservoir consists of both sylvatic and domesticated animals. In the case of rabies, for example, the disease typically spreads from a sylvatic reservoir (often bats, foxes, and skunks) to domestic pets from which humans may be infected. The wild animals constitute a reservoir for the rabies virus, but transmission to humans can be limited by vaccinating domestic pets.

Table 3 provides a brief view of some common zoonoses. Humans are usually dead-end hosts for zoonotic pathogens—that is, humans do not act as significant reservoirs

## CLINICAL CASE STUDY

### A Deadly Carrier

In 1937, a man employed to lay water pipes in Croyden, England, was found to be the source of a severe epidemic of typhoid fever. The man, an asymptomatic carrier of *Salmonella enterica* serotype Typhi, the bacterium that causes typhoid, habitually urinated at his job site. In the process, he contaminated the town's water supply with bacteria from his bladder. Over 300 cases of typhoid fever developed, and 43 people died before the man was identified as the carrier.

1. How do you think health officials were able to identify the source of this typhoid epidemic?

2. Given that antibiotics were not generally available in 1937, how could health officials end the epidemic short of removing the man from the job site?

for the reinfection of animal hosts—largely because the circumstances under which zoonoses are transmitted favor movement from animals to humans but not in the opposite direction. For example, animals do not often eat humans these days, and animals less frequently have contact with human wastes than humans have contact with animal wastes. Zoonotic diseases transmitted via the bites of bloodsucking arthropods are the most likely type to be transmitted back to animal hosts.

### Human Carriers

Experience tells you that humans with active diseases are important reservoirs of infection for other humans. What may not be so obvious is that people with no obvious symptoms before or after an obvious disease may also be infective in some cases. Further, some infected people remain both asymptomatic and infective for years. This is true of tuberculosis, syphilis, and AIDS, for example. Whereas some of these **carriers** incubate the pathogen in their body and eventually develop the disease, others remain a continued source of infection without ever becoming sick. Presumably many such healthy carriers have defensive systems that protect them from illness. An example of such a carrier is given in **Clinical Case Study: A Deadly Carrier.**

### Nonliving Reservoirs

Soil, water, and food can be **nonliving reservoirs** of infection. Soil, especially if fecally contaminated, can harbor *Clostridium* (klos-trid′ē-ŭm) bacteria, which cause botulism, tetanus, and other diseases. Water can be contaminated with feces and urine containing parasitic worm eggs, pathogenic protozoa, bacteria, and viruses. Meats and vegetables can also harbor pathogens. Milk can contain many pathogens, which is why it is routinely pasteurized in the United States.

# The Movement of Microbes into Hosts: Infection

In this section we examine events that occur when hosts are exposed to microbes from a reservoir, the sites at which microbes can gain entry into hosts, and the ways entering microbes become established in new hosts.

## Exposure to Microbes: Contamination and Infection

### Learning Objective

✓ Describe the relationship between contamination and infection.

In the context of the interaction between microbes and their hosts, **contamination** refers to the mere presence of microbes in or on the body. Some microbial contaminants reach the body in food, drink, or the air, whereas others are introduced via wounds, biting arthropods, or sexual intercourse. Several outcomes of contamination by microbes are possible. Some microbial contaminants remain where they first contacted the body (such as the skin or mucous membranes) without causing harm and subsequently become part of the resident microbiota; other microbial contaminants remain on the body for only a short time, as part of the transient microbiota. Still others overcome the body's external defenses, multiply, and become established in the body; such a successful invasion of the body by a pathogen is called an **infection.** An infection may or may not result in disease; that is, it may not adversely affect the body.

Next we consider in greater detail the various sites through which pathogens gain entry into the body.

## Portals of Entry

### Learning Objective

✓ Identify and describe the portals through which pathogens invade the body.

The sites through which most pathogens enter the body can be likened to the great gates or portals of a castle, because those sites constitute the routes by which microbes gain entry. Pathogens thus enter the body at several sites, called **portals of entry** (Figure 3), which are of three major types: the skin, the mucous membranes, and the placenta. A fourth entry point, the so-called *parenteral* (pă-ren′ter-ăl) *route,* is not a portal but a way of circumventing the usual portals. Next we consider each type in turn.

### Skin

Because the outer layer of skin is composed of relatively thick layers of tightly packed, dead, dry cells (Figure 4), it forms a formidable barrier to most pathogens so long as it remains intact. Still, some pathogens can enter the body through natural

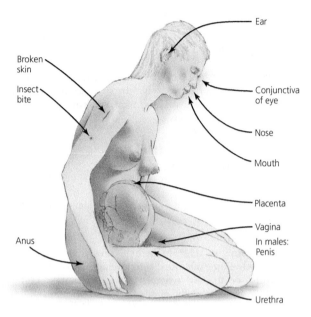

**Figure 3  Routes of entry for invading pathogens.** The portals of entry include the skin, placenta, conjunctiva, and mucous membranes of the respiratory, gastrointestinal, urinary, and reproductive tracts. The parenteral route involves a puncture through the skin.

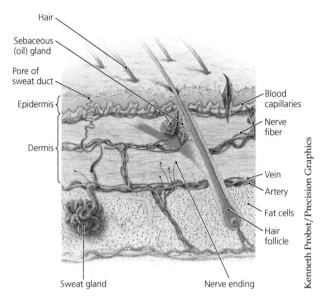

**Figure 4  A cross section of skin.** The layers of cells constitute a barrier to most microbes so long as the skin remains intact. Some pathogens can enter the body through hair follicles, the ducts of sweat glands, and parenterally.

openings in the skin, such as hair follicles and sweat glands. Abrasions, cuts, bites, scrapes, stab wounds, and surgeries open the skin to infection by con taminants. Additionally, the larvae of some parasitic worms are capable of burrowing through the skin to reach underlying tissues, and some fungi can digest the dead outer layers of skin, thereby gaining access to deeper, moister areas within the body.

### Mucous Membranes

The major portals of entry for pathogens are the *mucous membranes,* which line all the body cavities that are open to the outside world. They include the linings of the respiratory, gastrointestinal, urinary, and reproductive tracts, as well as the *conjunctiva* (kon-jŭnk-tī′vă), the thin membrane covering the surface of the eyeball and the underside of each eyelid. Like the skin, mucous membranes are composed of tightly packed cells; but unlike the skin, mucous membranes are relatively thin, moist, and warm, and their cells are living. Therefore, pathogens find mucous membranes more hospitable and easier portals of entry.

The respiratory tract is the most frequently used portal of entry. Pathogens enter the mouth and nose in the air, on dust particles, and in droplets of moisture. For example, the bacteria that cause whooping cough, diphtheria, pneumonia, strep throat, and meningitis, as well as some fungi, viruses, and protozoa, enter through the respiratory tract.

Surprisingly, many viruses enter the respiratory tract via the eyes. They are introduced onto the conjunctiva by contaminated fingers and are washed into the nasal cavity with tears. Cold and influenza viruses typically enter the body in this manner.

Some parasitic protozoa, helminths, bacteria, and viruses infect the body through the gastrointestinal mucous membranes. These parasites are able to survive the acidic pH of the stomach and the digestive juices of the intestinal tract. Noncellular pathogens called *prions* enter the body through oral mucous membranes.

### Placenta

A developing embryo forms an organ, called the *placenta,* through which it obtains nutrients from the mother. The placenta is in such intimate contact with the wall of the mother's uterus that nutrients and wastes diffuse between the blood vessels of the developing child and of the mother, but because the two blood supplies do not actually contact each other, the placenta typically forms an effective barrier to most pathogens. However, in about 2% of pregnancies, pathogens cross the placenta and infect the embryo or fetus, sometimes causing spontaneous abortion, birth defects, or premature birth. Some pathogens that can cross the placenta are listed in Table 4.

### The Parenteral Route

The **parenteral route** is not a portal of entry, but instead a means by which the portals of entry can be circumvented. To enter the body by the parenteral route, pathogens must be deposited directly into tissues beneath the skin or mucous membranes, such as occurs in punctures by a nail, thorn, or hypodermic needle. Some experts include breaks in the skin by cuts, bites, stab wounds, deep abrasions, or surgery in the parenteral route.

# The Role of Adhesion in Infection

## Learning Objectives

✓ List the types of adhesion factors and the roles they play in infection.

✓ Explain how a biofilm may facilitate contamination and infection.

After entering the body, symbionts must adhere to cells if they are to be successful in establishing colonies. The process by which microorganisms attach themselves to cells is called **adhesion** (ad-hē'zhŭn) (or *attachment*). To accomplish adhesion, pathogens use **adhesion factors,** which are either specialized structures or attachment proteins. Examples of such specialized structures are adhesion disks in some protozoa and suckers and hooks in some helminths. In contrast, viruses and many bacteria have surface lipoprotein and glycoprotein molecules called *ligands* that enable them to bind to complementary receptors on host cells (Figure 5). Ligands are also called *adhesins* on bacteria and *attachment proteins* on viruses. Adhesins are found on fimbriae, flagella, and glycocalyces of many pathogenic bacteria. Receptor molecules on host cells are typically glycoproteins containing sugar molecules such as mannose and galactose. If ligands or their receptors can be changed or blocked, infection can often be prevented.

The specific interaction of adhesins and receptors with chemicals on host cells often determines the specificity of pathogens for particular hosts. For example, *Neisseria gonorrhoeae* (nī-se'rē-ă go-nor-rē'ī) has adhesins on its fimbriae that adhere to cells lining the urethra and vagina of humans. Thus, this pathogen cannot affect other hosts.

Some bacteria, including *Bordetella* (bōr-dĕ-tel'ă), the cause of whooping cough, have more than one type of adhesin. Other pathogens, such as *Plasmodium* (plaz-mō'dē-um; the cause of malaria), change their adhesins over time, which helps the pathogen evade the body's immune system and allows the pathogen to attack more than one kind of cell. Bacterial cells and viruses that have lost the ability to make ligands— whether as the result of some genetic change (mutation) or exposure to certain physical or chemical agents (as occurs in the

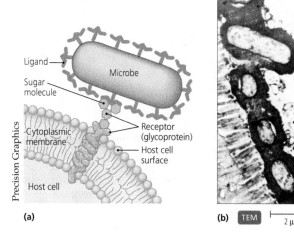

**▲ Figure 5** **The adhesion of pathogens to host cells.**
**(a)** An artist's rendition of the attachment of a microbial ligand to a complementary surface receptor on a host cell. **(b)** A photomicrograph of cells of a pathogenic strain of *E. coli* attached to the mucous membrane of the intestine. Although the thick glycocalyces (black), of the bacteria are visible, the bacteria's ligands are too small to be seen at this magnification.

production of some vaccines)—become harmless, or **avirulent** (ā-vir'ū-lent).

Some bacterial pathogens do not attach to host cells directly, but instead interact with each other to form a sticky web of bacteria and polysaccharides called a **biofilm,** which adheres to a surface within a host. A prominent example of a biofilm is dental plaque (Figure 6), which contains the bacteria that cause dental caries (tooth decay).

## CRITICAL **THINKING**

If a mutation occurred in *Escherichia coli* that deleted the gene for an adhesin, what effect might it have on the ability of *E. coli* to cause urinary tract infections?

## TABLE 4 — Some Pathogens That Cross the Placenta

| | Pathogen | Condition in the Adult | Effect on Embryo or Fetus |
|---|---|---|---|
| **Protozoan** | *Toxoplasma gondii* | Toxoplasmosis | Abortion, epilepsy, encephalitis, microcephaly, mental retardation, blindness, anemia, jaundice, rash, pneumonia, diarrhea, hypothermia, deafness |
| **Bacteria** | *Treponema pallidum* | Syphilis | Abortion, multiorgan birth defects, syphilis |
| | *Listeria monocytogenes* | Listeriosis | Granulomatosis infantiseptica (nodular inflammatory lesions and infant blood poisoning), death |
| **DNA viruses** | *Cytomegalovirus* | Usually asymptomatic | Deafness, microcephaly, mental retardation |
| | *Parvovirus* B19 | Erythema infectiosum | Abortion |
| **RNA viruses** | *Lentivirus* (HIV) | AIDS | Immunosuppression (AIDS) |
| | *Rubivirus* | German measles | Severe birth defects or death |

**Figure 6 Dental plaque.** This biofilm consists of bacteria that adhere to one another and to teeth by means of sticky capsules, slime layers, and fimbriae.

| TABLE **5** | Typical Manifestations of Disease | |
|---|---|
| **Symptoms (sensed by the patient)** | **Signs (detected or measured by an observer)** |
| Pain, nausea, headache, chills, sore throat, fatigue or lethargy (sluggishness, tiredness), malaise (discomfort), itching, abdominal cramps | Swelling, rash or redness, vomiting, diarrhea, fever, pus formation, anemia, leukocytosis/leukopenia (increase/decrease in the number of circulating white blood cells), bubo (swollen lymph node), tachycardia/bradycardia (increase/decrease in heart rate) |

# The Nature of Infectious Disease

## Learning Objective

✓ Compare and contrast the terms *infection, disease, morbidity, pathogenicity,* and *virulence.*

Most infections succumb to the body's defenses, but some infectious agents not only evade the defenses and multiply, but also affect body function. By definition, all parasites injure their hosts. When the injury is significant enough to interfere with the normal functioning of the body, the result is termed **disease.** Thus, disease, also known as **morbidity,** is any change from a state of health.

Infection and disease are not the same thing. Infection is the invasion of a pathogen; disease results only if the pathogen multiplies sufficiently to adversely affect the body. Some illustrations will help to clarify this point. While caring for a patient, a nurse may become contaminated with the bacterium *Staphylococcus aureus* (o'rē-ŭs). If the pathogen is able to gain access to his body, perhaps through a break in his skin, he will become infected. Then, if the multiplication of *Staphylococcus* results in the production of a boil, the nurse will have a disease. Another example: A drug addict who shares needles may become contaminated and subsequently infected with HIV without experiencing visible change in body function for years. Such a person is infected but not yet diseased.

## Manifestations of Disease: Symptoms, Signs, and Syndromes

### Learning Objective

✓ Contrast symptoms, signs, and syndromes.

Diseases may become manifest in different ways. **Symptoms** are *subjective* characteristics of a disease that can be felt by the patient alone, whereas **signs** are *objective* manifestations of disease that can be observed or measured by others. Symptoms include pain, headache, dizziness, and fatigue; signs include swelling, rash, redness, and fever. Sometimes pairs of symptoms and signs reflect the same underlying cause: Nausea is a symptom, and vomiting a sign; chills are a symptom, whereas shivering is a sign. Note, however, that even though signs and symptoms may have the same underlying cause, they need not occur together. Thus, for example, a viral infection of the brain may result in both a headache (a symptom) and the presence of viruses in the cerebrospinal fluid (a sign), but viruses in the cerebrospinal fluid are not invariably accompanied by headache. Symptoms and signs are used in conjunction with laboratory tests to make diagnoses. Some typical symptoms and signs are listed in Table 5.

A **syndrome** is a group of symptoms and signs that collectively characterizes a particular disease or abnormal condition. For example, acquired immunodeficiency syndrome (AIDS) is characterized by malaise, loss of certain white blood cells, diarrhea, weight loss, pneumonia, toxoplasmosis, and tuberculosis.

Some infections go unnoticed because they have no symptoms. Such cases are **asymptomatic** or **subclinical** infections. Note that even though asymptomatic infections by definition lack symptoms, in some cases certain signs may still be detected if the proper tests are performed. For example, leukocytosis (an excess of white blood cells) may be detected in a blood sample from an individual who feels completely healthy.

Table 6 lists some prefixes and suffixes used to describe various aspects of diseases and syndromes.

## Causation of Disease: Etiology

### Learning Objectives

✓ Define *etiology.*

✓ List Koch's postulates, explain their function, and describe their limitations.

Even though our focus in this chapter is infectious disease, it's obvious that not all diseases result from infections. Some diseases are *hereditary,* which means they are genetically transmitted from

**6**

## Terminology of Disease

| Prefix/Suffix | Meaning | Example |
|---|---|---|
| carcino- | cancer | carcinogenic: giving rise to cancer |
| col-, colo- | colon | colitis: inflammation of the colon |
| dermato- | skin | dermatitis: inflammation of the skin |
| -emia | pertaining to the blood | viremia: viruses in the blood |
| endo- | inside | endocarditis: inflammation of lining of heart |
| -gen, gen- | give rise to | pathogen: giving rise to disease |
| hepat- | liver | hepatitis: inflammation of the liver |
| idio- | unknown | idiopathic: pertaining to a disease of unknown cause |
| -itis | inflammation of a structure | meningitis: inflammation of the meninges (covering of the brain); endocarditis |
| -oma | tumor or swelling | papilloma: wart |
| -osis | condition of | toxoplasmosis: being infected with *Toxoplasma* |
| -patho, patho- | abnormal | pathology: study of disease |
| septi- | literally, *rotting*; refers to presence of pathogens | septicemia: pathogens in the blood |
| terato- | defects | teratogenic: causing birth defects |
| tox- | poison | toxin: harmful compound |

parents to offspring. Other diseases, called *congenital diseases,* are diseases that are present at birth, regardless of the cause (whether hereditary, environmental, or infectious). Still other diseases are classified as *degenerative, nutritional, endocrine, mental, immunological,* or *neoplastic.*[8] The various categories of diseases are described in Table 7. Note that some diseases can fall into more than one category. For example, liver cancer, which is usually associated with infection by hepatitis B and D viruses, can be classified as both neoplastic and infectious.

The study of the cause of a disease is called **etiology** (ē-tē-ol'ō-jē). Because our focus here and in subsequent chapters is on infectious diseases, we next examine how microbiologists investigate the causation of infectious diseases, beginning with a reexamination of the work of Robert Koch.

### Using Koch's Postulates

In our modern world, we take for granted the idea that specific microbes cause specific diseases, but this has not always been the case. In the past, disease was thought to result from a variety of causes, including bad air, imbalances in body fluids, or astrological forces. In the 19th century, Louis Pasteur, Robert Koch, and other microbiologists proposed the **germ theory of disease,** which states that disease is caused by infections of pathogenic microorganisms (at the time, called *germs*).

But which pathogen causes a specific disease? How can we distinguish between the pathogen, which causes a disease, and all the other biological agents (fungi, bacteria, protozoa, and

[8]Neoplasms are tumors, which may either remain in one place (benign tumors) or spread (cancers).

viruses) that are part of the normal microbiota and are in effect "innocent bystanders"?

Koch developed a series of essential conditions, or *postulates,* that scientists must demonstrate or satisfy to prove that a particular microbe is pathogenic and causes a particular disease. Using his postulates, Koch proved that *Bacillus anthracis* (ba-sil'ŭs an-thrā'sis) causes anthrax and that *Mycobacterium tuberculosis* (mī'kō-bak-tēr'ē-ŭm too-ber-kyū-lō'sis) causes tuberculosis.

To prove that a given infectious agent causes a given disease, a scientist must satisfy all of **Koch's postulates** (Figure 7):

1 The suspected agent (bacterium, virus, etc.) must be present in every case of the disease.

2 That agent must be isolated and grown in pure culture.

3 The cultured agent must cause the disease when it is inoculated into a healthy, susceptible experimental host.

4 The same agent must be reisolated from the diseased experimental host.

It is critical that all the postulates be satisfied in order. The mere presence of an agent does not prove that it causes a disease. Although Koch's postulates have been used to prove the cause of many infectious diseases in humans, animals, and plants, inadequate attention to the postulates has resulted in incorrect conclusions concerning some disease causation. For instance, in the early 1900s *Haemophilus influenzae* (hē-mof'i-lŭs in-flu-en'zī) was found in the respiratory systems of flu victims and identified as the causative agent of influenza based on its presence. Later, flu victims that lacked *H. influenzae* in their lungs were discovered. This discovery violated the first postulate, so *H. influenzae* cannot be the cause of flu. Today we know that an RNA virus causes flu, and that *H. influenzae* was part of

**1** The suspected agent must be present in every case of the disease.

Diseased subjects

Agent not typically found in healthy subjects.

Healthy subject

Petri plate

Bacterial colonies

**2** The agent must be isolated and grown in pure culture.

Streaked plates

Injection

**3** The cultured agent must cause the disease when it is inoculated into a healthy, susceptible experimental host (animal or plant).

**4** The same agent must be reisolated from the diseased experimental host.

◀ **Figure 7 Koch's postulates.**

the normal microbiota of those early flu patients. (Later studies, correctly using Koch's postulates, showed that *H. influenzae* can cause an often-fatal meningitis in children.)

### Exceptions to Koch's Postulates

Clearly, Koch's postulates are a cornerstone of the etiology of infectious diseases, but using them is not always feasible, for the following reasons:

- Some pathogens cannot be cultured in the laboratory. For example, pathogenic strains of *Mycobacterium leprae* (lep'rī), which causes leprosy, have never been grown on laboratory media.

- Some diseases are caused by a combination of pathogens, or by a combination of a pathogen and physical, environmental, or genetic cofactors. In such cases, the pathogen alone is avirulent, but when accompanied by another pathogen or the appropriate cofactor, disease results. For example, liver cancer can result when liver cells are infected by both the hepatitis B and hepatitis D viruses, but seldom when only one of the viruses infects the cells.

- Ethical considerations prevent applying Koch's postulates to diseases and pathogens that occur in humans only. In such cases the third postulate, which involves inoculation of a healthy susceptible host, cannot be satisfied within ethical boundaries. For this reason, scientists have never

## 7

## Categories of Diseases[a]

|  | Description | Examples |
|---|---|---|
| Hereditary | Caused by errors in the genetic code received from parents | Sickle-cell anemia, diabetes mellitus, Down syndrome |
| Congenital | Anatomical and physiological (structural and functional) defects present at birth; caused by drugs (legal and illegal), X-ray exposure, or infections | Fetal alcohol syndrome, deafness from rubella infection |
| Degenerative | Result from aging | Renal failure, age-related farsightedness |
| Nutritional | Result from lack of some essential nutrients in diet | Kwashiorkor, rickets |
| Endocrine (hormonal) | Due to excesses or deficiencies of hormones | Dwarfism |
| Mental | Emotional or psychosomatic | Skin rash, gastrointestinal distress |
| Immunological | Hyperactive or hypoactive immunity | Allergies, autoimmune diseases, agammaglobulinemia |
| Neoplastic (tumor) | Abnormal cell growth | Benign tumors, cancers |
| Infectious | Caused by an infectious agent | Colds, influenza, herpes infections |
| Iatrogenic[b] | Caused by medical treatment or procedures; are a subgroup of hospital-acquired diseases | Surgical error, yeast vaginitis resulting from antimicrobial therapy |
| Idiopathic[c] | Unknown cause | Alzheimer's disease, multiple sclerosis |
| Nosocomial[d] | Disease acquired in health care setting | *Pseudomonas* infection in burn patient |

[a]Some diseases may fall in more than one category.
[b]From Greek *iatros*, meaning physician.
[c]From Greek *idiotes*, meaning ignorant person, and *pathos*, meaning disease.
[d]From Greek *nosokomeion*, meaning hospital.

attempted to apply Koch's postulates to prove that HIV causes AIDS; however, observations of fetuses that were naturally exposed to HIV by their infected mothers, as well as accidentally infected health care and laboratory workers, have in effect satisfied the third postulate.

Additionally, some circumstances may make satisfying Koch's postulates difficult:

- It is not possible to establish a single cause for such infectious diseases as pneumonia, meningitis, and hepatitis, because the names of these diseases refer to conditions that can be caused by more than one pathogen. For these diseases, laboratory technicians must identify the etiologic agent involved in any given case.

- Some pathogens have been ignored. For example, gastric ulcers were long thought to be caused by excessive production of stomach acid in response to stress, but the majority of such ulcers are now known to be caused by a long-overlooked bacterium, *Helicobacter pylori* (hel'ĭ-kō-bak'ter pī'lō-rē).

If Koch's postulates cannot be applied to a disease condition for whatever reason, how can we positively know the causative agent of a disease? *Epidemiological* studies, discussed later in this chapter, can give statistical support to causation theories, but not absolute proof. For example, some researchers have proposed that the bacterium *Chlamydophila pneumoniae* (kla-mē-dof'ĭ-lă nū-mō'nē-ī) causes many cases of arteriosclerosis on the basis of the bacterium's presence in patients with the disease. Debate among scientists about such cases fosters a continued drive for knowledge and discovery. For example, we are

still searching for the causes of Parkinson's disease, multiple sclerosis, and Alzheimer's disease.

## Virulence Factors of Infectious Agents

### Learning Objective

✓ Explain how microbial extracellular enzymes, toxins, adhesion factors, and antiphagocytic factors affect virulence.

Microbiologists characterize the disease-related capabilities of microbes by using two related terms. The ability of a microorganism to cause disease is termed **pathogenicity** (path'ō-jĕ-nis'i-tē), and the *degree* of pathogenicity is termed **virulence.** In other words, virulence is the relative ability of a pathogen to infect a host and cause disease. Neither term addresses the severity of a disease; the pathogen causing rabbit fever is highly virulent but the disease is relatively mild. Organisms can be placed along a virulence continuum (Figure 8); highly virulent organisms almost always cause disease, while less virulent organisms (including opportunistic pathogens) cause disease only in weakened hosts or when present in overwhelming numbers.

Pathogens have a variety of traits that interact with a host and enable the pathogen to enter a host, adhere to host cells, gain access to nutrients, and escape detection or removal by the immune system. These traits are collectively called **virulence factors.** Virulent pathogens have one or more virulence factors that nonvirulent microbes lack. We discussed two virulence factors—adhesion factors and biofilm formation—previously;

▲ **Figure 8 Relative virulence of some microbial pathogens.**
Virulence involves ease of infection and the ability of a pathogen to cause disease; the term does not indicate the seriousness of a disease.

now we examine three other virulence factors: extracellular enzymes, toxins, and antiphagocytic factors. Other virulence factors can be examined online at www.masteringmicrobiology.com. **ANIMATIONS:** *Virulence Factors: Inactivating Host Defenses*

## Extracellular Enzymes

Many pathogens secrete enzymes that enable them to dissolve structural chemicals in the body and thereby maintain an infection, invade further, and avoid body defenses. Figure 9a illustrates the action of some extracellular enzymes of bacteria:

- Hyaluronidase and collagenase degrade specific molecules to enable bacteria to invade deeper tissues. Hyaluronidase digests hyaluronic acid, the "glue" that holds animal cells together, and collagenase breaks down collagen, the body's chief structural protein.

- Coagulase causes blood proteins to clot, providing a "hiding place" for bacteria within a clot.

- Kinases such as staphylokinase and streptokinase digest blood clots, allowing subsequent invasion of damaged tissues.

Many bacteria with these enzymes are virulent; mutant strains of the same species that have defective genes for these extracellular enzymes are usually avirulent.

Pathogenic eukaryotes also secrete enzymes that contribute to virulence. For example, fungi that cause "ringworm"

produce *keratinase,* which enzymatically digests keratin—the main component of skin, hair, and nails. *Entamoeba histolytica* (ent-ă-mē'bă his-tō-li'ti-kă) secretes *mucinase* to digest the mucus lining the intestinal tract, allowing the amoeba entry to the underlying cells where it causes amebic dysentery. **ANIMATIONS:** *Virulence Factors: Penetrating Host Tissues*

## Toxins

**Toxins** are chemicals that either harm tissues or trigger host immune responses that cause damage. The distinction between extracellular enzymes and toxins is not always clear, because many enzymes are toxic, and many toxins have enzymatic action. In a condition called **toxemia** (tok-sē'mē-ā), toxins enter the bloodstream and are carried to other parts of the body, including sites that may be far removed from the site of infection. There are two types of toxin: exotoxins and endotoxin.

**Exotoxins** Many microorganisms secrete **exotoxins** that are central to their pathogenicity in that they destroy host cells or interfere with host metabolism. Exotoxins are of three principal types:

- *Cytotoxins,* which kill host cells in general or affect their function (Figure 9b)

- *Neurotoxins,* which specifically interfere with nerve cell function

- *Enterotoxins,* which affect cells lining the gastrointestinal tract

Examples of pathogenic bacteria that secrete exotoxins are the clostridia that cause gangrene, botulism, and tetanus; pathogenic strains of *S. aureus* that cause food poisoning and other ailments; and diarrhea-causing *E. coli, Salmonella enterica* (sal'mŏ-nel'ă en-ter'i-kă), and *Shigella* (shē-gel'lă) species. Some fungi and marine dinoflagellates (protozoa) also secrete exotoxins. Specific exotoxins are discussed in the chapters that examine specific diseases. **ANIMATIONS:** *Virulence Factors: Exotoxins*

The body protects itself with **antitoxins,** which are protective molecules called *antibodies* that bind to specific toxins and neutralize them. Health care workers stimulate the production of antitoxins by administering immunizations composed of *toxoids,* which are toxins that have been treated with heat, formaldehyde, chlorine, or other chemicals to make them nontoxic but still capable of stimulating the production of antibodies.

**Endotoxin** Gram-negative bacteria have an outer (cell wall) membrane composed of lipopoly saccharide, phospholipids, and proteins. **Endotoxin,** also called **lipid A,** is the lipid portion of the membrane's lipopolysaccharide.

Endotoxin can be released when Gram-negative bacteria divide, die naturally, or are digested by phagocytic cells such as macrophages (see Figure 9b). Many types of lipid A stimulate the body to release chemicals that cause fever, inflammation, diarrhea, hemorrhaging, shock, and blood coagulation.

**Hyaluronidase and collagenase**

Bacterium
Hyaluronidase
Epithelial cells
Collagen layer
Collagenase

Invasive bacteria reach epithelial surface.

Bacteria produce hyaluronidase and collagenase.

Bacteria invade deeper tissues.

**(a) Extracellular enzymes**

**Coagulase and kinase**

Bacterium
Coagulase
Clotting protein
Clot
Kinase

Bacteria produce coagulase.

Clot forms.

Bacteria later produce kinase, dissolving clot and releasing bacteria.

**Exotoxin**

Bacterium
Exotoxin

Bacteria secrete exotoxins, in this case a cytotoxin.

Cytotoxin kills host's cells.

**(b) Toxins**

**Endotoxin**

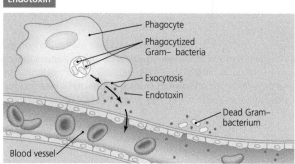

Phagocyte
Phagocytized Gram– bacteria
Exocytosis
Endotoxin
Dead Gram– bacterium
Blood vessel

Dead Gram-negative bacteria release endotoxin (lipid A) which induces effects such as fever, inflammation, diarrhea, shock, and blood coagulation.

**Phagocytosis blocked by capsule**

Capsule around bacterium
Phagocyte

**(c) Antiphagocytic factors**

**Incomplete phagocytosis**

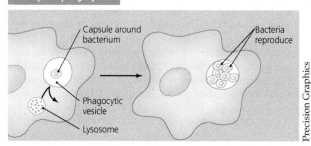

Capsule around bacterium
Bacteria reproduce
Phagocytic vesicle
Lysosome

Precision Graphics

▲ **Figure 9** **Some virulence factors. (a)** Extracellular enzymes. Hyaluronidase and collagenase digest structural materials in the body. Coagulase in effect "camouflages" bacteria inside a blood clot, whereas kinases digest clots to release bacteria. **(b)** Toxins. Exotoxins (including cytotoxin, shown here) are released from living pathogens and harm neighboring cells. Endotoxin is released from many dead Gram-negative bacteria and can trigger widespread disruption of normal body functions. **(c)** Antiphagocytic factors. Capsules, one antiphagocytic factor, can prevent phagocytosis or stop digestion by a phagocyte. *How can bacteria prevent a phagocytic cell from digesting them once they have been engulfed by pseudopodia?*

**Figure 9** *Some bacteria secrete a chemical that prevents the fusion of lysosomes with the phagosome containing the bacteria.*

## 8

## A Comparison of Bacterial Exotoxins and Endotoxin

| | Exotoxins | Endotoxin |
|---|---|---|
| Source | Mainly Gram-positive and Gram-negative bacteria | Gram-negative bacteria |
| Relation to bacteria | Metabolic product secreted from living cell | Portion of outer (cell wall) membrane released upon cell death |
| Chemical nature | Protein or short peptide | Lipid portion of lipopolysaccharide (lipid A) of outer (cell wall) membrane |
| Toxicity | High | Low, but may be fatal in high doses |
| Heat stability | Typically unstable at temperatures above 60°C | Stable for up to 1 hour at autoclave temperature (121°C) |
| Effect on host | Variable depending on source; may be cytotoxin, neurotoxin, enterotoxin | Fever, lethargy, malaise, shock, blood coagulation |
| Fever producing? | No | Yes |
| Antigenicity[a] | Strong: stimulates antitoxin (antibody) production | Weak |
| Toxoid formation for immunization? | By treatment with heat or fomaldehyde | Not feasible |
| Representative diseases | Botulism, tetanus, gas gangrene, diphtheria, cholera, plague, staphylococcal food poisoning | Typhoid fever, tularemia, endotoxic shock, urinary tract infections, meningococcal meningitis |

[a]Refers to the ability of a chemical to trigger a specific immune response, particularly the formation of antibodies.

Although infections by bacteria that produce exotoxins are generally more serious than infections with other bacteria, most Gram-negative pathogens can be potentially life threatening because the release of endotoxin from dead bacteria can produce serious, systemic effects in the host. **ANIMATIONS:** *Virulence Factors: Endotoxins*

Table 8 summarizes differences between exotoxins and endotoxins.

### Antiphagocytic Factors

Typically, the longer a pathogen remains in a host, the greater the damage and the more severe the disease. To limit the extent and duration of infections, the body's phagocytic cells, such as the white blood cells called macrophages, engulf and remove invading pathogens. Here we consider some virulence factors related to the evasion of phagocytosis, beginning with bacterial capsules. **ANIMATIONS:** *Phagocytosis: Microbes That Evade It*

**Capsules** The capsules of many pathogenic bacteria are effective virulence factors because many capsules are composed of chemicals normally found in the body (including polysaccharides); as a result, they do not stimulate a host's immune response. For example, hyaluronic acid capsules in effect deceive phagocytic cells into treating them and the enclosed bacteria as if they were a normal part of the body. Additionally, capsules are often slippery, making it difficult for phagocytes to surround and phagocytize them—their pseudopodia cannot grip the capsule, much as wet hands have difficulty holding a wet bar of soap (Figure 9c).

**Antiphagocytic Chemicals** Some bacteria, including the cause of gonorrhea, produce chemicals that prevent the fusion of lysosomes with phagocytic vesicles, which allows the bacteria to survive inside of phagocytes (see Figure 9c). *Streptococcus*

*pyogenes* (strep-tō-kok′ŭs pī-oj′en-ēz) produces a protein on its cell wall and fimbriae, called *M protein*, that resists phagocytosis and thus increases virulence. Other bacteria produce *leukocidins*, which are chemicals capable of destroying phagocytic white blood cells outright. **ANIMATIONS:** *Virulence Factors: Hiding from Host Defenses*

## The Stages of Infectious Diseases

### Learning Objective

✓  List and describe the five typical stages of infectious diseases.

Following exposure and infection, a sequence of events called the **disease process** can occur. Many infectious diseases have five stages following infection: an incubation period, a prodromal period, illness, decline, and convalescence (Figure 10).

### Incubation Period

The **incubation period** is the time between infection and occurrence of the first symptoms or signs of disease. The length of the incubation period depends on the virulence of the infective agent, the infective dose (initial number of pathogens), the state and health of the patient's immune system, the nature of the pathogen and its reproduction time, and the site of infection. Some diseases have typical incubation periods, whereas for others the incubation period varies considerably. Table 9 lists incubation periods for selected diseases.

### Prodromal Period

The **prodromal**[9] (prō-drō′măl) period is a short time of generalized, mild symptoms (such as malaise and muscle aches) that

---

[9]From Greek *prodromos*, meaning forerunner.

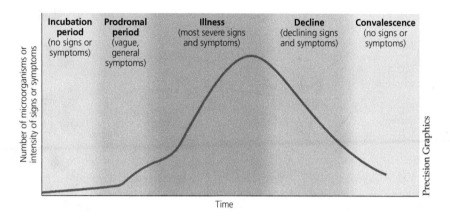

► **Figure 10**
**The stages of infectious diseases.**
Not every stage occurs in every disease.

precedes illness. Not all infectious diseases have a prodromal stage.

### Illness

**Illness** is the most severe stage of an infectious disease. Signs and symptoms are most evident during this time. Typically the patient's immune system has not yet fully responded to the pathogens, and their presence is harming the body. This stage is usually when a physician first sees the patient.

### Decline

During the period of **decline,** the body gradually returns to normal as the patient's immune response and/or medical treatment vanquish the pathogens. Fever and other signs and symptoms subside. Normally the immune response and its products (such as antibodies in the blood) peak during this stage. If the patient doesn't recover, then the disease is fatal.

### Convalescence

During **convalescence** (kon-vă-les′ens), the patient recovers from the illness; tissues are repaired and returned to normal. The length of a convalescent period depends on the amount of damage, the nature of the pathogen, the site of infection, and the overall health of the patient. Thus, whereas recovery from staphylococcal food poisoning may take less than a day, recovery from Lyme disease may take years.

A patient is likely to be infectious during every stage of disease. Even though most of us realize we are infective during the symptomatic periods, many people are unaware that infections can be spread during incubation and convalescence as well. For example, a patient who no longer has any obvious herpes sores is always capable of transmitting herpesviruses. Good aseptic technique can limit the spread of many pathogens from recovering patients.

## The Movement of Pathogens Out of Hosts: Portals of Exit

Just as infections occur through portals of entry, so pathogens must leave infected patients through **portals of exit** in order to infect others (Figure 11). Many portals of exit are essentially identical to portals of entry. However, pathogens often exit hosts in materials that the body secretes or excretes. Thus, pathogens may leave hosts in secretions (earwax, tears, nasal secretions, saliva, sputum, and respiratory droplets), in blood (via arthropod bites, hypodermic needles, or wounds), in vaginal secretions or semen, in milk produced by the mammary glands, and in excreted bodily wastes (feces and urine). As we will see, health care personnel must consider the portals of entry and exit in their efforts to understand and control the spread of diseases within populations.

**TABLE 9**

**Incubation Periods of Selected Infectious Diseases**

| Disease | Incubation Period |
|---|---|
| *Staphylococcus* foodborne infection | <1 day |
| Influenza | About 1 day |
| Cholera | 2 to 3 days |
| Genital herpes | About 5 days |
| Tetanus | 5 to 15 days |
| Syphilis | 10 to 21 days |
| Hepatitis B | 70 to 100 days |
| AIDS | 1 to >8 years |
| Leprosy | 10 to >30 years |

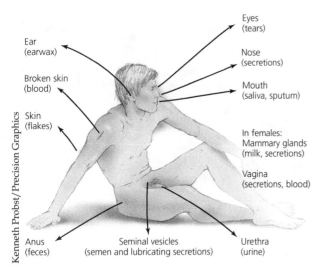

Kenneth Probst/Precision Graphics

▲ **Figure 11 Portals of exit.** Many portals of exit are the same sites as portals of entry. Pathogens often leave the body via bodily secretions and excretions produced at those sites.

Andrew Davidhazy, Photo Arts and Sciences at Rochester Institute of Technology

▲ **Figure 12 Droplet transmission.** In this case, droplets are propelled, primarily from the mouth, during a sneeze. By convention, such transmission is considered contact transmission only if droplets transmit pathogens to a new host within 1 meter of their source. *By what portal of entry does airborne transmission most likely occur?*

**Figure 12** *The most likely portal of entry of airborne pathogens is the respiratory mucous membrane.*

# Modes of Infectious Disease Transmission

## Learning Objectives

✓ Contrast contact, vehicle, and vector transmission of pathogens.

✓ Contrast *droplet transmission* and *airborne transmission.*

✓ Contrast *mechanical* and *biological* vectors.

By definition, an infectious disease agent must be transmitted from either a reservoir or a portal of exit to another host's portal of entry. Transmission can occur by numerous modes that are somewhat arbitrarily categorized into three groups: contact transmission, vehicle transmission, and vector transmission.
**ANIMATIONS:** *Epidemiology: Transmission of Disease*

## Contact Transmission

Contact transmission is the spread of pathogens from one host to another by direct contact, indirect contact, or respiratory droplets.

**Direct contact transmission,** including *person-to-person spread,* typically involves body contact between hosts. Touching, kissing, and sexual intercourse are involved in the transmission of such diseases as warts, herpes, and gonorrhea. Touching, biting, or scratching can transmit zoonoses such as rabies, ringworm, and tularemia from an animal reservoir to a human. The transfer of pathogens from an infected mother to a developing baby across the placenta is another form of direct contact transmission. Direct transmission within a single individual can also occur if the person transfers pathogens from a portal of exit directly to a portal of entry—as occurs, for example, when people with poor personal hygiene unthinkingly place fingers contaminated with fecal pathogens into their mouths.

**Indirect contact transmission** occurs when pathogens are spread from one host to another by **fomites** (fōm′i-tēz; singular: *fomes,* fō′mēz), which are inanimate objects that are inadvertently used to transfer pathogens to new hosts. Fomites include needles, toothbrushes, paper tissues, toys, money, diapers, drinking glasses, bedsheets, medical equipment, and other objects that can harbor or transmit pathogens. Contaminated needles are a major source of infection of the hepatitis B and AIDS viruses.

**Droplet transmission** is a third type of contact transmission. Pathogens can be transmitted within *droplet nuclei* (droplets of mucus) that exit the body during exhaling, coughing, and sneezing **(Figure 12)**. Pathogens such as cold and flu viruses may be spread in this manner. If pathogens travel more than 1 meter in respiratory droplets, the mode is considered to be *airborne transmission* (discussed shortly), rather than contact transmission.

## Vehicle Transmission

**Vehicle transmission** is the spread of pathogens via air, drinking water, and food, as well as bodily fluids being handled outside the body.

**Airborne transmission** involves the spread of pathogens farther than 1 meter to the respiratory mucous membranes of a new host via an **aerosol** (ār′ō-sol)—a cloud of small droplets and solid particles suspended in the air. Aerosols may contain pathogens either on dust or inside droplets. (Recall that transmission via droplet nuclei that travel less than 1 meter is considered to be a form of direct contact transmission.) Aerosols can come from

## TB in the Nursery

In the early fall, a neonatal nurse from a large metropolitan hospital became ill with a cough and fever. Her physician believed she had seasonal allergies and so treated her with cough suppressant, antihistamines, and aerosol steroids. She returned to work in the hospital's nursery.

Three weeks later her condition worsened; her symptoms were complicated by shortness of breath and bloody sputum. Upon further questioning, her physician noted that she was working in the United States on a work visa and was a native of the Philippines. She had a positive skin test for tuberculosis (TB) but had always believed this was her body's natural reaction to the TB vaccine she had received as a child. Her chest X rays in the past had always been clear of infection.

This time, however, her sputum smear tested positive for acid-fast bacilli. She was diagnosed with active tuberculosis and began a standard drug regimen for TB. She was restricted from work and placed in respiratory isolation for six weeks, but during the three weeks that she had continued to work in the nursery, she exposed over 900 obstetric patients including 620 newborns to TB, an airborne infectious disease.

1. How can private physicians quickly assess their clients for the possibility of an infectious disease?

2. What policies should be in place at hospitals to protect patients from exposure to infectious staff members?

3. How could doctors' offices improve public knowledge and protect the public from infectious diseases like tuberculosis?

Reference: Adapted from *MMWR* 54:1280–1283. 2005.

▲ **Figure 13 Poorly refrigerated foods can harbor pathogens and transmit diseases.**

sneezing and coughing, or they can be generated by such things as air conditioning systems, sweeping, mopping, changing clothes or bed linens, or even from flaming inoculating loops in microbiology labs. Dust particles can carry *Staphylococcus, Streptococcus,* and *Hantavirus* (han'tă-vī-rŭs), whereas measles virus and tuberculosis bacilli can be transmitted in dried, airborne droplets. Fungal spores of *Histoplasma* (his-tō-plaz'mă) and *Coccidioides* (kok-sid-ē-oy'dēz) are typically inhaled.

**Waterborne transmission** is important in the spread of many gastrointestinal diseases, including giardiasis, amebic dysentery, and cholera. Note that water can act as a reservoir as well as a vehicle of infection. **Fecal-oral infection** is a major source of disease in the world. Some waterborne pathogens, such as *Schistosoma* (skis-tō-sō'mă) worms and enteroviruses, are shed in the feces, enter through the gastrointestinal mucous membrane or skin, and subsequently can cause disease elsewhere in the body.

**Foodborne transmission** involves pathogens in and on foods that are inadequately processed, undercooked, or poorly

refrigerated (Figure 13). Foods may be contaminated with normal microbiota (e.g., *E. coli* and *S. aureus*), with zoonotic pathogens such as *Mycobacterium bovis* (bō'vis) and *Toxoplasma* (tok-sō-plaz'mă), and with parasitic worms that alternate between human and animal hosts. Contamination of food with feces and pathogens such as hepatitis A virus is another kind of fecal-oral transmission. Because milk is particularly rich in nutrients that microorganisms use (protein, lipids, vitamins, and sugars), it would be associated with the transmission of many diseases from infected animals and milk handlers if it were not properly pasteurized.

Because blood, urine, saliva, and other bodily fluids can contain pathogens, everyone—but especially health care workers—must take precautions when handling these fluids in order to prevent **bodily fluid transmission.** Special care must be taken to prevent such fluids—all of which should be considered potentially contaminated with pathogens—from contacting the conjunctiva or any breaks in the skin or mucous membranes. Examples of diseases that can be transmitted via bodily fluids are AIDS, hepatitis, and herpes, which as we have seen can also be transmitted via direct contact. The **Clinical Case Study** examines the transmission of West Nile virus via blood and infected organs.

## Vector Transmission

**Vectors** are animals that transmit diseases from one host to another. Vectors can be either biological or mechanical.

135

## Unusual Transmission of West Nile Virus

Ben Edwards/Stone/Getty Images

Although West Nile virus is primarily transmitted through mosquito bites, it can also be transmitted in at least two other ways. On August 1, 2002, four organs harvested from a single donor were transplanted into four patients. Within 17 days of transplantation, all four recipients became sick with West Nile virus–associated illnesses. Three of the patients developed meningoencephalitis, an inflammation of the brain and of the membranes surrounding the brain and spinal cord; the fourth patient developed West Nile virus fever. The organ donor's plasma tested positive for West Nile virus. It was determined that the donor herself was infected by a transfusion of WNV-positive blood a day before the organs were harvested.

In September 2005, another organ donor was likely infected by a mosquito rather than through blood transfusion. Lung and liver transplant recipients had severe West Nile virus encephalitis and still remain comatose. One kidney transplant recipient had a positive plasma test for West Nile virus but remains without symptoms. The other kidney recipient had no evidence of West Nile virus infection.

1. In addition to patients who had received organs from the infected donor, what other patients might be at risk of West Nile virus infection?

2. As a scientist, what questions would you seek to answer about the infected donor?

3. What precautions would you advise instituting in order to prevent transmission of West Nile virus infection via blood transfusion and organ transplantation?

References: Adapted from: *MMWR* 51:833–836. 2002. and *MMWR* 54:1021–1023. 2005.

**Biological vectors** not only transmit pathogens, they also serve as hosts for the multiplication of a pathogen during some stage of the pathogen's life cycle. The biological vectors of diseases affecting humans are typically biting arthropods, including mosquitoes, ticks, lice, fleas, bloodsucking flies, bloodsucking bugs, and mites. After pathogens replicate within a biological vector, often in its gut or salivary gland, the pathogens enter a new host through a bite. The bite site becomes contaminated with the vector's feces, or the vector's bite directly introduces pathogens into the new host.

**Mechanical vectors** are not required as hosts by the pathogens they transmit; such vectors only passively carry pathogens to new hosts on their feet or other body parts. Mechanical vectors such as houseflies and cockroaches may introduce pathogens such as *Salmonella* and *Shigella* into drinking water and food or onto the skin.

Table 10 lists some arthropod vectors and the diseases they transmit. Table 11 summarizes the modes of disease transmission.

# Classification of Infectious Diseases

### Learning Objectives

✓ Describe the basis for each of the various classification schemes of infectious diseases.

✓ Distinguish among acute, subacute, chronic, and latent diseases.

✓ Distinguish among communicable, contagious, and noncommunicable infectious diseases.

Infectious diseases can be classified in a number of ways. No one way is "*the* correct way"; each has its own advantages. One scheme groups diseases based upon the body systems affected. A difficulty with this method of classification is that many diseases involve more than one organ system. For example, AIDS begins as a sexually transmitted infection (reproductive system) or a parenteral infection of the blood (cardiovascular system). It then becomes an infection of the lymphatic system as viruses invade lymphocytes. Finally, the syndrome involves diseases and degeneration of the respiratory, nervous, digestive, cardiovascular, and lymphatic systems.

Another classification system deals with diseases according to taxonomic categories.

Every disease (not just infectious diseases) can also be classified according to its longevity and severity. If a disease develops rapidly but lasts a relatively short time, it is called an **acute disease.** An example is the common cold. In contrast, **chronic diseases** develop slowly (usually with less severe symptoms) and are continual or recurrent. Infectious mononucleosis, hepatitis C, tuberculosis, and leprosy are chronic diseases. **Subacute diseases** have durations and severities that lie somewhere between acute and chronic. Subacute bacterial endocarditis, a disease of heart valves, is one example. **Latent**

## TABLE 10 — Selected Arthropod Vectors

| | Disease | Causative Agent (bacteria unless otherwise indicated) |
|---|---|---|
| **Biological Vectors** | | |
| **Mosquitoes** | | |
| *Anopheles,* | Malaria | *Plasmodium* spp. (protozoan) |
| *Aedes* | Yellow fever | *Flavivirus* sp. (virus) |
| | Elephantiasis | *Wuchereria bancrofti* (helminth) |
| | Dengue | *Flavivirus* spp. (virus) |
| | Viral encephalitis | *Alphavirus* spp. (virus) |
| **Ticks** | | |
| *Ixodes* | Lyme disease | *Borrelia burgdorferi* |
| *Dermacentor* | Rocky Mountain spotted fever | *Rickettsia rickettsii* |
| **Flea** | | |
| *Xenopsylla* | Bubonic plague | *Yersinia pestis* |
| | Endemic typhus | *Rickettsia prowazekii* |
| **Louse** | | |
| *Pediculus* | Epidemic typhus | *Rickettsia typhi* |
| **Bloodsucking flies** | | |
| *Glossina* | African sleeping sickness | *Trypanosoma brucei* |
| *Simulium* | River blindness | *Onchocerca volvulus* (helminth) |
| **Bloodsucking bug** | | |
| *Triatoma* | Chagas' disease | *Trypanosoma cruzi* (protozoan) |
| **Mite (chigger)** | | |
| *Leptotrombidium* | Scrub typhus | *Orientia tsutsugamushi* |
| **Mechanical Vectors** | | |
| **Housefly** | | |
| *Musca* | Foodborne infections | *Shigella* spp., *Salmonella* spp., *Escherichia coli* |
| **Cockroaches** | | |
| *Blatella,* *Periplaneta* | Foodborne infections | *Shigella* spp., *Salmonella* spp., *Escherichia coli* |

**diseases** are those in which a pathogen remains inactive for a long period of time before becoming active. Herpes is an example of a latent disease.

When an infectious disease comes from another infected host, either directly or indirectly, it is a **communicable** disease. Influenza, herpes, and tuberculosis are examples of communicable diseases. If a communicable disease is easily transmitted between hosts, as is the case for chickenpox or measles, it is also called a **contagious** disease. **Noncommunicable** diseases arise outside of hosts or from normal microbiota. In other words, they are not spread from one host to another, and diseased patients are not a source of contamination for others. Tooth decay, acne, and tetanus are examples of noncommunicable diseases.

Table 12 defines these and other terms used to classify infectious diseases.

Yet another way in which all infectious diseases may be classified is by the effects they have on populations, rather than on individuals. Is a certain disease consistently found in a given group of people or geographic area? Under what circumstances is it more prevalent than normal in a given geographic area? How prevalent is "normal"? How is the disease transmitted throughout a population? We next examine issues related to diseases at the population level.

# Epidemiology of Infectious Diseases

## Learning Objective

✓ Define *epidemiology.*

Our discussion so far has centered on the negative impact of microorganisms on *individuals.* Now we turn our attention to the effects of pathogens on *populations.* **Epidemiology**[10] (ep-i-dĕ-mē-ol'ō-jē) is the study of where and when diseases occur, and how they are transmitted within populations. During the 20th century, epidemiologists expanded the scope of their work beyond infectious diseases to also consider injuries and deaths related to automobile and fireworks accidents, cigarette smoking, lead poisoning, and other causes; however, we will limit our discussion primarily to the epidemiology of infectious diseases. **ANIMATIONS:** *Epidemiology: Overview*

## Frequency of Disease

## Learning Objectives

✓ Contrast between incidence and prevalence.

✓ Differentiate among the terms *endemic, sporadic, epidemic,* and *pandemic.*

Epidemiologists keep track of the occurrence of diseases by using two measures: incidence and prevalence. **Incidence** is the number of *new* cases of a disease in a given area or population during a given period of time; **prevalence** is the *total number* of cases, both new and already existing, in a given area or population during a given period of time. In other words, prevalence is a cumulative number. Thus, for example, the reported number of new cases—the incidence—of AIDS in the United States in 2006 was 36,828. However, the prevalence of AIDS in 2006 was 436,690 because almost 400,000 patients who got the disease prior to 2006 still survived with the disease. Figure 14 illustrates this relationship between incidence and prevalence.

Epidemiologists report their data in many ways including maps, graphs, charts, and tables (Figure 15). Why do they report their data in so many different ways? Using a variety of formats enables epidemiologists to observe patterns that may give clues about the causes of or ways to prevent diseases. For example, shigellosis (an infection of *Shigella* characterized by

---

[10]From Greek *epidemios,* meaning among the people, and *logos,* meaning study of.

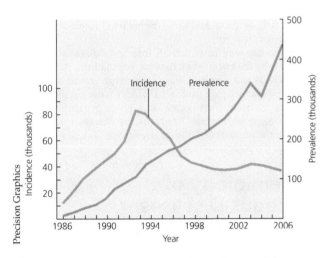

▲ **Figure 14** **Curves representing the incidence and the estimated prevalence of AIDS among U.S. adults.** Note that the scales for the two curves are different. *Why can the incidence of a disease never exceed the prevalence of that disease?*

*Figure 14 Because prevalence includes all cases, both old and new, prevalence must always be larger than incidence.*

diarrhea, abdominal pain, and fever) had an overall prevalence of 85 cases per million in the U.S. population in 2000, but when the data are reported by age group, it becomes apparent that the highest prevalence (350 cases per million) occurs in young children (see Figure 15c).

The occurrence of a disease can also be considered in terms of a combination of frequency and geographic distribution (Figure 16). A disease that normally occurs continually (at moderately regular intervals) at a relatively stable incidence within a given population or geographical area is said to be **endemic**[11] to that population or region. A disease is considered **sporadic** when only a few scattered cases occur within an area or population. Whenever a disease occurs at a greater frequency than is usual for an area or population, the disease is said to be **epidemic** within that area or population. ANIMATIONS: *Epidemiology: Occurrence of Disease*

The commonly held belief that a disease must infect thousands or millions to be considered an epidemic is mistaken. The time period and the number of cases necessary for an outbreak of disease to be classified as an epidemic are not specified; the important fact is that there are more cases than historical statistics indicate are expected. For example, less than 200 cases of *Hantavirus* pulmonary syndrome occurred in the Four Corners area[12] of the United States in 1993, but because they were the first cases of this disease ever reported for the region, the outbreak was considered an epidemic. At the same place, thousands of cases of flu occurred, but there was no flu epidemic because the number of cases observed did not exceed the number expected.

[11]From Greek *endemos*, meaning native.
[12]Four Corners is the geographic region surrounding the point at which Arizona, Utah, New Mexico, and Colorado meet.

(a)

(b)

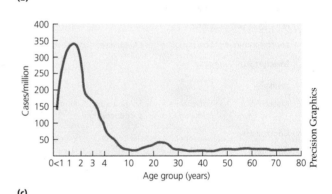

(c)

▲ **Figure 15** **Epidemiologists report data in a number of ways.** Here incidence of shigellosis in the U.S. in 2000 is presented **(a)** on a map by state, **(b)** by month, and **(c)** as cases per million by age group. The latter graph reveals that shigellosis in young children is much more prevalent (as high as 350 cases per million) than in the U.S. population as a whole, a fact not apparent unless the data are sorted by age.

Figure 17 illustrates how epidemics are defined according to the number of expected cases, and not according to the absolute number of cases.

If an epidemic occurs simultaneously on more than one continent, it is referred to as a **pandemic** (see Figure 16d). H1N1 flu, so-called swine flu, became pandemic worldwide in 2009.

▶ **Figure 16 Illustrations of the different terms for the occurrence of disease. (a)** An endemic disease, which is normally present in a region. **(b)** A sporadic disease, which occurs irregularly and infrequently. **(c)** An epidemic disease, which is present in greater frequency than is usual. **(d)** A pandemic disease, which is an epidemic disease occurring on more than one continent at a given time. *Regardless of where you live, name a disease that is endemic, one that is sporadic, and one that is epidemic in your state.*

**Figure 16** *Some possible answers: Flu is endemic in every state; tuberculosis is sporadic in most states; AIDS is epidemic in every state.*

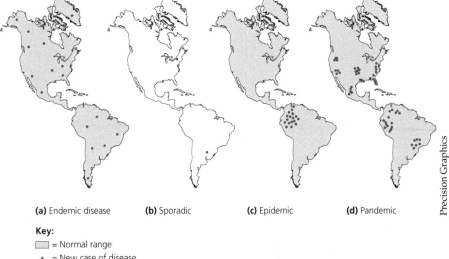

**(a)** Endemic disease    **(b)** Sporadic    **(c)** Epidemic    **(d)** Pandemic

**Key:**

☐ = Normal range

• = New case of disease

Obviously, for disease prevalence to be classified as either endemic, sporadic, epidemic, or pandemic, good records must be kept for each region and population. From such records, incidence and prevalence can be calculated, and then changes in these data can be noted. Health departments at the local and state levels require doctors and hospitals to report certain infectious diseases. Some are also nationally notifiable; that is, their occurrence must be reported to the Centers for Disease Control and Prevention (CDC) in Atlanta, Georgia, which is the headquarters and clearinghouse for national epidemiological research. Nationally notifiable diseases are listed in Table 13. Each week the CDC reports the number of cases of

▶ **Figure 17 Epidemics may have fewer cases than nonepidemics.** These two graphs demonstrate the independence between the absolute number of cases and a disease's designation as an epidemic. Even though the number of cases of disease A always exceeds the number of cases of disease B, only disease B is ever considered epidemic—at those times when the number of cases observed exceeds the number of cases expected. *How can scientists know the normal prevalence of a given disease?*

**Figure 17** *Scientists record every case of the disease so that they will have a "baseline" prevalence, which then becomes the expected prevalence for each disease.*

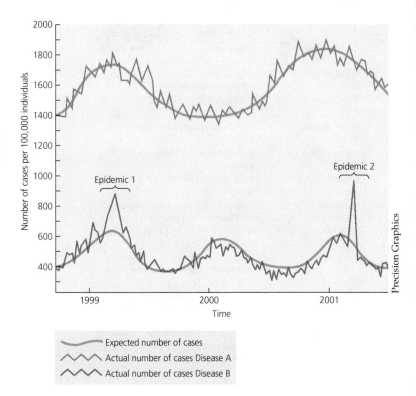

Expected number of cases

Actual number of cases Disease A

Actual number of cases Disease B

## TABLE 11

## Modes of Disease Transmission

| Mode of Transmission | Examples of Diseases Spread |
|---|---|
| **Contact Transmission** | |
| **Direct contact:** e.g., handshaking, kissing, sexual intercourse, bites | Cutaneous anthrax, genital warts, gonorrhea, herpes, rabies, staphylococcal infections, syphilis |
| **Indirect contact:** e.g., drinking glasses, toothbrushes, toys, punctures | Common cold, enterovirus infections, influenza, measles, Q fever, pneumonia, tetanus |
| **Droplet transmission:** e.g., droplets from sneezing (within 1 meter) | Whooping cough, streptococcal pharyngitis (strep throat) |
| **Vehicle Transmission** | |
| **Airborne:** e.g., dust particles or droplets carried more than 1 meter | Chickenpox, coccidioidomycosis, histoplasmosis, influenza, measles, pulmonary anthrax, tuberculosis |
| **Waterborne:** e.g., streams, swimming pools | *Campylobacter* infections, cholera, *Giardia* diarrhea |
| **Foodborne:** e.g., poultry, seafood, meat | Food poisoning (botulism, staphylococcal); hepatitis A, listeriosis, tapeworms, toxoplasmosis, typhoid fever |
| **Vector Transmission** | |
| **Mechanical:** e.g., on bodies of flies, roaches | *E. coli* diarrhea, salmonellosis, trachoma |
| **Biological:** e.g., lice, mites, mosquitoes, ticks | Chagas' disease, Lyme disease, malaria, plague, Rocky Mountain spotted fever, typhus fever, yellow fever |

## TABLE 12

## Terms Used to Classify Infectious Diseases

| Term | Definition |
|---|---|
| Acute disease | Disease in which symptoms develop rapidly and that runs its course quickly |
| Chronic disease | Disease with usually mild symptoms that develop slowly and last a long time |
| Subacute disease | Disease with time course and symptoms between acute and chronic° |
| Asymptomatic disease | Disease without symptoms |
| Latent disease | Disease that appears a long time after infection |
| Communicable disease | Disease transmitted from one host to another |
| Contagious disease | Communicable disease that is easily spread |
| Noncommunicable disease | Disease arising from outside of hosts or from opportunistic pathogen |
| Local infection | Infection confined to a small region of the body |
| Systemic infection | Widespread infection in many systems of the body; often travels in the blood or lymph |
| Focal infection | Infection that serves as a source of pathogens for infections at other sites in the body |
| Primary infection | Initial infection within a given patient |
| Secondary infection | Infections that follow a primary infection; often by opportunistic pathogens |

most of the nationally notifiable diseases in the *Morbidity and Mortality Weekly Report (MMWR)* (Figure 18).

## Epidemiological Studies

### Learning Objective

✓ Explain three approaches epidemiologists use to study diseases in populations.

Epidemiologists conduct research to study the dynamics of diseases in populations by taking three different approaches, called descriptive, analytical, and experimental epidemiology.

### Descriptive Epidemiology

**Descriptive epidemiology** involves the careful tabulation of data concerning a disease. Relevant information includes the location and time of cases of the disease, as well as information about the patients, such as ages, gender, occupations, health histories, and socioeconomic groups. Because the time course and chains of transmission of a disease are an important part of descriptive epidemiology, epidemiologists strive to identify the **index case** (the first case) of the disease in a given area or population. Sometimes it is difficult or impossible to identify an index case because the patient has recovered, moved, or died.

▶ **Figure 18 A page from the *MMWR*.** The CDC's *Morbidity and Mortality Weekly Report (MMWR)* provides epidemiological data state by state for the current week, for the current year to date, and for the previous year to date. The *MMWR* also publishes reports on epidemiological case studies. This page shows the incidence of three diseases in one week in 2008–2009.

TABLE II, (*Continued*) Provisional cases of selected notifiable diseases, United States, weeks ending January 3, 2009, and December 29, 2007 (53rd week)*

| Reporting area | Pertussis | | | | | Rabies, animal | | | | | Rocky Mountain spotted fever | | | | |
|---|---|---|---|---|---|---|---|---|---|---|---|---|---|---|---|
| | Current week | Previous 52 weeks Med | Previous 52 weeks Max | Cum 2008 | Cum 2007 | Current week | Previous 52 weeks Med | Previous 52 weeks Max | Cum 2008 | Cum 2007 | Current week | Previous 52 weeks Med | Previous 52 weeks Max | Cum 2008 | Cum 2007 |
| **United States** | 164 | 174 | 315 | 10,007 | 10,454 | 17 | 101 | 164 | 4,911 | 5,975 | 14 | 31 | 145 | 2,276 | 2,221 |
| **New England** | 4 | 11 | 35 | 620 | 1,552 | 6 | 7 | 20 | 372 | 522 | — | 0 | 2 | 4 | 10 |
| Connecticut | — | 0 | 4 | 34 | 89 | 3 | 4 | 17 | 203 | 219 | — | 0 | 0 | — | — |
| Maine[†] | — | 0 | 5 | 47 | 83 | 1 | 1 | 5 | 64 | 86 | N | 0 | 0 | N | N |
| Massachusetts | — | 8 | 32 | 420 | 1,178 | N | 0 | 0 | N | N | — | 0 | 1 | 1 | 9 |
| New Hampshire | 4 | 1 | 4 | 48 | 80 | — | 0 | 3 | 35 | 53 | — | 0 | 1 | 1 | 1 |
| Rhode Island | — | 0 | 7 | 59 | 59 | N | 0 | 0 | N | N | — | 0 | 2 | 2 | — |
| Vermont[†] | — | 0 | 2 | 12 | 63 | 2 | 1 | 6 | 70 | 164 | — | 0 | 0 | — | — |
| **Mid. Atlantic** | — | 19 | 41 | 1,051 | 1,314 | 6 | 28 | 63 | 1,536 | 997 | — | 1 | 5 | 80 | 85 |
| New Jersey | — | 1 | 6 | 71 | 229 | — | 0 | 0 | — | — | — | 0 | 2 | 12 | 32 |
| New York (Upstate) | — | 7 | 24 | 426 | 549 | 6 | 9 | 20 | 500 | 514 | — | 0 | 2 | 17 | 7 |
| New York City | — | 0 | 5 | 46 | 150 | — | 0 | 2 | 19 | 44 | — | 0 | 2 | 24 | 28 |
| Pennsylvania | — | 9 | 34 | 508 | 386 | — | 18 | 48 | 1,017 | 439 | — | 0 | 2 | 27 | 18 |
| **E.N. Central** | 84 | 30 | 189 | 1,919 | 1,495 | — | 3 | 28 | 247 | 414 | — | 1 | 15 | 150 | 60 |
| Illinois | — | 6 | 39 | 517 | 199 | — | 1 | 21 | 103 | 113 | — | 1 | 10 | 104 | 39 |
| Indiana | 27 | 1 | 15 | 139 | 68 | — | 0 | 2 | 10 | 13 | — | 0 | 3 | 8 | 6 |
| Michigan | — | 6 | 14 | 294 | 292 | — | 0 | 8 | 73 | 202 | — | 0 | 1 | 3 | 4 |
| Ohio | 57 | 10 | 176 | 846 | 609 | — | 1 | 7 | 61 | 86 | — | 0 | 4 | 34 | 10 |
| Wisconsin | — | 2 | 7 | 123 | 327 | N | 0 | 0 | N | N | — | 0 | 1 | 1 | 1 |
| **W.N. Central** | 18 | 17 | 120 | 1,378 | 909 | — | 3 | 13 | 206 | 276 | 1 | 4 | 32 | 456 | 369 |
| Iowa | — | 2 | 20 | 209 | 150 | — | 0 | 5 | 29 | 31 | — | 0 | 2 | 7 | 17 |
| Kansas | 1 | 1 | 13 | 78 | 104 | — | 0 | 0 | — | 110 | — | 0 | 0 | — | 12 |
| Minnesota | — | 2 | 26 | 224 | 393 | — | 0 | 10 | 65 | 40 | — | 0 | 0 | — | 6 |
| Missouri | 15 | 6 | 50 | 535 | 118 | — | 1 | 8 | 65 | 38 | 1 | 4 | 31 | 426 | 315 |
| Nebraska[†] | 2 | 2 | 35 | 281 | 70 | — | 0 | 0 | — | — | — | 0 | 4 | 20 | 14 |
| North Dakota | — | 0 | 1 | 1 | 14 | — | 0 | 7 | 34 | 30 | — | 0 | 0 | — | — |
| South Dakota | — | 0 | 7 | 50 | 60 | — | 0 | 2 | 23 | 27 | — | 0 | 1 | 3 | 5 |
| **S. Atlantic** | 16 | 17 | 44 | 937 | 978 | 4 | 37 | 101 | 2,024 | 2,184 | 13 | 12 | 71 | 928 | 1,020 |
| Delaware | — | 0 | 3 | 18 | 11 | — | 0 | 0 | — | — | — | 0 | 5 | 33 | 17 |
| District of Columbia | — | 0 | 1 | 7 | 9 | — | 0 | 0 | — | — | — | 0 | 2 | 8 | 3 |
| Florida | — | 5 | 20 | 306 | 211 | — | 0 | 77 | 139 | 128 | — | 0 | 3 | 20 | 19 |
| Georgia | — | 1 | 6 | 91 | 37 | — | 5 | 42 | 339 | 300 | — | 1 | 8 | 73 | 60 |
| Maryland[†] | 1 | 2 | 8 | 130 | 118 | — | 8 | 17 | 420 | 431 | — | 1 | 7 | 72 | 63 |
| North Carolina | 15 | 0 | 15 | 94 | 330 | 4 | 9 | 16 | 454 | 472 | 12 | 2 | 55 | 511 | 665 |
| South Carolina[†] | — | 2 | 10 | 129 | 102 | — | 0 | 0 | — | 46 | 1 | 1 | 9 | 55 | 64 |
| Virginia[†] | — | 3 | 10 | 152 | 128 | — | 11 | 24 | 591 | 730 | — | 2 | 15 | 149 | 123 |
| West Virginia | — | 0 | 2 | 10 | 32 | — | 1 | 9 | 81 | 77 | — | 0 | 1 | 7 | 6 |
| **E.S. Central** | 3 | 7 | 28 | 395 | 463 | — | 3 | 7 | 165 | 156 | — | 3 | 23 | 324 | 276 |
| Alabama[†] | — | 1 | 5 | 59 | 91 | — | 0 | 0 | — | — | — | 1 | 8 | 90 | 96 |
| Kentucky | 1 | 2 | 11 | 136 | 33 | — | 0 | 4 | 45 | 21 | — | 0 | 1 | 1 | 5 |
| Mississippi | 1 | 2 | 5 | 92 | 255 | — | 0 | 1 | 2 | 3 | — | 0 | 3 | 12 | 20 |
| Tennessee[†] | 1 | 1 | 14 | 108 | 84 | — | 2 | 6 | 118 | 132 | — | 2 | 19 | 221 | 155 |
| **W.S. Central** | 10 | 27 | 106 | 1,631 | 1,303 | — | 1 | 11 | 92 | 1,086 | — | 1 | 41 | 286 | 361 |
| Arkansas | 9 | 1 | 19 | 93 | 173 | — | 0 | 6 | 48 | 33 | — | 0 | 14 | 68 | 122 |
| Louisiana | — | 1 | 7 | 77 | 21 | — | 0 | 0 | — | 6 | — | 0 | 1 | 5 | 4 |
| Oklahoma | 1 | 0 | 21 | 56 | 58 | — | 0 | 10 | 42 | 78 | — | 0 | 26 | 170 | 186 |
| Texas[†] | — | 23 | 98 | 1,405 | 1,051 | — | 0 | 1 | 2 | 969 | — | 1 | 6 | 43 | 49 |
| **Mountain** | 8 | 15 | 34 | 814 | 1,137 | — | 1 | 8 | 77 | 97 | — | 1 | 3 | 43 | 37 |
| Arizona | — | 4 | 10 | 204 | 210 | N | 0 | 0 | N | N | — | 0 | 2 | 17 | 10 |
| Colorado | 6 | 3 | 6 | 160 | 307 | — | 0 | 0 | — | — | — | 0 | 1 | 1 | 3 |
| Idaho[†] | 2 | 0 | 5 | 38 | 45 | — | 0 | 0 | — | 12 | — | 0 | 1 | 1 | 4 |
| Montana[†] | — | 1 | 11 | 83 | 53 | — | 0 | 2 | 9 | 21 | — | 0 | 1 | 3 | 1 |
| Nevada[†] | — | 0 | 7 | 19 | 37 | — | 0 | 4 | 5 | 13 | — | 0 | 2 | 2 | — |
| New Mexico[†] | — | 1 | 8 | 68 | 74 | — | 0 | 3 | 25 | 15 | — | 0 | 1 | 2 | 6 |
| Utah | — | 4 | 13 | 226 | 397 | — | 0 | 6 | 14 | 16 | — | 0 | 1 | 7 | — |
| Wyoming | — | 0 | 2 | 16 | 24 | — | 0 | 3 | 24 | 20 | — | 0 | 2 | 10 | 13 |
| **Pacific** | 21 | 22 | 83 | 1,262 | 1,303 | 1 | 3 | 13 | 192 | 243 | — | 0 | 1 | 5 | 3 |
| Alaska | 1 | 3 | 21 | 258 | 89 | — | 0 | 4 | 15 | 45 | N | 0 | 0 | N | N |
| California | 1 | 7 | 23 | 392 | 590 | 1 | 3 | 12 | 163 | 186 | — | 0 | 1 | 2 | 1 |
| Hawaii | — | 0 | 2 | 17 | 19 | — | 0 | 0 | — | — | N | 0 | 0 | N | N |
| Oregon[†] | — | 3 | 10 | 176 | 123 | — | 0 | 4 | 14 | 12 | — | 0 | 1 | 3 | 2 |
| Washington | 19 | 5 | 63 | 419 | 482 | — | 0 | 0 | — | — | N | 0 | 0 | N | N |
| American Samoa | — | 0 | 0 | — | — | N | 0 | 0 | N | N | N | 0 | 0 | N | N |
| C.N.M.I. | — | — | — | — | — | — | — | — | — | — | — | — | — | — | — |
| Guam | — | 0 | 0 | — | — | — | 0 | 0 | — | — | N | 0 | 0 | N | N |
| Puerto Rico | — | 0 | 0 | — | — | — | 1 | 5 | 59 | 48 | N | 0 | 0 | N | N |
| U.S. Virgin Islands | — | 0 | 0 | — | — | N | 0 | 0 | N | N | N | 0 | 0 | N | N |

C.N.M.I.: Commonwealth of Northern Mariana Islands.
U: Unavailable.    —: No reported cases.    N: Not notifiable.    Cum: Cumulative year-to-date counts.    Med: Median.    Max: Maximum.
* Incidence data for reporting year 2008 is provisional.
[†] Contains data reported through the National Electronic Disease Surveillance System (NEDSS).

Precision Graphics

• Deaths from cholera
⊕ Pump

▲ **Figure 19** **A map showing cholera deaths in a section of London, 1854.** From the map he compiled, Dr. John Snow showed that cholera cases centered around the Broad Street pump. Snow's work was a landmark in epidemiological research.

The earliest descriptive epidemiological study was by John Snow (1813–1858), who studied a cholera outbreak in London in 1854. By carefully mapping the locations of the cholera cases in a particular part of the city, Snow found that the cases were clustered around the Broad Street water pump (Figure 19). This distribution of cases, plus the voluminous watery diarrhea of cholera patients, suggested that the disease was spread via contamination of drinking water by sewage.

### Analytical Epidemiology

**Analytical epidemiology** investigates a disease in detail, including analysis of data acquired in descriptive epidemiological studies, to determine the probable cause, mode of transmission, and possible means of prevention of the disease. Analytical epidemiology may be used in situations where it is not ethical to apply Koch's postulates. Thus, even though Koch's third postulate has never been fulfilled in the case of AIDS (because it

is unethical to intentionally inoculate a human with HIV), analytical epidemiological studies indicate that HIV causes AIDS and that it is transmitted primarily sexually.

Often analytical studies are *retrospective;* that is, they attempt to identify causation and mode of transmission after an outbreak has occurred. Epidemiologists compare a group of people who had the disease with a group who did not. The groups are carefully matched by factors such as gender, environment, and diet, and then compared to determine which pathogens and factors may play a role in morbidity.

### Experimental Epidemiology

**Experimental epidemiology** involves testing a hypothesis concerning the cause of a disease. The application of Koch's postulates is an example of experimental epidemiology. Experimental epidemiology also involves studies to test a hypothesis resulting from an analytical study such as the efficacy of a preventive measure or certain treatment. For example, analytical epidemiological studies suggested that the bacterium *Chlamydophila pneumoniae* may contribute to arteriosclerosis, resulting in heart attacks. Some scientists have hypothesized that antibacterial drugs could prevent heart attacks by killing the causative agent. To test this hypothesis the scientists administered either the antimicrobial drug azithromycin or a medicinally inactive placebo to 7700 patients, all of whom had a history of heart disease and were infected with *C. pneumoniae*. The researchers observed no significant difference in the number of heart attacks suffered by patients in the two groups over a 2-year period. Thus an experimental epidemiological study disproved a hypothesis suggested by an analytical epidemiological analysis.

The **Clinical Case Study:** *Legionella* **in the Produce Aisle** illustrates the work of epidemiologists.

## Hospital Epidemiology: Nosocomial Infections

### Learning Objectives

✓ Explain how nosocomial infections differ from other infections.

✓ Describe the factors that influence the development of nosocomial infections.

✓ Describe three types of nosocomial infections and how they may be prevented.

Of special concern to epidemiologists and health care workers are nosocomial (nos-ō-kō′mē-ăl) infections and nosocomial diseases. **Nosocomial infections** are those acquired by patients or health care workers while they are in health care facilities, including hospitals, dental offices, nursing homes, and doctors' waiting rooms. The CDC estimates that about 10% of American patients acquire a nosocomial infection each year. **Nosocomial diseases**—those acquired in a health care setting—increase the duration and cost of medical care and result in some 90,000 deaths annually in the U.S. **ANIMATIONS:** *Nosocomial Infections: Overview*

## 13

# Nationally Notifiable Infectious Diseases[a]

| | | | |
|---|---|---|---|
| Acquired immunodeficiency syndrome (AIDS) | *Hantavirus* pulmonary syndrome | Poliomyelitis, paralytic | *Streptococcus pneumoniae*, drug resistant |
| Anthrax | Hemolytic uremic syndrome, postdiarrheal | Poliovirus infection | *Streptococcus pneumoniae*, non-drug-resistant and invasive in children |
| Arboviral diseases | Hepatitis A | Psittacosis | |
| Botulism | Hepatitis B | Q fever | Syphilis, congenital |
| Brucellosis | Hepatitis C | Rabies, animal and human | Tetanus |
| Chancroid | HIV infection | Rocky Mountain spotted fever | Toxic-shock syndrome, non-streptococcal |
| *Chlamydia trachomatis*, genital infections | Influenza-associated pediatric mortality | Rubella | |
| | | Rubella, congenital syndrome | Trichinellosis |
| Cholera | Legionellosis | Salmonellosis | Tuberculosis |
| Coccidioidomycosis | Listeriosis | Severe acute respiratory syndrome (SARS) | Tularemia |
| Cryptosporidiosis | Lyme disease | | Typhoid fever |
| Cyclosporiasis | Malaria | Shiga-toxin-producing *Escherichia coli* | Vancomycin-resistant *Staphylococcus aureus* |
| Diphtheria | Measles | Shigellosis | |
| Ehrlichiosis/anaplasmosis | Meningococcal disease | Smallpox | Varicella |
| Giardiasis | Mumps | Streptococcal disease, invasive, Group A | Vibriosis |
| Gonorrhea | Novel influenza A infections | | Yellow fever |
| *Haemophilus influenzae*, invasive disease | Pertussis | Streptococcal toxic shock syndrome | |
| Hansen disease (leprosy) | Plague | | |

[a]Diseases for which hospitals, physicians, and other health care workers are required to report cases to state health departments, who then forward the data to the CDC.

## CLINICAL CASE STUDY

### *Legionella* in the Produce Aisle

Vincent P. Walter/Prentice Hall

The Lousiana state health department has received reports of 33 cases of Legionnaires' disease in the town of Bogalusa (population 16,000). Legionnaires' disease, or legionellosis, is a potentially fatal respiratory disease caused by the growth of a bacterium, *Legionella pneumophila,* in the lungs of patients. The bacterium enters humans via the respiratory portal in aerosols produced by cooling towers, air conditioners, whirlpool baths, showers, humidifiers, and respiratory therapy equipment.

Epidemiologists begin trying to ascertain the source of Bogalusa's Legionnaires' disease outbreak by interviewing the victims and their relatives to develop complete histories and to identify areas of commonality among the victims that were lacking among nonvictims. Victims include a range of ages, occupations, hobbies, religions, and types and locations of dwellings. Although no significant differences are identified among the lifestyles, ages, or smoking habits of victims and nonvictims, one curious fact is discovered: All the victims did their grocery shopping at the same store. However, healthy individuals also shopped at that store.

The air conditioning system of the grocery store proves to be free of *Legionella,* but the vegetable misting machine does not. The strain of *Legionella* isolated from the misting machine is identical to the strain recovered from the victims' lungs.

1. Would this outbreak be classified as endemic, epidemic, or pandemic?

2. Is this a descriptive, analytical, or experimental epidemiological study?

3. Knowing the epidemiology and causative agent of Legionnaires' disease, what questions would you ask of the victims or of their surviving relatives?

4. What, as an epidemiologist, would you examine at the store?

5. How did the victims become contaminated? Why didn't everyone who bought vegetables at the store get legionellosis? What could the owners of the store do to limit or prevent future infections?

Reference: Adapted from *MMWR* 39: 108–109. 1990.

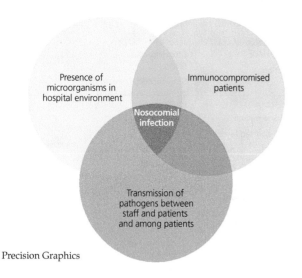

Precision Graphics

▲ **Figure 20** **The interplay of factors that result in nosocomial infections.** Although nosocomial infections can result from any one of the factors shown, most nosocomial infections are the product of the interaction of all three factors.

## Types of Nosocomial Infections

When most people think of nosocomial infections, what likely comes to mind are **exogenous** (eks-oj′ě-nŭs) infections, which are caused by pathogens acquired from the health care environment. After all, hospitals are filled with sick people shedding pathogens from every type of portal of exit. However, we have seen that members of the normal microbiota can become opportunistic pathogens as a result of hospitalization or medical treatments such as chemotherapy. Such opportunists cause **endogenous** (en-doj′ě-nŭs) nosocomial infections; that is, they arise from normal microbiota within the patient that become pathogenic because of factors within the health care setting.

**Iatrogenic** (ī-at-rō-jen′ik) **infections** (literally meaning "doctor induced" infections) are a subset of nosocomial infections that ironically are the direct result of modern medical procedures such as the use of catheters, invasive diagnostic procedures, and surgery.

*Superinfections* may result from the use of antimicrobial drugs that, by inhibiting some resident microbiota, allow others to thrive in the absence of competition. For instance, long-term antimicrobial therapy to inhibit a bacterial infection may allow *Clostridium difficile* (dif-fi′sil-ē), a transient microbe of the colon, to grow excessively and cause a painful condition called pseudomembranous colitis. Such superinfections are not limited to health care settings.

Nosocomial infections most often occur in the urinary, respiratory, cardiovascular, and integumentary (skin) systems, though surgical wounds can become infected and result in nosocomial infections in any part of the body.

## Factors Influencing Nosocomial Infections

Nosocomial infections arise from the interaction of several factors in the health care environment, which include the following (Figure 20):

- Exposure to numerous pathogens present in the health care setting, including many that are resistant to antimicrobial agents
- The weakened immune systems of patients who are ill, making them more susceptible to opportunistic pathogens
- Transmission of pathogens among patients and health care workers—from staff and visitors, to patients, and even from one patient to another via activities of staff members (including invasive procedures and other iatrogenic factors)

## Control of Nosocomial Infections

Aggressive control measures can noticeably reduce the incidence of nosocomial infections. These include disinfection; medical asepsis, including good housekeeping, handwashing, bathing, sanitary handling of food, proper hygiene, and precautionary measures to avoid the spread of pathogens among patients; surgical asepsis and sterile procedures, including thorough cleansing of the surgical field, use of sterile instruments, and use of sterile gloves, gowns, caps, and masks; isolation of particularly contagious or susceptible patients; and establishment of a nosocomial infection control committee charged with surveillance of nosocomial diseases and review of control measures. **ANIMATIONS:** *Nosocomial Infections: Prevention*

Numerous studies have shown that the single most effective way to reduce nosocomial infections is effective handwashing by all medical and support staff. In one study, deaths from nosocomial infections were reduced by over 50% when hospital personnel followed strict guidelines about washing their hands frequently.

# Epidemiology and Public Health

### Learning Objective

✓ List three ways public health agencies work to limit the spread of diseases.

As you have likely realized by now, epidemiologists gather information concerning the spread of disease within populations so that they can take steps to reduce the number of cases and improve the health of individuals within a community. In the following sections we will examine how the various public health agencies share epidemiological data, facilitate the interruption of disease transmission, and educate the public about public health issues. Public health agencies also implement immunization programs.

## EMERGING DISEASES

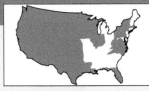

Precision Graphics

### HANTAVIRUS PULMONARY SYNDROME

▲ **The deer mouse,** *Peromyscus maniculatus.*

Doli was excited. Her Navajo basketball team had won the divisional championship for 1993, and she was high point (the high scorer) for the championship game. The thrill of the moment made her forget the argument with her parents earlier in the week about sweeping out the storage shed. They were champions, and life was good.

The next morning, Doli woke with deep muscle pain that she attributed to the exertions of the game. By noon she had a headache and was nauseous and experiencing the chill associated with a fever. "The flu," her mother concluded, and sent Doli to bed with acetaminophen and plenty of fluids. Over the next few days, Doli's lungs began to congest; she struggled to breathe, and her heart raced. Doli was drowning in her own bodily fluid.

Desperately worried, Doli's parents drove her 60 miles to the Navajo medical center, where bewildered doctors provided respiratory and cardiac care while searching for answers. They discovered three patients in the surrounding counties with the same signs and symptoms; all had died. Doli's prognosis was the same: She was comatose. Her blood platelet level had dropped precipitously. Excessive proteins were in her blood. Her kidneys' function was deteriorating. A week after her classmates had cheered their team's victory, they gathered to mourn their friend.

As heartbreaking as the deaths in this epidemic were, the cases advanced our medical understanding and put to use the power of modern epidemiology and genetic analysis. Within eight days of the initial case, epidemiologists had isolated a suspect virus, sequenced its genes, identified it as a previously unknown species of *Hantavirus*, and shown that the virus was the cause of the condition, which is now known as *Hantavirus* pulmonary syndrome (HPS). Scientists also showed that HPS is acquired when victims inhale the virus in aerosolized deer-mouse urine or feces stirred up by sweeping, enabling other residents of the region to take preventive measures.

Rob and Ann Simpson/Visuals Unlimited

**(MM)** Track *Hantavirus* pulmonary syndrome online by going to the Study Area at www.masteringmicrobiology.com.

### The Sharing of Data Among Public Health Organizations

Numerous agencies at the local, state, national, and global levels work together with the entire spectrum of health care personnel to promote public health. By submitting reports on incidence and prevalence of disease to public officials, physicians can subsequently learn of current disease trends. Additionally, public health agencies often provide physicians with laboratory and diagnostic assistance.

City and county health departments report data on disease incidence to state agencies. Because state laws govern disease reporting, state agencies play a vital role in epidemiological studies. States accumulate data similar to that in the *MMWR* and assist local health departments and medical practitioners with diagnostic testing for diseases such as rabies and Lyme disease.

Data collected by the states are forwarded to the CDC, which is but one branch of the United States Public Health Service, our national public health agency. In addition to epidemiological studies, the CDC and other branches of the Public Health Service conduct research in disease etiology and prevention, make recommendations concerning immunization schedules, and work with public health organizations of other countries.

The World Health Organization (WHO) coordinates efforts to improve public health throughout the world, particularly in poorer countries, and the WHO has undertaken ambitious projects to eradicate such diseases as polio, measles, and mumps. Some other current campaigns involve AIDS education, malaria control, and childhood immunization programs in poor countries.

### The Role of Public Health Agencies in Interrupting Disease Transmission

As we have seen, pathogens can be transmitted in air, food, and water, as well as by vectors and via fomites. Public health agencies work to limit disease transmission by a number of methods:

- Enforce standards of cleanliness in water and food supplies
- Work to reduce the number of disease vectors and reservoirs
- Establish and enforce immunization schedules
- Locate and prophylactically treat individuals exposed to contagious pathogens
- Establish isolation and quarantine measures to control the spread of pathogens

A water supply that is **potable** (fit to drink) is vital to good health. Organisms that cause dysentery, cholera, and typhoid fever are just some of the pathogens that can be spread in water contaminated by sewage. Filtration and chlorination processes are used to reduce the number of pathogens in water supplies. Local, state, and national agencies work to ensure that water supplies remain clean and healthful by monitoring both sewage treatment facilities and the water supply.

Food can harbor infective stages of parasitic worms, protozoa, bacteria, and viruses. National and state health officials ensure the safety of the food supply by enforcing standards in the use of canning, pasteurization, irradiation, and chemical preservatives, and by insisting that food preparers and handlers wash their hands and use sanitized utensils. The Department of Agriculture also provides for the inspection of meats for the presence of pathogens such as *E. coli* and tapeworms.

Milk is an especially rich food, and the same nutrients that nourish us also facilitate the growth of many microorganisms. In the past, contaminated milk has been responsible for epidemics of tuberculosis, brucellosis, typhoid fever, scarlet fever, and diphtheria. Today, public health agencies require the pasteurization of milk, and as a result disease transmission via milk has been practically eliminated in the United States.

Individuals should assume responsibility for their own health by washing their hands before and during food preparation, using disinfectants on kitchen surfaces, and using proper refrigeration and freezing procedures. It is also important to thoroughly cook all meats.

Public health officials also work to control vectors, especially mosquitoes and rodents, by eliminating breeding grounds such as stagnant pools of water and garbage dumps. Insecticides have been used with some success to control insects.

### Public Health Education

Diseases that are transmitted sexually or through the air are particularly difficult for public health officials to control. In these cases, individuals must take responsibility for their own health, and health departments can only educate the public to make healthy choices.

Colds and flu remain the most common diseases in the United States because of the ubiquity of the viral pathogens and their mode of transmission in aerosols and via fomites. Health departments encourage afflicted people to remain at home, use disposable tissues to reduce the spread of viruses, and avoid crowds of coughing, sneezing people. As we have discussed, handwashing is also important in preventing the introduction of cold and flu viruses onto the conjunctiva.

We as a society are faced with several epidemics of sexually transmitted diseases. Syphilis, gonorrhea, genital warts, and sexually transmitted AIDS are completely preventable if the chain of transmission is interrupted by abstinence or mutually faithful monogamy. Their incidence can be reduced, but not eliminated, by the use of condoms. Based on the premise that "an ounce of prevention is worth a pound of cure," public health agencies expend considerable effort in public campaigns to educate people to make good choices—those that can result in healthier individuals and improved health for the public at large.

## Chapter Summary

### Symbiotic Relationships Between Microbes and Their Hosts

1. Microbes live with their hosts in **symbiotic** relationships, including **mutualism,** in which both members benefit; **parasitism,** in which a parasite benefits while the **host** is harmed; and more rarely **commensalism,** in which one member benefits while the other is relatively unaffected. Any parasite that causes disease is called a **pathogen.**

2. Organisms called **normal microbiota** live in and on the body. Some of these microbes are resident, whereas others are transient.

3. **Opportunistic pathogens** cause disease when the immune system is suppressed, when normal **microbial antagonism (competition)** is affected by certain changes in the body, and when a member of the normal microbiota is introduced into an area of the body unusual for that microbe.

### Reservoirs of Infectious Diseases of Humans

1. Living and nonliving continuous sources of infectious disease are called **reservoirs of infection.** Animal reservoirs harbor agents of **zoonoses,** which are diseases of animals that may be spread to humans via direct contact with the animal or its waste products, or via an arthropod. Humans may be asymptomatic **carriers.**

2. **Nonliving reservoirs** of infection include soil, water, and inanimate objects.

### The Movement of Microbes into Hosts: Infection

1. Microbial **contamination** refers to the mere presence of microbes in or on the body or object. Microbial contaminants include harmless resident and transient members of the microbiota, as well as pathogens, which after a successful invasion cause an **infection.**

2. **Portals of entry** of pathogens into the body include skin, mucous membranes, and the placenta. These portals may be bypassed via the **parenteral route,** by which microbes are directly deposited into deeper tissues.

3. Pathogens attach to cells—a process called **adhesion**—via a variety of structures or attachment proteins called **adhesion factors.** Some bacteria and viruses lose the ability to make adhesion factors called adhesins and thereby become **avirulent.**

4. Some bacteria interact to produce a sticky web of cells and polysaccharides called a **biofilm** that adheres to a surface.

## The Nature of Infectious Disease

1. **Disease,** also known as **morbidity,** is a condition sufficiently adverse to interfere with normal functioning of the body.

2. **Symptoms** are subjectively felt by a patient, whereas an outside observer can observe **signs.** A **syndrome** is a group of symptoms and signs that collectively characterizes a particular abnormal condition.

3. **Asymptomatic** or **subclinical** infections may go unnoticed because of the absence of symptoms, even though clinical tests might reveal signs of disease.

4. **Etiology** is the study of the cause of a disease.

5. Nineteenth-century microbiologists proposed the **germ theory of disease,** and Robert Koch developed a series of essential conditions called **Koch's postulates** to prove the cause of infectious diseases. Certain circumstances can make the use of these postulates difficult or even impossible.

6. **Pathogenicity** is a microorganism's ability to cause disease; **virulence** is a measure of pathogenicity. **Virulence factors** such as adhesion factors, extracellular enzymes, toxins, and antiphagocytic factors affect the relative ability of a pathogen to infect and cause disease.
   **ANIMATIONS:** *Virulence Factors: Hiding from Host Defenses, Inactivating Host Defenses, Penetrating Host Tissues; Phagocytosis: Microbes That Evade It*

7. **Toxemia** is the presence in the blood of poisons called **toxins. Exotoxins** are secreted by pathogens into their environment. **Endotoxin,** also known as **lipid A,** is released from the cell wall of dead and dying Gram-negative bacteria and can have fatal effects.
   **ANIMATIONS:** *Virulence Factors: Exotoxins, Endotoxins*

8. **Antitoxins** are antibodies the host forms against toxins.

9. The **disease process**—the stages of infectious diseases—typically consists of the **incubation period, prodromal period, illness, decline,** and **convalescence.**

## The Movement of Pathogens Out of Hosts: Portals of Exit

1. **Portals of exit,** such as the nose, mouth, and urethra, allow pathogens to leave the body and are of interest in studying the spread of disease.

## Modes of Infectious Disease Transmission

**ANIMATIONS:** *Epidemiology: Transmission of Disease*

1. **Direct contact transmission** of infectious diseases involves person-to-person spread by body contact. When pathogens are transmitted via inanimate objects (called **fomites**), it is called **indirect contact transmission.**

2. **Droplet transmission** (a third type of contact transmission) occurs when pathogens travel less than 1 meter in droplets of mucus to a new host as a result of speaking, coughing, or sneezing.

3. **Vehicle transmission** involves **airborne, waterborne,** and **foodborne** transmission. **Aerosols** are clouds of water droplets, which travel more than 1 meter in airborne transmission. **Fecal-oral infection** can result from sewage-contaminated drinking water or from ingesting fecal contaminants. **Bodily fluid transmission** is the spread of pathogens via blood, urine, saliva, or other fluids.

4. **Vectors** transmit pathogens between hosts. **Biological** vectors are animals, usually biting arthropods, that serve as both host and vector of pathogens. **Mechanical vectors** are not hosts to the pathogens they carry.

## Classification of Infectious Diseases

1. There are various ways in which infectious disease may be grouped and studied. When grouped by time course and severity, disease may be described as **acute, subacute, chronic,** or **latent.**

2. When an infectious disease comes either directly or indirectly from another host, it is considered a **communicable** disease. If a communicable disease is easily transmitted from a reservoir or patient, it is called a **contagious** disease. **Noncommunicable** diseases arise either from outside of hosts or from normal microbiota.

## Epidemiology of Infectious Diseases

1. **Epidemiology** is the study of where and when diseases occur, and how they are transmitted within populations.
   **ANIMATIONS:** *Epidemiology: Overview*

2. Epidemiologists track the **incidence** (number of new cases) and **prevalence** (total number of cases) of a disease, and classify disease outbreaks as **endemic** (usually present), **sporadic** (occasional), **epidemic** (more cases than usual), or **pandemic** (epidemic on more than one continent).
   **ANIMATIONS:** *Epidemiology: Occurrence of Disease*

3. **Descriptive epidemiology** is the careful recording of data concerning a disease; it often includes detection of the **index case**—the first case of the disease in a given area or population. **Analytical epidemiology** seeks to determine the probable cause of a disease. **Experimental epidemiology** involves testing a hypothesis resulting from analytical studies.

4. **Nosocomial infections** and **nosocomial diseases** are acquired by patients or workers in health care facilities. They may be **exogenous** (acquired from the health care environment), **endogenous** (derived from normal microbiota that become opportunistic while in the hospital setting), or **iatrogenic** (induced by treatment or medical procedures).
   **ANIMATIONS:** *Nosocomial Infections: Overview*

5. Health care workers can help protect their patients and themselves from exposure to pathogens by handwashing and other aseptic and disinfecting techniques.
   **ANIMATIONS:** *Nosocomial Infections: Prevention*

6. Public health organizations such as the World Health Organization (WHO) use epidemiological data to promulgate rules and standards for clean, **potable** water and safe food, to prevent disease by controlling vectors and animal reservoirs, and to educate people to make healthy choices concerning the prevention of disease.

# Questions for Review
*Answers to the Questions for Review (except Short Answer questions) appear at the end of this chapter.*

## Multiple Choice

1. In which type of symbiosis do both members benefit from their interaction?
   a. mutualism
   b. parasitism
   c. commensalism
   d. pathogenesis

2. An axenic environment is one that
   a. exists in the human mouth.
   b. contains only one species.
   c. exists in the human colon.
   d. both a and c

3. Which of the following is *false* concerning microbial contaminants?
   a. Contaminants may become opportunistic pathogens.
   b. Most microbial contaminants will eventually cause harm.
   c. Contaminants may be a part of the transient microbiota.
   d. Contaminants may be introduced by a mosquito bite.

4. The most frequent portal of entry for pathogens is
   a. the respiratory tract.
   b. the skin.
   c. the conjunctiva.
   d. a cut or wound.

5. The process by which microorganisms attach themselves to cells is
   a. infection.
   b. contamination.
   c. disease.
   d. adhesion.

6. Which of the following is the correct sequence of events in infectious diseases?
   a. incubation, prodromal period, illness, decline, convalescence
   b. incubation, decline, prodromal period, illness, convalescence
   c. prodromal period, incubation, illness, decline, convalescence
   d. convalescence, prodromal period, incubation, illness, decline

7. Which of the following are most likely to cause disease?
   a. opportunistic pathogens in a weakened host
   b. pathogens lacking the enzyme kinase
   c. pathogens lacking the enzyme collagenase
   d. highly virulent organisms

8. The nature of bacterial capsules
   a. causes widespread blood clotting.
   b. allows phagocytes to readily engulf these bacteria.
   c. affects the virulence of these bacteria.
   d. has no effect on the virulence of bacteria.

9. When pathogenic bacterial cells lose the ability to make adhesins, they typically
   a. become avirulent.
   b. produce endotoxin.
   c. absorb endotoxin.
   d. increase in virulence.

10. A disease in which a pathogen remains inactive for a long period of time before becoming active is termed a(n)
    a. subacute disease.
    b. acute disease.
    c. chronic disease.
    d. latent disease.

11. Which of the following statements is the best definition of a pandemic disease?
    a. It normally occurs in a given geographic area.
    b. It is a disease that occurs more frequently than usual for a geographical area or group of people.
    c. It occurs infrequently at no predictable time scattered over a large area or population.
    d. It is an epidemic that occurs on more than one continent at the same time.

12. Which of the following types of epidemiologists is most like a detective?
    a. a descriptive epidemiologist
    b. an analytical epidemiologist
    c. an experimental epidemiologist
    d. a reservoir epidemiologist

13. Consider the following case. An animal was infected with a virus. A mosquito bit the animal, was contaminated with the virus, and proceeded to bite and infect a person. Which was the vector?
    a. animal
    b. virus
    c. mosquito
    d. person

14. A patient contracted athlete's foot after long-term use of a medication. His physician explained that the malady was directly related to the medication. Such infections are termed
    a. nosocomial infections.
    b. exogenous infections.
    c. iatrogenic infections.
    d. endogenous infections.

15. Which of the following phrases describes a contagious disease?
    a. a disease arising from fomites
    b. a disease that is easily passed from host to host in aerosols
    c. a disease that arises from opportunistic, normal microbiota
    d. both a and b

## Fill in the Blanks

1. A microbe that causes disease is called a _____.

2. Infections that may go unnoticed due to the absence of symptoms are called _____ infections.

3. The study of the cause of a disease is _____.

4. The study of where and when diseases occur and how they are transmitted within populations is _____.

5. Diseases that are naturally spread from their usual animal hosts to humans are called _____.

6. Nonliving reservoirs of disease, such as a toothbrush, drinking glass, and needle, are called _____.

7. _____ infections are those acquired by patients or staff while in health care facilities.

8. The total number of cases of a disease in a given area is its _____.

9. An animal that carries a pathogen and also serves as host for the pathogen is a _____ vector.

10. Endotoxin is the part of the cell wall known as _____ in a Gram-negative bacterium.

## Labeling

Each map below shows the locations (dots) of cases of a disease that normally occurs in the Western Hemisphere. Label each map with a correct epidemiological description of the disease's occurrence.

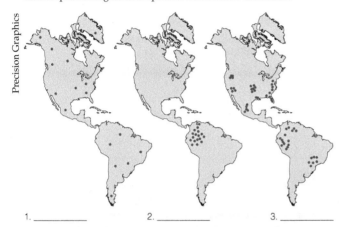

1. _____   2. _____   3. _____

## Short Answer

1. List three types of symbiotic relationships, and give an example of each.

2. List three conditions that create opportunities for pathogens to become harmful in a human.

3. List three portals through which pathogens enter the body.

4. List Koch's four postulates, and describe situations in which not all may be applicable.

5. List in the correct sequence the five stages of infectious diseases.

6. Describe three modes of disease transmission.

7. Describe the parenteral route of infection.

8. In general, contrast transient microbiota with resident microbiota.

9. Contrast the terms *infection* and *morbidity*.

10. Contrast iatrogenic and nosocomial diseases.

# Concept Mapping

Using the following terms, draw a concept map that describes disease transmission.
Or, complete this concept map online by going to the Study Area at www.masteringmicrobiology.com.

| | | | |
|---|---|---|---|
| Airborne | Direct contact | Mechanical | Vehicle transmission |
| Arthropods | Droplet transmission | Mosquito | Waterborne |
| Biological | Fomites | Sneezing | |
| Body | Foodborne | Tick | |
| Contact transmission | Indirect contact | Vector transmission | |

# Critical Thinking

1. Explain why Ellen H., a menopausal woman, may have developed gingivitis from normal microbiota.

2. Will P. died of *E. coli* infection after an intestinal puncture. Explain why this microbe, which normally lives in the colon, could kill this patient.

3. Examine the graph of the red epidemic and the blue epidemic. Neither red disease nor blue disease is treatable. A person with either disease is ill for only 1 day and recovers fully. Both epidemics began at the same time. Which epidemic affected more people during the first 3 days? What could explain the short time course for the red epidemic? Why was the blue epidemic longer lasting?

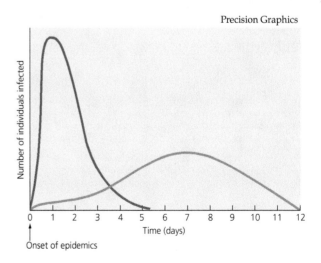

Precision Graphics

4. A 27-year-old female came to her doctor's office with a widespread rash, fever, malaise, and severe muscle pain. The symptoms had begun with a mild headache 3 days previously. She reported being bitten by a tick 1 week prior to that.

    The doctor correctly diagnosed Rocky Mountain spotted fever (RMSF) and prescribed tetracycline. The rash and other signs and symptoms disappeared in a couple of days, but she continued on her antibiotic therapy for 2 weeks.

    Draw a graph showing the course of disease and the relative numbers of pathogens over time. Label the stages of the disease.

5. Over 30 children younger than 3 years of age developed gastroenteritis after visiting a local water park. These cases represented 44% of the park visitors in this age group on the day in question. No older individuals were affected. The causative agent was determined to be a member of the bacterial genus *Shigella*. The disease resulted from oral transmission to the children.

Based only on the information given, can you classify this outbreak as an epidemic? Why or why not? If you were an epidemiologist, how would you go about determining which pools in the water park were contaminated? What factors might account for the fact that no older children or adults developed disease? What steps could the park operators take to reduce the chance of future outbreaks of gastroenteritis?

6. Describe the relationship between the photosynthetic member of the lichen and the fungus in terms of the type of symbiosis.

7. Using the data in the Clinical Case Study, calculate the incidence of Legionnaires' disease in Bogalusa, Louisiana.

Access more review material online in the Study Area at **www.masteringmicrobiology.com.** There, you'll find
- **Animations**
- **MP3 Tutor Sessions**
- **Concept Mapping Activities**
- **Flashcards**
- **Quizzes**

and more to help you succeed.

# Answers

Answers to multiple-choice, fill-in-blank, labeling, matching, and true/false questions are listed here. Answers for Short Answer and Critical Thinking questions are available for instructors only in the Instructor's Manual that accompanies this text.

**Multiple Choice**
1. a; 2. b; 3. b; 4. a; 5. d; 6. a; 7. d; 8. c; 9. a; 10. d; 11. d; 12. b; 13. c; 14. d; 15. b

**Fill in the Blanks**
1. pathogen; 2. asymptomatic or subclinical; 3. etiology; 4. epidemiology; 5. zoonoses; 6. fomites; 7. Nosocomial; 8. prevalence; 9. biological; 10. lipid A

**Labeling**
1. Endemic (or sporadic); 2. Epidemic; 3. Pandemic

# Innate
# Immunity

Each day the equivalent of a small room full of air enters your respiratory tract through your nose. With that air come dust, smoke, bacteria, viruses, fungi, pollen, soot, fuzz, sand, and more. Acting as a first line of defense, your respiratory mucous membrane uses nose hairs, ciliated epithelium, and mucus to cleanse the inhaled air of pathogens and certain harmful pollutants. Each day you swallow and subsequently digest about a liter of mucus, along with the trapped pathogens and pollutants it contains. Still more nasal mucus clumps around microbes and pollutants to form masses of mucus that may dry out or remain slimy, depending on how rapidly you're breathing and the humidity of the air. Yellowish or greenish mucus contains a large population of trapped bacteria, their waste products, and dead or dying defensive white blood cells.

Mucus is just one example of the body's general defenses against pathogens. The skin and certain protective cells, chemicals, and processes within the body are other ways the body limits early stages of infection by microbes. In this chapter we will focus on each of these aspects of the body's defenses.

**Take the pre-test for this chapter online. Visit the Study Area at www.masteringmicrobiology.com.**

Cilia, such as these lining the upper respiratory tract, move mucus and contaminants out of the body.

From Chapter 15 of *Microbiology with Diseases by Taxonomy*, Third Edition. Robert W. Bauman. Copyright © 2011 by Pearson Education, Inc. Published by Benjamin Cummings, Inc. All rights reserved.

A pathogen can cause a disease only if it can (1) gain access, either by penetrating the surface of the skin or by entering through some other portal of entry; (2) attach itself to host cells; and (3) evade the body's defense mechanisms long enough to produce harmful changes. In this chapter we will examine the structures, processes, and chemicals that respond in a general way to protect the body from all types of pathogens.

# An Overview of the Body's Defenses

## Learning Objectives

✓ List and briefly describe the three lines of defense in the human body.

✓ Explain the phrases *species resistance* and *innate immunity*.

Because the cells and certain basic physiological processes of humans are incompatible with those of most plant and animal pathogens, humans have what is termed **species resistance** to these pathogens. In many cases the chemical receptors these pathogens require for attachment to a host cell do not exist in the human body; in other cases the pH or temperature of the human body are incompatible with the conditions under which these pathogens can survive. Thus, for example, all humans have species resistance to both tobacco mosaic virus and to the virus that causes feline immunodeficiency syndrome in members of the cat family.

Nevertheless, we are confronted every day with pathogens that can cause disease in humans. Bacteria, viruses, fungi, protozoa, and parasitic worms come in contact with your body in the air you breathe, in the water you drink, in the food you eat, and during the contacts you have with other people. Your body must defend itself from these potential pathogens, and in some cases from members of your normal microbiota, which may become opportunistic pathogens.

It is convenient to cluster the structures, cells, and chemicals that act against pathogens into three main lines of defense, each of which overlaps and reinforces the other two. The first line of defense is chiefly composed of external physical barriers to pathogens, especially the skin and mucous membranes. The second line of defense is internal and is composed of protective cells, bloodborne chemicals, and processes that inactivate or kill invaders. Together, the first two lines of defense are called **innate immunity** because they are present at birth prior to contact with infectious agents or their products. Innate immunity is rapid and works against a wide variety of pathogens, including parasitic worms, protozoa, fungi, bacteria, and viruses.

By contrast, the third line of defense, **adaptive immunity,** responds against unique species or strains of pathogens and alters the body's defenses such that they act more effectively upon subsequent infection with the specific strain. Here we turn our attention to the two lines of innate immunity.
**ANIMATIONS:** *Host Defenses: Overview*

SEM | 40 μm

David Scharf/Peter Arnold

▲ **Figure 1** **A scanning electron micrograph of a section of skin.** Epidermal cells are dead, dry, and slough off, providing an effective barrier to most microorganisms.

# The Body's First Line of Defense

The body's initial line of defense is made up of structures, chemicals, and processes that work together to prevent pathogens from entering the body in the first place. Here we discuss the main components of the first line of defense: the skin and the mucous membranes of the respiratory, digestive, urinary, and reproductive systems. These structures provide a formidable barrier to the entrance of microorganisms. If these barriers are pierced, broken, or otherwise damaged, they become portals of entry for pathogens. In this section we examine aspects of the first line of defense, including the role of the normal microbiota.

## The Role of Skin in Innate Immunity

### Learning Objective

✓ Identify the physical and chemical aspects of skin that enable it to prevent the entrance of pathogens.

The skin—the organ of the body with the greatest surface area—is composed of two major layers: an outer **epidermis,** and a deeper **dermis,** which contains hair follicles, glands, and nerve endings. Both the physical structure and the chemical components of skin enable it to act as an effective defense.

The epidermis is composed of multiple layers of tightly packed cells. It constitutes a physical barrier to most bacteria, fungi, and viruses. Very few pathogens can penetrate the layers of epidermal cells unless the skin has been burned, broken, or cut.

The deepest cells of the epidermis continually divide, pushing their daughter cells toward the surface. As the daughter cells are pushed toward the surface, they flatten and die and are eventually shed in flakes (Figure 1). Microorganisms that attach to the skin's surface are sloughed off with the flakes of

# BENEFICIAL MICROBES

## WHAT HAPPENS TO ALL THAT SKIN?

▲ **Dust mite.** SEM 100 μm

Your body sheds tens of thousands of skin flakes every time you walk or move, and you shed at only a slightly lower rate when you stand still. That comes to about 10 billion skin cells per day, or 250 grams (about half a pound) of skin every year! What happens to all that skin?

Much of household dust is skin that you and your housemates have shed as you go about your lives. The skin flakes fall to the rug and upholstery, where they become food for microscopic mites that live sedentary and harmless lives waiting patiently for meals to rain down on them from above. They dwell not only in the rug, but also in your mattress and pillow, and even in the hair follicles of your eyebrows, benefiting you by catching skin cells cascading down your forehead before they can irritate your eyes.

By the way, house dust also contains mite feces and mite skeletons, which can trigger allergies. So after reading this chapter, you just might want to clean your carpet.

---

dead cells. **Beneficial Microbes: What Happens to All That Skin?** describes the fate of lost epidermal cells.

The epidermis also contains phagocytic cells called **dendritic[1] cells.** The slender, fingerlike processes of dendritic cells extend among the surrounding cells, forming an almost continuous network to intercept invaders. Dendritic cells both phagocytize pathogens nonspecifically and play a role in adaptive immunity.

The combination of the barrier function of the epidermis, its continual replacement, and the presence of phagocytic dendritic cells provides significant nonspecific defense against colonization and infection by pathogens.

The dermis also defends nonspecifically. It contains tough fibers of a protein called collagen. These give the skin strength and pliability to prevent jabs and scrapes from penetrating the dermis and introducing microorganisms. Blood vessels in the dermis deliver defensive cells and chemicals, which will be discussed shortly.

In addition to its physical structure, the skin has a number of chemical substances that nonspecifically defend against pathogens. Dermal cells secrete antimicrobial peptides and sweat glands secrete perspiration, which contains salt, antimicrobial peptides, and lysozyme. Salt draws water osmotically from invading cells, which inhibits their growth and kills them.

**Antimicrobial peptides** (sometimes called *defensins*) are positively charged chains of 20–50 amino acids that act against microorganisms. Sweat glands secrete a class of antimicrobial peptides called *dermicidins*. Dermicidins are broad-spectrum antimicrobials that are active against many Gram-negative and Gram-positive bacteria and fungi. As expected of a peptide active on the surface of the skin, dermicidins are insensitive to low pH and salt. The exact mechanism of dermicidin action is not known.

**Lysozyme** (lī'sō-zīm) is an enzyme that destroys the cell walls of bacteria by cleaving the bonds between the sugar subunits of the walls. Bacteria without cell walls are more

susceptible to osmotic shock and digestion by other enzymes within phagocytes (discussed later in the chapter as part of the second line of defense).

The skin also contains sebaceous (oil) glands that secrete **sebum** (sē'bŭm), an oily substance that not only helps keep the skin pliable and less sensitive to breaking or tearing but also contains fatty acids that lower the pH of the skin's surface to about pH 5, which is inhibitory to many bacteria.

Although salt, defensins, lysozyme, and acidity make the surface of the skin an inhospitable environment for most microorganisms, some bacteria, such as *Staphylococcus epidermidis* (staf'i-lō-kok'ŭs ep-i-der-mid'is), find the skin a suitable environment for growth and reproduction. Bacteria are particularly abundant in crevices around hairs and in the ducts of glands; usually they are nonpathogenic.

In summary, the skin is a complex barrier that limits access by microbes.

### CRITICAL THINKING

Some strains of *Staphylococcus aureus* produce exfoliative toxin, a chemical that causes portions of the entire outer layer of the skin to be sloughed off in a disease called scalded skin syndrome. Given that cells of the outer layer are going to fall off anyway, why is this disease dangerous?

## The Role of Mucous Membranes in Innate Immunity

### Learning Objectives

✓ Identify the locations of the body's mucous membranes.

✓ Explain how mucous membranes protect the body both physically and chemically.

Mucus-secreting (mucous) membranes, a second part of the first line of defense, cover all body cavities that are open to the outside environment. Thus mucous membranes line the

---

[1] Form Greek *dendron*, meaning tree, referring to their branched appearance.

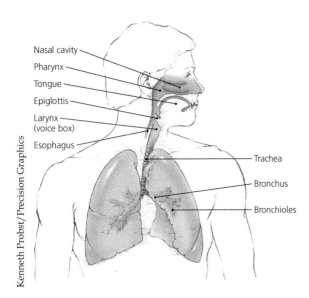

▲ **Figure 2** **The structure of the respiratory system, which is lined with a mucous membrane.** The epithelium of the trachea contains mucus-secreting goblet cells and ciliated cells whose cilia propel the mucus (and the microbes trapped within it) up to the larynx for removal. *What is the function of stem cells within the respiratory epithelium?*

*Figure 2 Stem cells in the respiratory epithelium undergo cytokinesis to form both ciliated cells and goblet cells to replace those lost during normal shedding.*

(Labels on figure:)
Nasal cavity
Pharynx
Tongue
Epiglottis
Larynx (voice box)
Esophagus
Trachea
Bronchus
Bronchioles

Kenneth Probst/Precision Graphics

| | Skin | Mucous Membrane |
|---|---|---|
| **Number of cell layers** | Many | One to a few |
| **Cells tightly packed?** | Yes | Yes |
| **Cells dead or alive?** | Outer layers: dead; inner layers: alive | Alive |
| **Mucus present?** | No | Yes |
| **Relative water content** | Dry | Moist |
| **Defensins present?** | Yes | With some |
| **Lysozyme present?** | Yes | With some |
| **Sebum present?** | Yes | No |
| **Cilia present?** | No | Trachea, uterine tubes |
| **Constant shedding and replacement of cells?** | Yes | Yes |

**TABLE 1**

# The First Line of Defense: A Comparison of the Skin and Mucous Membranes

lumens[2] of the respiratory, urinary, digestive, and reproductive tracts. Like the skin, mucous membranes act nonspecifically to limit infection both physically and chemically.

Mucous membranes are moist and have two distinct layers: the *epithelium,* in which cells from a covering that is superficial (closest to the surface, in this case the lumen), and a deeper connective tissue layer that provides mechanical and nutritive support for the epithelium. Epithelial cells of mucous membranes are packed closely together, like those of the epidermis, but they form only a thin layer. Indeed, in some mucous membranes, the epithelium is only a single cell thick. Unlike surface epidermal cells, surface cells of mucous membranes are alive and play roles in the diffusion of nutrients and oxygen (in the digestive, respiratory, and female reproductive systems) and in the elimination of wastes (in the urinary, respiratory, and female reproductive systems).

The thin epithelium on the surface of a mucous membrane provides a less efficient barrier to the entrance of pathogens than the multiple layers of dead cells found at the skin's surface. So how are microorganisms kept from invading through these thin mucous membranes? In some cases they are not, which is why some mucous membranes, especially those of the respiratory and reproductive systems, are common portals of entry for pathogens. Nevertheless, the epithelial cells of mucous membranes are tightly packed to prevent the entry of

[2]A lumen is a cavity or channel within any tubular structure or organ.

many pathogens, and the cells are continually shed and then replaced via the cytokinesis of **stem cells,** which are generative cells capable of dividing to form daughter cells of various types. One effect of such shedding is that it carries attached microorganisms away.

Dendritic cells reside below the mucous epithelium to phagocytize invaders. These cells are also able to extend pseudopodia between epithelial cells to "sample" the contents of the lumen, which helps prepare adaptive immune responses against particular pathogens that might breach the mucosal barrier.

In addition, the epithelia of some mucous membranes have still other means of removing pathogens. In the mucous membrane of the trachea, for example, the stem cells produce both *goblet cells,* which secrete an extremely sticky mucus that traps bacteria and other pathogens, and *ciliated columnar cells,* whose cilia propel the mucus and its trapped particles and pathogens up from the lungs (Figure 2). The effect of the action of the cilia is often likened to that of an escalator. Mucus carried into the throat is coughed up and either swallowed or expelled. Because the poisons and tars in tobacco smoke damage cilia, the lungs of smokers are not properly cleared of mucus, so smokers may develop severe coughs as their respiratory tracts attempt to expel excess mucus from the lungs. Smokers also typically succumb to more respiratory pathogens, because they are unable to effectively clear pathogens from their lungs.

In addition to these physical actions, mucous membranes produce chemicals that defend against pathogens. Nasal mucus contains lysozyme, which chemically destroys bacterial cell walls. Mucus also contains antimicrobial peptides (defensins). Table 1 compares the physical and chemical actions of the skin and mucous membranes in the body's first line of defense.

## The Role of the Lacrimal Apparatus in Innate Immunity

### Learning Objective

✓ Describe the lacrimal apparatus and the role of tears in combating infection.

The lacrimal apparatus is a group of structures that produce and drain away tears (Figure 3). Lacrimal glands, located above and to the sides of the eyes, secrete tears into lacrimal gland ducts and onto the surface of the eyes. The tears either evaporate or drain into small lacrimal canals, which carry them into nasolacrimal ducts that empty into the nose. There, the tears join the nasal mucus and flow into the pharynx, where they are swallowed. The blinking action of eyelids spreads the tears and washes the surfaces of the eyes. Normally, evaporation and flow into the nose balance the flow of tears onto the eye. However, if the eyes are irritated, increased tear production floods the eyes, carrying the irritant away. In addition to their washing action, tears contain lysozyme, which destroys bacteria.

## The Role of Normal Microbiota in Innate Immunity

### Learning Objective

✓ Define *normal microbiota* and explain how they help provide protection against disease.

The skin and mucous membranes of the body are normally home to a variety of protozoa, fungi, bacteria, and viruses. This **normal microbiota** plays a role in protecting the body by competing with potential pathogens in a variety of ways, a situation called **microbial antagonism.**

A variety of activities of the normal microbiota make it less likely that a pathogen can compete with them and produce disease. Microbiota consume nutrients, making them unavailable to pathogens. Additionally, normal microbiota can change the pH, creating an environment that is favorable for themselves but unfavorable to other microorganisms.

Further, the presence of microbiota stimulates the body's second line of defense (discussed shortly). Researchers have observed that animals raised in an *axenic*[3] (ā-zēn'ik) environment—that is, one free of all other organisms or viruses—are slower to defend themselves when exposed to a pathogen. Recent studies have shown that members of the normal microbiota in the intestines boost the production of anti microbial substances by the body.

Finally, the resident microbiota of the intestines improve overall health by providing several vitamins, including biotin and pantothenic acid (vitamin $B_5$), which are important in glucose metabolism; folic acid, which is essential for the production of the purine and pyrimidine bases of nucleic acids; and the precursor of vitamin K, which has an important role in blood clotting.

[3]From Greek *a*, meaning no, and *xenos*, meaning foreigner.

**Anterior view**

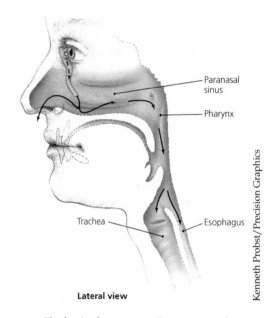

**Lateral view**

Kenneth Probst/Precision Graphics

▲ **Figure 3  The lacrimal apparatus.** These structures function in the body's first line of defense by bathing the eye with tears. Arrows indicate the route tears take across the eye and into the throat. *Name an antimicrobial protein found in tears.*

Figure 3 *Tears contain lysozyme, an antimicrobial protein that acts against the peptidoglycan of bacterial cell walls.*

## Other First-Line Defenses

### Learning Objective

✓ Describe antimicrobial peptides as part of the body's defenses.

Besides the physical barrier of the skin and mucous membranes, there are other hindrances to microbial invasion. Among these are additional antimicrobial peptides and other processes and chemicals.

## TABLE 2

### Secretions and Activities That Contribute to the First Line of Defense

| Secretion/Activity | Function |
| --- | --- |
| **Digestive System** | |
| Saliva | Washes microbes from teeth, gums, tongue, and palate; contains lysozyme, an antibacterial enzyme |
| Stomach acid | Digests and/or inhibits microorganisms |
| Gastroferritin | Sequesters iron being absorbed, making it unavailable for microbial use |
| Bile | Inhibitory to most microorganisms |
| Intestinal secretions | Digests and/or inhibits microorganisms |
| Peristalsis | Moves gastrointestinal contents through GI tract, constantly eliminating potential pathogens |
| Defecation | Eliminates microorganisms |
| Vomiting | Eliminates microorganisms |
| **Urinary System** | |
| Urine | Contains lysozyme; urine's acidity inhibits microorganisms; may wash microbes from ureters and urethra during urination |
| **Reproductive System** | |
| Vaginal secretions | Acidity inhibits microorganisms; contains iron-binding proteins that sequester iron, making it unavailable for microbial use |
| Menstrual flow | Cleanses uterus and vagina |
| Prostate secretion | Contains iron-binding proteins that sequester iron, making it unavailable for microbial use |
| **Cardiovascular System** | |
| Blood flow | Removes microorganisms from wounds |
| Coagulation | Prevents entrance of many pathogens |
| Transferrin | Binds iron for transport, making it unavailable for microbial use |

## Antimicrobial Peptides

As we saw in our examination of skin and mucous membranes, antimicrobial peptides (sometimes called defensins) act against microorganisms. Scientists have discovered hundreds of these antimicrobial peptides in organisms as diverse as silkworms, frogs, and humans. Besides being secreted onto the surface of the skin, antimicrobial peptides are found in mucous membranes and in neutrophils. These peptides act against a variety of potential pathogens, being triggered by sugar and protein molecules on the external surfaces of microbes. Some antimicrobial peptides act only against Gram-positive bacteria or Gram-negative bacteria, others act against both, and still others act against protozoa, enveloped viruses, or fungi.

Researchers have elucidated several ways in which antimicrobial peptides work. Some punch holes in the cytoplasmic membranes of the pathogens, while others interrupt internal signaling or enzymatic action. Some antimicrobial peptides are chemotactic factors that recruit leukocytes to the site.

### Other Processes and Chemicals

Many other body organs contribute to the first line of defense by secreting chemicals with antimicrobial properties that are secondary to their prime function. For example, stomach acid is primarily present to aid digestion of proteins, but it also prevents the growth of many potential pathogens. Likewise, saliva contains lysozyme as well as a digestive enzyme; further, saliva physically washes microbes from the teeth. The contributions of these and other processes and chemicals to the first line of defense are listed in Table 2.

# The Body's Second Line of Defense

### Learning Objective

✓ Compare and contrast the body's first and second lines of defense against disease.

When pathogens succeed in penetrating the skin or mucous membranes, the body's second line of innate defense comes into play. Like the first line of defense, the second line operates against a wide variety of pathogens, from parasitic worms to viruses. But unlike the first line of defense, the second line includes no barriers; instead, it is composed of cells (especially phagocytes), antimicrobial chemicals (peptides, complement, interferons), and processes (inflammation, fever). Some cells and chemicals from the first line of defense play additional roles in the second line of defense. We will consider each component of the second line of defense in some detail shortly, but because many of them are either contained in or originate in the blood, we first consider the components of blood.

## Defense Components of Blood

### Learning Objectives

✓ Discuss the components of blood and their functions in the body's defense.

✓ Explain how macrophages are named.

Blood is a complex liquid tissue composed of cells and portions of cells within a fluid called *plasma*. We begin our discussion of the defense functions of blood by briefly considering plasma.

### Plasma

**Plasma** is mostly water containing electrolytes (ions), dissolved gases, nutrients, and—most relevant to the body's defenses—a variety of proteins. Some plasma proteins are involved in inflammation (discussed later) and in blood clotting, a defense

▶ **Figure 4**
**A schematic representation of hematopoiesis.** In this process the division of stem cells in the bone marrow produces three types of formed (cellular) elements: erythrocytes, platelets, and leukocytes.

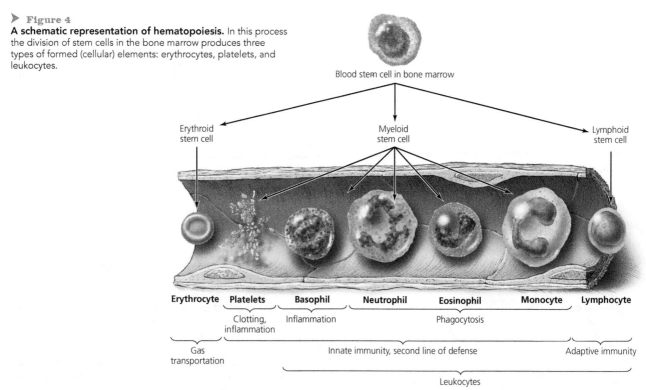

Blood stem cell in bone marrow

Erythroid stem cell

Myeloid stem cell

Lymphoid stem cell

| Erythrocyte | Platelets | Basophil | Neutrophil | Eosinophil | Monocyte | Lymphocyte |

Clotting, inflammation | Inflammation | Phagocytosis

Gas transportation | Innate immunity, second line of defense | Adaptive immunity

Leukocytes

Kenneth Probst/Precision Graphics

mechanism that reduces both blood loss and the risk of infection. When clotting factors have been removed from the plasma, as for instance when blood clots, the remaining liquid is called *serum.*

Most cells require iron for metabolism: it is a component of cytochromes of electron transport chains, functions as an enzyme cofactor, and is an essential part of hemoglobin—the oxygen-carrying protein of erythrocytes. Because iron is relatively insoluble, in humans it is transported in plasma to cells by a transport protein called *transferrin.* When transferrin-iron complexes reach cells with receptors for transferrin, the binding of the protein to the receptor stimulates the cell to take up the iron via endocytosis. Excess iron is stored in the liver bound to another protein called *ferritin.*

Though the main function of iron-binding proteins is transporting and storing iron, they play a secondary, defensive role—sequestering iron so that it is unavailable to microorganisms.

Some bacteria, such as *Staphylococcus aureus* (o'rē-ŭs), respond to a shortage of iron by secreting their own iron-binding proteins called *siderophores.* Because siderophores have a greater affinity for iron than does transferrin, bacteria that produce siderophores can in effect steal iron from the body. In response, the body produces *lactoferrin,* which retakes the iron from the bacteria by its even greater affinity. Thus, the body and the pathogens engage in a kind of chemical "tug-of-war" for the possession of iron.

Some pathogens bypass this contest altogether. For example, *Neisseria meningitidis* (nī-se'rē-ă me-nin-ji'ti-dis), a pathogen that causes often fatal meningitis, produces receptors for transferrin and plucks iron from the bloodstream as it flows by. *S. aureus* and related pathogens can secrete the protein *hemolysin,* which punches holes in the cytoplasmic membranes of red blood cells, releasing hemoglobin. Other bacterial proteins then bind hemoglobin to the bacterial membrane and strip it of its iron.

Another group of plasma proteins, called *complement proteins,* is an important part of the second line of defense and is discussed shortly. Still other plasma proteins, called *antibodies* or *immunoglobulins,* are a part of adaptive immunity, the body's third line of defense.

## Defensive Blood Cells: Leukocytes

Cells and cell fragments suspended in the plasma are called **formed elements.** In a process called *hematopoiesis,*[4] blood stem cells located principally in the bone marrow within the hollow cavities of the large bones produce three types of formed elements: **erythrocytes**[5] (ĕ-rith'rō-sītz), **platelets**[6] (plāt'letz), and **leukocytes**[7] (loo'kō-sīts) (Figure 4). Erythrocytes, the most numerous of the formed elements, carry oxygen and carbon dioxide in the blood. Platelets, which are pieces of large cells

[4]From Greek *haima,* meaning blood, and *poiein,* meaning to make.
[5]From Greek *erythro,* meaning red, and *cytos,* meaning cell.
[6]French for small plates. Platelets are also called thrombocytes, from Greek *thrombos,* meaning lump, and *cytos,* meaning cell, though they are technically not cells, but instead pieces of cells.
[7]From Greek *leuko,* meaning white, and *cytos,* meaning cell.

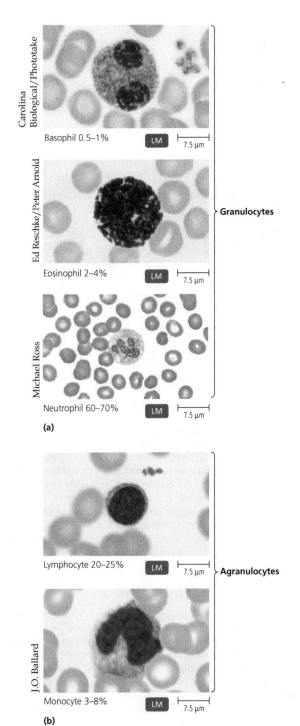

Carolina Biological/Phototake

Basophil 0.5–1% | LM | 7.5 μm

Ed Reschke/Peter Arnold

Eosinophil 2–4% | LM | 7.5 μm

Michael Ross

Neutrophil 60–70% | LM | 7.5 μm

**(a)**

} Granulocytes

Lymphocyte 20–25% | LM | 7.5 μm

J.O. Ballard

Monocyte 3–8% | LM | 7.5 μm

**(b)**

} Agranulocytes

▲ **Figure 5 Leukocytes as seen in stained blood smears.**
**(a)** Granulocytes: basophil, eosinophil, and neutrophil. **(b)** Agranulocytes: lymphocyte and monocyte. The numbers are the normal percentages of each cell type among all leukocytes.

called *megakaryocytes* that have split into small portions of cytoplasm surrounded by cytoplasmic membranes, are involved in blood clotting. Leukocytes, the formed elements that are directly involved in defending the body against invaders, are commonly called white blood cells because they form a whitish layer when the components of blood are separated within a test tube.

Based on their appearance in stained blood smears when viewed under the microscope, leukocytes are divided into two groups: *granulocytes* (gran′ū-lō-sītz) and *agranulocytes* (ā-gran′ū-lō-sītz) (Figure 5).

Granulocytes have large granules in their cytoplasm that stain different colors depending on the type of granulocyte and the dyes used: **basophils** (bā′sō-fils) stain blue with the basic dye methylene blue; **eosinophils** (ē-ō-sin′ō-fils) stain red to orange with the acidic dye eosin; and **neutrophils** (noo′trō-fils), also known as *polymorphonuclear leukocytes* (PMNs), stain lilac with a mixture of acidic and basic dyes. Both neutrophils and eosinophils phagocytize pathogens, and both can exit the blood to attack invading microbes in the tissues by squeezing between the cells lining capillaries (the smallest blood vessels). This process is called **diapedesis**[8] (dī′ă-pĕ-dē′sis) or *emigration*. As we will see later in the chapter, eosinophils are also involved in defending the body against parasitic worms and are present in large number during many allergic reactions, though their exact function in allergies is disputed. Basophils can also leave the blood, though they are not phagocytic; instead, they release inflammatory chemicals, an aspect of the second line of defense that will be discussed shortly.

The cytoplasm of agranulocytes appears uniform when viewed via light microscopy, though granules do become visible with an electron microscope. Agranulocytes are of two types: **lymphocytes** (lim′fō-sītz), which are the smallest leukocytes and have nuclei that nearly fill the cells, and **monocytes** (mon′ō-sītz), which are large agranulocytes with slightly lobed nuclei. Although most lymphocytes are involved in adaptive immunity, *natural killer (NK) lymphocytes* function in innate defense and thus are discussed later in this chapter. Monocytes leave the blood and mature into **macrophages** (mak′rō-fāj-ĕz), which are phagocytic cells of the second line of defense. Their initial function is to devour foreign objects, including bacteria, fungi, spores, and dust, as well as dead body cells.

Macrophages are named for their location in the body. *Wandering macrophages* leave the blood via diapedesis and perform their scavenger function while traveling throughout the body, including extracellular spaces. Other macrophages are fixed and do not wander. These include *alveolar* (al-vē′ō-lăr) *macrophages*[9] of the lungs and *microglia* (mī-krog′lē-ă) of the central nervous system. Fixed macrophages generally phagocytize within specific organs, such as the heart chambers, blood vessels, and lymphatic vessels.

[8]From Greek *dia*, meaning through, and *pedan*, meaning to leap.
[9]Alveoli are small pockets at the end of respiratory passages where oxygen and carbon dioxide exchange occurs between the lungs and the blood.

# CLINICAL CASE STUDY

## Evaluating an Abnormal CBC

**CBC Profile**

| | | |
|---|---|---|
| Name: Brown, Roger | Age/Sex: 61/M | Attend Dr: Kevin, Larry |
| Acct#: 04797747 | Status: ADM IN | |
| Reg: 11/27/09 | | |

| | | | |
|---|---|---|---|
| SPEC #: 0303:AS:H00102T | COLL: 12/03/09-0620 | STATUS: COMP | REQ #: 01797367 |
| | RECD: 12/03/09-0647 | SUBM DR: Kevin, Larry | |
| ENTERED: 12/03/09-0002 | | OTHER DR: NONE, PER PT | |
| ORDERED: CBC W/ MAN DIFF | | | |

| Test | Result | Flag | Reference | Site |
|---|---|---|---|---|
| *CBC* | | | | |
| WBC (white blood cells) | 0.8 | L | 4.8–10.8 K/mm3 | ML |
| RBC (red blood cells) | 3.09 | L | 4.20–5.40 M/mm3 | ML |
| HGB (hemoglobin) | 9.6 | L | 12.0–16.0 g/dL | ML |
| HCT (hematocrit) | 28.2 | L | 37.0–47.0 % | ML |
| MCV | 91.3 | | 81.0–99.0 fL | ML |
| MCH | 31.1 | H | 27.0–31.0 pg | ML |
| MCHC | 34.1 | | 32.0–36.0 g/dl | ML |
| RDW | 17.1 | H | 11.5–14.5 % | ML |
| PLT (platelets) | 21 | L | 150–450 K/mm3 | ML |
| MPV | 8.7 | | 7.4–10.4 fL | ML |
| *DIFF* | | | | |
| CELLS COUNTED | 100 | | #CELLS | ML |
| SEGS | 39 | | % | ML |
| BAND | 4 | | % | ML |
| LYMPH (lymphocytes) | 41 | | % | ML |
| MONO (monocytes) | 15 | | % | ML |
| EOS (eosinophils) | 1 | | % | ML |
| NEUT# (# neutrophils) | 0.3 | L | 1.9–8.0 K/mm3 | ML |
| LYMPH# | 0.3 | L | 0.9–5.2 K/mm3 | ML |
| MONO# | 0.1 | | 0.1–1.2 K/mm3 | ML |
| EOS# | 0.0 | | 0–0.8 K/mm3 | ML |
| PLATELET EST | DECREASED | * | | ML |
| RBC MORPHOLOGY | ABNORMAL | * | | ML |
| *CELL MORPHOLOGY* | | | | |
| ANISOCYTOSIS | MODERATE | * | | ML |
| POIKILOCYTOSIS | MODERATE | | | ML |
| TEAR DROP CELLS | PRESENT | * | | ML |

ML - MAIN LABORATORY

Roger Brown, an African American cancer patient, received a chemotherapeutic agent as a treatment for his disease. The drug used to destroy the cancer also produced an undesirable condition known as bone marrow depression. The complete blood count (CBC) profile shown here indicates that this patient is in trouble. Review the lab values and answer the following questions.

1. Note that the platelet count is very low. How does this affect the patient? Discuss measures to protect him.

2. Note that the white blood cell count is abnormally low. With the second line of defense impaired, how should the first line of defense be protected?

A special group of phagocytes are not white blood cells. These are the dendritic cells, mentioned previously, which are multibranched cells plentiful throughout the body, particularly in the skin and mucous membranes. Dendritic cells await microbial invaders, phagocytize them, and inform cells of adaptive immunity that there is a microbial invasion.

**Lab Analysis of Leukocytes** Analysis of blood for diagnostic purposes, including white blood cell counts, is one task of medical lab technologists. The proportions of leukocytes, as determined in a **differential white blood cell count**, can serve as a sign of disease. For example, an increase in the percentage of eosinophils can indicate allergies or infection with parasitic worms; bacterial diseases typically result in an increase in the number of leukocytes and an increase in the percentage of neutrophils, while viral infections are associated with an increase in the relative number of lymphocytes. The ranges for the normal values for each kind of white blood cell, expressed as a percentage of the total leukocyte population, are shown in Figure 5.

## CRITICAL THINKING

A medical laboratory technologist argues that granulocytes are a natural group, whereas agranulocytes are an artificial grouping. Based on Figure 4, do you agree or disagree with the lab tech? What evidence can you cite to justify your conclusion?

Now that we have some background concerning the defensive properties of plasma components and leukocytes, we turn our attention to the details of the body's second line of defense: phagocytosis, nonphagocytic killing by leukocytes, nonspecific chemical defenses, inflammation, and fever.

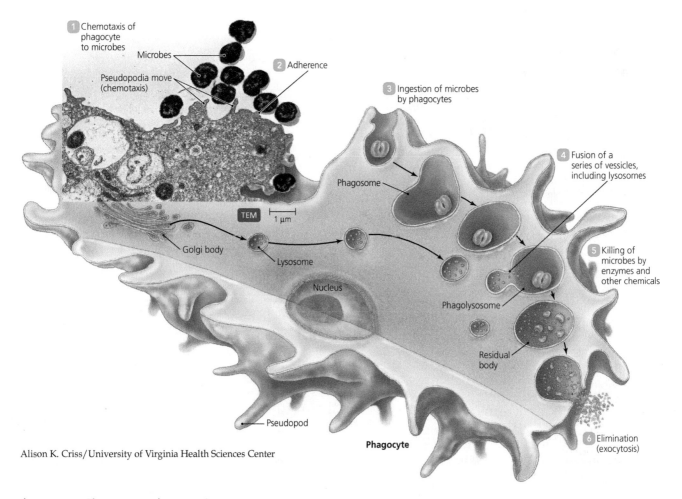

① Chemotaxis of phagocyte to microbes

Microbes

Pseudopodia move (chemotaxis)

② Adherence

③ Ingestion of microbes by phagocytes

④ Fusion of a series of vessicles, including lysosomes

Phagosome

TEM 1 μm

Golgi body

Lysosome

⑤ Killing of microbes by enzymes and other chemicals

Nucleus

Phagolysosome

Residual body

Pseudopod

Phagocyte

⑥ Elimination (exocytosis)

Alison K. Criss/University of Virginia Health Sciences Center

▲ **Figure 6 The events in phagocytosis.**
Here a neutrophil phagocytizes *Neisseria gonorrhoeae*.

## Phagocytosis

### Learning Objective

✓ Name and describe the six stages of phagocytosis.

We examined phagocytosis as a way by which a cell actively transports substances across the cytoplasmic membrane and into the cytoplasm. Here we consider how those cells of the body that are capable of phagocytosis—collectively known as **phagocytes** (fag′ō-sītz)—play a role against pathogens that get past the body's first line of defense. **ANIMATIONS:** *Phagocytosis: Overview*

Phagocytosis is a complex process that is still not completely understood. For the purposes of our discussion, we will divide the continuous process of phagocytosis into six steps: chemotaxis, adherence, ingestion, maturation, killing, and elimination (Figure 6).

### Chemotaxis

*Chemotaxis* is movement of a cell either toward a chemical stimulus (positive chemotaxis) or away from a chemical stimulus (negative chemotaxis). In the case of phagocytes, positive chemotaxis involves the use of *pseudopodia* (sū-dō-pō′dē-ă) to crawl toward microorganisms at the site of an infection (①). Chemicals that attract phagocytic leukocytes include microbial components and secretions, components of damaged tissues and white blood cells, and **chemotactic** (kem-ō-tak′tik) **factors.** Chemotactic factors include defensins, peptides derived from complement (discussed later in this chapter), and chemicals called **chemokines** (kē′mō-kīnz), which are released by leukocytes already at a site of infection.

### Adherence

After arriving at the site of an infection, phagocytes attach to microorganisms through the binding of complementary chemicals such as glycoproteins found on the membranes of cells (2). This process is called **adherence.**

Some bacteria have virulence factors, such as M protein of *Streptococcus pyogenes* (strep-tō-kok'ŭs pī-oj'en-ēz), or slippery capsules that hinder adherence of phagocytes and thereby increase the virulence of the bacteria. Such bacteria are more readily phagocytized if they are pushed up against a surface such as connective tissue, the wall of a blood vessel, or a blood clot.

All pathogens are more readily phagocytized if they are first covered with antimicrobial proteins such as complement proteins (discussed later) or the specific antimicrobial proteins called antibodies. This coating process is called **opsonization**[10] (op'sŭ-nī-zā'shun), and the proteins are called **opsonins.** Generally, opsonins increase the number and kinds of binding sites on a microbe's surface.

### Ingestion

After phagocytes adhere to pathogens, they extend *pseudopodia* to surround the microbe (3). The encompassed microbe is internalized as the pseudopodia fuse to form a food vesicle called a **phagosome.**

### Phagosome Maturation and Microbial Killing

A series of membranous organelles within the phagocyte fuse with newly formed phagosomes to form digestive vesicles. One organelle, the lysosome, adds digestive chemicals to the maturing phagosome, which is now called a **phagolysosome** (fag-ŏ-lī'sō-sōm) (4). Phagolysosomes contain antimicrobial substances, such as highly reactive, toxic forms of oxygen, in an environment with a pH of about 5.5 due to the active pumping of $H^+$ from the cytosol. These factors, along with 30 or so different enzymes such as lipases, proteases, nucleases, and a variety of others, destroy the engulfed microbes (5).

Most pathogens are dead within 30 minutes, though some bacteria contain virulence factors (such as M protein or waxy cell walls) that resist a lysosome's action. In the end, a phagolysosome is known as a *residual body.*

### Elimination

Digestion is not always complete, and phagocytes eliminate remnants of microorganisms via *exocytosis*, a process that is essentially the reverse of ingestion (6). Some microbial components are specially processed and remain attached to the cytoplasmic membrane of some phagocytes, particularly dendritic cells, a phenomenon that plays a role in the adaptive immune response.

**ANIMATIONS:** *Phagocytosis: Mechanism*

How is it that phagocytes destroy invading pathogens, and leave the body's own healthy cells unharmed? At least two mechanisms are responsible for this:

• Some phagocytes have cytoplasmic membrane receptors for various microbial surface components lacking on the body's cells, such as cell wall components or flagellar proteins.

• Opsonins such as complement and antibody provide a signal to the phagocyte.

## Nonphagocytic Killing

### Learning Objective

✓ Describe the role of eosinophils, NK cells, and neutrophils in nonphagocytic killing of microorganisms and parasitic helminths.

Phagocytosis involves killing a pathogen once it has been ingested—that is, once it is inside the phagocyte. In contrast, eosinophils, natural killer cells, and neutrophils can accomplish *killing* without phagocytosis.

### Killing by Eosinophils

As discussed earlier, eosinophils can phagocytize; however, this is not their usual mode of attack. Instead, eosinophils secrete antimicrobial chemicals. They attack parasitic helminths (worms) by attaching to the worm's surface, where they secrete extracellular protein toxins onto the surface of the parasite. These weaken the helminth and may even kill it. **Eosinophilia** (ē-ō-sin'ō-fil-e-ă), an abnormally high number of eosinophils in the blood, is often indicative of helminth infestation.

Besides their attacks against parasitic helminths, eosinophils have recently been discovered to use a never-before-seen tactic against bacteria: Lipopolysaccharide from Gram-negative bacterial cell walls triggers eosinophils to rapidly eject mitochondrial DNA, which combines with previously extruded eosinophil proteins to form a physical barrier. This extracellular structure binds to and then kills the bacteria. This is the first evidence that DNA can have antimicrobial activity, and scientists are investigating exactly how mitochondrial DNA acts as an antibacterial agent.

### Killing by Natural Killer Lymphocytes

**Natural killer lymphocytes** (or **NK cells**) are another type of defensive leukocyte of innate immunity that works by secreting toxins onto the surfaces of virally infected cells and neoplasms (tumors). NK cells identify and spare normal body cells because the latter express membrane proteins similar to those on the NK cells. The ability to distinguish one's own healthy cells from diseased cells and pathogens is discussed.

### Killing by Neutrophils

Neutrophils do not always devour pathogens; they can destroy nearby microbial cells without phagocytosis. They can do this in at least two ways. Enzymes in a neutrophil's cytoplasmic membrane add electrons to oxygen, creating highly reactive superoxide radical $O_2^-$ and hydrogen peroxide ($H_2O_2$). Another enzyme converts these into hypochlorite, the active antimicrobial ingredient in household bleach. These chemicals can kill nearby invaders. Yet another enzyme in the membrane makes nitric oxide, which is a powerful inducer of inflammation.

Scientists have recently discovered another way that neutrophils disable microorganisms in their vicinity. They generate

---

[10]From Greek *opsonein*, meaning to supply food, and *izein*, meaning to cause; thus, loosely, "to prepare for dinner."

## TABLE 3

### Toll-Like Receptors and Their Natural Microbial Binding Partners

| TLR/Location | PAMP (Microbial Molecule) |
|---|---|
| TLR1 Cytoplasmic membrane | Bacterial lipopeptides and certain proteins in multicellular parasites |
| TLR2 Cytoplasmic membrane | Bacterial lipopeptides, lipoteichoic acid (found in Gram-positive cell wall), and cell wall of yeast |
| TLR3 Phagosome membrane | Double-stranded RNA (found only in viruses) |
| TLR4 Cytoplasmic membrane | Lipid A (found in Gram-negative cell wall) |
| TLR5 Cytoplasmic membrane | Flagellin (bacterial flagella) |
| TLR6 Cytoplasmic membrane | Bacterial lipopeptides, lipoteichoic acid (found in Gram-positive cell wall), and cell wall of yeast |
| TLR7 Phagosome membrane | Single-stranded viral RNA |
| TLR8 Phagosome membrane | Single-stranded viral RNA |
| TLR9 Phagosome membrane | Unmethylated cytosine-guanine pairs of viral and bacterial DNA |
| TLR10 Unknown | Unknown |

webs of extracellular fibers nicknamed *NETs* for *neutrophil extracellular traps.* Neutrophils synthesize NETs via a unique form of cellular suicide involving the disintegration of their nuclei. As the nuclear envelope breaks down, DNA and histones are released into the cytosol, and the mixing of nuclear components with cytoplasmic granule membranes and proteins forms NET fibers. Reactive oxygen species—superoxide and peroxide— then kill the neutrophil. The NETs are released from the dying cell as its cytoplasmic membrane ruptures. NETs trap both Gram-positive and Gram-negative bacteria, immobilizing them and sequestering them along with antimicrobial peptides, which kill the bacteria. Thus, even in their dying moments, neutrophils fulfill their role as defensive cells.

## Nonspecific Chemical Defenses Against Pathogens

### Learning Objectives

✓ Define *Toll-like receptors* and describe their action in relation to pathogen-associated molecular patterns.

✓ Describe the location and functions of NOD proteins.

✓ Explain the roles of interferons in innate immunity.

✓ Describe the complement system, including its three activation pathways.

Chemical defenses augment phagocytosis in the second line of defense. The chemicals assist phagocytic cells either by enhancing other features of innate immunity or by directly attacking pathogens. Defensive chemicals include lysozyme and defensins (examined previously) as well as Toll-like receptors, NOD proteins, interferons, and complement.

### Toll-Like Receptors (TLRs)

**Toll-like receptors (TLRs)**[11] are integral membrane proteins produced by phagocytic cells. TLRs act as an early warning system, triggering your body's responses to a number of molecules that are shared by various bacterial or viral pathogens and are absent in humans. These microbial molecules include peptidoglycan, lipopolysaccharide, flagellin, unmethylated pairs of cytosine and guanine nucleotides from bacteria and viruses, double-stranded RNA, and single-stranded viral RNA. Such microbial components are collectively referred to as **pathogen-associated molecular patterns (PAMPs).**

Ten TLRs are known for humans. TLRs 1, 2, 4, 5, and 6 are found spanning cytoplasmic membranes, while TLRs 3, 7, 8, and 9 span phagosome membranes. Some TLRs act alone; others act in pairs to recognize a particular PAMP. For example, TLR3 binds to double-stranded RNA from viruses such as West Nile virus, and TLR2 and TLR6 in conjunction bind to lipoteichoic acid—a component of Gram-positive cell walls. Table 3 summarizes the PAMPs and the membrane locations of the ten known TLRs of humans.

Binding of a PAMP to a Toll-like receptor initiates a number of defensive responses, including apoptosis (cell suicide) of an infected cell, secretion of inflammatory mediators or interferons (both discussed shortly), or production of chemical stimulants of adaptive immune responses. If TLRs fail, much of immune response collapses, leaving the body open to attack by a myriad of pathogens.

Scientists are actively seeking ways to stimulate TLRs, so as to enhance the body's immune response to pathogens and immunizations. In contrast, methods to inhibit TLRs may provide us with ways to counter inflammatory disorders and some hyperimmune responses.

### NOD Proteins

**NOD[12] proteins** are another set of receptors for PAMPs, but NOD proteins are located in a host cell's cytosol rather than in its membranes. Scientists have mostly studied NOD proteins that bind to components of bacterial cell walls. NOD proteins trigger inflammation, apoptosis, and other innate immune responses against bacterial pathogens, though researchers are still elucidating their exact method of action. Mutations in NOD genes are associated with several inflammatory bowel diseases, including Crohn's disease.

---

[11]German, meaning fantastic. Originally referring to a gene of fruit flies, mutations of which cause the flies to be bizarre looking. Toll-like proteins are similar to fruit fly Toll in their amino acid sequence, though not in their function.

[12]Nucleotide-oligomerization domains, referring to their ability to bind a region of a finite number (oligomer) of DNA nucleotides.

## Interferons

So far in this chapter we have focused primarily on how the body defends itself against bacteria and eukaryotes. Now we consider how chemicals in the second line of defense act against viral pathogens.

Viruses use a host's metabolic machinery to produce new viruses. For this reason, it is often difficult to interfere with virus replication without also producing deleterious effects on the host. **Interferons** (in-ter-fēr'onz) are protein molecules released by host cells to nonspecifically inhibit the spread of viral infections. Their lack of specificity means that interferons produced against one viral invader protect somewhat against infection by other types of viruses as well. However, interferons also cause malaise, muscle aches, chills, headache, and fever, which are typically associated with viral infections.

Different cell types produce one of two basic types of interferon when stimulated by viral nucleic acid binding to TLR3, TLR7, or TLR8. Interferons within any given type share certain physical and chemical features, though they are specific to the species that produces them. In general, type I interferons—also known as alpha and beta interferons—are present early in viral infections, whereas type II (gamma) interferon appears somewhat later in the course of infection. Because their actions are identical, we examine alpha and beta interferons together before discussing gamma interferon.

**Type I (Alpha and Beta) Interferons** Within hours after infection, virally infected monocytes, macrophages, and some lymphocytes secrete small amounts of **alpha interferon (IFN-α);** similarly, fibroblasts, which are undifferentiated cells in such connective tissues as cartilage, tendon, and bone, secrete small amounts of **beta interferon (IFN-β)** when infected by viruses. The structures of alpha and beta interferons are similar, and their actions are identical.

Interferons do not protect the cells that secrete them—these cells are already infected with viruses. Instead, interferons activate natural killer lymphocytes and trigger protective steps in neighboring uninfected cells. Alpha and beta interferons bind to interferon receptors on the cytoplasmic membranes of neighboring cells. Such binding triggers the production of **antiviral proteins (AVPs),** which remain inactive within these cells until AVPs bind to viral nucleic acids, particularly double-stranded RNA, a molecule that is common among viruses but generally absent in eukaryotic cells (Figure 7).

At least two types of AVPs are produced: *oligoadenylate synthetase,* the action of which results in the degradation of mRNA, and *protein kinase,* which inhibits protein synthesis by ribosomes. Between them, these AVP enzymes essentially destroy the protein production system of the cell, preventing viruses from being replicated. Of course, cellular metabolism is also affected negatively. The antiviral state lasts three to four days, which may be long enough for a cell to rid itself of viruses but still a short enough period for the cell to survive without protein production.

**Type II (Gamma) Interferon** Gamma interferon (IFN-γ) is produced by activated T lymphocytes and NK lymphocytes. Because T lymphocytes are usually activated as part of an adaptive immune response days after an infection has occurred, gamma interferon appears later than either alpha or beta interferon. Its action in stimulating the activity of macrophages gives IFN-γ its other name: *macrophage activation factor.* Gamma interferon plays a small role in protecting the body against viral infections; mostly IFN-γ regulates the immune system, as in its activation of phagocytic activity.

Table 4 summarizes various properties of interferons in humans.

As scientists learned more about the effects of interferons, many thought these proteins might be a "magic bullet" against viral infections, but viruses can interfere with the effects of interferon, as discussed in **Highlight: How Do Viruses Thwart Interferon?** Many variations of interferons in all three classes have been produced in laboratories using recombinant DNA technology, in the hopes that antiviral therapy can be improved.

## Complement

The **complement system**—or **complement** for short—is a set of serum proteins designated numerically according to the order of their discovery. These proteins initially act as opsonins and chemotactic factors, and indirectly trigger inflammation and fever. The end result of full complement activation is lysis of foreign cells. **ANIMATIONS:** *Complement: Overview*

Complement is activated in three ways (Figure 8):

- In the *classical pathway,* antibodies activate complement.
- In the *alternative pathway,* pathogens or pathogenic products (such as bacterial endotoxins and glycoproteins) activate complement.
- In the *lectin pathway,* microbial polysaccharides bind to activating molecules.

As Figure 8 shows, the three pathways merge. Complement proteins react with one another in an amplifying sequence of chemical reactions, in which the product of each reaction becomes an enzyme that catalyzes the next reaction many times over. Such reactions are called *cascades* because they progress in a way that can be likened to a rock avalanche in which one rock dislodges several other rocks, each of which dislodges many others until a whole cascade of rocks is tumbling down the mountain. The products of each step in the complement cascade initiate other reactions, often with wide-ranging effects in the body.

**The Classical Pathway** Complement got its name from events in the originally discovered "classical" pathway. In this pathway the various proteins act to "complement," or act in conjunction with, the action of antibodies, which we now understand are part of adaptive immunity. As you study the

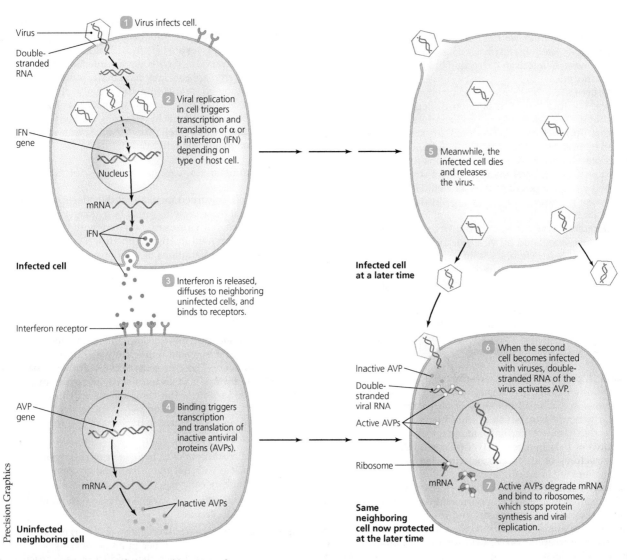

▲ **Figure 7** The actions of alpha and beta interferons.

**4**

## The Characteristics of Human Interferons

| Property | Type I | | Type II |
| --- | --- | --- | --- |
| | Alpha Interferon (IFN-α) | Beta Interferon (IFN-β) | Gamma Interferon (IFN-γ) |
| Principal source | Epithelium, leukocytes | Fibroblasts | Activated T lymphocytes and NK lymphocytes |
| Inducing agent | Viruses | Viruses | Adaptive immune responses |
| Action | Stimulates production of antiviral proteins | Stimulates production of antiviral proteins | Stimulates phagocytic activity of macrophages and neutrophils |
| Other names | Leukocyte-IFN | Fibroblast-IFN | Immune-IFN, macrophage activation factor |

**Figure 8**

**Pathways by which complement is activated.** In the classical pathway, the binding of antibodies to antigens activates complement. In the alternative pathway the binding of factors B, D, and P to endotoxin or glycoproteins in the cell walls of bacteria or fungi activates complement. The lectin pathway activates when lectins bind to microbial carbohydrates. *How did complement get that name?*

*Figure 8 Complement proteins add to—or complement—the action of antibodies.*

depiction of the classical complement cascade in **Figure 9**, keep the following concepts in mind:

- Complement enzymes in early events cleave other complement molecules to form *fragments,* which are designated with lowercase letters. For example, inactive complement protein 3 (C3) is cleaved into active fragments C3a and C3b.

- Most fragments have specific and important roles in achieving the functions of the complement system. Some combine together to form new enzymes; some act to increase vascular permeability, which increases diapedesis; others enhance inflammation; still others are involved as chemotactic factors or in opsonization.

## HIGHLIGHT

### HOW DO VIRUSES THWART INTERFERON?

Hepatitis C is a viral disease that chronically infects nearly 200 million people worldwide. In an effort to shed light on how viruses thwart the human body's defense mechanisms, researchers at the University of Texas have studied the tactics that the hepatitis C virus uses when infecting a host.

In the human body, interferon is part of the defense against viral infections. When a virus invades a cell, the cell's defense systems produce interferon, which inhibits the spread of the viral infection to neighboring cells. One way that viruses attempt to overcome the body's defenses is by preventing the production of interferon.

Researchers have found that the human body's defense against hepatitis C begins with a gene called *RIG-I.* This gene codes for a protein with a novel shape. The new shape signals other proteins to activate interferon regulatory factor 3 (IRF-3), which turns on the genes that produce interferon.

Hepatitis C virus interrupts this process by producing a protease. Protease chops up the proteins that are needed to carry RIG-I's signal to IRF-3. Since IRF-3 doesn't get the message, no interferon is produced.

Drugs known as protease inhibitors disable the viral protease. Widely used against the human immunodeficiency virus (HIV), protease inhibitors have shown promise in treating patients with hepatitis C. If researchers can identify the exact proteins that are attacked by the hepatitis C protease, they may be able to develop protease inhibitors that are more effective against hepatitis C.

The University of Texas discoveries have far-reaching implications. Tactics used by the hepatitis C virus are likely to

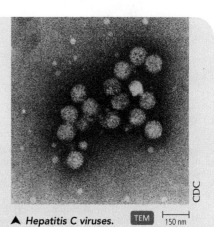

▲ *Hepatitis C viruses.* TEM |—| 150 nm

be similar to those of the West Nile, influenza, and common cold viruses. Understanding of these mechanisms may lead to the development of treatments against these viruses as well.

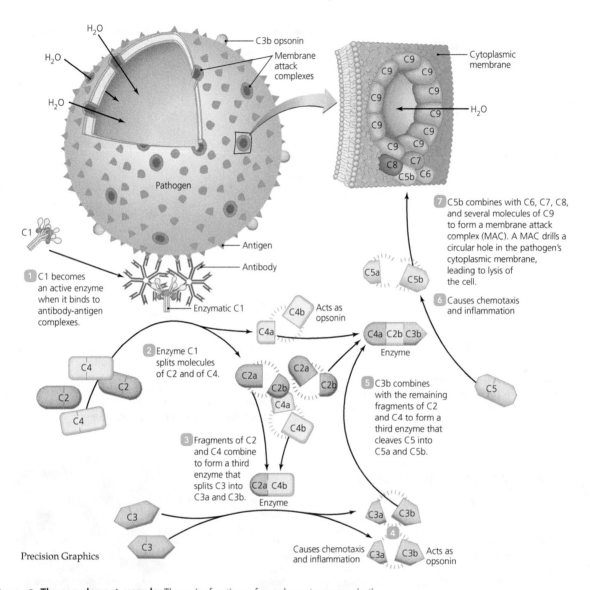

▲ **Figure 9 The complement cascade.** The major functions of complement are opsonization and mediation of chemotaxis, and inflammation. A membrane attack complex is a potent antimicrobial weapon that can form against a wide variety of bacterial and eukaryotic pathogens. *What proteins would be involved in activating a complement cascade if this were the alternative pathway?*

**Figure 9** *Whereas the classical pathway of complement activation involves proteins C1, C2, and C4, the alternative pathway involves factors B, D, and P (properdin).*

- One end product of a full cascade is a **membrane attack complex (MAC),** which forms a circular hole in a pathogen's membrane. The production of numerous MACs (Figure 10) leads to lysis in a wide variety of bacterial and eukaryotic pathogens. Gram-negative bacteria, such as the bacterium causing gonorrhea, are particularly sensitive to the production of MACs via the complement cascade be-

cause their outer membranes are exposed and susceptible. In contrast, a Gram-positive bacterium, which has a thick layer of peptidoglycan overlying its cytoplasmic membrane, is typically resistant to the MAC-induced lytic properties of complement, though it is susceptible to the other effects of the complement cascade.

In addition to its enzymatic role, fragment C3b acts as an opsonin. Fragment C4b also acts as an opsonin. Fragments C3a and C5a function as chemotactic factors, attracting phagocytes to the site of infection, and are also inflammatory agents that trigger increased vascular permeability and dilation. The inflammatory roles of these fragments are discussed in more detail shortly.

**The Alternative Pathway** The alternative pathway was so named because scientists discovered it second. As previously mentioned, antibodies bound to antigens are necessary for the classical activation of complement, whereas activation of the alternative pathway occurs independently of antibodies. The alternative pathway begins with the cleavage of C3 into C3a and C3b. This naturally occurs at a slow rate in the plasma but proceeds no further because C3b is cleaved into smaller fragments almost immediately. However, when C3b binds to microbial surfaces, it stabilizes long enough for a protein called factor B to adhere. Another plasma protein, factor D, then cleaves factor B, creating an enzyme composed of C3b and Bb. This enzyme, which is stabilized by a third protein—factor P (properdin)—cleaves more molecules of C3 into C3a and C3b, continuing the complement cascade and the formation of MACs.

The alternative pathway is useful in the early stages of an infection, before the adaptive immune response has created the antibodies needed to activate the classical pathway.

**The Lectin Pathway** Researchers have discovered a third pathway for complement activation that acts through the use of *lectins*. Lectins are chemicals that bind to specific sugar subunits of polysaccharide molecules; in this case, to mannose sugar in mannan polysaccharide on the surfaces of fungi, bacteria, or viruses. Mannose is rare in mammals. Lectins bound to mannose act to trigger a complement cascade by cleaving C2 and C4. The cascade then proceeds like the classical pathway (see steps ❸ to ❼ in Figure 9). **ANIMATIONS:** *Complement: Activation, Results*

### CRITICAL **THINKING**

A patient has a genetic disorder that makes it impossible for her to synthesize complement protein 8 (C8). Is her complement system nonfunctional? What major effects of complement could still be produced?

**Inactivation of Complement** We have seen that the complement system is nonspecific, and that MACs can form on any cell's exposed membrane. How do the body's own cells withstand the action of complement? Membrane-bound proteins on the body's cells bind with and break down activated complement proteins, which interrupts the complement cascade before damage can occur.

Sucharit Bhakdi

TEM | 1 μm

▲ **Figure 10 Membrane attack complexes.** Transmission electron micrograph of a cell damaged by numerous punctures produced by membrane attack complexes.

## Inflammation

### Learning Objective

✓ Discuss the process and benefits of inflammation.

Inflammation is a general, nonspecific response to tissue damage resulting from a variety of causes, including heat, chemicals, ultraviolet light (sunburn), abrasions, cuts, and pathogens. **Acute inflammation** develops quickly, is short lived, is typically beneficial, and results in the elimination or resolution of whatever condition precipitated it. Long-lasting **chronic inflammation** causes damage (even death) to tissues, resulting in disease. Both acute and chronic inflammation exhibit similar signs and symptoms, including redness in light-colored skin (rubor), localized heat (calor), edema (swelling), and pain (dolor). **ANIMATIONS:** *Inflammation: Overview*

It may not be obvious from this list of signs and symptoms that acute inflammation is beneficial; however, acute inflammation is an important part of the second line of defense because it results in (1) dilation and increased permeability of blood vessels, (2) migration of phagocytes, and (3) tissue repair. Although the chemical details of inflammation are beyond the scope of our study, we now consider these three aspects of acute inflammation.

### Dilation and Increased Permeability of Blood Vessels

Part of the body's initial response to an injury or invasion of pathogens is localized dilation (increase in diameter) of blood vessels in the affected region. The process of blood clotting triggers the conversion of a soluble plasma protein into a nine-amino-acid peptide chain called **bradykinin** (brad-e-ki'nin), which is a potent mediator of inflammation. Further, patrolling macrophages, using Toll-like receptors and NOD proteins to

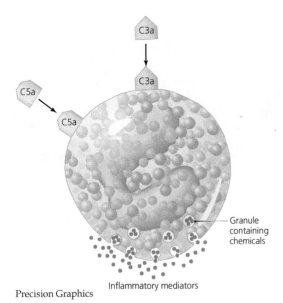

Precision Graphics

▲ **Figure 11 The stimulation of inflammation by complement.** The complement fragments C3a and C5a bind to platelets, basophils, and mast cells, causing them to release histamine, which in turn stimulates the dilation of arterioles.

identify invaders, release other inflammatory chemicals, including **prostaglandins** (pros-tă-glan′dinz) and **leukotrienes** (loo-kō-tri′ĕnz). Basophils, platelets, and specialized cells located in connective tissue—called **mast cells**—also release inflammatory mediators, such as **histamine** (his′tă-mēn), when they are exposed to complement fragments C3a and C5a (Figure 11). Recall that these complement peptides were cleaved from larger polypeptides during the complement cascade.

Bradykinin and histamine cause vasodilation of the body's smallest arteries (arterioles) (Figure 12). Vasodilation results in more blood being delivered to the site of infection, which in turn delivers more phagocytes, oxygen, and nutrients to the site. Inflammatory mediators cause cells that line blood vessels to make adhesion molecules, which are receptors for leukocytes. Bradykinin, prostaglandins, leukotrienes, and (to some extent) histamine also make small veins more permeable—that

is, they cause cells lining the vessels to contract and pull apart, leaving gaps in the walls through which phagocytes can move into the damaged tissue and fight invaders (Figure 13). Increased permeability also allows delivery of more bloodborne antimicrobial chemicals to the site.

Dilation of blood vessels in response to inflammatory mediators results in the redness and localized heat associated with inflammation. At the same time, prostaglandins and leukotrienes cause fluid to leak from the more permeable blood vessels and accumulate in the surrounding tissue, resulting in edema, which is responsible for much of the pain of inflammation as pressure is exerted on nerve endings.

Vasodilation and increased permeability also deliver fibrinogen, the blood's clotting protein. Clots forming at the site of injury or infection wall off the area and help prevent pathogens and their toxins from spreading. One result is the formation of *pus*, a fluid containing dead tissue cells, leukocytes, and pathogens in the walled-off area. Pus may push up toward the surface and erupt, or it may remain isolated in the body, where it is slowly absorbed over a period of days. Such an isolated site of infection is called an **abscess.** Pimples, boils, and pustules are examples of abscesses.

The signs and symptoms of inflammation can be treated with antihistamines, which block histamine receptors on blood vessel walls, or with antiprostaglandins. One of the ways aspirin and ibuprofen reduce pain is by acting as antiprostaglandins.

## Migration of Phagocytes

Increased blood flow due to vasodilation delivers monocytes and neutrophils to a site of infection. As they arrive, these leukocytes roll along the inside walls of blood vessels until they adhere to the receptors lining the vessels, in a process called **margination.** They then squeeze between the cells of the vessel's wall (diapedesis) and enter the site of infection, usually within an hour of tissue damage. The phagocytes then destroy pathogens via phagocytosis.

As mentioned previously, phagocytes are attracted to the site of infection by chemotactic factors, including C3a, C5a, leukotrienes, and microbial components and toxins. The first phagocytes to arrive are often neutrophils, which are then followed by monocytes. Once monocytes leave the blood, they

◀ **Figure 12 The dilating effect of inflammatory mediators on small blood vessels.** The release of mediators from damaged tissue causes nearby arterioles to dilate, which causes capillaries to expand and enables more blood to be delivered to the affected site. The increased blood flow causes the reddening and heat associated with inflammation.

**Normal permeability
of venule**

Venule wall

Small amount
of fluid

Monocyte

Small amount
of fluid

Kenneth Probst/Precision Graphics

**Increased permeability of venule
during inflammation**

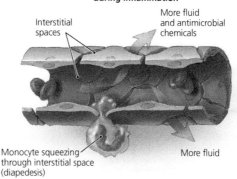

Interstitial
spaces

More fluid
and antimicrobial
chemicals

Monocyte squeezing
through interstitial space
(diapedesis)

More fluid

▲ **Figure 13 Increased vascular permeability during inflammation.** The presence of bradykinin, prostaglandins, leukotrienes, or histamine causes cells lining venules to pull apart, allowing phagocytes to leave the bloodstream and more easily reach a site of infection. The leakage of fluid and cells causes the edema and pain associated with inflammation.

change and become wandering macrophages, which are especially active phagocytic cells that devour pathogens, damaged tissue cells, and dead neutrophils. Wandering macrophages are a major component of pus.

### Tissue Repair

The final stage of inflammation is tissue repair, which in part involves the delivery of extra nutrients and oxygen to the site. Areas of the body where cells regularly undergo cytokinesis, such as the skin and mucous membranes, are repaired rapidly. Some other sites are not fully reparable and form scar tissue.

If the damaged tissue contains undifferentiated stem cells, tissues can be fully restored. For example, a minor skin cut is repaired to such an extent it is no longer visible. However, if cells called *fibroblasts* are involved to a significant extent, scar tissue is formed, inhibiting normal function. Some tissues, such as cardiac muscle and parts of the brain, do not replicate and thus tissue damage cannot be repaired. As a result, these tissues remain damaged following heart attacks and strokes.

Figure 14 gives an overview of the entire inflammatory process. Table 5 summarizes the chemicals involved in inflammation. ANIMATIONS: *Inflammation: Steps*

CRITICAL **THINKING**

While using a microscope to examine a sample of pus from a pimple, Maria observed a large number of macrophages. Is the pus from an early or a late stage of infection? How do you know?

## Fever

### Learning Objective

✓ Explain the benefits of fever in fighting infection.

**Fever** is a body temperature above 37°C. Fever augments the beneficial effects of inflammation, but like inflammation it also has unpleasant side effects, including malaise, body aches, and tiredness.

The hypothalamus, a portion of the brain just above the brain stem, controls the body's internal (core) temperature. Fever results when the presence of chemicals called **pyrogens**[13] (pī'rō-jenz) trigger the hypothalamic "thermostat" to reset at a higher temperature. Pyrogens include bacterial toxins, cytoplasmic contents of bacteria that are released upon lysis, antibody-antigen complexes formed in adaptive immune responses, and pyrogens released by

[13]From Greek *pyr*, meaning fire, and *genein*, meaning to produce.

**5**

## Chemical Mediators of Inflammation

| | |
|---|---|
| **Vasodilating chemicals** | Histamine, serotonin, bradykinin, prostaglandins |
| **Chemotactic factors** | Fibrin, collagen, mast cell chemotactic factors, bacterial peptides |
| **Substances with both vasodilating and chemotactic effects** | Complement fragments C5a and C3a, interferons, interleukins, leukotrienes, platelet secretions |

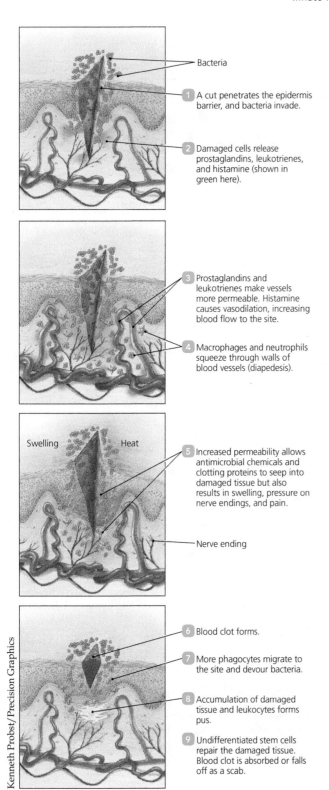

Bacteria

**1** A cut penetrates the epidermis barrier, and bacteria invade.

**2** Damaged cells release prostaglandins, leukotrienes, and histamine (shown in green here).

**3** Prostaglandins and leukotrienes make vessels more permeable. Histamine causes vasodilation, increasing blood flow to the site.

**4** Macrophages and neutrophils squeeze through walls of blood vessels (diapedesis).

Swelling    Heat

**5** Increased permeability allows antimicrobial chemicals and clotting proteins to seep into damaged tissue but also results in swelling, pressure on nerve endings, and pain.

Nerve ending

**6** Blood clot forms.

**7** More phagocytes migrate to the site and devour bacteria.

**8** Accumulation of damaged tissue and leukocytes forms pus.

**9** Undifferentiated stem cells repair the damaged tissue. Blood clot is absorbed or falls off as a scab.

Kenneth Probst/Precision Graphics

◀ **Figure 14** **An overview of the events in inflammation.** The process, which is characterized by redness, swelling, heat, and pain, ends with tissue repair. *In general, what types of cells are involved in tissue repair?*

**Figure 14** *Tissue repair is effected by cells that are capable of cytokinesis and differentiation. If fibroblasts are among them, scar tissue is laid down.*

phagocytes that have phagocytized bacteria. Although the exact mechanism of fever production is not known, the following discussion and Figure 15 present one possible explanation.

Chemicals produced by phagocytes (**1**) cause the hypothalamus to secrete prostaglandin, which resets the hypothalamic thermostat by an unknown mechanism (**2**). The hypothalamus then communicates the new temperature setting to other parts of the brain, which initiate nerve impulses that produce rapid and repetitive muscle contractions (shivering), an increase in metabolic rate, and constriction of blood vessels of the skin (**3**). These processes combine to raise the body's core temperature until it equals the prescribed temperature setting (**4**). Because blood vessels in the skin constrict as fever progresses, one effect of inflammation (vasodilation) is undone. The constricted vessels carry less blood to the skin, causing it to appear paler and feel cold to the touch, even though the body's core temperature is higher. This symptom is the *chill* associated with fever.

Fever continues as long as pyrogens are present. As an infection comes under control and fewer active phagocytes are involved, the level of pyrogens decreases, the thermostat is reset to 37°C, and the body begins to cool by perspiring, lowering the metabolic rate, and dilating blood vessels in the skin. These

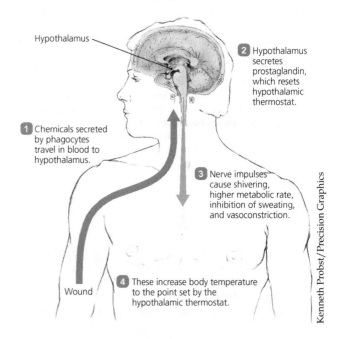

Hypothalamus

**2** Hypothalamus secretes prostaglandin, which resets hypothalamic thermostat.

**1** Chemicals secreted by phagocytes travel in blood to hypothalamus.

**3** Nerve impulses cause shivering, higher metabolic rate, inhibition of sweating, and vasoconstriction.

Wound

**4** These increase body temperature to the point set by the hypothalamic thermostat.

Kenneth Probst/Precision Graphics

▲ **Figure 15** **One theoretical explanation for the production of fever in response to infection.**

**6**

## A Summary of Some Nonspecific Components of the First and Second Lines of Defense (Innate Immunity)

| First Line | Second Line | | | | | | |
|---|---|---|---|---|---|---|---|
| **Barriers and Associated Chemicals** | **Phagocytes** | **Extracellular Killing** | **Complement** | **Interferons** | **Antimicrobial Peptides** | **Inflammation** | **Fever** |
| Skin and mucous membranes prevent the entrance of pathogens; chemicals (e.g., sweat, acid, lysozyme, mucus) enhance the protection | Macrophages, neutrophils, and eosinophils ingest and destroy pathogens | Eosinophils and NK lymphocytes kill pathogens without phagocytizing them | Components attract phagocytes, stimulate inflammation, and attack a pathogen's cytoplasmic membrane | Increase resistance of cells to viral infection, slow the spread of disease | Interfere with membranes, internal signaling, and metabolism; act against pathogens | Increases blood flow, capillary permeability, and migration of leukocytes into infected area; walls off infected region, increases local temperature | Mobilizes defenses, accelerates repairs, inhibits pathogens |

processes, collectively called the *crisis* of a fever, are a sign that the infection has been overcome and that body temperature is returning to normal.

The increased temperature of fever enhances the effects of interferons, inhibits the growth of some microorganisms, and is thought to enhance the performance of phagocytes, the activity of cells of specific immunity, and the process of tissue repair. However, if fever is too high, critical proteins are denatured; additionally, nerve impulses are inhibited, resulting in hallucinations, coma, and even death.

Because of the potential benefits of fever, many doctors recommend that patients refrain from taking fever-reducing drugs

unless the fever is prolonged or extremely high. Other physicians believe that the benefits of fever are too slight to justify enduring the adverse symptoms.

## CRITICAL **THINKING**

How do drugs such as aspirin and ibuprofen act to reduce fever? Should you take fever-reducing drugs or let a fever run its course?

Table 6 summarizes the barriers, cells, chemicals, and processes involved in the body's first two, nonspecific lines of defense.

# Chapter Summary

## An Overview of the Body's Defenses

1. Humans have **species resistance** to certain pathogens, as well as three overlapping lines of defense. The first two lines of defense compose **innate immunity**, which is generally nonspecific and protects the body against a wide variety of potential pathogens. A third line of defense is **adaptive immunity**, which is a specific response to a particular pathogen.
   **ANIMATIONS:** *Host Defenses: Overview*

## The Body's First Line of Defense

1. The first line of defense includes the skin, composed of an outer **epidermis** and a deeper **dermis. Dendritic cells** of the epidermis devour pathogens. Sweat glands of the skin produce salty sweat containing the enzyme called **lysozyme** and **antimicrobial peptides** (defensins), which are small peptide chains that act against a broad range of pathogens. **Sebum** is an oily substance of the skin that lowers pH, which deters the growth of many pathogens.

2. The mucous membranes, another part of the body's first line of defense, are composed of tightly packed cells that are replaced fre-

quently by **stem cell** division and often coated with sticky mucus secreted by goblet cells.

3. **Microbial antagonism,** the competition between **normal microbiota** and potential pathogens, also contributes to the body's first line of defense.

4. Tears contain antibacterial lysozyme and also flush invaders from the eyes. Saliva similarly protects the teeth. The low pH of the stomach inhibits most microbes that are swallowed.

## The Body's Second Line of Defense

1. The second line of defense includes cells (especially **phagocytes**), antimicrobial chemicals (Toll-like receptors, NOD proteins, interferons, complement, lysozyme, and antimicrobial peptides), and processes (phagocytosis, information, and fever).

2. Blood is composed of **formed elements** (cells and parts of cells) within a fluid called **plasma.** Serum is that portion of plasma without clotting factors. The formed elements are **erythrocytes** (red blood cells), **leukocytes** (white blood cells), and **platelets.**

3. Based on their appearance in stained blood smears, leukocytes are grouped as either granulocytes (**basophils, eosinophils,** and **neutrophils**) or agranulocytes (**lymphocytes, monocytes**). When monocytes leave the blood they become macrophages.

4. Basophils function to release histamine during inflammation, whereas eosinophils and neutrophils phagocytize pathogens. They exit capillaries via **diapedesis** (emigration).

5. **Macrophages,** neutrophils, and dendritic cells are phagocytic cells of the second line of defense. Many are named for their location in the body, for example, alveolar macrophages (the lungs) and microglia (the nervous system).

6. A **differential white blood cell count** is a lab technique that indicates the relative numbers of leukocyte types; it can be helpful in diagnosing disease.

7. **Chemotactic factors,** such as chemicals called **chemokines,** attract phagocytic leukocytes to the site of damage or invasion. Phagocytes attach to pathogens via a process called **adherence.**
   ANIMATIONS: *Phagocytosis: Overview*

8. **Opsonization,** the coating of pathogens by proteins called **opsonins,** makes those pathogens more vulnerable to phagocytes. A phagocyte's pseudopodia then surround the microbe to form a sac called a **phagosome,** which fuses with a lysosome to form a **phagolysosome,** in which the pathogen is killed.
   ANIMATIONS: *Phagocytosis: Mechanism*

9. Leukocytes can distinguish between the body's normal cells and foreign cells because leukocytes have receptor molecules for foreign cells' components or because the foreign cells are opsonized by complement or antibodies.

10. Eosinophils and **natural killer (NK) lymphocytes** attack nonphagocytically, especially in the case of helminth infections and cancerous cells. **Eosinophilia**—an abnormally high number of eosinophils in the blood—typically indicates such a helminth infection.

11. **Interferons (IFNs)** are protein molecules that inhibit the spread of viral infections. **Alpha interferons** and **beta interferons,** which are released within hours of infection, trigger **antiviral proteins** to prevent viral reproduction in neighboring cells. **Gamma interfer-**

**ons,** produced days after initial infection, activate macrophages and neutrophils.

12. Microbial molecules called **pathogen-associated molecular patterns (PAMPs)** bind to **Toll-like receptors (TLRs)** on host cells' membranes or to **NOD proteins** inside cells, triggering innate immune responses.

13. The **complement system** is a set of proteins that act as chemotactic attractants, trigger inflammation and fever, and ultimately can effect the destruction of foreign cells via the formation of **membrane attack complexes (MACs),** which result in multiple, fatal holes in pathogens' membranes. Complement is activated by a classical pathway involving antibodies, by an alternative pathway triggered by bacterial chemicals, or by a lectin pathway triggered by mannose found on microbial surfaces.
   ANIMATIONS: *Complement: Overview, Activation, Results*

14. **Acute inflammation** develops quickly and damages pathogens, whereas **chronic inflammation** develops slowly and can cause tissue damage that can lead to disease. Signs and symptoms of inflammation include redness, heat, swelling, and pain.
   ANIMATIONS: *Inflammation: Overview, Steps*

15. The process of blood clotting triggers formation of **bradykinin**—a potent mediator of inflammation.

16. Macrophages with Toll-like receptors or NOD proteins release **prostaglandins** and **leukotrienes,** which increase permeability of blood vessels. **Mast cells,** basophils, and platelets release **histamine** when exposed to peptides from the complement system. Blood clots may isolate an infected area to form an **abscess** such as a pimple or boil.

17. When leukocytes rolling along blood vessel walls reach a site of infection, they stick to the wall in a process called **margination** and then undergo diapedesis to arrive at the site of tissue damage. The increased blood flow of inflammation also brings extra nutrients and oxygen to the infection site to aid in repair.

18. **Fever** results when chemicals called **pyrogens,** including substances released by bacteria and phagocytes, affect the hypothalamus in a way that causes it to reset body temperature to a higher level. The exact process of fever and its control are not fully understood.

---

# Questions for Review   Answers to the Questions for Review (except Short Answer questions) appear at the end of this chapter.

## Multiple Choice

1. Phagocytes of the epidermis are called
   a. microglia.
   b. goblet cells.
   c. alveolar macrophages.
   d. dendritic cells.

2. Mucus-secreting membranes are found in the
   a. urinary system.
   b. digestive cavity.
   c. respiratory passages.
   d. all of the above

3. The complement system involves
   a. the production of antigens and antibodies.
   b. serum proteins involved in nonspecific defense.
   c. a set of genes that distinguish foreign cells from body cells.
   d. the elimination of undigested remnants of microorganisms.

4. The alternative complement activation pathway involves
   a. factors B, D, and P.
   b. the cleavage of C5 to form C9.
   c. binding to mannose sugar.
   d. recognition of antigens bound to specific antibodies.

5. Complement must be inactivated because if it were not,
   a. viruses could continue to multiply inside host cells using the host's own metabolic machinery.
   b. necessary interferons would not be produced.
   c. protein synthesis would be inhibited, thus halting important cell processes.
   d. it would make holes in the body's own cells.

6. The type of interferon present late in an infection is
   a. alpha interferon.    c. gamma interferon.
   b. beta interferon.     d. delta interferon.

7. Interferons
   a. do not protect the cell that secretes them.
   b. stimulate the activity of macrophages.
   c. cause muscle aches, chills, and fever.
   d. all of the above

8. Which of the following is not targeted by a Toll-like receptor?
   a. lipid A                      c. single-stranded RNA
   b. eukaryotic flagellar protein  d. lipoteichoic acid

9. Toll-like receptors (TLRs) act to
   a. bind microbial proteins and polysaccharides.
   b. induce phagocytosis.
   c. cause phagocytic chemotaxis.
   d. destroy microbial cells.

10. Which of the following binds iron?
    a. lactoferrin     c. transferrin
    b. siderophores    d. all of the above

## Modified True/False

Indicate which statements are true. Correct all false statements by changing the italicized words.

1. ____ The surface cells of the epidermis of the skin are *alive*.

2. ____ The surface cells of mucous membranes are *alive*.

3. ____ Wandering macrophages experience *diapedesis*.

4. ____ *Monocytes* are immature macrophages.

5. ____ *Lymphocytes* are large agranulocytes.

6. ____ *Phagocytes* exhibit chemotaxis toward a pathogen.

7. ____ In phagocytosis, adherence involves the binding between complementary chemicals on a phagocyte and on the membrane of a *body cell*.

8. ____ *Opsonization* occurs when a phagocyte's pseudopodia surround a microbe and fuse to form a sac.

9. ____ Lysosomes fuse with phagosomes to form *peroxisomes*.

10. ____ A membrane attack complex drills circular holes in a *macrophage*.

11. ____ Rubor, calor, swelling, and dolor are associated with *fever*.

12. ____ Acute and chronic inflammation exhibit *similar* signs and symptoms.

13. ____ The *hypothalamus* of the brain controls body temperature.

14. ____ Defensins are *phagocytic cells* of the second line of defense.

15. ____ NETs are webs produced by *neutrophils* to trap microbes.

## Matching

In the blank beside each cell, chemical, or process in the left column, write the letter of the line of defense that first applies. Each letter may be used several times.

1. ____ Inflammation      A. First line of defense
2. ____ Monocytes         B. Second line of defense
3. ____ Lactoferrin       C. Third line of defense

4. ____ Fever
5. ____ Dendritic cells
6. ____ Alpha interferon
7. ____ Mucous membrane of the digestive tract
8. ____ Neutrophils
9. ____ Epidermis
10. ____ Lysozyme
11. ____ Goblet cells
12. ____ Phagocytes
13. ____ Sebum
14. ____ T lymphocytes
15. ____ Antimicrobial peptides

Write the letter of the description that applies to each of the following terms.

1. ____ Goblet cell
2. ____ Lysozyme
3. ____ Stem cell
4. ____ Dendritic cell
5. ____ Cell from sebaceous gland
6. ____ Bone marrow stem cell
7. ____ Eosinophil
8. ____ Alveolar macrophage
9. ____ Microglia
10. ____ Wandering macrophage

A. Leukocyte that primarily attacks parasitic worms
B. Phagocytic cell in lungs
C. Secretes sebum
D. Devours pathogens in epidermis
E. Breaks bonds in bacterial cell wall
F. Phagocytic cell in central nervous system
G. Generative cell with many types of offspring
H. Develops into formed elements of blood
I. Intercellular scavenger
J. Secretes mucus

## Labeling

Label the steps of phagocytosis.

Peter Parks/imagequestmarine.com

## Short Answer

1. In order for a pathogen to cause disease, what three things must happen?

2. How does a phagocyte "know" it is in contact with a pathogen instead of another body cell?

3. Give three characteristics of the epidermis that make it an intolerable environment for most microorganisms.

4. What is the role of Toll-like receptors in innate immune responses?

5. Describe the classical complement cascade pathway from C1 to the MAC.

6. How do NOD proteins differ from Toll-like receptors?

 # Concept Mapping

Using the following terms, draw a concept map that describes phagocytosis.
Or, complete this concept map online by going to the Study Area at www.masteringmicrobiology.com.

| | | | |
|---|---|---|---|
| Adherence | Elimination | Killing | Opsonins |
| Chemotactic factors | Eosinophils | Lysosome | Phagolysosome |
| Chemotaxis | Exocytosis | Macrophages | Phagosome |
| Dendritic cells | Ingestion | Neutrophils | |

# Critical Thinking

1. John received a chemical burn on his arm and was instructed by his physician to take an over-the-counter, anti-inflammatory medication for the painful, red, swollen lesions. When Charles suffered pain, redness, and swelling from an infected cut on his foot, he decided to take the same anti-inflammatory drug because his symptoms matched John's symptoms. How is Charles's inflammation like that of John? How is it different? Is it appropriate for Charles to medicate his cut with the same medicine John used?

2. What might happen to someone whose body did not produce C3? C5?

3. My-lim, age 65, has had diabetes for 40 years, with resulting damage to the small blood vessels in her feet and toes. Her circulation is impaired. How might this condition affect her vulnerability to infection?

4. A patient's chart shows that eosinophils make up 8% of his white blood cells. What does this lead you to suspect? Would your suspicions change if you learned that the patient had spent the previous three years as an anthropologist living among an African tribe? What is the normal percentage of eosinophils?

5. There are two kinds of agranulocytes in the blood—monocytes and lymphocytes. Janice noted that monocytes are phagocytic and that lymphocytes are not. She wondered why two agranulocytes would be so different. What facts of hematopoiesis can help her answer her question?

6. A patient has a genetic disorder that prevents him from synthesizing C8 and C9. What effect does this have on his ability to resist bloodborne Gram-negative and Gram-positive bacteria? What would happen if C3 and C5 fragments were also inactivated?

7. Sweat glands in the armpits secrete perspiration with a pH close to neutral (7.0). How does this fact help explain body odor in this area as compared to other parts of the skin?

8. Scientists can raise "germ-free" animals in axenic environments. Would such animals be as healthy as their worldly counterparts?

9. Compare and contrast the protective structures and chemicals of the skin and mucous membranes.

10. Scientists are interested in developing antimicrobial drugs that act like the body's normal antimicrobial peptides. What advantage might such a drug have over antibiotics?

Access more review material online in the Study Area at
**www.masteringmicrobiology.com.** There, you'll find
- **Animations**
- **MP3 Tutor Sessions**
- **Concept Mapping Activities**
- **Flashcards**
- **Quizzes**
and more to help you succeed.

# Answers

Answers to multiple-choice, fill-in-blank, labeling, matching, and true/false questions are listed here. Answers for Short Answer and Critical Thinking questions are available for instructors only in the Instructor's Manual that accompanies this text.

**Multiple Choice**
1. d; 2. d; 3. b; 4. a; 5. d; 6. c; 7. d; 8. b; 9. a; 10. d

**Modified True/False**
1. *dead*; 2. True; 3. True; 4. True; 5. *monocytes*; 6. True; 7. *pathogen*; 8. *ingestion*; 9. *phagolysosomes*; 10. *pathogen's cytoplasmic membrane*; 11. *inflammation*; 12. True; 13. True; 14. *antimicrobial peptides*; 15. True

**Matching**
First section: 1. B; 2. B; 3. B; 4. B; 5. A; 6. B; 7. A; 8. B; 9. A; 10. A; 11. A; 12. B; 13. A; 14. C; 15. A
Second section: 1. J; 2. E; 3. G; 4. D; 5. C; 6. H; 7. A; 8. B; 9. F; 10. I

**Labeling**
See Figure 6.

# Adaptive Immunity

Imagine that your friend has been bitten on the hand by a dog. The skin is broken and the wound is deep. Your friend washes the wound with soap and water but does not use any of the more powerful antimicrobial agents. Within 24 hours, his hand and arm are swollen,

red, and painful and he is feeling seriously ill. His body's inflammatory response is in full force as manifested by the swelling and pain, but it isn't strong enough to overcome the virulent invading microorganisms.

Fortunately, infections like this trigger the body's *adaptive immunity* in addition to the innate defense responses. In this chapter we will explore what happens when facets of adaptive immunity—especially lymphocytes—enter the battle against microbial invaders.

 Take the pre-test for this chapter online. Visit the Study Area at www.masteringmicrobiology.com.

This chapter has *MicroFlix*. Go to **www.masteringmicrobiology.com** for 3-D movie-quality animations on immunology.

White blood cells called lymphocytes roll along blood vessel walls. Lymphocytes are the main cells of adaptive immune defenses.

We discussed innate immunity, which includes two lines of rapid defense against microbial pathogens. The first line includes intact skin and mucous membranes, whereas the second line includes phagocytosis, nonspecific chemical defenses, inflammation, and fever. As in the chapter opening story, innate defenses do not always offer enough protection in defending the body. Although the mechanisms of innate immunity are readily available and fast-acting, they do not adapt to enhance the effectiveness of response to the great variety of pathogens confronting us—a fever is a fever, whether it is triggered by a mild cold virus or the deadly Ebola virus. The body augments the mechanisms of innate immunity with a third line of defense that destroys invaders while becoming more effective in the process. This response is called *adaptive immunity.*

# Overview of Adaptive Immunity

## Learning Objectives

✓ Describe five distinctive attributes of adaptive immunity.

✓ List the two basic types of white blood cells involved in adaptive immunity.

✓ List two basic divisions of adaptive immunity and describe their targets.

**Adaptive immunity** is the body's ability to recognize and then mount a defense against distinct invaders and their products, whether they are protozoa, fungi, bacteria, viruses, or toxins. *Immunologists*—scientists who study the cells and chemicals involved in immunity—are continually refining and revising our knowledge of adaptive immunity. In this chapter, we will examine some of what they have discovered.

Adaptive immunity has five distinctive attributes:

- *Specificity.* Any particular adaptive immune response acts only against one particular molecular shape and not against others. Adaptive immune responses are precisely tailored reactions against specific attackers, whereas innate immunity involves more generalized responses to pathogen-associated molecular patterns (PAMPs)—molecular shapes common to many microbes.

- *Inducibility.* Cells of adaptive immunity activate only in response to specific pathogens.

- *Clonality.* Once induced, cells of adaptive immunity proliferate to form many generations of nearly identical cells, which are collectively called *clones.*

- *Unresponsiveness to self.* As a rule, adaptive immunity does not act against normal body cells; in other words, adaptive immune responses are self-tolerant. Several mechanisms help ensure that immune responses do not attack the body itself.

- *Memory.* An adaptive immune response has "memory" about specific pathogens; that is, it adapts to respond faster and more effectively in subsequent encounters with a particular type of pathogen or toxin.

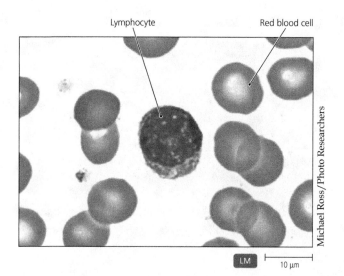

Lymphocyte    Red blood cell

Michael Ross/Photo Researchers

LM    |—————| 10 μm

▲ **Figure 1 Lymphocytes play a central role in adaptive immunity.** A resting lymphocyte is the smallest leukocyte—slightly larger than a red blood cell.

These aspects of adaptive immunity involve the activities of **lymphocytes** (lim′fō-sītz), which are a type of leukocyte (white blood cell) that acts against specific pathogens. Lymphocytes in their resting state are the smallest white blood cells, and each is characterized by a large, round, central nucleus surrounded by a thin rim of cytoplasm (Figure 1). Initially, lymphocytes of humans form in the *red bone marrow,* located in the ends of long bones in juveniles and in the centers of adult flat bones such as the ribs and hip bones. These sites contain *blood stem cells,* which are cells that give rise to all types of blood cells including lymphocytes.

Although lymphocytes appear identical in the microscope, scientists make distinctions between two main types—*B lymphocytes* and *T lymphocytes*—according to integral surface proteins that are part of each lymphocyte's cytoplasmic membrane. These proteins allow lymphocytes to recognize specific pathogens and toxins by their molecular shapes, and the proteins play roles in intercellular communication among immune cells.

Lymphocytes must undergo a maturation process. **B lymphocytes,** which are also called **B cells,** arise and mature in the red bone marrow of adults. (The designation "B" does not stand for bone marrow, but instead for the *bursa of Fabricius,* a unique lymphoid organ located near the end of the intestinal tract in birds, which is where B lymphocytes were originally identified. Mammals do not have this bursa, but the name "B cell" has been retained.)

**T lymphocytes,** also known as **T cells,** begin in bone marrow as well but do not mature there. Instead, T cells travel to and mature in the *thymus,* located in the chest near the heart. T lymphocytes are so called because of the role the thymus plays in their maturation.

Adaptive immunity consists of two basic types of responses. Historically, bodily fluids such as blood were called *humors* (the Latin word for moisture), and thus immunologists call immune activity centered in such fluids **humoral immune responses.** Descendants of activated B cells are the main defensive cells of humoral immunity. Once induced, they secrete soluble proteins called *antibodies* that act against *extracellular pathogens* such as bacteria and fungi in the body's fluids. In contrast, descendants of T cells regulate adaptive immune responses or attack *intracellular pathogens,* such as viruses replicating inside a cell. Such T lymphocytes mount **cell-mediated immune responses,** which do not involve antibodies. Long-lived descendants of B and T lymphocytes maintain the ability to mount adaptive immunological response against specific pathogens—an ability sometimes called immunological memory. **ANIMATIONS:** *Humoral Immunity: Overview* and *Cell-Mediated Immunity: Overview*

Both humoral immune responses against extracellular pathogens and cell-mediated immune responses against intracellular pathogens are powerful defensive reactions that have the potential to severely and fatally attack the body's own cells. The body must regulate adaptive immune responses to prevent damage; for example, an immune response requires multiple chemical signals before proceeding, thus reducing the possibility of randomly triggering an immune response against uninfected healthy tissue. Autoimmune disorders, hypersensitivities, or immunodeficiency diseases result when regulation is insufficient or overexcited.

# Elements of Adaptive Immunity

Just as the program at a dramatic presentation might present a synopsis of the performance and introduce the actors and their roles, the following sections present elements of adaptive immunity by describing the "stage" and introducing the "cast of characters" involved in adaptive immunity. We will examine the *lymphatic system*—the organs, tissues, and cells of adaptive immunity; then we consider the molecules called *antigens* that trigger adaptive immune responses; next, we take a look at *antibodies;* and finally we examine special *chemical signals* and *mediators* involved in coordinating and controlling a specific immune response.

First, we turn our attention to the "stage"—the lymphatic system, which plays an important role in the production, maturation, and housing of the cells that function in adaptive immunity.

## The Tissues and Organs of the Lymphatic System

### Learning Objectives

✓ Contrast the flow of lymph with the flow of blood.

✓ Describe the primary and secondary organs of the lymphatic system.

✓ Describe the importance of red bone marrow, the thymus, lymph nodes, and other lymphoid tissues.

The **lymphatic system** is composed of the *lymphatic vessels,* which conduct the flow of a liquid called *lymph;* and lymphatic cells, tissues, and organs, which are directly involved in adaptive immunity (Figure 2a). Taken together, the components of the lymphatic system constitute a surveillance system that screens the tissues of the body—particularly possible points of entry such as the throat and intestinal tract—for foreign molecules. We begin by examining lymphatic vessels.

### The Lymphatic Vessels and the Flow of Lymph

**Lymphatic vessels** form a one-way system that conducts **lymph** (pronounced limf) from local tissues and returns it to the circulatory system. Lymph is a colorless, watery liquid similar in composition to blood plasma; indeed, lymph arises from fluid that has leaked out of blood vessels into the surrounding intercellular spaces. Unlike blood which supplies nutrients, lymph contains wastes such as degraded proteins and toxins. Lymph is first collected by remarkably permeable *lymphatic capillaries* (Figure 2b), which are located in most parts of the body (exceptions include the bone marrow, brain, and spinal cord). From the lymphatic capillaries, lymph passes into increasingly larger lymphatic vessels until it finally flows via two large *lymphatic ducts* into blood vessels near the heart. One-way valves ensure that lymph flows only toward the heart as skeletal muscular activity squeezes the lymphatic vessels. Unlike the cardiovascular system, the lymphatic system has no unique pump and is not circular; that is, lymph flows in only one direction—toward the heart. Located at various points within the system of lymphatic vessels are about 1000 *lymph nodes,* which house leukocytes that recognize and attack foreigners present in the lymph, allowing for immune system surveillance and interactions.

### Lymphoid Organs

Once lymphocytes have arisen and matured in the *primary lymphoid organs* of the red bone marrow and thymus, they migrate to *secondary lymphoid organs* and *tissues,* including lymph nodes, spleen, and other less-organized accumulations of lymphoid tissue, where they in effect lie in wait for foreign microbes. The hundreds of **lymph nodes** are located throughout the body but concentrated in the cervical (neck), inguinal (groin), axillary (armpit), and abdominal regions (see Figure 2a). Each lymph node receives lymph from numerous *afferent* (inbound) *lymphatic vessels* and drains lymph into just one or two *efferent* (outbound) *lymphatic vessels* (Figure 2c). Essentially, lymph nodes are sites to facilitate interactions among immune cells and between immune cells and material in the lymph arriving from throughout the body.

A node has a medullary (central) maze of passages, which filter the lymph passing through and house numerous lymphocytes that survey the lymph for foreign molecules and mount specific immune responses against them. The cortex (outer) portion of a lymph node consists of a tough capsule surrounding *germinal centers,* which is where clones of B cells replicate.

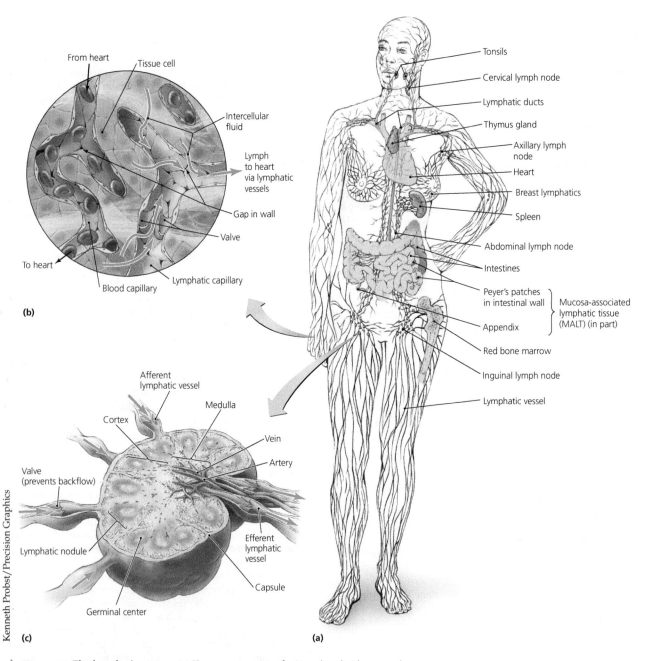

**(b)**

From heart
Tissue cell
Intercellular fluid
Lymph to heart via lymphatic vessels
Gap in wall
Valve
To heart
Blood capillary
Lymphatic capillary

**(c)**

Afferent lymphatic vessel
Medulla
Cortex
Vein
Artery
Valve (prevents backflow)
Efferent lymphatic vessel
Lymphatic nodule
Capsule
Germinal center

Kenneth Probst/Precision Graphics

**(a)**

Tonsils
Cervical lymph node
Lymphatic ducts
Thymus gland
Axillary lymph node
Heart
Breast lymphatics
Spleen
Abdominal lymph node
Intestines
Peyer's patches in intestinal wall
Appendix
Red bone marrow
Inguinal lymph node
Lymphatic vessel

Mucosa-associated lymphatic tissue (MALT) (in part)

▲ **Figure 2  The lymphatic system. (a)** The system consists of primary lymphoid organs—bone marrow (not shown) and thymus gland—and secondary lymphoid organs, including lymphatic vessels, lymph nodes, tonsils, and other lymphatic tissue. **(b)** Lymphatic capillaries collect lymph from intercellular spaces. **(c)** Afferent lymphatic vessels carry lymph into lymph nodes; efferent vessels carry it away. The cortex contains germinal centers, where B lymphocytes proliferate; the lymphocytes in the medulla encounter foreign molecules. *Why do lymph nodes enlarge during an infection?*

**Figure 2** *During an infection, lymphocytes multiply profusely in lymph nodes. This proliferation and swelling cause lymph nodes to enlarge.*

The lymphatic system contains other secondary lymphoid tissues and organs, including the spleen, the tonsils, and *mucosa-associated lymphatic tissue.* The spleen is similar in structure and function to lymph nodes, except that it filters blood instead of lymph. The spleen removes bacteria, viruses, toxins, and other foreign matter from the blood. It also cleanses the blood of old and damaged blood cells, stores blood platelets (which are required for the proper clotting of blood), and stores blood components such as iron.

The tonsils and MALT lack the tough outer capsules of lymph nodes and the spleen, but they function in somewhat the same way by physically trapping foreign particles and microbes. MALT includes the appendix; lymphoid tissue of the respiratory tract, vagina, urinary bladder, and mammary glands; and discrete bits of lymphoid tissue called *Peyer's patches* in the wall of the small intestine. MALT contains most of the body's lymphocytes.

We are considering adaptive immunity in terms of a "play" taking place on the stage of the lymphatic system. Now, let's meet the "villain actors"—the foreign molecules that lymphocytes recognize.

## Antigens

### Learning Objectives

✓ Identify the characteristics of antigens that stimulate effective immune responses.

✓ Distinguish among exogenous antigens, endogenous antigens, and autoantigens.

Adaptive immune responses are not directed against whole bacteria, fungi, protozoa, or viruses, but instead against portions of cells, viruses, and even parts of single molecules that the body recognizes as foreign and worthy of attack. Immunologists call these biochemical shapes **antigens**[1] (an'ti-jenz). They bind to lymphocytes and can trigger adaptive immune responses. Antigens from pathogens and toxins are the "villains" of our story.

## Properties of Antigens

Not every molecule is an effective antigen. Among the properties that make certain molecules more effective at provoking adaptive immunity are a molecule's *shape, size,* and *complexity.* The body recognizes antigens by the three-dimensional shapes of regions called **epitopes,** which are also known as *antigenic determinants,* because they are the actual part of an antigen that determines an immune response (Figure 3a).

In general, larger molecules with molecular masses (often called molecular weights) between 5000 and 100,000 daltons are better antigens than smaller ones. The most effective antigens are large foreign macromolecules such as proteins and glycoproteins, but carbohydrates and lipids can be antigenic. Small molecules, especially those with a molecular mass under 5000 daltons, make poor antigens by themselves because they evade detection. Such small molecules, called *haptens,* can become antigenic when bound to larger, carrier molecules (often proteins). For example, the fungal product penicillin is too small by itself (molecular mass: 302 daltons) to trigger a specific immune response. However, bound to a carrier protein in the blood, penicillin can become antigenic and trigger an allergic response in some patients.

Complex molecules make better antigens than simple ones because they have more epitopes, like a gemstone with its many facets. For example, starch, which is a very large polymer of repeating glucose subunits, is not a good antigen despite its large size, because it lacks structural complexity. In contrast, complicated molecules, such as glycoproteins and phospholipids, have multiple distinctive shapes and novel combinations of subunits that cells of the immune system recognize as foreign.

Examples of antigens include components of bacterial cell walls, capsules, pili, and flagella, as well as the external and internal proteins of viruses, fungi, and protozoa. Many toxins and some nucleic acid molecules are also antigenic. Invading microorganisms are not the only source of antigens; for example, food may contain antigens called *allergens* that provoke allergic reactions, and inhaled dust contains mite feces, pollen grains, dander (flakes of skin), and other antigenic and allergenic particles.

## Types of Antigens

Though immunologists categorize antigens in various ways, one especially important way is to group antigens according to their relationship to the body:

- **Exogenous**[2] **antigens** (Figure 3b). Exogenous (eks-oj'en-us) antigens include toxins and other secretions and components of microbial cell walls, membranes, flagella, and pili.

- **Endogenous**[3] **antigens** (Figure 3c). Protozoa, fungi, bacteria, and viruses that reproduce inside a body's cells produce endogenous antigens. The immune system cannot

---

[1] From *antibody generator;* antibodies are proteins secreted during a humoral immune response that bind to specific regions of antigens.
[2] From Greek *exo,* meaning without, and *genein,* meaning to produce.
[3] From Greek *endon,* meaning within.

**(a)** Epitopes (antigenic determinants)

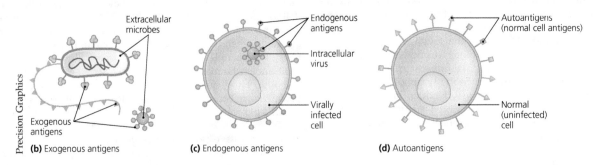

**(b)** Exogenous antigens  **(c)** Endogenous antigens  **(d)** Autoantigens

▲ **Figure 3** **Antigens, molecules that provoke a specific immune response.**
**(a)** Epitopes, or antigenic determinants, are three-dimensional regions of antigens whose shapes are recognized by cells of the immune system. **(b–d)** Categories of antigens based on their relationship to the body. Exogenous antigens originate from microbes located outside the body's cells; endogenous antigens are produced by intracellular microbes and are typically incorporated into a host cell's cytoplasmic membrane; autoantigens are components of normal body cells.

assess the health of the body's cells; it responds to endogenous antigens only if the body's cells incorporate such antigens into their cytoplasmic membranes, leading to their external display.

• **Autoantigens[4]** **(Figure 3d)**. Antigenic molecules derived from normal cellular processes are autoantigens (or *self-antigens*). As we will discuss more fully in a later section, immune cells that treat autoantigens as if they were foreign are normally eliminated during the development of the immune system. This phenomenon, called *self-tolerance,* prevents the body from mounting an immune response against itself.

So far, we have examined two aspects of immune responses in terms of an analogy to a stage play—the lymphoid organs and tissues provide the stage, and antigens of pathogens are the villains that induce an immune response with their epitopes (antigenic determinants). Next, we examine the activities of lymphocytes in more detail. Recall that B and T lymphocytes act against antigens; they are the "heroes" of the action. We begin by considering B lymphocytes.

---
[4]From Greek *autos,* meaning self.

# B Lymphocytes (B cells) and Antibodies

## Learning Objectives

✓ Describe the characteristic of B lymphocytes that furnishes them specificity.

✓ Describe the basic structure of an immunoglobulin molecule.

✓ Contrast the structure and function of the five classes of immunoglobulins.

B lymphocytes are found in the spleen, MALT, and primarily in the germinal centers of lymph nodes. A small percentage of B cells circulate in the blood. The major function of B cells is the secretion of soluble antibodies, which we examine in more detail shortly. As we have established, B cells function in humoral immune responses, each of which is against only a particular epitope. How is such specificity developed and maintained? Specificity comes from membrane proteins called *B cell receptors.*

## Specificity of the B Cell Receptor (BCR)

The surface of each B lymphocyte is covered with about 500,000 identical copies of a protein called the **B cell receptor (BCR).** A BCR is a type of *immunoglobulin* (im'yū-nō-glob'yū-lin) *(Ig).*

A simple immunoglobulin contains four polypeptide chains—two identical longer chains called *heavy chains,* and two identical shorter *light chains* (Figure 4). The terms *heavy* and *light* refer to their relative molecular masses. Disulfide bonds, which are covalent bonds between sulfur atoms in two different amino acids, link the light chains to the heavy chains in such a way that a simple immunoglobulin looks like the letter Y. A BCR has two *arms* and a *transmembrane portion*. Each arm's end is a *variable region,* because terminal ends of each heavy and each light chain vary in amino acid sequence among B cells. The transmembrane portion anchors the BCR in the cytoplasmic membrane and consists of the stem of the Y (composed of the tails of the two heavy chains) and two other polypeptides.

Each B cell randomly generates a single BCR gene during its development in the bone marrow. Scientists estimate that there are fewer than 25,000 genes in a human cell, yet there are billions of different BCR proteins in an individual. Obviously, a person cannot have a separate gene for each BCR; instead, a developing B cell randomly recombines segments from three immunoglobulin regions of DNA and combines these segments to develop novel BCR genes. B cells may also randomly change BCR genes to develop even more diversity. Each newly formed BCR gene codes for a specific and unique BCR. **Highlight: BCR Diversity: The Star of the Show** expands on the genetic explanation for the extensive BCR diversity.

All the BCRs of any particular cell are identical because the variable regions of every BCR on a single cell are identical—the two light chain variable regions are identical and the two heavy chain variable regions are identical. Together the two variable regions form **antigen-binding sites** (see Figure 4). Antigen-binding sites are complementary in shape to the three-dimensional shape of an epitope and bind precisely to it. Exact binding between antigen-binding site and epitope accounts for the specificity of a humoral immune response.

Though all of the BCRs on a single B cell are the same, the BCRs of one cell differ from the BCRs of all other B cells, much as each snowflake is distinct from all others. Scientists estimate that each person forms no less than $10^9$ and likely as many as $10^{13}$ B lymphocytes—each with its own BCR. Since an antigen, for example a bacterial protein, typically has numerous epitopes of various shapes, many different BCRs will recognize any particular antigen's epitopes, but each BCR recognizes only one epitope. BCR genes are randomly generated in sufficient numbers that the entire repertoire of BCRs (each carried by a particular B lymphocyte) is capable of recognizing the entire repertoire of thousands of millions of different epitopes. In other words, at least one BCR is fortuitously complementary to any given specific epitope the body may or may not encounter.

An analogy will serve to clarify this point. Imagine a locksmith who has a copy of every possible key to fit every possible lock. If a customer arrives at the shop with a lock needing a key, the locksmith can provide it (though it may take a while to find the correct key). Similarly, you have a BCR complementary to every possible epitope in the environment, though you will not be infected with every epitope. For example, you have lymphocytes with BCRs complementary to epitopes of stingray venom, though it is unlikely you will ever be stabbed by a stingray.

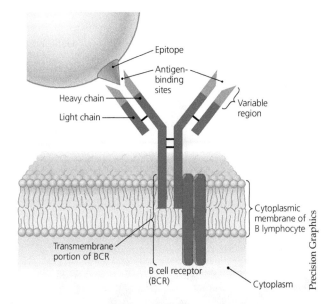

▲ **Figure 4 B cell receptor (BCR).** The B cell receptor is composed of a symmetrical, epitope-binding, Y-shaped protein in association with two transmembrane polypeptides.

When an antigenic epitope stimulates a specific B cell via the B cell's unique BCR, the B cell responds by undergoing cell division, giving rise to nearly identical offspring that secrete immunoglobulins into the blood or lymph. The immunoglobulins act against the epitope shape that stimulated the B cell. Activated, immunoglobulin-secreting B lymphocytes are called **plasma cells.** They have extensive rough endoplasmic reticulum and many Golgi bodies involved in the synthesis, packaging, and secreting of the immunoglobulins. Next we consider the structure and functions of the secreted immunoglobulins, which are called antibodies.

## Specificity and Antibody Structure

**Antibodies** are immunoglobulins and similar to BCRs in shape, though antibodies are secreted and lack the bulk of the transmembrane portions of BCRs (Figure 5). Thus, a basic antibody molecule is Y-shaped with two identical heavy chains and two identical light chains and is nearly identical to the secreting cell's BCR. The antigen-binding sites of antibodies from a given plasma cell are identical to one another and to the antigen-binding sites of that cell's BCR. Antibodies carry the same specificity for an epitope as the BCR of the activated B cell.

Because the arms of an antibody molecule contain antigen-binding sites, they are also known as the $F_{ab}$ *regions* (*fragment, antigen-binding*). The angle between the $F_{ab}$ regions and the stem can change because the point at which they join is hinge-like. An antibody stem, which is formed of the lower portions of the two heavy chains, is also called the $F_c$ *region* (because it forms a *fragment* that is *crystallizable*).

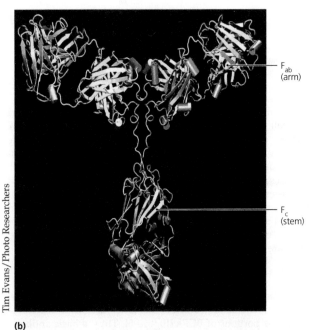

**(b)**

▲ **Figure 5  Basic antibody structure. (a)** Artist's rendition. Each antibody molecule, which is shaped like the letter Y, consists of two identical heavy chains and two identical light chains held together by disulfide bonds. Five different kinds of heavy chains form an antibody's stem ($F_c$ region). The arms ($F_{ab}$ regions) terminate in variable regions to form two antigen-binding sites. The hinge region is flexible, allowing the arms to bend in almost any direction. **(b)** Three-dimensional shape of an antibody based on X-ray crystallography. *Why are the two antigen-binding sites on a typical antibody molecule identical?*

**Figure 5** *The amino acid sequences of the two light chains of an antibody molecule are identical, as are the sequences of the two heavy chains, so the binding sites—each composed of the ends of one light chain and one heavy chain—must be identical.*

There are five basic types of $F_c$ region, designated by the Greek letters *mu, gamma, alpha, epsilon,* and *delta.* A plasma cell attaches the gene for its heavy chain variable region to one of the five $F_c$ region genes to form one of five classes of antibodies known as IgM, IgG, IgA, IgE, and IgD.

## Antibody Function

As we have seen, antigen-binding sites of antibodies are complementary to epitopes; in fact, the shapes of the two can match so very closely that most water molecules are excluded from the area of contact, producing a strong, noncovalent, hydrophobic interaction. Additionally, hydrogen bonds and other molecular attractions mediate antibody binding to epitope. The binding of antibody to epitope is the central functional feature of humoral adaptive immune responses. Once bound, antibodies function in several ways. These include activation of complement and inflammation, neutralization, opsonization, direct killing, agglutination, and antibody-dependent cytoxicity.

**Activation of Complement and Inflammation** $F_c$ regions of two or more antibodies bind to complement protein 1 (C1), activating it to become enzymatic. This begins the classical complement pathway, which releases inflammatory mediators. Some types of antibodies leave the blood during inflammation. More fully examines the defense reactions of complement activation and inflammation.

**Neutralization** Antibodies can neutralize a toxin by binding to a critical portion of the toxin so that it can no longer function against the body. Similarly, antibodies can block adhesion molecules on the surface of a bacterium or virus, neutralizing the pathogen's virulence because it cannot adhere to its target cell (Figure 6a).

**Opsonization** Antibodies act as **opsonins**[5]—molecules that stimulate phagocytosis. Neutrophils and macrophages have receptors for the $F_c$ regions of IgG molecules; therefore, these leukocytes bind to the stems of antibodies. Once antibodies are so bound, the leukocytes phagocytize them, along with the antigens they carry, at a faster rate compared to antigens lacking bound antibody. Changing the surface of an antigen so as to enhance phagocytosis is called **opsonization** (op'sŏ-nī-zā'shŭn) (Figure 6b).

**Killing by Oxidation** Recently, scientists have shown that some antibodies have catalytic properties that allow them to kill bacteria directly (Figure 6c). Specifically, antibodies catalyze the production of hydrogen peroxide, ozone, and other potent oxidants that kill bacteria.

**Agglutination** Because each basic antibody has two antigen-binding sites, each can attach to two epitopes at once. Numerous antibodies can aggregate antigens together—a state called **agglutination** (ă-glū-ti-nā'shŭn) (Figure 6d). Agglutination of

[5]From Greek *opsonein,* meaning to supply food, and *izein,* meaning to cause; thus, loosely, "to prepare for dinner."

soluble molecules typically causes them to become insoluble and precipitate. Agglutination may hinder the activity of pathogenic organisms and increases the chance that they will be phagocytized or filtered out of the blood by the spleen.

**Antibody-Dependent Cellular Cytoxicity (ADCC)** Antibodies often coat a target cell by binding to epitopes all over the target's surface. The antibodies' $F_c$ regions can then bind to receptors on special lymphocytes called *natural killer lymphocytes (NK cells)*, which are neither B nor T cells. NK lymphocytes lyse target cells with proteins called **perforin** (per'fōr-in) and **granzyme** (gran'zīm). Perforin molecules form into a tubular structure in the target cell's membrane, forming a channel through which granzyme enters the cell and triggers **apoptosis**[6] (programmed cell suicide) (Figure 6e). ADCC is similar to opsonization in that antibodies cover the target cell; however, with ADCC the target dies by apoptosis, whereas with opsonization the target is phagocytized. **ANIMATIONS:** *Humoral Immunity: Antibody Function*

## Classes of Antibodies

Threats confronting the immune system can be extremely variable, so it is not surprising that there are several classes of antibody. The class involved in any given humoral immune response depends on the type of invading foreign antigens, the portal of entry involved, and the antibody function required. Here, we consider the structure and functions of the five classes of antibodies.

Every B cell begins by attaching its variable region gene to the gene for the mu $F_c$ region and thus begins by making class M—**immunoglobulin M (IgM).** Some simple IgM molecules are put into the cytoplasmic membrane to act as a BCR, but most IgM is secreted during the initial stages of an immune response. A secreted IgM molecule is more than five times larger than the basic Y-shape because secreted IgM is a pentamer, consisting of five basic units linked together in a circular fashion via disulfide bonds and a short polypeptide *joining (J) chain* (see Table 1). Each IgM subunit has a conventional immunoglobulin structure, consisting of two light chains and two mu heavy chains. IgM is most efficient at complement activation, which also triggers inflammation, and can be involved in agglutination and neutralization.

In a process called **class switching,** a plasma cell then combines its variable region gene to the gene for a different $F_c$ region and begins secreting a new class of antibodies. The most common switch is to the gene for heavy chain gamma; that is, the plasma cell switches to synthesizing immunoglobulin G.

**Immunoglobulin G (IgG)** is the most common and longest-lasting class of antibody in the blood, accounting for about 80% of serum antibodies, possibly because IgG has many functions. Each molecule of IgG has the basic Y-shaped antibody structure.

**(a) Neutralization**

**(b) Opsonization**

**(c) Oxidation**

**(d) Agglutination**

**(e) Antibody-dependent cellular cytotoxicity (ADCC)**

Precision Graphics

▲ **Figure 6 Four functions of antibodies.** Drawings are not to scale. **(a)** Neutralization of toxins and microbes. **(b)** Opsonization. **(c)** Oxidation by toxic forms of oxygen such as $^1O_2$ (singlet oxygen), $H_2O_2$ (hydrogen peroxide), and $O_3$ (ozone). **(d)** Agglutination. **(e)** Antibody-dependent cellular cytotoxicity.

[6]Greek, meaning falling off.

# BCR DIVERSITY: THE STAR OF THE SHOW

How does your body generate billions of unique B cell receptor proteins (BCRs) so as to recognize the thousand of millions of foreign epitopes on pathogens that attack you? There isn't enough DNA in a cell to have individual genes for so many receptors. It would require several thousand times more DNA than you have. The answer to the problem of BCR diversity lies in the ingenious way in which B cells use their relatively small number of diverse BCR genes.

Genes for BCRs occur in discrete stretches of DNA called *loci* (singular: *locus*). Genes for the constant region are located downstream from loci for the variable regions. We will consider the variable region genes first, because it is in the variable region that BCR diversity is greatest.

BCR variable region genes occur in three loci on each of two chromosomes—one locus for the heavy chain variable region and two loci (called *kappa* and *lambda*) for the light chain variable region. Each cell is diploid—having two of each type of chromosome—so there are six loci all together. However, a developing B cell uses only one chromosome's loci for each of its heavy and light chains. Once a locus on a particular chromosome is used, the other chromosome's corresponding locus is inhibited.

Each locus is divided further into distinct genetic segments coding for portions of its respective chain. The heavy chain variable region locus has three segments called *variable* ($V_H$), *diversity* ($D_H$), and *junction* ($J_H$) segments. In each of your developing B cells there are 65 variable segment genes, 27 diversity segment genes, and 6 junction segment genes. Each light chain variable region locus has an additional *variable segment* ($V_L$) and a *junction segment* ($J_L$). For the kappa locus, there are 40 variable segment genes and 5 junction genes. The lambda locus is less variable, having only 30 V genes and a single J gene.

1 RAG randomly combines one D segment with one J segment.

2 RAG randomly combines DJ with one V segment.

3 Transcription and translation of polypeptide completed.

BCR

A great variety of BCRs form during B cell maturation as the B cell uses an enzyme called RAG—the *recombination activating gene* protein—to randomly combine one of each kind of the various segments to form its BCR gene. An analogy will help your understanding of this concept. Imagine that you have a wardrobe consisting of 65 different pairs of shoes, 27 different shirts, and 6 different pairs of pants that can be combined to create outfits. You can choose any one pair of shoes, any one shirt, and any one pair of pants each day, so with these 98 pieces of clothing, you will potentially have 10,530 different outfits ($65 \times 27 \times 6$). Your roommate might have the same numbers of items, but in different colors and styles; so between you, you will have twice as many potential outfits—21,060! Similarly, each developing B cell has 10,530 possible combinations of $V_H$, $D_H$, and $J_H$ segments on each of its two chromosomes for a total of 21,060 possible heavy chain variable region gene combinations.

The developing B cell also uses RAG to recombine the segments of the light chain variable loci. Since there are

200 ($40 \times 5$) possible kappa genes and 30 ($30 \times 1$) possible lambda genes on each chromosome, there are a total of 460 possible light chain genes on the two chromosomes. Therefore, each B cell can make one of a possible 9,687,600 ($21,060 \times 460$) different BCRs using only 348 genetic segments in the heavy and light chain loci on its two chromosomes.

Still, these nearly 10 million different BCRs do not account for all the variability seen among BCRs. Each B cell creates additional diversity: RAG randomly removes portions of D and J segments before joining the two together. Another enzyme randomly adds nucleotides to each heavy chain VDJ combination, and B cells in the germinal centers of lymph nodes undergo random point mutations in their V regions. The result of RAG recombinations, random deletions, random insertions, and point mutations is tremendous potential variability. Scientists estimate that you may have about $10^{23}$ B cell receptors possibilities. That's one hundred billion trillion—a number ten times greater than all the stars in the universe! Your B cells are indeed stars of the show.

HIGHLIGHT

IgG molecules play a major role in antibody-mediated defense mechanisms, including complement activation, opsonization, neutralization, and antibody-dependent cellular cytotoxicity (ADCC). IgG molecules can leave blood vessels to enter extracellular spaces more easily than can the other immunoglobulins. This is especially important during inflammation, because it enables IgG to bind to invading pathogens before they get into the circulatory systems. IgG molecules are also the only antibodies that cross a placenta to protect a developing child.

**Immunoglobulin A (IgA),** which has alpha heavy chains, is the immunoglobulin most closely associated with various body secretions. Some of the body's IgA is a monomer with the basic Y-shape that circulates in the blood, constituting about 12% of total serum antibody. However, plasma cells in the tear ducts, mammary glands, and mucous membranes synthesize **secretory IgA,** which is composed of two monomeric IgA molecules linked via a J chain and another short polypeptide (called a *secretory component*). Plasma cells add secretory component during the transport of secretory IgA across mucous membranes. Secretory component protects secretory IgA from digestion by intestinal enzymes.

Secretory IgA agglutinates and neutralizes antigens and is of critical importance in protecting the body from infections arising in the gastrointestinal, respiratory, urinary, and reproductive tracts. IgA provides nursing newborns some protection against foreign antigens because mammary glands secrete IgA into milk. Thus, nursing babies receive antibodies directed against antigens that have infected their mothers and are likely to infect them as well.

**Immunoglobulin E (IgE)** is a typical Y-shaped immunoglobulin with two epsilon heavy chains. Because it is found in extremely low concentrations in serum (less than 1% of total antibody), it is not critical for most antibody functions. Instead, IgE antibodies act as signal molecules—they attach to receptors on eosinophil cytoplasmic membranes to trigger the release of cell-damaging molecules onto the surface of parasites, particularly parasitic worms. IgE antibodies also trigger mast cells and basophils to release inflammatory chemicals such as histamine. In developed countries, IgE is more likely associated with allergies than with parasitic worms.

**Immunoglobulin D (IgD)** is characterized by delta heavy chains. IgD molecules are not secreted but are membrane-bound antigen receptors on B cells that are often seen during the initial phases of a humoral immune response. In this regard, IgD antibodies are like BCRs. Not all mammals have IgD, and animals that lack IgD show no observable ill effects; therefore, scientists do not know the exact function or importance of this class of antibody.

Table 1 compares the different classes of immunoglobulins and adds some details of antibody structure.

### CRITICAL **THINKING**

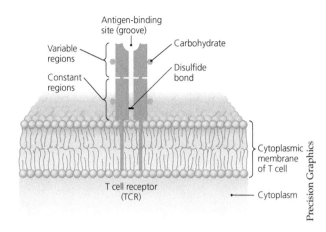

▲ **Figure 7 A T cell receptor (TCR).** A TCR is an asymmetrical surface molecule composed of two polypeptides containing a single antigen-binding site between them.

In most cases, B cells do not act alone to mount a humoral immune response. Instead, they respond to antigens only with the assistance of certain T lymphocytes. We will continue discussion of the details of humoral immune responses after we consider the various T cells.

## T Lymphocytes (T Cells)

### Learning Objectives

✓ Describe the importance of the thymus to the development of T lymphocytes.

✓ Describe the basic characteristics common to T lymphocytes.

✓ Compare and contrast three types of T cells.

A human adult's red bone marrow produces T lymphocytes. Sticky, adhesive molecules coupled with the action of chemotactic molecules attract these lymphocytes to the thymus from blood vessels. T cells mature in the thymus under the influence of molecular signals from the thymus. Following maturation, T cells circulate in the lymph and blood and migrate to the lymph nodes, spleen, and Peyer's patches. They account for about 70–85% of all lymphocytes in the blood.

T lymphocytes are like B cells in their specificity. Each T cell has about half a million copies of a **T cell receptor (TCR)** on its cytoplasmic membrane. Each T cell randomly chooses and combines segments of DNA in TCR gene regions to create a novel gene that codes for that cell's unique and specific TCR. The random production of diverse TCRs accomplished by recombining TCR genes is similar to the way BCRs are produced.

### Specificity of the T Cell Receptor (TCR)

In contrast to a BCR, a TCR is composed of only two glycopolypeptide chains; however, like BCRs, the terminal ends of TCRs are composed of variable regions that grant each cell's TCR specific binding properties. The groove between the polypeptides acts as the antigen-binding site (Figure 7). Similarly to binding by a BCR, a TCR recognizes and binds to a

# Characteristics of the Five Classes of Antibodies

TABLE 1

Precision Graphics

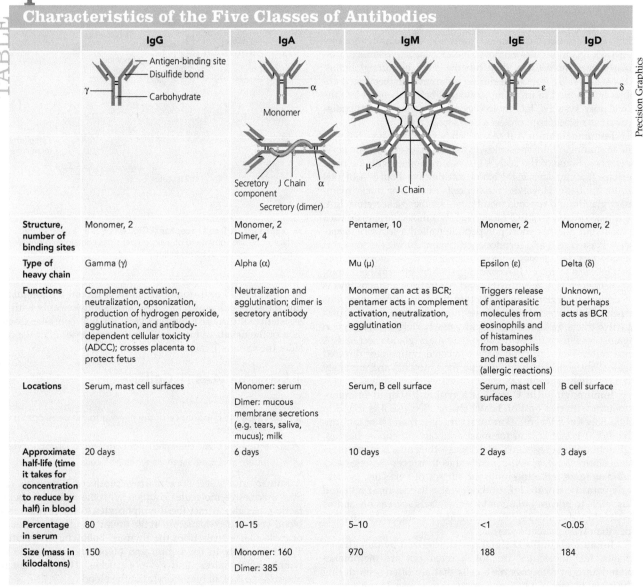

| | IgG | IgA | IgM | IgE | IgD |
|---|---|---|---|---|---|
| Structure, number of binding sites | Monomer, 2 | Monomer, 2<br>Dimer, 4 | Pentamer, 10 | Monomer, 2 | Monomer, 2 |
| Type of heavy chain | Gamma (γ) | Alpha (α) | Mu (μ) | Epsilon (ε) | Delta (δ) |
| Functions | Complement activation, neutralization, opsonization, production of hydrogen peroxide, agglutination, and antibody-dependent cellular toxicity (ADCC); crosses placenta to protect fetus | Neutralization and agglutination; dimer is secretory antibody | Monomer can act as BCR; pentamer acts in complement activation, neutralization, agglutination | Triggers release of antiparasitic molecules from eosinophils and of histamines from basophils and mast cells (allergic reactions) | Unknown, but perhaps acts as BCR |
| Locations | Serum, mast cell surfaces | Monomer: serum<br>Dimer: mucous membrane secretions (e.g. tears, saliva, mucus); milk | Serum, B cell surface | Serum, mast cell surfaces | B cell surface |
| Approximate half-life (time it takes for concentration to reduce by half) in blood | 20 days | 6 days | 10 days | 2 days | 3 days |
| Percentage in serum | 80 | 10–15 | 5–10 | <1 | <0.05 |
| Size (mass in kilodaltons) | 150 | Monomer: 160<br>Dimer: 385 | 970 | 188 | 184 |

complementary shape, but TCRs do not recognize epitopes directly. A TCR binds only to an epitope associated with a particular protein called *MHC protein,* which will be discussed shortly. There are at least $10^9$ different TCRs—each specific TCR type on a different T cell—which is enough for every epitope–MHC protein.

T lymphocytes act primarily against body cells that harbor intracellular pathogens such as viruses, though they also can act against body cells that produce abnormal cell-surface proteins (such as cancer cells). Because T cells act directly against antigens (they do not secrete immunoglobulins), their immune activities are called cell-mediated immune responses.

## Types of T Lymphocytes

Immunologists recognize types of T cells based on surface glycoproteins and characteristic functions. These are *cytotoxic T cells, helper T cells,* and *regulatory T cells.*

**Cytotoxic T Lymphocyte** Every **cytotoxic T cell (Tc or CD8 cell)** is distinguished by copies of its own unique TCR as well as the presence of CD8 cell-surface glycoprotein. CD (for *cluster of differentiation*) glycoproteins are named with internationally accepted designations consisting of a number following the prefix. These numbers reflect the order in which the glycoproteins were discovered, not the order in which they are produced or function. As the name *cytotoxic T cell* implies, these lymphocytes directly kill other cells—those infected with viruses and other intracellular pathogens, as well as abnormal cells, such as cancer cells.

**Helper T Lymphocyte** Immunologists distinguish **helper T cells (Th or CD4 cells)** by the presence of the CD4 glycoproteins. These cells are called "helpers" because their function is to assist in regulating the activity of B cells and cytotoxic T cells during immune responses by providing necessary signals and growth factors. There are two main subpopulations of helper T cells: *type 1 helper T cells (Th1 cells),* which assist cytotoxic T cells and innate macrophages, and *type 2 helper T cells (Th2 cells),* which function in conjunction with B cells. Immunologists distinguish between Th1 and Th2 cells on the basis of their secretions and by characteristic cell-surface proteins.

Helper T cells secrete various soluble protein messengers called *cytokines* that regulate the entire immune system, both adaptive and innate portions. We will consider the types and effects of cytokines shortly. **Highlight: The Loss of Helper T Cells in AIDS Patients** describes some of the effects of the destruction of helper T cells in individuals infected with the human immunodeficiency virus (HIV). **ANIMATIONS:** *Cell-Mediated Immunity: Helper T Cells*

**Regulatory T Lymphocyte** **Regulatory T cells (Tr cells),** previously known as *suppressor T cells,* repress adaptive immune responses and prevent autoimmune diseases. Tr cells express CD4 and CD25 glycoproteins. Scientists have not fully characterized the manner in which Tr cells work, but it is known that they are activated by contact with other immune cells and they

secrete some immunologically active chemicals called *cytokines,* which we examine in a subsequent section.

Table 2 compares and contrasts the features of various types of lymphocytes. We have considered the primary lymphocytes involved in immune responses. Now, we turn our attention to the way in which the body eliminates T cells and B cells that recognize normal body antigens by means of their BCRs and TCRs, respectively.

## Clonal Deletion
### Learning Objectives

✓ Describe apoptosis and explain its role in lymphocyte editing by clonal deletion.

✓ Compare and contrast clonal deletion of T cells and clonal deletion of B cells.

Given that both T and B lymphocytes randomly generate the shapes of their receptors (TCRs and BCRs respectively), every population of maturing lymphocytes includes numerous cells with receptors complementary to normal body components—the autoantigens mentioned earlier. It is vitally important that specific immune responses not be directed against autoantigens; the immune system must be tolerant of "self." When self-tolerance is impaired, the result is an *autoimmune disease.*

The body eliminates self-reactive lymphocytes via **clonal deletion,** so named because elimination of a cell deletes its potential offspring (clones). In this process, lymphocytes are exposed to autoantigens, and those lymphocytes that react to autoantigens undergo apoptosis (programmed cell suicide) and

---

▲ *HIV budding from Th cells.*

SEM | 400 nm

Andrejs Liepins/SPL/Photo Researchers

**THE LOSS OF HELPER T CELLS IN AIDS PATIENTS**

Neither B cells nor cytotoxic T cells respond effectively to most antigens without the participation of helper T cells, because signals are passed more effectively among leukocytes when the CD4 molecules of helper T cells bind to certain leukocytes.

We also saw that in order for viruses to enter cells and replicate, they must first attach to a specific protein on their target cells' surface. In the case of human immunodeficiency virus (HIV), the causative agent of AIDS, the surface protein to which it attaches is CD4, and its target cells are helper T cells. Once HIV enters a helper T cell, it, like other viruses, takes over the cell's protein-synthesizing machinery and directs the cell to produce more viruses.

Because they are essential to mounting an effective immune response, the body normally has a surplus of helper T cells—usually about three times as many as it needs. As a result, individuals infected with HIV can typically lose up to about two-thirds of their helper T cells before signs of immune deficiency appear. Cell-mediated immunity is usually affected first; even though B cells require the assistance of helper T cells to function optimally, they can still be stimulated directly by large quantities of antigen. Normal human blood typically contains about three CD4 helper T cells for every two CD8 cytotoxic T cells—a CD4 to CD8 ratio of 3:2. During the course of HIV infection, however, CD4 helper T cells are lost, reducing the CD4 to

CD8 ratio such that individuals with full-blown AIDS may have a ratio lower than 1:7.

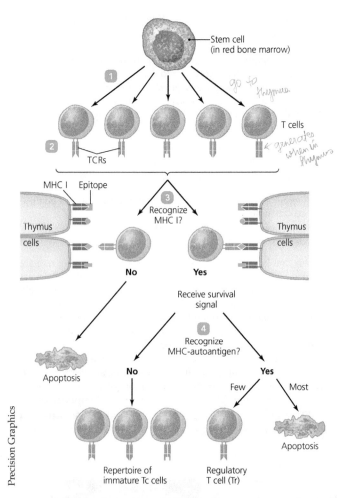

are thereby deleted from the repertoire of lymphocytes. Apoptosis is the critical feature of clonal deletion and the development of self-tolerance. The result of clonal deletion is that surviving lymphocytes respond only to foreign antigens.

In humans, clonal deletion occurs in the thymus for T lymphocytes and in the bone marrow for B lymphocytes. Lymphocyte clonal deletion is slightly different in T cells than it is in B cells. We will examine each in turn.

## Clonal Deletion of T Cells

As we have seen, T cells recognize epitopes only when the epitopes are bound to MHC protein. Young T lymphocytes spend about a week in the thymus being exposed to all of the body's natural epitopes though a unique feature of thymus cells. As a group, these cells express all of the body's normal proteins, including proteins that have no function in the thymus. For example, some thymus cells synthesize lysozyme, hemoglobin, and muscle cell proteins, though these proteins are not expressed externally to the cells. Rather, thymus cells process these autoantigens so as to express their epitopes in association with an MHC protein. Since the cells collectively synthesize polypeptides from the body's proteins, together they process and present all the body's autoantigens to young T cells.

Immature T cells undergo one of four fates (Figure 8):

- Those T cells that do not recognize the body's MHC protein undergo apoptosis, in other words, clonal deletion. Since they do not recognize the body's own MHC protein, they will be of no use identifying foreign epitopes carried by MHC protein. T cells that do recognize the body's MHC protein receive a signal to survive.

- Those that subsequently recognize autoantigen in conjunction with MHC protein mostly die by apoptosis, further clonal deletion.

- A few of these "self-recognizing" T cells remain alive to become regulatory T cells.

- The remaining T cells are those that will recognize the body's own MHC protein in conjunction with foreign epitopes and not with autoantigens. These T lymphocytes become the repertoire of protective T cells, which leave the thymus to circulate in the blood and lymph.

▲ **Figure 8  Clonal deletion of T cells.** ① Stem cells in the red bone marrow generate a host of lymphocytes that move to the thymus. ② In the thymus, each lymphocyte randomly generates a TCR with a particular shape. Note that each cell's TCR binding sites differ from those of other cells. ③ T cells pass through a series of "decision questions" in the thymus: Are their TCRs complementary to the body's MHC I protein? If "no," they undergo apoptosis—*clonal deletion*. If "yes," they survive. ④ Do the surviving cells recognize MHC I protein bound to any autoantigen? If "no," they survive and become the repertoire of immature T cells. If "yes," then most undergo apoptosis (more clonal deletion); a few survive as regulatory T cells (Tr).

*Precision Graphics*

## 2

## Characteristics of Selected Lymphocytes

| Lymphocyte | Site of Maturation | Representative Cell-Surface Glycoproteins | Selected Secretions |
|---|---|---|---|
| B cell | Red bone marrow | CD40 and distinctive BCR | Antibodies |
| Helper T cell type 1 (Th1) | Thymus | CD4, CCR5, and distinctive TCR | Interleukin 2, IFN-γ |
| Helper T cell type 2 (Th2) | Thymus | CD4, CCR3, CCR4, and distinctive TCR | Interleukin 4 |
| Cytotoxic T cell (Tc) | Thymus | CD8, CD95L, and distinctive TCR | Perforin, granzyme |
| Regulatory T cell (Tr) | Thymus | CD4, CD25, and distinctive TCR | Cytokines such as interleukin 10 |

TABLE

### Clonal Deletion of B Cells

Clonal deletion of B cells occurs in the bone marrow in a similar fashion (**Figure 9**), though self-reactive B cells may become inactive or change their BCR rather than undergo apoptosis. In any case, self-reactive B cells are removed from the active B cell repertoire, so that humoral immunity does not act against autoantigens. Tolerant B cells leave the bone marrow and travel to the spleen where they undergo further maturation before circulating in the blood and lymph.

Surviving B and T lymphocytes move into the blood and lymph, where they form the lymphocyte repertoire that scans for antigens. They communicate among one another and with other body cells via chemical signals called *cytokines*. In terms of our analogy of a stage play, there is dialogue among the cast of characters, but in our story the dialogue consists of chemical signals.

## Immune Response Cytokines

### Learning Objective

✓ Describe five types of cytokines.

**Cytokines** (sī'tō-kīnz) are soluble regulatory proteins that act as intercellular messages when released by certain body cells including those of the kidney, skin, and immunity. Here we are concerned with cytokines that signal among various immune leukocytes. For example, cytotoxic T cells (Tc) do not respond to antigens unless they are first signaled by cytokines.

Immune system cytokines are secreted by various leukocytes and affect diverse cells. Many cytokines are redundant; that is, they have almost identical effects. Such complexity has given rise to the concept of a *cytokine network*—a complex web of signals among all the cell types of the immune system. The nomenclature of cytokines is not based on a systematic relationship among them; instead, scientists named cytokines after their cells of origin, their function, and/or the order in which they were discovered. Cytokines of the immune system include the following substances:

- **Interleukins**[7] (in-ter-lū'kinz) **(ILs).** As their name suggests, ILs signal among leukocytes, though cells other than leukocytes may also use interleukins. Immunologists named interleukins sequentially as they were discovered. Currently, scientists have identified about 35 interleukins.

- **Interferons** (in-ter-fēr'onz) **(IFNs).** These antiviral proteins, may also act as cytokines. The most important interferon with such a dual function is gamma interferon (IFN-γ), which is a potent phagocytic activator secreted by Th1 cells.

- **Growth factors.** These proteins stimulate leukocyte stem cells to divide, ensuring that the body is supplied with sufficient white blood cells of all types. The body can control the progression of an adaptive immune response by limiting the production of growth factors.

- **Tumor necrosis**[8] **factor (TNF).** Macrophages and T cells secrete TNF to kill tumor cells and to regulate immune responses and inflammation.

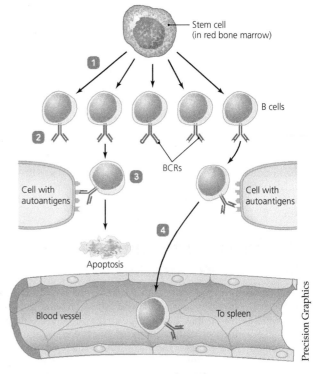

▲ **Figure 9 Clonal deletion of B cells.** **1** Stem cells in the red bone marrow generate a host of B lymphocytes. **2** Each newly formed B cell randomly generates a BCR with a particular shape. Note that each cell's BCR binding sites differ from those of other cells. **3** Cells whose BCR is complementary to some autoantigen bind with that autoantigen, stimulating the cell to undergo apoptosis. Thus, an entire set of potential daughter B cells (a clone) that are reactive with the body's own cells are eliminated—*clonal deletion.* **4** B cells with a BCR that is not complementary to any autoantigen are released from the bone marrow and into the blood. *Of the B cells shown, which is likely to undergo apoptosis?*

**Figure 9** *The second and third B lymphocytes from the left will undergo apoptosis; their active sites are complementary to the second and fourth autoantigens from the top, respectively.*

- **Chemokines** (kē'mō-kīnz). Chemokines are chemotactic cytokines; that is, they signal leukocytes to move—for example, to rush to a site of inflammation or infection, or to move within tissues.

Table 3 summarizes some properties of selected cytokines.

We have been considering adaptive immunity as a stage play. To this point, we have examined the "stage" and the "cast of characters" involved in adaptive immunity. The latter are: antigens with their epitopes, B cells with their BCRs, plasma cells and their antibodies, and T cells with their TCRs. The dialogue consists of cytokines. Actors who would disrupt the play—those T cells and B cells that recognize autoantigens—have been eliminated by

---

[7]From Latin *inter*, meaning between, and Greek *leukos*, meaning white.
[8]From Latin *necare*, meaning to kill.

191

| TABLE | Selected Immune Response Cytokines | | | |
|---|---|---|---|---|
| | **Cytokine** | **Representative Source** | **Representative Target** | **Representative Action** |
| | Interleukin 2 (IL-2) | Type 1 helper T (Th1) cell, cytotoxic T (Tc) cell | Tc cell | Cloning of Tc cell |
| | Interleukin 4 (IL-4) | Type 2 helper T (Th2) cell | B cell | B cell differentiates into plasma cell |
| | Interleukin 12 (IL-12) | Dendritic cell | Helper T (Th) cell | Th cell differentiates into Th1 cell |
| | Gamma interferon (IFN-γ) | Th1 cell | Macrophage | Increases phagocytosis |
| | Tumor necrosis factor (TNF) | Macrophages, T cells | Body tissues | Triggers inflammation or apoptosis |

clonal deletion. Before we finish examining the processes involved in humoral immune and cell-mediated immune responses, we need to consider some other initial preparations the body makes before the "play" begins.

# Preparation for an Adaptive Immune Response

The body equips itself for specific immune responses by making *major histocompatibility complex proteins* (MHC proteins) and processing antigens so that T lymphocytes can recognize epitopes. We will examine each of these preparations of adaptive immunity, beginning with the roles of the major histocompatibility complex.

## The Roles of the Major Histocompatibility Complex

### Learning Objective

✓ Describe the two classes of major histocompatibility complex (MHC) proteins with regard to their location and function.

When scientists first began grafting tissue from one animal into another so as to determine a method for treating burn victims, they discovered that if the animals were not closely related, the recipients swiftly rejected the grafts. When they analyzed the reason for such rapid rejection, they found that a graft recipient mounted a very strong immune response against a specific type of antigen found on the cells of unrelated grafts. When the antigen on a graft's cells was sufficiently dissimilar from antigens on the host's cells, as seen with unrelated animals, the grafts were rejected. This is how scientists came to understand how the body is able to distinguish "self" from "nonself."

Immunologists named these types of antigens *major histocompatibility*[9] *antigens* to indicate their importance in determining the compatibility of tissues in successful grafting. Further research revealed that major histocompatibility antigens are glycoproteins found in the membranes of most cells of vertebrate animals. Major histocompatibility antigens are coded by a cluster of genes called the **major histocompatibility complex (MHC).** In humans, an MHC is located on each copy of chromosome 6.

Because organ grafting is a modern surgical procedure with no counterpart in nature, scientists reasoned that MHC proteins must have some other "real" function. Indeed, immunologists have determined that MHC proteins in cytoplasmic membranes function to hold and position epitopes for presentation to T cells. Each MHC molecule has an *antigen-binding groove* that lies between two polypeptides. Inherited variations in the amino acid sequences of the polypeptides modify the shapes of MHC binding sites and determine which epitopes can be bound and presented. It is important to recall that TCRs recognize only epitopes that are bound to MHC molecules.

MHC proteins are of two classes (Figure 10). Class I MHC molecules are found on the cytoplasmic membranes of all nucleated cells. Thus red blood cells, which do not have nuclei, do not express MHC proteins, whereas cells such as those of skin and muscles do express MHC class I molecules. Special cells called **antigen-presenting cells (APCs)** also have class II MHC proteins. Professional antigen-presenting cells—those that regularly present antigen—are B cells, macrophages, and most importantly **dendritic cells,** which are so named because they have many long, thin cytoplasmic processes called *dendrites*[10] (Figure 11). Phagocytic dendritic cells are found under the surface of the skin and mucous membranes. Some dendritic cells extend dentrites to a mucous surface to sample antigens, much like a submarine extends a periscope to get a view of surface activity. After acquiring antigens, dendritic cells migrate to lymph nodes to interact with B and T lymphocytes. Certain other phagocytes, such as *microglia* in the brain and *Kupffer cells* in the liver, may also present antigen under certain conditions. These cells are termed *nonprofessional antigen-presenting cells.*

The cytoplasmic membrane of a professional APC has about 100,000 MHC II molecules, each of which varies in the epitope it can bind. Their diversity is dependent on an individual's genotype. If an antigen fragment cannot be bound to an MHC molecule, it typically does not trigger an immune response. Thus, MHC molecules determine which antigen fragments might trigger immune responses.

## Antigen Processing

### Learning Objectives

✓ Explain the roles of antigen-presenting cells (e.g., dendritic cells and macrophages) and MHC molecules in antigen processing and presentation.

✓ Contrast endogenous antigen processing with exogenous antigen processing.

---

[9]From Greek *histos*, meaning tissue, and Latin *compatibilis*, meaning agreeable.
[10]From Greek *dendron*, meaning tree, referring to long cellular extensions that look like branches of a tree.

**(a)**

**(b)**

Precision Graphics

▲ **Figure 10 The two classes of major histocompatibility complex (MHC) proteins.** Each is composed of two polypeptides that form an antigen-binding groove. **(a)** MHC class I glycoproteins, which are found on all cells except red blood cells. **(b)** MHC class II glycoproteins, which are expressed only by B cells and special antigen-presenting cells (APCs).

Before MHC proteins can display epitopes, antigens must be processed. Antigen processing occurs via somewhat different processes according to whether the antigen is endogenous or exogenous. Recall that endogenous antigens come from the cells' cytoplasm or from pathogens living within the cells, whereas exogenous antigens have extracellular sources, such as lymph. **ANIMATIONS:** *Antigen Processing and Presentation: Overview*

### Processing Endogenous Antigens

A few molecules of new polypeptides produced within nucleated cells—including some polypeptides produced by intracellular bacteria or polypeptides coded by viruses—are catabolized into smaller pieces containing about 8–12 amino acids. These pieces will include epitopes from larger polypeptides. Peptides containing epitopes bind onto complementary antigen-binding

Cécile Chalouni, Genentech

LM | 10 μm

▲ **Figure 11 Dendritic cells.** These important antigen-presenting cells in the body are found in the skin and mucous membranes. They have numerous thin cytoplasmic processes called dendrites.

grooves of MHC class I molecules during biosynthesis in the membrane of the endoplasmic reticulum. This membrane, loaded with MHC class I proteins and epitopes, is then packaged into a vesicle by a Golgi body and inserted into the cytoplasmic membrane. The result is that the cell displays the MHC class I protein–epitope complex on the cell's surface (Figure 12). All nucleated cells express MHC class I molecules and epitopes in this manner.

### Processing Exogenous Antigens

For exogenous antigens, a professional antigen-presenting cell (APC), which is usually a dendritic cell, internalizes the invading pathogen and enzymatically catabolizes the pathogen's molecules, producing peptide epitopes, which are contained in a phagolysosome. A vesicle already containing MHC class II molecules in its membrane fuses with the phagolysosome, and each peptide then attempts to bind to an antigen-binding groove of a complementary MHC class II molecule. The fused vesicle inserts successful MHC class II protein–epitope complexes into the cytoplasmic membrane such that the epitopes are presented on the outside (Figure 13). Empty MHC molecules are not stable on a cell's surface and are degraded. **ANIMATIONS:** *Antigen Processing and Presentation: Steps, MHC*

So far, we have set the stage for the immune system "play" by examining the organs, cells, secretions, and signaling molecules of the immune system, as well as the preparatory steps of antigen processing, antigen presentation, and clonal deletion. We have seen that adaptive immunity is specific, due to the precise and accurate fit of lymphocyte receptors with their complements; that adaptive immunity involves clones of B and T cells,

▲ **Figure 12  The processing of T-dependent endogenous antigens.** Epitopes from all polypeptides synthesized within a nucleated cell load onto complementary MHC I proteins, which are exported to the cytoplasmic membrane.

▲ **Figure 13  The processing of T-dependent exogenous antigens.** Antigens arising outside the body's cells are phagocytized by an APC, which then loads epitopes into complementary antigen-binding grooves of MHC II molecules. The MHC II protein–epitope complexes are then displayed on the outside of the APC's cytoplasmic membrane.

**1 Antigen presentation**

Dendritic cell

MHC I

CD8 — Epitope

TCR

Tc cell

Immunological synapse

MHC II protein
Epitope
TCR
Th cell

DC

IL-12

Inactive Tc cell

IL-2 receptor (IL-2R)

**2 Th differentiation**

Th1 cell

IL-2

**3 Clonal expansion**

Memory T cell

IL-2R

Active Tc cells

IL-2

IL-2

**4 Self-stimulation**

IL-2R

Active Tc cells

IL-2

Precision Graphics

▲ **Figure 14  Activation of a clone of cytotoxic T (Tc) cells.** 1 Antigen-presenting cells, here a dendritic cell, present epitopes in conjunction with MHC I protein to inactive T cells. 2 Infected APCs secrete IL-12, which causes helper T cells to differentiate into Th1 cells. 3 Signaling from the APC and IL-2 from the Th1 cell activate Tc cells that recognize the MHC I protein–epitope complex. IL-2 triggers Tc cells to divide, forming a clone of active Tc cells as well as memory T cells. 4 Active Tc cells secrete IL-2, becoming self-stimulatory.

which are unresponsive to self (due to clonal deletion); and that immune responses are inducible against foreign antigens. Now, we can examine cell-mediated and humoral immune responses in more detail. We begin with cell-mediated immunity.

# Cell-Mediated Immune Responses

## Learning Objectives

✓ Describe a cell-mediated immune response.

✓ Compare and contrast the two pathways of cytotoxic T cell action.

The body uses cell-mediated immune responses to fight intracellular pathogens and abnormal body cells. Recall that inducibility and specificity are two hallmark characteristics of adaptive immunity. The body induces cell-mediated immune responses

only against specific endogenous antigens. Given that many common intracellular invaders are viruses, our examination of cell-mediated immunity will focus on these pathogens. However, cell-mediated immune responses are also mounted against cancer cells, intracellular parasitic protozoa, and intracellular bacteria such as *Mycobacterium tuberculosis* (mī'kō-bak-tēr'-ē-ŭm too-ber-kyū-lō'sis), which causes tuberculosis. **Highlight: Attacking Cancer with Lab-Grown T Cells** describes an experimental use of T cells to treat one form of cancer.

## Activation of T Cell Clones and Their Functions

The body does not initiate adaptive immune responses at the site of an infection but rather in lymphoid organs, usually lymph nodes, where antigen-presenting cells interact with lymphocytes. The initial event in cell-mediated immunity is the activation of a specific clone of cytotoxic T cells as depicted in **Figure 14**:

HIGHLIGHT

## ATTACKING CANCER WITH LAB-GROWN T CELLS

The body naturally manufactures T cells that attack cancer cells, but it sometimes does not make enough of them to shrink tumors and effectively halt the tumor's progress. Recent studies have focused on patients with malignant melanoma, an aggressive form of skin cancer. Researchers took samples of the patients' own cancer-fighting T cells and cloned them in a laboratory until they numbered in the billions. These billions of identical T cells were then injected back into the individuals that first produced them. The results were

encouraging. Many of the patients became "virtually cancer free," while tumors were substantially reduced in other patients.

Such T cell therapy remains experimental and is still some time away from becoming a generally accepted cancer treatment. Scientists do not yet understand why the therapy works in some patients and not others. To date, the therapy has primarily been tested against malignant melanoma, but planning to test it against other types of cancer is under way, and some scientists

believe that a similar therapy may be effective against viral diseases such as hepatitis.

Tc cell

▲ *T cell (green) attacking a cancer cell.* SEM 0.25 μm

Andrejs Liepins/SPL/ Photo Researchers

1. **Antigen presentation.** A virus-infected antigen-presenting cell (APC), typically a dendritic cell, migrates to a nearby lymph node where it presents virus epitopes in conjunction with MHC I protein. Because of the vast repertoire of randomly generated TCRs, at least one Tc cell will have a TCR complementary to the presented MHC I protein–epitope complex. This Tc cell binds to the dendritic cell to form a cell-cell contact site called an *immunological synapse.* CD8 glycoprotein of the Tc cell, which specifically binds to MHC I protein, stabilizes the synapse.

2. **Helper T cell differentiation.** When the interaction between Tc and APC is not particularly strong, a nearby CD4-bearing helper T (Th) lymphocyte helps. The Th cell binds to the APC via the TCR of the helper cell (which is complementary to an MHC II protein–epitope complex presented on the APC) and induces the APC to more vigorously signal the Tc cell. Viruses and some intracellular bacteria induce dendritic cells to secrete interleukin 12 (IL-12), which stimulates the helper T cells to become a clone of type 1 helper T (Th1) cells. Th1 cells in turn secrete IL-2. Lacking the assistance of Th cells, an immunological synapse between the APC and the Tc cell fails to progress. This limits improper immune responses.

3. **Clonal expansion.** The dendritic cell imparts a second required signal in the immunological synapse. This signal, in conjunction with any IL-2 from a Th1 cell that may be present, activates the cytotoxic T (Tc) cell to secrete its own IL-2. Interleukin 2 triggers cell division and differentiation in Tc cells. Activated Tc cells reproduce to form memory T cells (discussed shortly) and more Tc progeny—a process known as **clonal expansion.**

4. **Self-stimulation.** Daughter Tc cells activate and produce both IL-2 receptors (IL-2R) and more IL-2, thereby becoming self-stimulating—they no longer require either an APC or a helper T cell. They leave the lymph node and are now ready to attack virally infected cells.

As previously discussed, when any nucleated cell synthesizes proteins, it displays epitopes from them in the antigen-binding grooves of MHC class I molecules on its cytoplasmic membrane. Thus, when viruses are replicated inside cells, epitopes of viral proteins are displayed on the host cell's surface. An active Tc cell binds to an infected cell via its TCR, which is complementary to the MHC I protein–epitope complex, and via its CD8 glycoprotein, which is complementary to the MHC class I protein of the infected cell (Figure 15a).

Cytotoxic T cells kill their targets through one of two pathways: the *perforin-granzyme pathway,* which involves the synthesis of special killing proteins, or the *CD95 pathway,* which is mediated through a glycoprotein found on the body's cells. **ANIMATIONS:** *Cell-Mediated Immunity: Cytotoxic T Cells* .

## The Perforin-Granzyme Cytotoxic Pathway

The cytoplasm of cytotoxic T cells has vesicles containing two key protein cytotoxins—*perforin* and *granzyme,* which are also used by NK cells in conjunction with antibody-dependent cellular cytotoxicity (discussed previously). When a cytotoxic T cell first attaches to its target, vesicles containing the cytotoxins release their contents. Perforin molecules aggregate into a channel through which granzyme enters, activating apoptosis in the target cell (Figure 15b). Having forced its target to commit suicide, the cytotoxic T cell disengages and moves on to another infected cell.

### CRITICAL **THINKING**

Why did scientists give the name "perforin" to a molecule secreted by Tc cells?

## The CD95 Cytotoxic Pathway

The **CD95 pathway** of cell-mediated cytotoxicity involves an integral glycoprotein called *CD95* that is present in the cytoplasmic membranes of many body cells. Activated Tc cells insert *CD95L*—

> **Figure 15  A cell-mediated immune response.**
> **(a)** The binding of a virus-infected cell by an active cytotoxic T (Tc) cell. **(b)** The perforin-granzyme cytotoxic pathway. After perforins and granzymes have been released from Tc cell vesicles, granzymes enter the infected cell through the perforin complex pore and activate the enzymes of apoptosis. **(c)** The CD95 cytotoxic pathway. Binding of CD95L on the Tc cell activates the enzymatic portion of the infected cell's CD95 such that apoptosis is induced.

(a)

(b)

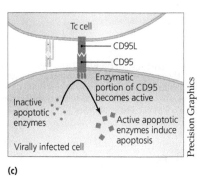

(c)

Precision Graphics

the receptor for CD95—into their cytoplasmic membranes. When an activated Tc cell comes into contact with its target, its CD95L binds to CD95 on the target, which then activates enzymes that trigger apoptosis, killing the target cells (Figure 15c).

## Memory T Cells

### Learning Objective

✓ Describe the establishment of memory T cells.

Some activated T cells become **memory T cells,** which may persist for months or years in lymphoid tissues. If a memory T cell subsequently contacts an epitope–MHC I protein complex matching its TCR, it responds immediately (without a need for interaction with APCs) and produces cytotoxic T cell clones that recognize the offending epitope. These cells need fewer regulatory signals and become functional immediately. Further, since the number of memory T cells is greater than the number of T cells that recognized the antigen during the initial exposure, a subsequent cell-mediated immune response to a previously encountered antigen is much more effective than a primary response. An enhanced cell-mediated immune response upon subsequent exposure to the same antigen is called a **memory response.**[11]

---

[11]Sometimes also called anamnestic responses, from Greek *ana*, meaning again, and *mimneskein*, meaning to call to mind.

## T Cell Regulation

### Learning Objective

✓ Explain the process and significance of the regulation of cell-mediated immunity.

The body carefully regulates cell-mediated immune responses so that T cells do not respond to autoantigens. As we have seen, T cells require several signals from an antigen-presenting cell to activate. If the T cells do not receive these signals in a specific sequence—like the sequence of numbers in a combination padlock—they will not respond. Thus, when a T cell and an antigen-presenting cell interact in an immunological synapse, the two cell types have a chemical dialogue that stimulates the T cell to fully respond to the antigen. If a T cell does not receive the signals required for its activation, it will "shut down" as a precaution against autoimmune responses.

Regulatory T (Tr) cells also moderate cytotoxic T cells by mechanisms that are beyond the scope of our discussion. Suffice it to say that Tr cells provide one more level of control over potentially dangerous cell-mediated immune responses.

## Humoral Immune Responses

As we have discussed, the body induces humoral immune responses against the antigens of exogenous pathogens. Recall that inducibility is one of the main characteristics of adaptive

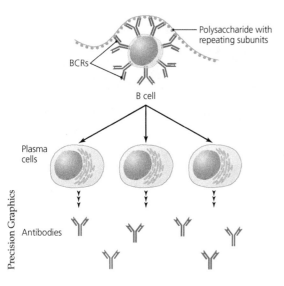

▲ **Figure 16 The effects of the binding of a T-independent antigen by a B cell.** When a molecule with multiple repeating epitopes (such as the polysaccharide shown here) cross-links the BCRs on a B cell, the cell is activated: it proliferates, and its daughter cells become plasma cells that secrete antibodies.

Steve Gschmeissner/Photo Researchers, Inc.

▲ **Figure 17 A plasma cell.** Plasma cells are almost twice as large as inactive B cells and are filled with endoplasmic reticulum and Golgi bodies for the synthesis and secretion of antibodies.

immunity: humoral immunity activates only in response to specific pathogens. The following sections examine the activity of B lymphocytes in humoral immune responses.

## Inducement of T-Independent Humoral Immunity

### Learning Objectives

✓ Contrast T-dependent and T-independent antigens in terms of size and repetition of subunits.

✓ Describe the inducement and action of a T-independent humoral response.

A few large antigens have many identical, repeating epitopes. These antigens can induce a humoral immune response without the assistance of a helper T cell (Th cell); therefore, these antigens are called *T-independent antigens,* and they trigger response of **T-independent humoral immunity** (Figure 16).

The repeating subunits of T-independent antigens allow extensive cross-linking between numerous BCRs on a B cell, stimulating the B cell to proliferate. Simultaneous interaction between Toll-like receptors on the B cell, innate mediators, and/or bacterial chemicals may facilitate activation of the B cell. Clones of the activated B cell become plasma cells, which have an extensive cytoplasm rich in rough endoplasmic reticulum and Golgi bodies and which secrete antibodies (Figure 17). Though these events occur without the direct involvement of Th cells, cytokines such as tumor necrosis factor (TNF) are required. T-independent humoral immune responses are fast because they do not depend on interactions with Th cells. Their speed is similar to that of innate immunity, but T-independent humoral immunity is relatively weak, disappears quickly, and induces little immunological memory.

T-independent responses are stunted in children, possibly because the repertoire and abundance of B cells is not fully developed in children; therefore, pathogens displaying T-independent antigens can cause childhood diseases, which are rare in adults. An example of such a T-independent antigen and its disease is the capsule of *Haemophilus influenzae* (hē-mof′i-lŭs in-flu-en′zī) type B that causes most cases of meningitis in unvaccinated children. The capsules of other bacteria, lipopolysaccharide of Gram-negative cell walls, bacterial flagella, and the capsids (outer covering) of some viruses constitute other T-independent antigens.

Most humoral immune responses are of the T-dependent type. We consider them next.

## Inducement of T-Dependent Humoral Immunity with Clonal Selection

### Learning Objectives

✓ Describe the formation and functions of plasma cells and memory B cells.

✓ Describe the steps and effect of clonal selection.

*T-dependent antigens* lack the numerous, repetitive, and identical epitopes and the large size of T-independent antigens, and immunity against them requires the assistance of type 2 helper T (Th2) cells. **T-dependent humoral immunity** begins with the action of an antigen-presenting cell, which is usually a dendritic cell. After endocytosis and processing of the antigen, the dendritic cell presents epitopes in conjunction with MHC II proteins. This APC will induce the specific helper T (CD4) lymphocyte with a TCR complementary to the presented MHC II–epitope complex. The activated Th2 cell must in turn induce the equally rare B cell that recognizes the same antigen. Lymph nodes facilitate and cytokines mediate interactions among the antigen-presenting cells and lymphocytes, increasing the chance that the appropriate cells find each other.

Thus, a T-dependent humoral immune response involves a series of interactions among antigen-presenting cell, helper T cells, and B cells, all of which are mediated and enhanced by cytokines. Now we will examine each step in more detail (Figure 18):

1. **Antigen presentation for Th activation and cloning.** A dendritic cell, after acquiring antigens in the skin or mucous membrane, moves via the lymph to a local lymph node. The trip takes about a day. As helper T (Th, CD4) cells pass through the lymph node, they survey all the resident APCs for complementary epitopes in conjunction with MHC II proteins. Antigen presentation depends on chance encounters between Th cells and the dendritic cells, but immunologists estimate that every lymphocyte browses the dendritic cells in every lymph node every day; therefore, complementary cells eventually find each other. Once they have established an immunological synapse, CD4 molecules in membrane rafts of the Th cell's cytoplasmic membrane recognize and bind to MHC II, stabilizing the synapse.

    As we saw in cell-mediated immune responses, helper T cells need further stimulation before they activate. The requirement for a second signal helps prevent accidental inducement of an immune response. As before, the APC imparts the second signal by displaying an integral membrane protein in the immunological synapse. This induces the Th cell to proliferate, producing a clone.

2. **Differentiation of helper T cells into Th2 cells.** In humoral immune responses, the cytokine interleukin 4 (IL-4) acts as a signal to the Th cells to become type 2 helper T cells (Th2 cells). Immunologists do not know the source of IL-4, but it may be secreted initially by innate cells such as mast cells or secreted later in a response by the Th cells themselves.

3. **Clonal selection of B cell.** A B cell attaches to and phagocytizes a complementary antigen, which is a BCR-mediated event. It then displays the pathogen's epitopes in association with MHC II proteins. Antigen binding primes these B cells to participate in humoral immune responses. This is called **clonal selection.**

4. **Activation of B cell.** The repertoire of B cells and newly formed Th2 cells survey one another. A Th2 cell binds to the B cell with an MHC II protein–epitope complex that is complementary to the TCR of the Th2 cell. CD4 glycoprotein again stabilizes the immunological synapse.

    Th2 cells secrete more chemical signal molecules, which induce the selected B cell to move to the cortex of the lymph node. A Th2 cell in contact with an MHC II protein–epitope on a B cell is stimulated, expresses new gene products, and inserts a protein called CD40L into its cytoplasmic membrane. CD40L binds to CD40, which is found on B cells. This provides a second signal in the immunological synapse, triggering B cell activation. The B cell moves to the cortex of the lymph node.

    The activated B cell proliferates rapidly to produce a population of cells (clone) that make up a germinal center in the lymph node. The clone differentiates into two types of cells—*memory B cells* (discussed shortly) and antibody-secreting *plasma cells*. **ANIMATIONS:** *Humoral Immunity: Clonal Selection and Expansion*

Most members of a clone become plasma cells. The initial plasma cell descendants of any single activated B cell secrete antibodies with binding sites identical to one another and complementary to the specific antigen recognized by their parent cell. However, as the plasma cell clones replicate, the cells slightly modify their antigen-binding-site genes such that they secrete antibodies with slightly different variable regions. Plasma cells that secrete antibodies with a higher affinity for the epitope have a selective survival advantage over plasma cells secreting antibodies with a less good fit; that is, active B cells with BCRs that bind the epitope more closely survive at a higher rate. Thus, as the humoral immune response progresses, there are more and more plasma cells, secreting antibodies whose fitness gets progressively better.

Each plasma cell produces about 2000 molecules of antibody per second. They begin by secreting IgM and then, through class switching, they secrete IgG. Some cells later switch a second time and begin secreting IgA or IgE. As discussed previously, antibodies activate complement, trigger inflammation, agglutinate and neutralize antigen, act as opsonins, directly kill pathogens, and induce antibody-dependent cytoxicity.

Individual plasma cells are short lived, at least in part because of their high metabolic rate; they die within a few days of activation, although their antibodies can remain in body fluids for several weeks. Providentially, their descendants persist for years to maintain long-term adaptive responses.

## CRITICAL **THINKING**

In general, what sorts of pathogens would successfully attack a patient with an inability to synthesize B lymphocytes?

# Memory B Cells and the Establishment of Immunological Memory

## Learning Objective

✓ Contrast primary and secondary immune responses.

# Adaptive Immunity

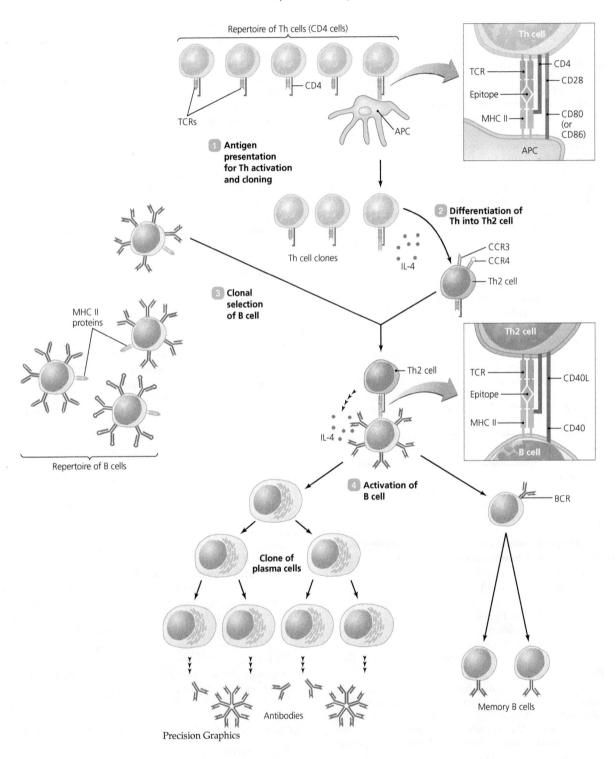

Repertoire of Th cells (CD4 cells)

TCRs

CD4

APC

Th cell

TCR — CD4
Epitope — CD28
MHC II — CD80 (or CD86)

APC

**1** Antigen presentation for Th activation and cloning

Th cell clones

IL-4

**2** Differentiation of Th into Th2 cell

CCR3
CCR4
Th2 cell

**3** Clonal selection of B cell

MHC II proteins

Repertoire of B cells

Th2 cell

Th2 cell

TCR — CD40L
Epitope
MHC II — CD40

B cell

IL-4

**4** Activation of B cell

BCR

Clone of plasma cells

Antibodies

Memory B cells

Precision Graphics

**Figure 18** **A T-dependent humoral immune response.**
**1** Antigen presentation, in which an APC, typically a dendritic cell, presents antigen to a complementary Th cell. **2** Differentiation of the Th cell into a Th2 cell. **3** Clonal selection, in which the Th2 cell binds to the B cell clone that recognizes the antigen. **4** Activation of the B cell in response to secretion of IL-4 by the Th2 cell, which causes the B cell to differentiate into antibody-secreting plasma cells and long-lived memory cells.

**(MM)** To see a 3-D animation on immunology, go to the Study Area at **www.masteringmicrobiology.com** and watch the *MicroFlix*.

(a)

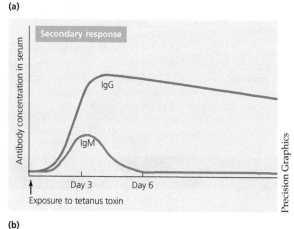

(b)

A small percentage of the cells produced during B cell proliferation do not secrete antibodies but survive as **memory B cells**—that is, long-lived cells with BCRs complementary to the specific epitope that triggered their production. In contrast to plasma cells, memory cells retain their BCRs and persist in lymphoid tissues, surviving for more than 20 years, ready to initiate antibody production if the same epitope is encountered again. Let's examine how memory cells provide the basis for immunization to prevent disease, using tetanus immunization as an example.

Because the body produces an enormous variety of B cells (and therefore BCRs), a few Th cells and B cells bind to and respond to epitopes of *tetanus toxoid* (deactivated tetanus toxin), which is used for tetanus immunization. In a **primary response** (Figure 19a), relatively small amounts of antibodies are produced, and it may take days before sufficient antibodies are made to completely eliminate the toxoid from the body. Though some antibody molecules may persist for three weeks, a primary immune response basically ends when the plasma cells have lived out their normal life spans. **ANIMATIONS:** *Humoral Immunity: Primary Immune Response*

Memory B cells, surviving in lymphoid tissue, constitute a reserve of antigen-sensitive cells that become active when there is another exposure to the antigen, in this case, toxin from infecting tetanus bacteria. Exposure may be many years later. Thus, tetanus toxin produced during the course of a bacterial infection will restimulate a population of memory cells, which proliferate and differentiate rapidly into plasma cells. The newly differentiated plasma cells produce large amounts of antibody within a few days (Figure 19b), and the tetanus toxin is neutralized before it can cause disease. Since many memory cells recognize and respond to the antigen, such a **secondary immune response** is much faster and more effective than the primary response. **ANIMATIONS:** *Humoral Immunity: Secondary Immune Response*

As you might expect, a third exposure (whether to tetanus toxin or to toxoid in an immunization booster) results in an even more effective response. Enhanced immune responses triggered by subsequent exposure to antigens are memory responses, which are the basis of *immunization*.

## CRITICAL **THINKING**

Plasma cells are vital for protection against infection, but memory B cells are not. Why not?

▲ **Figure 19** **The production of primary and secondary humoral immune responses.** This example depicts some events following the administration of a tetanus toxoid in immunization.
**(a)** Primary response. After the tetanus toxoid is introduced into the body, the body slowly removes the toxoid while producing memory B cells.
**(b)** Secondary response. Upon exposure to active tetanus toxin during the course of an infection, memory B cells immediately differentiate into plasma cells and proliferate, producing a response that is faster and results in greater antibody production than occurs in the primary response.

In summary, the body's response to infectious agents seldom relies on one mechanism alone, because this course of action would be far too risky. Therefore, the body typically uses several different mechanisms to combat infections. In the example from the chapter opener, the body's initial response to intruders was inflammation (a nonspecific, innate response), but a specific immune response against the invading microorganisms was also necessary. APCs phagocytize some of the invaders, process their epitopes, and induce clones of lymphocytes in both humoral and cell-mediated immune responses. Key to enduring protection are the facts that adaptive immunity is unresponsive to self and involves immunological memory brought about by long-lived memory B and T cells.

Cell-mediated adaptive immune responses involve the activity of cytotoxic T lymphocytes in killing cells infected with

## EMERGING DISEASES

Precision Graphics

### MICROSPORIDIOSIS

iStockPhoto

Darius is sick, which is not surprising for an HIV-infected man. But he is sick in several new ways. Sick of having to stay within 20 feet of a toilet. Sick of the cramping, the gas, the pain, and the nausea. Sick with irregular, but persistent, watery diarrhea. He is losing weight because food is passing through him undigested. Most days over the past seven months have been disgusting despite his use of over-the-counter remedies, which provide a few days of intermittent relief. His belief that these normal days signaled the end of the ordeal have kept him from the doctor. But now his eyes have begun to hurt, and his vision is blurry. Whatever it is, it's attacking him at both ends. Time to get stronger drugs from his doctor.

Microscopic examination of Darius's stool sample reveals that he is being assaulted by *Encephalitozoon intestinalis*, a member of a group of emerging pathogens called microsporidia. The single-celled pathogens are also seen on smears from Darius's nose and eyes. Microsporidia were long thought to be simple single-celled animals, but genetic analysis and comparison with other organisms reveal that they are closer to zygomycete yeasts.

Microsporidia appear to infect humans who engage in unprotected sexual activity, eat contaminated food, or drink or swim in contaminated water. People with active T cells rarely have symptoms; but people with suppressed immunity become easy targets for the fungus.

Microsporidia attack by uncoiling a flexible, hollow filament that stabs into a host cell and serves as a conduit for the microsporidium's cytoplasm to invade. In this way, the pathogens become intracellular parasites. They can destroy the intestinal lining, causing diarrhea, and spread to infect the eyes, muscles, or lungs.

Fortunately for Darius, an antimicrobial, albendazole, kills the parasite, and the effects of the infection are reversed. Unfortunately for Darius, the loss of helper T cells in AIDS means that another emerging, reemerging, or opportunistic infection is sure to follow.

(MM) Track microsporidiosis online by going to the Study Area at www.masteringmicrobiology.com.

---

intracellular bacteria and viruses. Humoral adaptive immunity involves the secretion of specific antibodies that have a variety of functions. T-independent humoral immune responses are rare, but can occur when an adult is challenged with T-independent antigens such as bacterial flagella or capsules. In contrast, T-dependent humoral immune responses are more common. A T-dependent humoral immune response occurs when an APC binds to a specific Th cell and signals the Th cell to proliferate.

The relative importance of each of these pathways depends on the type of pathogen involved and on the mechanisms by which they cause disease. In any case, adaptive immune responses are specific, inducible, involve clones, are unresponsive to self, and give the body long-term memory against their antigenic triggers. **ANIMATIONS:** *Host Defenses: The Big Picture*

### CRITICAL **THINKING**

What sorts of pathogens could successfully attack a patient with an inability to produce T lymphocytes?

# Types of Acquired Immunity

### Learning Objective

✓ Contrast active versus passive acquired immunity, and naturally acquired versus artificially acquired immunity.

As we have seen, adaptive immunity is acquired during an individual's life. Immunologists categorize immunity as either naturally or artificially acquired. Naturally acquired immunity occurs when the body mounts an immune response against antigens, such as influenzaviruses or food antigens, encountered during the course of daily life. Artificial immunity is the body's response to antigens introduced in vaccines, as occurs with immunization against tetanus and flu. Immunologists further distinguish acquired immune responses as either *active* or *passive;* that is, the immune system either responds actively to antigens via humoral or cell-mediated responses, or the body passively receives antibodies from another individual. Next we consider each of four types of acquired immunity.

### Naturally Acquired Active Immunity

**Naturally acquired active immunity** occurs when the body responds to exposure to pathogens and environmental antigens by mounting specific immune responses. The body is naturally and actively engaged in its own protection. As we have seen, once an immune response occurs, immunological memory persists—on subsequent exposure to the same antigen, the immune response will be rapid and powerful and often provides the body complete protection.

## TABLE 4

## A Comparison of the Types of Acquired Immunity

| | Active | Passive |
| --- | --- | --- |
| **Naturally acquired** |  PBWPIX / Alamy<br><br>The body responds to antigens that enter naturally, such as during infections. |  Diane Macdonald/Stockbyte/ Getty Images<br><br>Antibodies are transferred from mother to offspring, either across the placenta (IgG) or in breast milk (secretory IgA). |
| **Artificially acquired** |  SUPRI/Reuters/Landov<br><br>Health care workers introduce antigens in vaccines; the body responds with humoral or cell-mediated immune responses, including the production of memory cells. |  Barbara Rice, CDC<br><br>Health care workers give patients antisera or antitoxins, which are preformed antibodies obtained from immune individuals or animals. |

## Naturally Acquired Passive Immunity

Although newborns possess the cells and tissues needed to mount an immune response, they respond slowly to antigens. If required to protect themselves solely via naturally acquired active immunity, they might die of infectious disease before their immune systems were mature enough to respond adequately. However, they are not on their own; in the womb, IgG molecules cross the placenta from the mother's bloodstream to provide protection, and after birth, children receive secretory IgA in breast milk. Via these two processes, a mother provides her baby with antibodies that protect it during its early months. Because the baby is not actively producing its own antibodies, this type of protection is known as **naturally acquired passive immunity.**

## Artificially Acquired Active Immunity

Physicians induce immunity in their patients by introducing antigens in the form of vaccines. The patients' own immune systems then mount active responses against the foreign antigens, just as if the antigens were part of a naturally acquired pathogen. Such **artificially acquired active immunity** is the basis of immunization.

## Artificially Acquired Passive Immunotherapy

Active immunity usually requires days to weeks to develop fully, and in some cases such a delay can prove detrimental or even fatal. For instance, an active immune response may be too slow to protect against infection with rabies or exposure to rattlesnate venom. Therefore, medical personnel routinely harvest antibodies specific for toxins and pathogens that are so deadly or so fast-acting that an individual's active immune response is inadequate. They acquire these antibodies from the blood of immune humans or animals, typically a horse. Physicians then inject such *antisera* or *antitoxins* into infected patients to confer **artificially acquired passive immunotherapy.**

Active immune responses, whether naturally or artificially induced, are advantageous because they result in immunological memory and protection against future infections. However, they are slow-acting. Passive processes, in which individuals are provided fully formed antibodies, has the advantage of speed but does not confer immunological memory because B and T lymphocytes are not activated. Table 4 summarizes the four types of acquired immunity.

# Chapter Summary

 This chapter has *MicroFlix*. Go to **www.masteringmicrobiology.com** for 3-D movie-quality animations on immunology.

## Overview of Adaptive Immunity

1. **Adaptive immunity** is the ability of a vertebrate to recognize and defend against distinct species or strains of invaders. Adaptive immunity is characterized by specificity, inducibility, clonality, unresponsiveness to self, and memory.

2. **B lymphocytes (B cells)** attack extracellular pathogens in **humoral immune responses,** involving soluble proteins called antibodies. **T lymphocytes (T cells)** carry out **cell-mediated immune responses** against intracellular pathogens.
   **ANIMATIONS:** *Humoral Immunity: Overview; Cell-Mediated Immunity: Overview; Host Defenses: The Big Picture*

## Elements of Adaptive Immunity

1. The **lymphatic system** is composed of **lymphatic vessels,** which conduct the flow of **lymph,** and lymphoid tissues and organs that are directly involved in specific immunity. The latter include **lymph nodes,** the thymus, the spleen, the tonsils, and mucosa-associated lymphoid tissue (MALT). Lymphocytes originate and mature in the red bone marrow and express characteristic membrane proteins. They migrate to and persist in various lymphoid organs, where they are available to encounter foreign invaders in the blood and lymph.

2. **Antigens** are substances that trigger specific immune responses. Effective antigen molecules are large, usually complex, stable, degradable, and foreign to their host. An **epitope** (or antigenic determinant) is the three-dimensional shape of a region of an antigen that is recognized by the immune system.

3. **Exogenous** antigens are found on microorganisms that multiply outside the cells of the body; **endogenous** antigens are produced by pathogens multiplying inside the body's cells.

4. Ideally, the body does not attack antigens on the surface of its normal cells, called **autoantigens;** this phenomenon is called self-tolerance.

5. B lymphocytes (B cells), which mature in the red bone marrow, make immunoglobulins (Ig) of two types—**B cell receptors (BCRs)** and **antibodies.** Immunoglobulins are complementary to epitopes and consist of two light chains and two heavy chains joined via disulfide bonds to form Y-shaped molecules. BCRs are inserted into the cytoplasmic membranes of B cells via a transmembrane polypeptide, and antibodies are secreted.

6. Together the variable regions of a heavy and a light chain form an **antigen-binding site,** and the upper portions of antibody molecules are called $F_{ab}$ regions. Each B cell randomly chooses (once in its life) genes for its $F_{ab}$ region; therefore, the $F_{ab}$ regions are called variable regions, because they differ from cell to cell. Each basic antibody molecule has two antigen-binding sites and can potentially bind two epitopes.

7. Antibodies function in complement activation, inflammation, **neutralization** (blocking the action of a toxin or attachment of a pathogen), **opsonization** (enhanced phagocytosis), direct killing by oxidation, **agglutination,** and **antibody-dependent cellular cytotoxicity (ADCC).**
   **ANIMATIONS:** *Humoral Immunity: Antibody Function*

8. Antibodies are of five basic classes based upon their stems ($F_c$ regions), which differ in their type of heavy chain.

9. **IgM,** a pentamer with 10 antigen-binding sites, is the predominant class of antibody produced first during a primary humoral response. **IgG** is the predominant antibody found in the bloodstream and is largely responsible for defense against invading bacteria. IgG can cross a placenta to protect the fetus. Two molecules of IgA are attached via J chains and a polypeptide secretory component to produce **secretory IgA,** which is found in milk, tears, and mucous membrane secretions. **IgE** triggers inflammation and allergic reactions. It also functions during helminth infections. Immunoglobulin D (**IgD**) is found in cytoplasmic membranes of some animals.

10. Through a process called **class switching,** antibody-producing cells change the class of antibody they secrete, beginning with IgM and then producing IgG and then possibly IgA or IgE.

11. T cells have **T cell receptors (TCRs)** for antigens, mature under influence of signals from the thymus, and attack cells that harbor endogenous pathogens during cell-mediated immune responses.

12. In cell-mediated immunity, **cytotoxic T cells (Tc or CD8 cells)** act against infected or abnormal body cells, including virus-infected cells, bacteria-infected cells, some fungal- or protozoan-infected cells, some cancer cells, and foreign cells that enter the body as a result of organ transplantation.

13. Two types of **helper T (Th) cells**—Th1 and Th2—are characterized by **CD4.** They direct cell-mediated and humoral immune responses respectively.
    **ANIMATIONS:** *Cell-Mediated Immunity: Helper T Cells*

14. T cells that do not recognize MHC I protein and most T cells that recognize MHC I protein in conjunction with autoantigens are removed by apoptosis. This is **clonal deletion.** A few self-recognizing T cells are retained and become **regulatory T cells (Tr cells).** T cells that recognize MHC I protein but not autoantigens become the repertoire of immature T cells.

15. B cells with B cell receptors that respond to autoantigens are selectively killed via apoptosis—further clonal deletion. Only B cells that respond to foreign antigens survive to defend the body.

16. **Cytokines** are soluble regulatory proteins that act as intercellular signals to direct activities in immune responses. Cytokines include **interleukin (ILs), interferons (IFNs), growth factors, tumor necrosis factors (TNFs),** and **chemokines.**

## Preparation for an Adaptive Immune Response

1. Nucleated cells display epitopes of their own proteins and epitopes from intracellular pathogens such as viruses on **major histocompatibility complex (MHC)** class I proteins.

2. The initial step in mounting an immune response is that antigens are captured, ingested, and degraded into epitopes by **antigen-presenting cells (APCs)** such as B cells, macrophages, and **dendritic cells.** Epitopes are inserted into major histocompatibility complex (MHC) class II proteins.

    **ANIMATIONS:** *Antigen Processing and Presentation: Overview, Steps, MHC*

## Cell-Mediated Immune Responses

1. Once activated by dendritic cells, cytotoxic T cells (Tc cells) recognize abnormal molecules presented by MHC I protein on the surface of infected, cancerous, or foreign cells. Sometimes cytotoxic T cells require cytokines from Th1 cells.

2. Activated Tc cells reproduce to form memory T cells and more Tc progeny in a process called **clonal expansion.**

3. Cytotoxic T cells destroy their target cells via two pathways: the perforin-granzyme pathway, which kills the affected cells by secreting **perforins** and **granzymes,** or the **CD95 pathway,** in which CD95L binds to CD95 on the target cell, triggering target cell apoptosis. Cytotoxic T cells may also form **memory T cells,** which function in **memory responses.**

    **ANIMATIONS:** *Cell-Mediated Immunity: Cytotoxic T Cells*

## Humoral Immune Responses

1. T-independent antigens, such as bacterial capsules, trigger **T-independent humoral immune responses,** which are more common in adults than in children.

2. In **T-dependent humoral immunity,** an APC's MHC II protein–epitope complex activates a helper T cell (Th cell) bearing a complementary TCR. CD4 stabilizes the connection between the cells, which is an example of an immunological synapse. Interleukin 4 (IL-4) then induces the Th cell to become a type 2 helper T cell (Th2).

3. In **clonal selection,** an immunological synapse forms between the Th2 cell and a B cell bearing a complementary MHC II protein–epitope complex. The Th2 cell secretes IL-4, which induces the B cell to divide. Its offspring, collectively called a clone, become **plasma cells** or **memory B cells.**

    **ANIMATIONS:** *Humoral Immunity: Clonal Selection and Expansion*

4. Plasma cells live for only a short time but secrete large amounts of antibodies, beginning with IgM and class switching as they get older. Memory B cells migrate to lymphoid tissues to await a subsequent encounter with the same antigen.

5. The **primary response** to an antigen is slow to develop and of limited effectiveness. When that antigen is encountered a second time, the activation of memory cells ensures that the immune response is rapid and strong. This is a **secondary immune response.** Such enhanced humoral immune responses are memory responses.

    **ANIMATIONS:** *Humoral Immunity: Primary Immune Response, Secondary Immune Response*

## Types of Acquired Immunity

1. When the body mounts a specific immune response against an infectious agent, the result is called **naturally acquired active immunity.**

2. The passing of maternal IgG to the fetus and the transmission of secretory IgA in milk to a baby are examples of **naturally acquired passive immunity.**

3. **Artificially acquired active immunity** is achieved by deliberately injecting someone with antigens in vaccines to provoke an active response, as in the process of immunization.

4. **Artificially acquired passive immunotherapy** involves the administration of preformed antibodies in antitoxins or antisera to a patient.

# Questions for Review    Answers to the Questions for Review (except Short Answer questions) appear at the end of this chapter.

## Multiple Choice

1. Antibodies function to
    a. directly destroy foreign organ grafts.
    b. mark invading organisms for destruction.
    c. kill intracellular viruses.
    d. promote cytokine synthesis.
    e. stimulate T cell growth.

2. MHC class II molecules bind to _____ and trigger _____.
    a. endogenous antigens, cytotoxic T cells
    b. exogenous antigens, cytotoxic T cells
    c. antibodies, B cells
    d. endogenous antigens, helper T cells
    e. exogenous antigens, helper T cells

3. Rejection of a foreign skin graft is an example of
    a. destruction of virus-infected cells.
    b. tolerance.
    c. antibody-mediated immunity.
    d. a secondary immune response.
    e. a cell-mediated immune response.

4. An autoantigen is
    a. an antigen from normal microbiota.
    b. a normal body component.
    c. an artificial antigen.
    d. any carbohydrate antigen.
    e. a nucleic acid.

5. Among the key molecules that mediate cell-mediated cytotoxicity are
   a. perforin.
   b. immunoglobulins.
   c. complement.
   d. cytokines.
   e. interferons.

6. Which of the following lymphocytes predominates in blood?
   a. T cells
   b. B cells
   c. plasma cells
   d. memory cells
   e. all are about equally prevalent

7. The major class of immunoglobulin found on the surfaces of the walls of the intestines and airways is secretory
   a. IgG.
   b. IgM.
   c. IgA.
   d. IgE.
   e. IgD.

8. Which cells express MHC class I molecules?
   a. red blood cells
   b. antigen-presenting cells only
   c. neutrophils only
   d. all nucleated cells
   e. dendritic cells only

9. In which of the following sites in the body can B cells be found?
   a. lymph nodes
   b. spleen
   c. red bone marrow
   d. intestinal wall
   e. all of the above

10. Tc cells recognize epitopes only when the latter are held by
    a. MHC proteins.
    b. B cells.
    c. interleukin 2.
    d. granzyme.

## Modified True/False

Mark each statement as either true or false. Rewrite false statements to make them true by changing the italicized words.

1. ____ MHC class II molecules are found on *T cells*.

2. ____ *Apoptosis* is the term used to describe cellular suicide.

3. ____ Lymphocytes with CD8 glycoprotein are *helper* T cells.

4. ____ *Cytotoxic T cells* secrete immunoglobulin.

5. ____ Secretion of antibodies by activated B cells is a form of *cell-mediated* immunity.

## Matching

1. Match each cell in the left column with its associated protein from the right column.

   ____ Plasma cell            A. MHC II molecule

   ____ Cytotoxic T cell       B. Interleukin 4

   ____ Th2 cell               C. Perforin and granzyme

   ____ Dendritic cell         D. Immunoglobulin

2. Match each type of immunity in the left column with its associated example from the right column.

   ____ Artificially acquired       A. Production of IgE in
        passive immunotherapy          response to pollen

   ____ Naturally acquired          B. Acquisition of maternal
        active immunity                antibodies in breast milk

   ____ Naturally acquired          C. Administration of tetanus
        passive immunity               toxoid

   ____ Artificially acquired       D. Administration of antitoxin
        active immunity

## Labeling

Label the parts of the immunoglobulin below.

Precision Graphics

## Short Answer

1. When is antigen processing an essential prerequisite for an immune response?

2. Why does the body have both humoral and cell-mediated immune responses?

# Concept Mapping

Using the following terms, draw a concept map that describes antibodies. Or, complete this concept map online by going to the Study Area at www.masteringmicrobiology.com.

| | | | |
|---|---|---|---|
| Agglutination | IgD | Inflammation | Target bacteria |
| Antigens | IgE | Neutralization | Toxins |
| Antigen-stimulated B cells | IgG | Opsonization | Viruses |
| Death by Oxidation | IgM | Phagocytosis (2) | |
| IgA | Immunoglobulins | Plasma cells | |

# Critical Thinking

1. Why is it advantageous for the lymphatic system to lack a pump?

2. Contrast innate defenses with adaptive immunity.

3. What is the benefit to the body of requiring the immune system to process antigen?

4. Scientists can develop genetically deficient strains of mice. Describe the immunological impairments that would result in mice deficient in each of the following: class I MHC, class II MHC, TCR, BCR, IL-2 receptor, and IFN-γ.

5. Human immunodeficiency virus (HIV) preferentially destroys CD4 cells. Specifically, what effect does this have on humoral and cell-mediated immunity?

6. What would happen to a person who failed to make MHC molecules?

7. Why does the body make five different classes of immunoglobulins?

8. Some materials such as metal bone pins and plastic heart valves can be implanted into the body without fear of rejection by the patient's immune system. Why is this? What are the ideal properties of any material that is to be implanted?

9. What nonmembranous organelle is prevalent in plasma cells? What membranous organelle is prevalent?

MasteringMICROBIOLOGY™

Access more review material online in the Study Area at **www.masteringmicrobiology.com.** There, you'll find
- **Animations**
- **Microflix**
- **MP3 Tutor Sessions**
- **Concept Mapping Activities**
- **Flashcards**
- **Quizzes**

and more to help you succeed.

# Answers

Answers to multiple-choice, fill-in-blank, labeling, matching, and true/false questions are listed here. Answers for Short Answer and Critical Thinking questions are available for instructors only in the Instructor's Manual that accompanies this text.

**Multiple Choice**
1. b; 2. e; 3. e; 4. b; 5. a; 6. a; 7. c; 8. d; 9. e; 10. a

**Modified True/False**
1. *antigen-presenting cells*; 2. True; 3. *cytotoxic*; 4. *Plasma cells*; 5. *humoral*

**Matching**
1. D Plasma cell; C Cytotoxic cell; B Th2 cell; A Dendritic cell;
2. D Artificially acquired passive immunity;

A Naturally acquired active immunity;
B Naturally acquired passive immunity;
C Artificially acquired active immunity

**Labeling**
See Figures 4 and 5.

# Immunization and Immune Testing

From Chapter 17 of *Microbiology with Diseases by Taxonomy*, Third Edition. Robert W. Bauman. Copyright © 2011 by Pearson Education, Inc. Published by Benjamin Cummings, Inc. All rights reserved.

# Immunization and Immune Testing

A 13-month-old girl is brought into the hospital, coughing and crying. Her mother tells the pediatrician that she had noticed a mucous discharge pooling in the corners of her child's eyes the previous evening. The pediatrician checks the girl's medical record and notes that she has not yet received her first measles/mumps/rubella (MMR) vaccination. The doctor then swabs the child's throat, arranges for a blood sample to be taken, and tells the mother that they are going to have the lab perform a "special immune test" to confirm the diagnosis: measles. Because the pediatrician has seen several children with measles in the past few weeks and the child's symptoms support the diagnosis, a nurse administers an intramuscular injection of immunoglobulin against measles. The nurse explains that this injection will protect the child against the most severe form of the illness, which can be fatal. The physician also schedules the daughter for a routine measles/mumps/rubella immunization. Mother and daughter return home to rest and recuperate.

How do immunoglobulins and vaccines work? How do immunological tests aid in the diagnosis of specific diseases? This chapter is an introduction to the important topics of immunization and immune testing.

 Take the pre-test for this chapter online. Visit the Study Area at www.masteringmicrobiology.com.

Andrew Brookes/Corbis

▲ Immunizations have done more to decrease human disease than any other medical advancement. Here, vaccine vials await shipment.

In this chapter we will discuss three applications of immunology: active immunization (vaccination); passive immunotherapy using immunoglobulins (antibodies); and immune testing. Vaccination has proven the most efficient and cost-effective method of controlling infectious diseases. Without the use of effective vaccines, millions more people worldwide would suffer each year from potentially fatal infectious diseases, including measles, mumps, and polio. The administration of immunoglobulins has further reduced morbidity and mortality from certain infectious diseases, such as hepatitis A and yellow fever, in unvaccinated individuals. Medical personnel also make practical use of the immune response as a diagnostic procedure. For example, the detection of antibodies to HIV in a person's blood indicates that the individual has been exposed to that virus and may develop AIDS. The remarkable specificity of antibodies also enables the detection of drugs in urine, recognition of pregnancy at early stages, and the identification or characterization of other biological material. The many tests developed for these purposes are the focus of the discipline of *serology* (sĕ-rol'ō-jē) and are discussed in the second half of this chapter.

# Immunization

An individual may be made immune to an infectious disease by two artificial methods: *active immunization,* which involves administering antigens to a patient so that the patient actively mounts an adaptive immune response, and *passive immunotherapy,* in which a patient acquires temporary immunity through the transfer of antibodies formed by other individuals or animals.

In the following sections we will review the history of immunization before examining immunization and immunotherapy in more detail.

## Brief History of Immunization

### Learning Objective

✓ Discuss the history of vaccination from the 12th century through the present.

As early as the 12th century, the Chinese noticed that children who recovered from smallpox never contracted the disease a second time. They therefore adopted a policy of deliberately infecting young children with particles of ground smallpox scabs from children who had survived mild cases. By doing so, they succeeded in significantly reducing the population's overall morbidity and mortality from the disease. News of this procedure, called *variolation* (var'ē-ō-lā'shŭn), spread westward through central Asia, and the technique was widely adopted.

Lady Mary Montagu (1689–1762), the wife of the English ambassador to the Ottoman Empire, learned of the procedure, had it performed on her own children, and told others about it upon her return to England in 1721. As a result, variolation came into use in England and in the American colonies. Although effective and usually successful, variolation caused death from smallpox in 1–2% of recipients and in people exposed to recipients, so in time the procedure was outlawed.

Thus, when the English physician Edward Jenner demonstrated in 1796 that protection against smallpox could be conferred by inoculation with crusts from a person infected with cowpox—a related but very mild disease—the new technique was adopted. Because cowpox was also called *vaccinia*[1] (vak-sin'ē-ă), Jenner called the new technique **vaccination** (vak'si-nā'shŭn), and the protective inoculum a **vaccine** (vak-sēn'). Today we use the term **immunization** to refer to the administration of any antigenic inoculum, which are all called vaccines. For many years thereafter, vaccination against smallpox was widely practiced, even though no one understood how it worked or whether similar techniques could protect against other diseases.

In 1879, Louis Pasteur conducted experiments on the bacterium *Pasteurella multocida* (pas-ter-el'ă mul-tŏ'si-da) and demonstrated that he could make an effective vaccine against this organism (which causes a disease in birds called fowl cholera). Once the basic principle of vaccine manufacture was understood, vaccines against anthrax and rabies rapidly followed. After it was discovered that these vaccines provide protection through the actions of antibodies, the technique of transferring protective antibodies to susceptible individuals—that is, *passive immunotherapy* (im'ū-nō-thār'ă-pē)—was developed soon thereafter.

By the late 1900s, immunologists and health care providers had formulated vaccines that significantly reduced the number of cases of many infectious diseases (Figure 1). We also have successful vaccines against some types of cancer. Health care providers, governments, and international organizations working together have rid the world of naturally occurring smallpox, and we hope for the worldwide eradication of polio, measles, mumps, and rubella. **Highlight: Why Isn't There a Cold Vaccine?** discusses why a vaccine for the common cold does not yet exist.

Even though immunologists have produced vaccines that protect people against many deadly diseases, a variety of political, social, economic, and scientific problems prevent vaccines from reaching all those who need them. In developing nations worldwide, over 3 million children still die each year from vaccine-preventable infectious diseases, primarily because of political obstacles. Additionally, some pathogens, such as the protozoa of malaria and the virus of AIDS, still frustrate attempts to develop effective vaccines against them. Furthermore, the existence of vaccine-associated risks—both medical risks (the low but persistent incidence of vaccine-caused diseases) and financial risks (the high costs of developing and producing vaccines, and the risk of lawsuits by vaccine recipients who have adverse reactions)—has in recent years discouraged investment in new vaccines. Thus, although the history of immunization is marked by stunning advancements in public health, the future of immunization poses immense challenges.

Next we take a closer look at active immunization, commonly known as vaccination.

---

[1]From Latin *vacca,* meaning cow.

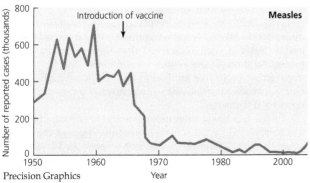

Precision Graphics

▲ **Figure 1** **The effect of immunization in reducing the prevalence of two infectious diseases in the United States.** Polio is no longer endemic in the United States. Measles is nearly eradicated.

## Active Immunization

### Learning Objectives

✓ Describe the advantages and disadvantages of five types of vaccines.

✓ Describe three methods by which recombinant genetic techniques can be used to develop improved vaccines.

✓ Delineate the risks and benefits of routine vaccination in healthy populations, mentioning contact immunity and herd immunity.

In the following subsections we examine types of vaccines, the roles of technology in producing modern vaccines, and issues concerning vaccine safety.

### Vaccine Types

Scientists are constantly striving to develop vaccines of maximal efficacy and safety. In each case, a pathogen is altered or inactivated so that it is less likely to cause illness; however, not all types of vaccines are equally safe or effective. Effectiveness can be checked by measuring the antibody (IgG and IgM) level—called the **titer** (tī′ter)—in the blood. When the titer is low, antibody production can be bolstered by administration of more antigen—a *booster immunization.*

Barry Dowsett and David A. J. Tyrrell

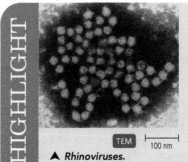

**HIGHLIGHT**

## WHY ISN'T THERE A COLD VACCINE?

We have vaccines for the flu, so why don't we have a vaccine for the common cold? The reason is that whereas strains of only one influenzavirus cause flu, over 200 different adenoviruses, coronaviruses, and rhinoviruses are known to cause the common cold, and each of these viruses has its own distinct antigens and antigenic strains, making it extremely difficult to create a single vaccine to prevent them all. To further complicate matters, viruses can mutate, resulting in changes in their antigens; with over 200 different cold viruses in existence, such mutations create immense logistical challenges in vaccine development. Fortunately, the common cold typically lasts only a few days and is adequately treated with rest and self-care.

▲ *Rhinoviruses.*

The general types of vaccines, each of which has its own combination of strengths and weaknesses, are attenuated (live) vaccines, killed (or inactivated) vaccines, toxoid vaccines, combination vaccines, and recombinant gene vaccines. Each of these is named for the type of antigen used in the inoculum.

**Attenuated (Live) Vaccines** Virulent microbes are normally not used in vaccines, because they cause disease. Instead, immunologists reduce virulence so that, although still active, the pathogens no longer cause disease. The process of reducing virulence is called **attenuation** (ă-ten-ū-ā′shŭn). The most common method for attenuating viruses involves raising them for numerous generations in tissue culture cells until the viruses lose the ability to produce disease. For example, rabies viruses, which preferentially attack nerve cells, are subjected to prolonged tissue culture until their virulence to nerve cells is lost; the resulting avirulent viruses can be used in vaccines. Bacteria may be made avirulent by culturing them under unusual conditions or by using genetic manipulation.

Attenuated vaccines—those containing attenuated microbes—are also called *modified live vaccines.* Because they contain active but avirulent organisms or viruses, these vaccines cause very mild infections but no serious disease under normal conditions. Attenuated viruses in such a vaccine infect host cells and replicate; the infected cells then process endogenous viral antigens. As a result, modified live viral vaccines trigger a cell-mediated immune response dominated by type 1 helper T cells (Th1) and cytotoxic T cells (Tc). Because modified live vaccines contain active microbes, a large number of antigen molecules are available to stimulate an immune response. Further, vaccinated individuals can infect those around them, providing **contact**

## TABLE 1 Some Common Adjuvants

| Adjuvant | Effects |
|---|---|
| Aluminum phosphate (alum) | Slows processing and degradation of antigen |
| Saponin (soaplike plant product)[a] | Stimulates T cell responses |
| Mineral oil[a] | Slows processing and degradation of antigen |
| Freund's complete adjuvant (mineral oil containing killed mycobacteria)[a] | Slows processing and degradation of antigen; stimulates T cell responses |

[a]Considered too toxic for humans; used in vaccinating animals only.

**immunity**—that is, immunity beyond the individual receiving the vaccine.

Although usually very effective, attenuated vaccines can be hazardous because modified microbes may retain enough residual virulence to cause disease in immunosuppressed people. Pregnant women should not receive live vaccines because of the danger that the attenuated pathogen will cross the placenta and harm the fetus. Occasionally, modified viruses actually revert to wild type or mutate to a form that causes persistent infection or disease. For example, in 2000 a polio epidemic in the Dominican Republic and Haiti resulted from the reversion of an attenuated live virus in oral polio vaccine to a virulent poliovirus. For this reason, we no longer use live polio vaccine to immunize children in the United States.

Health care providers and government agencies must carefully balance the benefits of attenuated vaccines against their risks. As a result, they may change their recommended immunization schedules.

**Inactivated (Killed) Vaccines** For some diseases, live vaccines have been replaced by **inactivated vaccines,** which are of two types: *whole agent vaccines* are produced with deactivated but whole microbes, whereas *subunit vaccines* are produced with antigenic fragments of microbes. Because neither whole agent nor subunit vaccines can replicate, revert, mutate, or retain residual virulence, they are safer than live vaccines. However, because they cannot replicate, several "booster"doses must be administered to achieve full immunity, and immunized individuals do not stimulate contact immunity. Also, with whole agent vaccines, nonantigenic portions of the microbe occasionally stimulate a painful inflammatory response in some individuals. As a result, whole agent pertussis vaccine is now being replaced with a subunit vaccine called acellular pertussis vaccine.

When microbes are killed for use in vaccines, it is important that their antigens remain as similar to those of living organisms as possible. If chemicals are used for killing, they must not alter the antigens responsible for stimulating protective immunity. A commonly used inactivating agent is *formaldehyde,* which denatures proteins and nucleic acids.

Because the microbes of inactivated vaccines cannot reproduce, they do not present as many antigenic molecules to the body as do live vaccines; therefore, inactivated vaccines are antigenically weak. They are administered in high doses or in multiple doses, or incorporated with materials called **adjuvants** (ad'joo-văntz), substances that increase the effective antigenicity of the vaccine by stimulating Toll-like receptors and their actions. Unfortunately, high individual doses and multiple dosing increase the risk of producing allergies, and the use of adjuvants to increase antigenicity may stimulate local inflammation. Table 1 lists some common adjuvants and their effects in enhancing the efficacy of vaccines.

Because all types of killed vaccines are recognized by the immune system as exogenous antigens, they stimulate an antibody immune response.

**Toxoid Vaccines** For some bacterial diseases, notably tetanus and diphtheria, it is more efficacious to induce an immune response against toxins than against cellular antigens. **Toxoid** (tok'soyd) **vaccines** are chemically or thermally modified toxins that are used in vaccines to stimulate active immunity. As with killed vaccines, toxoids stimulate antibody-mediated immunity. Because toxoids have few antigenic determinants, effective immunization requires multiple childhood doses as well as reinoculations every 10 years for life. **ANIMATIONS:** *Vaccines: Function, Types*

**Combination Vaccines** The Centers for Disease Control and Prevention (CDC) has approved several **combination vaccines** for routine use. These vaccines combine antigens from several toxoids and inactivated pathogens that are administered simultaneously. Examples include MMR—vaccine against measles, mumps, and rubella—and Pentacel, which is a vaccine against diphtheria, tetanus, pertussis (whooping cough), polio, and diseases of *Haemophilus influenzae* (hē-mof'i-lŭs in-flu-en'zī).

**Vaccines Using Recombinant Gene Technology** Although live, inactivated, and toxoid vaccines have been highly successful in controlling infectious diseases, researchers are always seeking ways to make vaccines more effective, cheaper, and safer and to make new vaccines against pathogens that have been difficult to protect against. For example, scientists have developed a recombinant DNA vaccine against a fungus, *Blastomyces* (blas-tō-mī'sēz)—the first vaccine against a fungal pathogen. Scientists can also use a variety of genetic recombinant techniques to make improved vaccines. For example, they can selectively delete virulence genes from a pathogen, producing an irreversibly attenuated microbe, one that cannot revert to a virulent pathogen (Figure 2a).

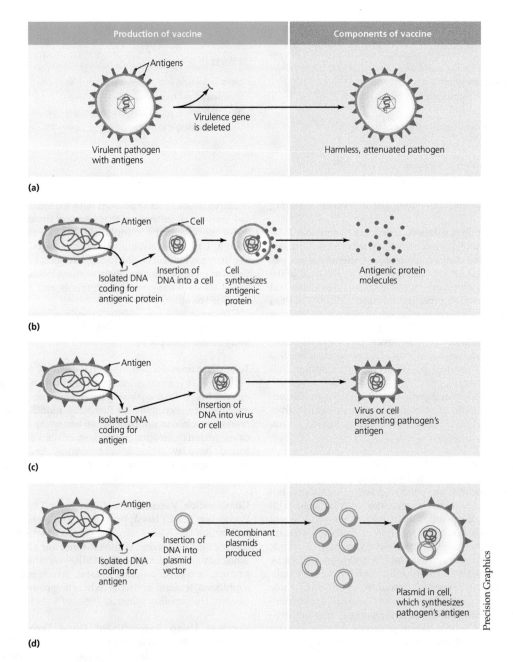

Production of vaccine | Components of vaccine

(a)
Antigens
Virulence gene is deleted
Virulent pathogen with antigens
Harmless, attenuated pathogen

(b)
Antigen — Cell
Isolated DNA coding for antigenic protein
Insertion of DNA into a cell
Cell synthesizes antigenic protein
Antigenic protein molecules

(c)
Antigen
Isolated DNA coding for antigen
Insertion of DNA into virus or cell
Virus or cell presenting pathogen's antigen

(d)
Antigen
Isolated DNA coding for antigen
Insertion of DNA into plasmid vector
Recombinant plasmids produced
Plasmid in cell, which synthesizes pathogen's antigen

Precision Graphics

▲ **Figure 2  Some uses of recombinant DNA technology for making improved vaccines.**
**(a)** Deletion of virulence gene(s) to create an attenuated pathogen for use in a vaccine.
**(b)** Insertion of gene that codes for a selected antigenic protein into a cell, which then produces
large quantities of the antigen for use in a vaccine. **(c)** Insertion of a gene that codes for a selected
antigenic protein into a cell or virus, which displays the antigen. The entire recombinant is used in a
vaccine. **(d)** Injection of DNA containing a selected gene (in this case, as part of a plasmid) into an
individual. Once some of this DNA is incorporated into the genome of a patient's cells, those cells
synthesize and process the antigen, which stimulates a cell-mediated immune response.

Scientists also use recombinant techniques to produce large quantities of very pure viral or bacterial antigens for use in vaccines. In this process, scientists isolate the gene that codes for an antigen and insert it into a bacterium, yeast, or other cell, which then expresses the antigen (Figure 2b). Vaccine manufacturers produce hepatitis B vaccine in this manner using recombinant yeast cells.

Alternatively, a genetically altered microbial cell or virus may itself be used as a live recombinant vaccine (Figure 2c). Experimental recombinant vaccines of this type have used adenoviruses, herpesviruses, poxviruses, and bacteria such as Salmonella (sal'mŏ-nel'ă). Vaccinia virus (a poxvirus) is used because it is easy to administer by dermal scratching or orally, and because its large genome makes inserting a new gene into it relatively easy.

Another innovative method of immunization involves injection not of antigens but instead of the DNA that codes for the antigen. For example, the DNA coding for a pathogen's antigen can be inserted into a plasmid vector, which is then injected into the body (Figure 2d). The body's cells then transcribe and translate the gene to produce antigen, which triggers a cell-mediated immune response.

### Vaccine Manufacture

Manufacturers mass-produce many vaccines by growing microbes in laboratory culture vessels, but because viruses require a host cell to reproduce, they are cultured inside chicken eggs. Availability of sterile eggs is thus critical for manufacturing viral vaccines such as flu vaccines. Because the vaccines are produced in eggs, physicians must withhold such immunizations from patients with egg allergies. Research on gene-based vaccines and development of vaccines in genetically modified plants may result in safer vaccines.

### Recommended Immunizations

The CDC and medical associations publish recommended immunization schedules for children, adults, and special populations such as health care workers and HIV-positive individuals. The recommendations are frequently modified to reflect changes in the relationships between pathogens and the human population. Figure 3 highlights the general 2009 immunization schedules recommended by the CDC. In Table 2, facts concerning the types of vaccines available for immunizing against each of the diseases in the vaccination schedule as well as some other available vaccines are listed. Vaccines against anthrax, cholera, plague, tuberculosis, and other diseases are available, but the CDC does not recommend them for the general U.S. population.

It is important that patients follow the recommended immunization schedule not only to protect themselves but also to provide society with **herd immunity.** Herd immunity is the protection provided all individuals in a population due to the inability of a pathogen to effectively spread when a large proportion of individuals (typically more than 75%) are resistant. When immunization compliance in a population has fallen, local epidemics have resulted.

### Vaccine Safety

Health care providers must carefully weigh the risks associated with vaccines against their benefits. A common vaccine-associated problem is mild toxicity. Some vaccines—especially whole agent vaccines that contain adjuvants—may cause pain at the injection site for several hours or days after injection. In rare cases, toxicity may result in general malaise and possibly a fever high enough to induce seizures. Although not usually life threatening, the potential for these symptoms may be sufficient to discourage people from being immunized or having their infants immunized.

A much more severe problem associated with immunization is the risk of *anaphylactic shock,* an allergic reaction, which may develop to some component of the vaccine, such as egg proteins, adjuvants, or preservatives. Because people are rarely aware of such allergies ahead of time, recipients should remain for several minutes in the physician's office, where epinephrine is readily available to counter any signs of an allergic reaction.

A third major problem associated with immunization is that of residual virulence, which we previously discussed. Attenuated viruses occasionally cause disease, not only in fetuses and immunosuppressed patients but also in healthy children and adults. A good example is the attenuated oral poliovirus vaccine (OPV), which was commonly used in the United States until the late 1990s. Though a very effective vaccine, it causes clinical poliomyelitis in 1 of every 2 million recipients or their close contacts. Medical personnel in the United States eliminated this problem by switching to inactivated polio vaccine (IPV).

Over the past two decades, lawsuits in the United States and Europe have alleged that certain vaccines against childhood diseases cause or trigger disorders such as autism, diabetes, and asthma. Extensive research has failed to substantiate these allegations, and to date no conclusive evidence for such a link has been found. Indeed, vaccine manufacturing methods have improved tremendously in recent years, ensuring that modern vaccines are much safer than those in use even a decade ago. The U.S. Food and Drug Administration (FDA) has established a Vaccine Adverse Event Reporting System for monitoring vaccine safety.

The CDC and FDA have determined that the problems associated with immunization are far less serious than the suffering and death that would result if we stopped immunizing people. **Beneficial Microbes: Smallpox: To Vaccinate or Not to Vaccinate?** discusses the issues surrounding the administration of smallpox vaccinations to the general public.

## Passive Immunotherapy

### Learning Objectives

- ✓ Identify two sources of antibodies for use in passive immunotherapy.
- ✓ Compare the relative advantages and disadvantages of active immunization and passive immunotherapy.

## CDC Recommended Immunization Schedule – United States, 2009

| Vaccine | Birth | 1 mo | 2 mos | 4 mos | 6 mos | 12 mos | 15 mos | 18 mos | 19–23 mos | 2–3 yrs | 4–6 yrs | 7–10 yrs | 11–12 yrs | 13–14 yrs | 15 yrs | 16–18 yrs | 19–49 yrs | 50–64 yrs | ≥ 65 yrs |
|---------|-------|------|-------|-------|-------|--------|--------|--------|-----------|---------|---------|----------|-----------|-----------|--------|-----------|-----------|-----------|----------|
| | | | | | | | | | | | | | **Adolescent** | | | | **Adult** | | |
| Hepatitis B (Hep B) | Dose 1 | Dose 2 | | | Dose 3 | | | | Catch-up immunization | | | | | | | | | | |
| Rotavirus | | | 1 | 2 | | | | | | | | | | | | | | | |
| Diphtheria, tetanus, pertussis (DTaP) | | | 1 | 2 | 3 | | 4 | | | | 5 | | 6 | | | | Tdap* every 10 yrs | | |
| Human papillomavirus (HPV) (females only) | | | | | | | | | | | | | 1 2 3 | | | | | | |
| Meningococcal | | | | | | | | | | | | | 1 | | | | | | |
| Haemophilus influenzae type b (Hib) | | | 1 | 2 | 3 | 4 | | | | | | | | | | | | | |
| Pneumococcal (PCV) | | | 1 | 2 | 3 | 4 | | | | | | | | | | | | | 5 |
| Inactivated polio (IPV) | | | 1 | 2 | | 3 | | | | | 4 | | | | | | | | |
| Influenza | | | | | Annually | | | | | | | | | | | | Annually | | |
| Measles, mumps, rubella (MMR) | | | | | | 1 | | | | | 2 | | | | | | 1 or 2 | | |
| Varicella-zoster | | | | | | 1 | | | | | 2 | | | | | | 1 2 | | |
| Hepatitis A | | | | | | 1 | | 2 | | | | | | | | | | | |

Range of recommended ages for immunization

Range for catch-up immunization

\* Tdap, used for adult boosters, is a slightly different vaccine than the childhood vaccine, DTap.

▲ **Figure 3**
**The CDC's recommended immunization schedule for the general population.**
Adult meningococcal vaccine recommended for college students who live in dormitories.
Three doses of human papillomavirus vaccine (HPV) recommended for women aged 19–26.

Passive immunotherapy (sometimes called passive immunization) involves the administration of preformed antibodies to a patient. Physicians use passive immunotherapy when protection against a recent infection or an ongoing disease is needed quickly. Rapid protection is achieved because passive immunotherapy does not require the body to mount a response; instead, preformed antibodies are immediately available to bind to antigen, enabling neutralization and opsonization to proceed without delay. For example, in a case of botulism poisoning [caused by the toxin of *Clostridium botulinum* (klos-trid′ē-ŭm bo-tū-lī′num)],

passive immunotherapy with preformed antibodies against the toxin can prevent death.

Antibodies directed against toxins are also called *antitoxins* (an-tē-tok′sinz); *antivenin* used to treat snakebites is an antitoxin. In some cases, infections with certain viruses—hepatitis A and B, measles, rabies, Ebola, chickenpox, and shingles—are treated with antibodies directed against the causative viruses.

For much of the time since passive immunotherapy was first developed, immunologists harvested the desired antibodies from human or animal donors that have either experienced natural

**2**

## Principal Vaccines to Prevent Human Diseases

| Vaccine | Disease Agent | Disease | Vaccine Type | Method of Administration |
|---|---|---|---|---|
| **Recommended by CDC** | | | | |
| Hepatitis B | Hepatitis B virus | Hepatitis B | Inactive subunit from recombinant yeast | Intramuscular |
| Rotavirus | *Rotavirus* | Gastroenteritis | Attenuated, recombinant | Oral |
| Diphtheria/ tetanus/ acellular pertussis (DTaP) | Diphtheria toxin Tetanus toxin *Bordetella pertussis* | Diphtheria Tetanus Whooping cough | Toxoid Toxoid Inactivated subunit (inactivated whole also available) | Intramuscular |
| Human papillomavirus (HPV) | Human papillomaviruses | Genital warts, cervical cancer | Inactive recombinant | Intramuscular |
| Meningococcal | *Neisseria meningiditis* | Meningitis | Inactive | Subcutaneous or intramuscular |
| *Haemophilus influenzae* type b (Hib) | *Haemophilus influenzae* | Meningitis, pneumonia, epiglottitis | Inactivated subunit | Intramuscular |
| Pneumococcal (PCV) | *Streptococcus pneumoniae* | Pneumonia | Inactivated subunit | Intramuscular |
| Polio | Poliovirus | Poliomyelitis | Inactivated (attenuated also available) | Subcutaneous or intramuscular (attenuated: oral) |
| Influenza | Influenzaviruses | Flu | Inactivated subunit | Intramuscular or oral |
| Measles/ mumps/ rubella (MMR) | Measles virus Mumps virus Rubella virus | Measles Mumps Rubella (German measles) | Attenuated Attenuated Attenuated | Subcutaneous |
| Varicella-zoster | Chickenpox virus | Chickenpox, shingles | Attenuated | Subcutaneous |
| Hepatitis A | Hepatitis A virus | Hepatitis A | Inactivated whole | Intramuscular |
| **Available But Not Recommended for General Population in the U.S.** | | | | |
| Anthrax | *Bacillus anthracis* | Anthrax | Inactivated whole | Subcutaneous |
| BCG (bacillus of Calmette and Guérin) | *Mycobacterium tuberculosis, M. leprae* | Tuberculosis, leprosy | Attenuated | Intradermal |
| Japanese encephalitis vaccine | Japanese encephalitis virus | Encephalitis | Inactive | Subcutaneous |
| Rabies | Rabies virus | Rabies | Inactivated whole | Intramuscular or intradermal |
| Typhoid fever vaccine | *Salmonella enterica* | Typhoid fever | Attenuated (inactive also available) | Oral (inactive: subcutaneous or intramuscular) |
| Vaccinia (cowpox) | Smallpox virus, monkeypox virus | Smallpox, monkeypox | Attenuated | Subcutaneous |
| Yellow fever | Yellow fever virus | Yellow fever | Attenuated | Subcutaneous |

causes of a disease or were actively immunized against it. To do so, immunologists remove the cells and clotting factors from the blood to acquire *serum*, which contains a variety of antibodies. When used for passive immunotherapy, such serum is called **antiserum** (an-tē-sē′rŭm) or sometimes *immune serum*. Antisera are typically collected from human blood plasma donors, or from horses intentionally exposed to the disease agent of interest because their large blood volume contains more antibodies than can be obtained from smaller animals. Pooled antisera from a group of human donors can be administered intravenously (intravenous immunoglobulins, IVIg) to treat immunodeficiencies and some autoimmune and inflammatory diseases.

Antisera have the following limitations:

- Repeated injections of horse-derived antisera can trigger a serious allergic response called *serum sickness,* in which the recipient mounts an immune response against horse antigens found in the antisera.
- Viral pathogens may contaminate antisera.
- The antibodies of horse-derived antisera are degraded relatively quickly by the recipient. The half-life of such antibodies is about 3 weeks; that is, half the molecules are degraded every 3 weeks.

Scientists have overcome the limitations of antisera by developing **hybridomas** (hī-brid-ō′mǎz), which are tumor cells created

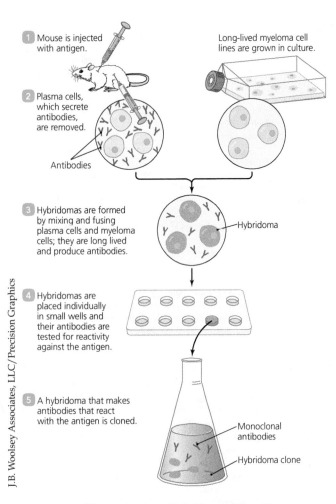

1 Mouse is injected with antigen.

2 Plasma cells, which secrete antibodies, are removed.

Antibodies

Long-lived myeloma cell lines are grown in culture.

3 Hybridomas are formed by mixing and fusing plasma cells and myeloma cells; they are long lived and produce antibodies.

Hybridoma

4 Hybridomas are placed individually in small wells and their antibodies are tested for reactivity against the antigen.

5 A hybridoma that makes antibodies that react with the antigen is cloned.

Monoclonal antibodies

Hybridoma clone

▲ **Figure 4** **The production of hybridomas.** After a laboratory animal is injected with the antigen of interest 1, plasma cells are removed from the animal and isolated 2. When these plasma cells are fused with cultured cancer cells called myelomas, the results are hybridomas 3. Once the hybridomas are cultured individually and the hybridoma that produces antibodies against the antigen of interest is identified 4, it is cloned to produce a large number of hybridomas, all of which secrete identical antibodies called monoclonal antibodies 5.

by fusing antibody-secreting plasma cells with cancerous plasma cells called *myelomas* (mī-ĕ-lō′ măz) **(Figure 4)**. Each hybridoma divides continuously (because of the cancerous plasma cell component) to produce clones of itself, and each clone secretes large amounts of a single antibody molecule. These identical antibodies are called **monoclonal** (mon-ō-klō′ năl) **antibodies** because all of them are secreted by clones originating from a single plasma cell. Once scientists have identified the hybridoma that secretes antibodies complementary to the antigen of interest, they maintain it in tissue culture to produce the antibodies needed for passive immunotherapy. For example, physicians use such a monoclonal antibody to treat newborns infected with respiratory syncytial virus.

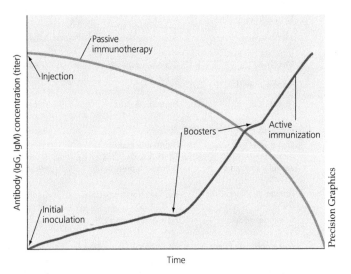

▲ **Figure 5** **The characteristics of immunity produced by active immunization (red) and passive immunotherapy (green).** Passive immunotherapy provides strong and immediate protection, but it disappears relatively quickly. Active immunity takes some time and may require additional booster inoculations to reach protective levels, but it is long lasting and capable of restimulation.

Active immunization and passive immunotherapy are used in different circumstances because they provide protection with different characteristics **(Figure 5)**. As just noted, passive immunotherapy with preformed antibodies is used whenever immediate protection is required. However, because preformed antibodies are removed rapidly from the blood and no memory B cells are produced, protection is temporary, and the recipient becomes susceptible again. Active immunization provides long-term protection that is capable of restimulation. Thus, when initiated before any exposure to *C. tetani* has occurred, active immunization using a tetanus toxoid develops long-lasting protection that is readily available upon exposure to the toxin.

# Antibody-Antigen Immune Testing

## Learning Objectives

✓ Distinguish between direct and indirect immune testing using antibody-antigen interactions.

✓ Define *serology*.

✓ In general terms, compare and contract precipitation, agglutination, neutralization, complement fixation, and labeled antibody tests.

There are two basic categories of immune testing using antibody-antigen interactions. For *direct testing*, the investigator is looking for the presence of an antigen, often a pathogen, in a specimen, which is typically taken from a site of infection. *Indirect testing* involves checking the blood or serum for antibodies that have formed against a particular antigen. Thus, in each category the

## BENEFICIAL MICROBES

### SMALLPOX: TO VACCINATE OR NOT TO VACCINATE?

▲ **Vaccinia necrosum.** |—— 10 mm ——|

Dr. Edward Jenner developed an early use for a beneficial microbe in medicine. Medical personnel in the United States followed Jenner's example by regularly administering cowpox virus—as the smallpox vaccine—to the general public until 1971, at which time the risk of contracting smallpox was deemed too low to justify required vaccinations. Indeed, in 1980 the World Health Assembly declared smallpox successfully eradicated from the natural world. However, recent concerns about the potential use of smallpox virus as an agent of bioterrorism has sparked debate about whether or not citizens should once again be vaccinated against it.

Although safe and effective for most healthy adults, for others the attenuated cowpox virus can result in serious side effects—even death. Individuals with compromised immune systems (such as AIDS patients or cancer patients undergoing chemotherapy) are considered to be at particularly high risk for developing adverse reactions. Pregnant women, infants, and individuals with a history of the skin condition eczema are also considered poor candidates for the vaccine. Though rare, adverse reactions to the vaccine may also develop in certain otherwise healthy individuals. The more serious side effects include vaccinia necrosum (characterized by progressive cell death in the area of vaccination) and encephalitis (inflammation of the brain). Approximately 1 in every million individuals receiving cowpox virus as a vaccine for the first time develops a fatal reaction to it.

Is the risk of a bioterrorist smallpox attack great enough to warrant the exposure to the known risks of administering smallpox vaccine to the general population? If you were a public health official, what would you decide?

---

investigator uses either antibody or antigen to test for the presence of its complement—antibody locates antigen in direct testing, whereas antigen locates antibody in indirect testing. The latter process can be used either to monitor the spread of an infection through a population or to establish a diagnosis in an individual. For example, the presence of antibodies against HIV in an adult's serum is strong evidence that this individual has been infected with HIV, and a patient's immune response to tuberculosis antigen indicates exposure to *Mycobacterium tuberculosis* (mī'kō-bak-tē'rē-ŭm too-ber-kyū-lō'sis).

The study and diagnostic use of antigen-antibody interactions in blood serum is called **serology** (sĕ-rol'ō-jē). Researchers have developed a wide variety of serologic tests to visualize antibody-antigen interactions, ranging from simple, automated processes to complex tests requiring skilled technicians. Physicians and medical laboratory technologists choose a particular test based on the suspected diagnosis, the cost to perform the test, and the speed with which a result can be obtained. In the following subsections we will consider several types of serologic tests: precipitation tests, agglutination tests, neutralization tests, and several tagged antibody tests. Some of these procedures are presented for historical reasons—more accurate and faster modern tests have replaced them.

## Precipitation Tests

### Learning Objectives

✓ Describe the general principles of precipitation testing.
✓ Describe the technique of immunodiffusion.
✓ Discuss the production of anti-antibodies for immune testing.

One of the simplest of serologic tests relies on the fact that when antigens and antibody are mixed in proper proportions, they form huge, insoluble, lattice-like complexes called precipitates. When, for example, a solution of a soluble antigen, such as that of the fungus *Coccidioides immitis* (kok-sid-ē-oy'dēz im'mi-tis), is mixed with an antiserum containing antibodies against the antigen, the mixture quickly becomes cloudy due to formation of a precipitate consisting of antigen-antibody complexes (*also called* **immune complexes**).

When a given amount of antibody is added to each of a series of test tubes containing increasing amounts of antigen, the amount of precipitate increases gradually until it reaches a maximum (**Figure 6a**). In test tubes containing still more antigen molecules, the amount of precipitate declines; in fact, in test tubes containing antigen in great excess over antibody, no precipitate at all develops. Thus, a graph of the amount of precipitate versus the amount of antigen has a maximum in the middle and lower values on either side.

The reasons behind this pattern of precipitation reactions are simple. Complex antigens are generally multivalent—each possesses many epitopes—and antibodies have pairs of active sites and therefore can simultaneously cross-link the same epitope on two antigen molecules. When there is excess antibody, each antigen molecule is covered with many antibody molecules, preventing extensive cross-linkage and thus precipitation (**Figure 6b**). Such soluble immune complexes can activate complement in the kidneys, leading to inflammatory damage to blood vessels in the kidneys.

**(a)**

**(b)**

Precision Graphics

◀ **Figure 6 Characteristics of precipitation reactions. (a)** When increasing amounts of antigen are placed in tubes containing a constant amount of antibody, precipitate forms only in tubes having moderate amounts of antigen. The overlay graph shows the amount of precipitate formed versus the amount of antigen present. **(b)** In the presence of excess antigen or antibody, immune complexes are small and soluble; only when antigen and antibody are in optimal proportions do large complexes form and precipitate.

When the reactants are in optimal proportions, the ratio of antigen to antibody is such that cross-linking and lattice formation are extensive. As this lattice grows, it precipitates.

In mixtures in which antigen is in excess, each antigen molecule is bound to only two antibody molecules. There is no cross-linkage; because these complexes are small and soluble, no precipitation occurs. In the body, phagocytic cells do not easily remove these small immune complexes. As a result, immune complexes may be deposited in the joints and in the tiny blood vessels of the kidneys, where they trigger allergic reactions.

Because precipitation requires the mixing of antigen and antibody in optimal proportions, it is not possible to perform a precipitation test by combining just any two solutions containing these reagents. To ensure that the optimal concentrations of antibody and antigen come together, scientists can use a technique involving movement of the molecules through an agar gel: immunodiffusion.

## Immunodiffusion

In the precipitation technique called **immunodiffusion** (im′ū-nō-di-fu′zhŭn), also known as *double immunodiffusion* or an *Ouchterlony* (ok′ter-lō-nē) *test,* a researcher cuts cylindrical holes called *wells* in an agar plate. One well is filled with a solution of antigen and the other with a solution of antibodies against the antigen. The antigen and antibody molecules diffuse in all directions out of the wells and into the surrounding agar, and where they meet in optimal proportions, a line of precipitation appears (Figure 7a). If the solutions contain many different antigens and antibodies, each complementary pair of reactants reaches optimal proportions at different positions, and numerous lines of precipitation are produced—one for each interacting antigen-antibody pair (Figure 7b). Such an immunodiffusion test has

**(a)**

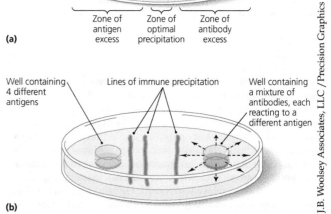

**(b)**

J.B. Woolsey Associates, LLC / Precision Graphics

▲ **Figure 7 Immunodiffusion, a type of precipitation reaction. (a)** Antigen and antibody placed in wells diffuse out and through the agar; where they meet in optimal proportions, a line of precipitation forms. **(b)** When multiple antigens and antibodies are placed in the wells, multiple lines of precipitation mark the sites where different antigen-antibody combinations occurred in optimal proportions. *Why did only three lines of precipitation occur when the antigen well contained four antigens?*

**Figure 7** *None of the antibodies used in the test was complementary to the fourth antigen.*

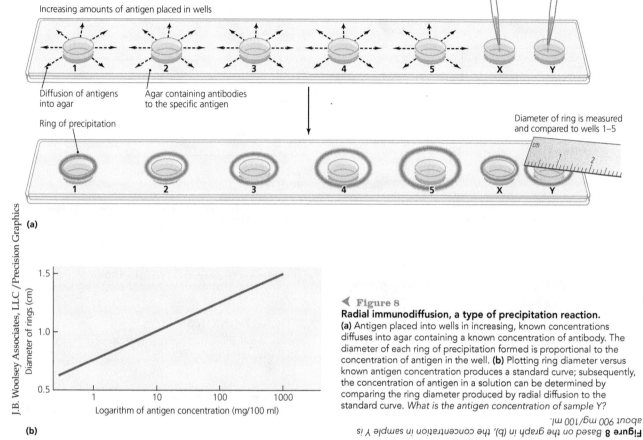

Increasing amounts of antigen placed in wells

Unknown concentrations of antigen

Sample X    Sample Y

Diffusion of antigens into agar

Agar containing antibodies to the specific antigen

Ring of precipitation

Diameter of ring is measured and compared to wells 1–5

**(a)**

J.B. Woolsey Associates, LLC / Precision Graphics

Diameter of rings (cm)

Logarithm of antigen concentration (mg/100 ml)

**(b)**

◀ **Figure 8**
**Radial immunodiffusion, a type of precipitation reaction.**
**(a)** Antigen placed into wells in increasing, known concentrations diffuses into agar containing a known concentration of antibody. The diameter of each ring of precipitation formed is proportional to the concentration of antigen in the well. **(b)** Plotting ring diameter versus known antigen concentration produces a standard curve; subsequently, the concentration of antigen in a solution can be determined by comparing the ring diameter produced by radial diffusion to the standard curve. *What is the antigen concentration of sample Y?*

**Figure 8** *Based on the graph in (b), the concentration in sample Y is about 900 mg/100 ml.*

been used to indicate exposure to complex mixtures of antigens from fungal pathogens. Only exposed patients have serum antibodies—and show precipitation—against the fungal antigens.

Another useful variation on precipitation is called *radial immunodiffusion* (Figure 8a). In this technique, an antigen in solution diffuses from a well into agar that contains a known concentration of specific antibodies. The diameter of the ring of precipitate that forms around the antigen well is directly proportional to the concentration of antigen in the well. By using a series of wells containing increasing but known concentrations of antigen, researchers construct a standard curve that relates ring diameter to antigen concentration (Figure 8b). Subsequently, the amount of antigen in a solution can be accurately assayed by comparing the ring diameter produced in other radial diffusion tests to the standard line. For example, investigators use radial immunodiffusion to measure the level of complement protein 3 (C3), which is often low in patients with lupus.

Scientists can also use radial immunodiffusion to measure the concentrations of specific antibodies or immunoglobulins in a person's serum. To do this, they take advantage of the fact that, because antibodies are complex proteins, they are antigenic

when injected into an individual of another species. Thus, purified human antibodies injected into a rabbit stimulate the rabbit to produce rabbit antibodies against the human antibodies. Such antibodies directed against other antibodies are called *antiantibodies*. So, in a radial immunodiffusion test to measure the concentration of a specific human antibody, the "antigen" in the test is the human immunoglobulin, and the antibody in the test is rabbit anti–human antibody.

## Agglutination Tests

### Learning Objectives

✓ Contrast agglutination and precipitation tests.

✓ Describe how agglutination is used in immunological testing, including titration.

Not all antigens are soluble proteins that can be precipitated by antibody. Because of their multiple antigen-binding sites, antibodies can also cross-link particles, such as whole bacteria or antigen-coated latex beads, causing **agglutination** (ă-gloo-ti-nā′shŭn) (clumping). The difference between agglutination and

Anti-A antibody added

Anti-B antibody added

Blood sample

A          B

A          B

Negative result: no agglutination of blood cells

Positive result: agglutination of blood cells

J.B. Woolsey Associates, LLC

**(a)**

Karen E. Petersen, Dept. of Biology, University of Washington

**(b)**

Serum added in increasing dilutions

1:1    1:10    1:100    1:1000    1:10,000    Control (no specimen added)

Antigen (identical in each well)

++++          +++          ++          +          −          Control
Very strong agglutination                                    No agglutination

J.B. Woolsey Associates, LLC

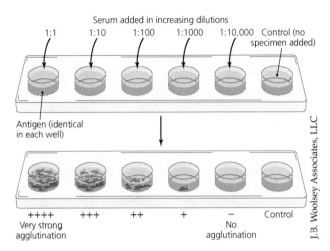

▲ **Figure 10  Titration, the use of agglutination to quantify the amount of antibody in a serum sample.** Serial dilutions of serum are added to wells containing a constant amount of antigen. At lower serum dilutions (higher concentrations of antibody), agglutination occurs; at higher serum dilutions, antibody concentration is too low to produce agglutination. The serum's titer is the highest dilution at which agglutination can be detected—in this case, 1:1000.

## CRITICAL **THINKING**

Draw a picture showing, at *both the molecular and cellular levels*, IgM agglutinating red blood cells.

▲ **Figure 9  The use of hemagglutination to determine blood types in humans. (a)** Antibodies with active sites that bind to either of two red blood cell surface antigens (antigen A or antigen B) are added to portions of a given blood sample. Where the antibodies react with the surface antigens, the blood cells can be seen to agglutinate or clump together. **(b)** Photo of actual test. *What is the blood type of the person whose blood was used in this hemagglutination reaction?*

**Figure 9** *The individual who donated the blood sample has type B+ blood.*

precipitation is that agglutination involves the clumping of insoluble particles, whereas precipitation involves the aggregation of soluble molecules. Agglutination reactions are easy to see and interpret with the unaided eye. IgM antibodies, which have 10 active sites, are more efficient than IgG antibodies (with only 2 active sites) at causing agglutination.

When the particles agglutinated are red blood cells, the reaction is called *hemagglutination* (hē-mă-gloo′ti-nā′shŭn). One use of hemagglutination is to determine blood type in humans. Blood is considered type A if the red blood cells possess surface antigens called A antigen, type B if they possess B antigens, type AB if they possess both antigens, and type O if they have neither antigen. In a hemagglutination reaction to determine blood type (Figure 9), two portions of a given blood sample are placed on a slide. Anti-A antibodies are added to one portion, and anti-B antibodies to the other; the antibodies agglutinate those blood cells that possess complementary antigens.

Another use of agglutination is in a type of test that determines the concentration of antibodies in a clinical sample. Although the simple *detection* of antibodies is sufficient for many purposes, it is often more desirable to measure the *amount* of antibodies in serum. By doing so, clinicians can determine whether a patient's antibody levels are rising, as occurs in response to the presence of active infectious disease, or falling, as occurs during the successful conclusion of a fight against an infection. One way of measuring antibody levels in blood sera is by **titration** (tī-trā′shŭn). In titration, the serum being tested undergoes a regular series of dilutions, and each dilution is then tested for agglutinating activity (Figure 10). Eventually, the antibodies in the serum become so dilute that they can no longer cause agglutination. The highest dilution of serum giving a positive reaction is the titer. Thus, a serum that must be greatly diluted before agglutination ceases (for example, has a titer of 1000) contains more antibodies than a serum that no longer agglutinates after minimal dilution (has a titer of 10).

## Neutralization Tests

### Learning Objectives

✓ Explain the purpose of neutralization tests.

✓ Contrast a viral hemagglutination inhibition test with a hemagglutination test.

**Neutralization tests** work because antibodies can *neutralize* the biological activity of many pathogens and their toxins. For example, combining antibodies against tetanus toxin with a sample of toxin renders the sample harmless to mice because the antibodies have reacted with and neutralized the toxin. Next we briefly consider two neutralization tests that, although not simple to perform, effectively reveal the biological activity of antibodies.

### Viral Neutralization

One neutralization test is **viral neutralization,** which is based on the fact that many viruses introduced into appropriate cell cultures will invade and kill the cells, a phenomenon called a *cytopathic effect* (seen in plaque formation). However, if the viruses are first mixed with specific antibodies against them, their ability to kill culture cells is neutralized. In a viral neutralization test, the lack of cytopathic effects when a mixture containing serum and a known pathogenic virus is introduced into a cell culture indicates the presence of antibodies against that virus in the serum. For example, if a mixture containing an individual's serum and a sample of hantavirus produces no cytopathic effect in a culture of susceptible cells, then it can be concluded that the individual's serum contains antibodies to hantavirus, and these antibodies neutralized the virus. Viral neutralization tests are sufficiently sensitive and specific to ascertain whether an individual has been exposed to a particular virus or viral strain.

### Viral Hemagglutination Inhibition Test

Because not all viruses are cytopathic—they do not kill their host cell—a neutralization test cannot be used to identify all viruses. However, many viruses (including influenzaviruses) have surface proteins that naturally clump red blood cells. (This natural process, called *viral hemagglutination,* must not be confused with the hemagglutination test we discussed previously—viral hemagglutination is not an antibody-antigen reaction.) Antibodies against influenzavirus inhibit viral hemagglutination; therefore, if serum from an individual stops viral hemagglutination, we know that the individual's serum contains antibodies to the influenzavirus. Such **viral hemagglutination inhibition tests** can be used to detect antibodies against influenza, measles, mumps, and other viruses that naturally agglutinate red blood cells.

## The Complement Fixation Test

### Learning Objective

✓ Briefly explain the phenomenon that is the basis for a complement fixation test.

Activation of the classical complement system by antibody leads to the generation of membrane attack complexes (MACs) that disrupt cytoplasmic membranes. This phenomenon is the basis for the **complement fixation** (kom'plĕ-ment fik-sā'shŭn) **test,** which is a complex assay used to detect the presence of specific antibodies in an individual's serum. The test can detect the presence of small amounts of antibody—amounts too small to detect by agglutination—though complement fixation tests have been replaced by other serological methods such as ELISA (discussed shortly) or genetic analysis using polymerase chain reaction (PCR).

## Labeled Antibody Tests

### Learning Objectives

✓ List three tests that use labeled antibodies to detect either antigen or antibodies.

✓ Compare and contrast the direct and indirect fluorescent antibody tests, and identify at least three uses for these tests.

✓ Compare and contrast the methods, purposes, and advantages of ELISA and the western blot tests.

A different form of serologic testing involves *labeled* (or *tagged*) *antibody tests,* so named because these tests use antibody molecules that are linked to some molecular "label" that enables them to be detected easily. Labeled antibody tests using radioactive or fluorescent labels can be used to detect either antigens or antibodies. In the following sections we will consider fluorescent antibody tests, ELISA, and the western blot test.

### Fluorescent Antibody Tests

Fluorescent dyes are used as labels in several important serologic tests. One of these dyes is *fluorescein* (flōr-es'ē-in), which can be chemically linked to an antibody without affecting the antibody's ability to bind antigen. When exposed to ultraviolet light (as in a fluorescent microscope), fluorescein glows bright green. Fluorescein-labeled antibodies are used in direct and indirect fluorescent antibody tests.

**Direct fluorescent antibody tests** identify the presence of antigen in a tissue. The test is straightforward: A scientist floods a tissue sample suspected of containing the antigen with labeled antibody, waits a short time to allow the antibody to bind to the antigen, washes the preparation to remove any unbound antibody, and examines it with a fluorescent microscope. If the suspected antigen is present, labeled antibody will adhere to it, and the scientist will see fluorescence. This is not a quantitative test—the amount of fluorescence observed is not directly related to the amount of antigen present.

Scientists use direct fluorescent antibody tests to identify small numbers of bacteria in patient tissues. This technique has been used to detect *Mycobacterium tuberculosis* in sputum and rabies viruses infecting a brain. In one use, medical laboratory technologists employ a direct fluorescent antibody test to detect the presence of yeast in a sample (**Figure 11**).

**Indirect fluorescent antibody tests** are used to detect the presence of specific antibodies in an individual's serum via a two-step process (**Figure 12a**):

1 After an antigen of interest is fixed to a microscope slide, the individual's serum is added for long enough to allow serum antibodies, if present, to bind to the antigen. The serum is then washed off, leaving the antibodies bound to the antigen (but not yet visible).

2 Antibodies against human antibodies (anti–human antibody antibodies; in this example, anti-IgG) labeled with a

LM | 10 μm

▲ **Figure 11 The direct fluorescent antibody test.** Fluorescence from labeled antibodies against the opportunistic yeast pathogen *Candida albicans* clearly reveals budding yeast cells.

fluorescent dye are added to the slide and bind to the antibodies already bound to the antigen. After washing to remove unbound anti-antibodies, the slide is examined with a fluorescent microscope.

The presence of fluorescence indicates the presence of the labeled anti-antibodies, which are bound to serum antibodies bound to the fixed antigen; thus fluoresence indicates that the individual has serum antibodies against the antigen of interest.

Indirect fluorescent antibody testing is used to detect antibodies against many viruses and some bacterial pathogens, including *Neisseria gonorrhoeae* (nĭ-se′rē-ă go-nor-rē′ĭ), the causative agent of gonorrhea (Figure 12b).

Scientists routinely identify and separate B and T lymphocytes by using specific monoclonal antibodies produced against each cell type. The researchers can attach differently colored fluorescent dyes to the antibodies, allowing them to differentiate between types of lymphocytes. Such identification tests can quantify the numbers and ratios of lymphocyte subsets, information critical in diagnosing and monitoring disease progression and effectiveness of treatment in patients with AIDS and other immunodeficiency diseases.

## ELISAs

In another type of labeled antibody test, called an **enzyme-linked immunosorbent assay** (im′ū-nō-sōr′bent as′sā; ELISA), the label is not a dye, but instead an enzyme that reacts with its substrate to produce a colored product that indicates a positive test. One form of ELISA is used to detect the presence and quantify the abundance of antibodies in serum. This test, which often takes place in commercially produced plates, has five steps (Figure 13):

1 Each of the wells in the plate is coated with antigen molecules in solution.

1 Antigen is attached to slide and flooded with patient's serum.

Antigen bound to slide

IgG from patient's serum

2 Fluorescent-labeled anti-Ig antiglobulin is added.

Fluorescent label
Anti-IgG (antiglobulin, anti-antibody)

Precision Graphics

(a)

LM | 10 μm

(b)

▲ **Figure 12 The indirect fluorescent antibody test.** This test detects the presence of a specific antibody in a patient's serum. **(a)** The test procedure. 1 Antigen is attached to the slide, which is then flooded with an individual's serum to allow specific antibodies in the serum to bind to the antigen. 2 After fluorescein-labeled anti-antibodies are added and then washed off, the slide is examined with a fluorescent microscope. **(b)** A positive indirect antibody test, in which fluorescence indicates the presence of antibodies against *Neisseria gonorrhoeae* (the agent of gonorrhea) in the individual's serum.

2 Excess antigen molecules are washed off, and another protein (such as gelatin) is added to the well to completely coat any of the surface not coated with antigen.

3 A sample of each of the sera being tested is added to a separate well. Whenever a serum sample contains antibodies against the antigen, they bind to the antigen affixed to the plate.

4 Anti-antibodies labeled with an enzyme are added to each well.

> **Figure 13 The enzyme-linked immunosorbent assay (ELISA).**
> Shown is one well in a plate. **1** Antigen added to the well attaches to it irreversibly. **2** After excess antigen is removed by washing, gelatin is added to cover any portion of the well not covered by antigen. **3** Test serum is added to the well; any specific antibodies in it bind to the antigen. **4** Enzyme-labeled anti-antibodies are added to the well and bind to any bound antibody. **5** The enzyme's substrate is added to the well, and the enzyme converts the substrate into a colored product; the amount of color, which can be measured via spectrophotometry, is directly proportional to the amount of antibody bound to the antigen.

**5** The enzyme's substrate is added to each well. The enzyme and substrate are chosen because their reaction results in products that cause a visible color change.

A positive reaction in a well, indicated by the development of color, can occur only if the labeled anti-antibody has bound to antibodies attached to the antigen of interest. The intensity of the color, which can be estimated visually or measured accurately using a spectrophotometer, is proportional to the amount of antibody present in the serum.

ELISA has become a test of choice for many diagnostic procedures, such as determination of HIV infection, because of its many advantages:

- Like other labeled antibody tests, ELISA can detect either antibody or antigen.
- ELISAs are sensitive, able to detect very small amounts of antibody (or antigen).
- Unlike some diffusion and fluorescent tests, ELISA can quantify amounts of antigen or antibody.
- ELISAs are easy to perform.
- ELISAs are relatively inexpensive.
- ELISAs can simultaneously test many samples quickly.
- ELISAs lend themselves to efficient automation and can be read easily, either by direct observation or by machine.
- Plates coated with antigen and gelatin can be stored for testing whenever they are needed.

A modification of the ELISA technique, called an *antibody sandwich ELISA,* is commonly used to detect antigen (**Figure 14**). In testing for the presence of HIV in blood serum, for example, the plates are first coated with antibody against HIV (instead of antigen). Then the sera from individuals being tested for HIV are added to the wells, and any HIV in the sera will bind to the antibody attached to the well. Finally, each well is flooded with enzyme-labeled antibodies specific to the antigen. The name "antibody sandwich ELISA" refers to the fact that the antigen being tested for is "sandwiched" between two antibody molecules. Such tests can also be used to quantify the amount of antigen in a given sample.

## CRITICAL **THINKING**

A diagnostician used an ELISA to show that a newborn had antibodies against HIV in her blood. However, six months later the same test was negative. How can this be?

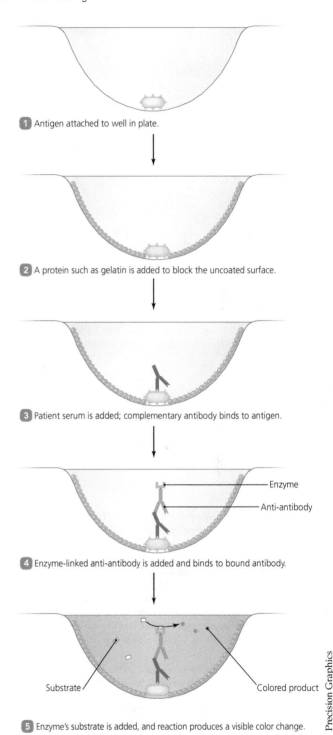

**1** Antigen attached to well in plate.

**2** A protein such as gelatin is added to block the uncoated surface.

**3** Patient serum is added; complementary antibody binds to antigen.

Enzyme

Anti-antibody

**4** Enzyme-linked anti-antibody is added and binds to bound antibody.

Substrate

Colored product

**5** Enzyme's substrate is added, and reaction produces a visible color change.

Precision Graphics

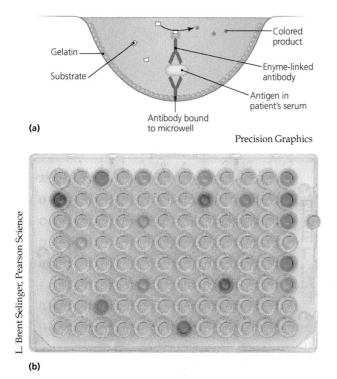

Gelatin

Substrate

Colored product

Enyme-linked antibody

Antigen in patient's serum

Antibody bound to microwell

**(a)**

Precision Graphics

**(b)**

L. Brent Selinger, Pearson Science

▲ **Figure 14** **An antibody sandwich ELISA.** Because this variation of ELISA is used to test for the presence of antigen, antibody is attached to the well in the initial step. A second antibody sandwiches the antigen. **(a)** Artist's rendition. **(b)** Actual results. *How many wells are positive?*

**Figure 14** *Seventeen wells are positive.*

## Western Blot Test

A technique for detecting antibodies against multiple antigens in a complex mixture is a **western blot test.** The name "western blot" is a play on words that refers to the similarity of this technique to a Southern blot test, named for the man who developed it. Western blots are also called *immunoblots.*

Western blot tests are currently used to verify the presence of antibodies against HIV in the serum of individuals who are antibody-positive by ELISA. Compared to other tests, western blot tests can detect more types of antibodies and are less subject to misinterpretation. A western blot test has three steps (Figure 15a):

1. Electrophoresis. Antigens in a solution (in this example, HIV proteins) are placed into wells and separated by gel electrophoresis. Each of the proteins in the solution is resolved into a single band, producing invisible protein bands.

2. Blotting. The protein bands are transferred to an overlying nitrocellulose membrane by absorbing the solution into absorbent paper—a process called blotting. The nitrocellulose membrane is then cut into strips.

3. ELISA. Each nitrocellulose strip is incubated with a test solution—in this example, those from each of six individuals

Wells containing antigens

Polyacrylamide gel

1 Electrophoresis (not shown)

Polyacrylamide gel

2 Blotting

Nitrocellulose filter

Filter paper

Polyacrylamide gel

Sponge

Nitrocellulose (blot) is cut into strips

3 ELISA is performed on strips

Polypeptides

Precision Graphics

**(a)**

Patient 1

2

3

4

5

6

Positive control

Negative control

**(b)**

Museum of Science and Industry, Chicago

◀ **Figure 15** **A western blot.** This technique demonstrates the presence of antibodies against multiple antigens in a complex mixture. **(a)** Steps in a western blot. ① Antigens are separated by gel electrophoresis. ② Separated proteins are transferred to a nitrocellulose membrane. ③ Test solutions, enzyme-labeled anti-antibody, and the enzyme's substrate are added; color changes are detected wherever antibody in the test solutions has bound to HIV proteins. **(b)** The results of a western blot. Patient 3 tested positive for antibodies.

who are being tested for antibodies against HIV. After the strips are washed, an enzyme-labeled anti-antibody solution is added for a time; then the strips are washed again and exposed to the enzyme's substrate.

Color develops wherever antibodies against the HIV proteins in the test solutions have bound to their substrates, as shown in the positive control. In this example, the individual tested in strip 3 is positive for antibodies against HIV, whereas the other five individuals are negative for antibodies against HIV. Colored bands common to all patients are normal serum proteins.

## Recent Developments in Antibody-Antigen Immune Testing

### Learning Objectives

✓ Discuss the benefits of using immunofiltration assays rather than an ELISA.

✓ Contrast immunofiltration and immunochromatographic assays.

Recent years have seen the development of simple immunoassays that give clinicians useful results within minutes. The most commonly used of these are *immunofiltration* and *immunochromatography* assays. These tests are not quantitative but rapidly give a positive or negative result, making them very useful in arriving at a diagnosis.

**Immunofiltration** (im′ū-nō-fil-trā′shŭn) **assays** are rapid ELISAs based on the use of antibodies bound to a membrane filter rather than to plates. Because of the large surface area of a membrane filter, reactions proceed faster and assay times are significantly reduced as compared to a traditional ELISA.

**Immunochromatographic** (im′ū-nō-krō′mat-ō-graf′ik) **assays** are still faster and easier to read immunoassays. In these systems, an antigen solution (such as diluted blood or sputum) flowing through a porous material encounters antibody labeled with either pink colloidal[2] gold or blue colloidal selenium. Where antigen and antibody bind, colored immune complexes form in the fluid, which then flows through a region where the complexes encounter antibody against them, resulting in a clearly visible pink or blue line, depending on the label used. These assays are used for pregnancy testing, which tests for *human chorionic growth hormone*—a hormone produced only by an embryo or fetus—and for rapid identification of infectious agents such as HIV, *Escherichia coli* (esh-ĕ-rik′ē-ă kō′lē) O157:H7, group A *Streptococcus,* respiratory syncytial virus (RSV), and influenzaviruses. In one adaptation, the antibodies are coated on

---
[2]*Colloidal* refers to small particles suspended in a liquid or gas.

▲ **Figure 16** **Immunochromatographic dipstick.** The dipstick is impregnated with colloidal metal particles linked to movable antibodies against particular antigens at one end, and anti-antibodies fixed in a line closer to the other end of the membrane.

Precision Graphics

membrane strips, which serve as dipsticks. At one end, anti-antibodies are fixed in a line so that they cannot move in the membrane. The lower portion of the membrane is coated with antibodies against the antigen in question. These antibodies are linked to a color indicator in the form of a colloidal metal and are free to move in the membrane by capillary action.

**Figure 16** illustrates the procedure used to test for the presence of group A *Streptococcus* in the nasal secretion of a patient. A technician prepares a nasal swab from the patient so as to release *Streptococcus* antigens if they are present. She then dips the membrane into the solution. The membrane's antibodies bind to streptococcal antigens, forming complexes. The complexes move up the membrane by capillary action until they reach the line of anti-antibodies, where they bind and must stop because the anti-antibodies are chemically bound to the strip. Previously the complexes were invisible because they were dilute; now they are concentrated at the line of anti-antibodies and become visible, indicating that this patient had group A *Streptococcus* in his nose. The procedure from antigen preparation to diagnosis takes less than 10 minutes.

**Table 3** lists some antibody-antigen immune tests that can be used to diagnose selected bacterial and viral diseases.

## 3 TABLE
### Antibody-Antigen Immunological Tests and Some of Their Uses

| Test | Use |
|------|-----|
| Immunodiffusion (precipitation) | Diagnosis of syphilis, pneumococcal pneumonia |
| Agglutination | Blood typing; pregnancy testing; diagnosis of salmonellosis, brucellosis, gonorrhea, rickettsial infection, mycoplasma infection, yeast infection, typhoid fever, meningitis caused by *Haemophilus* |
| Viral neutralization | Diagnosis of infections by specific strains of viruses |
| Viral hemagglutination inhibition | Diagnosis of viral infections including influenza, measles, mumps, rubella, mononucleosis |
| Complement fixation | In the past, diagnosis of measles, influenza A, syphilis, rubella, rickettsial infections, scarlet fever, rheumatic fever, infections of respiratory syncytial virus and *Coxiella* |
| Direct fluorescent antibody | Diagnosis of rabies, infections of group A *Streptococcus*, identification of lymphocyte subsets |
| Indirect fluorescent antibody | Diagnosis of syphilis, mononucleosis |
| ELISA | Pregnancy testing; presence of drugs in urine; diagnosis of hepatitis A, hepatitis B, rubella; initial diagnosis of HIV infection |
| Western blot | Verification of infection with HIV; diagnosis of Lyme disease |

# Chapter Summary

## Immunization

1. The first **vaccine** was developed by Edward Jenner against small-pox. He called the technique **vaccination. Immunization** is a more general term referring to the use of vaccines against rabies, anthrax, measles, mumps, rubella, polio, and other diseases.

2. Individuals can be protected against many infections by either active immunization or passive immunotherapy.
**ANIMATIONS:** *Vaccines: Function*

3. Active immunization involves giving antigen in the form of either **attenuated vaccines, inactivated (killed) vaccines, toxoid vaccines,** or recombinant gene vaccines. Antibody **titer** refers to the amount of antibody produced.
**ANIMATIONS:** *Vaccines: Types*

4. Pathogens in attenuated vaccines are weakened so that they no longer cause disease, though they are still alive or active and can provide **contact immunity** in unimmunized individuals who associate with immunized people.

5. Inactivated vaccines are either whole agent or subunit vaccines and often contain **adjuvants,** which are chemicals added to increase their ability to stimulate active immunity.

6. Toxoid vaccines use modified toxins to stimulate antibody-mediated immunity.

7. A **combination vaccine** is composed of antigens from several pathogens so they can be administered to a patient at once.

8. Having a large proportion of immunized individuals (>75%) in a population interrupts disease transmission, providing protection to unimmunized individuals. Such protection is called **herd immunity.**

9. Passive immunotherapy (a type of passive immunization) involves administration of an **antiserum** containing preformed antibodies. Serum sickness results when the patient makes antibodies against the antiserum.

10. The fusion of myelomas (cancerous plasma cells) with plasma cells results in **hybridomas,** the source of **monoclonal antibodies,** which can be used in passive immunization.

## Antibody-Antigen Immune Testing

1. **Serology** is the study and use of immunological tests to diagnose and treat disease or identify antibodies or antigens. Direct testing involves using antibodies to find an antigen in a specimen. Indirect testing involves using an antigen to find antibodies in serum or blood.

2. The simplest of the serologic tests is a precipitation test, in which antigen and antibody meet in optimal proportions to form immune complexes, which are often insoluble. Often this test is performed in clear gels, where it is called **immunodiffusion.**

3. **Agglutination tests** involve the clumping of antigenic particles by antibodies. The amount of these antibodies, called the titer, is measured by diluting the serum in a process called **titration.**

4. Antibodies to viruses or toxins can be measured using a **neutralization test,** such as a **viral neutralization** test. Infection by viruses that naturally agglutinate red blood cells can be demonstrated using a **viral hemagglutination inhibition test.**

5. The **complement fixation test** is a complex assay used to determine the presence of specific antibodies.

6. Fluorescently labeled antibodies—those chemically linked to a fluorescent dye—can be used in a variety of **direct** and **indirect fluorescent antibody** tests. The presence of labeled antibodies is visible through a fluorescent microscope.

7. **Enzyme-linked immunosorbent assays (ELISAs)** are a family of simple tests that can be readily automated and read by machine. These tests are among the most common serologic tests used. A variation of the ELISA is the **western blot test,** which is used to detect antibodies against multiple antigens in a mixture.

8. **Immunofiltration assays** and **immunochromatographic assays** are modifications of ELISA tests that can give much more rapid diagnostic results.

# Questions for Review

Answers to the Questions for Review (except Short Answer questions) appear at the end of this chapter.

## Multiple Choice

1. In order to obtain immediate immunity against tetanus, a patient should receive
   a. an attenuated vaccine of *Clostridium tetani*.
   b. a modified live vaccine of *C. tetani*.
   c. tetanus toxoid.
   d. immunoglobulin against tetanus toxin (antitoxin).
   e. a subunit vaccine against *C. tetani*.

2. Which of the following vaccine types is commonly given with an adjuvant?
   a. an attenuated vaccine       d. an immunoglobulin
   b. a modified live vaccine     e. an agglutinating antigen
   c. a chemically killed vaccine

3. Which of the following viruses was widely used in living vaccines?
   a. coronavirus      d. retrovirus
   b. vaccinia virus   e. myxovirus
   c. influenzavirus

4. When antigen and antibodies combine, maximal precipitation occurs when
   a. antigen is in excess.
   b. antibody is in excess.
   c. antigen and antibody are at equivalent concentrations.
   d. antigen is added to the antibody.
   e. antibody is added to the antigen.

5. An anti-antibody is used when
   a. an antigen is not precipitating.
   b. an antibody is not agglutinating.
   c. an antibody does not activate complement.
   d. an antigen is insoluble.
   e. the antigen is an antibody.

6. The many different proteins in serum can be analyzed by
   a. an anti-antibody test.      d. an agglutination test.
   b. a complement fixation test. e. an immunodiffusion test.
   c. a precipitation test.

7. A direct fluorscent antibody test requires which of the following?
   a. heat-inactivated serum    d. heated plasma
   b. fluorescent serum         e. antibodies against the
   c. immune complexes             antigen

8. An ELISA uses which of the following reagents?
   a. an enzyme-labeled        c. a source of complement
      anti-antibody            d. an enzyme-labeled antigen
   b. a radioactive anti-antibody e. an enzyme-labeled antibody

9. A direct fluorescent antibody test can be used to detect the presence of
   a. hemagglutination.    d. complement.
   b. specific antigens.   e. precipitated antigen-
   c. antibodies.             antibody complexes.

10. Which of the following is a good test to detect rabies virus in the brain of a dog?
    a. agglutination                 d. western blot
    b. hemagglutination inhibition   e. direct immunofluorescence
    c. virus neutralization

11. Attenuation is
    a. the process of reducing virulence.
    b. a necessary step in vaccine manufacture.
    c. a form of variolation.
    d. similar to an adjuvant.

12. An antiserum is
    a. an anti-antibody.
    b. an inactivated vaccine.
    c. formed of monoclonal antibodies.
    d. the liquid portion of blood used for immunization.

13. Monoclonal antibodies
    a. are produced by hybridomas.
    b. are secreted by clone cells.
    c. can be used for passive immunization.
    d. all of the above

14. The study of antibody-antigen interaction in the blood is
    a. attenuation.
    b. agglutination.
    c. precipitation.
    d. serology.

15. Anti–human antibody antibodies are
    a. found in immunocompromised individuals.
    b. used in direct fluorescent antibody tests.
    c. formed by animals reacting to human immunoglobulins.
    d. an alternative method in ELISA.

## True/False

1. ____ Passive immunotherapy provides more prolonged immunity than active immunization.

2. ____ It is standard to attenuate killed virus vaccines.

3. ____ One single serologic test is inadequate for an accurate diagnosis of HIV infection.

4. ____ ELISA is very easily automated.

5. ____ ELISA has basically replaced the western blot test.

## Matching

Match the characteristic in the first column with the therapy it most closely describes in the second column. Some choices may be used more than once.

1. ____ Induces rapid onset of immunity

2. ____ Induces mainly an antibody response

3. ____ Induces good cell-mediated immunity

4. ____ Increases antigenicity

5. ____ Uses antigen fragments

6. ____ Uses attenuated microbes

A. Attenuated viral vaccine
B. Adjuvant
C. Subunit vaccine
D. Immunoglobulin
E. Residual virulence

## Labeling

Identify the chemicals represented by this artist's conception of an ELISA.

1. _____
2. _____
3. _____
4. _____
5. _____
6. _____

Precision Graphics

## Short Answer

1. Compare and contrast the Chinese practice of variolation with Jenner's vaccination procedure.

2. What are the advantages and disadvantages of attenuated vaccines?

3. Compare the advantages and disadvantages of passive immunotherapy and active immunization.

4. How does precipitation differ from agglutination?

5. Explain how a pregnancy test works at the molecular level.

6. Compare and contrast herd immunity and contact immunity.

# Concept Mapping

Using the following terms, draw a concept map that describes vaccines.
Or, complete this concept map online by going to the Study Area at www.masteringmicrobiology.com.

Active immunity
Antigenic fragments
Attenuated whole agents
Hepatitis B vaccine
Immunizations

Inactivated whole agents
Inactivated polio vaccine
Killed vaccine
Live vaccines
Measles vaccine

Microorganisms
Modified toxins
Reduced virulence
Subunits
Tetanus toxoid

Toxoids
Varicella vaccine

# Critical Thinking

1. Is it ethical to approve the use of a vaccine that causes significant illness in 1% of patients, if it protects immunized survivors against a serious disease?

2. Which is worse: to use a diagnostic test for HIV that may falsely indicate that a patient is not infected (false negative), or to use one that sometimes falsely indicates that a patient is infected (false positive)? Defend your choice.

3. Discuss the importance of costs and technical skill in selecting a practical serologic test. Under what circumstances does automation become important?

4. What bodily fluids, in addition to blood serum, might be usable for immune testing?

5. Why might a serologic test give a false positive result?

6. Some researchers want to distinguish between B cells and T cells in a mixture of lymphocytes. How could they do this without killing the cells?

7. Describe three ways by which genetic recombinant techniques could be used to develop safer, more effective vaccines.

8. How does a toxoid vaccine differ from an attenuated vaccine?

9. Explain why many health organizations promote breast feeding of newborns. What risks are involved in such nursing?

10. Contrast a hemagglutination test with a viral hemagglutination inhibition test.

11. Sixty years ago parents would have done almost anything to get a protective vaccine against polio for their children. Now parents fear the vaccine, not the disease. Why?

## MasteringMICROBIOLOGY™

Access more review material online in the Study Area at **www.masteringmicrobiology.com**. There, you'll find
- Animations
- MP3 Tutor Sessions
- Concept Mapping Activities
- Flashcards
- Quizzes

and more to help you succeed.

# Answers

Answers to multiple-choice, fill-in-blank, labeling, matching, and true/false questions are listed here. Answers for Short Answer and Critical Thinking questions are available for instructors only in the Instructor's Manual that accompanies this text.

**Multiple Choice**
1. d; 2. c; 3. b; 4. c; 5. e; 6. e; 7. e; 8. a; 9. b; 10. e; 11. a; 12. d; 13. d; 14. d; 15. c

**True/False**
1. False; 2. False; 3. True; 4. True; 5. False

**Matching**
1. D; 2. C; 3. A; 4. B; 5. C; 6. A

**Labeling**
See Figure 14.

# Immune Disorders

It is summer, and you are hiking along a densely wooded trail wearing shorts and a T-shirt. You spot a beautiful **wildflower** just a few feet away and wander briefly off the trail to get a better look, wading through knee-high foliage. The next morning, an itchy red **rash** has developed on both of your legs. Within days, the rash has progressed to painful, oozing blisters. You realize, unhappily, that you have contacted **poison ivy** and will be treating the blisters until they heal—typically within 14 to 20 days.

A poison ivy rash is caused by an **allergic** response to urushiol, a chemical that coats poison ivy leaves. About 85% of the population experiences an allergic reaction when exposed to urushiol. The body's **immune system** essentially overreacts to the urushiol: it identifies the chemical as a foreign substance and initiates an immune response that results in allergic contact dermatitis (inflammation of the skin). In the absence of an immune response, poison ivy would be harmless.

In this chapter we examine a variety of immune system disorders, including allergies and other immune **hypersensitivities**, autoimmune diseases, and immune deficiencies.

**(MM)** Take the pre-test for this chapter online. Visit the Study Area at www.masteringmicrobiology.com.

The attractive, glistening tripartite leaves and interesting fruit of poison ivy belie its allergic potential.

From Chapter 18 of *Microbiology with Diseases by Taxonomy*, Third Edition. Robert W. Bauman. Copyright © 2011 by Pearson Education, Inc. Published by Benjamin Cummings, Inc. All rights reserved.

The immune system is an absolutely essential component of the body's defenses. However, if the immune system functions abnormally—either by over reacting or underreacting—the malfunction may cause significant disease, even death. If the immune system functions excessively, the body develops any of a variety of *immune hypersensitivities*. An important example of a hypersensitivity is an allergy, which occurs when the immune system reacts to generally harmless substances such as pollen. Further, *autoimmune diseases* develop when the immune system attacks the body's own tissues. Finally, diseases that result from a failure of the immune system are called *immunodeficiency* (im'ū-nō-dē-fish'en-sē) *diseases*. In this chapter we discuss each of these three categories of derangements of the immune system.

# Hypersensitivities

## Learning Objective

✓ Compare and contrast the four types of hypersensitivity.

**Hypersensitivity** (hī'per-sen-si-tiv'i-tē) may be defined as any immune response against a foreign antigen that is exaggerated beyond the norm. For example, most people can wear wool, smell perfume, or dust furniture without experiencing itching, wheezing, runny nose, or watery eyes. When these symptoms do occur, the person is said to be experiencing a hypersensitivity response. In the following sections we examine each of the four main types of hypersensitivity response, designated as type I through type IV.

## Type I (Immediate) Hypersensitivity

### Learning Objectives

✓ Describe the two-part mechanism by which type I hypersensitivity occurs.

✓ Explain the roles of three inflammatory chemicals (mediators) released from mast cell granules.

✓ Describe three disease conditions resulting from type I hypersensitivity mechanisms.

Type I hypersensitivities are localized or systemic (whole body) reactions that result from the release of inflammatory molecules (such as histamine) in response to an antigen. These reactions are termed *immediate hypersensitivity* because they develop within seconds or minutes following exposure to the antigen. They are also commonly called **allergies,**[1] and the antigens that stimulate them are called **allergens** (al'er-jenz).

In the next two subsections we will examine the two-part mechanism of a type I hypersensitivity reaction: sensitization upon an initial exposure to an allergen, and the degranulation of sensitized cells.

---

[1] From Greek *allos*, meaning other, and *ergon*, meaning work.

## Sensitization upon Initial Exposure to an Allergen

All of us are exposed to antigens in the environment, against which we typically mount immune responses that result in the production of IgG. But when cytokines (especially interleukin 4) from type 2 helper T (Th2) cells stimulate B cells in allergic individuals, the B cells become plasma cells that produce not IgG, but instead switch to IgE (Figure 1a). Typically, IgE is directed against parasitic worms, which rarely infect most Americans, so IgE is found at low levels in the blood serum. However, in allergic individuals plasma cells produce IgE in response to allergens.

The precise reason that only some people produce high levels of IgE (and thereby suffer from allergies) is a matter of intense research. Some researchers think that environmental factors—including exposure during infancy and childhood to high levels of indoor antigens such as cigarette smoke, dust mites, and molds—sensitize people, making them hypersensitive (allergic). Conversely, other researchers believe that childhood exposure to such antigens is protective, that young children who experience multiple bacterial and viral infections as well as exposure to pet dander (flakes of animal skin) are less likely to develop allergies than those who have been relatively sheltered from infectious diseases and unexposed to pets. **Highlight: Can Pets Help Decrease Children's Allergy Risks?** examines the second hypothesis.

In any case, following initial exposure to allergens, the plasma cells of allergic individuals secrete IgE, which binds very strongly via its stem ($F_c$ region) to three types of defense cells—*mast cells*, *basophils*, and *eosinophils*—sensitizing these cells to respond to subsequent exposures to the allergen.

## Degranulation of Sensitized Cells

When the same allergen reenters the body, it binds to the active sites of IgE molecules on the surfaces of sensitized cells (described shortly). This binding triggers a cascade of internal biochemical reactions that causes the sensitized cells to release the inflammatory chemicals from their granules into the surrounding intercellular space—an event called *degranulation* (dē-gran-ū-lā'shŭn) (Figure 1b). It is these inflammatory mediators that generate the characteristic symptoms of type I hypersensitivity reactions: respiratory distress, rhinitis (inflammation of the nasal mucous membranes commonly called "runny nose"), watery eyes, inflammation, and reddening of the skin.

## The Roles of Degranulating Cells in an Allergic Reaction

**Mast cells** are specialized relatives of white blood cells, deriving from other stem cells in the bone marrow. They are distributed throughout the body in connective tissues other than blood. These large, round cells are most often found in sites close to body surfaces, including the skin and the walls of the

▶ **Figure 1**
**The mechanisms of a type I hypersensitivity reaction.**
**(a)** Sensitization. After normal processing of an antigen (allergen) by an antigen-presenting cell ( 1 ), Th2 cells are stimulated to secrete IL-4 ( 2 ). This cytokine stimulates a B cell ( 3 ), which becomes a plasma cell that secretes IgE ( 4 ), which then binds to and sensitizes mast cells, basophils, and eosinophils ( 5 ). **(b)** Degranulation. When the same allergen is subsequently encountered, its binding to the IgE molecules on the surfaces of sensitized cells triggers rapid degranulation and the release of inflammatory chemicals from the cells.

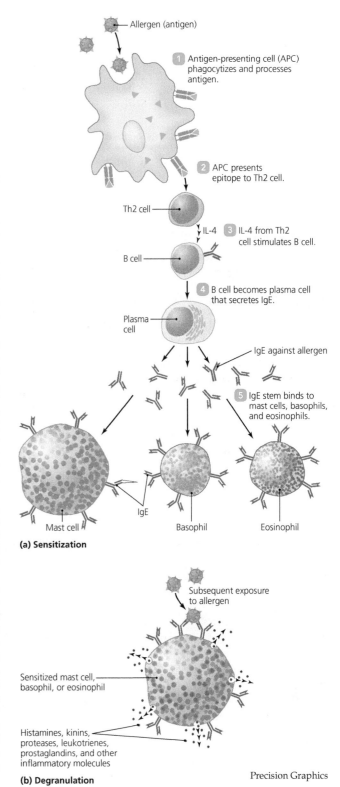

Allergen (antigen)

1 Antigen-presenting cell (APC) phagocytizes and processes antigen.

2 APC presents epitope to Th2 cell.

Th2 cell

IL-4   3 IL-4 from Th2 cell stimulates B cell.

B cell

4 B cell becomes plasma cell that secretes IgE.

Plasma cell

IgE against allergen

5 IgE stem binds to mast cells, basophils, and eosinophils.

IgE

Mast cell          Basophil          Eosinophil

**(a) Sensitization**

Subsequent exposure to allergen

Sensitized mast cell, basophil, or eosinophil

Histamines, kinins, proteases, leukotrienes, prostaglandins, and other inflammatory molecules

**(b) Degranulation**

Precision Graphics

intestines and airways. Their characteristic feature is cytoplasm packed with large granules that are loaded with a mixture of potent inflammatory chemicals.

One significant chemical released from mast cell granules is **histamine** (his′tă-mēn), a small molecule related to the amino acid histidine. Histamine stimulates strong contractions in the smooth muscles of the bronchi, gastrointestinal tract, uterus, and bladder, and it also makes small blood vessels dilate (expand) and become leaky. As a result, tissues in which mast cells degranulate become red and swollen. Histamine also stimulates nerve endings, causing itching and pain. Finally, histamine is a potent stimulator of bronchial mucus secretion, tear formation, and salivation.

Other mediators of allergies released by degranulating mast cells include **kinins** (kī′ninz), which are powerful inflammatory chemicals, and **proteases** (prō′tē-ās-ez)—enzymes that destroy nearby cells, activating the complement system, which in turn results in the release of still more inflammatory chemicals. Proteases account for more than half the proteins in a mast cell granule. In addition, the binding of allergens to IgE on mast cells activates other enzymes that trigger the production of **leukotrienes** (loo-kō-trī′ēnz) and **prostaglandins** (prostă-glan′dinz), lipid molecules that are potent inflammatory agents. Table 1 summarizes the inflammatory molecules released from mast cells.

**Basophils,** the least numerous type of leukocyte in blood, contain cytoplasmic granules that stain intensely with basic dyes and are filled with inflammatory chemicals similar to those found in mast cells. Sensitized basophils bind IgE and degranulate in the same way as mast cells when they encounter allergens.

The blood and tissues of allergic individuals also accumulate many **eosinophils,** leukocytes that contain numerous cytoplasmic granules that stain intensely with the red dye eosin and function primarily to destroy parasitic worms. The process during type I hypersensitivity reactions that results in the accumulation of eosinophils in the blood—a condition termed *eosinophilia*—begins with mast cell degranulation, which releases peptides that stimulate the release of eosinophils from the bone marrow. Once in the bloodstream, eosinophils are attracted to the site of mast cell degranulation, where they themselves degranulate. Eosinophil granules contain unique inflammatory mediators and produce large amounts of leukotrienes, which increase vascular permeability and stimulate smooth muscle contraction, thereby contributing greatly to the severity of a hypersensitivity response.

TABLE 1

## Inflammatory Molecules Released from Mast Cells

| Molecules | Role in Hypersensitivity Reactions |
| --- | --- |
| **Released During Degranulation** | |
| Histamine | Causes smooth muscle contraction, increased vascular permeability, and irritation |
| Kinins | Cause smooth muscle contraction, inflammation, and irritation |
| Proteases | Damage tissues and activate complement |
| **Synthesized in Response to Inflammation** | |
| Leukotrienes | Cause slow, prolonged smooth muscle contraction, inflammation, and increased vascular permeability |
| Prostaglandins | Some contract smooth muscle; others relax it |

### Clinical Signs of Localized Allergic Reactions

Type I hypersensitivity reactions are usually mild and localized. The site of the reaction depends on the portal of entry of the antigens. For example, inhaled allergens may provoke a response in the upper respiratory tract commonly known as **hay fever,** a local allergic reaction marked by a profuse watery nasal discharge, sneezing, itchy throat and eyes, and excessive tear production. Fungal (mold) spores; pollens from grasses, flowering plants, and some trees; and feces and dead bodies of house dust mites are among the more common allergens (Figure 2).

If inhaled allergen particles are sufficiently small, they may reach the lungs. A type I hypersensitivity in the lungs can cause an episode of severe difficulty in breathing known as **asthma,** characterized by wheezing, coughing, excessive production of a thick, sticky mucus, and constriction of the smooth muscles of the bronchi. Although a localized reaction, asthma can be life threatening: without medical intervention, the increased mucus and bronchial constriction can quickly cause suffocation.

Other allergens—including latex, wool, certain metals, and the venom or saliva of wasps, bees, fire ants, deer flies, fleas, and other stinging or biting insects—may cause a local dermatitis (inflammation of the skin). As a result of the release of histamine and other mediators, plus the ensuing leakage of serum from local blood vessels, the individual suffers raised, red areas called *hives* or **urticaria**[2] (er'ti-kar'i-ă; Figure 3). These lesions are very itchy because histamine irritates local nerve endings.

### Clinical Signs of Systemic Allergic Reactions

Following a sensitized individual's contact with an allergen, many mast cells may degranulate simultaneously, releasing massive amounts of histamine and other inflammatory mediators into the bloodstream. The release of chemicals may exceed the body's ability to adjust, resulting in **acute anaphylaxis**[3] (an'ă-fĭ-lak'sis), or **anaphylactic shock.**

[2] From Latin *urtica*, meaning nettle.
[3] From Greek *ana*, meaning away from, and *phylaxis*, meaning protection.

**▲ Figure 2 Some common allergens. (a)** Spores of the fungus, *Aspergillus* on stalks.
**(b)** Pollen of *Ambrosia trifida* (ragweed), the most common cause of hay fever in the United States.
**(c)** A house dust mite. Mites' fecal pellets and dead bodies may become airborne and trigger allergic responses.

A common cause of acute anaphylaxis is a bee sting in an allergic and sensitized individual. The first sting produces sensitization and the formation of IgE antibodies, and successive stings—which may occur years later—produce an anaphylactic reaction. Other allergens commonly implicated in acute anaphylaxis are certain foods (notoriously peanuts), vaccines,

antibiotics such as penicillin, iodine dyes, local anesthetics, blood products, and certain narcotics such as morphine.

The clinical signs of acute anaphylaxis are those of rapid suffocation. Bronchial smooth muscle, which is highly sensitive to histamine, contracts violently. In addition, increased leakage of fluid from blood vessels causes swelling of the larynx and other tissues. The patient also experiences contraction of the smooth muscle of the intestines and bladder. Without prompt administration of *epinephrine* (ep'i-nef'rin) (discussed shortly), an individual in anaphylactic shock may suffocate, collapse, and die within minutes.

### Diagnosis of Type I Hypersensitivity

Clinicians diagnose type I hypersensitivity with a test variously called *ImmunoCAP Specific IgE blood test, CAP RAST,* or *Pharmacia CAP*, in which suspected allergens are mixed with samples of the patient's blood. The specifics of the test are beyond the scope of this chapter, but basically the test detects the amount of IgE directed against each allergen. High levels of a specific IgE indicate a hypersensitivity against that allergen.

Alternatively, physicians diagnose type I hypersensitivity by injecting a very small quantity of a dilute solution of the allergens being tested into the skin. In most cases the individual is screened for more than a dozen potential allergens simultaneously, using the forearms as injection sites. When the individual tested is sensitive to an allergen, local histamine release causes redness and swelling at the injection site within a few minutes (Figure 4).

### Prevention of Type I Hypersensitivity

Prevention of type I hypersensitivity begins with *identification* and *avoidance* of the allergens responsible. Filtration of air and avoidance of rural areas during pollen season can reduce upper respiratory allergies provoked by some pollens. Encasing

BISP/Photo Researchers, Inc.

**▲ Figure 3 Urticaria.** These red, itchy patches on the skin are prompted by the release of histamine in response to an allergen. *What causes fluid to accumulate in the patches seen in urticaria?*

**Figure 3** *The fluid accumulates because histamine from degranulated mast cells causes blood capillaries to become more permeable.*

SUI/Visuals Unlimited

▲ **Figure 4** **Skin tests for diagnosing type I hypersensitivity.** The presence of redness and swelling at an injection site indicates sensitivity to the allergen injected at that site.

bedding in mite-proof covers, frequent vacuuming, and avoidance of home furnishings that trap dust (such as wall-to-wall carpeting and heavy drapes) can reduce the severity of other household allergies. A dehumidifier can reduce mold in a home. The best way for individuals to avoid allergic reactions to pets is to find out whether they are allergic before they get a pet. If an allergy develops afterward, they may have to find a new home for the animal.

Food allergens can be identified and then avoided by using a medically supervised elimination diet in which foods are removed one at a time from the diet to see when signs of allergy cease. Peanuts and shellfish are among the foods more commonly implicated in anaphylactic shock; allergic individuals must scrupulously avoid consuming even minute amounts (see **Highlight: When Kissing Triggers Allergic Reactions**). For example, individuals sensitized against shellfish can suffer anaphylactic shock from consuming meat sliced on an unwashed cutting board previously used to prepare shellfish. Some vaccines contain small amounts of egg proteins and should not be given to individuals allergic to eggs.

Health care workers should assess a patient's medical history carefully before administering penicillin, iodine dyes, and other potential allergens. Therapies such as antidotes and respiratory stimulants should be immediately available if a patient's sensitivity status is unknown.

In addition to avoidance of allergens, type I hypersensitivity reactions can be prevented by *immunotherapy* (im'ū-nō-thār'-ă-pē), commonly called "allergy shots," which involves the administration of a series of injections of dilute allergen, usually once a week for many months. It is unclear just how allergy shots work, but they may alter the helper T cell balance from Th2 cells to Th1 cells, reducing the production of antibodies, or they may stimulate the production of IgG, which binds antigen before the antigen can react with IgE on mast cells, basophils, and eosinophils. Immunotherapy reduces the severity of allergy symptoms by roughly 50% in about two-thirds of patients with upper respiratory allergies; however, the series of injections must be repeated every two to three years. Immunotherapy is not effective in treating asthma.

## Treatment of Type I Hypersensitivity

One way to treat type I hypersensitivity is to administer drugs that specifically counteract the inflammatory mediators released by degranulating cells. Thus, **antihistamines** are administered to counteract histamine. However, because histamine is but one of many mediators released in type I hypersensitivity, antihistamines do not completely eliminate all clinical signs. Indeed, because antihistamines are essentially useless in patients with asthma, asthmatics are typically prescribed an inhalant containing *glucocorticoid* (gloo-kō-kōr'ti-koyd) and a *bronchodilator* (brong-kō-dī-lā'ter), which counteract the effects of inflammatory mediators.

The hormone *epinephrine* quickly neutralizes many of the lethal mechanisms of anaphylaxis by relaxing smooth muscle tissue in the lungs, contracting smooth muscle of blood vessels, and reducing vascular permeability. Epinephrine is thus the drug of choice for the emergency treatment of both severe asthma and anaphylactic shock. Patients who suffer from severe type I hypersensitivities may carry a prescription epinephrine kit so that they can inject themselves before their allergic reactions become life threatening.

## HIGHLIGHT

### WHEN KISSING TRIGGERS ALLERGIC REACTIONS

Individuals with particularly severe food allergies not only need to watch what they eat—they also need to watch who kisses them. In a study from the University of California at Davis, researchers found that of 316 patients with severe allergies to peanuts, tree nuts, and/or seeds, 20 (about 6%) reported developing allergic reactions after being kissed. In nearly all of the cases, the kisser had eaten nuts to which the allergic individual was sensitive. In some of the cases, the allergic individuals were so sensitive that they developed reactions even though the kissers had brushed their teeth or had consumed the nuts several hours earlier. Food allergists believe that the duration and intensity of a kiss may also be a factor—that is, longer kisses involving exchange of saliva may be more likely to elicit allergic reactions than a quick buss on the cheek.

Tom and Dee Ann McCarthy/Corbis

The moral of the story: if you have a severe food allergy, you might want to tell your romantic partner about it!

## The First Time's Not the Problem

Steven, an eight-year-old boy, is brought to your office Monday morning by his father to have his upper arm checked for a possible infection. Dad is worried because the area of a bee sting on the boy's arm is getting more red, itchy, and tender. The father gave him some children's acetaminophen yesterday, which relieved the discomfort somewhat.

There is no history of medical problems or allergies, and the child takes no regular medication. The child is otherwise feeling well, and his father tells you he is playing and eating normally. There is no previous history of bee stings, and Steven proudly tells you he "hardly even cried" when he got stung.

There is a half-dollar-sized area on his left upper arm that is puffy and red, but there is no streaking or drainage, and the area does not appear to to be infected. Steven's temperature is normal and his lungs are clear.

1. What type of hypersensitivity reaction is Steven manifesting?

2. What other over-the-counter medication might relieve the itching?

3. What mechanism is causing the signs and symptoms you are seeing?

4. Since the area is not infected, what future health risk for his son should the father be made aware of?

5. What can be done to determine future risk from a bee sting?

6. How would you recognize a severe allergic reaction?

7. What precautions can the family take to protect the boy from future reactions?

## Type II (Cytotoxic) Hypersensitivity

### Learning Objectives

✓ Discuss the mechanisms underlying transfusion reactions.

✓ Construct a table comparing the key features of the four blood types in the ABO blood group system.

✓ Describe the mechanisms and treatment of hemolytic disease of the newborn.

The second major form of hypersensitivity results when cells are destroyed by an immune response—typically by the combined activities of complement and antibodies. This *cytotoxic hypersensitivity* is part of many autoimmune diseases, which we will discuss later in this chapter, but the most significant examples of type II hypersensitivity are the destruction of donor red blood cells following an incompatible blood transfusion and the destruction of fetal red blood cells in hemolytic disease of the newborn. We begin our discussion by focusing on these two manifestations of type II hypersensitivity.

### The ABO System and Transfusion Reactions

Red blood cells have many different glycoprotein and glycolipid molecules on their surface. Some surface molecules of red blood cells, called **blood group antigens,** have various functions, including transportation of glucose and ions across the cytoplasmic membrane.

There are several sets of blood group antigens that vary in complexity. The ABO group system is most famous and consists of just two antigens arbitrarily given the names A antigen and B antigen. Each person's red blood cells have either A antigen, B antigen, both A and B antigens, or neither antigen. Individuals with neither antigen are said to have blood type O.

As you probably know, blood can be transfused from one person to another; however, if blood is transfused to an individual with a different blood type, then the donor's blood group antigens may stimulate the production of antibodies in the recipient. These bind to and eventually destroy the transfused cells. The result can be a potentially life-threatening *transfusion reaction*. Note that it is a blood recipient's own immune system that causes problems; the donated cells merely trigger the response.

Transfusion reactions, the most problematic of which involve the ABO group, develop as follows:

- If the recipient has preexisting antibodies to foreign blood group antigens, then the donated blood cells will be destroyed immediately—either the antibody-bound cells will be phagocytized by macrophages and neutrophils, or the antibodies will agglutinate the cells, and complement will rupture them, a process called *hemolysis* (Figure 5). Hemolysis releases hemoglobin into the bloodstream, which may cause severe kidney damage. At the same time, the membranes of the ruptured blood cells trigger blood clotting within blood vessels, blocking them and causing circulatory failure, fever, difficulty in breathing, coughing, nausea, vomiting, and diarrhea. If the patient survives, recovery follows the elimination of all the foreign red blood cells.

- If the recipient has no preexisting antibodies to the foreign blood group antigens, then the transfused cells circulate and function normally, but only for a while—that is, until the recipient's immune system mounts a primary response against the foreign antigens and produces enough antibody to destroy the foreign cells. This happens gradually over a long enough time that the severe symptoms and signs mentioned above do not occur.

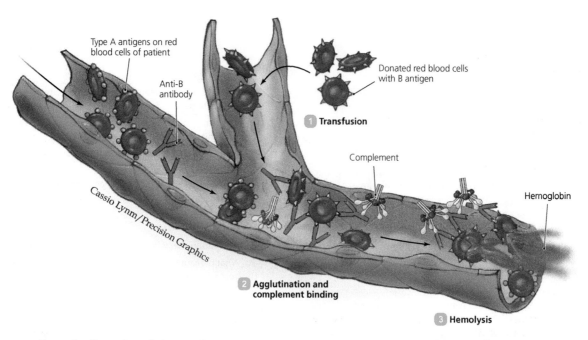

Type A antigens on red
blood cells of patient

Anti-B
antibody

Donated red blood cells
with B antigen

1 **Transfusion**

Complement

Cassio Lynm/Precision Graphics

Hemoglobin

2 **Agglutination and
complement binding**

3 **Hemolysis**

▲ **Figure 5 Events leading to hemolysis.** One of the negative consequences of a transfusion
reaction (here illustrated by a transfusion of type B blood into a patient with type A blood): When
antibodies against a foreign ABO antigen combine with the antigen on transfused red blood cells
(1), the cells are agglutinated, and the complexes bind complement (2). The resulting hemolysis
releases large amounts of hemoglobin into the bloodstream (3), and produces additional negative
consequences throughout the body.

To prevent transfusion reactions, laboratory personnel
must cross-match ABO blood types between donors and recipients. Before a recipient receives a blood transfusion, the red
cells and serum of the donor can be mixed with the serum and
red cells of the recipient. If any signs of agglutination are seen,
then that blood is not used, and an alternative donor is sought.
Table 2 presents the characteristics of the ABO blood group,
and the compatible donor/recipient matches that can be made.

In most people, production of antibodies against foreign
ABO antigens is not stimulated by exposure to foreign blood
cells but instead by exposure to antigenically similar molecules
found on a wide range of plants and bacteria. Individuals

encounter and make antibodies against these antigens on a
daily basis, but only upon receipt of a mismatched blood transfusion are they problematic.

## CRITICAL **THINKING**

During the Iraq war in 2009, an Army corporal with type AB blood
received a life-saving blood transfusion from his sergeant who had type
O blood. Later the sergeant was involved in a traumatic accident and
needed blood desperately. The corporal wanted to help but was told
his blood was incompatible. Explain the immunological reasons the
corporal could receive from but could not give to the sergeant.

**TABLE 2**

## ABO Blood Group Characteristics and Donor/Recipient Matches

| ABO Blood Group | ABO Antigen(s) Present | Antibodies Present | Can Donate To | Can Receive From |
|---|---|---|---|---|
| A | A | Anti-B | A or AB | A or O |
| B | B | Anti-A | B or AB | B or O |
| AB | A and B | None | AB | A, B, AB, or O (universal recipient) |
| O | None | Both anti-A and anti-B | A, B, AB, or O (universal donor) | O |

## The Rh System and Hemolytic Disease of the Newborn

Many decades ago, researchers discovered the existence of an antigen common to the red blood cells of humans and rhesus monkeys. They called this antigen, which transports anions and glucose across the cytoplasmic membrane, *rhesus* (rē′sŭs) antigen or **Rh antigen.** Laboratory analysis of human blood samples eventually showed that the Rh antigen is present on the red blood cells of about 85% of humans; that is, about 85% of the population is *Rh positive* (*Rh+*), and about 15% of the population is *Rh negative* (*Rh−*).

In contrast to the situation with ABO antigens, preexisting antibodies against Rh antigen do not occur. Although a transfusion reaction can occur in an Rh-negative patient who receives more than one transfusion of Rh-positive blood, such a reaction is usually minor because Rh antigen molecules are less abundant than A or B antigens. Instead, the primary problem posed by incompatible Rh antigen is the risk of **hemolytic** (hē-mō-lit′ik) **disease of the newborn** (Figure 6).

This hypersensitivity reaction develops when an Rh− mother is pregnant with an Rh+ baby (who inherited an Rh gene from its father). Normally, the placenta keeps fetal red blood cells separate from the mother's blood, so fetal cells do not enter the mother's bloodstream. However, in 20–50% of pregnancies—especially during the later weeks of pregnancy, during a clinical or spontaneous abortion, or during childbirth—fetal red blood cells escape into the mother's blood. The Rh− mother's immune system recognizes these Rh+ fetal cells as foreign and initiates a humoral immune response by developing antibodies against the Rh antigen. Initially, only IgM antibodies are produced, and because IgM is a very large molecule that cannot cross the placenta, no problems arise during this first pregnancy.

However, IgG antibodies can cross the placenta, so if during subsequent pregnancies the fetus is Rh+, anti-Rh IgG molecules produced by the mother cross the placenta and destroy the fetus's Rh+ red blood cells. Such destruction may be limited, or it may be severe enough—especially in a third or subsequent pregnancy—to cause grave problems. One classic feature of hemolytic disease of the newborn is severe jaundice from excessive *bilirubin* (bil-i-roo′bin), a yellowish blood pigment released during the degradation of hemoglobin from lysed red blood cells. The liver is normally responsible for removing bilirubin, but because of the immaturity of the fetal liver and overload from the hemolytic process, the bilirubin may instead be deposited in the brain, causing severe neurological damage or death during the latter weeks of pregnancy or shortly after the baby's birth.

In the past, when prevention of hemolytic disease of the newborn was impossible, this terrible disease occurred in about 1 of every 300 births. Today, however, physicians can routinely and drastically reduce the prevalence of the disease by administering anti-Rh immunoglobulin (IgG), called *RhoGAM*, to Rh-negative pregnant women at 28 weeks' gestation and also within 72 hours following abortion, miscarriage, or childbirth. Any fetal red cells that may have entered the mother's body are

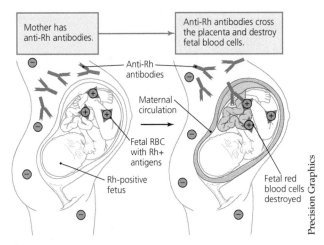

**(a)** First pregnancy

**(b)** Subsequent pregnancy

Precision Graphics

▲ **Figure 6** Events in the development of hemolytic disease of the newborn. **(a)** During an initial pregnancy, Rh+ red blood cells from the fetus enter the Rh− mother's circulation, often during childbirth. As a result, the mother produces anti-Rh antibodies. **(b)** During a subsequent pregnancy with another Rh+ child, anti-Rh IgG molecules cross the placenta and trigger destruction of the fetus's red blood cells. *How is it possible that the child of an Rh− mother is Rh+?*

**Figure 6** *The father of the child is Rh positive.*

destroyed by RhoGAM before the fetal cells can trigger an immune response. As a result, sensitization of the mother does not occur, and subsequent pregnancies are safer.

### Drug-Induced Cytotoxic Reactions

Another kind of type II hypersensitivity involves cytotoxic reactions to drugs. Although the molecules of such drugs as quinine, penicillin, or sulfanilamide are too small to trigger an

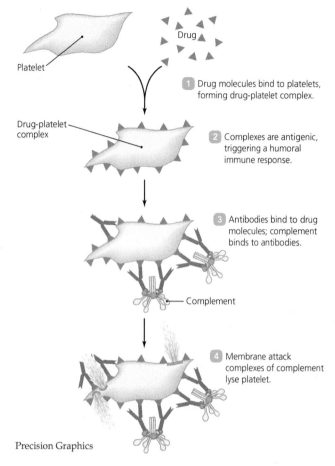

1  Drug molecules bind to platelets, forming drug-platelet complex.

2  Complexes are antigenic, triggering a humoral immune response.

3  Antibodies bind to drug molecules; complement binds to antibodies.

4  Membrane attack complexes of complement lyse platelet.

Precision Graphics

▲ **Figure 7 Events in the development of immune thrombocytopenic purpura.** This disease results from a drug-induced type II (cytotoxic) hypersensitivity reaction. The destruction of platelets through the action of bound antibodies and complement produces the inhibition of blood clotting characteristic of this disease. *What similar disease results from type II (cytotoxic) destruction of red blood cells?*

**Figure 7** *Hemolytic anemia is the type II (cytotoxic) destruction of red blood cells.*

immune response by themselves, they can be *haptens;* that is, when they bind to larger molecules, they become antigenic and stimulate production of antibodies (a humoral immune response).

When such antibodies and then complement bind to drug molecules already bound to blood platelets, the platelets are lysed, producing a disease called **immune thrombocytopenic[4] purpura** (throm′bō-sī-tō-pē′nik pūr′pū-ră) (Figure 7). The destruction of the platelets inhibits the ability of the blood to clot correctly, which leads to the production of purple hemorrhages, called *purpura*[5] (pŭr′poo-ră), under the skin. Similar destruction

---

[4] *Thrombocyte* is another name for platelet.
[5] From Latin, meaning purple.

of leukocytes is one form of *agranulocytosis,* and that of red blood cells is called *hemolytic anemia* (ă-nē′mē-ă).

## Type III (Immune Complex–Mediated) Hypersensitivity

### Learning Objectives

✓  Outline the basic mechanism of type III hypersensitivity.

✓  Describe hypersensitivity pneumonitis and glomerulonephritis.

✓  List the signs and symptoms of rheumatoid arthritis.

✓  Discuss the cause and signs of systemic lupus erythematosus.

The formation of complexes of antigen bound to antibody, called **immune complexes,** initiates several molecular processes, including complement activation. Normally, immune complexes are eliminated from the body via phagocytosis. However, in *type III (immune complex–mediated) hypersensitivity* reactions, the immune complexes escape phagocytosis, and so circulate in the bloodstream until they become trapped in organs, joints, and tissues (such as the walls of blood vessels). In these sites they trigger mast cells to degranulate, releasing inflammatory chemicals that damage the tissues. Figure 8 illustrates the mechanism of type III reactions.

Type III hypersensitivities may be localized or may affect a number of body systems simultaneously. There is no cure for these diseases, though steroids that suppress the immune system may provide some relief. Two localized conditions resulting from immune complex–mediated hypersensitivity are hypersensitivity pneumonitis and glomerulonephritis; two systemic disorders are rheumatoid arthritis and systemic lupus erythematosus.

### Hypersensitivity Pneumonitis

Type III hypersensitivities can affect the lungs, causing a form of pneumonia called **hypersensitivity pneumonitis** (noo-mō-nī′tus). Individuals become sensitized when minute mold spores or other antigens are inhaled deep into the lungs, stimulating the production of antibodies. A hypersensitivity reaction occurs when the subsequent inhalation of the same antigen stimulates the formation of immune complexes that then activate complement.

One form of hypersensitivity pneumonitis, called *farmer's lung,* occurs in farmers chronically exposed to spores from moldy hay. Many other syndromes in humans develop via a similar mechanism and are usually named after the source of the inhaled allergen. Thus, *pigeon breeder's lung* arises following exposure to the dust from pigeon feces, *mushroom grower's lung* is a response to the soil or fungal spores encounted when cultivating mushrooms, and *librarian's lung* results from inhalation of dust from old books.

### Glomerulonephritis

**Glomerulonephritis** (glō-mār′ū-lō-nef-rī′tis) occurs when immune complexes circulating in the bloodstream are deposited in the walls of *glomeruli,* which are networks of minute blood

> **Figure 8 The mechanism of type III (immune complex–mediated) hypersensitivity.** After immune complexes form (**1**), the complexes that are not phagocytized lodge in certain tissues (in this case, the wall of a blood vessel) (**2**). Trapped complexes then activate complement (**3**), which attracts and activates neutrophils (**4**). The release of inflammatory chemicals from the activated neutrophils leads to the destruction of tissue (**5**).

vessels in the kidneys. Immune complexes damage the glomerular cells, leading to enhanced local production of cytokines that stimulate nearby cells to produce more of the intercellular proteins that underlie the cells, impeding blood filtration. Sometimes, the immune complexes are deposited in the center of the glomeruli, where they stimulate local cells to proliferate and compress nearby blood vessels, again interfering with kidney function. The net result is kidney failure; the glomeruli lose their ability to filter wastes from the blood, ultimately resulting in death.

## Rheumatoid Arthritis

**Rheumatoid arthritis** (roo′mă-toyd ar-thrī′tis) commences when B cells secrete IgM that binds to certain IgG molecules. IgM-IgG complexes are deposited in the joints, where they activate complement and mast cells, which release inflammatory chemicals. The resulting inflammation causes the tissues to swell, thicken, and proliferate into the joint, resulting in severe pain. As the altered tissue extends into the joint, the inflammation further erodes and destroys joint cartilage and the neighboring bony structure, until the joints begin to break down and fuse; as a result, affected joints become distorted and lose their range of motion (Figure 9). The course of rheumatoid arthritis is often intermittent; however, with each recurrence, the lesions and damage get progressively more severe.

The trigger of rheumatoid arthritis is not well understood. The fact that there are no animal models (because the disease appears to affect humans only) significantly hinders research on its cause. Many cases demonstrate that rheumatoid arthritis commonly follows an infectious disease in a genetically susceptible individual. Possession of certain MHC genes appears to increase susceptibility.

Physicians treat rheumatoid arthritis by administering anti-inflammatory drugs such as ibuprofen to prevent additional joint damage and immunosuppressive drugs to inhibit the humoral immune response.

## Systemic Lupus Erythematosus

An example of type III hypersensitivity disease that affects multiple organs is **systemic lupus erythematosus** (loo′pŭs er-ĭ-thē′mă-tō-sus) **(SLE)**, often shortened to *lupus*. Patients with this generalized immunological disorder make antibodies against numerous self-antigens found in normal organs and tissues, giving rise to many different pathological lesions and clinical manifestations. One consistent feature of SLE is the

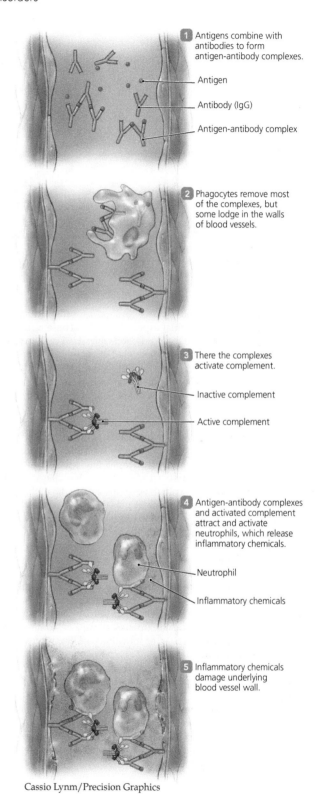

**1** Antigens combine with antibodies to form antigen-antibody complexes.

— Antigen

— Antibody (IgG)

— Antigen-antibody complex

**2** Phagocytes remove most of the complexes, but some lodge in the walls of blood vessels.

**3** There the complexes activate complement.

— Inactive complement

— Active complement

**4** Antigen-antibody complexes and activated complement attract and activate neutrophils, which release inflammatory chemicals.

— Neutrophil

— Inflammatory chemicals

**5** Inflammatory chemicals damage underlying blood vessel wall.

Cassio Lynm/Precision Graphics

243

P. Marazzi/Photo Researchers

▲ **Figure 9** The crippling distortion of joints characteristic of rheumatoid arthritis.

A. Doria and R. Rondinone, Dept. of Rheumatology, University of Padova, Italy

▲ **Figure 10** The characteristic facial rash of systemic lupus erythematosus. Its shape corresponds to areas most exposed to sunlight, which worsens the condition.

development of such self-reactive antibodies, called autoantibodies, against nucleic acids, especially DNA. These autoantibodies combine with free DNA released from dead cells to form immune complexes that are deposited in glomeruli, causing glomerulonephritis and kidney failure. Thus, SLE is an immune complex–mediated hypersensitivity reaction. Immune complexes may also be deposited in joints, where they give rise to arthritis.

The disease's curious name—systemic lupus erythematosus—stems from two features of the disease: *Systemic* simply reflects the fact that it affects different organs throughout the body; *lupus* is Latin for wolf, and *erythematosus* refers to a redness of the skin, so these latter two words describe the characteristic red, butterfly-shaped rash that develops on the face of many patients, giving them what is sometimes described as a wolflike appearance (Figure 10). This rash is caused by deposition of nucleic acid–antibody complexes in the skin and is worse in skin areas exposed to sunlight.

Although autoantibodies to nucleic acids are characteristic of SLE, many other autoantibodies are also produced. Autoantibodies to red blood cells cause hemolytic anemia; autoantibodies to platelets give rise to bleeding disorders; antilymphocyte antibodies alter immune reactivity; and autoantibodies against muscle cells cause muscle inflammation and, in some cases, damage to the heart. Because of its variety of symptoms, SLE can be misdiagnosed.

The trigger of lupus is unknown, though a lupus-like disease can be induced by some drugs. It is likely that SLE has many causes.

Physicians treat lupus with immunosuppressive drugs that reduce autoantibody formation and with glucocorticoids that reduce the inflammation associated with the deposition of immune complexes. Scientists are currently testing a battery of novel drugs for treating lupus.

# Type IV (Delayed or Cell-Mediated) Hypersensitivity

## Learning Objectives

✓ Outline the mechanism of type IV hypersensitivity.

✓ Describe the significance of the tuberculin test.

✓ Identify four types of grafts.

✓ Compare four types of drugs commonly used to prevent graft rejection.

When certain antigens contact the skin of sensitized individuals, they provoke inflammation that begins to develop at the site only after 12–24 hours. Such **delayed hypersensitivity reactions** result not from the action of antibodies but rather from interactions among antigen, antigen-presenting cells, and T cells; thus, a type IV reaction is also called *cell-mediated hypersensitivity.* The delay in this cell-mediated response reflects the time it takes for macrophages and T cells to migrate to and proliferate at the site of the antigen. We begin our discussion of type IV reactions by considering two common examples: the tuberculin response and allergic contact dermatitis. Then we discuss two type IV hypersensitivity reactions involving the interactions between the body and tissues grafted to (transplanted into) it—graft rejection and graft-versus-host disease—before considering donor-recipient matching and tissue typing.

### The Tuberculin Response

The **tuberculin** (too-ber′kū-lin) **response** is an important example of a delayed hypersensitivity reaction in which the skin of an individual exposed to tuberculosis or tuberculosis vaccine reacts to a subcutaneous injection of *tuberculin*—a protein solution obtained from *Mycobacterium tuberculosis* (mī′kō-bak-tēr′ē-ŭm too-ber-kyū-lō′sis). Health care providers use the tuberculin test, also called a

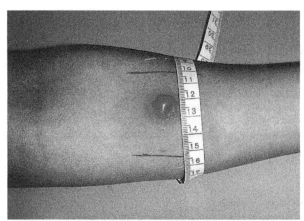

Princess Margaret Hospital/Dept. of Pediatrics

▲ **Figure 11** **A positive tuberculin test.** The hard, red swelling 10 mm or greater in diameter that is characteristic of the tuberculin response indicates that the individual has been vaccinated against *Mycobacterium tuberculosis* or is now or has been previously infected with the bacterium.

*Mantoux* (mahn-too′) *test* after the French physician who perfected it, to diagnose contact with antigens of *M. tuberculosis*.

When tuberculin is injected into the skin of a healthy, never-infected or unvaccinated individual, no response occurs. In contrast, when tuberculin is injected into someone currently or previously infected with *M. tuberculosis* or an individual previously immunized with tuberculosis vaccine, a red, hard swelling (10 mm or greater in diameter) indicating a positive tuberculin test develops at the site (Figure 11). Such inflammation reaches its greatest intensity within 24–72 hours and may persist for several weeks before fading. Microscopic examination of the lesion reveals that it is infiltrated with lymphocytes and macrophages.

A tuberculin response is mediated by memory T cells. When an individual is first infected by or immunized against *M. tuberculosis*, the resulting cell-mediated immune response generates memory T cells that persist in the body. When a sensitized individual is subsequently injected with tuberculin, phagocytic cells migrate to the site and attract memory T cells, which secrete a mixture of cytokines that attract still more T cells and macrophages, giving rise to a slowly developing inflammation. The macrophages ingest and destroy the injected tuberculin, allowing the tissues eventually to return to normal.

### Allergic Contact Dermatitis

*Urushiol* (ŭ-rū′shē-ŏl), the oil of poison ivy (*Toxicodendron radicans*, toks′si-kō-den′dron rā′dē-kanz) and related plants, is a highly reactive hapten that binds to almost any protein it contacts—including proteins in the skin of anyone who rubs against the plant. The body regards these chemically modified skin proteins as foreign, triggering a cell-mediated immune response and resulting in an intensely irritating skin rash called **allergic contact dermatitis** (der-mă-tī′tis). In severe cases,

Seelevel.com

▲ **Figure 12** **Allergic contact dermatitis, a type IV hypersensitivity response.** The response in this case is to poison ivy. Note the large, acellular, fluid-filled blisters that result from the destruction of skin cells.

Tc cells destroy so many skin cells that acellular, fluid-filled blisters develop (Figure 12).

Other haptens that combine chemically with skin proteins can also induce allergic contact dermatitis. Examples include formaldehyde; some cosmetics, dyes, drugs, and metal ions; and chemicals used in the production of latex for hospital gloves and tubing.

Because T cells mediate allergic contact dermatitis, epinephrine and other drugs used for the treatment of immediate hypersensitivity reactions are ineffective. T cell activities and inflammation can, however, be suppressed by corticosteroid treatment. Good strategies for dealing with exposure to poison ivy include washing the area thoroughly and immediately with a strong soap and washing all exposed clothes as soon as possible.

### Graft Rejection

A special case of type IV hypersensitivity is the rejection of **grafts** (or transplants), which are tissues or organs, such as livers, kidneys, or hearts, that have been transplanted, whether between sites within an individual or between a donor and an unrelated recipient. Even though advances in surgical technique enable surgeons to move grafts freely from site to site, grafts perceived as foreign by a recipient undergo rejection, a highly destructive phenomenon that can severely limit the success of organ and tissue transplantation. Graft rejection is a normal immune response against foreign major histocompatibility complex (MHC) proteins on the surface of graft cells. The likelihood of graft rejection depends on the degree to which the graft is foreign to the recipient, which in turn is related to the type of graft.

Scientists name graft types according to the degree of relatedness between the donor and the recipient (Figure 13). A graft is called an **autograft** (aw′tō-graft) when tissues are moved to a different location within the same individual. Autografts do not trigger immune responses because they do not express foreign antigens. Examples of autografts include the grafting of

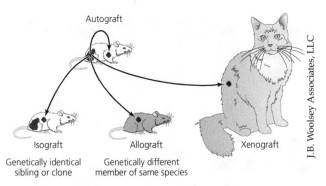

**▲ Figure 13 Types of grafts.** The names are based on the degree of relatedness between donor and recipient. Autografts are grafts moved from one location to another within a single individual. In isografts, the donor and recipient are either genetically identical siblings or clones. In allografts, the donor and recipient are genetically distinct individuals of the same species. In xenografts, the donor and recipient are of different species.

J.B. Woolsey Associates, LLC

skin from one area of the body to another to cover a burn area, or the use of a leg vein to bypass blocked coronary arteries.

**Isografts** (ī′sō-graftz) are grafts transplanted between two genetically identical individuals; that is, between identical siblings or clones. Because these individuals have identical MHC proteins, the immune system of the recipient cannot differentiate between the grafted cells and its own normal body cells. As a result, isografts are not rejected.

**Allografts** (al′ō-graftz) are grafts transplanted between genetically distinct members of the same species. Most grafts performed in humans are allografts. Because the MHC proteins of the allograft are different from those of the recipient, allografts typically induce a strong type IV hypersensitivity, resulting in graft rejection. Rejection must be suppressed with immunosuppressive drugs if the graft is to survive.

**Xenografts** (zēn′ō-graftz) are grafts transplanted between individuals of different species. Thus, the transplant of a baboon's heart into a human is a xenograft. Because xenografts are usually very different from the tissues of the recipient, both biochemically and immunologically, they usually provoke a rapid, intense rejection that is very difficult to suppress. Therefore, xenografts from mature animals are not commonly used therapeutically.

### Graft-Versus-Host Disease

Physicians often use bone marrow allografts as a component of the treatment for leukemias and lymphomas (cancers of leukocytes). In this procedure, physicians use total body irradiation combined with cytotoxic drugs to kill tumor cells in the patient's bone marrow. In the process, the patient's existing leukocytes are also destroyed, which completely eliminates the body's ability to mount any kind of immune response. Physicians then inject the patient with donated bone marrow which

produces a new set of leukocytes. Ideally, within a few months, a fully functioning bone marrow is restored.

Unfortunately, when they are transplanted, donated bone marrow T cells may regard the patient's cells as foreign, mounting an immune response against them and giving rise to a condition called **graft-versus-host disease.** If the donor and recipient mainly differ in MHC class I molecules, the grafted T cells attack all of the recipient's tissues, producing especially destructive lesions in the skin and intestine. If the donor and recipient differ mainly in MHC class II molecules, then the grafted T cells attack the antigen-presenting cells of the host, leading to immunosuppression and leaving the recipient vulnerable to infections. The same immunosuppressive drugs used to prevent graft rejection (discussed shortly) can limit graft-versus-host disease.

### Donor-Recipient Matching and Tissue Typing

Although it is usually not difficult to ensure that donor and recipient have identical blood groups, MHC compatibility is much harder to achieve. The reason is the very high degree of MHC variability, which ensures that unrelated individuals differ widely in their MHCs. In general, the more closely donor and recipient are related, the smaller their MHC difference. Given that in most cases an identical sibling is not available, it is usually preferable that grafts be donated by a parent or sibling possessing MHC antigens similar to those of the recipient.

In practice, of course, closely related donors are not always available. And even though a paired organ (such as a kidney) or a portion of an organ (such as liver tissue) may be available from a living donor, unpaired organs (such as the heart) almost always come from an unrelated cadaver. In such cases, attempts are made to match donor and recipient as closely as possible by means of *tissue typing.* Physicians examine the white cells of potential graft recipients to determine what MHC proteins they have. When a donor organ becomes available, it too is typed. Then the individual whose MHC proteins most closely match those of the donor is chosen to receive the graft. Though a perfect match is rarely achieved, the closer the match, the less intense the rejection process, and the greater the chance of successful grafting. A match of 50% or less of the MHC proteins is usually acceptable for most organs, but near absolute matches are required for successful bone marrow transplants.

Table 3 summarizes the major characteristics of the four types of hypersensitivity.

### CRITICAL **THINKING**

A patient arrives at the doctor's office with a rash covering her legs. How could you determine whether the rash is a type I or a type IV hypersensitivity?

Next we turn our attention to the actions of various types of immunosuppressive drugs used in situations in which the immune system is overactive.

## TABLE 3 — The Characteristics of the Four Types of Hypersensitivity Reactions

| Descriptive | Name | Cause | Time Course | Characteristic Cells Involved |
|---|---|---|---|---|
| Type I | Immediate hypersensitivity | Antibody (IgE) on sensitized cells' membranes binds antigen, causing degranulation | Seconds to minutes | Mast cells, basophils, and eosinophils |
| Type II | Cytotoxic hypersensitivity | Antibodies and complement lyse target cells | Minutes to hours | Red blood cells |
| Type III | Immune complex–mediated hypersensitivity | Nonphagocytized complexes of antibodies and antigens trigger mast cell degranulation | Several hours | Neutrophils |
| Type IV | Delayed hypersensitivity | T cells attack the body's cells | Several days | Activated T cells |

### The Actions of Immunosuppressive Drugs

The development of potent immunosuppressive drugs has played a large role in the dramatic success of modern transplantation procedures. These drugs can also be effective in combating certain autoimmune diseases (discussed shortly). In the following discussion we consider four classes of immunosuppressive drugs: glucocorticoids, cytotoxic drugs, cylosporine, and lymphocyte-depleting therapies.

**Glucocorticoids,** sometimes called *corticosteroids* and commonly referred to as steroids, have been used as immunosuppressive agents for many years. Glucocorticoids such as *prednisone* (pred'ni-sōn) and *methylprednisolone* suppress the response of T cells to antigen and inhibit such mechanisms as T cell cytotoxicity and cytokine production. These drugs have a much smaller effect on B cell function.

**Cytotoxic** (sī-tō-tok'sik) **drugs** inhibit mitosis and cytokinesis (cell division). Given that lymphocyte proliferation is a key feature of specific immunity, blocking cellular reproduction is a potent, although very nonspecific, method of immunosuppression. Among the cytotoxic drugs that have been used, the following are noteworthy:

- *Cyclophosphamide* (sī-klō-fos'fă-mīd) cross-links daughter DNA molecules in mitotic cells, preventing their separation and blocking mitosis. It impairs both B cell and T cell responses.
- *Azathioprine* (ā-ză-thī'ō-prēn) is a purine analog; it competes with purines during the synthesis of nucleic acids, thus blocking DNA replication and suppressing both primary and secondary antibody responses.

Three other cytotoxic drugs used for immunosuppression include *mycophenolate mofetil,* which inhibits purine synthesis, and *brequinar sodium* and *leflunomide,* which each inhibit pyrimidine synthesis and thereby inhibit cellular replication.

Drugs such as **cyclosporine** (sī-klō-spōr'ēn), a polypeptide derived from fungi, prevent production of interleukins and interferons by T cells, thereby blocking Th1 responses. Because cyclosporine acts only on activated T cells and has no effect on resting T cells, it is far less toxic than the nonspecific drugs previously described. When it is given to prevent allograft rejection, only activated T cells attacking the graft are suppressed.

Because steroids have a similar effect, the combination of glucocorticoids and cyclosporine is especially potent and can enhance survival of allografts.

Scientists have developed techniques involving relatively specific *lymphocyte-depleting therapies* in an attempt to reduce the many adverse side effects associated with the use of less-specific immunosuppressive drugs. One technique involves administering an antiserum called *antilymphocyte globulin,* which is specific for lymphocytes. Another, more specific antilymphocyte technique uses monoclonal antibodies against CD3, which is found only on T cells. An even more specific monoclonal antibody is directed against the interleukin 2 receptor (IL-2R), which is expressed mainly on activated T cells. Such immunosuppressive therapies are effective in reversing graft rejection. Because they target a narrow range of cells, they produce fewer undesirable side effects than less-specific drugs.

Table 4 lists some drugs, and their actions, for each of the four classes of the immunosuppressive drugs.

# Autoimmune Diseases

Just as today's military must control its arsenal of sophisticated weapons to avert losses of its own soldiers from "friendly fire," the immune system must be carefully regulated so that it does not damage the body's own tissues. However, an immune system does occasionally produce antibodies and cytotoxic T cells that target normal body cells—a phenomenon called *autoimmunity.* Although such responses are not always damaging, they can give rise to **autoimmune diseases,** some of which are life threatening.

## Causes of Autoimmune Diseases

### Learning Objective

✓ Briefly discuss seven hypotheses concerning the causes of autoimmunity and autoimmune diseases.

Most autoimmune diseases appear to develop spontaneously and at random, with no obvious predisposing factor. Nevertheless, scientists have noted some common features of autoimmune disease. For example, they occur more often in older individuals, and they are also much more common in women

## 4 The Four Classes of Immunosuppressive Drugs

| Class | Examples | Action |
|---|---|---|
| Glucocorticoids | Prednisone, methylprednisolone | Anti-inflammatory; kills T cells |
| Cytotoxic drugs | Cyclophosphamide, azathioprine, mycophenolate mofetil, brequinar sodium, leflunomide | Blocks cell division nonspecifically |
| Cyclosporine | Cyclosporine | Blocks T cell responses |
| Lymphocyte-depleting therapies | Antilymphocyte globulin, monoclonal antibodies | Kills T cells nonspecifically, kills activated T cells, inhibits IL–2 reception |

than in men, although the reasons for this gender difference are unclear.

Hypotheses to explain the etiology of autoimmunity abound. They include the following:

- Estrogen may stimulate the destruction of tissues by cytotoxic T cells.

- During pregnancy, some maternal cells may cross the placenta and colonize the fetus. These cells are more likely to survive in a daughter than in a son and might trigger an autoimmune disease later in the daughter's life.

- Conversely, fetal cells may also cross the placenta and trigger autoimmunity in the mother.

- Environmental factors may contribute to the development of autoimmune disorders. Some autoimmune diseases—type I diabetes mellitus (dī-ă-bē'tēz mĕ-lī'tĕs) and rheumatoid arthritis, for example—develop in a few patients following their recovery from viral infections, though other individuals who develop these diseases have no history of such viral infections.

- Genetic factors may play a role in autoimmune diseases. MHC genes that in some way promote autoimmunity are found in individuals with autoimmune diseases, whereas MHC genes that somehow protect against autoimmunity may dominate in other individuals. MHC genes may also determine susceptibility to autoimmune disease by regulating the elimination of self-reactive T cells in the thymus.

- Some autoimmune diseases develop when T cells encounter self-antigens that are normally "hidden" in sites where T cells rarely go. For example, because sperm develop within the testes during puberty, long after the body has selected its T cell population, men may have T cells that recognize their own sperm as foreign. This is normally of little consequence because sperm are sequestered from the blood. But if the testes are injured, T cells may enter the site of damage and mount an autoimmune response against the sperm, resulting in infertility.

- Infections with a variety of microorganisms may trigger autoimmunity as a result of **molecular mimicry,** which occurs when an infectious agent has an epitope that is very similar or identical to a self-antigen. In responding to the invader, the body produces antibodies that are *autoantibodies* (antibodies against self-antigens), which

damage body tissues. For example, children infected with some strains of *Streptococcus pyogenes* (strep-tō-kok'ŭs pī-oj'en-ēz) may produce antibodies to heart muscle and so develop heart disease. Other strains of streptococci trigger the production of antibodies that cross-react with glomerular basement membranes and so cause kidney disease. It is possible that some virally triggered autoimmune diseases may also result from molecular mimicry.

- Other autoimmune responses may result from failure of the normal control mechanisms of the immune system. Thus even though harmful, self-reactive T lymphocytes are normally destroyed via apoptosis triggered through the cell-surface receptor CD95 defects in CD95 can cause autoimmunity by permitting abnormal T cells to survive and cause disease.

## Examples of Autoimmune Diseases

### Learning Objective

✓ Describe a serious autoimmune disease associated with each of the following: blood cells, endocrine glands, nervous tissue, and connective tissue.

Regardless of the specific mechanism that causes an autoimmune disease, immunologists categorize them into two major categories: systemic autoimmune diseases such as lupus (discussed previously) and single-organ autoimmune diseases, which affect a single organ or tissue. Among the many single-organ autoimmune diseases recognized, common examples affect blood cells, endocrine glands, nervous tissue, or connective tissue.

### Autoimmunity Affecting Blood Cells

Individuals with **autoimmune hemolytic anemia** produce antibodies against their own red blood cells. These autoantibodies hasten the destruction of the red blood cells, and the patient becomes severely anemic. Different hemolytic anemia patients make antibodies of different classes. Some patients make IgM autoantibodies, which bind to red blood cells and activate the classical complement pathway; the red blood cells are lysed, and degration products from hemoglobin are released into the bloodstream. Other hemolytic anemia patients make IgG autoantibodies, which serve as opsonins that promote phagocytosis. In this case, red blood cells are removed by macrophages in the liver, spleen, and bone marrow. Even though these latter patients have no hemoglobin in their urine, they are still severely anemic.

The precise causes of all cases of autoimmune hemolytic anemia are unknown, but some cases follow infections with viruses or treatment with certain drugs, both of which alter the surface of red blood cells such that they are recognized as foreign and trigger an immune response.

### Autoimmunity Affecting Endocrine Organs

Other common targets of autoimmune attack are the endocrine (hormone-producing) organs. For example, patients can develop autoantibodies or produce T cells against cells of the islets of Langerhans within the pancreas or against cells of the thyroid gland. In most cases, the ensuing autoimmune reaction results in damage to or destruction of the gland and in hormone deficiencies as endocrine cells are killed.

Immunological attack on the islets of Langerhans results in a loss of the ability to produce the hormone *insulin*, which leads to the development of **type I diabetes mellitus** (also known as *juvenile-onset diabetes*). As with other autoimmune diseases, the exact trigger of type I diabetes is unknown, but many patients endured a severe viral infection some months before the onset of diabetes. Additionally, some patients are known to have a genetic predisposition to developing type I diabetes that is associated with the possession of certain class I MHC molecules. Some physicians have been successful in delaying the onset of type I diabetes by treating at-risk patients with immunosuppressive drugs before damage to the islets of Langerhans becomes apparent.

An autoimmune response can lead to stimulation rather than to inhibition or destruction of glandular tissue. An example of this is **Graves' disease,** which involves the thyroid gland. This major endocrine gland located in the neck secretes iodine-containing hormones, which help regulate metabolic rate in the body. Like other autoimmune diseases, Graves' disease may be triggered by a viral infection in individuals with certain genetic backgrounds. Affected patients (usually women) make autoantibodies that bind to and stimulate receptors on the cytoplasmic membranes of thyroid cells, which elicits excessive production of thyroid hormone and growth of the thyroid gland. Such patients develop an enlarged thyroid gland—called a goiter—protruding eyes, rapid heartbeat, fatigue, and weight loss despite increased appetite. Physicians treat Graves' disease with antithyroid medicines, radioactive iodine, or, in nonresponsive patients, by surgically removing most of the thyroid tissue.

### Autoimmunity Affecting Nervous Tissue

Of the group of autoimmune diseases affecting nervous tissue, the most frequent is **multiple sclerosis** (sklĕ-rō'sis) **(MS).** The exact cause of MS is unknown, but it appears that a cell-mediated immune response against a bacterium or virus generates cytotoxic T cells that mistakenly attack and destroy the myelin sheaths that normally insulate brain and spinal cord neurons and increase the speed of nerve impulses along the length of the

neurons. Consequently, MS patients experience deficits in vision, speech, and neuromuscular function that may be quite mild and intermittent or may ultimately lead to death.

### Autoimmunity Affecting Connective Tissue

Rheumatoid arthritis (discussed previously) is another crippling autoimmune disease resulting from a type III hypersensitivity. Autoantibodies are formed against connective tissue in joints.

CRITICAL **THINKING**

A 43-year-old woman has been diagnosed with rheumatoid arthritis. Unable to find relief from her symptoms, she seeks treatment from a doctor in another country who injects antibodies and complement into her afflicted joints. Do you expect the treatment to improve her condition? Explain your reasoning.

# Immunodeficiency Diseases

## Learning Objective

✓ Differentiate between primary and acquired immunodeficiencies, and cite one disease caused by each form of immunodeficiency.

You may have noticed that during periods of increased emotional or physical stress you are more likely to succumb to a cold or a bout of the flu. You are not imagining this phenomenon; stress has long been known to decrease the efficiency of the immune system. Similarly, chronic defects in the immune system typically first become apparent when affected individuals show increased susceptibility to infections of opportunistic pathogens (or even of organisms not normally considered pathogens). Such opportunistic infections are the hallmarks of *immunodeficiency diseases,* which are conditions resulting from defective immune mechanisms.

Researchers have characterized a large number of immunodeficiency diseases in humans, which are of two general types:

- **Primary immunodeficiency diseases,** which are detectable near birth and develop in infants and young children, result from some genetic or developmental defect.

- **Acquired (secondary) immunodeficiency diseases** develop in later life as a direct consequence of some other recognized cause, such as malnutrition, severe stress, or infectious disease.

Next we consider each general type of immunodeficiency disease in turn.

## Primary Immunodeficiency Diseases

Many different inherited defects have been identified in all of the body's lines of defense, affecting first and second lines of defense as well as humoral and cell-mediated immune responses.

## SCID: "BUBBLE BOY" DISEASE

As a result of the widely publicized case of David Vetter—a Houston, Texas, resident commonly known as the "bubble boy" because he lived from birth until age 12 in a sterile, plastic-enclosed environment —*severe combined immunodeficiency disease (SCID)* has been known as "bubble boy" disease since the 1970s. Like all SCID patients, David had no immune system—his body produced neither B cells nor T cells—so the slightest infection could be lethal. As a result, contact with him could occur only through a pair of antiseptic rubber gloves built into one of the walls of his plastic enclosure. At age 12, David underwent an experimental bone marrow transplant in the hope that marrow donated by his older sister would enable him to build up an immune system. Unfortunately, the donated cells turned out to be infected with Epstein-Barr virus (a common virus that causes mononucleosis), ultimately killing David.

Today, there is much more hope for patients with SCID. Virus-free bone marrow transplants are now possible. More recently, more than 20 children have undergone gene therapy, in which the gene for an enzyme (adenine deaminase) missing in SCID patients is inserted, via retroviral vectors, into clones of the patient's bone marrow cells. These genetically altered cells are then returned to the child, where they grow and synthesize sufficient enzyme to normalize the immune response. Though successful in several children studied in a French trial, the therapy was halted in 2002 after three children developed leukemia following treatment. Investigations into whether or not the illness was caused by the gene therapy are under way; however,

▲ *David Vetter.*    NASA

scientists remain hopeful that gene therapy can achieve a cure for SCID—without side effects—in the near future.

---

One of the more important inherited defects in the second line of defense is **chronic granulomatous disease,** in which children have recurrent infections characterized by the inability of their phagocytes to destroy bacteria. The reason is that these children have an inherited inability to make reactive forms of oxygen, which are necessary to destroy phagocytized bacteria.

Most primary immunodeficiencies are associated with defects in the components of the third line of defense—adaptive immunity. For example, some children fail to develop any lymphoid stem cells whatsoever, and as a result they produce neither B cells nor T cells and cannot mount immune responses. The resulting defects in the immune system cause **severe combined immunodeficiency disease (SCID),** which is discussed in **Highlight: SCID: "Bubble Boy" Disease.**

Other children suffer from T cell deficiencies alone. For example, **DiGeorge syndrome** results from a failure of the thymus to develop. Consequently, there are no T cells. The importance of T cells in protecting against viruses is emphasized by the observation that individuals with DiGeorge syndrome generally die of viral infections while remaining resistant to most bacteria. Physicians treat DiGeorge syndrome with a thymic stem cell transplant.

B cell deficiencies also occur in children. The most severe of the B cell deficiencies, called **Bruton-type agammaglobulinemia**[6] (ā-gam′ă-glob′ū-li-nē′mē-ă), is an inherited disease in which

[6]Agammaglobulinemia means an absence of gamma globulin (IgG).

affected babies, usually boys, cannot make immunoglobulins. These children experience recurrent bacterial infections but are usually resistant to viral, fungal, and protozoan infections.

Inherited deficiencies of individual immunoglobulin classes are more common than a deficiency of all classes. Among these, IgA deficiency is the most common. Because affected children cannot produce secretory IgA, they experience recurrent infections in the respiratory and gastrointestinal tracts.

### CRITICAL THINKING

Two boys have autoimmune diseases: One has Bruton-type agammaglobulinemia, and the other has DiGeorge syndrome. On a camping trip, each boy is stung by a bee and each falls into poison ivy. What hypersensitivity reactions might each boy experience as a result of his camping mishaps?

Table 5 summarizes the major primary immunodeficiency diseases.

## Acquired Immunodeficiency Diseases

Unlike inherited primary immunodeficiency diseases, acquired immunodeficiency diseases affect older individuals who had a previously healthy immune system.

## 5

### Some Primary Immunodeficiency Diseases

| Disease | Defect | Manifestation |
|---|---|---|
| Chronic granulomatous disease | Ineffective phagocytes | Uncontrolled infections |
| Severe combined immunodeficiency disease (SCID) | A lack of T cells and B cells | No resistance to any type of infection, leading to rapid death |
| Bruton-type agammaglobulinemia | A lack of B cells and thus a lack of immunoglobulins | Death from overwhelming bacterial infections |
| DiGeorge syndrome | A lack of T cells and thus no cell-mediated immunity | Death from overwhelming viral infections |

Acquired immunodeficiencies result from a number of causes. In all humans the immune system (but especially T cell production) deteriorates with increasing age; as a result, older individuals normally have less effective immunity, especially cell-mediated immunity, than younger individuals, leading to an increased incidence of both viral diseases and certain types of cancer. Severe stress can also lead to immunodeficiencies by prompting the secretion of increased quantities of glucocorticoids, which are toxic to T cells and thus suppress cell-mediated immunity. This is why, for example, cold sores may "break out" on the faces of students during final exams: the causative herpes simplex viruses, which are controlled by a fully functioning cell-mediated immune response, escape immune control in stressed individuals. Malnutrition and certain environmental toxins can also cause acquired immunodeficiency diseases by inhibiting the normal production of B cells and T cells.

Of course, the most significant example of the result of an acquired immunodeficiency is **acquired immunodeficiency syndrome (AIDS).** From the time of its discovery in 1981 to its emergence as a worldwide pandemic, no affliction has affected modern life as much.

AIDS is not a single disease but a **syndrome;** that is, a group of signs, symptoms, and diseases associated with a common pathology. Currently, epidemiologists define this syndrome as the presence of several opportunistic or rare infections associated with a severe decrease in the number of CD4 cells and a positive test showing the presence of human immunodeficiency virus (HIV). The infections include diseases of the skin, such as shingles and herpes; diseases of the nervous system, including meningitis, toxoplasmosis, and *Cytomegalovirus* (sī-tō-meg′ă-lō-vī′rŭs) disease; diseases of the respiratory system, such as tuberculosis, *Pneumocystis* (nū-mō-sis′ tis) pneumonia, histoplasmosis, and coccidioidomycosis; and diseases of the digestive system, including chronic diarrhea, thrush, and oral hairy leukoplakia. A rare cancer of blood vessels called Kaposi's sarcoma is also commonly seen in AIDS patients. AIDS often results in dementia during the final stages.

## Chapter Summary

1. Immunological responses may give rise to inflammatory reactions called **hypersensitivities.** An immunological attack on normal tissues gives rise to autoimmune disorders. A failure of the immune system to function normally may give rise to **immunodeficiency diseases.**

### Hypersensitivities

1. Type I hypersensitivity gives rise to **allergies.** Antigens that trigger this response are called **allergens.**

2. Allergies result when allergens bind to IgE molecules that are already bound to **mast cells, basophils,** and **eosinophils.** This causes the sensitized cells to degranulate and release **histamine, kinins, proteases, leukotrienes,** and **prostaglandins.**

3. Depending on the amount of these molecules and the site at which they are released, the result can produce various clinical syndromes, including **hay fever, asthma, urticaria** (hives), or various other allergies. When the inflammatory mediators exceed the body's coping mechanisms, **acute anaphylaxis (anaphylactic shock)** may occur. The specific treatment for anaphylaxis is epinephrine.

4. Type I hypersensitivity can be diagnosed by skin testing and can be partially prevented by avoidance of allergens and immunotherapy. Some type I hypersensitivities are treated with **antihistamines.**

5. Type II cytotoxic hypersensitivities, such as incompatible blood transfusions and hemolytic disease of the newborn, result when cells are destroyed by an immune response.

6. Red blood cells have **blood group antigens** on their surface. If incompatible blood is transfused into a recipient, a severe transfusion reaction can result.

7. The most important of the blood group antigens is the ABO group, which is largely responsible for transfusion reactions.

8. Approximately 85% of the human population carries **Rh antigen,** which is also found in rhesus monkeys. If an Rh-negative pregnant woman is carrying an Rh-positive fetus, the fetus may be at risk of **hemolytic disease of the newborn,** in which antibodies made by the mother against the Rh antigen may cross the placenta and destroy the fetus's red blood cells. RhoGAM administered to pregnant Rh– women may prevent this disease.

9. Drugs bound to blood platelets may subsequently bind antibodies and complement, causing **immune thrombocytopenic purpura,** in which the platelets lyse.

10. In type III hypersensitivity, excessive amounts of **immune complexes** are deposited in tissues, where they cause significant tissue damage. Immune complexes deposited in the lung cause a **hypersensitivity pneumonitis,** of which the most common example is farmer's lung. If large amounts of immune complexes form in the bloodstream, they may be filtered out by the glomeruli of the kidney, causing **glomerulonephritis,** which can result in kidney failure.

11. In **rheumatoid arthritis,** immune complexes result in the growth of inflammatory tissue within joints.

12. **Systemic lupus erythematosus** (SLE, lupus) is a systemic, autoimmune, type III hypersensitivity in which autoantibodies bind to many autoantigens, especially the patient's DNA.

13. Type IV hypersensitivity, also known as **delayed hypersensitivity,** is a T cell–mediated inflammatory reaction that takes 24–72 hours to reach maximal intensity.

14. A good example of a delayed hypersensitivity reaction is the **tuberculin response,** generated when tuberculin, a protein extract of *Mycobacterium tuberculosis,* is injected into the skin of an individual who has been infected with or vaccinated against *M. tuberculosis.*

15. Another example of a type IV hypersensitivity reaction is **allergic contact dermatitis,** which is T cell–mediated damage to chemically modified skin cells. The best-known example is a reaction to poison ivy.

16. An organ or tissue **graft** can be made between different sites within a single individual (an **autograft**), between genetically identical individuals (an **isograft**), between genetically dissimilar individuals (an **allograft**), or between individuals of different species (a **xenograft**). Most surgical organ grafting involves allografts, which, if not treated with immunosuppressive drugs, lead to **graft rejection.**

17. In **graft-versus-host disease,** an organ donor's cells attack the recipient's body.

18. Commonly used immunosuppressive drugs include **glucocorticoids, cytotoxic drugs, cyclosporine,** and lymphocyte-depleting therapies, which involve treatment with antibodies against T cells or their receptors.

## Autoimmune Diseases

1. **Autoimmune diseases** may result when an individual begins to make autoantibodies or cytotoxic T cells against normal body components.

2. There are many hypotheses concerning the cause of autoimmune disease. One involves **molecular mimicry,** in which microorganisms with epitopes similar to self-antigens trigger autoimmune tissue damage. Others implicate estrogen, pregnancy, and environmental and genetic factors.

3. One group of autoimmune diseases involve only a single organ or cell type. Examples of such diseases include **autoimmune hemolytic anemia, type I diabetes mellitus, Graves' disease, multiple sclerosis**, and rheumatoid arthritis.

4. A second group of autoimmune diseases, such as systemic lupus erythematosus, involves multiple organs or body systems.

## Immunodeficiency Diseases

1. Immunodeficiency diseases may be classified as **primary immunodeficiency diseases,** which result from mutations or developmental anomalies and occur in young children, and **acquired** or **secondary immunodeficiency diseases,** which result from other known causes such as viral infections.

2. Examples of primary immunodeficiency diseases include **chronic granulomatous disease,** in which a child's neutrophils are incapable of killing ingested bacteria. Inability to produce both T cells and B cells is called **severe combined immunodeficiency disease.** In **DiGeorge syndrome,** the thymus fails to develop. In **Bruton-type agammaglobulinemia,** B cells fail to function.

3. **Acquired immunodeficiency syndrome (AIDS),** a condition marked by the presence of antibodies against HIV in conjunction with certain opportunistic infections, is the most common acquired immunodeficiency disease.

4. A **syndrome** is a complex of signs, symptoms, and diseases with a common cause. AIDS is defined by a presence of a number of opportunistic infections in the presence of antibodies against HIV.

# Questions for Review
*Answers to the Questions for Review (except Short Answer questions) appear at the end of this chapter.*

## Multiple Choice

1. The immunoglobulin class that mediates type I hypersensitivity is
   a. IgA.
   b. IgM.
   c. IgG.
   d. IgD.
   e. IgE.

2. The major inflammatory mediator released by degranulating mast cells in type I hypersensitivity is
   a. immunoglobulin.
   b. complement.
   c. histamine.
   d. interleukin.
   e. prostaglandin.

3. Hemolytic disease of the newborn is caused by antibodies against which major blood group antigen?
   a. MHC protein
   b. MN antigen
   c. ABO antigen
   d. rhesus antigen
   e. type II protein

4. Farmer's lung is a hypersensitivity pneumonitis resulting from
   a. a type I hypersensitivity reaction to grass pollen.
   b. a type II hypersensitivity to red cells in the lung.
   c. a type III hypersensitivity to mold spores.
   d. a type IV hypersensitivity to bacterial antigens.
   e. none of the above

5. A positive tuberculin skin test indicates that a patient not immunized against tuberculosis
   a. is free of tuberculosis.
   b. is shedding *Mycobacterium*.
   c. has been exposed to tuberculosis antigens.
   d. is susceptible to tuberculosis.
   e. is resistant to tuberculosis.

6. Which of the following is an autoimmune disease?
   a. a heart attack
   b. acute anaphylaxis
   c. farmer's lung
   d. graft-versus-host disease
   e. systemic lupus erythematosus

7. When a surgeon conducts a cardiac bypass operation by transplanting a piece of vein from a patient's leg to the same patient's heart, this is
   a. a rejected graft.
   b. an autograft.
   c. an allograft.
   d. a type IV hypersensitivity.
   e. a cardiograft.

8. A deficiency of both B cells and T cells is most likely
   a. a secondary immunodeficiency.
   b. a complex immunodeficiency.
   c. an acquired immunodeficiency.
   d. a primary immunodeficiency.
   e. an induced immunodeficiency.

9. Infection with HIV causes
   a. primary immunodeficiency disease.
   b. acquired hypersensitivity syndrome.
   c. acquired immunodeficiency syndrome.
   d. anaphylactic immunodeficiency diseases.
   e. combined immunodeficiency diseases.

10. What do medical personnel administer to counteract various type I hypersensitivities?
    a. antihistamine
    b. bronchodilator
    c. glucocorticoid
    d. epinephrine
    e. all of the above

## Modified True/False

Indicate whether each statement is true or false. If the statement is false, change the italicized word or phrase to make the statement true.

1. ____ *Cyclosporine is* released by degranulating mast cells.

2. ____ *Type III* hypersensitivity reactions may lead to the development of glomerulonephritis.

3. ____ ABO blood group antigens are found on *nucleated* cells.

4. ____ The tuberculin reaction is a *type I* hypersensitivity.

5. ____ Graft-versus-host disease can follow a bone marrow *isograft*.

## Matching

Match the immune system complication in the first column with the types of hypersensitivities in the second column. Choices may be used more than once or not at all.

1. ____ Acute anaphylaxis
2. ____ Allergic contact dermatitis
3. ____ Systemic lupus erythematosus
4. ____ Allograft rejection
5. ____ AIDS
6. ____ Graft-versus-host disease
7. ____ Milk allergy
8. ____ Farmer's lung
9. ____ Asthma
10. ____ Hay fever

A. Type I hypersensitivity
B. Type II hypersensitivity
C. Type III hypersensitivity
D. Type IV hypersensitivity
E. Not a hypersensitivity

## Labeling

Label the four types of grafts on the figure below.

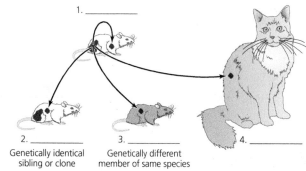

1. _____

2. _____
Genetically identical sibling or clone

3. _____
Genetically different member of same species

4. _____

J.B. Woolsey Associates, LLC/Precision Graphics

## Short Answer

1. Why is AIDS more accurately termed a "syndrome" rather than a mere disease?

2. Why is a child born to an Rh+ mother not susceptible to Rh-related hemolytic disease of the newborn?

3. Why is a person who produces a large amount of IgE more likely to experience anaphylactic shock than a person who instead produces a large amount of IgG?

4. Contrast autografts, isografts, allografts, and xenografts.

5. Compare and contrast the functions of four classes of immunosuppressive drugs.

# Concept Mapping

Using the following terms, draw a concept map that describes immediate hypersensitivity. Or, complete this concept map online by going to the Study Area at www.masteringmicrobiology.com.

Allergens
Allergy symptoms
Anaphylactic shock
Anaphylaxis
Antihistamine
Asthma
Basophils
Bee venom

Dust mites
Epinephrine
Hay fever
Histamine
IgE
Increased vascular
   permeability
Localized

Mast cells
Peanuts
Pollen
Smooth muscle
   contraction
Systemic
Type I hypersensitivity

Urticaria
Vasodilation

# Critical Thinking

1. What possible advantages might an individual gain from making class E antibodies (IgE)?

2. Why can't physicians use skin tests similar to the tuberculin reaction to diagnose other bacterial diseases?

3. In both Graves' disease and juvenile onset diabetes mellitus, autoantibodies are directed against cytoplasmic membrane receptors. Speculate on the clinical consequences of an autoimmune response to estrogen receptors.

4. In general, people with B cell defects acquire numerous bacterial infections, whereas those with T cell defects get viral diseases. Explain why this is so.

5. What types of illnesses cause death in patients with combined immunodeficiencies or AIDS?

6. Because of the severe shortage of organ donors for transplants, many scientists are examining the possibility of using organs from nonhuman species such as pigs. What special clinical problems might be encountered when using these xenografts?

7. Why do the blisters of positive tuberculin reactions resemble the blisters of poison ivy?

Access more review material online in the Study Area at **www.masteringmicrobiology.com.** There, you'll find
- **MP3 Tutor Sessions**
- **Concept Mapping Activities**
- **Flashchards**
- **Quizzes**

and more to help you succeed.

# Answers

**Multiple Choice**
1. e; 2. c; 3. d; 4. c; 5. c; 6. e; 7. b; 8. d; 9. c; 10. e

**Modified True/False**
1. *Histamine, kinins, and/or proteases are;*
2. True; 3. *red blood;* 4. *type IV;* 5. *allograft*

**Matching**
1. A; 2. D; 3. E; 4. D; 5. E; 6. D; 7. A; 8. C; 9. A; 10. A

**Labeling**
See Figure 13.

# Characterizing and Classifying Prokaryotes

From Chapter 11 of *Microbiology with Diseases by Taxonomy*, Third Edition. Robert W. Bauman. Copyright © 2011 by Pearson Education, Inc. Published by Benjamin Cummings, Inc. All rights reserved.

# Characterizing and Classifying Prokaryotes

Microbiologist Tony Walsby startled the scientific world by announcing the discovery of something no one had seen before: a rectangular-shaped prokaryote. This novel archaeon was named *Haloarcula*, meaning "salt box," because of its unusual boxy shape and its habitat, the salt-encrusted Dead Sea. Until this extraordinary find, scientists had only seen spherical, rod-shaped, or spiral prokaryotes. *Haloarcula* was a surprise, one that forced scientists to reconsider some of their assumptions about prokaryotic life forms.

More recently, we have discovered species of archaea that may offer clues to whether or not there is life on other planets. And among the millions of unknown microorganisms that live on Earth, there may very well exist entirely new categories of life. The vast and diverse world of prokaryotes continues to surprise and amaze us.

 **Take the pre-test for this chapter online. Visit the Study Area at www.masteringmicrobiology.com.**

Iconotec/Alamy

▲ The Dead Sea, the lowest point on the Earth's surface, is also one of the saltiest, but it isn't really dead—rectangular-shaped halophilic archaea live there.

Prokaryotes are by far the most numerous and diverse group of cellular microbes. Scientists estimate there are more than $5 \times 10^{30}$ prokaryotes on Earth. They thrive in various habitats: from Antarctic glaciers to thermal hot springs, from the colons of animals to the cytoplasm of other prokaryotes, from distilled water to supersaturated brine, and from disinfectant solutions to basalt rocks thousands of meters below the Earth's surface. In part because of such great diversity, only a very few prokaryotes have enzymes, toxins, or cellular structures that enable them to colonize humans and cause disease. In this chapter we will begin by examining general prokaryotic characteristics and conclude with a survey of specific prokaryotic taxa.

# General Characteristics of Prokaryotic Organisms

Previously, we considered the general characteristics of prokaryotic cells, including their cellular structure, metabolism, growth, and genetics. Here we will consider prokaryotes not merely as cells, but as distinct organisms, focusing on their cellular shapes, their reproductive processes, their spatial arrangements, and the ability of some to survive unfavorable conditions by forming resistant structures within themselves.

## Morphology of Prokaryotic Cells

### Learning Objective

✓ Identify six basic shapes of prokaryotic cells.

Prokaryotic cells exist in a variety of shapes, or morphologies (Figure 1). The three basic shapes are **cocci** (kok'sī, roughly spherical), **bacilli** (bă-sil'ī, rod-shaped), and **spirals**. Cocci are not all perfectly spherical; for example, there are pointed, kidney-shaped, and oval cocci. Similarly, bacilli vary in shape; for example, some bacilli are pointed, spindle shaped, or threadlike (filamentous). Spiral-shaped prokaryotes are either **spirilla,**

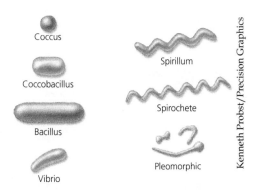

Coccus

Coccobacillus

Bacillus

Vibrio

Spirillum

Spirochete

Pleomorphic

Kenneth Probst/Precision Graphics

▲ **Figure 1 Typical prokaryotic morphologies.** *What is one difference between a spirillum and a spirochete?*

Figure 1 *Generally, spirilla are stiff, whereas spirochetes are flexible.*

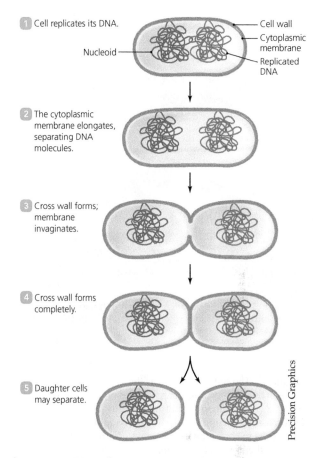

1. Cell replicates its DNA.

Nucleoid — Replicated DNA — Cell wall — Cytoplasmic membrane

2. The cytoplasmic membrane elongates, separating DNA molecules.

3. Cross wall forms; membrane invaginates.

4. Cross wall forms completely.

5. Daughter cells may separate.

Precision Graphics

▲ **Figure 2 Binary fission.** The cell replicates its DNA, elongates, forms a cross wall, and divides into two equal-sized daughter cells.

which are stiff, or **spirochetes** (spī'rō-kētz), which are flexible. Slightly curved rods are **vibrios,** and the term **coccobacillus** is used to describe cells that are intermediate in shape between cocci and bacilli; that is, when it is difficult to ascertain if a cell is an elongated coccus or a short bacillus. In addition to these basic shapes, there are star-shaped, triangular, and rectangular prokaryotes, as well as prokaryotes that are **pleomorphic**[1] (plē-ō-mōr'fik); that is, they vary in shape and size.

## Reproduction of Prokaryotic Cells

### Learning Objectives

✓ List three common types of reproduction in prokaryotes.

✓ Describe snapping division as a type of binary fission.

All prokaryotes reproduce asexually; none reproduce sexually. The most common method of asexual reproduction is **binary fission,** which proceeds as follows (Figure 2): 1 The cell replicates its DNA; each DNA molecule is attached to the cytoplasmic

---

[1]From Greek *pleon*, meaning more, and *morphe*, meaning form.

257

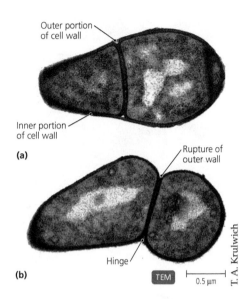

**(a)**

**(b)**

T. A. Krulwich

▲ **Figure 3** **Snapping division, a variation of binary fission.**
**(a)** Only the inner portion of the cell wall forms a cross wall. **(b)** As the
daughter cells grow, tension snaps the outer portion of the cell wall,
leaving the daughter cells connected by a hinge of old cell wall material.

Kim Findlay, John Innes Centre, Norfolk, UK

▲ **Figure 4** **Spores of actinomycetes.** Filamentous vegetative cells
produce chains of spores, shown here in *Streptomyces.*

membrane. ② The cell grows; and as the cytoplasmic membrane
elongates, it moves the daughter molecules of DNA apart. ③ The
cell forms a cross wall, invaginating the cytoplasmic membrane.
④ The cross wall completely divides daughter cells. ⑤ The
daughter cells may or may not separate. The parental cell disappears with the formation of progeny. **ANIMATIONS:** *Bacterial
Growth: Overview*

A variation of binary fission called **snapping division** occurs
in some Gram-positive bacilli (Figure 3). In snapping division,
only the inner portion of the cell wall is deposited across the
dividing cell. The thickening of this new transverse wall puts
tension on the outer layer of the old cell wall, which still holds
the two cells together. Eventually, as the tension increases, the
outer wall breaks at its weakest point with a snapping movement
that tears it most of the way around. The daughter cells then remain hanging together, held at an angle by a small remnant of
the original outer wall that acts like a hinge.

A few prokaryotes have other methods of reproduction.
The parental cell retains its identity during and after these
methods. The *actinomycetes* (ak'ti-nō-mī-sētz) produce reproductive cells called **spores** at the ends of their filamentous cells
(Figure 4). Each spore can develop into a clone of the original
organism. Some *cyanobacteria* reproduce by fragmentation into
small motile filaments that glide away from the parental strand.
Still other prokaryotes reproduce by **budding,** in which an out-
growth of the original cell (a bud) receives a copy of the genetic
material and enlarges. Eventually the bud is cut off from the
parental cell, typically while it is still quite small (Figure 5).

*Epulopiscium* (ep'yoo-lō-pis'sē-ŭm), the giant bacterial
symbiont of surgeonfish, and many of its relatives have a

truly unique method of reproduction among prokaryotes:
They give "birth" to as many as 12 live offspring that emerge
from the body of a dead mother cell. The production of live offspring within a mother is called *viviparity,* and this is the first
documented case of viviparous behavior in the prokaryotic
world. In these bacteria, formation of internal offspring
proceeds in a manner similar to the early stages of endospore
formation.

Kenneth Probst/Precision Graphics

Nucleoid replicates

New nucleoid is
moved into bud

Young bud

Daughter cell

▲ **Figure 5** **Budding.** *How does budding differ from binary fission?*

*Figure 5* In binary fission, the parent cell disappears with the formation
of two equal-sized offspring; in contrast, a bud is often much smaller
than its parent, and the parent remains to produce more buds.

Mike Dyall-Smith, Dept. of Microbiology and Immunology, University of Melbourne, Australia

Eastman Kodak

L. Brent Selinger, Pearson Science

▲ **Figure 6** **Arrangements of cocci. (a)** The diplococci of *Neisseria gonorrhoeae.* **(b)** The streptococci of *Streptococcus pyogenes.* **(c)** Tetrads, in this case of *Micrococcus luteus.* **(d)** The genus *Sarcina* is characterized by sarcinae. **(e)** The staphylococci of *Staphylococcus aureus.*

## Arrangements of Prokaryotic Cells

### Learning Objective

✓ Draw and label five arrangements of prokaryotes.

The arrangements of prokaryotic cells result from two aspects of division during binary fission: the planes in which cells divide and whether or not daughter cells separate completely or remain attached to each other. Cocci that remain attached in pairs are **diplococci** (Figure 6a), and long chains of cocci are called **streptococci**[2] (Figure 6b). Some cocci divide in two planes and

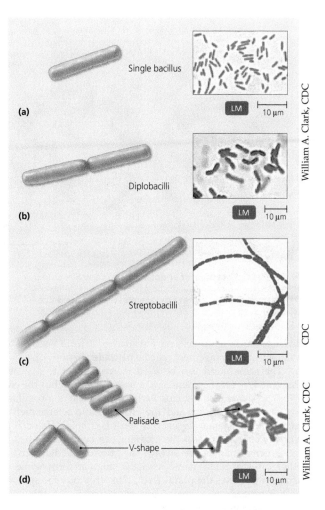

William A. Clark, CDC

CDC

William A. Clark, CDC

▲ **Figure 7** **Arrangements of bacilli. (a)** A single bacillus of *Escherichia coli.* **(b)** Diplobacilli in a young culture of *Bacillus cereus.* **(c)** Streptobacilli in an older culture of *Bacillus cereus.* **(d)** V-shape and a palisade of *Corynebacterium diphtheriae.*

remain attached to form **tetrads** (Figure 6c); others divide in three planes to form cuboidal packets called **sarcinae**[3] (sar'si-nī) (Figure 6d). Clusters called **staphylococci**[4] (staf'i-lo-kok-sī), which look like bunches of grapes, form when the planes of cell division are random (Figure 6e).

Bacilli are less varied in their arrangements than cocci because bacilli divide transversely—that is, perpendicular to the long axis. Daughter bacilli may separate to become single cells or stay attached as either pairs or chains (Figure 7a–c). Because the cells of *Corynebacterium diphtheriae* (kŏ-rī'nē-bak-tēr'ē-ŭm dif-thi'rē-ī), the causative agent of diphtheria, divide by snapping

[2]From Greek *streptos*, meaning twisted, because long chains tend to twist.
[3]Latin for bundles.
[4]From Greek *staphyle*, meaning bunch of grapes.

259

**(a)** LM 10 μm

**(b)** LM 10 μm

▲ **Figure 8 Locations of endospores. (a)** Central endospores of *Bacillus*. **(b)** Subterminal endospores of *Clostridium botulinum*. The enlarged endospores have swollen the vegetative cells that produced them.

division, the daughter cells remain attached to form V-shapes and a side-by-side arrangement called a **palisade**[5] (Figure 7d).

The same word can be used to refer either to a general shape and/or arrangement or to a specific genus. Thus the characteristic shape of the genus *Bacillus* (ba-sil′ŭs) is a bacillus, a rod-shaped bacterium, and the characteristic arrangement of bacteria in the genus *Sarcina* (sar′si-nă) is cuboidal. In such potentially confusing cases the meaning can be distinguished because genus names are always capitalized and italicized. In other cases a genus name uses the singular form while the arrangement uses the plural form; thus streptococci—spherical cells arranged in a chain—are characteristic of the genus *Streptococcus* (strep-tō-kok′ŭs).

## Endospores

### Learning Objective

✓ Describe the formation and function of bacterial endospores.

The Gram-positive bacteria *Bacillus* and *Clostridium* (klos-trid′-ē-ŭm) produce **endospores,** which are important for several reasons, including their durability and potential pathogenicity. Endospores constitute a defensive strategy against hostile or unfavorable conditions. They are stable resting stages that barely metabolize and germinate only when conditions improve.

Though some people refer to endospores as "spores," endospores should not be confused with the reproductive spores of actinomycetes, algae, and fungi. A single bacterial cell, called a *vegetative* cell to distinguish it from an endospore, transforms into only one endospore, which then germinates to grow into a single vegetative cell; therefore, endospores are not reproductive structures.

The process of endospore formation, called *sporulation*, requires 8 to 10 hours and proceeds in seven steps. Depending on the species, a cell forms endospores either *centrally, subterminally* (near one end), or *terminally* (at one end) (Figure 8).

Food processors, health care professionals, and governments are concerned about endospore formation because endospores are so resistant and because many endospore-forming bacteria produce deadly toxins that cause fatal diseases such as anthrax, tetanus, and gangrene.

## Modern Prokaryotic Classification

### Learning Objectives

✓ Explain the general purpose of *Bergey's Manual of Systematic Bacteriology*.

✓ Discuss the veracity and limitations of any taxonomic scheme.

Scientists called *taxonomists* group similar organisms into categories called *taxa*. At one time the smallest taxa of prokaryotes (that is, genera and species) were based solely on growth habits and the characteristics we considered in the previous section, especially morphology and arrangement. More recently, the classification of living things has been based more on genetic relatedness. Accordingly, modern taxonomists place all organisms into three *domains*—Archaea (ar′kē-ă), Bacteria, and Eukarya—which are the largest, most inclusive taxa. Bacteria and Archaea (both prokaryotic) occupy smaller taxa primarily on the basis of similarities in DNA, RNA, and protein sequences.

We previously noted as well that the vast majority of prokaryotes—perhaps as many as 99.5%, and probably millions of species—have never been isolated or cultured and are known only from their rRNA "fingerprints"; that is, they are known only from sequences of rRNA that do not match any known rRNA sequences. In light of this information, taxonomists now construct modern classification schemes of prokaryotes based on the relative similarities of rRNA sequences found in various prokaryotic groups (Figure 9).

Perhaps the most authoritative reference in modern prokaryotic systematics is *Bergey's Manual of Systematic Bacteriology*, which classifies prokaryotes into 27 phyla—3 in Archaea and 24 in Bacteria. The five volumes of the second edition of *Bergey's Manual* discuss the great diversity of prokaryotes based in large part (but not exclusively) on their possible evolutionary relationships as reflected in their rRNA sequences.

Our examination of prokaryotic diversity in this text is for the most part organized to reflect the taxonomic scheme that appears in *Bergey's Manual*, but it is important to note that as authoritative as *Bergey's Manual* is, it is not an "official" list of prokaryotic taxa. The reason is that taxonomy is partly a matter of opinion and judgment, and not all taxonomists agree. Because there is room in taxonomy for honest differences of

---

[5]From Latin *palus*, meaning stake, referring to a fence made of adjoining stakes.

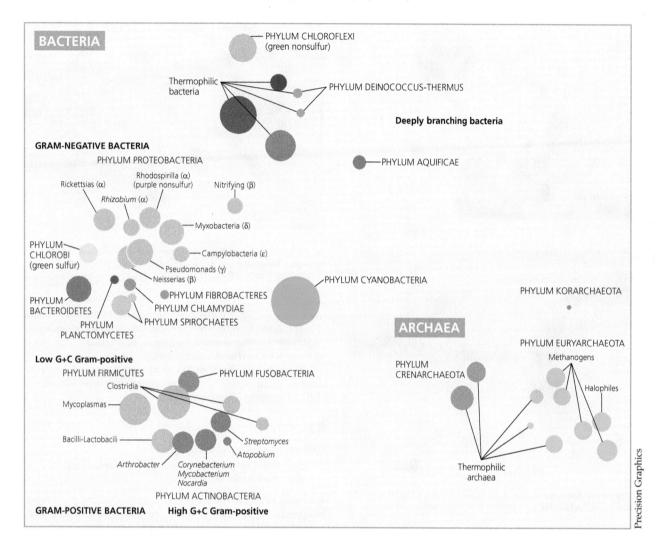

**BACTERIA**

PHYLUM CHLOROFLEXI
(green nonsulfur)

Thermophilic
bacteria

PHYLUM DEINOCOCCUS-THERMUS

**Deeply branching bacteria**

PHYLUM AQUIFICAE

**GRAM-NEGATIVE BACTERIA**

PHYLUM PROTEOBACTERIA

Rickettsias (α)

Rhodospirilla (α)
(purple nonsulfur)

Nitrifying (β)

*Rhizobium* (α)

Myxobacteria (δ)

PHYLUM
CHLOROBI
(green sulfur)

Campylobacteria (ε)

Pseudomonads (γ)

PHYLUM CYANOBACTERIA

PHYLUM KORARCHAEOTA

Neisserias (β)

PHYLUM FIBROBACTERES

PHYLUM
BACTEROIDETES

PHYLUM CHLAMYDIAE

PHYLUM EURYARCHAEOTA

PHYLUM SPIROCHAETES

**ARCHAEA**

PHYLUM
PLANCTOMYCETES

Methanogens

**Low G+C Gram-positive**

PHYLUM FIRMICUTES

PHYLUM
CRENARCHAEOTA

PHYLUM FUSOBACTERIA

Clostridia

Halophiles

Mycoplasmas

Bacilli-Lactobacili

*Streptomyces*

*Atopobium*

Arthrobacter

*Corynebacterium*
*Mycobacterium*
*Nocardia*

Thermophilic
archaea

PHYLUM ACTINOBACTERIA

**GRAM-POSITIVE BACTERIA**    **High G+C Gram-positive**

Precision Graphics

▲ **Figure 9 Prokaryotic taxonomy.** This scheme is based on relatedness according to rRNA sequences. The closer together the disks, the more similar are the rRNA sequences of the species within the group. The sizes of disks are proportional to the number of species known for that group. Note that archaea are distinctly separate from bacteria. The discussion in this chapter is largely based on the scheme depicted in this figure. Not all phyla are shown.
(In phylum Proteobacteria, classes are indicated by a Greek letter, α = alpha, β = beta, γ = gamma, δ = delta, and ε = epsilon.)
(Adapted from *Road Map to Bergey's*. 2002, Bergey's Manual Trust.)

opinion, and because legitimately differing views often change as more information is uncovered and examined, *Bergey's Manual* is merely a consensus of experts at a given time. More information about *Bergey's Manual* can be found on the textbook website at www.masteringmicrobiology.com.

In the following sections we examine representative prokaryotes in each major phylum. We begin our exploration of prokaryotic diversity with a survey of Archaea.

# Survey of Archaea

## Learning Objective

✓ Identify the common features of microbes in the domain Archaea.

Scientists originally identified archaea as a distinct type of prokaryotes on the basis of unique rRNA sequences. Archaea also share other common features that distinguish them from bacteria:

From: Extending the upper temperature limit for life. K. Kashefi, D. R. Lovley. *Science.* 2003 August 15; 301(5635): 934, fig1A. Reprinted with permission. © 2003 AAAS

(a) TEM | 1 μm

Reinhard Rachel

(b) TEM | 1.0 μm

▲ **Figure 10 Archaea. (a)** *Geogemma*, which has a tuff of flagella. **(b)** *Pyrodictium*, which has disk-shaped cells with filamentous extensions.

- Archaea lack true peptidoglycan in their cell walls.
- Their cell membrane lipids have branched hydrocarbon chains.
- The initial amino acid in their polypeptide chains, coded by the AUG start codon, is methionine (as in eukaryotes and in contrast to the *N*-formylmethionine used by bacteria).

Archaea are currently classified in three phyla—Crenarchaeota (kren-ar′kē-ō-ta), Euryarchaeota (ū-rē-ar′kē-ō-ta), and Korarchaeota (kor-ar′kē-ō-ta)—based primarily upon rRNA sequences. In fact, the latter phylum is known only from environmental RNA samples; no members have been observed visually. Researchers have discovered RNA from another un-culturable archaeon—*Nanoarchaeum* (nan-o-ar′kē-um)—that may represent a fourth archaeal phylum, though there is not con-sensus on this taxon.

Archaea reproduce by binary fission, budding, or fragmen-tation. Known archaeal cells are cocci, bacilli, spirals, or pleo-morphic (**Figure 10**). Archaeal cell walls vary among taxa and

Sascha Burkard/Shutterstock

▲ **Figure 11 Some hyperthermophilic archaea live in hot springs.** Orange archaea thrive along the edge of this pool in Yellowstone National Park.

are composed of a variety of compounds, including proteins, glycoproteins, lipoproteins, and polysaccharides; all lack pepti-doglycan. Another interesting feature of archaea is that not one of them is known to cause diseases.

Though most Archaea live in moderate environmental con-ditions, noted archaea are *extremophiles*, which we discuss next, and *methanogens* (discussed shortly).

## Extremophiles

### Learning Objective

✓ Compare and contrast the two kinds of extremophiles discussed in this section.

**Extremophiles** are microbes that require extreme conditions of temperature, pH, and/or salinity to survive. Prominent among the extremophiles are *thermophiles* and *halophiles.*

### Thermophiles

**Thermophiles**[6] are prokaryotes whose DNA, RNA, cytoplas-mic membranes, and proteins do not function properly at tem-peratures lower than 45°C. Prokaryotes that require tempera-tures over 80°C are called **hyperthermophiles.** Most thermophilic archaea are in the phylum Crenarchaeota, though some are also found in the phylum Euryarchaeota.

Two representative genera of thermophiles are *Geogemma* (jē′ō-jem-a) and *Pyrodictium* (pī-rō-dik′tē-um; see Figure 10). These microorganisms live in acidic hot springs such as those found in deep ocean rifts and similar terrestrial volcanic habi-tats (**Figure 11**). *Geogemma* is the current record holder for surviving high temperatures—it can survive 2 hours at 130°C! The cells of *Pyrodictium,* which live in deep-sea hydrothermal

---

[6]From Greek *thermos*, meaning heat, and *philos*, meaning love.

vents, are irregular disks with elongated protein tubules that attach them to grains of sulfur, which they use as final electron acceptors in respiration.

Scientists use thermophiles and their enzymes in recombinant DNA technology applications because thermophiles' cellular structure and enzymes are stable and functional at temperatures that denature most proteins and nucleic acids and kill other cells. DNA polymerase from hyperthermophilic archaea makes possible the automated amplification of DNA in a thermocycler. Heat-stable enzymes are also ideal for many industrial applications, including their use as additives in laundry detergents.

### Halophiles

**Halophiles**[7] are classified in the phylum Euryarchaeota. They inhabit extremely saline habitats such as the Dead Sea, the Great Salt Lake, and solar evaporation ponds used to concentrate salt for use in seasoning and for the production of fertilizer (Figure 12). Halophiles can also colonize and spoil such foods as salted fish, sausages, and pork.

The distinctive characteristic of halophiles is their absolute dependence on a concentration of NaCl greater than 9% (that is, a 1.5 molar solution) to maintain the integrity of their cell walls. Most halophiles grow and reproduce within an optimum range of 17–23% NaCl, and many species can survive in a saturated saline solution (35% NaCl). Many halophiles contain red to orange pigments that probably play a role in protecting them from intense visible and ultraviolet light.

The most studied halophile is *Halobacterium salinarium* (hā'lō-bak-tēr'ē-ŭm sal-ē-nar'ē-um), which is an archaeon despite its name. It is a photoheterotroph, using light energy to drive the synthesis of ATP, but deriving carbon from organic compounds. *Halobacterium* lacks photosynthetic pigments—chlorophylls and bacteriochlorophylls. Instead, it synthesizes purple proteins, called **bacteriorhodopsins** (bak-tēr'ē-ō-rō-dop'sinz), that absorb light energy to pump protons across the cytoplasmic membrane to establish a proton gradient. Cells use the energy of proton gradients to produce ATP via chemiosmosis.) *Halobacterium* also rotates its flagella with energy from the proton gradient so as to position itself at the proper water depth for maximum light absorption.

## Methanogens

### Learning Objective

✓ List at least four significant roles played by methanogens in the environment.

**Methanogens** are obligate anaerobes in the phylum Euryarchaeota that convert $CO_2$, $H_2$, and organic acids into methane gas ($CH_4$). These microbes constitute the largest known group of archaea. Most species are mesophilic, though a few thermophilic methanogens are known. For example, *Methanopyrus*[8] (meth'a-nō-pī'rŭs) has an optimum growth temperature of 98°C and

[7]From Greek *halos*, meaning salt.
[8]From Greek *pyrus*, meaning fire.

*San Francisco Chronicle*

▲ **Figure 12** **The habitat of halophiles: highly saline water.** These are solar evaporation ponds near San Francisco. Halophiles often contain red to orange pigments, possibly to protect them from intense solar energy.

grows in 110°C seawater around submarine hydrothermal vents. Scientists have also discovered halophilic methanogens.

Methanogens play significant roles in the environment by converting organic wastes in pond, lake, and ocean sediments into methane. Other methanogens living in the colons of animals are one of the primary sources of environmental methane. Methanogens dwelling in the intestinal tract of a cow, for example, can produce 400 liters of methane a day. Methanogens have produced about 10 trillion tons of methane—twice the known amount of oil, natural gas, and coal combined—that lies buried in mud on the ocean floor. Sometimes the production of methane in swamps and bogs is so great that bubbles rise to the surface as "swamp gas." Methane is a so-called *greenhouse gas;* that is, methane in the atmosphere traps heat, which adds to global warming. It is about 25 times more potent as a greenhouse gas than carbon dioxide. If all the methane trapped in ocean sediments were released, it would wreak havoc with the world's climate.

Methanogens also have useful industrial applications. An important step in sewage treatment is the digestion of sludge by methanogens, and some sewage treatment plants burn methane to heat buildings and generate electricity.

Though we have concentrated our discussion on extremophiles and methanogens, many archaea live in more moderate habitats. For example, archaea make up about a third of the prokaryotic biomass in coastal Antarctic water, providing food for marine animals.

### CRITICAL **THINKING**

A scientist who discovers a prokaryote living in a hot spring at 100°C suspects that it belongs to the archaea. Why does he think it might be archaeal? How could he prove that it is not bacterial?

# Survey of Bacteria

As we noted previously, our survey of prokaryotes in this chapter reflects the classification scheme that is featured in the still-incomplete second edition of *Bergey's Manual.* Whereas the classification scheme for bacteria in the first edition of the *Manual* emphasized morphology, Gram reaction, and biochemical characteristics, the second edition largely bases its classification of bacteria on differences in 16S rRNA sequences. We begin our survey of bacteria by considering the deeply branching and phototrophic bacteria.

## Deeply Branching and Phototrophic Bacteria

### Learning Objectives

✓ Provide a rationale for the name "deeply branching bacteria."

✓ Explain the function of heterocysts in terms of both photosynthesis and nitrogen fixation.

### Deeply Branching Bacteria

The **deeply branching bacteria** are so named because their rRNA sequences and growth characteristics lead scientists to conclude that these organisms are similar to the earliest bacteria; that is, they appear to have branched off the "tree of life" at an early stage. For example, the deeply branching bacteria are autotrophic, and early organisms must have been autotrophs because heterotrophs by definition must derive their carbon from autotrophs. Further, many of the deeply branching bacteria live in habitats similar to those some scientists think existed on the early Earth—hot, acidic, anaerobic, and exposed to intense ultraviolet radiation from the sun.

One representative of these microbes—the Gram-negative, microaerophilic *Aquifex* (ăk'wē-feks), a bacterium in the phylum Aquificae—is considered to represent the earliest branch of bacteria. It is chemoautotrophic, hyperthermophilic, and anaerobic, deriving energy and carbon from inorganic sources in very hot habitats containing little oxygen.

Another representative of deeply branching bacteria is *Deinococcus* (dī-nō-kok'ŭs), in phylum Deinococcus-Thermus which grows as tetrads of Gram-positive cocci. Interestingly, the cell wall of *Deinococcus* has an outer membrane similar to that of Gram-negative bacteria, but the cells stain purple like typical Gram-positive microbes. *Deinococcus* is extremely resistant to radiation because of the way it packages its DNA and the presence of radiation-absorbing pigments, unique lipids within its membranes, and high cytoplasmic levels of manganese, which protect its DNA repair proteins from radiation damage. Even when exposed to 5 million rad of radiation, which is enough energy to shatter its chromosome into hundreds of fragments, its enzymes can repair the damage. Not surprisingly, researchers have isolated *Deinococcus* from sites severely contaminated with radioactive wastes.

### Phototrophic Bacteria

Phototrophic bacteria acquire the energy needed for anabolism by absorbing light with pigments located in thylakoids called *photosynthetic lamellae.* They lack the membrane-bound thylakoids seen in eukaryotic chloroplasts. Most phototrophic bacteria are also autotrophic—they produce organic compounds from carbon dioxide.

Phototrophs are a diverse group of microbes that are taxonomically confusing. Based on their pigments and their source of electrons for photosynthesis, phototrophic bacteria can be divided into the following five groups:

- Blue-green bacteria (cyanobacteria)
- Green sulfur bacteria
- Green nonsulfur bacteria
- Purple sulfur bacteria
- Purple nonsulfur bacteria

These five groups of organisms are classified into four phyla. We consider all of them in the following sections because of their common phototrophic metabolism.

**Cyanobacteria** Cyanobacteria are Gram-negative phototrophs that vary greatly in shape, size, and method of reproduction. They range in size from 1 μm to 10 μm in diameter and are either coccoid or disk shaped. Coccal forms can be single or arranged in pairs, tetrads, chains, or sheets (Figure 13a, b); disc-shaped forms are often tightly appressed end to end to form filaments, which can be either straight, branched, or helical and are frequently contained in a gelatinous glycocalyx called a *sheath* (Figure 13c). Some filamentous cyanobacteria are motile, moving along surfaces by *gliding.* Cyanobacteria generally reproduce by binary fission, with some species also reproducing by motile fragments or by thick-walled spores called akinetes (ā-kin-ēts'; see Figure 13a).

Like plants and algae, cyanobacteria utilize chlorophyll *a* and are oxygenic (generate oxygen) during photosynthesis:

$$12 H_2O + 6 CO_2 \xrightarrow{\text{light}} C_6H_{12}O_6 + 6 H_2O + 6 O_2 \qquad (1)$$

For this reason, cyanobacteria were formerly called *blue-green algae;* however, the name *cyanobacteria* properly emphasizes their true prokaryotic nature.

Photosynthesis by cyanobacteria is thought to have transformed the anaerobic atmosphere of the early Earth into our oxygen-containing one, and according to the endosymbiotic theory, chloroplasts developed from cyanobacteria. Indeed, chloroplasts and cyanobacteria have similar rRNA and structures such as 70S ribosomes and photosynthetic membranes.

Nitrogen is an essential element in proteins and nucleic acids. Though nitrogen constitutes about 79% of the atmosphere, relatively few organisms can utilize this gas. A few species of filamentous cyanobacteria and proteobacteria (discussed later in the chapter) reduce nitrogen gas ($N_2$) to ammonia ($NH_3$) via a process called **nitrogen fixation.** Nitrogen fixation is essential for life on Earth because nitrogen-fixers not only are able to enrich their own growth but also provide nitrogen in a usable form to other organisms.

Vegetative cell

Heterocyst

Akinete

Microbial Culture Collection, MCC-NIES, Japan

(a)

LM    10 µm

Yuuji Tsukii, Hosei University, Tokyo, Japan

(b)

LM    5 µm

Biodisc/Visuals Unlimited/Alamy

Sheath

(c)

LM    10 µm

▲ **Figure 13 Examples of cyanobacteria with different growth habits. (a)** *Anabaena*, which grows as a filament of cocci with differentiated cells. Heterocysts fix nitrogen; akinetes are reproductive cells. **(b)** *Merismopedia*, which grows as a flat sheet of cocci surrounded by a gelatinous glycocalyx. **(c)** *Oscillatoria*, which forms a filament of tightly appressed disk-shaped cells.

Because the enzyme responsible for nitrogen fixation is inhibited by oxygen, nitrogen-fixing cyanobacteria are faced with a problem—how to segregate nitrogen fixation, which is inhibited by oxygen, from oxygenic photosynthesis, which produces oxygen. Nitrogen-fixing cyanobacteria solve this problem in one of two ways. Most cyanobacteria isolate the enzymes of nitrogen fixation in specialized, thick-walled, nonphotosynthetic cells called **heterocysts** (see Figure 13a). Heterocysts transport reduced nitrogen to neighboring cells in exchange for glucose. Other cyanobacteria photosynthesize during daylight hours and fix nitrogen at night, thereby separating nitrogen fixation from photosynthesis in time rather than in space.

**Green and Purple Phototrophic Bacteria** Green and purple bacteria differ from plants, algae, and cyanobacteria in two ways: They use *bacteriochlorophylls* for photosynthesis instead of chlorophyll *a*, and they are *anoxygenic;* that is, they do not generate oxygen during photosynthesis. Green and purple phototrophic bacteria commonly inhabit anaerobic muds rich in hydrogen sulfide at the bottoms of ponds and lakes. These microbes are not necessarily green and purple in color; rather, the terms refer to pigments in some of the better-known members of the groups.

As previously indicated, the green and purple phototrophic bacteria include both sulfur and nonsulfur forms. Whereas nonsulfur bacteria derive electrons for the reduction of $CO_2$ from organic compounds such as carbohydrates and organic acids, sulfur bacteria derive electrons from the oxidation of hydrogen sulfide to sulfur, as follows:

$$12\,H_2S + 6\,CO_2 \xrightarrow{\text{light}} C_6H_{12}O_6 + 6\,H_2O + 12\,S \qquad (2)$$

Green sulfur bacteria deposit the resultant sulfur outside their cells, whereas purple sulfur bacteria deposit sulfur within their cells (Figure 14).

At the beginning of the 20th century, a prominent question in biology concerned the origin of the oxygen released by photosynthetic plants. It was initially thought that oxygen was derived from carbon dioxide, but a comparison of photosynthesis in cyanobacteria (Equation 1) with that in sulfur bacteria (Equation 2) provided evidence that free oxygen is derived from water.

Whereas green sulfur bacteria are placed in phylum Chlorobi, green nonsulfur bacteria are members of phylum Chloroflexi. The purple bacteria (both sulfur and nonsulfur) are placed in three classes of phylum Proteobacteria, which is composed of Gram-negative bacteria and is discussed shortly. Table 1 summarizes the characteristics of phototrophic bacteria. **ANIMATIONS:** *Photosynthesis: Comparing Prokaryotes and Eukaryotes*

Now we turn our attention to various groups of Gram-positive bacteria, and to a different characteristic of microbes that is used in the classification of Gram-positive bacteria—*G + C ratio.* This ratio is the percentage of all base pairs in a genome that are guanine-cytosine base pairs—and is a useful criterion in classifying microbes. Bacteria with G + C ratios below 50% are considered "low G + C bacteria"; the remainder are

LM | 4.0 µm

▲ **Figure 14** **Deposits of sulfur within purple sulfur bacteria in the genus *Chromatium*.** These bacteria oxidize H$_2$S to produce the granules of elemental sulfur evident in this photomicrograph. *Where do green sulfur bacteria deposit sulfur grains?*

Figure 14 *Green sulfur bacteria deposit sulfur grains externally.*

considered "high G + C bacteria." Because taxonomists have discovered that Gram-positive bacteria with low G + C ratios have similar sequences in their 16S rRNA, and that those with high G + C ratios also have rRNA sequences in common, they have assigned low G + C bacteria and high G + C bacteria to different phyla. We discuss the low G + C bacteria first.

# Low G + C Gram-Positive Bacteria

## Learning Objectives

✓ Discuss the lack of cell walls in mycoplasmas.

✓ Identify significant beneficial or detrimental effects of the genera *Clostridium*, *Bacillus*, *Listeria*, *Lactobacillus*, *Streptococcus*, and *Staphylococcus*.

The low G + C Gram-positive bacteria are classified within phylum Firmicutes (fer-mik'ū-tēz), which includes three groups: clostridia, mycoplasmas, and other low G + C Gram-positive bacilli and cocci. Next we consider these three groups in turn.

### Clostridia

Clostridia are rod-shaped, obligate anaerobes, many of which form endospores. The group is named for the genus *Clostridium,*[9] which is important both in medicine—in large part because its members produce potent toxins that cause a variety of diseases in humans—and in industry because their endospores enable them to survive harsh conditions, including many types of disinfection and antisepsis. Examples of clostridia include *C. tetani* (te'tan-ē, which causes tetanus), *C. perfringens* (per-frin'jens, gangrene), *C. botulinum* (bo-tū-lī'num, botulism), and *C. difficile* (di-fi'sil-ē, severe diarrhea). **Beneficial Microbes: Botulism and Botox** describes how a deadly toxin produced by *C. botulinum* has been put to use for cosmetic purposes.

Microbes related to *Clostridium* include sulfate-reducing microbes, which produce H$_2$S from elemental sulfur during

---

[9]From Greek *kloster*, meaning spindle.

# TABLE 1

## Characteristics of the Major Groups of Phototrophic Bacteria

| | Phylum | | | | |
|---|---|---|---|---|---|
| | **Cyanobacteria** | **Chlorobi** | **Chloroflexi** | **Proteobacteria** | **Proteobacteria** |
| Class | Cyanobacteria | Chlorobia | Chloroflexi | Gammaproteobacteria | Alphaproteobacteria and one genus in betaproteobacteria |
| Common name(s) | Blue-green bacteria ("blue-green algae") | Green sulfur bacteria | Green nonsulfur bacteria | Purple sulfur bacteria | Purple nonsulfur bacteria |
| Major photosynthetic pigments | Chlorophyll *a* | Bacteriochlorophyll *a* plus *c, d,* or *e* | Bacteriochlorophylls *a* and *c* | Bacteriochlorophyll *a* or *b* | Bacteriochlorophyll *a* or *b* |
| Types of photosynthesis | Oxygenic | Anoxygenic | Anoxygenic | Anoxygenic | Anoxygenic |
| Electron donor in photosynthesis | H$_2$O | H$_2$, H$_2$S, or S | Organic compounds | H$_2$, H$_2$S, or S | Organic compounds |
| Sulfur deposition | None | Outside of cell | None | Inside of cell | None |
| Nitrogen fixation | Some species | None | None | None | None |
| Motility | Nonmotile or gliding | Nonmotile | Gliding | Motile with polar or peritrichous flagella | Nonmotile or motile with polar flagella |

anaerobic respiration, and *Veillonella* (vī-lō-nel'ă), a genus of anaerobic cocci that live as part of the biofilm (plaque) that forms on the teeth of warm-blooded animals. *Veillonella* is unusual because even though it has a typical Gram-positive cell wall structure, it has a negative Gram reaction—it stains pink.

## Mycoplasmas

A second class of low G + C bacteria are the **mycoplasmas**[10] (mī'kō-plaz'mas). These facultative or obligate anaerobes lack cell walls, which means they stain pink when Gram stained. Indeed, until their nucleic acid sequences proved their similarity to Gram-positive organisms, mycoplasmas were classified as Gram-negative microbes, instead of in phylum Firmicutes with other low G + C Gram-positive bacteria.

Mycoplasmas are able to survive without cell walls in part because they colonize osmotically protected habitats such as animal and human bodies, and because they have tough cytoplasmic membranes, many of which contain lipids called *sterols* that give the membranes strength and rigidity. Because they lack cell walls, they are pleomorphic. They were named "mycoplasmas" because their filamentous forms resemble the filaments of fungi. Mycoplasmas have diameters ranging from 0.2 μm to 0.8 μm, making them the smallest free-living cells, and many mycoplasmas have a terminal structure that is used for attachment to eukaryotic cells and that gives the bacterium a pearlike shape. They require organic growth factors, such as cholesterol, fatty acids, vitamins, amino acids, and nucleotides, which they acquire from their host or which must be added to laboratory media. When growing on solid media, most species form a distinctive "fried egg" appearance because cells in the center of the colony grow into the agar while those around the perimeter only spread across the surface (Figure 15).

In animals, mycoplasmas colonize mucous membranes of the respiratory and urinary tracts and are associated with pneumonia and urinary tract infections. Pathogenic mycoplasmas and the diseases they cause are discussed more fully.

---

[10]From Greek *mycos*, meaning fungus, and *plassein*, meaning to mold.

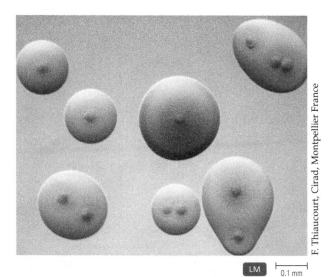

F. Thiaucourt, Cirad, Montpellier France

LM   0.1 mm

▲ **Figure 15** **The distinctive "fried egg" appearance of** ***Mycoplasma* colonies.** This visual feature is unique to this group of bacteria, growing on an agar surface.

## Other Low G + C Bacilli and Cocci

A third group of low G + C Gram-positive organisms is composed of bacilli and cocci that are significant in environmental, industrial, and health care settings. Among the genera in this group are *Bacillus, Listeria* (lis-tēr'ē-ă), *Lactobacillus* (lak'tō-bă-sil'ŭs), *Streptococcus, Enterococcus* (en'ter-ō-kok'ŭs), and *Staphylococcus* (staf'i-lō-kok'ŭs).

***Bacillus*** The genus *Bacillus* includes endospore-forming aerobes and facultative anaerobes that typically move by means of peritrichous flagella. Numerous species of *Bacillus* are common in soil.

*Bacillus thuringiensis* (thur-in-jē-en'sis) is beneficial to farmers and gardeners. During sporulation, this bacterium produces a

---

## BENEFICIAL MICROBES

### BOTULISM AND BOTOX

Rick Gomez/Corbis

*Clostridium botulinum* produces botulinum toxins, some of the deadliest toxins known. When absorbed in the body, botulism toxins interfere with the release of acetylcholine, the neurotransmitter that

signals muscles to contract. As a result, muscle cells cannot contract, and a slow but progressive paralysis spreads throughout the body. Death occurs when paralysis of respiratory muscles results in respiratory failure.

Purified type A botulinum toxin is marketed as Botox, extremely small doses of which are injected into facial muscles that cause skin wrinkles. The toxin paralyzes or weakens the muscles, smoothing the skin. Such treatments last approximately 6 months and must be repeated in order to maintain the desired effects.

Bacillus thuringiensis          Bt toxin

SciMAT/Photo Researchers

SEM    1 μm

▲ **Figure 16 Crystals of Bt toxin, produced by the endospore-forming *Bacillus thuringiensis*.** The crystalline protein kills caterpillars that ingest it.

crystalline protein that is toxic to caterpillars that ingest it (Figure 16). Gardeners spray *Bt toxin*, as preparations of the bacterium and toxin are known, on plants to protect them from caterpillars. Scientists have achieved the same effect, without the need of spraying, by introducing the gene for Bt toxin into plants' chromosomes. Other beneficial species of *Bacillus* include *B. polymyxa* (po-lē-miks′ă) and *B. licheniformis* (lī-ken-i-for′mis), which synthesize the antibiotics polymyxin and bacitracin, respectively.

*Bacillus anthracis* (an-thrā′sis), which causes anthrax, gained notoriety in 2001 as an agent of bioterrorism. Its endospores are either inhaled or enter the body through breaks in the skin. When they germinate, the vegetative cells produce toxins that kill surrounding tissues. Untreated *cutaneous anthrax* is fatal in 20% of patients; untreated inhalational *anthrax* is generally 100% fatal without prompt aggressive treatment. As discussed, refrigeration prevents the excessive growth of this and other contaminants.

**Listeria** Another pathogenic low G + C Gram-positive rod is *Listeria monocytogenes* (mo-nō-sī-tah′je-nēz), which can contaminate milk and meat products. This microbe, which does not produce endospores, is notable because it continues to reproduce under refrigeration, and it can survive inside phagocytic white blood cells. *Listeria* rarely causes disease in adults, but it can kill a fetus in an infected woman when it crosses the placental barrier. It also causes meningitis[11] and bacteremia[12] when it infects immunocompromised patients such as the aged and patients with AIDS, cancer, or diabetes.

**Lactobacillus** Organisms in the genus *Lactobacillus* are non-spore-forming rods normally found growing in the human mouth, stomach, intestinal tract, and vagina. These organisms rarely cause disease; instead, they protect the body by inhibit-

ing the growth of pathogens—a situation called *microbial antagonism.* Lactobacilli are used in industry in the production of yogurt, buttermilk, pickles, and sauerkraut. The Beneficial Microbes box discusses the growing role of *Lactobacillus* in promoting human health.

**Streptococcus and Enterococcus** The genera *Streptococcus* and *Enterococcus* are diverse groups of Gram-positive cocci associated in pairs and chains (see Figure 6b). They cause numerous human diseases, including pharyngitis (strep throat), scarlet fever, impetigo, fetal meningitis, wound infections, pneumonia, and diseases of the inner ear, skin, blood, and kidneys. In recent years, health care providers have become concerned over strains of multi-drug-resistant streptococci. Of particular concern are so-called flesh-eating streptococci, which produce toxins that destroy muscle and fat tissue.

**Staphylococcus** Among the common inhabitants of humans is *Staphylococcus aureus*[13] (o′rē-ŭs), which is typically found growing harmlessly in clusters on the skin. A variety of toxins and enzymes allow some strains of *S. aureus* to invade the body and cause such diseases as bacteremia, pneumonia, wound infections, food poisoning, toxic shock syndrome, and diseases of the joints, bones, heart, and blood.

The characteristics of the low G + C Gram-positive bacteria are summarized in the first part of Table 2. These bacteria, which are classified into three classes within phylum Firmicutes, include the anaerobic endospore-forming rod *Clostridium*, the pleomorphic *Mycoplasma*, the aerobic and facultative aerobic endospore-forming rod *Bacillus*, the non-endospore-forming rods *Listeria* and *Lactobacillus*, and the cocci *Streptococcus*, *Enterococcus*, and *Staphylococcus*.

Next we consider Gram-positive bacteria that have high G + C ratios.

## High G + C Gram-Positive Bacteria

### Learning Objectives

✓ Explain the slow growth of *Mycobacterium*.

✓ Identify significant beneficial or detrimental properties of the genera *Corynebacterium, Mycobacterium, Actinomyces, Nocardia,* and *Streptomyces.*

Taxonomists classify Gram-positive bacteria with a G + C ratio greater than 50% in the phylum Actinobacteria, which includes species with rod-shaped cells (many of which are significant human pathogens) and filamentous bacteria, which resemble fungi in their growth habit and in the production of reproductive spores.

---

[11]Inflammation of the membranes covering the brain and spinal cord; from Greek *meninx*, meaning membrane.
[12]The presence of bacteria, particularly those that produce disease symptoms, in the blood.
[13]From Latin *aurum*, meaning gold, because it produces yellow pigments.

## 2

## Characteristics of Selected Gram-Positive Bacteria

| Phylum/Class | G + C Ratio | Representative Genera | Special Characteristics | Diseases |
|---|---|---|---|---|
| **Firmicutes** | | | | |
| Clostridia | Low (less than 50%) | Clostridium | Obligate anaerobic rods; endospore formers | Tetanus |
| | | | | Botulism |
| | | | | Gangrene |
| | | | | Severe diarrhea |
| | | Epulopiscium | Giant rods | |
| | | Veillonella | Part of oral biofilm on human teeth; stain like Gram-negative bacteria (pink) | Dental caries |
| Mollicutes | Low (less than 50%) | Mycoplasma | Lack cell walls; pleomorphic; smallest free-living cells; stain like Gram-negative bacteria (pink) | Pneumonia |
| | | | | Urinary tract infections |
| Bacilli | Low (less than 50%) | Bacillus | Facultative anaerobic rods; endospore formers | Anthrax |
| | | Listeria | Contaminates dairy products | Listeriosis |
| | | Lactobacillus | Produce yogurt, buttermilk, pickles, sauerkraut | Rare blood infections |
| | | Streptococcus | Cocci in chains | Strep throat, scarlet fever, and others |
| | | Staphylococcus | Cocci in clusters | Bacteremia, food poisoning, and others |
| **Actinobacteria** | | | | |
| Actinobacteria | High (greater than 50%) | Corynebacterium | Snapping division; metachromatic granules in cytoplasm | Diphtheria |
| | | Mycobacterium | Waxy cell walls (mycolic acid) | Tuberculosis and meningitis |
| | | Actinomyces | Filaments | Actinomycosis |
| | | Nocardia | Filaments; degrade pollutants | Lesions |
| | | Streptomyces | Produce antibiotics | Rare sinus infections |

### Corynebacterium

Members of the genus *Corynebacterium* are pleomorphic—though generally rod-shaped—aerobes and facultative anaerobes. They reproduce by snapping division, which often causes the cells to form V-shapes and palisades (see Figures 3 and 7d). Corynebacteria are also characterized by their stores of phosphate within inclusions called **metachromatic granules,** which stain differently from the rest of the cytoplasm when the cells are stained with methylene blue or toluidine blue. The best-known species is *C. diphtheriae,* which causes diphtheria.

### Mycobacterium

The genus *Mycobacterium* (mī'kō-bak-tēr'ē-um) is composed of aerobic species that are slightly curved to straight rods that sometimes form filaments. Mycobacteria grow very slowly, often requiring a month or more to form a visible colony on an agar surface. Their slow growth is partly due to the time and energy required to enrich their cell walls with high concentrations of long carbon-chain waxes called **mycolic acids,** which make the cells resistant to desiccation and to staining with water-based dyes. Microbiologists developed the *acid-fast stain* for mycobacteria because they are difficult to stain by standard staining techniques such as the Gram stain. Though some mycobacteria are free-living, the most prominent species are pathogens of animals and humans, including *Mycobacterium tuberculosis* (too-ber-kyū-lō'sis) and *Mycobacterium leprae* (lep'rī), which cause tuberculosis and leprosy, respectively. Mycobacteria should not be confused with the low G + C mycoplasmas discussed earlier.

### Actinomycetes

**Actinomycetes** (ak'ti-nō-mī-sētz) are high G + C Gram-positive bacteria that form branching filaments resembling fungi (Figure 17). Of course, in contrast to fungi, the filaments of actinomycetes are composed of prokaryotic cells. As we have seen, some actinomycetes also resemble fungi in the production of chains of reproductive spores at the ends of their filaments (see Figure 4). These spores should not be confused with endospores, which are resting stages and not reproductive cells. Actinomycetes may cause disease, particularly in immunocompromised patients. Among the important actinomycete genera are *Actinomyces* (which gives this group its name), *Nocardia,* and *Streptomyces.*

▲ **Figure 17 The branching filaments of actinomycetes.** This photograph shows filaments of a colony of *Streptomyces* sp. growing on agar. *How do the filaments of actinomycetes compare to the filaments of fungi?*

**Figure 17** *Filaments of actinomycetes are thinner than those of fungi, and they are composed of prokaryotic cells.*

**Actinomyces** Species of *Actinomyces* (ak′ti-nō-mī′sēz) are facultative capneic[14] filaments that are normal inhabitants of the mucous membranes lining the oral cavity and throats of humans. *Actinomyces israelii* (is-rā′el-ē-ē) growing as an opportunistic pathogen in humans destroys tissue to form abscesses and can spread throughout the abdomen, consuming every vital organ.

**Nocardia** Species of *Nocardia* (nō-kar′dē-ă) are soil- and water-dwelling aerobes that typically form aerial and subterranean filaments that make them resemble fungi. *Nocardia* is notable because it can degrade many pollutants of landfills, lakes, and streams, including waxes, petroleum hydrocarbons, detergents, benzene, polychlorinated biphenyls (PCBs), pesticides, and rubber. Some species of *Nocardia* cause lesions in humans.

**Streptomyces** Bacteria in the genus *Streptomyces* (strep-tō-mī′-sēz) are important in several realms. Ecologically, they recycle nutrients in the soil by degrading a number of carbohydrates, including cellulose, lignin (the woody part of plants), chitin (the skeletal material of insects and crustaceans), latex, aromatic chemicals (organic compounds containing a benzene ring), and keratin (the protein that forms hair, nails, and horns). The metabolic by-products of *Streptomyces* give soil its musty smell. Medically, *Streptomyces* produce most of the important antibiotics, including chloramphenicol, erythromycin, and tetracycline. **Highlight:** *Streptomyces* **and the European Beewolf** discusses a species of *Streptomyces* that resides in the antennal glands of a wasp.

Table 2 includes a summary of the characteristics of the genera of high G + C Gram-positive bacteria (phylum Actinobacteria) discussed in this chapter.

Gudrun Herzner

## HIGHLIGHT

### STREPTOMYCES AND THE EUROPEAN BEEWOLF

The female European beewolf is a wasp that takes motherhood seriously. True to its name, the beewolf catches bees, paralyzes them with its sting, and then tucks them into holes in the ground, where the (still living) bees serve as food for the beewolf's young. To protect her young, the female beewolf also enlists the help of bacteria. She secretes a goolike substance from her antennal glands, which, as scientists have recently learned, contains a previously unidentified species of *Streptomyces* bacteria. It appears that the goo, with the help of these bacteria, somehow defends young beewolves from threats such as pathogens in their environment. Studies have shown that beewolf larvae deprived of contact with the goo were less likely to live to adulthood than larvae allowed contact with the goo—suggesting that the European beewolf may have bacteria to thank for keeping her young secure.

## CRITICAL **THINKING**

We discussed the identification of microbes using dichotomous taxonomic keys. Design a key for all the genera of Gram-positive bacteria listed in Table 2.

To this point we have discussed archaea and deeply branching, phototrophic, and Gram-positive bacteria. Now we turn our attention to the Gram-negative bacteria that are grouped together within the phylum Proteobacteria.

## Gram-Negative Proteobacteria

Phylum **Proteobacteria**[15] constitutes the largest and most diverse group of bacteria (see Figure 9). Though they have a variety of shapes, reproductive strategies, and nutritional types, they are all Gram-negative and share common 16S rRNA nucleotide sequences. The G + C ratio of Gram-negative species is not critical in delineating taxa of most Gram-negative organisms, so we will not consider this characteristic in our discussion of these bacteria.

There are five distinct classes of proteobacteria, designated by the first five letters of the Greek alphabet—alpha, beta, gamma, delta, and epsilon. These classes are distinguished by minor differences in their rRNA sequences. Here we will focus

---

[14]Meaning they grow best with a relatively high concentration of carbon dioxide.
[15]Named for the Greek god *Proteus*, who could assume many shapes.

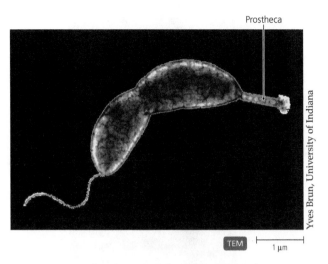

Prostheca

TEM |———| 1 μm

Yves Brun, University of Indiana

▲ **Figure 18  A prostheca.** This extension of an alphaproteobacterial cell increases surface area for absorbing nutrients and serves as an organ of attachment. This prosthecate bacterium, *Hyphomicrobium facilis*, also produces buds from its prostheca.

Visuals Unlimited/Getty Images

▲ **Figure 19  Nodules on pea roots.** *Rhizobium*, a nitrogen-fixing alphaproteobacterium, stimulates the growth of such nodules.

our attention on species with novel characteristics as well as species with practical importance.

### Alphaproteobacteria

Learning Objective

✓ Describe the appearance and function of prosthecae in alphaproteobacteria.

**Alphaproteobacteria** are typically aerobes capable of growing at very low nutrient levels. Many have unusual methods of metabolism, as we will see shortly. They may be rods, curved rods, spirals, coccobacilli, or pleomorphic. Many species have unusual extensions called *prosthecae* (pros-thē'kē), which are composed of cytoplasm surrounded by the cytoplasmic membrane and cell wall (Figure 18). They use prosthecae for attachment and to increase surface area for nutrient absorption. Some prosthecate species produce buds at the ends of the extensions.

**Nitrogen Fixers** Two genera of nitrogen-fixers in the class Alphaproteobacteria—*Azospirillum* (ā-zō-spī'ril-ŭm) and *Rhizobium* (ri-zō' be-ŭm)—are important in agriculture. They grow in association with the roots of plants, where they make atmospheric nitrogen ($N_2$) available to the plants as ammonia ($NH_3$), often called fixed nitrogen. *Azospirillum* associates with the outer surfaces of roots of tropical grasses, such as sugar cane. In addition to supplying nitrogen to the grass, this bacterium also releases chemicals that stimulate the plant to produce numerous root hairs, which increase a root's surface area and thus its uptake of nutrients.

*Rhizobium* grows within the roots of leguminous plants such as peas, beans, and clover, stimulating the formation of nodules on their roots (Figure 19). *Rhizobium* cells within the nodules make ammonia available to the plant, encouraging growth. Scientists are actively seeking ways to successfully insert the genes

of nitrogen fixation into plants such as corn, which require large amounts of nitrogen.

**Nitrifying Bacteria** Chemoautotrophic organisms derive their carbon from carbon dioxide and their energy from inorganic chemicals. Those that derive electrons from the oxidation of nitrogenous compounds are called **nitrifying bacteria.** These microbes are important in the environment and in agriculture because they convert reduced nitrogen compounds, such as ammonia ($NH_3$), and ammonium ($NH_4^+$), into nitrate ($NO_3^-$)—a process called **nitrification.** Nitrate moves more easily through soil than reduced nitrogenous compounds and is thereby more available to plants. Nitrifying alphaproteobacteria oxidize ammonia or ammonium and are in the genus *Nitrobacter* (nī-trō-bak'ter).

### CRITICAL **THINKING**

Contrast the processes of nitrogen fixation and nitrification.

**Purple Nonsulfur Phototrophs** With one exception (the betaproteobacterium *Rhodocyclus*), purple nonsulfur phototrophs are classified as alphaproteobacteria. Purple nonsulfur bacteria grow in the upper layer of mud at the bottoms of lakes and ponds. As we discussed earlier, they harvest light as an energy source by using bacteriochlorophylls, and they do not generate oxygen during photosynthesis. Morphologically, they may be rods, curved rods, or spirals; some species are prosthecate. Refer to Table 1 to review the characteristics of all phototrophic bacteria.

**Pathogenic Alphaproteobacteria** Notable pathogens among the alphaproteobacteria include *Rickettsia* (ri-ket'sē-ă), and *Brucella* (broo-sel'lă).

*Rickettsia* is a genus of small, Gram-negative, aerobic rods that live and reproduce inside mammalian cells. They cause a number

Rock or other substrate

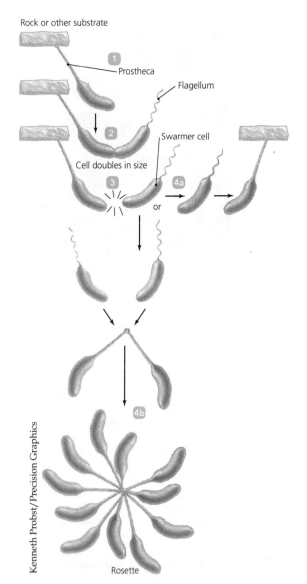

Prostheca

Flagellum

Swarmer cell

Cell doubles in size

or

Rosette

Kenneth Probst/Precision Graphics

▲ **Figure 20 Growth and reproduction of *Caulobacter*.**
1 A cell attached to a substrate by its prostheca. 2 Growth and production of an apical flagellum. 3 Division by asymmetrical binary fission to produce a flagellated daughter cell called a swarmer cell. 4a Attachment of a swarmer cell to a substrate by a prostheca that replaces the flagellum. 4b Attachment of a swarmer cell to other cells to form a rosette.

of human diseases, including typhus and Rocky Mountain spotted fever. Rickettsias cannot use glucose as a nutrient; instead they oxidize amino acids and Krebs cycle intermediates such as glutamic acid and succinic acid. For this reason they are obliged to live within other cells where these nutrients are produced.

*Brucella* is a coccobacillus that causes *brucellosis,* a disease of mammals characterized by spontaneous abortions and sterility in animals. In contrast, infected humans suffer chills, sweating, fatigue, and fever. *Brucella* is notable because it survives phago-

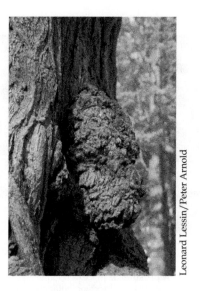

Leonard Lessin/Peter Arnold

▲ **Figure 21 A plant gall.** Infecting cells of *Agrobacterium* have inserted into a plant chromosome a plasmid carrying a plant growth hormone gene. The hormone causes the proliferation of undifferentiated plant cells. These gall cells synthesize nutrients for the bacteria.

cytosis by white blood cells—normally an important step in the body's defense against disease.

**Other Alphaproteobacteria** Other alphaproteobacteria are important in industry and the environment. For example, *Acetobacter* (a-sē′tō-bak-ter) and *Gluconobacter* (gloo-kon′ō-bak-ter) are used to synthesize acetic acid (vinegar). *Caulobacter* (kaw′lō-bak-ter) is a common prosthecate rod-shaped microbe that inhabits nutrient-poor seawater and freshwater; it can also be found in laboratory water baths.

*Caulobacter* has a unique reproductive strategy (Figure 20). A cell that has attached to a substrate with its prostheca (1) grows until it has doubled in size, at which time it produces a flagellum at its apex (2); it then divides by asymmetric binary fission (3). The flagellated daughter cell, which is called a swarmer cell, then swims away. The swarmer cell can either attach to a substrate with a new prostheca that replaces the flagellum (4a) or attach to other swarmer cells to form a rosette of cells (4b). The process of reproduction repeats about every 2 hours. **Beneficial Microbes: A Microtube of Super Glue** examines an amazing property of *Caulobacter* prosthecae.

Scientists are very interested in the usefulness of another alphaproteobacterium, *Agrobacterium* (ag′ro-bak-tēr′ē-ŭm), which infects plants to form tumors called *galls* (Figure 21). The bacterium inserts a plasmid called Ti, which carries a gene for a plant growth hormone, into a chromosome of the plant. The growth hormone causes the cells of the plant to proliferate into a gall and to produce nutrients for the bacterium. Scientists have discovered that they can insert almost any DNA sequence into the plasmid, making it an ideal vector for genetic manipulation of plants.

Characteristics of selected members of the alphaproteobacteria are listed in Table 3.

**3**

**TABLE**

## Characteristics of Selected Gram-Negative Bacteria

| Phylum/Class | Representative Members | Special Characteristics | Diseases |
|---|---|---|---|
| **Proteobacteria** | | | |
| Alphaproteobacteria | *Azospirillum* | Nitrogen fixer | |
| | *Rhizobium* | Nitrogen fixer | |
| | *Nitrobacter* | Nitrifying bacterium | |
| | Purple nonsulfur bacteria | Anoxygenic phototrophs | |
| | *Rickettsia* | Intracellular pathogen | Typhus and Rocky Mountain spotted fever |
| | *Brucella* | Coccobacillus | Brucellosis |
| | *Acetobacter, Gluconobacter* | Synthesize acetic acid | |
| | *Caulobacter* | Prosthecate bacterium | |
| | *Agrobacterium* | Causes galls in plants; vector for gene transfer in plants | |
| Betaproteobacteria | *Nitrosomonas* | Nitrifying bacterium | |
| | *Neisseria* | Diplococcus | Gonorrhea and meningitis |
| | *Bordetella* | | Pertussis |
| | *Burkholderia* | | Lung infection of cystic fibrosis patients |
| | *Thiobacillus* | Colorless sulfur bacterium | |
| | *Zoogloea* | Used in sewage treatment | |
| | *Sphaerotilus* | Blocks sewage treatment pipes | |
| Gammaproteobacteria | Purple sulfur bacteria | | |
| | *Legionella* | Intracellular pathogen | Legionnaires' disease |
| | *Coxiella* | Intracellular pathogen | Q fever |
| | *Methylococcus* | Oxidizes methane | |
| | Glycolytic facultative anaerobes | Facultative anaerobes that catabolize carbohydrates via glycolysis and the pentose phosphate pathway | See Table 4 |
| | *Pseudomonas* | Aerobe that catabolizes carbohydrates via Entner-Doudoroff and pentose phosphate pathways | Urinary tract infections, external otitis |
| | *Azotobacter Azomonas* | Nitrogen fixers not associated with plant roots | |
| Deltaproteobacteria | *Desulfovibrio* | Sulfate reducer | |
| | *Bdellovibrio* | Pathogen of Gram-negative bacteria | |
| | Myxobacteria | Reproduces by forming differentiated fruiting bodies | |
| Epsilonproteobacteria | *Campylobacter* | Curved rod | Gastroenteritis |
| | *Helicobacter* | Spiral | Gastric ulcers |
| **Chlamydiae** | | | |
| Chlamydiae | *Chlamydia* | Intracellular pathogen; lacks peptidoglycan | Neonatal blindness and lymphogranuloma venereum |
| **Spirochaetes** | | | |
| "Spirochaetes"[a] | *Treponema* | Motile by axial filaments | Syphilis |
| | *Borrelia* | Motile by axial filaments | Lyme disease |
| **"Bacteroidetes"** | | | |
| "Bacteroidetes" | *Bacteroides* | Anaerobe that lives in animal colons | Abdominal infections |
| "Sphingobacteria" | *Cytophaga* | Digests complex polysaccharides | |

[a]The names of taxa in quotations are not officially recognized.

## BENEFICIAL MICROBES

### A MICROTUBE OF SUPERGLUE

Yves Brun/Indiana University

▲ *Caulobacter crescentus.* SEM 1 μm

A swarmer cell of the Gram-negative, alphaproteobacterium *Caulobacter crescentus* attaches itself to an environmental substrate by secreting an organic adhesive from its prostheca as if it were a tube of glue. This polysaccharide-based bonding agent is the strongest known glue of biological origin, beating out such contenders as barnacle glue, mussel glue, and the adhesion of gecko lizard bristles. One way scientists gauge adhesive strength is to measure the force required to break apart two glued objects.

Commercial superglues typically lose their grip when confronted with a shear force of 18 to 28 newtons (N) per square millimeter (1 newton is the amount of force needed to accelerate a 1-kg mass 1 meter per second per second). Dental cements bond with strengths up to 30 $N/mm^2$, but *Caulobacter* glue is more than twice as adhesive. It maintains its grip up to 68 $N/mm^2$! That is equivalent to being able to hang an adult female elephant on a wall with a spot of glue the size of an American quarter. And remember, this bacterium lives in water; its glue works even when submerged.

Scientists are researching the biophysical and chemical mechanisms that give this biological glue such incredible gripping power. One critical component of the glue is N-acetylglucosamine, one of the sugar subunits of peptidoglycan found in bacterial cell walls. Scientists are struggling to characterize the other molecules that make up the glue. The problem? They cannot pry the glue free to analyze it.

Some potential applications of such a bacterial superglue include use as a biodegradable suture in surgery, as a more durable dental adhesive, or as an adhesive to stick anti-biofilm disinfectants onto surfaces such as medical devices and ships' hulls.

### Betaproteobacteria

#### Learning Objective

✓ Name three pathogenic and three useful betaproteobacteria.

**Betaproteobacteria** are another diverse group of Gram-negative bacteria that thrive in habitats with low levels of nutrients. They differ from alphaproteobacteria in their rRNA sequences, though metabolically the two groups overlap. One example of the metabolic overlap is *Nitrosomonas* (nī-trō-sō-mō′nas), an important nitrifying bacterium of soils; instead of oxidizing ammonia or ammonium to nitrate, however, it oxidizes nitrite to nitrate. In this section we will discuss a few interesting betaproteobacteria.

**Pathogenic Betaproteobacteria** Species of *Neisseria* (ni-se′rē-ă) are Gram-negative diplococci that inhabit the mucous membranes of mammals and cause such diseases as gonorrhea, meningitis, pelvic inflammatory disease, and inflammation of the cervix, pharynx, and external lining of the eye.

Other pathogenic betaproteobacteria include *Bordetella* (bŏr-dĕ-tel′ă), which is the cause of pertussis (whooping cough) (see **Emerging Diseases: Pertussis**), and *Burkholderia* (burk-hol-der′ē-ă), which recycles numerous organic compounds in nature. *Burkholderia* commonly colonizes moist environmental surfaces (including laboratory and medical equipment) and the respiratory passages of patients with cystic fibrosis.

**Other Betaproteobacteria** Members of the genus *Thiobacillus* (thī-ō-bă-sil′ŭs) are colorless sulfur bacteria that are important in recycling sulfur in the environment by oxidizing hydrogen sulfide ($H_2S$) or elemental sulfur ($S^0$) to sulfate ($SO_4^{2-}$). Miners use *Thiobacillus* to leach metals from low-grade ore, though the bacterium does cause extensive pollution when it releases metals and acid from mine wastes.

Sewage treatment supervisors are interested in *Zoogloea* (zō′ō-glē-ă) and *Sphaerotilus* (sfēr-ō′til-us), two genera that form *flocs*—slimy, tangled masses of bacteria and organic matter in sewage. *Zoogloea* forms compact flocs that settle to the bottom of treatment tanks and assist in the purification process. *Sphaerotilus*, in contrast, forms loose flocs that do not settle and thus impede the proper flow of waste through a treatment plant.

The characteristics of the genera of betaproteobacteria discussed in this section are summarized in Table 3.

### Gammaproteobacteria

#### Learning Objective

✓ Describe the gammaproteobacteria.

The **gammaproteobacteria** make up the largest and most diverse class of proteobacteria; almost every shape, arrangement of cells, metabolic type, and reproductive strategy is represented in this group. Ribosomal studies indicate that gammaproteobacteria can be divided into several subgroups:

- Purple sulfur bacteria
- Intracellular pathogens
- Methane oxidizers
- Facultative anaerobes that utilize Embden-Meyerhof gly-
  colysis and the pentose phosphate pathway
- Pseudomonads, which are aerobes that catabolize carbohy-
  drates by the Entner-Doudoroff and pentose phosphate
  pathways

Here we will examine some representatives of these groups.

**Purple Sulfur Bacteria** Whereas the purple *non*sulfur bacteria are distributed among the alpha- and betaproteobacteria, **purple sulfur bacteria** are all gammaproteobacteria (Figure 22). Purple sulfur bacteria are obligate anaerobes that oxidize hydrogen sulfide to sulfur, which they deposit as internal granules. They are found in sulfur-rich zones in lakes, bogs, and oceans. Some species form intimate relationships with marine worms, covering the body of a worm like strands of hair.

**Intracellular Pathogens** Organisms in the genera *Legionella* (lē-jŭ-nel'lă) and *Coxiella* (kok-sē-el'ă) are pathogens of humans that avoid digestion by white blood cells, which are normally part of a body's defense; in fact, they thrive inside these defensive cells. *Legionella* derives energy from the metabolism of amino acids, which are more prevalent inside cells than outside. *Coxiella* grows best at low pH, such as is found in the

David J. Patterson, http://micro*scope.mbl.edu.

LM     5 μm

▲ **Figure 22  Purple sulfur bacteria.**

phagolysomes of white blood cells. The bacteria in these genera cause Legionnaires' disease and Q fever, respectively.

**Methane Oxidizers** Methane oxidizers, such as *Methylococcus* (meth-i-lō-kok'ŭs), are Gram-negative bacteria that utilize methane as a carbon source and as an energy source. Like

---

**EMERGING DISEASES**

MIXA Co., Ltd./ Alamy

### PERTUSSIS

Jeeyun was coughing again. She had been coughing off and on for two weeks. If she had thought of it, she might have noticed that the coughing spells began soon after her flight from New York, where she had visited her grandmother. Within a week of her return to California, she had developed coldlike signs—runny nose, sneezing, and a slight fever—but she didn't remember these things. What she did know was that the coughing was worse; her chest hurt from the constant hacking. Then, the coughing broke two ribs.

The surprising pain caused Jeeyun to involuntarily urinate. When the coughing stopped, she vomited and fainted in a heap on the floor. This was no ordinary cough! Jeeyun's roommate called 911. Later, emergency room staff at the hospital bandaged her chest to stabilize the broken ribs and diagnosed the cough as pertussis.

Pertussis, commonly known as whooping cough, is usually considered a childhood disease, but it can strike adults. Older patients seldom develop the characteristic "whooping" sound associated with gasping inhalation, but in Jeeyun's case, the severity and length of the coughing led to a speedy diagnosis.

Immunization is the only way to control pertussis, but adults have been lax in vaccinating children and receiving boosters for themselves. As a result, whooping cough is reemerging as a major problem in the industrialized world. Infected people spread *Bordetella* in respiratory droplets to their neighbors, as happened to Jeeyun in an airplane's cabin on a long flight.

Precision Graphics

**(MM)  Track pertussis online by going to the Study Area at www.masteringmicrobiology.com.**

K. S. Kim/Peter Arnold

SEM | 2.0 μm

▲ **Figure 23** Two dividing *Pseudomonas* cells and their characteristic polar flagella.

archaeal methanogens, methane oxidizers inhabit anaerobic environments worldwide, growing just above the anaerobic layers that contain methanogens. Although methane is one of the so-called greenhouse gases that retains heat in the atmosphere, methane oxidizers digest most of the methane in their local environment before it can adversely affect the world's climate.

**Glycolytic Facultative Anaerobes** The largest group of gammaproteobacteria is composed of Gram-negative, facultatively anaerobic rods that catabolize carbohydrates by glycolysis and the pentose phosphate pathway. This group, which is divided into three families (Table 4), contains numerous human pathogens. Members of the family Enterobacteriaceae, including *Escherichia coli* (esh-ĕ-rik'ē-ă kō'lē), are frequently used for laboratory studies of metabolism, genetics, and recombinant DNA technology.

**Pseudomonads** Bacteria called **pseudomonads** are Gram-negative, aerobic, flagellated, straight to slightly curved rods that catabolize carbohydrates by the Entner-Doudoroff and pentose phosphate pathways. These organisms are noted for their ability to break down numerous organic compounds. Many of them are important pathogens of humans and animals and are involved in the spoilage of refrigerated milk, eggs, and meat because they can grow and catabolize proteins and lipids at 4°C. The pseudomonad group is named for its most important genus: *Pseudomonas* (soo-dō-mō'nas; Figure 23), which causes diseases such as urinary tract infections and external otitis (swimmer's ear). Other pseudomonads such as *Azotobacter* (ā-zō-tō-bak'ter) and *Azomonas* (ā-zō-mō'nas) are soil-dwelling, nonpathogenic nitrogen fixers; however, in contrast to nitrogen-fixing alphaproteobacteria, these gammaproteobacteria do not associate with the roots of plants.

The characteristics of the members of the gammaproteobacteria discussed in this section are summarized in Table 3.

### Deltaproteobacteria

Learning Objective

✓ List several members of deltaproteobacteria.

The **deltaproteobacteria** are not a large assemblage, but like other proteobacteria they include a wide variety of metabolic types. *Desulfovibrio* (dē'sul-fō-vib'rē-ō) is a sulfate-reducing microbe that is important in the sulfur cycle. It is also an important member of bacterial communities living in the sediments of polluted streams and sewage treatment lagoons, where its presence is often apparent by the odor of hydrogen sulfide that it releases during anaerobic respiration. Hydrogen sulfide reacts

**TABLE 4**

## Representative Glycolytic Facultative Anaerobes of the Class Gammaproteobacteria

| Family | Special Characteristics | Representative Genera | Typical Human Diseases |
|---|---|---|---|
| Enterobacteriaceae | Straight rods; oxidase negative; peritrichous flagella or nonmotile | *Escherichia* | Gastroenteritis |
| | | *Enterobacter* | (Rarely pathogenic) |
| | | *Serratia* | (Rarely pathogenic) |
| | | *Salmonella* | Enteritis |
| | | *Proteus* | Urinary tract infection |
| | | *Shigella* | Shigellosis |
| | | *Yersinia* | Plague |
| | | *Klebsiella* | Pneumonia |
| Vibrionaceae | Vibrios; oxidase positive; polar flagella | *Vibrio* | Cholera |
| Pasteurellaceae | Cocci or straight rods; oxidase positive; nonmotile | *Haemophilus* | Meningitis in children |

From: Bdellovibrio bacteriovorus—a predatory bacterial parasite. *Naturwissenschaften.* H. Stolp. 1968 February; 55(2):57–63. With permission of Springer Science and Business Media

**(b)**

◀ **Figure 24** *Bdellovibrio,* **a Gram-negative pathogen of other Gram-negative bacteria. (a)** Life cycle, including the elapsed times between events. **(b)** *Bdellovibrio* invading the periplasmic space of its host.

with iron to form iron sulfide, so sulfate-reducing bacteria play a primary role in the corrosion of iron pipes in heating systems, sewer lines, and other structures.

*Bdellovibrio* (del-lō-vib′rē-ō) is not pathogenic to eukaryotes, but instead attacks other Gram-negative bacteria. It has a complex and unusual life cycle (Figure 24a):

1  A free *Bdellovibrio* swims rapidly through the medium until it attaches via fimbriae to a Gram-negative bacterium.

2  It rapidly drills through the cell wall of its prey by secreting hydrolytic enzymes and rotating in excess of 100 revolutions per second (Figure 24b).

3  Once inside, *Bdellovibrio* lives in the periplasmic space—the space between the cytoplasmic membrane and the cell wall. It kills its host by disrupting the host's cytoplasmic membrane and inhibiting DNA, RNA, and protein synthesis.

4  The invading bacterium uses the nutrients released from its dying prey and grows into a long filament.

5  Eventually, the filament divides into many smaller cells, each of which, when released from the dead cell, produces a flagellum, and swims off to repeat the process. Multiple fissions to produce many offspring is a rare form of reproduction.

**Myxobacteria** are Gram-negative, aerobic, soil-dwelling bacteria with a unique life cycle for prokaryotes in that individuals cooperate to produce differentiated reproductive structures. The life cycle of myxobacteria can be summarized as follows (Figure 25a):

1  Vegetative myxobacteria glide on slime trails through their environment, digesting yeasts and other bacteria or scavenging nutrients released from dead cells. When nutrients and cells are plentiful, the myxobacteria divide by binary fission; when nutrients are depleted, however, they aggregate by gliding into a mound of cells.

2  Myxobacteria within the mound differentiate to form a macroscopic *fruiting body* ranging in height from 50 μm to 700 μm.

3  Some cells within the fruiting body develop into dormant *myxospores* that are enclosed within walled structures called *sporangia* (singular: *sporangium;* Figure 25b).

4  The sporangia release the myxospores, which can resist desiccation and nutrient deprivation for a decade or more.

5  When nutrients are again plentiful, the myxospores germinate and become vegetative cells.

Myxobacteria live worldwide in soils that have decaying plant material or animal dung. Though certain species live in the arctic and others in the tropics, most myxobacteria live in temperate regions.

## CRITICAL **THINKING**

What do the names *Desulfovibrio* and *Bdellovibrio* tell you about the morphology of these deltaproteobacteria?

## Epsilonproteobacteria

**Epsilonproteobacteria** are Gram-negative rods, vibrios, or spirals. Important genera are *Campylobacter* (kam′pi-lō-bak′ter),

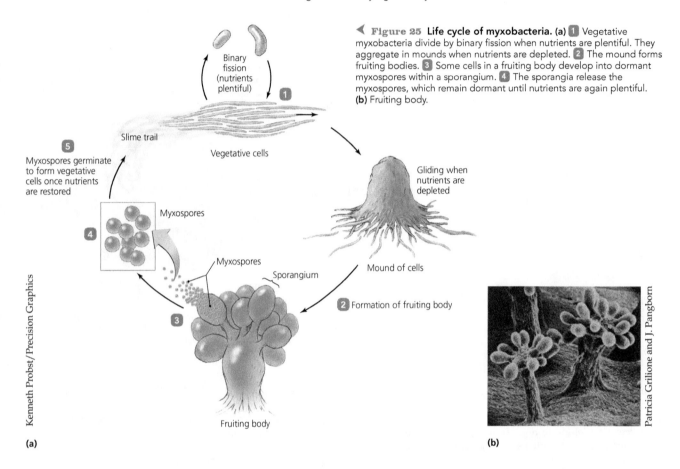

**◄ Figure 25 Life cycle of myxobacteria. (a) ①** Vegetative myxobacteria divide by binary fission when nutrients are plentiful. They aggregate in mounds when nutrients are depleted. **②** The mound forms fruiting bodies. **③** Some cells in a fruiting body develop into dormant myxospores within a sporangium. **④** The sporangia release the myxospores, which remain dormant until nutrients are again plentiful. **(b)** Fruiting body.

Binary fission (nutrients plentiful)

**①**

Slime trail

Vegetative cells

**⑤** Myxospores germinate to form vegetative cells once nutrients are restored

Gliding when nutrients are depleted

Myxospores

**④**

Myxospores

Sporangium

Mound of cells

**②** Formation of fruiting body

**③**

Fruiting body

Kenneth Probst/Precision Graphics

Patricia Grilione and J. Pangborn

**(a)**

**(b)**

which causes blood poisoning and inflammation of the intestinal tract, and *Helicobacter* (hel′ĭ-kō-bak′ter), which causes ulcers.

The characteristics of the delta- and epsilonproteobacteria are summarized in Table 3.

CRITICAL **THINKING**

Design a dichotomous key for the proteobacteria discussed in this chapter.

## Other Gram-Negative Bacteria

### Learning Objectives

✓ Describe the unique features of chlamydias and spirochetes.

✓ Describe the ecological importance of bacteroids.

In the final section of this chapter we consider an assortment of Gram-negative bacteria that are classified in the second edition of *Bergey's Manual* into nine phyla that are grouped together for convenience rather than because of genetic relatedness. Species in six of the nine phyla are of relatively minor importance. Here we discuss representatives from the three phyla that are either of particular ecological concern or significantly affect human

health: the chlamydias (phylum Chlamydiae), the spirochetes (phylum Spirochaetes), and the bacteroids (phylum Bacteroidetes) (see Figure 9).

### Chlamydias

Microorganisms called **chlamydias** (kla-mid′ē-ăz) are small, Gram-negative cocci that grow and reproduce only within the cells of mammals, birds, and a few invertebrates. The smallest chlamydias—0.2 μm in diameter—are smaller than the largest viruses; however, in contrast to viruses, chlamydias have both DNA and RNA, cytoplasmic membranes, functioning ribosomes, reproduction by binary fission, and metabolic pathways. Like other Gram-negative prokaryotes, chlamydias have two membranes, but in contrast they lack peptidoglycan.

Because chlamydias and rickettsias share an obvious characteristic—both have a requirement for intracellular life—these two types of organisms were grouped together in a single taxon in the first edition of *Bergey's Manual*. Now, however, the rickettsias are classified with the alphaproteobacteria, and the chlamydias are in their own phylum. Chlamydias cause neonatal blindness, pneumonia, and a sexually transmitted disease called *lymphogranuloma venereum;* in fact, chlamydias are the most common sexually transmitted bacteria in the United States.

Chlamydias have a unique method of reproduction. After invading a host cell, a chlamydial cell forms an **initial body** (also called a *reticulate body*). The initial body grows and undergoes repeated binary fissions until the host cell is filled with reticulate bodies. These then change into **elementary bodies,** which contain electron-dense material and have rigid outer boundaries formed when they cross-link their two membranes with disulfide bonds. Each elementary body, which is relatively resistant to drying, is an infective stage. When the host cell dies, the elementary bodies are released to drift until they contact and attach to other host cells, triggering their own endocytosis by the new host cells. Once inside a host cell, elementary bodies transform back into initial bodies, and the cycle repeats.

### Spirochetes

**Spirochetes** are unique helical bacteria that are motile by means of axial filaments—flagella-like structures that lie within the periplasmic space. When the axial filaments rotate, the entire cell corkscrews through the medium.

Spirochetes have a variety of types of metabolism and live in diverse habitats. They are frequently isolated from the human mouth, marine environments, moist soil, and the surfaces of protozoa that live in termites' guts. In the latter case, they may coat the protozoan so thickly that they look, and act, like cilia. The spirochetes *Treponema* (trep-ō-ne′mă) and *Borrelia* (bo-rē′lē-ā) cause syphilis and Lyme disease, respectively, in humans.

### Bacteroids

**Bacteroids** are yet another diverse group of Gram-negative microbes that are grouped together on the basis of similarities in their rRNA nucleotide sequences. The group is named for *Bacteroides* (bak-ter-oy′dēz), a genus of obligately anaerobic rods that normally inhabit the digestive tracts of humans and animals. Bacteroids assist in digestion by catabolizing substances such as cellulose and other complex carbohydrates that are indigestible by mammals. About 30% of the bacteria isolated from human feces are *Bacteroides*. Some species of *Bacteroides* cause abdominal, pelvic, blood, and other infections; in fact, they are the most common anaerobic human pathogen.

Bacteroids in the genus *Cytophaga* (sī-tof′ă-gă) are aquatic, gliding, rod-shaped aerobes with pointed ends. These bacteria degrade complex polysaccharides such as agar, pectin, chitin, and even cellulose, so they cause damage to wooden boats and piers; they also play an important role in the degradation of raw sewage. Their ability to glide allows these bacteria to position themselves at sites with optimum nutrients, pH, temperature, and oxygen levels. Organisms in *Cytophaga* differ from other gliding bacteria, such as cyanobacteria and myxobacteria, in that they are nonphotosynthetic and do not form fruiting bodies.

The characteristics of these groups of Gram-negative bacteria are listed in Table 3.

### CRITICAL **THINKING**

Design a dichotomous key for the genera of Gram-negative bacteria listed in Table 3.

## Chapter Summary

### General Characteristics of Prokaryotic Organisms

1. Three basic shapes of prokaryotic cells are spherical **cocci,** rod-shaped **bacilli,** and **spirals.** Spirals may be stiff **(spirilla)** or flexible **(spirochetes).**

2. Other variations in shapes include **vibrios** (slightly curved rods), **coccobacilli** (intermediate to cocci and bacilli), and **pleomorphic** (variable shape and size).

3. Cocci may typically be found in groups, including long chains **(streptococci),** pairs **(diplococci),** foursomes **(tetrads),** cuboidal packets **(sarcinae),** and clusters **(staphylococci).**

4. Bacilli are found singly, in pairs, in chains, or in a **palisade** arrangement.

5. Prokaryotes reproduce asexually by **binary fission, snapping division** (a type of binary fission), **spore** formation, and **budding.**
   **ANIMATIONS:** *Bacterial Growth: Overview*

6. Environmentally resistant **endospores** are produced within vegetative cells of the Gram-positive genera *Bacillus* and *Clostridium.* Depending on the species in which they are formed, the endospores may be terminal, subterminal, or centrally located.

### Modern Prokaryotic Classification

1. Living things are now classified into three domains—Archaea, Bacteria, and Eukarya—based largely on genetic relatedness.

2. The most authoritative reference in modern prokaryotic systematics is *Bergey's Manual of Systematic Bacteriology,* 2nd ed., which classifies prokaryotes into 3 phyla of Archaea and 24 phyla of Bacteria. The organization of this text's survey of prokaryotes largely follows Bergey's classification scheme.

### Survey of Archaea

1. The domain Archaea includes **extremophiles,** microbes that require extreme conditions of temperature, pH, and/or salinity to survive. One archaeal phylum is known only from rRNA sequences.

2. **Thermophiles** and **hyperthermophiles** (in the phyla Crenarchaeota and Euryarchaeota) live at temperatures above 45°C and 80°C, respectively, because their DNA, membranes, and proteins do not function properly at lower temperatures.

3. **Halophiles** (phylum Euryarchaeota) depend on high concentrations of salt to keep their cell walls intact. Halophiles such as *Halobacterium salinarium* synthesize purple proteins called **bacteriorhodopsins** that harvest light energy to synthesize ATP.

4. **Methanogens** (phylum Euryarchaeota) are obligate anaerobes that produce methane gas and are useful in sewage treatment.

## Survey of Bacteria

1. **Deeply branching bacteria** have rRNA sequences thought to be similar to those of earliest bacteria. They are autotrophic and live in hot, acidic, and anaerobic environments, often with intense exposure to sun.

2. Phototrophic bacteria trap light energy with photosynthetic lamellae. The five groups of phototrophic bacteria are cyanobacteria, green sulfur bacteria, green nonsulfur bacteria, purple sulfur bacteria, and purple nonsulfur bacteria.

3. Many **cyanobacteria** reduce atmospheric $N_2$ to $NH_3$ via a process called **nitrogen fixation.** Cyanobacteria must separate (in either time or space) the metabolic pathways of nitrogen fixation from those of oxygenic photosynthesis because nitrogen fixation is inhibited by the oxygen generated during photosynthesis. Many cyanobacteria fix nitrogen in thick-walled cells called **heterocysts.**

4. Green and purple bacteria use bacteriochlorophylls for anoxygenic photosynthesis. Nonsulfur forms derive electrons from organic compounds; sulfur forms derive electrons from $H_2S$.
   **ANIMATIONS:** *Photosynthesis: Comparing Prokaryotes and Eukaryotes*

5. The phylum Firmicutes contains bacteria with a G + C ratio (the proportion of all base pairs that are guanine-cytosine base pairs) of less than 50%. Firmicutes includes clostridia, mycoplasmas, and other low G + C cocci and bacilli.

6. Clostridia include the genus *Clostridium* (pathogenic bacteria that cause gangrene, tetanus, botulism, and diarrhea), *Epulopiscium* (which is large enough to be seen without a microscope), and *Veillonella* (often found in dental plaque).

7. **Mycoplasmas** are Gram-positive, pleomorphic, facultative anaerobes and obligate anaerobes that lack cell walls and therefore stain pink with Gram stain. They are frequently associated with pneumonia and urinary tract infections.

8. Low G + C Gram-positive bacilli and cocci important to human health and industry include *Bacillus* (which contains species that cause anthrax and food poisoning, and includes beneficial Bt-toxin bacteria), *Listeria* (which causes bacteremia and meningitis), *Lactobacillus* (used to produce yogurt and pickles), *Streptococcus* (which causes strep throat and other diseases), *Enterococcus* (which can cause endocarditis and other diseases), and *Staphylococcus* (which causes a number of human diseases).

9. High G + C bacteria (*Corynebacterium, Mycobacterium,* and actinomycetes) are classified in phylum Actinobacteria.

10. Bacteria in *Corynebacterium* store phosphates in **metachromatic granules;** *C. diphtheriae* causes diphtheria.

11. Members of the genus *Mycobacterium,* including species that cause tuberculosis and leprosy, grow slowly and have unique, resistant cell walls containing waxy **mycolic acids.**

12. **Actinomycetes** resemble fungi in that they produce spores and form filaments; this group includes *Actinomyces* (normally found in human mouths), *Nocardia* (useful in degradation of pollutants), and *Streptomyces* (produces important antibiotics).

13. Phylum **Proteobacteria** is a very large group of Gram-negative bacteria divided into five classes—the alpha-, beta-, gamma-, delta-, and epsilonproteobacteria.

14. The **alphaproteobacteria** include a variety of aerobes, many of which have unusual cellular extensions called prosthecae. *Azospirillum* and *Rhizobium* are nitrogen fixers that are important in agriculture.

15. Some members of the alphaproteobacteria are **nitrifying bacteria,** which oxidize $NH_3$ to $NO_3$ via a process called **nitrification.** Nitrifying alphaproteobacteria are in the genus *Nitrobacter.*

16. Most purple nonsulfur phototrophs are alphaproteobacteria.

17. Pathogenic alphaproteobacteria include *Rickettsia* (typhus and Rocky Mountain spotted fever) and *Brucella* (brucellosis).

18. There are many beneficial alphaproteobacteria, including *Acetobacter* and *Gluconobacter,* both of which are used to synthesize acetic acid. *Caulobacter* is of interest in reproductive studies, and *Agrobacterium* is used in genetic recombination in plants.

19. The **betaproteobacteria** include the nitrifying *Nitrosomonas* and pathogenic species such as *Neisseria* (gonorrhea), *Bordetella* (whooping cough), and *Burkholderia* (which colonizes the lungs of cystic fibrosis patients).

20. Other betaproteobacteria include *Thiobacillus* (ecologically important), *Zoogloea* (useful in sewage treatment), and *Sphaerotilus* (hampers sewage treatment).

21. The **gammaproteobacteria** constitute the largest class of proteobacteria; they include **purple sulfur bacteria,** intracellular pathogens, facultative anaerobes that utilize glycolysis and the pentose phosphate pathway, and pseudomonads.

22. Both *Legionella* and *Coxiella* are intracellular, pathogenic gammaproteobacteria.

23. Numerous human pathogens are facultatively anaerobic gammaproteobacteria that catabolize carbohydrates by glycolysis.

24. **Pseudomonads,** including pathogenic *Pseudomonas* and nitrogen-fixing *Azotobacter* and *Azomonas,* utilize the Entner-Doudoroff and pentose phosphate pathways for catabolism of glucose.

25. The **deltaproteobacteria** include *Desulfovibrio* (important in the sulfur cycle and in corrosion of pipes), *Bdellovibrio* (pathogenic to bacteria), and **myxobacteria.** The latter form stalked fruiting bodies containing resistant, dormant myxospores.

26. The **epsilonproteobacteria** include some important human pathogens, including *Campylobacter* and *Helicobacter.*

27. **Chlamydias** are Gram-negative cocci typified by the genus *Chlamydia;* they cause neonatal blindness, pneumonia, and a sexually transmitted disease. Within a host cell, chlamydias form **initial bodies,** which change into smaller **elementary bodies** released when the host cell dies.

28. **Spirochetes** are flexible, helical bacteria that live in diverse environments. *Treponema* (syphilis) and *Borrelia* (Lyme disease) are important spirochetes.

29. **Bacteroids** include *Bacteroides,* an obligate anaerobic rod that inhabits the digestive tract, and *Cytophaga,* an aerobic rod that degrades wood and raw sewage.

# Questions for Review
*Answers to the Question for Review (except Short Answers questions) appear at the end of this chapter.*

## Modified True/False

For each of the following statements that is true, write "true" in the blank. For each statement that is false, write the word(s) that should be substituted for the italicized word(s) to make the statement correct.

1. _____ All prokaryotes reproduce *sexually.*

2. _____ A *bacillus* is a bacterium with a slightly curved rod shape.

3. _____ If you were to view *staphylococci,* you should expect to see clusters of cells.

4. _____ *Initial* bodies are stable resting stages that do not metabolize but will germinate when conditions improve.

5. _____ Archaea are classified into phyla based primarily on *tRNA sequences.*

6. _____ *Halophiles* inhabit extremely saline habitats such as the Great Salt Lake.

7. _____ Pigments located in thylakoids in phototrophic bacteria trap *light* energy for metabolic processes.

8. _____ Most *cyanobacteria* form heterocysts in which nitrogen fixation occurs.

9. _____ A giant bacterium that is large enough to be seen without a microscope is *Veillonella.*

10. _____ When environmental nutrients are depleted, *myxobacteria* aggregate in mounds to form fruiting bodies.

## Matching

Match the bacterium on the left with the term with which it is most closely associated.

1. _____ *Bacillus anthracis*      A. wood damage

2. _____ *Veillonella*             B. dental biofilm (plaque)

3. _____ *Clostridium perfringens* C. gangrene

4. _____ *Clostridium botulinum*   D. botox

5. _____ *Bacillus licheniformis*  E. anthrax

6. _____ *Streptococcus*           F. lymphogranuloma venereum

7. _____ *Streptomyces*            G. leprosy

8. _____ *Corynebacterium*         H. tetracycline

9. _____ *Gluconobacter*           I. vinegar

10. _____ *Bordetella*             J. yogurt

11. _____ *Zoogloea*               K. impetigo

12. _____ *Azotobacter*            L. bacitracin

13. _____ *Desulfovibrio*          M. iron pipe corrosion

14. _____ *Chlamydia*              N. pertussis

15. _____ *Cytophaga*              O. nitrogen fixation

P. floc formation

Q. diphtheria

## Multiple Choice

1. The type of reproduction in prokaryotes that results in a palisade arrangement of cells is called
   a. pleomorphic division.
   b. endospore formation.
   c. snapping division.
   d. binary fission.

2. The thick-walled reproductive spores produced in the middle of cyanobacterial filaments are called
   a. akinetes.
   b. terminal endospores.
   c. metachromatic granules.
   d. heterocysts.

3. Which of the following terms best describes stiff, spiral-shaped prokaryotic cells?
   a. cocci
   b. bacilli
   c. spirilla
   d. spirochetes

4. Endospores
   a. can remain alive for decades.
   b. can remain alive in boiling water.
   c. live in a state of suspended animation.
   d. all of the above

5. *Halobacterium salinarium* is distinctive because
   a. it is absolutely dependent on high salt concentrations to maintain its cell wall.
   b. it is found in terrestrial volcanic habitats.
   c. it photosynthesizes without chlorophyll.
   d. it can survive 5 million rad of radiation.

6. Photosynthetic bacteria that also fix nitrogen are
   a. mycoplasmas.
   b. spirilla.
   c. bacteroids.
   d. cyanobacteria.

7. Which genus is the most common anaerobic human pathogen?
   a. *Bacteroides*
   b. *Spirochetes*
   c. *Chlamydia*
   d. *Methanopyrus*

8. Flexible spiral-shaped prokaryotes are
   a. spirilla.
   b. spirochetes.
   c. vibrios.
   d. rickettsias.

9. Bacteria that convert nitrogen gas into ammonia are
   a. nitrifying bacteria.
   b. nitrogenous.
   c. nitrogen fixers.
   d. nitrification bacteria.

10. The presence of mycolic acid in the cell wall characterizes
    a. *Corynebacterium.*       c. *Nocardia.*
    b. *Listeria.*              d. *Mycobacterium.*

## Labeling

Label the shapes of these prokaryotic cells.

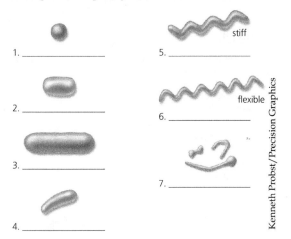

1. _____

2. _____

3. _____

4. _____

5. _____ stiff

6. _____ flexible

7. _____

Kenneth Probst/Precision Graphics

## Short Answer

1. Whereas the first edition of *Bergey's Manual* relied on morphological and biochemical characteristics to classify microbes, the new edition focuses on ribosomal RNA sequences. List several other criteria for grouping and classifying bacteria.

2. What are extremophiles? Describe two kinds and give examples.

3. Name and describe three types of bacteria mentioned in this chapter that "glide."

4. Name three groups of low G + C Gram-positive bacteria.

5. Sketch and label six shapes of bacteria.

6. A student was memorizing the arrangements of bacteria and noticed that there are more arrangements for cocci than for bacilli. Why might this be so?

7. How is *Agrobacterium* used in recombinant DNA technology?

8. Name and describe five distinct classes of phylum Proteobacteria.

9. Explain why organisms formerly known as blue-green algae are now called cyanobacteria.

10. Contrast the processes of nitrification and nitrogen fixation.

## Concept Mapping

Using the following terms, draw a concept map that describes the domain archaea. Or, complete this concept map online by going to the Study Area at www.masteringmicrobiology.com.

| | | | | | |
|---|---|---|---|---|---|
| >45°C | Acidophiles | Extremophiles | Hydrothermal vents | Methane | Prokaryotes |
| >80°C | Animal colons | Great Salt Lake | Hyperthermophiles | Methanogens | Sewage treatment |
| 17–25% salt | Disease | Halophiles | Low pH | Peptidoglycan | Thermophiles |

## Critical Thinking

1. A microbiology student described "deeply branching bacteria" as having a branched filamentous growth habit akin to *Streptomyces*. Do you agree with this description? Why or why not?

2. Iron oxide (rust) forms when iron is exposed to oxygen, particularly in the presence of water. Nevertheless, iron pipes typically corrode more quickly when they are buried in moist *anaerobic* soil than when they are buried in soil containing oxygen. Explain why this is the case.

3. Why is it that Gram-positive species don't have axial filaments?

4. Even though *Clostridium* is strictly an anaerobic bacterium, it can be isolated easily from the exposed surface of your skin. Explain how this can be.

5. Louis Pasteur said, "The role of the infinitely small in nature is infinitely large." Explain what he meant by using examples of the roles of microorganisms in health, industry, and the environment.

6. How are bacterial endospores different from the spores of actinomycetes?

Access more review material online in the Study Area at
**www.masteringmicrobiology.com.** There, you'll find
- **Animations**
- **MP3 Tutor Sessions**
- **Concept Mapping Activities**
- **Flashcards**
- **Quizzes**
and more to help you succeed.

# Answers

Answers to multiple-choice, fill-in-blank, labeling, matching, and true/false questions are listed here. Answers for Short Answer and Critical Thinking questions are available for instructors only in the Instructor's Manual that accompanies this text.

**Modified True/False**
1. *asexually*; 2. *vibrio*; 3. True; 4. *Elementary*; 5. *rRNA sequences*; 6. True; 7. True; 8. True; 9. *Epulopiscium*; 10. True

**Matching**
1. E; 2. B; 3. C; 4. D; 5. L; 6. K; 7. H; 8. Q; 9. I; 10. N; 11. P; 12. O; 13. M; 14. F; 15. A

**Multiple Choice**
1. c; 2. a; 3. c; 4. d; 5. a; 6. d; 7. a; 8. b; 9. c; 10. d

**Labeling**
See Figure 1.

# Pathogenic Gram-Positive Bacteria

We are all familiar with acne, the common skin disorder characterized by pimples and other blemishes. But did you know that acne is often caused by a Gram-positive bacterium called *Propionibacterium acnes*? *P. acnes* grows in the sebaceous (oil) glands of the skin. Teenagers are especially prone to developing acne because the hormonal changes of adolescence can trigger the production of excess oil, stimulating bacterial growth. The bacteria secrete chemicals that attract the body's leukocytes, which phagocytize the bacteria and trigger inflammation. Pus-filled pimples result when lymphocytes and dead bacteria clog the skin's pores.

In this chapter we will learn more about *P. acnes* and about other medically important Gram-positive pathogens, including *Staphylococcus*, *Streptococcus*, and *Bacillus*. A general characteristic of Gram-positive pathogens is that the disease symptoms they cause often result from the toxins they secrete.

 Take the pre-test for this chapter online. Visit the Study Area at www.masteringmicrobiology.com.

Dennis Kunkel/Phototake

Gram-positive *Propionibacterium acnes* is a major cause of teenagers' acne.

From Chapter 19 of *Microbiology with Diseases by Taxonomy*, Third Edition. Robert W. Bauman. Copyright © 2011 by Pearson Education, Inc. Published by Benjamin Cummings, Inc. All rights reserved.

We examined the general features of prokaryotes, including some pathogens. In this chapter we explore the major Gram-positive bacterial pathogens in more detail. Recall that Gram-positive bacteria stain purple when Gram stained and generally fall within the phylum Firmicutes. We will discuss the major pathogens of this group.

Taxonomists currently group Gram-positive bacteria into two major groups: low G + C Gram-positive bacteria and high G + C Gram-positive bacteria. As the names indicate, these classifications are based on the ratio of guanine-cytosine nucleotide base pairs to adenine-thymine nucleotide base pairs in these organisms' DNA. Low G + C Gram-positive bacteria include three genera of pathogenic spherical cells (cocci): *Staphylococcus, Streptococcus,* and *Enterococcus;* three genera of pathogenic rod-shaped cells (bacilli): *Bacillus, Clostridium,* and *Listeria;* and the *mycoplasmas,* a group of bacteria that lack cell walls. Mycoplasmas have historically been classified as Gram-negative bacteria because they stain pink when Gram stained. However, studies of their nucleotide sequences have revealed that they are genetically more similar to low G + C Gram-positive bacteria.

The high G + C Gram-positive pathogens include rod-shaped genera *Corynebacterium, Mycobacterium,* and *Propionibacterium,* and the filamentous, fungus-like *Nocardia* and *Actinomyces.*

We begin our discussion of Gram-positive bacteria with *Staphylococcus.*

# Staphylococcus

Bacteria in the genus *Staphylococcus* (staf'i-lō-kok'ŭs) are living and reproducing on almost every square inch of your skin right now. They are normal members of every human's microbiota, which usually go unnoticed. However, they can be opportunistic pathogens, causing minor to life-threatening diseases.

## Structure and Physiology

### Learning Objective

✓ Contrast the virulence of *S. aureus* with that of *S. epidermidis* in humans.

*Staphylococcus*[1] is a genus of Gram-positive, facultatively anaerobic prokaryotes whose spherical cells are typically clustered in grapelike arrangements (Figure 1). This arrangement results from two characteristics of cell division: cell divisions occur in successively different planes, and daughter cells remain attached to one another. Staphylococcal cells are 0.5–1.0 μm in diameter, nonmotile, and salt tolerant—they are capable of growing in media that are up to 10% NaCl, which explains how they tolerate the salt deposited on human skin by sweat glands. Additionally, they are tolerant of desiccation, radiation, and heat (up to 60°C for 30 min), allowing them to survive on environmental surfaces in addition to skin. Further, *Staphylococcus* synthesizes catalase—a characteristic that dis-tinguishes this genus from other low G + C Gram-positive cocci.

SEM    2 μm

David M. Phillips/Photo Researchers

▲ **Figure 1** *Staphylococcus.* Gram-positive cells appear in grapelike clusters.

Two species are commonly associated with staphylococcal diseases in humans:

- *Staphylococcus aureus*[2] (o'rē-ŭs) is the more virulent, producing a variety of disease conditions and symptoms depending on the site of infection.

- *Staphylococcus epidermidis* (e-pi-der-mid'is), as its name suggests, is a part of the normal microbiota of human skin, but it is an opportunistic pathogen in immunocompromised patients or when introduced into the body via intravenous catheters or on prosthetic devices such as artificial heart valves.

## Pathogenicity

### Learning Objective

✓ Discuss the structural and enzymatic features and toxins of *Staphylococcus* that enable it to be pathogenic.

What are commonly called "staph" infections result when staphylococci breach the body's physical barriers (skin or mucous membranes); entry of only a few hundred bacteria can ultimately result in disease. The pathogenicity of *Staphylococcus* results from three features: structures that enable it to evade phagocytosis, the production of enzymes, and the production of toxins.

### Structural Defenses Against Phagocytosis

The cells of *S. aureus* are uniformly coated with a protein, called *protein A,* that interferes with humoral immune responses by binding to the $F_c$ regions (stems) of class G antibodies (IgG). Recall that antibodies are opsonins—they enhance phagocytosis—precisely because phagocytic cells have receptors for antibody stems; therefore, protein A, by binding stems, effectively inhibits opsonization. Protein A also inhibits

---

[1]From Greek *staphle,* meaning small bunch of grapes, and *kokkos,* meaning a berry.
[2]Latin for golden, for the golden color of its colonies growing on the surface of a solid medium.

the complement cascade, which is triggered by antibody molecules bound to antigen.

The outer surfaces of most pathogenic strains of *S. aureus* also contain *bound coagulase,* an enzyme that converts the soluble blood protein fibrinogen into long, insoluble fibrin molecules, which are threads that form blood clots around the bacteria. Fibrin clots in effect hide the bacteria from phagocytic cells.

Both *S. aureus* and *S. epidermidis* also evade the body's defenses by synthesizing loosely organized polysaccharide slime layers (sometimes called capsules) that inhibit chemotaxis of and endocytosis by leukocytes, particularly neutrophils. The slime layer also facilitates attachment of *Staphylococcus* to artificial surfaces such as catheters, shunts, artificial heart valves, and synthetic joints.

In summary, protein A, bound coagulase, and a slime layer allow *S. aureus* to evade the body's defenses, whereas *S. epidermidis* relies almost exclusively on its slime layer.

### Enzymes

Staphylococci produce a number of enzymes that contribute to their survival and pathogenicity:

- *Cell-free coagulase,* like bound coagulase, triggers blood clotting. Cell-free coagulase does not act on fibrin directly but instead combines with a blood protein before becoming enzymatic and converting fibrinogen to fibrin threads. Only *S. aureus* synthesizes coagulase; *S. epidermidis* and other species of *Staphylococcus* are coagulase negative.

- *Hyaluronidase* breaks down hyaluronic acid, which is a major component of the matrix between cells. Hyaluronidase, found in 90% of *S. aureus* strains, enables the bacteria to spread between cells throughout the body.

- *Staphylokinase* (produced by *S. aureus*) dissolves fibrin threads in blood clots, allowing *S. aureus* to free itself from clots. Thus, *Staphylococcus* can escape the immune system by enclosing itself in a fibrin clot (via coagulase), and then, when space and nutrients become limiting, it can digest its way out of the clot with staphylokinase and spread to new locations.

- *Lipases* digest lipids, allowing staphylococci to grow on the surface of the skin and in cutaneous oil glands. All staphylococci produce lipases.

- *β-lactamase (penicillinase),* now present in over 90% of *S. aureus* strains, breaks down penicillin. Though β-lactamase plays no role in inhibiting the natural defenses of the body, it does allow the bacteria to survive treatment with beta-lactam antimicrobial drugs such as penicillin and cephalosporin.

### Toxins

*Staphylococcus aureus* and (less frequently) *S. epidermidis* also possess several toxins that contribute to their pathogenicity, including the following:

- *Cytolytic toxins.* So-called alpha, beta, gamma, and delta toxins are proteins, coded by chromosomal genes, that

| TABLE 1 A Comparison of the Virulence Factors of Staphylococcal Species | *S. aureus* | *S. epidermidis* |
|---|---|---|
| Protein A | + | – |
| Coagulase | + | – |
| Catalase | + | + |
| Hyaluronidase | + | – |
| Staphylokinase | + | – |
| Lipase | + | + |
| β-Lactamase (penicillinase) | + | – |

disrupt the cytoplasmic membranes of a variety of cells including leukocytes. Leukocidin is a fifth cytolytic toxin that lyses leukocytes specifically, providing *Staphylococcus* with some protection against phagocytosis.

- *Exfoliative toxins.* Each of two distinct proteins causes the dissolution of epidermal *desmosomes* (intercellular bridge proteins that hold adjoining cytoplasmic membranes together), causing the patient's skin cells to separate from each other and slough off the body.

- *Toxic shock syndrome (TSS) toxin.* This protein causes toxic shock syndrome (discussed shortly).

- *Enterotoxins.* These five proteins (designated A through E) stimulate the intestinal muscle contractions, nausea, and intense vomiting associated with staphylococcal food poisoning. Enterotoxins are heat stable, remaining active at 100°C for up to 30 minutes.

Table 1 compares and contrasts the virulence factors of *S. aureus* and *S. epidermidis*.

## Epidemiology

*Staphylococcus epidermidis* is ubiquitous on human skin, whereas *S. aureus* is commonly found only on moist skin folds. Both species also grow in the upper respiratory, gastrointestinal, and urogenital tracts of humans. Both bacteria are transmitted through direct contact between individuals, as well as via fomites such as contaminated clothing, bed sheets, and medical instruments; as a result, proper handwashing and aseptic techniques are essential in preventing their transfer in health care settings.

## Staphylococcal Diseases

### Learning Objectives

✓ Describe the symptoms and prevention of staphylococcal food poisoning.

✓ List and describe six pyogenic lesions caused by *Staphylococcus aureus*.

✓ Discuss five systemic and potentially fatal diseases caused by *Staphylococcus*.

From: Images in clinical medicine. Staphylococcal scalded skin syndrome. L. A. Schenfeld. *New England Journal of Medicine*. 2000 Apr 20; 342(16):1178, fig. 1. Used by permission of the Massachusetts Medical Society.

▲ **Figure 2** **Staphylococcal scalded skin syndrome.**
Exfoliative toxin, produced by some strains of *Staphylococcus aureus*, causes reddened patches of the epidermis to slough off.

Medical Online/Alamy Images

▲ **Figure 3** **Impetigo.** Reddened patches of skin become pus-filled vesicles that eventually crust over.

*Staphylococcus* causes a variety of medical problems, depending on the site of infection, the immune state of its host, and the toxins and enzymes a particular species or strain secretes. Staphylococcal syndromes and diseases can be categorized as noninvasive, cutaneous, and systemic diseases.

## Noninvasive Disease

*Staphylococcus aureus* is one of the more common causes of food poisoning (more specifically, this is food intoxication, because disease is caused by enterotoxin-contaminated food rather than by invasion of bacteria). Commonly affected foods include processed meats, custard pastries, potato salad, and ice cream that have been contaminated with bacteria from human skin. (In *S. aureus* food poisoning, unlike many other forms of food poisoning, animals are not involved.) The food must remain at room temperature or warmer for several hours for the bacteria to grow, reproduce, and secrete toxin. Warming or reheating inoculated food does not inactivate enterotoxins, which are heat stable, although heating does kill the bacteria. Food contaminated with staphylococci does not appear or taste unusual.

Symptoms, which include nausea, severe vomiting, diarrhea, headache, sweating, and abdominal pain, usually appear within four hours following ingestion. Consumed staphylococci do not continue to produce toxins, so the course of the disease is rapid, usually lasting 24 hours or less.

## Cutaneous Diseases

*Staphylococcus aureus* causes localized *pyogenic*[3] (pī-ō-jen'ik) lesions. **Staphylococcal scalded skin syndrome** is a reddening of the skin that typically begins near the mouth, spreads over the

[3] From Greek *pyon*, meaning pus, and *genein*, meaning to produce.

entire body, and is followed by large blisters that contain clear fluid lacking bacteria or white blood cells—consistent with the fact that the disease is caused by a toxin released by bacteria growing on the skin. Within two days the affected outer layer of skin (epidermis) peels off in sheets, as if it had been dipped into boiling water (Figure 2). The seriousness of scalded skin syndrome results from secondary bacterial infections in denuded areas.

Small, flattened, red patches on the face and limbs, particularly of children whose immune systems are not fully developed, characterize **impetigo** (im-pe-tī'gō) (Figure 3). The patches develop into pus-filled vesicles that eventually crust over. The pus is filled with bacteria and white blood cells, which distinguishes impetigo from scalded skin syndrome. *S. aureus* acting alone causes about 80% of impetigo cases; about 20% of cases also involve streptococci.

**Folliculitis** (fo-lik'ū-lī'tis) is an infection of a hair follicle in which the base of the follicle becomes red, swollen, and pus filled. When this condition occurs at the base of an eyelid, it is called a **sty.** A **furuncle** (fū'rŭng-kl) or boil is a large, painful, raised nodular extension of folliculitis into surrounding tissue. When several furuncles coalesce, they form a **carbuncle** (kar'-bŭng-kl), which extends deeper into the tissues, triggering the fever and chills that are characteristic of innate immunity. As staphylococci spread into underlying tissues, multiple organs and systems can become involved.

## Systemic Diseases

*Staphylococcus aureus*, and to a lesser extent *S. epidermidis*, cause a wide variety of potentially fatal systemic infections when they

▲ **Figure 4 Staphylococcal toxic shock syndrome (STSS).** Fatal infections involve not only red rash (as shown here) but internal organs as well.

are introduced into deeper tissues of the body, including the blood, heart, lungs, and bones.

**Staphylococcal Toxic Shock Syndrome** When strains of *Staphylococcus* that produce TSS toxin grow in a wound or in an abraded vagina, the toxin can be absorbed into the blood and cause **staphylococcal toxic shock syndrome (STSS),** characterized by fever, vomiting, red rash, extremely low blood pressure, and loss of sheets of skin (Figure 4). STSS is fatal to 5% of patients when their blood pressure falls so low that the brain, heart, and other vital organs have an inadequate supply of oxygen—a condition known as *shock.*

Staphylococcal toxic shock syndrome occurs in both males and females, but in 1980 epidemiologists noted an epidemic of STSS among menstruating women. Researchers subsequently discovered that *S. aureus* grows exceedingly well in super-absorbent tampons, especially when the tampon remains in place for a prolonged period. As a result of the withdrawal of this type of tampon from the market, plus government-mandated reduction in the absorbency of all tampons and mandatory inclusion of educational information concerning the risks of STSS on every package of tampons, the number of cases of STSS declined rapidly (Figure 5).

**Bacteremia** *S. aureus* is a common cause of **bacteremia** (bak-tēr-ē'mē-ă), the presence of bacteria in the blood. After staphylococci enter the blood from a site of infection, they travel to other organs of the body, which may become infected. Furuncles, vaginal infections, infected surgical wounds, and contaminated medical devices such as intravascular catheters have all been implicated in cases of bacteremia. Nosocomial (hospital-acquired) infections account for about half of all cases of staphylococcal bacteremia. Physicians fail to identify the initial site of infection in about a third of patients, but it is presumed to be an innocuous skin infection.

**Endocarditis** *S. aureus* may attack the lining of the heart (including its valves), producing a condition called **endocarditis**[4] (en'dō-kar-dī'tis). Typically, patients with endocarditis have nonspecific, flulike symptoms, but their condition quickly deteriorates as the amount of blood pumped from the heart drops precipitously. About 50% of patients with endocarditis do not survive.

▲ **Figure 5 The incidence of staphylococcal toxic shock syndrome in the United States since 1979.** *Use of what product puts women at increased risk of STSS?*

Figure 5 *Use of tampons is a risk factor for STSS.*

**Pneumonia and Empyema** *Staphylococcus* in the blood can invade the lungs, causing **pneumonia** (noo-mŏ'nē-ă)—an inflammation of the lungs in which the alveoli (air sacs) and bronchioles (smallest airways) become filled with fluid. In 10% of patients with staphylococcal pneumonia this fluid is pus—a condition known as **empyema**[5] (em-pī-ē'mă).

**Osteomyelitis** When *Staphylococcus* invades a bone, either through a traumatic wound or via the blood during bacteremia, it causes **osteomyelitis**[6] (os'tē-ō-mī-e-lī'tis)—inflammation of the bone marrow and the surrounding bone. Osteomyelitis is characterized by pain in the infected bone accompanied by high fever. In children the disease typically occurs in the growing regions of long bones, which are areas with well-developed blood supplies. In adults, osteomyelitis is more commonly seen in vertebrae.

## Diagnosis, Treatment, and Prevention
### Learning Objectives
✓ Describe how staphylococcal species are distinguished from one another during diagnosis.
✓ Discuss briefly the history of staphylococcal resistance to antimicrobial drugs.

Physicians diagnose staphylococcal infection by detecting grape-like arrangements of Gram-positive bacteria isolated from pus, blood, or other fluids. If staphylococci isolated from an infection

[4]From Greek *endon*, meaning within; *kardia*, meaning heart; and *itis*, meaning inflammation.
[5]From Greek *en*, meaning in, and *pyon*, meaning pus.
[6]From Greek *osteon*, meaning bone; *myelos*, meaning marrow; and *itis*, meaning inflammation.

## CLINICAL CASE STUDY

### A Fatal Case of Methicillin-Resistant *S. Aureus*

SEM ⊢──── 1 μm ────⊣

▲ **Methicillin-resistant *S. aureus*.**

A five-year-old girl was admitted to the hospital with a temperature of 103°F and pain in her right hip. After pus was surgically drained from the hip joint, she was treated with a semisynthetic cephalosporin. Her physicians changed the antibiotic regimen after 24-hour cultures of blood and pus revealed the presence of MRSA. On the third day, she suffered respiratory failure and empyema and was placed on mechanical ventilation. She died from pulmonary hemorrhage and pneumonia after five weeks of hospitalization. The girl had been previously healthy with no recent hospitalizations. She had skinned her knee while learning to ride a bicycle two days before admittance to the hospital.

1. How might the girl have been infected?
2. How did her hip joint become infected?
3. Describe the series of diseases she suffered.
4. What was likely the second antibiotic she received?

are able to clot blood, then they are coagulase-positive *S. aureus*. Coagulase-negative staphylococci are usually *S. epidermidis,* which is a normal part of the microbiota of the skin; their presence in a clinical sample is usually not indicative of a staphylococcal infection.

During the latter half of the 20th century, genes for β-lactamase, which convey resistance to natural penicillin, spread among *Staphylococcus* species. Thus, 90% of staphylococci were susceptible to penicillin in 1945, but only 5% are susceptible today. For this reason, the semisynthetic form of penicillin—methicillin, which is not inactivated by β-lactamase—became the drug of choice for staphylococcal infections. Unfortunately, **methicillin-resistant *Staphylococcus aureus* (MRSA)** has emerged as a major problem, initially in health care settings but now increasingly in day care centers, high school locker rooms, and prisons. In fact, more people die from MRSA than from HIV in the United States.

MRSA is also resistant to many other common antimicrobial drugs, including penicillin, macrolides, aminoglycosides, and cephalosporin; as a result, *vancomycin* has been used to treat MRSA infections. Physicians are very concerned about the increasing prevalence of **vancomycin-resistant *staphylococcus aureus* (VRSA).**

Clinical practice has shown how crucial it is that abscesses be drained of pus and cleansed if subsequent antibiotic therapy is to be effective. Systemic infections such as endocarditis and osteomyelitis require long-term therapy with antimicrobial drugs.

Because strains of *Staphylococcus* resistant to antimicrobial agents have become more common, especially in hospitals, it is imperative that health care workers take precautions against introducing the bacterium into patients. Of course, given that *Staphylococcus* is ubiquitous on human skin, staphylococcal infection cannot be eliminated. Fortunately, because a large inoculum is required to establish an infection, proper cleansing of wounds and surgical openings, attention to aseptic use of catheters and indwelling needles, and the appropriate use of antiseptics will prevent infections in most healthy patients. Health care workers with staphylococcal infections may be barred from delivery rooms, nurseries, and operating rooms. The most important measure for protecting against nosocomial infection is frequent handwashing.

Scientists are currently testing the efficacy and safety of a vaccine that has proven effective in protecting dialysis patients from *S. aureus* infections. Such immunization, if it proves safe and effective in preventing other infections, may have a significant effect on nosocomial disease. It would be especially good news for health care providers who are battling resistant strains of *Staphylococcus.*

## *Streptococcus*

### Learning Objectives

✓ Describe the classification of streptococcal strains.

✓ Describe seven diseases caused by *S. pyogenes* and the treatments available.

The genus *Streptococcus* (strep-tō-kok'ŭs) is a diverse assemblage of Gram-positive cocci 0.5–1.2 μm in diameter and arranged in pairs or chains. They are catalase negative (unlike *Staphylococcus*), although they do synthesize peroxidase and thus are facultatively anaerobic.

Researchers differentiate species of *Streptococcus* using several different, overlapping schemes, including serological classification based on the reactions of antibodies to specific bacterial antigens, type of hemolysis (alpha, beta, or gamma), cell arrangement, and physiological properties as revealed by biochemical tests. In this chapter we will largely use a serological classification scheme, developed by Rebecca Lancefield (1895–1981), that divides streptococci into serotype groups based on the bacteria's antigens (known, appropriately, as Lancefield antigens). The serotypes in this scheme include Lancefield groups A through H and K through V. Whereas the more significant streptococcal pathogens of humans are in groups A and B, two other significant streptococcal pathogens of humans lack Lancefield antigens. We begin our survey of the streptococci with group A *Streptococcus*.

# Group A *Streptococcus: Streptococcus pyogenes*

## Learning Objectives

✓ Describe two structures in *Streptococcus pyogenes* that enable this organism to survive the body's defenses.

✓ Identify four enzymes and a type of toxin that facilitate the spread of *S. pyogenes* in the body.

✓ Identify the conditions under which group A *Streptococcus* causes disease.

**Group A *Streptococcus***, which is synonymously known as *S. pyogenes* (pī-oj'en-ēz), is a coccus that forms white colonies 1–2 mm in diameter surrounded by a large zone of beta-hemolysis after 24 hours on blood agar plates. Pathogenic strains of this species often form capsules. The following sections discuss the pathogenesis and epidemiology of this species, as well as the diagnosis, treatment, and prevention of the diseases it causes.

## Pathogenicity

Strains of *Streptococcus pyogenes* have a number of structures, enzymes, and toxins that enable them to survive as pathogens in the body.

Two main structural features enable cells of *S. pyogenes* to evade phagocytosis:

- *M protein.* A membrane protein called *M protein* destabilizes complement, thereby interfering with opsonization and lysis.

- *Hyaluronic acid capsule.* Because hyaluronic acid is normally found in the body, white blood cells may ignore bacteria "camouflaged" by this type of capsule.

Researchers have identified two *streptokinases* that break down blood clots, presumably enabling group A *Streptococcus* to rapidly spread through infected and damaged tissues. Similarly, four distinct *deoxyribonucleases* depolymerize DNA that has been released from dead cells in abscesses, reducing the firmness of the pus surrounding the bacteria and facilitating bacterial spread. *C5a peptidase* breaks down the complement protein C5a, which acts as a chemotactic factor. Thus, *S. pyogenes* decreases the movement of white blood cells into a site of infection. Finally, hyaluronidase facilitates the spread of streptococci through tissues by breaking down hyaluronic acid.

Group A *Streptococcus* secretes three distinct *pyrogenic*[7] (pī-rō-jen'ik) *toxins* that stimulate macrophages and helper T lymphocytes to release cytokines that in turn stimulate fever, a widespread rash, and shock. Because these toxins cause blood capillaries near the surface to dilate, producing a red rash, some scientists call them *erythrogenic*[8] (e-rith-rō-jen'ik) *toxins.* The genes for these toxins are carried on temperate bacteriophages, so only lysogenized bacteria—bacteria in which a virus has become part of the bacterial chromosome—secrete the toxins. Fever-stimulating *pyrogenic* toxins should not be confused with pus-producing *pyogenic* toxins.

[7]From Greek *pyr*, meaning fire, and *genein*, meaning to produce.
[8]From Greek *erythros*, meaning red, and *genein*, meaning to produce.

CDC

▲ **Figure 6** **Pharyngitis.**

*S. pyogenes* also produces two different, membrane-bound proteins, called *streptolysins,* which lyse red blood cells, white blood cells, and platelets; thus, these proteins interfere with the oxygen-carrying capacity of the blood, immunity, and blood clotting. After they have been phagocytized, group A *Streptococcus* releases streptolysins into the cytoplasm of the phagocyte, causing lysosomes to release their contents, which lyses the phagocyte and releases the bacteria.

## Epidemiology

Group A *Streptococcus* frequently infects the pharynx or skin, but the resulting abscesses are usually temporary, lasting only until adaptive immune responses against bacterial antigens (particularly M protein and streptolysins) clear the pathogens. Typically, *Streptococcus pyogenes* causes disease only when normal competing microbiota are depleted; when a large inoculum enables the streptococci to gain a rapid foothold before antibodies are formed against them; or when adaptive immunity is impaired. Following colonization of the skin or a mucous membrane, *S. pyogenes* can invade deeper tissues and organs through a break in such barriers. People spread *S. pyogenes* among themselves via respiratory droplets, especially under crowded conditions such as those in classrooms and day care centers.

Before the discovery of antimicrobials, a major cause of human disease was group A streptococcal infection, which claimed the lives of millions. Because it is sensitive to antimicrobial drugs, its significance as a pathogen has declined, but group A streptococci still sicken thousands of Americans annually.

## Group A Streptococcal Diseases

Group A *Streptococcus* causes a number of diseases, depending on the site of infection, the strain of bacteria, and the immune responses of the patient.

**Pharyngitis** A sore throat caused by streptococci, commonly known as "strep throat," is a kind of **pharyngitis** (far-in-jī'tis)—inflammation of the pharynx (Figure 6)—that is accompanied

P. Marazzi/Photo Researchers

▲ **Figure 7 Erysipelas.** The localized, pus-filled lesions are caused by group A streptococci *(Streptococcus pyogenes)*. *What is the meaning of the word* pyogenes?

Figure 7 *Pyogenes means pus-producing.*

by fever, malaise,[9] and headache. The back of the pharynx typically appears red, with swollen lymph nodes and *purulent* (pus-containing) abscesses covering the tonsils. Some microbiologists estimate that only 50% of patients diagnosed with strep throat actually have it; the rest have viral pharyngitis. Given that the symptoms and signs for the two diseases are identical, a sure diagnosis requires bacteriological or serological tests. Correct diagnosis is essential because bacterial pharyngitis is treatable with antibacterial drugs, which of course have no effect on viral pharyngitis.

**Scarlet Fever** The disease known as **scarlet fever** or as *scarlatina* often accompanies streptococcal pharyngitis when the infection involves a lysogenized strain of *S. pyogenes*. After one to two days of pharyngitis, pyrogenic toxins released by the streptococci trigger a diffuse rash that typically begins on the chest and spreads across the body. The tongue usually becomes strawberry red. The rash disappears after about a week and is followed by sloughing of the skin.

**Pyoderma and Erysipelas** A **pyoderma** (pī-ō-der'mă) is a confined, pus-producing lesion that usually occurs on the exposed skin of the face, arms, or legs. One cause is group A streptococcal infection following direct contact with an infected person or contaminated fomites. This condition is also known as *impetigo* because of its similar appearance to the staphylococcal disease of the same name. After a pus-filled lesion breaks open, it forms a yellowish crust. This stage is highly contagious, and scratching may convey bacteria to the surrounding skin, spreading the lesions.

When a streptococcal infection also involves surrounding lymph nodes and triggers pain and inflammation, the condition is called **erysipelas**[10] (er-i-sip'ĕ-las) **(Figure 7)**. Erysipelas occurs most commonly on the faces of children.

Ben Barankin, Dermatlas

▲ **Figure 8 Necrotizing fasciitis.** So-called flesh-eating group A streptococci *(Streptococcus pyogenes)* cause this condition.

**Toxic-Shock-Like Syndrome** Group A streptococci can spread, albeit rarely, from an initial site of infection, particularly in patients infected with HIV or suffering with cancer, heart disease, pulmonary disease, or diabetes mellitus. Such spread leads to bacteremia and severe multisystem infections producing **toxic-shock-like syndrome (TSLS).** Patients experience inflammation at sites of infection, as well as pain, fever, chills, malaise, nausea, vomiting, and diarrhea. These signs and symptoms are followed by increased pain, organ failure, shock—and over 40% of patients die.

**Necrotizing Fasciitis** Another serious disease caused by *S. pyogenes* is **necrotizing**[11] **fasciitis** (ne'kro-tī-zing fas-ē-ī'tis), sensationalized by the news media as "flesh-eating bacteria." In this disease, streptococci enter the body through breaks in the skin, secrete enzymes and toxins that destroy tissues, and eventually destroy muscle and fat tissue **(Figure 8)**. The bacteria spread deep within the body along the *fascia,* which are fibrous sheets of connective tissue surrounding muscles and binding them to one another—hence the word *fasciitis* in the disease's name. Necrotizing fasciitis also involves *toxemia* (toxins in the blood), failure of many organs, and death of more than 50% of patients.

**Rheumatic Fever** A complication of untreated *S. pyogenes* pharyngitis is **rheumatic** (rū-mat'ik) **fever,** in which inflammation leads to damage of heart valves and muscle. Though the exact cause of the damage is unknown, it appears that rheumatic fever is not caused directly by *Streptococcus* but instead is an autoimmune response in which antibodies directed against streptococcal antigens cross-react with heart antigens. Damage to the heart valves may be so extensive that they must be replaced when the patient reaches middle age. Rheumatic fever was much more prevalent before the advent of antimicrobial drugs.

**Glomerulonephritis** For an undetermined reason, antibodies bound to the antigens of some strains of group A *Streptococcus* are not removed from circulation, but instead accumulate in the *glomeruli* (small blood vessels) of the kidneys' *nephrons* (filtering

---

[9]French, meaning discomfort.
[10]From Greek *erythros,* meaning red, and *pella,* meaning skin.
[11]From Greek *nekros,* meaning corpse.

units). The result is **glomerulonephritis** (glō-măr'ū-lō-nef-rī'tis)—inflammation of the glomeruli and nephrons, which obstructs blood flow through the kidneys and leads to hypertension (high blood pressure) and low urine output. Blood and proteins are often secreted in the urine. Young patients usually recover fully from glomerulonephritis, but progressive and irreversible kidney damage may occur in adults.

### Diagnosis, Treatment, and Prevention

Because *Streptococcus* is not a normal member of the microbiota of the skin, the observation of Gram-positive bacteria in short chains or pairs in cutaneous specimens can provide a rapid preliminary diagnosis of pyoderma, erysipelas, and necrotizing fasciitis. In contrast, streptococci are normally in the pharynx, so their presence in a respiratory sample is of little diagnostic value; instead, physicians must use immunological tests that identify the presence of group A streptococcal antigens.

Penicillin is very effective against *S. pyogenes.* Erythromycin or cephalosporin is used to treat penicillin-sensitive patients. *S. pyogenes* is also susceptible to the topical antimicrobial bacitracin—a characteristic that distinguishes it from group B *Streptococcus* (discussed shortly). Necrotizing fasciitis must be treated with aggressive surgical removal of nonviable tissue and infecting bacteria. Because rheumatic fever and glomerulonephritis are the result of an immune response against group A streptococci, they cannot be treated directly; instead, the underlying infection must be arrested.

Antibodies against M protein provide long-term protection against *S. pyogenes.* However, antibodies directed against the M protein of one strain provide no protection against other strains; this explains why a person can have strep throat more than once.

## Group B *Streptococcus:* *Streptococcus agalactiae*

### Learning Objectives

✓ Contrast group B *Streptococcus* with group A *Streptococcus* in terms of structure.

✓ Discuss the epidemiology, diagnosis, treatment, and prevention of infections with *Streptococcus agalactiae.*

**Group B** *Streptococcus,* or *S. agalactiae* (a-ga-lak'tē-ī), is a Gram-positive coccus, 0.6–1.2 μm in diameter, that divides to form chains. Like group A *Streptococcus, S. agalactiae* is beta-hemolytic, but it can be distinguished from the former by three qualities: it has group-specific, polysaccharide cell wall antigens; it forms buttery colonies that are 2–3 mm in diameter and have a small zone of beta-hemolysis after 24 hours of growth on blood agar; and it is bacitracin resistant.

### Pathogenicity

Even though *S. agalactiae* forms capsules, antibodies target its capsular antigens, so the capsules are not protective. For this reason *S. agalactiae* has a predilection for newborns who have not yet formed type-specific antibodies and whose mothers are uninfected (and so do not provide passive immunity across the placenta or in milk).

Group B streptococci produce enzymes—proteases (that catabolize protein), hemolysins (that lyse red blood cells), deoxyribonuclease, and hyaluronidase—that probably play a role in causing disease, though such a role has not been proven.

### Epidemiology

Group B streptococci normally colonize the lower gastrointestinal (GI), genital, and urinary tracts. Diseases in adults primarily follow wound infections and childbirth, though group B *Streptococcus* is emerging as a significant pathogen in the elderly.

Sixty percent of newborns are inoculated with group B streptococcal strains either during passage through the birth canal or by health care personnel. Such infections do not cause disease when maternal antibodies have crossed the placenta; but mortality rates can exceed 50% in children of uninfected mothers. Infections in newborns less than one week old cause *early-onset disease;* infections occurring in infants one week to three months of age cause *late-onset disease.*

### Diseases

Even though microbiologists initially described *Streptococcus agalactiae* as the cause of *puerperal*[12] (pyu-er'per-ăl) *(childbirth) fever* in women, today the bacterium is most often associated with neonatal bacteremia, meningitis, and pneumonia, at least one of which occurs in approximately 3 of every 1000 newborns. Mortality has been reduced to about 5% as a result of rapid diagnosis and supportive care, but about 25% of infants surviving group B streptococcal meningitis have permanent neurological damage, including blindness, deafness, or severe mental retardation. Immunocompromised older patients are also at risk from group B streptococcal infections, and about 25% of them die from streptococcal diseases.

### Diagnosis, Treatment, and Prevention

Medical laboratory technologists identify group B streptococcal infections by means of ELISA tests utilizing antibodies directed against the bacteria's distinctive cell wall polysaccharides. Samples of clinical specimens can also be incubated in blood media containing the antimicrobial drug bacitracin, which inhibits the growth of other beta-hemolytic bacteria.

Penicillin G is the drug of choice for use against group B *Streptococcus,* though some strains tolerate concentrations of the drug more than 10 times greater than that needed to inhibit group A *Streptococcus.* For this reason, physicians may prescribe an aminoglycoside such as streptomycin in addition to penicillin.

The CDC recommends prophylactic administration of penicillin at birth to children whose mothers' urinary tracts are colonized with group B streptococci. Implementation of this guideline in 1996 reduced early-onset disease morbidity and

---

[12]From Latin *puer,* meaning child, and *pario,* meaning to bring forth.

Capsule

Electron micrograph by Vincent A. Fischetti, Rockefeller University, NY

TEM 200 nm

▲ **Figure 9** ***Streptococcus pneumoniae.*** Cells of this most common cause of pneumonia are paired and covered with a capsule. *What is pneumonia?*

*Figure 9 Pneumonia is inflammation of the lungs, resulting in fluid buildup.*

mortality by 70% by 2001. Additionally, physicians can immunize women against group B streptococci, preventing infection of future children.

## Other Beta-Hemolytic Streptococci

### Learning Objective

✓ Contrast *Streptococcus equisimilis* and *S. anginosus* in terms of polysaccharide composition, diseases caused, and treatment.

*Streptococcus equisimilis* (ek-wi-si′mil-is) and *S. anginosus* (an-ji-nō′sŭs) are the only other pathogenic beta-hemolytic streptococci. Although members of both species typically have group C polysaccharides, some strains of *S. anginosus* have group F or group G antigens instead—an example of the confusing status of the classification of the streptococci.

*S. equisimilis* causes pharyngitis (and occasionally glomerulonephritis) but, unlike group A streptococci, these cases of pharyngitis never lead to rheumatic fever. *S. anginosus* produces pus-containing abscesses. Penicillin is effective against both species.

## Alpha-Hemolytic Streptococci: The Viridans Group

### Learning Objective

✓ Identify the normal sites of viridans streptococci in the human body, and list three serious diseases they cause.

Many alpha-hemolytic streptococci lack group-specific carbohydrates, and thus they are not part of any Lancefield group. Instead, microbiologists classify them as the **viridans**[13] **streptococci** (vir′i-danz strep′tō-kok′sī) because many of them produce a green pigment when grown on blood media. The taxonomic relationships of these microorganisms are poorly

understood; European and American microbiologists do not always agree about the names assigned to species, and some microbiologists place these microbes in a separate genus: *Abiotrophia.* Some of the names given by Americans to viridans streptococci are *S. mitis* and *S. sanguis.* Members of the group are alpha-hemolytic and susceptible to penicillin.

Viridans streptococci normally inhabit the mouth, pharynx, GI tract, genital tract, and urinary tract of humans. They are opportunists that produce purulent abdominal infections, and are one cause of dental **caries**[14] (kār′ēz, cavities). They stick to dental surfaces via an insoluble polysaccharide, *dextran,* which they produce from glucose. Large quantities of dextran allow viridans streptococci and other bacteria to colonize the enamel of teeth, forming biofilms known as *dental plaque.* Viridans streptococci are not highly invasive, entering the blood only through surgical wounds and lacerations of the gums, including undetectable cuts produced by chewing hard candy, brushing the teeth, or dental procedures. Once in the blood they can cause meningitis and endocarditis.

## *Streptococcus pneumoniae*

### Learning Objectives

✓ Describe how the structure of *Streptococcus pneumoniae* affects its pathogenicity.

✓ Describe the route of *Streptococcus pneumoniae* through the body, describing the chemical and physical properties that allow it to cause pneumonia.

✓ Discuss the diagnosis, treatment, and prevention of pneumococcal diseases.

Louis Pasteur discovered *Streptococcus pneumoniae* (nū-mō′nē-ī) in pneumonia patients in 1881. The bacterium is a Gram-positive coccus, 0.5–1.2 μm in diameter, that forms short chains or, more commonly, pairs (Figure 9). In fact, it was once classified in its own genus, "Diplococcus." Ninety-two different strains of *S. pneumoniae,* collectively called *pneumococci,* are known to infect humans.

Colonies of *S. pneumoniae* grown for 24 hours are 1–3 mm in diameter, round, mucoid, unpigmented, and dimpled in the middle because of the death of older cells. Colonies are alpha-hemolytic on blood agar when grown aerobically, and beta-hemolytic when grown anaerobically. This bacterium lacks Lancefield antigens but does incorporate a species-specific teichoic acid into its cell wall.

### Pathogenicity

*Streptococcus pneumoniae* is a normal member of the pharyngeal microbiota that can colonize the lungs, sinuses, and middle ear. Even though microbiologists have studied the pneumococci extensively—the entire genomes of more than 10 strains have been sequenced—they still do not fully understand their pathogenicity; nevertheless, certain structural and chemical properties are known to be required.

---

[13]From Latin *viridis*, meaning green.
[14]Latin, meaning dry rot.

The cells of virulent strains of *S. pneumoniae* are surrounded by a polysaccharide capsule, which protects them from digestion after endocytosis. A capsule is required for virulence; unencapsulated strains are avirulent. Microbiologists distinguish 90 unique serotypes based on differences in the antigenic properties of the capsules among various strains.

In addition, cells of *S. pneumoniae* insert into their cell walls a chemical called *phosphorylcholine.* Its binding to receptors on cells in the lungs, in the meninges, and blood vessel walls stimulates the cells to engulf the bacteria. Together, the polysaccharide capsule and phosphorylcholine enable pneumococci to "hide" inside body cells. *S. pneumoniae* can then pass across these cells into the blood and brain.

Pathogenic pneumococci secrete *protein adhesin,* a poorly defined protein that mediates binding of the cells to epithelial cells of the pharynx. From there the bacteria enter the lungs.

The body limits migration of bacteria into the lungs by binding the microbes with the active sites of secretory IgA. The rest of the antibody molecule then binds to mucus, trapping the bacteria where they can be swept from the airways by the action of ciliated epithelium. The bacterium counteracts this defense by secreting *secretory IgA protease,* which destroys IgA, and *pneumolysin,* which binds to cholesterol in the cytoplasmic membranes of ciliated epithelial cells, producing transmembrane pores that result in the lysis of the cells. Pneumolysin also suppresses the digestion of endocytized bacteria by interfering with the action of lysosomes.

### Epidemiology

*Streptococcus pneumoniae* grows in the mouths and pharynges of 75% of humans, without causing harm; however, when pneumococci travel to the lungs, they cause disease. Typically, the incidence of pneumococcal disease is highest in children and the elderly, groups whose immune responses are not fully active.

### Pneumococcal Diseases

*Streptococcus pneumoniae* causes a variety of diseases, which we explore next.

**Pneumococcal Pneumonia** The most prevalent disease caused by *S. pneumoniae* is **pneumococcal pneumonia** (nū-mō′nē-ă), which constitutes about 85% of all cases of pneumonia. The disease results when pneumococci are inhaled from the pharynx into lungs damaged either by a previous viral disease, such as influenza or measles, or by other conditions, such as alcoholism, congestive heart failure, or diabetes mellitus. As the bacteria multiply in the alveoli (air sacs), they damage the alveolar lining, allowing fluid, red blood cells, and leukocytes to enter the lungs. The leukocytes attack *Streptococcus,* in the process secreting inflammatory and pyrogenic chemicals. The onset of clinical symptoms is abrupt and includes a fever of 39–41°C and severe shaking chills. Most patients have a productive cough, slightly bloody sputum, and chest pain.

**Sinusitis and Otitis Media** Following viral infections of the upper respiratory tract, *S. pneumoniae* can also invade the sinuses and middle ear, where it causes **sinusitis** (sī-nŭ-sī′tis; inflammation of

---

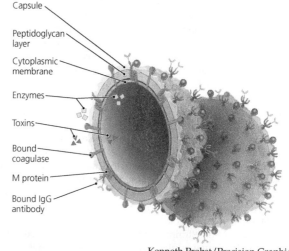

## MICROBE AT A GLANCE

### *Streptococcus pneumoniae*

**Taxonomy:** Domain Bacteria, phylum Firmicutes, class "Bacilli," order "Lactobacillales," family Streptococcaceae

**Other names:** Pneumococcus, formerly "Diplococcus pneumoniae"

**Cell morphology and arrangement:** Cocci in pairs

**Gram reaction:** Positive

**Virulence factors:** Polysaccharide capsule, phosphorylcholine, protein adhesin, secretory IgA protease, pneumolysin

**Diseases caused:** Pneumococcal pneumonia, sinusitis, otitis media, bacteremia, endocarditis, pneumococcal meningitis

**Treatment for diseases:** Penicillin, cephalosporin, erythromycin, chloramphenicol

**Prevention of disease:** Vaccine against 23 common strains is long lasting in adults with unimpaired immunity

Capsule

Peptidoglycan layer

Cytoplasmic membrane

Enzymes

Toxins

Bound coagulase

M protein

Bound IgG antibody

Kenneth Probst/Precision Graphics

---

the nasal sinuses) and **otitis media** (ō-tī′tis mē′dē-ă; inflammation of the middle ear). Pus production and inflammation in these cavities create pressure and pain. Sinusitis occurs in patients of all ages. Otitis media is more prevalent in children because their narrow auditory tubes connecting the pharynx with the middle ears are nearly horizontal, which facilitates the flow of infected fluid from the pharynx into the middle ears. The tubes become wider and more vertical when the shape of the head changes as children grow, making infection less likely in adults.

**Bacteremia and Endocarditis** *Streptococcus pneumoniae* can enter the blood either through lacerations (as might result from vigorous tooth brushing, chewing hard foods, or dental procedures) or as a result of tissue damage in the lungs during pneumonia. Bacteria generally do not enter the blood during sinusitis or otitis media. As with *Staphylococcus, S. pneumoniae* can colonize the lining of the heart, causing endocarditis. The heart valves, once involved, are typically destroyed.

**Pneumococcal Meningitis** Pneumococci can spread to the meninges via bacteremia, during sinusitis or otitis media, or following head or neck surgery or trauma that opens a passage between the pharynx and the subarachnoid space of the meninges. The mortality rate of pneumococcal meningitis, which is primarily a disease of children, is up to 20 times that of meningitis caused by other microorganisms.

### Diagnosis, Treatment, and Prevention

Medical laboratory technologists can quickly identify pneumococci in Gram stains of sputum smears and confirm their presence with the *Quellung*[15] *reaction,* in which anticapsular antibodies cause the capsule to swell. Antibodies against particular strains trigger Quellung reactions only against those strains. Antibody agglutination tests can also be used to identify specific strains. Culture of sputum samples is often difficult because pneumococci have fastidious nutritional requirements and cultures are often overgrown by normal oral microbiota. *S. pneumoniae* is sensitive to most antimicrobial drugs; therefore, samples for culture must be obtained before antibacterial therapy has begun. Laboratory technologists can distinguish pneumococcal colonies from other colonies of alpha-hemolytic strains by adding a drop of bile to a colony. Bile triggers chemicals present in pneumococci to lyse the cells, dissolving the colony in just a few minutes.

Penicillin has long been the drug of choice against *S. pneumoniae,* though penicillin-resistant strains have emerged in the last decade; about a third of peumococcal isolates are now resistant. Cephalosporin, erythromycin, and chloramphenicol are also effective treatments.

Prevention of pneumococcal diseases is focused on a vaccine made from purified capsular material from the 23 most common pathogenic strains. The vaccine is immunogenic and long lasting in normal adults, but unfortunately it is not as efficacious in patients at greatest risk, such as the elderly, young children, and AIDS patients.

# *Enterococcus*

## Learning Objective

✓ Identify two species of *Enterococcus,* and describe their pathogenicity and the diagnosis, treatment, and prevention of their diseases.

We have discussed two Gram-positive cocci that are pathogenic in humans: catalase-positive *Staphylococcus* and catalase-negative *Streptococcus.* Now we turn our attention to another genus of Gram-positive, catalase-negative cocci—*Enterococcus* (en'ter-ō-kok'ŭs), so named because all enterococci are spherical and live in the intestinal tracts of animals. Lancefield classified entero-

*Enterococcus*

Mike Miller, CDC

LM    10 μm

▲ **Figure 10** *Enterococcus* **faecalis in lung tissue.**
The Gram-positive cells are arranged in pairs and short chains, but (unlike *S. pneumoniae*) lack capsules. *Why are these bacteria called "enterococci"?*

Figure 10 *They are called "enterococci" because they are spherical bacteria that live in the intestinal tracts of animals.*

cocci with group D streptococci, but they differ significantly from other members of group D in that *Enterococcus* is unencapsulated, produces gas during fermentation of sugars, and is typically nonhemolytic (i.e., gamma-hemolytic). Because of these and other differences, microbiologists now classify *Enterococcus* as a separate genus.

## Structure and Physiology

Enterococci form short chains and pairs; they do not form capsules (Figure 10). Enterococci grow at temperatures up to 45°C, at pH as high as 9.6, and in 6.5% NaCl or 40% bile salt broths—all conditions that severely inhibit the growth of *Streptococcus.* The two species that are significant pathogens of humans are *E. faecalis*[16] (fē-kă'lis) and *E. faecium*[17] (fē'sē-ŭm).

## Pathogenesis, Epidemiology, and Diseases

*E. faecalis* is ubiquitous in the human colon. *E. faecium* is found less often. Because both species lack structural and chemical elements that make them virulent, they are rarely pathogenic in the intestinal tract. Nevertheless, they do have the ability to adhere to human epithelial cells, and they secrete *bacteriocins,* which are chemicals that inhibit the growth of other bacteria.

*E. faecalis* and *E. faecium* can cause serious disease if they are introduced into other parts of the body, such as the lungs, urinary tract, or bloodstream, via poor personal hygiene or intestinal laceration. Enterococci account for about 10% of nosocomial infections and cause bacteremia, endocarditis, and wound infections.

[15]German, meaning swelling.
[16]Latin, meaning pertaining to feces.
[17]Latin, meaning of feces.

## Diagnosis, Treatment, and Prevention

Even though a Gram stain of *Enterococcus* looks similar to one of *S. pneumoniae,* the two genera can be distinguished readily in that *Enterococcus* is not sensitive to bile.

Enterococcal infections are very difficult to treat because strains resistant to frequently used antimicrobials—lactams, aminoglycosides, and vancomycin—are relatively common. This is particularly troublesome in that the genes for antimicrobial resistance occur on plasmids that can be transmitted to other bacteria.

It is difficult to prevent enterococcal infections, particularly in health care settings, where patients' immune systems are weakened. Health care workers should always use good hygiene and aseptic techniques to minimize the transmission of these microorganisms.

Table 2 summarizes the features of the major pathogenic, Gram-positive streptococci—*Streptococcus* and *Enterococcus.* Now we turn our attention to the Gram-positive pathogenic bacilli, beginning with the low G + C, endospore-forming genera *Bacillus* and *Clostridium.*

## *Bacillus*

Scientists divide Gram-positive bacilli (rod-shaped cells) into endospore-forming and non-endospore-forming genera. The endospore-forming genera are *Bacillus* and *Clostridium.* In this section we examine *Bacillus anthracis*—one of the 51 species of *Bacillus* and a strict pathogen of animals and humans. The following section discusses *Clostridium.*

*Bacillus anthracis*

SEM   10 µm

A. Dowsett/Health Protection Agency/SPL/Photo Researchers

▲ Figure 11 *Bacillus anthracis* as it appears in tissue.

## Structure, Physiology, and Pathogenicity

### Learning Objective

✓ Identify the structural features of *Bacillus* that contribute to its pathogenicity.

*Bacillus anthracis*[18] (ba-sil′ŭs an-thrā′sis) is a large (1 µm × 3–5 µm) rod-shaped, facultatively anaerobic bacterium that normally dwells in soil. Its cells are arranged singly, in pairs, or in chains (Figure 11). In laboratory culture, prominent endospores form in the middle of cells, which lack capsules. In contrast, bacteria in clinical specimens typically lack endospores

[18]Greek, meaning charcoal.

## Characteristics of Pathogenic Streptococci

**TABLE 2**

| Lancefield Group | Scientific Name | Hemolytic Pattern | Significant Characteristics | Characteristic Diseases |
|---|---|---|---|---|
| A | S. pyogenes | Large zone of beta-hemolysis | 1- to 2-mm white colonies on blood agar; bacitracin sensitive | Pharyngitis, scarlet fever, pyoderma, erysipelas, toxic-shock-like syndrome, necrotizing fasciitis, rheumatic fever, glomerulonephritis |
| B | S. agalactiae | Small zone of beta-hemolysis | 2- to 3-mm buttery colonies on blood agar; bacitracin resistant | Puerperal fever, neonatal bacteremia, meningitis, pneumonia |
| C | S. equisimilis | Large zone of beta-hemolysis | 1- to 2-mm white colonies on blood agar | Pharyngitis, glomerulonephritis |
| C, F, or G | S. anginosus | Small zone of beta-hemolysis | 1- to 2-mm white colonies on blood agar | Purulent abscess |
| — | S. mutans | Alpha-hemolysis | Viridans group (produce green pigment when grown on blood agar) | Dental caries; rarely bacteremia, meningitis, endocarditis |
| — | S. pneumoniae | Alpha-hemolysis (aerobic); beta-hemolysis (anaerobic) | Diplococci; capsule required for pathogenicity; bile sensitive | Pneumonia, sinusitis, otitis media, bacteremia, endocarditis, meningitis |
| D | Enterococcus faecalis, E. faecium | None (gamma-hemolysis) | Diplococci; no capsule; bile insensitive | Urinary tract infections, bacteremia, endocarditis, wound infections |

Greater Southern Area Health Service, NSW Australia

▲ **Figure 12** **Cutaneous anthrax.** Black eschars are characteristic of cutaneous anthrax.

and possess protective capsules. The tough external coat and the internal chemicals of endospores make these structures resistant to harsh environmental conditions, enabling *Bacillus* to survive in the environment for centuries or perhaps even longer. A vegetative (non-endospore) cell of *Bacillus* can survive in the body because it has multiple copies of a plasmid coding for a capsule, which is composed solely of glutamic acid. The capsule inhibits effective phagocytosis by white blood cells.

Pathogenic strains of *B. anthracis* cause disease because they contain multiple copies of another plasmid coding for *anthrax toxins*—three distinct polypeptides that work together in a lethal combination. Seven copies of one toxin combine to form a protein pore that breaches the cytoplasmic membrane of a host cell. The other two toxins enter the cell through the pore. Once in the cell, the toxins interfere with intracellular signaling, severely affect cellular metabolism, and ultimately cause the cell to undergo apoptosis (programmed cell suicide). Scientists are investigating the precise mechanisms by which the three components of anthrax toxin work in hopes of developing techniques for neutralizing them. Anthrax can be deadly even after treatment, because antimicrobial drugs do not inactivate accumulated anthrax toxin.

## Epidemiology

### Learning Objective

✓ List three methods of transmission of anthrax.

**Anthrax** is primarily a disease of herbivores; humans contract the disease from infected animals. Anthrax is not normally transmitted from individual to individual, but can invade via one of three routes: inhalation of endospores, inoculation of endospores into the body through a break in the skin, or ingestion of endospores. Ingestion anthrax is the normal means of transmission among animals but is rare in humans. In the 25 years between January 1976 and September 2001, only 15 cases of anthrax were reported in the United States; thus epidemiologists suspected bioterrorism when over a dozen cases of anthrax were reported in New York, Florida, and Washington, D.C., in the fall of 2001.

## Disease

### Learning Objectives

✓ List and describe three clinical manifestations of *Bacillus anthracis* infections.

✓ Identify the diagnosis, treatment, and prevention of anthrax.

*Bacillus anthracis* causes only one disease—anthrax—but it can have three clinical manifestations. The first, *gastrointestinal anthrax,* is very rare in humans but is common in animals; it results in intestinal hemorrhaging and eventually death.

*Cutaneous anthrax* begins when a painless, solid, raised nodule forms on the skin at the site of infection. The cells in the affected area die, and the nodule spreads to form a painless, swollen, black, crusty ulcer called an *eschar* (es′kar) **(Figure 12)**. It is from the black color of eschars that anthrax, which means "charcoal" in Greek, gets its name. *B. anthracis* growing in the eschar releases anthrax toxin into the blood, producing toxemia. Untreated cutaneous anthrax is fatal for 20% of patients.

*Inhalation anthrax* is also rare in humans, as it requires inhalation of airborne endospores. After endospores germinate in the lungs, they secrete toxins that are absorbed into the blood-

## BENEFICIAL MICROBES

### MICROBES TO THE RESCUE?

▲ *Lactobacillus,* a potential probiotic. SEM 5 μm

The digestive tract is home to viruses, bacteria, protozoa, fungi, and parasitic helminths. The normal microbiota helps protect the body by competing with pathogens for nutrients and space. Some research indicates that consumption of living microbes in food or dietary supplements may change the normal microbiota of the digestive tract. Such microbes may help ward off bowel problems such as irritable bowel syndrome, reduce incidence of yeast infection, alleviate symptoms of gastroenteritis, and shorten the duration of colds by 36 hours. Probiotics, as such microbes are called, are often bacteria used to ferment food, particularly species of *Lactobacillus* or the related genus *Bifidobacterium*. Despite favorable anecdotal evidence and partial support in laboratory studies for the benefits of probiotics, many scientists remain skeptical that consumers can successfully change the makeup of their intestinal microbiota or that probiotics are really helpful.

stream, producing toxemia. Early signs and symptoms include fatigue, malaise, fever, aches, and cough—all of which are common to many pulmonary diseases. In a later phase, victims of inhalation anthrax have a high fever and labored breathing due to localized swelling, and they go into shock. Historically, mortality rates have been high—approaching 100% even when treated—perhaps in part because the disease is often not suspected until it is irreversible, and because antimicrobial drugs do not neutralize toxins released during the course of the disease. During the bioterrorism attack of 2001, physicians learned that early and aggressive treatment of inhalation anthrax with antimicrobial drugs accompanied by persistent drainage of fluid from around the lungs increased the survival rate to greater than 50%.

## Diagnosis, Treatment, and Prevention

Large, nonmotile, Gram-positive bacilli in clinical samples from the lungs or skin are diagnostic. As mentioned previously, endospores are not typically seen in clinical samples but are produced after a few days in culture.

Penicillin, erythromycin, chloramphenicol, and many other antimicrobial agents are effective against *B. anthracis.* Ciprofloxacin (Cipro) gained fame in 2001 as physicians were encouraged to use it in the fear that the bioterrorists had genetically altered the microorganism to be penicillin resistant—a fear that proved unfounded.

Prevention of naturally occurring disease in humans requires control of the disease in animals. Farmers in areas where anthrax is endemic must vaccinate their stock and bury or burn the carcasses of infected animals. Anthrax vaccine has proven effective and safe for humans, but requires six doses over 18 months plus annual boosters. Researchers are developing an alternative vaccine.

# Clostridium

### Learning Objective

✓ Characterize the four major species of *Clostridium.*

*Clostridium* (klos-trid′ē-ŭm) is an anaerobic, Gram-positive, endospore-forming bacillus that is ubiquitous in soil, water, sewage, and the gastrointestinal tracts of animals and humans. Several species are significant human pathogens. Pathogenicity is due in great part to the ability of endospores to survive harsh conditions, and to the secretion by vegetative cells of potent *histolytic toxins, enterotoxins* (toxins affecting the GI tract), and *neurotoxins.* The most common pathogenic clostridia are *C. perfringens, C. difficile, C. botulinum,* and *C. tetani.*

## Clostridium perfringens

### Learning Objective

✓ Identify the mechanisms accounting for the pathogenesis of *Clostridium perfringens* infections.

✓ Describe the diagnosis, treatment, and prevention of *Clostridium perfringens* infections.

SPL/Photo Researchers

▲ **Figure 13** **Gas gangrene, a life-threatening disease caused by** *Clostridium perfringens.* The blackening is the result of the death of muscle tissue (myonecrosis), whereas the "bubbling" appearance results from the production of gaseous waste products by the bacteria.

*Clostridium perfringens* (per-frin′jens), the clostridium most frequently isolated from clinical specimens, is a large, almost rectangular, Gram-positive bacillus. Although it is nonmotile, its rapid growth enables it to proliferate across the surface of laboratory media, resembling the spread of motile bacteria. Endospores are rarely observed either in clinical samples or in culture. *C. perfringens* type A, known by its specific antigens, is the most virulent serotype.

### Pathogenesis, Epidemiology, and Disease

*C. perfringens* produces 11 toxins that lyse erythrocytes and leukocytes, increase vascular permeability, reduce blood pressure, and kill cells, resulting in irreversible damage. Because *C. perfringens* commonly grows in the digestive tracts of animals and humans, it is nearly ubiquitous in fecally contaminated soil and water.

The severity of diseases caused by *C. perfringens* ranges from mild food poisoning to life-threatening illness. Clostridial food poisoning is a relatively benign disease characterized by abdominal cramps and watery diarrhea, but not fever, nausea, or vomiting. It lasts for less than 24 hours. Such food poisoning typically results from the ingestion of large numbers ($10^8$ or more) of *C. perfringens* type A in contaminated meat.

*C. perfringens* is not invasive, but when some traumatic event (such as a surgical incision, a puncture, a gunshot wound, crushing trauma, or a compound fracture) introduces endospores into the body, they can germinate in the anaerobic environment of deep tissues. The immediate result is intense pain at the initial site of infection as clostridial toxins induce swelling and tissue death. The rapidly reproducing bacteria can then spread into the surrounding tissue, causing the death of muscle and connective tissue that is typically accompanied by the production of abundant, foul-smelling, gaseous, bacterial waste products—hence the common name for the disease: **gas gangrene**[19] (**Figure 13**). Shock, kidney failure, and death can follow, often within a week of infection.

[19]From Greek *gangraina,* meaning an eating sore.

## Diagnosis, Treatment, and Prevention

Medical laboratory technologists show that *Clostridium* is involved in food poisoning by demonstrating more than $10^5$ bacteria in a gram of food or $10^6$ cells per gram of feces. The appearance of gas gangrene is usually diagnostic by itself, though the detection of large Gram-positive bacilli is confirmatory.

Clostridial food poisoning is typically self-limiting—the pathogens and their toxins are eliminated in the resulting watery stool. In contrast, physicians must quickly and aggressively intervene to stop the spread of necrosis in gas gangrene by surgically removing dead tissue and administering large doses of antitoxin and penicillin. Oxygen applied under pressure may also be effective. Despite all therapeutic care, mortality of gas gangrene exceeds 40%.

It is difficult to prevent infections of *C. perfringens* because the organism is so common; however, refrigeration of food prevents toxin formation and reduces the chance of clostridial food poisoning. Alternatively, reheating contaminated food destroys any toxin that has formed. Given that gas gangrene occurs when endospores are introduced deep in the tissues, proper cleaning of wounds can prevent many cases.

## *Clostridium difficile*

### Learning Objectives

✓ Discuss the role of antimicrobial drugs in the development of gastrointestinal diseases caused by *Clostridium difficile*.

✓ Discuss the diagnosis, treatment, and prevention of *C. difficile* infections.

*Clostridium difficile* (di-fi′sil-ē) is a motile, anaerobic intestinal bacterium with cells about 1.5 μm in width and 3–6.5 μm in length that form oval, subterminal endospores. The bacterium produces two toxins (called toxins A and B) and the enzyme hyaluronidase.

### Pathogenesis, Epidemiology, and Disease

Although so-called *C. diff.* is a common member of the intestinal microbiota, it can be an opportunistic pathogen in patients treated with broad-spectrum antimicrobial drugs, such as penicillin and cephalosporin. In such patients, the normal proportions of different bacteria in the colon can be significantly altered. In many cases the hardy endospores of *C. difficile* germinate, enabling it to become the predominant intestinal bacterium, such that the toxins and enzymes it produces cause hemorrhagic death of the intestinal wall. In minor infections these lesions result in a self-limiting explosive diarrhea; however, in more serious cases, *C. difficile* produces life-threatening **pseudomembranous colitis,** in which large sections of the colon wall slough off, potentially perforating the colon, and leading to massive internal infection by fecal bacteria and eventual death.

### Diagnosis, Treatment, and Prevention

Diarrhea in patients undergoing antimicrobial therapy is suggestive of *C. difficile* infection, and laboratory microbiologists confirm the diagnosis either by isolating the organism from feces using selective media or by demonstrating the presence of the toxins via immunoassays.

Discontinuation of the implicated antimicrobial drug, which allows the microbiota to return to normal, usually resolves minor infections with *C. difficile.* More serious cases are treated with vancomycin or metronidazole, though endospores survive such therapy in about a third of patients, causing a relapse. Further treatment of relapses with either vancomycin or metronidazole is often successful.

*C. difficile* is frequently found in hospitals, and hospital personnel can easily transmit it between patients. Proper hygiene—particularly frequent handwashing—is critical for limiting nosocomial infections.

## *Clostridium botulinum*

### Learning Objectives

✓ Contrast the three manifestations of botulism.

✓ Describe the use of mice in the diagnosis of botulism.

✓ Describe three treatments of botulism and explain how to prevent it.

*Clostridium botulinum*[20] (bo-tū-lī′num) is an anaerobic, endospore-forming, Gram-positive bacillus that is common in soil and water worldwide. Its endospores survive improper canning of food, germinating to produce vegetative cells that grow and release into the jar or can a powerful neurotoxin that causes **botulism** (bot′ū-lizm).

### Pathogenesis

Strains of *C. botulinum* produce one of seven antigenically distinct *botulism toxins* (A through G). Some scientists consider botulism toxins among the deadliest toxins known—30 grams of pure toxin would be enough to kill every person in the United States. Botulism toxins are extremely potent; even a small taste of contaminated food can cause full-blown illness or death.

Each of the seven toxins is a quaternary protein composed of a single neurologically active polypeptide associated with one or more nontoxic polypeptides that prevent the inactivation of the toxin by stomach acid. To understand the action of botulism toxins, we must consider the way the nervous system controls muscle contractions.

Each of the many ends of a motor neuron (nerve cell) forms an intimate connection with a muscle cell at a *neuromuscular junction;* however, the two cells do not actually touch—a small gap, called a *synaptic cleft,* remains between them (Figure 14a). The neuron stores a chemical, called *acetylcholine,* in vesicles near its terminal cytoplasmic membrane. Acetylcholine is one of a family of chemicals called neurotransmitters that mediate communication among neurons and between neurons and other cells.

When a signal arrives at the terminus of a motor neuron (①), the vesicles containing acetylcholine fuse with the neuron's cytoplasmic membrane, releasing acetylcholine into the synaptic

---

[20]From Latin, *botulus,* meaning sausage.

(a) Normal neuromuscular junction

(b) Neuromuscular junction with botulism toxin present

▲ **Figure 14 How botulism toxin acts at a neuromuscular junction. (a)** Normal function at a neuromuscular junction. ❶ A nerve impulse from the central nervous system causes vesicles filled with acetylcholine to fuse with the neuron's cytoplasmic membrane, ❷ releasing acetylcholine into the synaptic cleft. The binding of acetylcholine to receptors on the muscle cell's cytoplasmic membrane stimulates a series of events that result in contraction of the muscle cell (not shown). **(b)** Botulism toxin blocks the fusion of the vesicles with the neuron's cytoplasmic membrane, thereby preventing secretion of the neurotransmitter into the synaptic cleft; as a result, the muscle cell does not contract.

cleft (❷). Molecules of acetylcholine then diffuse across the cleft and bind to receptors on the cytoplasmic membrane of the muscle cell. The binding of acetylcholine to muscle cell receptors triggers a series of events inside the muscle cell that results in muscle contraction (not shown).

Botulism toxins act by binding irreversibly to neuronal cytoplasmic membranes, thereby preventing the fusion of vesicles and secretion of acetylcholine into the synaptic cleft (Figure 14b). Thus, these neurotoxins prevent muscular contraction, resulting in a *flaccid paralysis*.

### Epidemiology and Diseases

*Botulism* is not an infection, but instead an *intoxication* (poisoning) caused by botulism toxin. Clinicians recognize three manifestations of botulism: foodborne botulism, infant botulism, and wound botulism. Fortunately, all three are rare.

About 25 cases of foodborne botulism occur in the United States each year, usually within one to two days following the consumption of toxin in home-canned foods or preserved fish. Contaminated food may not appear or smell spoiled. Patients are initially weak and dizzy and have blurred vision, dry mouth, dilated pupils, constipation, and abdominal pain, followed by a progressive paralysis that eventually affects the diaphragm. The patient remains mentally alert throughout the ordeal. When fatal, death results from the inability of muscles of respiration to effect inhalation; victims asphyxiate because they cannot inhale. Survivors recover very slowly as their nerve cells grow new endings

over the course of months or years, replacing the debilitated termini. (See **Highlight: Botulism in Alaska**.)

In contrast to foodborne botulism, infant botulism results from the ingestion of endospores, which then germinate and colonize the infant's gastrointestinal tract. Infants are susceptible to colonization because their GI tracts do not have a sufficient number of benign microbiota to compete with *C. botulinum* for nutrients and space. Botulism toxin is absorbed into the blood from an infected infant's GI tract, causing nonspecific symptoms: crying, constipation, and "failure to thrive." Fortunately, paralysis and death are rare. About 100 cases of infant botulism are reported in the United States each year, though some cases reported as sudden infant death syndrome may be fatal infant botulism instead.

Wound botulism usually begins four or more days following the contamination of a wound by endospores. With the exception that the gastrointestinal system is not typically involved, the symptoms are the same as those of foodborne botulism.

### Diagnosis, Treatment, and Prevention

The symptoms of botulism are diagnostic; culturing the organism from contaminated food, from feces, or from the patient's wounds confirms the diagnosis. Further, toxin activity can be detected by using a mouse bioassay. In this laboratory procedure, specimens of food, feces, and/or serum are divided into two portions. Botulism antitoxin is mixed with one of the portions, and the portions are then inoculated into two sets of mice. If the mice receiving the antitoxin survive while the other mice die, botulism is confirmed.

Precision Graphics

## HIGHLIGHT

Flip Nicklin/Minden Pictures

### BOTULISM IN ALASKA

For some indigenous Alaskans living near the Bering Sea, an adult beluga whale beached on the coast in July 2002 seemed a feast fit for a king. The villagers carved up the tail and enjoyed a traditional delicacy known as "muktuk"—skin and pink blubber eaten raw. Within 36 hours, however, 8 of the 14 diners came down with symptoms of dry mouth, blurred vision, swallowing difficulties, and progressive paralysis: telltale signs of botulism.

Sure enough, local authorities discovered that the whale meat had been contaminated with botulism toxin type E, which is found uniquely in marine mammals. Apparently, the whale had been dead for some weeks before it was eaten—enough time for it to become an incubator for *Clostridium botulinum,* an anaerobe that prefers a moist, low-acid environment. That July, the temperature rose high enough to match the lower temperature limit for toxin production, a weather phenomenon that may have been a result of global warming. All patients recovered thanks to the prompt administration of antitoxin and ventilator support.

Treatment of botulism entails three approaches:

- Repeated washing of the intestinal tract to remove *Clostridium.*
- Administration of antibodies against botulism toxin to neutralize toxin in the blood before it can bind to neurons.
- Administration of antimicrobial drugs to kill clostridia in infant and wound botulism cases. (This approach is not effective in treating foodborne botulism, which results from the ingestion of toxin, not of the bacteria themselves.)

Note that damage resulting from any prior binding of toxin to any particular nerve ending is irreversible, so signs and symptoms of botulism may persist despite aggressive medical care.

Foodborne botulism is prevented by destroying all endospores in contaminated food by proper canning techniques, by preventing endospores from germinating by using refrigeration or establishing an acidic environment (pH <4.5), or by destroying the toxin by heating to at least 80°C for 20 minutes or more. Because infant botulism is often associated with the consumption of honey, parents are advised not to feed honey to infants under age one because their intesinal microbiota are not suffciently developed to inhib the germination *C. botulinum* endospores and their growth as toxin-producing vegetative cells.

### MICROBE AT A GLANCE

## *Clostridium botulinum*

**Taxonomy:** Domain Bacteria, phylum Firmicutes, class "Clostridia," order Clostridiales, family Clostridiaceae

**Cell morphology and arrangement:** Endospore-forming bacillus

**Gram reaction:** Positive

**Virulence factors:** Endospore, botulism toxins A–G

**Diseases caused:** Foodborne botulism, infant botulism, and wound botulism

**Treatment for diseases:** Repeated washing to intestinal tract to remove *Clostridium*, administration of antitoxin (antibodies against the toxins), antimicrobial drugs used for cases of infant botulism and wound botulism; damage to nerve endings irreversible

**Prevention of disease:** Proper canning to kill endospores; refrigeration to prevent endospores from germinating; heating to 80°C for 20 minutes to destroy toxin; refrain from feeding honey to infants

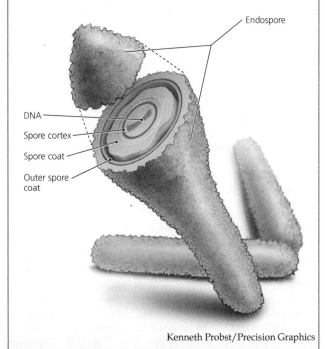

Endospore

DNA

Spore cortex

Spore coat

Outer spore coat

Kenneth Probst/Precision Graphics

 Download the Microbe at a Glance flashcards from the Study Area at www.masteringmicrobiology.com.

## Clostridium tetani

### Learning Objectives

✓ Describe the epidemiology of tetanus.

✓ List treatments for and preventative measures against *Clostridium tetani* infections.

*Clostridium tetani*[21] (te'tan-ē) is a small, motile, obligate anaerobe that produces a terminal endospore, giving the cell a distinctive lollipop appearance (Figure 15). *C. tetani* is ubiquitous in soil, dust, and the GI tracts of animals and humans. Its vegetative cells are extremely sensitive to oxygen and live only in anaerobic environments, but its endospores survive for years. Its toxin causes the disease **tetanus.**

### Pathogenesis

Contrary to popular belief, deep puncture wounds by rusty nails are not the only (or even primary) source of tetanus. Even a tiny break in the skin or mucous membranes can allow endospores of *C. tetani* access to an anaerobic environment in which they germinate, grow, and produce a fatal disease caused by **tetanospasmin** (tetanus toxin)—a potent neurotoxin released by *C. tetani* cells when they die. To understand the action of tetanospasmin, we must further consider the control of muscles by the central nervous system.

As we have seen, the secretion of acetylcholine at neuromuscular junctions stimulates muscles to contract. Skeletal muscles are typically arranged in competing pairs on opposite sides of a joint: When a motor nerve stimulates one muscle of the pair to contract, the muscle on the other side of the joint relaxes, but there is no "relaxing" neurotransmitter. Relaxation occurs because the muscle is unstimulated by nerve impulses. Inhibitory neurons of the central nervous system release neurotransmitters that inhibit the motor neuron, which therefore cannot stimulate the muscle (Figure 16).

Tetanospasmin is composed of two polypeptides held together by a disulfide bond. The heavier of the two polypeptides binds to a receptor on a neuron's cytoplasmic membrane. The neuron then endocytizes the toxin, removes the lighter of the two polypeptides, and transports it to the central nervous system. There the smaller polypeptide enters an inhibitory neuron and blocks the release of inhibitory neurotransmitter. With inhibition blocked, excitatory activity is unregulated, and both muscles in an antagonistic pair are signaled to contract simultaneously (Figure 16b). The result is that muscles on both sides of the joint contract and do not relax. Opposing contractions can be so severe they break bones.

### Disease and Epidemiology

The incubation period of tetanus ranges from a few days to a week depending on the distance of the site of infection from the central nervous system. Typically the initial and diagnostic sign of tetanus is tightening of the jaw and neck muscles—which is why tetanus is also called *lockjaw.* Other early symptoms include

[21]From Greek *tetanos*, meaning to stretch.

Endospore

Rich Robison, Pearson Science

LM  10 μm

▲ **Figure 15 Cells of *Clostridium tetani*, with terminal endospores.** The cells have a distinctive lollipop shape. *How does the location of* C. tetani *endospores distinguish this bacterium from* Bacillus anthracis?

**Figure 15** *The endospores of C. tetani are terminal, whereas those of* Bacillus anthracis *are located centrally.*

sweating, drooling, grouchiness, and constant back spasms. If the toxin spreads to autonomic neurons, then heartbeat irregularities, fluctuations in blood pressure, and extensive sweating result. Spasms and contractions may spread to other muscles, becoming so severe that the arms and fists curl tightly, the feet curl down, and the body assumes a stiff backward arch as the heels and back of the head bend toward one another (Figure 17). Complete, unrelenting contraction of the diaphragm results in a final inhalation; patients die because they cannot exhale.

Over a million cases of tetanus occur annually worldwide, mostly in underdeveloped countries where vaccination is unavailable or medical care is inadequate. The effect of tetanospasmin is irreversible at any particular synapse, so recovery depends on the growth of new neuronal terminals to replace those affected. The mortality rate of tetanus is about 50% among all patients, though the mortality of neonatal tetanus, resulting most commonly from infection of the umbilical stump, exceeds 90%.

### Diagnosis, Treatment, and Prevention

The diagnostic feature of tetanus is the characteristic muscular contraction, which is often noted too late to save the patient. The bacterium itself is rarely isolated from clinical samples because it grows slowly in culture and is extremely sensitive to oxygen.

Treatment involves thorough cleaning of wounds to remove all endospores, immediate passive immunization with immunoglobulin directed against the toxin, the administration of antimicrobials such as penicillin, and active immunization with tetanus toxoid. Cleansing and antimicrobials eliminate the bacteria, whereas the immunoglobulin binds to and neutralizes tetanospasmin before it can attach to neurons. Active immunization stimulates the formation of antibodies that neutralize the toxin. Once the toxin binds to a neuron, treatment is limited to supportive care.

(a)

(b)

Cassio Lynm/Precision Graphics

**▲ Figure 16 The action of tetanospasmin (tetanus toxin) on a pair of antagonistic muscles. (a)** Normally, when the muscle on one side of a joint is stimulated to contract, neurons controlling the antagonistic muscle are inhibited, so the antagonistic muscle relaxes. **(b)** Tetanospasmin blocks the inhibitory neurotransmitter. As a result, motor neurons controlling the antagonistic muscle are not inhibited, but instead can generate nerve impulses that stimulate muscle contraction.

CDC

**◀ Figure 17 A patient with tetanus.** Prolonged muscular contractions result from the action of tetanus toxin.

**▲ Figure 18 How *Listeria* avoids the host's immune system while infecting new cells. (a)**
After *Listeria* is initially endocytized (①), the intracellular bacterium escapes the phagosome (②)
and reproduces within the phagocyte (③). The bacterium then polymerizes the host cell's actin
filaments into a "tail" (④) that pushes the bacterium into a pseudopod (⑤) that is subsequently
endocytized by a new host cell (⑥). **(b)** A photomicrograph showing the endocytosis of a
pseudopod containing a *Listeria* cell.

The number of cases of tetanus in the United States has
steadily declined as a result of effective immunization with
tetanus toxoid. The CDC currently recommends five doses
beginning at two months of age, followed by a booster every
10 years for life.

In the previous two sections we examined two pathogenic,
Gram-positive bacilli that form endospores: *Bacillus,* which is
facultatively anaerobic, and *Clostridium,* which is anaerobic.
Next we consider the low G + C, rod-shaped *Listeria,* and the
unusual low G + C mycoplasmas that Gram stain pink because
they lack cell walls.

# *Listeria*

## Learning Objectives

✓ Describe the structures of *Listeria monocytogenes* that
account for its pathogenicity.

✓ Discuss the signs and symptoms, diagnosis, treatment, and
prevention of listeriosis.

*Listeria monocytogenes* (lis-tēr′ē-ă mo-nō-sī-tah′je-nēz) is a low
G + C, Gram-positive, non-endospore-forming bacillus found
in soil, water, mammals, birds, fish, and insects. It enters the
body in contaminated food and drink.

## Pathogenesis, Epidemiology, and Disease

*L. monocytogenes* binds to the surfaces of a macrophage or liver or
gallbladder cell, triggering its own endocytosis to become a facultative intracellular parasite. Once inside a human cell's phagosome, *Listeria* synthesizes a pore-forming protein, called
*listeriolysin O,* that punctures the phagosome membrane, releasing the bacterium into the host cell's cytosol before a lysosome
can fuse with the phagosome. *Listeria* then grows and reproduces
in the cytosol, sheltered from the humoral immune system.

*Listeria* continues to avoid exposure to the immune system
via a unique method of transferring itself to neighboring cells
without having to leave host cells (Figure 18). The pathogen
polymerizes the host cell's actin molecules to form stiff actin
filaments that lengthen and push the bacterium through the
cytosol to the cell's surface, where it forms a pseudopod. A
neighboring macrophage or epithelial cell then endocytizes the
pseudopod, and *Listeria* once again "tunnels" its way out of the
phagosome to continue its intracellular parasitic existence within
a new host cell.

*Listeria's* virulence is directly related to its ability to live
within cells, which is conferred by listeriolysin O and the membrane protein that triggers endocytosis; it produces no toxins or
enzymes that make it virulent. Interestingly, some mRNA in
*Listeria* is inactive until it is at 37°C in a human body. As a result,
the bacterium reproduces rapidly only when it is in a host.

*Listeria* is rarely pathogenic in healthy adults, who experience either no symptoms or only a mild flulike illness. In contrast, infection in pregnant women, fetuses, newborns, the elderly, and immunocompromised patients (particularly those with suppressed cell-mediated immunity) can be quite severe. In these patients, *Listeria* travels via the bloodstream to the brain, causing meningitis and possibly death. Human-to-human transmission is limited to the transfer of *Listeria* from pregnant women to fetuses, leading to premature delivery, miscarriage, stillbirth, or meningitis in the newborn.

## Diagnosis, Treatment, and Prevention

Because *Listeria* most commonly causes meningitis, clinicians look for it in the cerebrospinal fluid (CSF) of people with symptoms of meningitis. Unfortunately, only a few *Listeria* cells are required to produce disease, so the bacterium is rarely seen in Gram-stained preparations of phagocytes.

*Listeria* can be cultured from blood and CSF specimens on many laboratory media, especially when a technique called *cold enrichment* is used. In this procedure, the specimen is held at 4°C—a temperature that inhibits most bacteria, but not *Listeria*—and samples are periodically inoculated onto media. Even with cold enrichment, colonies of *Listeria* may take four weeks or longer to become visible.

The bacterium exhibits a characteristic end-over-end "tumbling" motility that occurs at room temperature but not at 37°C. Tumbling motility is so distinctive that it can provide the basis for an initial diagnosis, although serological testing is required for positive identification.

Most antimicrobial drugs, including penicillin and erythromycin, inhibit *Listeria*, though the bacterium is resistant to tetracycline and trimethoprim. Prevention of infections is difficult because the organism is ubiquitous. Individuals at greatest risk should avoid undercooked vegetables, unpasteurized milk, undercooked meat, and all soft cheeses such as feta, Brie, and Camembert. Aged cheeses made from raw milk should be particularly avoided because *Listeria* can grow during refrigeration. Further, people at a high risk of infection should thoroughly cook raw meat and heat prepared meats—including cold cuts, luncheon meats, and hot dogs—before consuming them.

# Mycoplasmas

## Learning Objectives

✓ List at least four characteristics of all mycoplasmas.

✓ Explain why mycoplasmas have been classified with both Gram-negative and Gram-positive organisms.

✓ Compare and contrast mycoplasmas and viruses.

**Mycoplasmas** (mī′kō-plaz-măz) are unique bacteria named for their most common representative, the genus *Mycoplasma*. Bacteria in the genus *Ureaplasma* (yū-rē′ă-plaz′mă) are also part of this group. Mycoplasmas lack cytochromes (which are present in many other organisms' electron transport chains), enzymes of the Krebs cycle, and cell walls—indeed, they are incapable of synthesizing peptidoglycan and its precursors.

Alan Rodwell

2.5 µm

▲ **Figure 19 Pleomorphic forms of *Mycoplasma*.** These bacteria can be either coccoid or filamentous because they lack a cell wall.

Moreover, most mycoplasmas have *sterols* in their cytoplasmic membranes, a feature lacking in other prokaryotes. They are distinct from all other organisms in that the codon UGA neither serves as a stop codon nor codes for selenocysteine, but instead codes for the amino acid tryptophan.

Before analysis of the nucleic acid sequences of mycoplasmal rRNA revealed that they are genetically Gram-positive organisms, mycoplasmas were classified in a separate phylum of Gram-negative bacteria—phylum Mollicutes. Modern taxonomists and the second edition of *Bergey's Manual of Systematic Bacteriology* now categorize organisms in Mollicutes as a class of low G + C, Gram-positive bacteria in the phylum Firmicutes. Nevertheless, they appear pink when stained with the Gram stain (because they have no cell walls).

Because they lack cell walls, mycoplasmas[22] are pleomorphic, taking on a variety of shapes, including cocci and thin, unicellular filaments up to 150 µm long that resemble the hyphae of fungi (Figure 19). Mycoplasmas are able to withstand osmotic stress despite having no walls because they colonize osmotically protected habitats such as animal and human bodies, and the sterols in their membranes convey sufficient strength and rigidity.

Mycoplasmas have diameters ranging from 0.1 µm to 0.8 µm, making them the smallest *free-living* microbes—that is, those that can grow and reproduce independently of other cells. Originally, many mycoplasmas were thought to be viruses because their small, flexible cells enabled them to squeeze through the 0.45-µm pores of filters that were at one time used to remove bacteria from solutions; however, mycoplasmas contain both functional RNA and DNA, and they divide by binary fission—traits that viruses lack.

[22]From Greek *mycos*, meaning fungus, and *plasma*, meaning anything formed or molded.

Mycoplasmas require organic growth factors, including cholesterol, fatty acids, vitamins, amino acids, and nucleotides; these factors must either be acquired from a host or supplied in laboratory media. With exception of the strictly aerobic *Mycoplasma pneumoniae* (nū-mō′nē-ī), mycoplasmas are facultative anaerobes.

Most mycoplasmas form distinctive colonies on solid media. The colonies are so small that often they must be viewed through a microscope, and the colonies of most species resemble fried eggs (because cells at the center of colonies tend to grow into the agar, whereas those at the periphery remain on the surface of the medium). However, two important pathogenic mycoplasmas, *M. pneumoniae* and *Ureaplasma,* are exceptions in that their colonies do not resemble fried eggs.

Mycoplasmas can colonize mucous membranes of the respiratory and urinary tracts and are associated with pneumonia and urinary tract infections. Of the two genera that cause diseases in humans, *Mycoplasma* is unable to utilize urea (that is, it is urease negative), whereas *Ureaplasma* does hydrolyze urea to form ammonia.

Over 100 species of *Mycoplasma* have been identified, but only a few cause significant diseases in humans. We begin our examination of these species with *M. pneumoniae.*

## *Mycoplasma pneumoniae*

### Learning Objective

✓ Describe the damage done to respiratory epithelial cells by *Mycoplasma pneumoniae.*

### Pathogenesis and Epidemiology

*Mycoplasma pneumoniae* (Figure 20) has an adhesive protein that attaches specifically to receptors located at the bases of cilia on epithelial cells lining the respiratory tracts of humans. Attachment causes the cilia to stop beating, and mycoplasmal colonization eventually kills the epithelial cells. This interrupts the normal removal of mucus from the respiratory tract, allowing colonization by other bacteria and causing a buildup of mucus that irritates the upper respiratory tract. Early symptoms of *M. pneumoniae* infections—including fever, malaise, headache, and sore throat—are not typical of other types of pneumonia; thus the disease is called **primary atypical pneumonia.** The body subsequently responds with a persistent, unproductive cough in an attempt to clear the lungs.

Primary atypical pneumonia may last for several weeks, but it is usually not severe enough to require hospitalization or to cause death. Because symptoms can be mild, the disease is also sometimes called *walking pneumonia.*

Nasal secretions spread *M. pneumoniae* among people in close contact, such as classmates and family members. The disease appears to be uncommon in children under age 5 or in adults older than 20, though it is probably the most common form of pneumonia seen in children 5–15 years old. However, because primary atypical pneumonia is not a reportable disease and is difficult to diagnose, the actual incidence of infection is unknown.

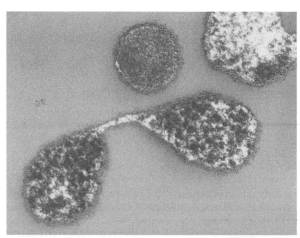

Kari Lounatmaa/Photo Researchers

TEM ⊢——⊣ 0.3 μm

▲ **Figure 20** *Mycoplasma pneumoniae.*

Primary atypical pneumonia occurs throughout the year. This lack of seasonality is in contrast to pneumococcal pneumonia (caused by *Streptococcus pneumoniae*), which is more commonly seen in the fall and winter.

### Diagnosis, Treatment, and Prevention

Diagnosis is difficult because mycoplasmas are small and difficult to detect in clinical specimens or tissue samples. Further, mycoplasmas grow slowly in culture, requiring two to six weeks before colonies can be seen. As previously noted, the colonies of *M. pneumoniae* differ from the colonies of other mycoplasmas in lacking a fried egg appearance; instead, the colonies have a uniform granular appearance. Complement fixation, hemagglutination, and immunofluorescent tests are sometimes used to confirm a diagnosis, but such tests are nonspecific and are not by themselves positively diagnostic.

Physicians treat primary atypical pneumonia with erythromycin or tetracycline. Prevention is difficult because patients are often infectious for long periods of time without signs or symptoms, and they remain infectious even while undergoing antimicrobial treatment. Nevertheless, frequent hand antisepsis, avoidance of contaminated fomites, and reducing aerosol dispersion can limit the spread of the pathogen and the number of cases of disease. No vaccine against *M. pneumoniae* is available.

### CRITICAL **THINKING**

*Mycoplasma pneumoniae*, like many pathogenic bacteria, is resistant to penicillin; however, unlike most resistant species, *Mycoplasma* does not synthesize β-lactamase. Explain why *Mycoplasma* is resistant to penicillin.

## Other Mycoplasmas

### Learning Objectives

✓ List three mycoplasmas associated with urinary and genital tract infections.

✓ Describe pelvic inflammatory disease.

Three other mycoplasmas are associated with diseases of humans: *M. hominis* (ho′mi-nis), *M. genitalium* (jen-ē-tal′ē-ŭm), and *Ureaplasma urealyticum* (ū-rē′ă-li′ti-kŭm) often colonize the urinary and genital tracts of newborn girls, though such infections rarely persist through childhood. However, the incidence of genital reinfections increases after puberty as a result of sexual activity; approximately 15% of sexually active adult Americans (males and females) are currently infected with *M. hominis,* and 70% are infected with *Ureaplasma.*

*M. genitalium* and *U. urealyticum* cause *nongonococcal urethritis*—that is, inflammation of the urethra not caused by *Neisseria gonorrhoeae* (nī-se′rē-ă go-nor-rē′ī). By contrast, *M. hominis* can cause **pelvic inflammatory disease (PID)** in women. Pelvic inflammatory disease is characterized by inflammation of the organs in the pelvic cavity, fever, and abdominal pain.

Infections of either *M. genitalium* or *U. urealyticum* are treated with erythromycin or tetracycline, whereas clindamycin is used to treat *M. hominis,* which is commonly resistant to tetracycline and erythromycin. Abstinence, mutually faithful monogamy, and proper use of condoms prevent the spread of these sexually transmitted organisms.

### CRITICAL **THINKING**

Why do pediatricians refrain from using tetracycline to treat mycoplasmal infections in children?

We have examined low G + C pathogenic, Gram-positive cocci; endospore-forming bacilli; non-endospore-forming, rod-shaped *Listeria;* and wall-less mycoplasmas. Now we turn our attention to the high G + C, Gram-positive pathogens, beginning with *Corynebacterium.*

# *Corynebacterium*

### Learning Objectives

✓ Characterize the arrangements of *Corynebacterium* cells.

✓ Describe the transmission of *Corynebacterium diphtheriae* and the effect of diphtheria toxin.

✓ Discuss the diagnosis, treatment, and prevention of diphtheria.

*Corynebacterium* (kŏ-rī′nē-bak-tēr′ē-ŭm) is a genus of high G + C, pleomorphic, non-endospore-forming bacteria that are ubiquitous on plants and in animals and humans, where they colonize the skin and the respiratory, gastrointestinal, urinary, and genital tracts. The bacteria divide via a type of binary fission called *snapping division,* in which daughter cells remain attached to form characteristic V-shapes and side-by-side *palisade*

G. W. Willis

LM  |— 20 μm

▲ **Figure 21** **Gram-stained *Corynebacterium diphtheriae.*** The characteristic arrangement of the cells results from the type of binary fission called snapping division.

arrangements (Figure 21). Another distinctive feature is that methylene blue or toluidine blue dyes color the cytoplasm of corynebacteria differentially, revealing storage granules called *metachromatic granules.* Although all species of corynebacteria can be pathogenic, the agent of diphtheria is most widely known.

## Pathogenesis, Epidemiology, and Disease

*Corynebacterium diphtheriae*[23] (dif-thi′rē-ī) is transmitted from person to person via respiratory droplets or skin contact. Diphtheria is endemic in poorer parts of the world that lack adequate immunization. The bacterium normally contains a lysogenic bacteriophage that codes for *diphtheria toxin,* which is directly responsible for the signs and symptoms of diphtheria. Cells lacking the phage are not pathogenic.

Like many bacterial toxins, diphtheria toxin consists of two polypeptides. One polypeptide binds to a growth factor receptor found on many types of human cells, triggering endocytosis of the toxin by these cells. Once inside a cell, proteolytic enzymes cleave the toxin, releasing the second polypeptide into the cytosol. This portion of the toxin enzymatically destroys *elongation factor,* a protein required for synthesis of polypeptides in eukaryotes. Because the action of the toxin is enzymatic, a single molecule of toxin sequentially destroys every molecule of elongation factor in the cell, completely blocking all polypeptide synthesis and resulting in cell death. Diphtheria toxin is thus one of the more potent toxins known.

Infections with *C. diphtheriae* have different effects depending on the host's immune status and the site of infection. Infections in

---

[23]From Greek *koryne,* meaning club; *bakterion,* meaning small rod; and *diphthera,* meaning leather membrane.

immune individuals are asymptomatic, whereas infections in partially immune individuals result in a mild respiratory disease. Respiratory infections of nonimmune patients are most severe, resulting in the sudden and rapid signs and symptoms of **diphtheria** (dif-thē-rē'ă), including sore throat, localized pain, fever, pharyngitis, and the oozing of a fluid composed of intracellular fluid, blood clotting factors, leukocytes, bacteria, and the remains of dead cells lining the larynx and pharynx. The fluid thickens into a *pseudomembrane* (Figure 22) that can adhere so tightly to the tonsils, uvula, palate, pharynx, and larynx that it cannot be dislodged without causing bleeding in the underlying tissue. In severe cases the pseudomembrane completely occludes the respiratory passages, resulting in death by suffocation.

In a similar way, cutaneous diphtheria causes cell death and the formation of a pseudomembrane on the skin. With both cutaneous and respiratory infections, toxin absorbed into the blood can kill heart cells and nerve cells throughout the body, resulting in cardiac arrhythmia, coma, and death of 5–10% of patients.

## Diagnosis, Treatment, and Prevention

Initial diagnosis is based on the presence of a pseudomembrane. Laboratory examination of the membrane or of tissue collected from the site of infection does not always reveal bacterial cells because the effects are due largely to the action of diphtheria toxin and not the cells directly. Culture of specimens on *Loffler's medium,* which was developed especially for the culture of *C. diphtheriae,* produces three colonial morphologies. Some colonies are large, irregular, and gray; others are small, flat, and gray; and still others are small, round, convex, and black. Even though observations of these distinctive colonies are useful, absolute certainty of diagnosis results from an immunodiffusion assay, called an **Elek test,** in which antibodies against the toxin react with toxin in a sample of fluid from the patient.

The most important aspect of treatment is the administration of antitoxin (immunoglobulins against the toxin) to neutralize toxin before it binds to cells; once the toxin binds to a cell, it enters via endocytosis and kills the cell. Penicillin or erythromycin kills the bacterium, preventing the synthesis of more toxin. In severe cases, a blocked airway must be opened surgically or bypassed with a tracheostomy tube.

Because humans are the only known host for *C. diphtheriae,* the most effective way to prevent diphtheria is immunization. Before immunization, hundreds of thousands of cases occurred in the United States each year; in contrast, only 15 cases total were reported between 1994 and 2009. Toxoid (deactivated toxin) is administered as part of the DTaP vaccine, which combines diphtheria and tetanus toxoids with antigens of the pertussis bacterium, at 2, 4, 6, 18 and 60 months of age, followed by booster immunizations with a slightly different vaccine (Tdap) every 10 years.

### CRITICAL **THINKING**

Why must diphtheria and tetanus vaccines be boosted every 10 years?

Medical-on-Line/Alamy

▲ **Figure 22** **A pseudomembrane.** This feature is characteristic of diphtheria.

# *Mycobacterium*

## Learning Objective

✓ Characterize mycobacteria in terms of endospore formation, cell wall composition, growth rate, and resistance to antimicrobial drugs.

Another devastating high G + C, non-endospore-forming pathogen is *Mycobacterium* (mī-kō-bak-tēr'ē-ŭm). Species in this genus have cell walls containing an abundance of a waxy lipid, called **mycolic** (mī-kol'ik) **acid,** that is composed of chains of 60–90 carbon atoms. This unusual cell wall is directly responsible for the unique characteristics of this pathogen. Specifically, mycobacteria:

- Grow slowly (because of the time required to synthesize numerous molecules of mycolic acid). The generation time varies from hours to several days.
- Are protected from lysis once they are phagocytized.
- Are capable of intracellular growth.
- Are resistant to Gram staining, detergents, many common antimicrobial drugs, and desiccation. Because mycobacteria stain only weakly with the Gram procedure (if at all), the acid-fast staining procedure was developed to differentially stain mycobacteria.

Even though almost 75 species of mycobacteria are known, most mycobacterial diseases in humans are caused by two species: *M. tuberculosis,* and *M. leprae,* which cause tuberculosis and leprosy, respectively. *M. avium-intracellulare* and *M. ulcerans* cause emerging mycobacterial diseases.

## Tuberculosis

### Learning Objectives

✓ Identify two effects of cord factor of *Mycobacterium tuberculosis.*

✓ Describe the transmission of *M. tuberculosis,* and its subsequent action within the human body.

✓ Discuss the diagnosis, treatment, and prevention of tuberculosis.

Biophoto Associates/Photo Researchers

LM    15 µm

▲ **Figure 23** *Mycobacterium tuberculosis.* The pink appearance of the bacteria when prepared with an acid-fast stain. Note the corded growth (parallel alignments) of daughter cells, a result of the presence of cord factor in the cell walls of virulent strains.

**Tuberculosis (TB),** the primary mycobacterial disease, is fundamentally a respiratory disease caused by *Mycobacterium tuberculosis* (too-ber-kyū-lō´sis). This bacterium forms dull-yellow raised colonies after growth for weeks on a special differential medium called Lowenstein-Jensen agar. Virulent strains of *M. tuberculosis* have a cell wall component, called **cord factor,** that produces strands of daughter cells that remain attached to one another in parallel alignments **(Figure 23).** Cord factor also inhibits migration of neutrophils and is toxic to mammalian cells. Mutant mycobacteria that are unable to synthesize cord factor do not cause disease.

## Pathogenesis and Disease

The waxy wall protects *Mycobacterium* from desiccation, and it can remain viable in dried aerosol droplets for eight months. The pathogen is not particularly virulent, as only about 5% of people infected with the bacterium develop disease; however, it kills about 50% of untreated diseased patients. Clinicians divide tuberculosis into three types; *primary TB, secondary* (or *reactivated*) *TB,* and *disseminated TB.*

**Primary Tuberculosis** Although *M. tuberculosis* can infect any organ, 85% of infections remain in the lungs. Primary infection, which typically occurs in children, involves the formation of small, hard nodules in the lungs called **tubercles** (too´ber-klz), which are characteristic of TB and give it its name. The five stages of a primary infection are as follows **(Figure 24a):**

1 *Mycobacterium* typically infects the respiratory tract via inhalation of respiratory droplets formed when infected individuals talk, sing, cough, or sneeze. A respiratory droplet is about 5 mm in diameter and carries 1–3 bacilli. The minimum infectious dose is about 10 cells. *Mycobacterium* has adhesive pili that attach to an extracellular human protein, laminin.

2 Macrophages in the alveoli (air sacs) of the lungs phagocytize the pathogens but are unable to digest them in part because the mycobacteria prevent fusion of lysosomes with phagosomes. *M. tuberculosis* also invades cells lining the alveoli.

3 The bacteria replicate freely within host cells, gradually killing them. Infected cells of the alveolar lining release chemokines that attract more macrophages. Bacteria released from dead macrophages are phagocytized by other macrophages, beginning the cycle anew. This stage of infection, which lasts for a few weeks, is typically asymptomatic or associated with a mild fever.

4 Infected macrophages present antigen to T lymphocytes, which produce lymphokines that attract and activate more macrophages and trigger inflammation. Tightly appressed macrophages surround the site of infection, forming a tubercle.

5 Other cells of the body deposit collagen fibers, enclosing infected macrophages and lung cells within the tubercle. Infected cells in the center of the tubercle die, releasing *M. tuberculosis* and producing *caseous*[24] necrosis—the death of tissue that takes on a cheeselike consistency due to the presence of protein and fat released from dying cells. Sometimes, for an unknown reason, the center liquefies and subsequently becomes filled with air. Such a tubercle is called a *tuberculous cavity.*

In most patients the immune system reaches a stalemate with the bacterium at this juncture: The immune system is able to prevent further spread of the pathogen and stop the progression of the disease, but it is not able to rid the body of all mycobacteria. *M. tuberculosis* may remain dormant for decades within macrophages and in the centers of tubercles. If the immune system breaks the stalemate by killing all the mycobacteria, the body deposits calcium around the tubercles, which are then called *Ghon complexes.*

**Secondary or Reactivated Tuberculosis** Secondary tuberculosis results when *M. tuberculosis* breaks the stalemate, ruptures the tubercule, and reestablishes an active infection in which the bacteria spread through the lungs via the bronchioles **(Figure 24b).** Reactivated TB is a common occurrence in TB-infected individuals with suppressed immune systems.

**Disseminated Tuberculosis** Disseminated TB results when some macrophages carry the pathogens via the blood and lymph to a variety of sites, including the bone marrow, spleen, kidneys, spinal cord, and brain. The signs and symptoms observed in disseminated TB correspond to complications arising at the various sites involved. The common name for TB in the early 1900s—*consumption*—reflects the wasting away of the body resulting from the involvement of multiple sites in disseminated TB.

## Epidemiology

Even though tuberculosis is on the decline in the United States, it is pandemic in other parts of the world, killing almost 2 million people annually. Over one-third of the world's population is infected with *M. tuberculosis,* and 10% of them develop a life-threatening case of tuberculosis. Patients with lowered immunity

---

[24]From Latin *caseus,* meaning cheese.

(a) Primary tuberculosis infection

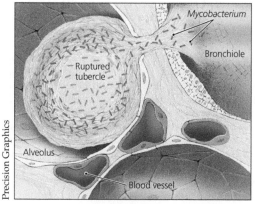

(b) Secondary or reactivated tuberculosis

▲ **Figure 24 Development of tuberculosis in the lungs.**
**(a)** The formation of tubercules in primary tuberculosis. **(b)** Events in secondary (reactivated) tuberculosis.

are at the greatest risk of infection; other risk factors include diabetes, poor nutrition, stress, crowded living conditions, alcohol and drug abuse, and smoking.

TB is prevalent in the countries of the former Soviet Union, where the breakdown of essential medical services has allowed a resurgence, and in Africa, where TB is the number one killer of AIDS patients. Someone in the world is infected with *M. tuberculosis* every second.

## Diagnosis, Treatment, and Prevention

A **tuberculin skin test** is used to screen patients for possible exposure to tuberculosis. In this test, a health care worker injects about 0.1 ml of cell wall antigens from *M. tuberculosis* into a patient's skin. The appearance of a hard, red swelling at the test site within 24 to 72 hours is a positive test (Figure 25a). The reaction is a type IV (cell-mediated) hypersensitivity response, indicating past infection or vaccination but not necessarily current disease.

A positive tuberculin skin test is not sufficient to distinguish patients who have been exposed to antigen but are currently

311

B. Lopez Oblare' (www.fotogeriatria.net)

**(a)**

Tubercles

Biophoto Associates/Photo Researchers

**(b)**

▲ **Figure 25** **Diagnosis of tuberculosis. (a)** The enlarged, reddened, and raised inoculation site of a positive tuberculin skin test. **(b)** An X-ray of a tuberculosis patient showing white patches indicative of tubercules. *What does a positive tuberculin test indicate?*

*Figure 25 A positive tuberculin skin test indicates that a patient has cell-mediated memory against antigens of M. tuberculosis, as a result of either infection or immunization.*

uninfected, chronic carriers from patients with active disease. Chest X-rays can reveal the presence of tubercles in the lungs (Figure 25b); primary tuberculosis appears as tubercles in the lower and central areas of the lungs, whereas secondary tuberculosis more commonly appears higher in the lungs. The presence of acid-fast cells and cords in sputum (see Figure 23b) confirms an active case of tuberculosis.

Common antimicrobials such as penicillin and erythromycin have little effect on *Mycobacterium tuberculosis,* because it grows so slowly that the drugs are cleared from the body by the liver and kidneys before they have any significant effect. Further, antimicrobial drugs have little impact on *M. tuberculosis* living within macrophages. The currently recommended treatment is a combination of isoniazid (INH), rifampin, pyrazinamide, and

ethambutol for two months, followed by INH and rifampin alone for four months.

Epidemiologists and physicians are concerned about strains of *M. tuberculosis* that are resistant to more than one of the standard antituberculosis drugs. Such *multi-drug resistant (MDR)* strains have developed in many countries. For example, MDR strains account for over 10% of tuberculosis cases in Germany, Denmark, and New Zealand. No one knows the extent of MDR cases in developing countries, but it is suspected that the situation there is even worse. MDR-TB must be treated with more expensive antimicrobials, such as fluoroquinolones in combination with kanamycin, for as long as two years. This increases the cost of treatment as much as 100-fold over treatment of drug-sensitive TB.

And now, TB strains with resistance to the most effective anti-TB antimicrobials have emerged, especially in populations with high incidence of infection with human immunodeficiency virus (HIV). These strains, called *extensively drug resistant TB (XDR-TB),* may infect as many as 30,000 people per year in 41 countries, according to the World Health Organization. Researchers are urgently seeking new antimicrobials to treat MDR-TB and XDR-TB lest the progress made toward TB control and eradication be reversed.

The World Health Organization and the CDC recommend a strategy of drug delivery called *Directly Observed Treatment, Shortcourse (DOTS),* in which health care workers observe patients to ensure they take their medications on schedule. Obviously, DOTS treatment is quite labor intensive and expensive.

Physicians use antibacterial drugs prophylactically to treat patients who have either shown a recent conversion from a negative to a positive tuberculin skin test or undergone significant exposure to active cases of tuberculosis. In countries where tuberculosis is common, health care workers immunize patients with *BCG*[25] vaccine, which is composed of attenuated *M. bovis* (bō'vis), a species that causes tuberculosis in cattle and is only rarely transmitted to humans via contaminated milk. The vaccine is not used for immunocompromised patients because it can cause disease.

Studies on the efficacy of TB vaccine vary widely from 80% protected to no protection at all. Nevertheless, the vaccine may reduce the spread of disease, and the World Health Organization (WHO) recommends all children be vaccinated at birth. In the United States, the cost of mass immunization is not warranted because of the relatively low prevalence of tuberculosis. Further, immunized patients may have a positive skin reaction for the rest of their lives, even if they have not been infected with *M. tuberculosis,* and such "false positive" results would hinder the work of epidemiologists trying to track the spread of the disease.

The prediction that tuberculosis would be eliminated in the United States by 2000 was not realized because of a resurgence of tuberculosis among AIDS patients, and its subsequent spread to drug abusers and the homeless. Nevertheless, both renewed efforts to detect and stop infection and the implementation of

---

[25]For bacillus of Calmette and Guérin, named after the two French developers of the vaccine.

DOTS reduced the number of reported U.S. cases in 2008 to the lowest incidence since reporting began in 1953.

## CRITICAL **THINKING**

Why don't physicians try to prevent the spread of TB by simply administering prophylactic antimicrobial drugs to everyone living in endemic areas?

## Leprosy

### Learning Objectives

✓ Compare and contrast tuberculoid leprosy with lepromatous leprosy.

✓ Discuss the diagnosis, treatment, and prevention of leprosy.

*Mycobacterium leprae* (lep'rī) causes **leprosy** (lep'rō-sē)—which is also called by the less dreaded name *Hansen's disease*, after Gerhard Hansen (1841–1912), a Norwegian bacteriologist who discovered its cause in 1873. *M. leprae* is a high G + C, Gram-positive bacillus. Because of the abundance of mycolic acid in the cell wall, bacilli do not Gram stain purple and must instead be stained with an acid-fast stain. *M. leprae* grows best at 30°C, showing a preference for cooler regions of the human body, particularly peripheral nerve endings and skin cells in the fingers, toes, lips, and earlobes. The bacterium does not grow in cell-free laboratory culture, a fact that has hindered research and diagnostic studies. Armadillos, which have a normal body temperature of 30°C, are its only other host and have proven valuable in studies on leprosy and on the efficacy of leprosy treatments.

### Pathogenesis, Epidemiology, and Disease

Leprosy has two different manifestations depending on the immune response of the patient: Patients with a strong cell-mediated immune response are able to kill cells infected with the bacterium, resulting in a nonprogressive form of the disease called *tuberculoid leprosy*. Regions of the skin that have lost sensation as a result of nerve damage are characteristic of this form of leprosy.

By contrast, patients with a weak cell-mediated immune response develop *lepromatous* (lep-rō-mă-tŭs) *leprosy* (Figure 26), in which bacteria multiply in skin and nerve cells, gradually destroying tissue and leading to the progressive loss of facial features, digits (fingers and toes), and other body structures. Development of signs and symptoms is very slow; incubation may take years before the disease is evident. Death from leprosy is rare and usually results from the infection of leprous lesions by other pathogens.

Lepromatous leprosy is the more virulent form of the disease, but fortunately it is becoming relatively rare: In the 1990s about 12 million cases were diagnosed annually worldwide, but in 2007 this number had decreased to 254,525.

Leprosy is transmitted via person-to-person contact. Given that the nasal secretions of patients with lepromatous leprosy are loaded with mycobacteria, infection presumably occurs via inhalation of respiratory droplets. Alternatively, infection may

Reuters/Rupak De Chowdhuri/Landov

▲ **Figure 26 Lepromatous leprosy can result in severe deformities.**

occur through breaks in the skin. In any case, leprosy is not particularly virulent; individuals are typically infected only after years of intimate social contact with a victim.

Why, then, does a diagnosis of leprosy elicit such dread? Much of the public's aversion to leprosy stems from Biblical references calling for the quarantine of lepers and from the horrible disfigurement lepers can suffer. During the Middle Ages lepers were often required to wear bells to warn passersby of their presence and forced to live in special villages or in isolated areas of the forests.

The 12th-century English king Henry II took lepraphobia (fear of leprosy and lepers) a step further; he ordered that those with the disease be burned at the stake. Not to be outdone, his great-grandson Edward I ordained that lepers be accorded a complete funeral service—before they were led to the cemetery and buried alive. Patients with leprosy are no longer quarantined because the disease is so rarely transmitted and is fully treatable.

### Diagnosis, Treatment, and Prevention

Diagnosis of leprosy is based on signs and symptoms of disease—a loss of sensation in skin lesions in the case of tuberculoid leprosy and disfigurement in the case of lepromatous leprosy. Diagnosis is confirmed by a positive skin test with leprosy antigen (similar to the tuberculin skin test) or through direct observation of acid-fast rods (AFRs) in tissue samples or nasal secretions (in the case of lepromatous leprosy).

As with *M. tuberculosis*, *M. leprae* quickly develops resistance to single antimicrobial agents, so therapy consists of administering multiple drugs, such as clofazimine, rifampin, or dapsone, for 12 months, though treatment can be lifelong for some patients.

BCG vaccine provides some protection against leprosy (as well as against tuberculosis), but prevention is primarily achieved by limiting exposure to the pathogen and by the prophylactic

# EMERGING DISEASES

## BURULI ULCER

Precision Graphics

Jacques liked living in the Democratic Republic of the Congo (DRC)—opportunities abounded for exploration, adventure, and wildlife photography, the countryside was beautiful, and he found the people generally friendly. It was on a photographic excursion to the east that Jacques met a not-so-friendly resident of the DRC, an emerging mycobacterial pathogen.

The photographer thought little of the small scratch he received while documenting wildlife in the swamps along the great Congo River, but he should have been concerned; *Mycobacterium ulcerans* had found a new home in his hand. Jacques would pay a grievous price for his lack of circumspection.

He continued to ignore the infection when it produced a small, painless nodule. He even ignored it when his finger swelled to twice its normal size; it was painless and he could still meet his busy schedule. But the bacterium was producing a potent toxin known as mycolactone that destroys cells below the skin, especially fat and muscle cells. Though his hand continued to swell, making it difficult to work normally, there still was no pain.

After six weeks of this condition, pain began suddenly and excruciatingly. The swollen finger ruptured, and a foul-smelling fluid saturated his camera. It was time to see a doctor.

The physician diagnosed Buruli ulcer, an emerging disease that affects more people each year as a result of human encroachment into the swamps where *M. ulcerans* lives. After two surgeries to remove dead tissue and the focus of the infection, several skin grafts, and two months of treatment with the antimicrobial drugs rifampicin and streptomycin, Jacques was released with scars that forever remind him of his adventure with *Mycobacterium ulcerans*.

Track Buruli ulcer online by going to the Study Area at www.masteringmicrobiology.com.

use of antimicrobial agents when exposure occurs. The World Health Organization (WHO) has set a goal to reduce the prevalence of leprosy below one case per 10,000 population. WHO epidemiologists predict that such a low prevalence will permanently interfere with the spread of the bacterium, and leprosy will be eliminated.

## Other Mycobacterial Infections

### Learning Objective

✓ Explain why the incidence of infections with *Mycobacterium avium-intracellulare*, long thought to be harmless to humans, has been increasing.

*Mycobacterium avium-intracellulare* (ā'vē-ŭm in'tra-sel-yu-la'rē) which is commonly found in soil, water, and food, was long thought to be a harmless occasional member of the respiratory microbiota. However, the advent of the AIDS epidemic has unmasked it as an important opportunistic pathogen and the cause of an emerging disease, which is the most common mycobacterial infection among AIDS patients in the United States. (*M. tuberculosis* is more common in countries where tuberculosis is epidemic.) Infections are believed to result from the ingestion of contaminated food or water; direct person-to-person transmission does not occur. The bacterium spreads throughout the body via the lymph.

In contrast to infections with other mycobacteria, *M. avium-intracellulare* simultaneously affects almost every organ of the body. In some tissues, every cell is packed with mycobacteria,

and during the terminal stages of AIDS the blood is often filled with thousands of bacteria per milliliter. The disease remains asymptomatic until organ failure occurs on a massive scale.

Treatment consists of trial-and-error administration of antimicrobial agents; the disseminated nature of the infection often makes treatment ineffectual.

**Emerging Diseases: Buruli Ulcer** examines another disease of mycobacteria.

## *Propionibacterium*

### Learning Objectives

✓ Identify the species of *Propionibacterium* most commonly involved in infections of humans.

✓ Explain the role of *P. acnes* in the formation of acne.

Propionibacteria are small, Gram-positive rods commonly found growing on the skin. They are so named because they produce propionic acid as a by-product of the fermentation of carbohydrates. The species most commonly involved in infections of humans is *Propionibacterium acnes* (prō-pē-on-i-bak-tēr'-ē-ŭm ak'nēz), which causes **acne** in 85% of adolescents and young adults. The bacterium can also be an opportunistic pathogen in patients with intrusive medical devices such as catheters, artificial heart valves, artificial joints, and cerebrospinal fluid shunts.

In its role in the development of acne (**Figure 27**), *Propionibacterium* typically grows in the sebaceous (oil) glands of

▶ **Figure 27  The development of acne.** Normally, oily sebum produced by glands reaches the hair follicle and is discharged from the pore and onto the skin surface ( 1 ). When inflammation resulting from bacteria infecting the hair follicle causes the skin to swell over the pore, sebum and the colonizing bacteria accumulate to form a whitehead ( 2 ). The blockage of the pore by a plug of dead and dying bacteria and sebum produces a blackhead ( 3 ). When the inflammation of the follicle becomes severe enough, pustules form ( 4 ) and rupture, producing cystic acne, which is often resolved by the formation of scar tissue. *Which bacterial pathogen is a common cause of cystic acne?*

*Figure 27  Propionibacterium acnes is a common cause of acne.*

the skin ( 1 ). Excessive oil production triggered by the hormones of adolescence, particularly testosterone in males, stimulates the growth and reproduction of the bacterium, which secretes chemicals that attract leukocytes. The leukocytes phagocytize the bacteria and release chemicals that stimulate local inflammation. The combination of dead bacteria and dead and living leukocytes makes up the white pus associated with the pimples of acne ( 2 ). A blackhead is formed when a plug of dead and dying bacteria blocks the gland's pore ( 3 ). In *cystic acne,* a particularly severe form of the disease, bacteria form inflamed pustules (cysts) ( 4 ) that rupture, triggering the formation of scar tissue.

There are many common misconceptions about acne. Cleaning the surface of the skin is not particularly effective in preventing the development of acne because the bacteria live deep in the sebaceous glands, though frequent cleansing may dry the skin, which helps loosen plugs from hair follicles. Scientists have not shown any connection between acne and diet, including chocolate or oily foods.

In most cases the immune system is able to control *Propionibacterium,* and no treatment is required. Dermatologists may prescribe antimicrobial drugs such as erythromycin and clindamycin, which have proven effective in controlling the bacterium. However, long-term antibiotic use can destroy susceptible normal bacterial microbiota, making the individual more vulnerable to opportunistic fungal and bacterial infections that are resistant to antimicrobial drugs. *Retinoic acid (Accutane),* a derivative of vitamin A, inhibits the formation of oil. Because this drug can cause intestinal bleeding, it is prescribed only for severe cases of acne. Further, it causes birth defects and thus should not be used by pregnant women.

In the previous few sections we have discussed pathogenic, non-endospore-forming, high G + C rods in the genera *Corynebacterium, Mycobacterium,* and *Propionibacterium.* Now we will consider filamentous, high G + C pathogens in the genera *Nocardia* and *Actinomyces.*

# *Nocardia* and *Actinomyces*

## Learning Objective

✓ Compare and contrast *Nocardia asteroides* and *Actinomyces* in terms of appearance, cell wall composition, and role in producing disease.

*Nocardia* and *Actinomyces* have elongated filamentous cells that resemble fungal hyphae. The cell walls of *Nocardia* contain mycolic

**1  Normal skin**
Oily sebum produced by glands reaches the hair follicle and is discharged onto the skin surface via the pore.

**2  Whitehead**
Inflamed skin swells over the pore when bacteria infect the hair follicle, causing the accumulation of colonizing bacteria and sebum.

**3  Blackhead**
Dead and dying bacteria and sebum form a blockage of the pore.

**4  Pustule formation**
Severe inflammation of the hair follicle causes pustule formation and rupture, producing cystic acne, which is often resolved by scar tissue formation.

Cassio Lynm

315

DERMNET

▲ **Figure 28** A *Nocardia* infection.

acid, so the cells are difficult to Gram stain, but they are acid-fast. *Actinomyces* stains purple in a Gram stain.

## Nocardia asteroides

*Nocardia asteroides* (nō-kar′dē-ă as-ter-oy′dēz), a common inhabitant of soils rich in organic matter, is the most common pathogen in this genus, accounting for about 90% of infections.

### Pathogenesis, Epidemiology, and Disease

*N. asteroides* is an opportunistic bacterial pathogen that infects numerous sites, including the lungs, skin, and central nervous system. Pulmonary infections develop following inhalation; cutaneous infections result from introduction of the bacteria into wounds; and infections of the central nervous system and other internal organs follow the spread of the bacterium in the blood.

In the lungs, *Nocardia* causes pneumonia accompanied by signs and symptoms typical of pulmonary infections—cough, shortness of breath, and fever. Cutaneous infections may produce **mycetoma,** a painless, long-lasting infection characterized by swelling, pus production, and draining sores (Figure 28).

### Diagnosis, Treatment, and Prevention

Microscopic examination of samples of skin, sputum, pus, or cerebrospinal fluid is usually sufficient to suspect infection with *Nocardia;* the presence of long, acid-fast, hypha-like cells is diagnostic. Treatment usually involves six weeks of an appropriate antimicrobial drug; sulfonamides are the drugs of choice. Although such treatment is usually sufficient for localized infections in patients with normal immune systems, the prognosis for immunocompromised patients with widespread infections is poor. Prevention of nocardial diseases involves avoiding exposure to the bacterium in soil, especially by immunocompromised patients.

## Actinomyces

*Actinomyces* is another genus characterized by hypha-like cells (Figure 29a), as reflected in the name of the genus, which means "ray fungus" in Greek. Despite the name, *Actinomyces* is not a fungus but a bacterium. Unlike *Nocardia, Actinomyces* is not acid-fast and stains purple when Gram-stained.

Colonies of *Actinomyces* form visible concretions resembling grains of sand. Even though the yellow of these multicellular structures has prompted the name "sulfur granules," they are in fact held together by calcium phosphate.

### Pathogenesis, Epidemiology, and Disease

*Actinomyces* is a normal member of the surface microbiota of human mucous membranes. It can become an opportunistic pathogen of the respiratory, gastrointestinal, urinary, and female

From: *Infections in Medicine, 1992; 9(9)*

(a)

LM ⊢———⊣ 30 μm

(b)

Lester V. Bergman/Corbis

▲ **Figure 29** *Actinomyces.* **(a)** A Gram stain of pus containing the bacteria, which resemble fungal hyphae and may form visible yellow aggregations that look like grains of sand. **(b)** Lesions of actinomycosis.

genital tracts, and it sometimes causes dental caries (cavities). It also causes a disease called *actinomycosis* when it enters breaks in the mucous membranes resulting from trauma, surgery, or infection by other pathogens. Actinomycosis is characterized by the formation of many abscesses connected by channels in the skin or mucous membranes (Figure 29b).

### Diagnosis, Treatment, and Prevention

Diagnosis of actinomycosis is difficult because other organisms cause similar symptoms, and it is difficult to show that the presence of *Actinomyces* is not merely contamination from its normal site on the mucous membranes. Often a health care worker collects and crushes a "sulfur granule" to reveal the presence of filamentous cells.

Treatment involves surgical removal of the infected tissue and the administration of penicillin, tetracycline, or erythromycin for 4–12 months. Prevention of *Actinomyces* infections involves good oral hygiene, and the prolonged use of prophylactic antimicrobials should trauma or surgery broach the mucous membranes.

## Chapter Summary

### Staphylococcus

1. *Staphylococcus aureus* and *Staphylococcus epidermidis* are found on the skin and in the upper respiratory, gastrointestinal, and urogenital tracts. *S. aureus* is the more virulent, partly because of its production of various enzymes (including coagulase and staphylokinase) and several toxins.

2. Food poisoning is a noninvasive disease caused by *Staphylococcus*. Cutaneous diseases caused by *Staphylococcus* include **staphylococcal scalded skin syndrome, impetigo, folliculitis, sties, furuncles,** and **carbuncles.**

3. Potentially fatal systemic infections caused by *Staphylococcus* include **staphylococcal toxic shock syndrome (STSS), bacteremia, endocarditis, pneumonia, empyema,** and **osteomyelitis.**

4. **Methicillin-resistant *Staphylococcus aureus* (MRSA),** which is resistant to many antimicrobials including methicillin, is an emerging nosocomial and community-acquired threat. **Vancomycin-resistant *S. aureus* (VRSA)** is also emerging as a threat as vancomycin is used against MRSA.

### Streptococcus

1. Cells of **group A *Streptococcus* (*Streptococcus pyogenes*)** produce M protein and a hyaluronic acid capsule, each of which contributes to the virulence of the species. Enzymes and toxins produced by *S. pyogenes* dissolve blood clots, stimulate fever, and lyse blood cells.

2. The diseases caused by group A streptococci include **pharyngitis** ("strep throat"), **scarlet fever** (scarlatina), **pyoderma** (impetigo), **erysipelas, toxic-shock-like syndrome (TSLS), necrotizing fasciitis** ("flesh-eating bacteria"), **rheumatic fever,** and **glomerulonephritis.**

3. Cells of **group B *Streptococcus* (*S. agalactiae*)** occur normally in the lower GI, genital, and urinary tracts. They are associated with neonatal diseases and are treated with penicillin.

4. The **viridans group** of alpha-hemolytic streptococci include members that inhabit the mouth, pharynx, GI tract, and genitourinary tracts, cause dental **caries** (cavities), and can enter the blood to cause bacteremia, meningitis, and endocarditis.

5. Virulent strains of *Streptococcus pneumoniae* are protected by polysaccharide capsules and phosphorylcholine in their cell walls. These bacteria secrete protein adhesin, secretory IgA protease, and pneumolysin, which lyses cells in the lungs.

6. **Pneumococcal pneumonia** is the most prevalent disease caused by *Streptococcus pneumoniae* infection. Other diseases include **sinusitis** (inflammation of the nasal sinuses), **otitis media** (inflammation of the middle ear), bacteremia, endocarditis, and meningitis.

### Enterococcus

1. *Enterococci* are normal members of the intestinal microbiota that can cause nosocomial bacteremia, endocarditis, and wound infections.

### Bacillus

1. *Bacillus anthracis* secretes anthrax toxin, which can cause three forms of **anthrax:** gastrointestinal anthrax (rare and fatal, with intestinal hemorrhaging), cutaneous anthrax (can be fatal if untreated), and inhalation anthrax (often fatal).

### Clostridium

1. *Clostridium perfringens* produces 11 toxins that lyse blood cells and cause diseases such as food poisoning and **gas gangrene.**

2. *Clostridium difficile* is an intestinal bacterium that can cause a self-limiting explosive diarrhea or a life-threatening **pseudomembranous colitis.**

3. *Clostridium botulinum* is an anaerobic, endospore-forming bacterium that can release an extremely poisonous toxin in improperly canned food, causing **botulism.** Infant botulism occurs when the pathogen grows in the gastrointestinal tract of an infant. Wound botulism results when the bacterial endospores germinate in surgical or traumatic wounds.

4. *Clostridium tetani* is a ubiquitous bacterium that enters the body via a break in the skin and causes **tetanus** due to the action of **tetanospasmin.** Immunization is effective in preventing this disease.

### Listeria

1. *Listeria monocytogenes* is rarely pathogenic but can cause severe disease in pregnant women, newborns, the elderly, and immunocompromised patients.

## Mycoplasmas

1. **Mycoplasmas,** the smallest free-living microbes, lack cell walls. They are mostly facultative anaerobes. The colonies of most mycoplasmas have a "fried egg" appearance.

2. *Mycoplasma pneumoniae* is a human pathogen that affects the epithelial cells of the respiratory tract and cause **primary atypical pneumonia** (walking pneumonia). It does not form "fried-egg" colonies on agar.

3. *Mycoplasma hominis* can cause **pelvic inflammatory disease** in women.

4. *Mycoplasma genitalium* and *Ureaplasma urealyticum* cause nongonococcal urethritis.

5. Venereal mycoplasmal diseases can be prevented by abstinence, mutually faithful monogamy, and the proper use of condoms.

## Corynebacterium

1. *Corynebacterium diphtheriae,* transmitted via respiratory droplets, contains a bacteriophage that codes for diphtheria toxin, which causes the symptoms of the potentially fatal disease **diphtheria.** Diagnosis results from an immunodiffusion assay called an **Elek test.**

## Mycobacterium

1. Cell walls of *Mycobacterium* contain **mycolic acid.** *Mycobacterium tuberculosis* with a cell wall component called **cord factor** causes

**tuberculosis,** a lung disease in which the bacteria replicate within macrophages. The **tuberculin skin test** screens for possible TB exposure.

2. *Mycobacterium leprae* causes **leprosy.** Tuberculoid leprosy is a nonprogressive form of the disease, whereas lepromatous leprosy results in progressive destruction of body structures.

3. *Mycobacterium avium-intracellulare* is an opportunistic pathogen that can become pathogenic in AIDS patients. It adversely affects almost every organ of the body.

## Propionibacterium

1. *Propionibacterium acnes* living in the sebaceous glands of the skin causes adolescent **acne.** The bacterium may also infect patients who have intrusive medical devices. Antimicrobial drugs are more effective than topical products in the treatment of acne.

## Nocardia and Actinomyces

1. The opportunistic pathogen *Nocardia asteroides* has elongated cells resembling fungal hyphae; it is acid-fast because of the presence of mycolic acid in its cell wall. Cutaneous infections may produce **mycetoma.**

2. *Actinomyces* is another opportunistic pathogen with elongated cells, but it is not acid-fast. It causes *actinomycosis*.

# Questions for Review
Answers to the Questions for Review (except Short Answer questions) appear at the end of this chapter.

## Multiple Choice

1. Which of the following bacteria causes a type of food poisoning?
   a. *Streptococcus sanguis*
   b. *Clostridium perfringens*
   c. *Staphylococcus aureus*
   d. *Streptococcus pyogenes*

2. How does *Staphylococcus aureus* affect the matrix between cells in the human body?
   a. *S. aureus* triggers blood clotting, which coats the matrix and inhibits cellular communication.
   b. *S. aureus* produces an enzyme that dissolves hyaluronic acid and thus enables it to pass between the cells.
   c. *S. aureus* contains a hyaluronic acid capsule that causes leukocytes to ignore the bacterium as if it were camouflaged.
   d. *S. aureus* does not affect the matrix but instead produces a necrotizing agent that dissolves body cells.

3. Which of the following conditions is a systemic disease caused by *Staphylococcus*?
   a. impetigo
   b. folliculitis
   c. carbuncle
   d. toxic shock syndrome

4. A bacterium associated with bacteremia, meningitis, and pneumonia in newborns is
   a. *Staphylococcus aureus*.
   b. *Staphylococcus epidermidis*.
   c. *Streptococcus pyogenes*.
   d. *Streptococcus agalactiae*.

5. Which type of anthrax is much more common in animals than in humans?
   a. cutaneous anthrax
   b. inhalation anthrax
   c. gastrointestinal anthrax
   d. mucoid anthrax

6. Of the following genera, which can survive the harshest conditions?
   a. *Staphylococcus*
   b. *Clostridium*
   c. *Mycobacterium*
   d. *Actinomyces*

7. Pathogenic strains that have become resistant to antimicrobial drugs are found in which of the following genera?
   a. *Staphylococcus*
   b. *Mycobacterium*
   c. *Enterococcus*
   d. all of the above

8. The bacterium causing pseudomembranous colitis is
   a. *Clostridium difficile*.
   b. *Streptococcus pyogenes*.
   c. *Mycobacterium avium-intracellulare*.
   d. *Corynebacterium diphtheriae*.

9. Mycoplasmas
   a. lack cell walls.
   b. are pleomorphic.
   c. have sterol in their membranes.
   d. all of the above

10. In which of the following diseases would a patient experience a pseudomembrane covering the tonsils, pharynx, and larynx?
    a. tuberculoid leprosy
    b. diphtheria
    c. arrhythmia
    d. tetanus

11. Which of the following is *not* characteristic of mycoplasmas?
    a. cytochromes
    b. sterols in cytoplasmic membranes
    c. use of UGA codon for tryptophan
    d. rRNA nucleotide sequences similar to those of Gram-positive bacteria

## Matching

For each of the following diseases or conditions, indicate the genus (or genera) of bacterium that causes it.

1. ____ Scalded skin syndrome
2. ____ Osteomyelitis
3. ____ Pharyngitis
4. ____ Scarlet fever
5. ____ Pyoderma
6. ____ Rheumatic fever
7. ____ Glomerulonephritis
8. ____ Sinusitis
9. ____ Otitis media
10. ____ Anthrax
11. ____ Myonecrosis
12. ____ Diphtheria
13. ____ Leprosy
14. ____ Dental caries
15. ____ Acne

A. *Staphylococcus*
B. *Streptococcus*
C. *Mycobacterium*
D. *Listeria*
E. *Propionibacterium*
F. *Corynebacterium*
G. *Bacillus*
H. *Clostridium*
I. *Actinomyces*

## Short Answer

1. Why are mycoplasmas able to survive a relatively wide range of osmotic conditions, even though these bacteria lack cell walls?

2. *Mycobacterium avium-intracellulare* was considered relatively harmless until the late 20th century, when it became common in certain infections. Explain how this bacterium's pathogenicity changed.

3. Contrast tuberculoid leprosy with lepromatous leprosy in terms of pathogenesis. How does the cellular immune response of a patient affect the form of the disease?

4. On a trans-Atlantic flight, a Latvian passenger with tuberculosis sits next to a Canadian businessman, who later develops tuberculosis and dies. Trace the path of *Mycobacterium tuberculosis* from a droplet of mucus leaving the European passenger to within the businessman, and explain how the disease became fatal.

5. Explain how mice are used in the diagnosis of botulism poisoning.

6. Why do pediatricians recommend that children under one year never be fed honey?

7. Explain why Gram-positive mycoplasmas appear pink in a Gram stained smear.

8. Explain the different actions of pyogenic and pyrogenic toxins.

9. Explain why *Staphylococcus epidermidis* is rarely pathogenic while the similar *S. aureus* is more commonly virulent.

10. Why did epidemiologists immediately suspect terrorism in the cases of anthrax in the fall of 2001?

11. Explain the action of the toxin of *Clostridium tetani*.

12. Why is mycolic acid a virulence factor for mycobacteria?

13. Compare and contrast mycoplasmas and viruses.

 # Concept Mapping

Using the following terms, draw a concept map that describes pathogenic clostridia. Or, complete this concept map on-line by going to the Study Area at www.masteringmicrobiology.com.

Antibiotic-associated diarrhea
Botox
Botulism toxin
*C. botulinum*
*C. difficile*
*C. perfringens*

*C. tetani*
Cosmetic applications
Endospore formers
Food poisoning
Foodborne botulism
Gas gangrene

Genus *Clostridium*
Gram positive bacilli
Infant botulism
Medical applications
Pseudomembranous colitis

Strict anaerobes
Tetanus
Tetanus toxin
Tetanus toxoid vaccine
Wound botulism

# Critical Thinking

1. We discussed the identification of microbes using dichotomous taxonomic keys. Design a key for the genera of Gram-positive cocci discussed in this chapter. Design a second key for identifying the Gram-positive bacilli discussed in the chapter.

2. A few days after the death of a child hospitalized with an MRSA infection, another child, who had been admitted to the hospital with viral pneumonia, worsened and died. An autopsy revealed that the second child also died from complications of MRSA. By what route was the second child likely infected? What should hospital personnel do to limit the transfer of MRSA and other bacteria among patients?

3. An elderly man is admitted to the hospital with severe pneumonia, from which he eventually dies. What species is the most likely cause of his infection? What antimicrobial drug is effective against this species? How could the man have been protected from infection? Is the hospital staff at significant risk of infection from the man? Which groups of patients would be at risk if the man had visited their rooms before he died?

4. Botulism toxin can be used as an antidote for tetanus. Can tetanus toxin be used as an antidote for botulism? Why or why not?

5. A blood bank refused to accept blood from a potential donor who had just had his teeth cleaned by a dental hygienist. Why did they refuse the blood?

6. Match the genera of pathogens to their appearance in stained smears: *Actinomyces, Bacillus, Clostridium, Mycobacterium, Staphylococcus, Streptococcus.*

L. Brent Selinger, Pearson Science

**(a)** Gram
From: *Infections in Medicine,* 1992; 9(9)

**(b)** Gram

**(c)** Gram

CDC

**(d)** Acid fast
Biophoto Associates/ Photo Researchers

**(e)** Gram
Eastman Kodak

**(f)** Gram

Rich Robison, Pearson Science

---

Mastering**MICROBIOLOGY**™

Access more review material online in the Study Area at **www.masteringmicrobiology.com.** There, you'll find
- **Concept Mapping Activities**
- **Flashcards**
- **Quizzes**

and more to help you succeed.

---

# Answers

Answers to multiple-choice, fill-in-blank, labeling, matching, and true/false questions are listed here. Answers for Short Answer and Critical Thinking questions are available for instructors only in the Instructor's Manual that accompanies this text.

**Multiple Choice**
1. c; 2. b; 3. d; 4. d; 5. c; 6. b; 7. d; 8. a; 9. d; 10. b; 11. a

**Matching**
1. A; 2. A; 3. B, F; 4. B; 5. B; 6. B; 7. B; 8. B; 9. B; 10. G; 11. B, H; 12. F; 13. C; 14. B, I; 15. E

# Pathogenic Gram-Negative Cocci and Bacilli

A New Mexico couple vacationing in New York City fell ill with flulike symptoms. A few days later they were admitted to a hospital, suffering from chills and a high fever. The wife had developed a "bubo" (a severely swollen lymph node) on her thigh, leading doctors to suspect bubonic plague—the dreaded "black death" that killed one-third of all Europeans during the 14th century but had not been seen in New York City in over 100 years. Subsequent tests confirmed that they were indeed infected with *Yersinia pestis*, the causative bacterium of plague. The wife was administered antibiotics and recovered quickly, but her husband worsened, requiring amputation of both feet and hospitalization for three months. Authorities later determined that the couple had most likely contracted the disease from infected fleas encountered near their property in rural New Mexico.

*Y. pestis* is one example of a Gram-negative pathogen—a group that also includes the genera *Escherichia*, *Salmonella*, and *Legionella*. Gram-negative pathogens cause a wide variety of human diseases. In this chapter we study important Gram-negative cocci and bacilli and major human diseases they cause.

*Yersina pestis*, a Gram-negative, rod-shaped bacterium, causes one of history's more feared diseases—bubonic plague.

Take the pre-test for this chapter online. Visit the Study Area at www.masteringmicrobiology.com.

From Chapter 20 of *Microbiology with Diseases by Taxonomy*, Third Edition. Robert W. Bauman. Copyright © 2011 by Pearson Education, Inc. Published by Benjamin Cummings, Inc. All rights reserved.

Numerous Gram-negative, cocci, bacilli, and coccobacilli are bacterial pathogens of humans. In fact, Gram-negative bacteria constitute the largest group of human bacterial pathogens, in part because the outer membrane of a Gram-negative bacterial cell wall contains lipid A. Lipid A triggers fever, vasodilation, inflammation, shock, and **disseminated intravascular coagulation (DIC)**—the formation of blood clots within blood vessels throughout the body. Almost every Gram-negative bacterium that can breach the skin or mucous membranes, grow at 37°C, and evade the immune system can cause disease and death in humans; however, most of the Gram-negative bacteria that cause disease fall into fewer than 30 genera.

We have seen that it is possible to group these organisms according to a variety of criteria. We considered the Gram-negative bacteria according to their placement in *Bergey's Manual,* which is based largely on genomic similarities; here we primarily consider them according to a different organizational scheme, one that traditionally has been used for many clinical purposes—according to their shapes, oxygen requirements, and other biochemical properties.

First we survey the primary genus of Gram-negative cocci that are pathogenic to humans; then we consider 15 genera of pathogenic, facultatively anaerobic bacilli in the families Enterobacteriaceae and Pasteurellaceae, which account for almost half of all Gram-negative pathogens. Finally, we examine a heterogeneous collection of 10 genera of pathogenic, Gram-negative aerobic bacilli before concluding by considering two genera of strictly anaerobic pathogenic bacilli.

# Pathogenic Gram-Negative Cocci: *Neisseria*

*Neisseria* (nī-se′rē-ă) is the only genus of Gram-negative cocci that regularly causes disease in humans. *Neisseria* is placed in the class Betaproteobacteria of the phylum Proteobacteria. Morphologically similar pathogenic bacteria in the genera *Moraxella* (mōr′ak-sel′ă) and *Acinetobacter* (as-i-nē′tō-bak′ter), considered coccobacilli, are now known to be more closely related to aerobic bacilli in class Gammaproteobacteria and thus are discussed in a later section.

## Structure and Physiology of *Neisseria*

### Learning Objective

✓ List three structural features of *Neisseria* that contribute to its pathogenicity.

The cells of all strains of *Neisseria* are nonmotile and typically arranged as diplococci (pairs) with their common sides flattened in a manner reminiscent of coffee beans (Figure 1). In addition to their shape, these aerobic bacteria are distinguished from many other Gram-negative pathogens by being *oxidase positive* (see Figure 4); that is, their electron transport chains contain the enzyme *cytochrome oxidase*. Pathogenic strains of *Neisseria* also have fimbriae and polysaccharide capsules, as well as a major cell wall antigen called *lipooligosaccharide* (lip′ō-ol-i-gō-sak′a-rīd, *LOS*), composed of lipid A (endotoxin) and

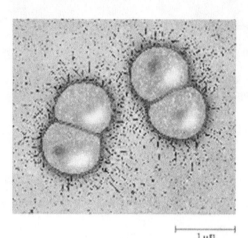

▲ **Figure 1 Diplococci of *Neisseria gonorrhoeae.*** *What function of gonococcal fimbriae (not visible here) contributes to the bacterium's pathogenicity?*

**Figure 1** *The fimbriae act as adhesins, enabling gonococci to adhere to cells lining the cervix and urethra and to sperm, which allows Neisseria to travel far into the female reproductive tract.*

sugar molecules—all of which enable the bacteria to attach to and invade human cells. Cells of *Neisseria* that lack any one of these three structural features are typically avirulent.

In the laboratory, *Neisseria* is fastidious in its growth requirements. Microbiologists culture this bacterium on either autoclaved blood agar (called *chocolate agar* because of its appearance) or a selective medium called *modified Thayer-Martin medium. Neisseria* is particularly susceptible to drying and extremes of temperature. A moist culture atmosphere containing 5% carbon dioxide enhances their growth. Laboratory personnel may use sugar fermentation tests to distinguish among strains of *Neisseria;* pathogenic strains, for example, are unable to ferment maltose, sucrose, or lactose.

Two species of *Neisseria* are pathogenic to humans: the so-called gonococcus, *N. gonorrhoeae* (go-nor-rē′ī), which causes gonorrhea, and the meningococcus, *N. meningitidis* (me-nin-ji′ti-dis), which causes a type of meningitis.

## The Gonococcus: *Neisseria gonorrhoeae*

### Learning Objectives

✓ Compare and contrast the symptoms of gonorrhea in men and women.

✓ Discuss the difficulties researchers face in developing an effective vaccine against *Neisseria gonorrhoeae.*

### Pathogenesis, Epidemiology, and Disease

*Neisseria gonorrhoeae* causes **gonorrhea** (gon-ō-rē′ă), which has been known as a sexually transmitted disease for centuries, although the disease was confused with syphilis until the 19th century. In the 2nd century A.D., the Roman physician Claudius Galen named gonorrhea for what he thought was its cause—an excess of semen (gonorrhea means "flow of seed" in Greek).

The disease is sometimes called "clap" from an archaic French word *clapoir,* meaning brothel.

Gonorrhea occurs in humans only. Even though it is one of the more common sexually transmitted diseases in the United States, the number of cases among civilians has been declining over the past few decades (Figure 2a). Most U.S. cases of gonorrhea occur in adolescents, particularly among those who engage in a promiscuous sexual lifestyle in several southeastern states (Figure 2b). The Centers for Disease Control and Prevention (CDC) has a goal to reduce the incidence of gonorrhea to below 19 cases per 100,000 population. This incidence will theoretically eliminate the disease in the United States.

The disease is 19 times more common among blacks than nonblacks and more common among females than males. Whereas women have a 50% chance of becoming infected during a single sexual encounter with an infected man, men have only a 20% chance of infection during a single encounter with an infected woman. An individual's risk of infection increases with increasing frequency of sexual encounters.

Gonococci adhere, via their fimbriae and capsules, to epithelial cells of the mucous membranes lining the genital, urinary, and digestive tracts of humans. As few as 100 pairs of cells can cause disease. The cocci protect themselves from the immune system by secreting a protease enzyme that cleaves secretory IgA in mucus. Further, endocytized bacteria survive and multiply within neutrophils. As the bacteria multiply, they invade deeper connective tissues, often while being transported intracellularly by phagocytes.

In men, gonorrhea is usually insufferably symptomatic—acute inflammation typically occurs two to five days after infection in the urethra of the penis, causing extremely painful urination and a purulent (pus-filled) discharge. Rarely, gonococci invade the prostate or epididymis, where the formation of scar tissue can render the man infertile. In contrast, recently acquired gonorrhea in women is often asymptomatic; about 50% of infected women have no symptoms or obvious signs of infection. Even when women do have symptoms, they often mistake them for a bladder infection or vaginal yeast infection.

*Neisseria* cannot attach to cells lining the vagina; instead, the bacteria most commonly infect the cervix of the uterus. Gonococci can infect deep in the uterus and even the uterine (Fallopian) tubes by "hitchhiking" to these locations on sperm to which they attach by means of fimbriae or LOS. In the uterine tubes they can trigger inflammation, fever, and abdominal pain—a condition known as **pelvic inflammatory disease (PID).** Chronic infections can lead to scarring of the tubes, resulting in *ectopic*[1] *pregnancies* or sterility.

Gonococcal infection of organs outside the reproductive tracts can also occur. Because a woman's urethral opening is close to her vaginal opening, the urethra can become infected with gonococci during sexual intercourse. Anal intercourse can lead to *proctitis* (inflammation of the rectum), and oral sexual intercourse can infect the pharynx or gums, resulting in *pharyngitis* and *gingivitis,* respectively. Oral and anal infections

<hr />

[1]From Greek *ektopos,* meaning out of place.

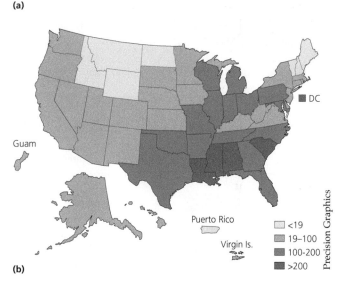

(a)

(b)

▲ **Figure 2** **Incidence of gonorrhea in the United States**
**(a)** The number of new cases annually, 1977–2008. **(b)** The geographic distribution of cases reported in 2007. The incidences shown are the number of new cases per 100,000 individuals in each state. *What organism causes gonorrhea?*

**Figure 2** *Gonorrhea is caused by Neisseria gonorrhoeae.*

are most commonly seen in men who have sex with men. In very rare cases, gonococci enter the blood and travel to the joints, meninges, or heart, causing arthritis, meningitis, and endocarditis, respectively.

Gonococcal infection of a child during birth can result in inflammation of the cornea, *ophthalmia neonatorum* (inflammation of the conjunctiva in newborns), or blindness. Gonococci can also infect the respiratory tracts of newborns during their passage through the birth canal. Infection of older children with *N. gonorrhoeae* is strong evidence of sexual abuse by an infected adult.

## MICROBE AT A GLANCE

### *Neisseria gonorrhoeae*

**Taxonomy:** Domain Bacteria, phylum Proteobacteria, class Betaproteobacteria, order Neisseriales, family Neisseriaceae

**Other names:** Gonococcus

**Cell morphology and arrangement:** Cocci in pairs

**Gram reaction:** Negative

**Virulence factors:** Capsule, fimbriae, and lipooligosaccharide adhere to human cells; IgA protease; can survive inside phagocytic cells; variable surface antigens

**Diseases caused:** Gonorrhea, pelvic inflammatory disease, ophthalmia neonatorum, proctitis, pharyngitis, gingivitis

**Treatment for diseases:** Cephalosporins

**Prevention of disease:** Sexual abstinence, mutually faithful monogamy, consistent and proper use of condoms

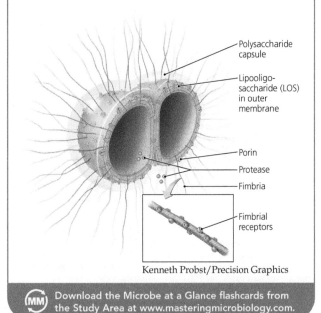

Polysaccharide capsule

Lipooligo-saccharide (LOS) in outer membrane

Porin

Protease

Fimbria

Fimbrial receptors

Kenneth Probst/Precision Graphics

(MMM) Download the Microbe at a Glance flashcards from the Study Area at www.masteringmicrobiology.com.

### Diagnosis, Treatment, and Prevention

The presence of Gram-negative diplococci in pus from an inflamed penis is sufficient for a diagnosis of symptomatic gonorrhea in men. For diagnosis of asymptomatic cases of gonorrhea in men and women, commercially available genetic probes provide direct, accurate, rapid detection of *N. gonorrhoeae* in clinical specimens. Alternatively, the bacterium can be cultured on selective media, such as Thayer-Martin agar.

The treatment of gonorrhea has been complicated in recent years by the worldwide spread of gonococcal strains resistant to penicillin, tetracycline, erythromycin, and aminoglycosides. Currently, the CDC recommends broad-spectrum oral cephalosporins to treat gonorrhea.

Long-term specific immunity against *N. gonorrhoeae* does not develop, and thus promiscuous people can be infected multiple times. This lack of immunity is explained in part by the highly variable surface antigens of this bacterium; immunity against one strain often provides no protection against other strains. Further, the existence of many different strains has prevented the development of an effective vaccine.

Except for the routine administration of antimicrobial agents to newborns' eyes, which successfully prevents ophthalmic disease, chemical prophylaxis is ineffective in preventing disease. In fact, the use of antimicrobials to prevent genital disease may select for hardier resistant strains, worsening the situation. The most effective methods of prevention, in order, are sexual abstinence; monogamy with an uninfected, faithful partner; and consistent and proper use of condoms. Efforts to stem the spread of gonorrhea focus on education, aggressive detection, and the screening of all sexual contacts of carriers.

### CRITICAL **THINKING**

Penicillin-resistant strains of *N. gonorrhoeae* produce a plasmid-coded β-lactamase, which degrades penicillin. What changes in structure or metabolism could explain resistance to other antimicrobial drugs in this bacterium?

## The Meningococcus: *Neisseria meningitidis*

### Learning Objectives

✓ Describe how meningococci survive and thrive in humans.

✓ Discuss the epidemiology of meningococcal diseases.

*Neisseria meningitidis* causes life-threatening diseases when it invades the blood or cerebrospinal fluid.

### Pathogenicity, Epidemiology, and Disease

Of the 13 known antigenic strains of meningococci, strains known as A, B, C, and W 135 cause most cases of disease in humans. The polysaccharide capsule of *N. meningitidis* resists lytic enzymes of the body's phagocytes, allowing phagocytized meningococci to survive, reproduce, and be carried throughout the body within neutrophils and macrophages. In the United States, the bacterium causes most cases of meningitis in children and adults under 20. Much of the damage caused by *N. meningitidis* results from *blebbing*—a process in which the bacterium sheds extrusions of outer membrane. The lipid A component of LOS thereby released into extracellular spaces triggers fever, vasodilation, inflammation, shock, and DIC.

*N. meningitidis* is a common member of the normal microbiota in the upper respiratory tracts of up to 40% of healthy people. As a result of crowded living conditions, meningococci are more prevalent in children and young adults from lower economic groups.

John Radcliffe Hospital/SPL/Photo Researchers

**(a)**

Ken Greer/Visuals Unlimited

**(b)**

▲ **Figure 3** **Petechiae in meningococcal septicemia.** These lesions can either be small and relatively diffuse **(a)** or may coalesce in areas containing dead cells **(b)**.

Respiratory droplets transmit the bacteria among people living in close contact, especially families, soldiers living in barracks, prisoners, and college students living in dormitories. In fact, meningococcal disease can be 23 times more prevalent in students living in dormitories than in the general population. Individuals whose lungs have been irritated by dust are more susceptible to airborne *Neisseria*. For example, annual outbreaks of meningococcal meningitis can kill tens of thousands in sub-Saharan Africa when dry winter winds create irritating dust storms. Even though meningococcal diseases occur worldwide, cases are relatively rare in countries with advanced health care systems and access to antimicrobial drugs.

The incidence of meningococcal disease in the United States is about 0.3 cases per 100,000 population. Most of these cases are meningitis, usually involving abrupt sore throat, fever, headache, stiff neck, vomiting, and convulsions. (Very young children may have only fever and vomiting.) Arthritis and partial loss of hearing occasionally result. Meningococcal meningitis can progress so rapidly that death results within six hours of the initial symptoms.

Meningococcal septicemia (blood poisoning) can also be life threatening. LOS may trigger shock, devastating blood coagulation in many organs, and *petechiae* (pe-tē'kē-ē)—minute hemorrhagic skin lesions—on the trunk and lower extremities (Figure 3a). Petechiae may coalesce and combine with regions of cell death to form large black lesions (Figure 3b). In some patients, however, septicemia produces only mild fever, arthritis, and petechiae.

### Diagnosis, Treatment, and Prevention

Because meningococcal meningitis constitutes a medical emergency, rapid diagnosis is critical. The demonstration of Gram-negative diplococci within phagocytes of the central nervous system is diagnostic for meningococcal disease. *N. meningitidis* can ferment maltose in laboratory culture, which distinguishes it from *N. gonorrhoeae*. Further, serological tests can demonstrate the presence of antibodies against *N. meningitidis*, though

strain B is relatively nonimmunogenic and therefore does not react well in such tests.

Despite the fact that meningococcal meningitis proceeds rapidly and is ordinarily 100% fatal when left untreated, immediate treatment with antimicrobial drugs has reduced mortality to less than 10%. Intravenously administered ceftriaxone, a semisynthetic cephalosporin, is the drug of choice.

Because healthy asymptomatic carriers are common, eradication of meningococcal disease is unlikely. Prevention involves prophylactic treatment with ceftriaxone, ciprofloxacin, or rifampin of anyone exposed to individuals with meningococcal disease, including family, classmates, day care center contacts, roommates, and health care workers. The CDC recommends immunization with a vaccine against strains A, C, and Y, though this vaccine cannot be used with children under two years old. As previously noted, strain B is weakly immunogenic, so immunity to it cannot be induced artificially and must instead develop following a natural infection.

### CRITICAL **THINKING**

Investigations of *Mycobacterium tuberculosis* have clearly demonstrated that this pathogen can be transmitted among airline passengers; however, as of 2008, no cases of in-flight transmission of the similarly transmitted *N. meningitidis* had been reported to the CDC. What are some possible explanations for the lack of documented cases of in-flight transmission of meningocci?

# Pathogenic, Gram-Negative, Facultatively Anaerobic Bacilli

Learning Objective

✓ Describe how members of the family Enterobacteriaceae are distinguished from members of the family Pasteurellaceae.

▲ **Figure 4** **The oxidase test.** The test distinguishes members of the family Enterobacteriaceae (left), which are oxidase negative, from members of the family Pasteurellaceae, which are oxidase positive, as indicated by a purple color.

Two families of facultatively anaerobic bacilli and coccobacilli in the class Gammaproteobacteria—Enterobacteriaceae and Pasteurellaceae—contain most of the Gram-negative pathogens of humans. Scientists distinguish between members of the two families by performing an oxidase test: members of the Enterobacteriaceae are oxidase negative, whereas members of the Pasteurellaceae are oxidase positive (Figure 4).

We begin our survey of these microorganisms by examining the family Enterobacteriaceae, which contains about 150 species in 41 genera, including some of the more important nosocomial pathogens of humans (Figure 5).

## The Enterobacteriaceae: An Overview

### Learning Objectives

- ✓ Discuss how members of the family Enterobacteriaceae are distinguished in the laboratory.
- ✓ List six virulence factors found in members of the family Enterobacteriaceae.
- ✓ Describe the diagnosis, treatment, and prevention of diseases of enteric bacteria.

As their name suggests, prokaryotes in the family **Enterobacteriaceae** (en'ter-ō-bak-tēr-ē-ā'sē-ē)—also called **enteric bacteria**—are members of the intestinal microbiota of most animals and humans. They are also ubiquitous in water, soil, and decaying vegetation. Some species are always pathogenic in humans, whereas others are opportunists normally found in the intestinal microbiota that become pathogenic when introduced into other body sites.

As a group, enteric bacteria are the most common Gram-negative pathogens of humans. Though most enteric bacteria can be pathogenic in humans, over 95% of the medically important species are in the 13 genera we discuss shortly.

### Structure and Physiology of the Enterobacteriaceae

Enteric bacteria are coccobacilli or bacilli that measure about 1 μm × 1.2–3 μm (Figure 6). Those members that are motile have peritrichous flagella. Some have prominent capsules,

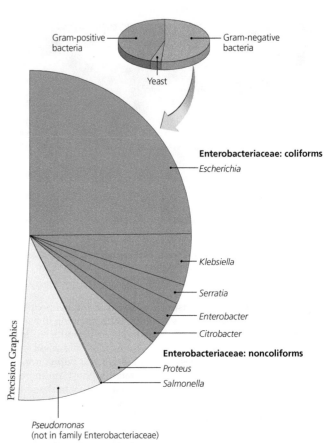

Gram-positive bacteria

Gram-negative bacteria

Yeast

**Enterobacteriaceae: coliforms**
- *Escherichia*
- *Klebsiella*
- *Serratia*
- *Enterobacter*
- *Citrobacter*

**Enterobacteriaceae: noncoliforms**
- *Proteus*
- *Salmonella*

*Pseudomonas* (not in family Enterobacteriaceae)

▲ **Figure 5** **Relative causes of nosocomial infections in the United States.** Gram-negative bacteria in the family Enterobacteriaceae account for most nosocomial infections. *What is a nosocomial infection?*

Figure 5 *An infection acquired in a health care setting.*

(a)  LM  10 μm     (b)  LM  10 μm

▲ **Figure 6** **Gram stains of bacteria in the family Enterobacteriaceae. (a)** *Enterobacter aerogenes*, a coccobacillus. **(b)** *Escherichia coli*, a bacillus. Note the similarity in staining properties.

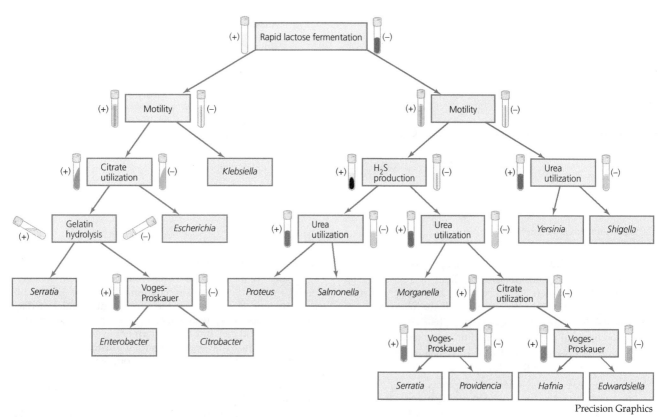

▲ **Figure 7** **A dichotomous key for distinguishing among enteric bacteria.** This key, based on biochemical tests and motility, is but one of many possible keys. *What characteristics do all enteric bacteria share?*

**Figure 7** *All enteric bacteria are Gram-negative, oxidase negative, and able to metabolize nitrate to nitrite.*

Precision Graphics

whereas others have only a loose slime layer. All members of the family reduce nitrate to nitrite and ferment glucose anaerobically, though most of them grow better in aerobic environments. As previously noted, all of them are also oxidase negative.

Given that all enteric bacteria are similar in microscopic appearance and staining properties, scientists traditionally distinguish among them by using biochemical tests, motility, and colonial characteristics on a variety of selective and nonselective media (for example, MacConkey agar and blood agar). Figure 7 presents one dichotomous key, based on motility and biochemical tests, for distinguishing among the 13 genera of enteric bacteria discussed in this chapter.

### Pathogenicity of the Enterobacteriaceae

Members of the Enterobacteriaceae have an outer membrane that contains lipopolysaccharide composed of three antigenic components:

- A core polysaccharide, shared by all of the enteric bacteria and called *common antigen.*

- So-called *O polysaccharide,* which has various antigenic varieties among strains and species.

- Lipid A, which, when released in a patient's blood, can trigger fever, vasodilation, inflammation, shock, and DIC. Because of the presence of lipid A, most of the enteric bacteria can cause serious disease and death.

Other antigens of certain enteric bacteria include protein and polysaccharide capsular antigens called K antigens (called Vi antigens in *Salmonella*) and flagellar proteins called H antigens. By controlling the genetic expression of K and H antigens, alternately producing and not producing the antigens, the bacteria survive by evading their host's immune system. Scientists use serological identification of antigens to distinguish among strains and species of enteric bacteria. For example, *Escherichia coli* O157:H7, a potentially deadly bacterium, is so designated in part because of its antigenic components. The specificity of serological tests can also be used in diagnosis and in epidemiological studies to identify the source of a particular infecting agent.

**Antigens**

Outer membrane:
(common antigen,
O antigen, lipid A)

Type III
secretion
system

Capsular antigens
(K; Vi in *Salmonella*)

Flagellar
antigens (H)

**Virulence Factors**

Fimbria

Exotoxin

Adhesin

Plasmid
(virulence genes)

Iron-binding protein

Hemolysin

◄ **Figure 8 Antigens and virulence factors of typical enteric bacteria.** *What is the function of a type III system?*

**Figure 8** A type III secretion system is a virulence factor that enables enteric bacteria to insert chemicals directly into the cytosol of a eukaryotic cell.

Kenneth Probst/Precision Graphics

Among the variety of virulence factors possessed by pathogenic enteric bacteria, some (for example, lipid A) are common to all genera, whereas others are unique to certain strains. Virulence factors seen in the Enterobacteriaceae include the following:

- *Capsules* that protect the bacteria from phagocytosis and antibodies, and provide a poorly immunogenic surface.

- *Fimbriae* and proteins called *adhesins,* which enable the bacteria to attach tightly to human cells.

- *Exotoxins* that cause a variety of symptoms such as diarrhea. The genes for exotoxins, fimbriae, and adhesins are frequently located on plasmids, which increases the likelihood that they will be transferred among bacteria.

- *Iron-binding compounds* called **siderophores** that capture iron and make it available to the bacteria.

- *Hemolysins,* which release nutrients such as iron by lysing red blood cells.

- A so-called *type III secretion system,* a complex structure composed of 20 different polypeptides that is synthesized by several pathogenic enteric species. Once assembled, the system spans the two membranes and peptidoglycan of the bacterial cell and inserts into a host cell's cytoplasmic membrane like a hypodermic needle. The bacterium then introduces proteins into the host cell. Because bacteria synthesize type III systems only after they have contacted a host cell, the proteins of a type III system are not exposed to immune surveillance.

Figure 8 illustrates the locations of the major types of antigens and virulence factors of enteric bacteria. **ANIMATIONS:** *Virulence Factors: Enteric Pathogens*

### Diagnosis, Treatment, and Prevention of Diseases of the Enterobacteriaceae

The presence of enteric bacteria in urine, blood, or cerebrospinal fluid is always diagnostic of infection or disease. To culture members of the Enterobacteriaceae from clinical specimens, clinicians use selective and differential media such as

eosin methylene blue (EMB) agar and MacConkey agar. In their role as selective media, these media inhibit the growth of many members of the normal microbiota and allow the growth of enteric bacteria (Figure 9a); in their role as differential media, they enable laboratory technicians to distinguish between enteric bacteria that can and cannot ferment lactose (Figure 9b). Commercially available systems using sophisticated biochemical tests can accurately distinguish among enteric bacteria in 4–24 hours.

Treatment of diarrhea involves treating the symptoms with fluid and electrolyte replacement. Often, antimicrobial drugs are not used to treat diarrhea because diarrhea is typically self-limiting—expulsion of the organisms from the body is often a more effective therapy than the action of antimicrobials. Also, antimicrobial therapy can worsen the prognosis by

*Escherichia coli*      *Escherichia coli*

David M. Phillips/Visuals Unlimited

Gladden Willis/Visuals Unlimited

*Staphylococcus aureus*      *Salmonella enterica* serotype Choleraesius

(a)      (b)

▲ **Figure 9 The use of MacConkey agar. (a)** This selective and differential medium allows growth of Gram-negative bacteria (here, *E. coli*) and inhibits Gram-positive bacteria (here, *Staphylococcus aureus*). **(b)** Additionally, colonies of lactose-fermenters (here, *E. coli*) are pink, differentiating them from other enteric bacteria that do not ferment lactose (here, *Salmonella enterica*).

killing many bacteria at once, which releases a large amount of toxic lipid A.

Treatment of internal infections involves selection of an appropriate antimicrobial drug, which often necessitates a susceptibility test such as a Kirby-Bauer test. Susceptible bacteria may develop resistance to antimicrobial drugs, presumably because enteric bacteria exchange plasmids readily; for example, many enterics can exchange DNA via conjugation. Antibiotics administered to control infections in the blood also kill the normal enteric bacteria, opening a niche for opportunistic resistant bacteria such as the endospore-forming, Gram-positive bacterium *Clostridium difficile* (klos-trid'ē-ŭm di-fi'sil-ē).

Given that enteric bacteria are a major component of the normal microbiota, preventing infections with them is almost impossible. Health care practitioners give prophylactic antimicrobial drugs to patients whenever mucosal barriers are breached by trauma or surgery, while avoiding prolonged unrestricted use of antimicrobials, a practice that selects for resistant strains of bacteria. Good personal hygiene (particularly handwashing) and proper sewage control are important in limiting the risk of infection. Specific methods of control and prevention associated with particular genera of enteric bacteria are discussed in the following sections.

## CLINICAL CASE STUDY

### A Painful Problem

Norman Jacobs, CDC

LM | 20 µm

A 20-year-old male reports to his physician that he has experienced painful urination, as if he were urinating molten solder. He has also noticed a puslike discharge from his penis. A stained smear of the discharge is shown in the photo.

The patient reports having been sexually active with two or three women in the previous six months. Because his partners reported being "absolutely sure" that they carried no sexually transmitted diseases, the patient had not used a condom.

1. What disease does this patient most likely have? What are the medical and common names for this disease?

2. How did the patient acquire the disease?

3. What could explain the lack of any history of sexually transmitted disease in his sexual partners?

4. What is the likely treatment?

5. Is the patient immune to future infections with this bacterium?

Scientists, researchers, and health care practitioners find it useful to categorize the pathogenic members of the Enterobacteriaceae into three groups:

- Coliforms, which rapidly ferment lactose, are part of the normal microbiota, and may be opportunistic pathogens.
- Noncoliform opportunists, which do not ferment lactose.
- True pathogens.

In the next three sections we will examine the important members of the Enterobacteriaceae according to this scheme, beginning with opportunistic coliforms.

## Coliform Opportunistic Enterobacteriaceae

Learning Objectives

✓ Compare and contrast *Escherichia, Klebsiella, Serratia, Enterobacter, Hafnia,* and *Citrobacter.*

✓ Describe the pathogenesis and diseases of *Escherichia coli* O157:H7.

**Coliforms** (kol'i-formz) are defined as aerobic or facultatively anaerobic, Gram-negative, rod-shaped bacteria that ferment lactose to form gas within 48 hours of being placed in a lactose broth at 35°C. Coliforms are found in the intestinal tracts of animals and humans, in soil, and on plants and decaying vegetation. The presence of fecal coliforms in water is indicative of impure water and of poor sewage treatment. The most common of the opportunistic coliform pathogens are bacteria in the genera *Escherichia, Klebsiella, Serratia, Enterobacter, Hafnia,* and *Citrobacter.*

### Escherichia coli

*Escherichia coli* (esh-ĕ-rik'ē-ă kō'lē)—the most common and important of the coliforms—is well known as a laboratory research organism.

Scientists have described numerous O, H, and K antigens of *E. coli,* which epidemiologists use to identify particular strains. Some antigens, such as O157, O111, H8, and H7, are associated with virulence. Virulent strains also have genes (located on virulence plasmids) for fimbriae, adhesins, and a variety of exotoxins, enabling these strains to colonize human tissue and cause disease. Such plasmids can be transferred among bacteria.

*E. coli* is responsible for a number of diseases, including septicemia, urinary tract infections (UTIs), neonatal meningitis, and gastroenteritis. *E. coli* in the blood can colonize the lining of the heart, triggering inflammation and the destruction of heart valves.

Gastroenteritis, the most common disease associated with *E. coli,* is often mediated by exotoxins, called *enterotoxins,* that bind to proteins on cells lining the intestinal tract. A portion of the toxin then enters the cell and triggers a series of chemical reactions that cause the loss of sodium, chloride, potassium, bicarbonate, and

329

Capsules

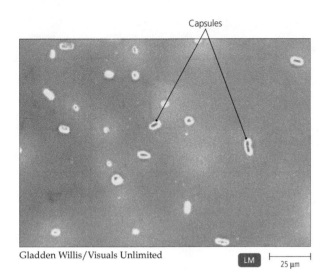

Gladden Willis/Visuals Unlimited

LM ├──────┤ 25 μm

▲ **Figure 10** **The prominent capsule of *Klebsiella pneumoniae.*** *How does the capsule function as a virulence factor?*

**Figure 10** *Capsules inhibit phagocytosis and intracellular digestion by phagocytic cells.*

water from the cells, producing watery diarrhea, cramps, nausea, and vomiting. Enterotoxin-producing strains are common in developing countries and are important causes of pediatric diarrhea, accounting for up to a third of the cases of this life-threatening disease in some countries.

*E. coli* is the most common cause of non-nosocomial urinary tract infections. Women, with their shorter urethras, are 15 times more likely to acquire UTIs than are men. Surprisingly, girls are less likely to acquire UTIs than are women, perhaps because of the hormonal influences of adulthood or an increased likelihood of UTIs following sexual intercourse. About 32% of adult women will suffer uncomplicated mild bladder infections by *E. coli* sometime during their lifetimes. In some cases, the bacterium ascends the ureters from the bladder, infecting the kidneys and causing a more serious disease called *acute pyelonephritis,* which involves fever, flank pain, bacteriuria (bacteria in the urine), profuse perspiration, nausea, and vomiting.

*E. coli* O157:H7, first described as a cause of human illness in 1982, is now the most prevalent strain of pathogenic *E. coli* in developed countries. The ingestion of as few as 10 organisms can result in disease, which ranges from bloody diarrhea, to severe or fatal hemorrhagic colitis, to a severe kidney disorder called *hemolytic uremic syndrome* in which renal function ceases.

Urinary tract and blood infections with this organism can be fatal, especially in children and immunocompromised adults. Most epidemics of *E. coli* O157:H7 have been associated with the consumption of undercooked ground beef or unpasteurized milk or fruit juice contaminated with feces. Despite its notoriety, fewer than 1 in 10 million deaths in the United States is caused by a U.S. citizen experiencing death or injury from strain O157:H7 in ground beef.

*E. coli* O157:H7 produces a type III secretion system through which it introduces two types of proteins into intestinal cells.

**CLINICAL CASE STUDY**

## A Heart-Rending Experience

L. Brent Selinger, Pearson Science

▲ *E. coli* in a blood smear.

LM ├──┤ 7 μm

A construction worker in his mid-30s visited his physician complaining of shortness of breath and a persistent cough that had lasted more than three weeks. Upon examination the doctor noted that the client had a history of asthma and intravenous drug use. Believing him to have an upper respiratory disturbance, the physician ordered a steroid to reduce swelling in the airways.

Two weeks later the construction worker's condition was worse, so he sought help at an emergency room. When he arrived, his heart rate was accelerated, and he appeared to be dehydrated. The ER staff administered a rapid IV infusion of fluids, took blood for analysis, and X-rayed his chest. Shortly after the infusion, the man's respiratory situation deteriorated to the point that he was placed on a ventilator. The X ray revealed an abnormally enlarged heart and fluid throughout both lungs. The blood culture contained *Escherichia coli.*

1. How could the patient have gotten *E. coli* in his blood?

2. What had *E. coli* done to the inner structures of his heart?

3. What factors in the medical treatment may have exacerbated the disease? Why?

Proteins of one type disrupt the cell's metabolism; proteins of the other type become lodged in the cell's cytoplasmic membrane, where they act as receptors for the attachment of additional *E. coli* O157:H7 bacteria. Such attachment apparently enables this strain of *E. coli* to displace normal, harmless strains.

*E. coli* O157:H7 also produces *Shiga-like toxin,* which inhibits protein synthesis in host cells. Shiga-like toxin, which was first identified in *Shigella* (discussed shortly), attaches to the surfaces of neutrophils and is spread by them throughout the body, causing widespread death of host cells and tissues. Antimicrobial drugs induce *E. coli* O157:H7 to increase its production of Shiga-like toxin, exacerbating the disease.

### Klebsiella

Species of the genus *Klebsiella* (kleb-sē-el'ă) grow in the digestive and respiratory systems of humans and animals. They are nonmotile, and their prominent capsules (Figure 10) give *Klebsiella* colonies a mucoid appearance and protect the bacteria from phagocytosis, enabling them to become opportunistic pathogens.

James A. Shapiro, University of Chicago

▲ **Figure 11** **Red colonies of *Serratia marcescens*.** Color develops in colonies grown at room temperature.

John J. Farmer, CDC

▲ **Figure 12** **The wavelike concentric rings of the swarming *Proteus microbilis*.** This characteristic of the bacterium is beautiful, but it makes isolation of *Proteus* difficult.

The most commonly isolated pathogenic species is *K. pneumoniae* (nū-mō'nē-ī), which causes pneumonia and may be involved in bacteremia, meningitis, wound infections, and UTIs. Pneumonia caused by *K. pneumoniae* often involves destruction of alveoli and the production of bloody sputum. Alcoholics and patients with compromised immunity are at greater risk of pulmonary disease because of their poor ability to clear aspirated oral secretions from their lower respiratory tracts.

### Serratia

The motile coliform *Serratia marcescens* (se-rat'ē-a mar-ses'enz) produces a red pigment when grown at room temperature (Figure 11). For many years, scientists considered *Serratia* to be totally benign; in fact, researchers intentionally introduced this bacterium into various environments to track the movement of bacteria in general. Using this method, scientists have followed the movement of *Serratia* from the mouth into the blood of dental patients, and throughout hospitals via air ducts. In a series of tests performed between 1949 and 1968, the U.S. government released large quantities of *S. marcescens* into the air over New York City and San Francisco to mimic the movement of a discharged biological weapon.

Now, however, we know that *Serratia* can grow on catheters, in saline solutions, and on other hospital supplies, and that it is a potentially life-threatening opportunistic pathogen in the urinary and respiratory tracts of immunocompromised patients. The bacterium is frequently resistant to antimicrobial drugs.

### Enterobacter, Hafnia, and Citrobacter

Other motile coliforms that can be opportunistic pathogens are *Enterobacter* (en'ter-ō-bak'ter), *Hafnia* (haf'nē-ǎ), and *Citrobacter* (sit'rō-bak-ter). These bacteria, like other coliforms, ferment

lactose and reside in the digestive tracts of animals and humans as well as in soil, water, decaying vegetation, and sewage. *Enterobacter* can be a contaminant of dairy products. All three genera are involved in nosocomial infections of the blood, wounds, surgical incisions, and urinary tracts of immunocompromised patients. Treatment of such infections can be difficult because these prokaryotes, especially *Enterobacter*, are often resistant to most antibacterial drugs.

## Noncoliform Opportunistic Enterobacteriaceae

### Learning Objectives

✓ Differentiate between coliform and noncoliform opportunists.

✓ Describe the diseases caused by noncoliform opportunistic enteric bacteria.

The family Enterobacteriaceae also contains genera that cannot ferment lactose; several of these genera are opportunistic pathogens. These noncoliform opportunists include *Proteus*, *Morganella*, *Providencia*, and *Edwardsiella*.

### Proteus

Like the mythical Greek god Proteus, who could change shape, the Gram-negative, facultative anaerobe *Proteus* (prō'tē-ŭs) is a typical rod-shaped bacterium with a few polar flagella when cultured in broth, but differentiates into an elongated cell that swarms by means of numerous peritrichous flagella when cultured on agar. Swarming cells produce concentric wavelike patterns on agar surfaces (Figure 12). The roles of the two morphologies in human infections are not clear.

*Proteus mirabilis* (mi-ra'bi-lis) is the most common species of *Proteus* associated with disease in humans, particularly with urinary tract infections in patients with long-term urinary

## MICROBE AT A GLANCE

### *Escherichia coli*

**Taxonomy:** Domain Bacteria, phylum Proteobacteria, class Gammaproteobacteria, order Enterobacteriales, family Enterobacteriaceae

**Cell morphology and arrangement:** Bacilli, single

**Gram reaction:** Negative

**Virulence factors:** Capsule, fimbriae, endotoxin, adhesins, exotoxins (enterotoxins), type III secretion system; strain O157:H7 produces Shiga-like toxin

**Diseases caused:** Septicemia; urinary tract infections, including hemolytic uremic syndrome; neonatal meningitis; gastroenteritis, including diarrhea and severe to fatal hemorrhagic colitis

**Treatment for diseases:** Various antimicrobials

**Prevention of disease:** Prevent fecal contamination of food and water, good personal hygiene

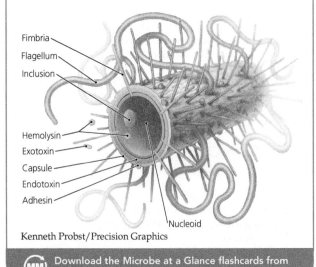

Fimbria
Flagellum
Inclusion
Hemolysin
Exotoxin
Capsule
Endotoxin
Adhesin
Nucleoid

Kenneth Probst/Precision Graphics

catheters. One study showed that 44% of catheterized patients had *P. mirabilis* growing in their urine.

In the presence of urea, as is found in the bladder, this microorganism releases a large amount of the enzyme *urease,* which breaks down urea into carbon dioxide and ammonia. Ammonia raises the pH of urine in the bladder and kidneys such that ions that are normally soluble at the acidic pH of urine (around pH 6.0) precipitate, often around bacterial cells, to form infection-induced kidney stones composed of magnesium ammonium phosphate or calcium phosphate. Kidney stones produced in this manner can contain hundreds of *P. mirabilis* cells.

Because *Proteus* is resistant to many antimicrobial drugs, health care workers must determine proper treatment following a susceptibility test. Researchers have been able to immunize mice against urinary tract infections with *Proteus.* This success is encouraging to those seeking protection for patients who must have long-term urinary catheters.

### *Morganella, Providencia,* and *Edwardsiella*

Nosocomial infections of immunocompromised patients by *Morganella* (mōr'gan-el'-ă), *Providencia* (prov'i-den'sē-ă), and *Edwardsiella* (ed'ward-sē-el'lă) are becoming more frequent. These organisms are primarily involved in urinary tract infections. *Providencia* contains a plasmid that codes for urease and thus triggers the formation of kidney stones.

## Truly Pathogenic Enterobacteriaceae

### Learning Objectives

✓ Describe the diseases caused by truly pathogenic enteric bacteria.

✓ Contrast salmonellosis and shigellosis.

✓ Describe the life cycle of *Yersinia pestis* and contrast bubonic and pneumonic plague.

Three important non-lactose-fermenting bacteria in the family Enterobacteriaceae are *Salmonella, Shigella,* and *Yersinia.* These genera are not considered members of the normal microbiota of humans, because they are almost always pathogenic due to their numerous virulence factors. All three genera synthesize type III secretion systems through which they introduce proteins that inhibit phagocytosis, rearrange the cytoskeletons of eukaryotic cells, or induce apoptosis. We begin our discussion with *Salmonella,* which is the most common of the three pathogens.

### *Salmonella*

*Salmonella* (sal'mŏ-nel'ă) is a genus of motile, Gram-negative, peritrichous bacilli that live in the intestines of virtually all birds, reptiles, and mammals and are eliminated in their feces. These bacteria do not ferment lactose, but they do ferment glucose, usually with gas production. They are urease negative and oxidase negative, and most produce hydrogen sulfide ($H_2S$). Scientists have identified more than 2000 unique serotypes (strains) of *Salmonella.* Analysis of the DNA sequences of their genes indicates that all of them properly belong to a single species—*S. enterica* (en-ter'i-ka). This taxonomically correct approach has not been well received by researchers or medical professionals, so we will consider the various strains of this single species with modern terminology as well as according to their traditional specific epithets, such as *S. typhi* (tī'fē) and *S. paratyphi* (par'a-tī'fē).

Most infections of humans with salmonellae result from the consumption of food contaminated with animal feces, often from pet reptiles. The pathogen is also common in foods containing poultry or eggs—about one-third of chicken eggs are contaminated. *Salmonella* released during the cracking of an egg on a kitchen counter and inoculated into other foods can reproduce into millions of cells in just a few hours. Some strains, such as *S. enterica* serotype Dublin, are acquired through the consumption of inadequately pasteurized contaminated milk. Infections with fewer than 1 million cells of most strains of *Salmonella* are usually asymptomatic in people with healthy immune systems.

Larger infective doses can result in **salmonellosis** (sal'mo-nel-o'sis), which is characterized by nonbloody diarrhea, nausea, and vomiting. Fever, myalgia (muscle pain), headache, and abdominal cramps are also common. The events in the course of salmonellosis are depicted in Figure 13. After the salmonellae pass through the stomach, they attach to the cells lining the small intestine ( 1 ). The bacteria then use type III secretion systems to insert proteins into the host cells, inducing the normally nonphagocytic cells to endocytize the bacteria ( 2 ). The salmonellae then reproduce within endocytic vesicles ( 3 ), eventually killing the host cells ( 4 ) and inducing the signs and symptoms of salmonellosis. Cells of some strains can subsequently enter the blood, causing bacteremia ( 5 ) and localized infections throughout the body, including in the lining of the heart, the bones, and the joints.

Humans are the sole hosts of *Salmonella enterica* serotype Typhi *(S. typhi),* which causes **typhoid fever.** (A mild form of typhoid fever is also produced by serotype Paratyphi.) Infection occurs via the ingestion of food or water contaminated with sewage containing bacteria from carriers, who are often asymptomatic. (For the story of perhaps the most notorious asymptomatic carrier, see **Highlight: The Tale of "Typhoid Mary".**) An infective dose of *S. enterica* Typhi is only about 1000–10,000 cells. The bacteria pass through the intestinal cells into the bloodstream; there they are phagocytized but not killed by phagocytic cells, which carry the bacteria to the liver, spleen, bone marrow, and gallbladder. Patients typically experience gradually increasing fever, headache, muscle pains, malaise, and loss of appetite that may persist for a week or more. Bacteria may reproduce in the gallbladder and be released to reinfect the intestines, producing gastroenteritis and abdominal pain, and then a recurrence of bacteremia. In some patients the bacteria ulcerate and perforate the intestinal wall, allowing bacteria from the intestinal tract to enter the abdominal cavity and cause *peritonitis.* Figure 14 contrasts the incidences of salmonellosis and typhoid fever in the United States since 1935.

Treatment for salmonellosis involves fluid and electrolyte replacement. Typhoid fever is treated with antimicrobial drugs such as ampicillin or ciprofloxacin. Physicians sometimes remove the gallbladder of a carrier to ensure that others are not infected. Researchers have developed vaccines that provide temporary protection for travelers to areas where typhoid fever is still endemic.

### Shigella

The genus *Shigella* (shĕ-gel'lă) contains Gram-negative, oxidase-negative, nonmotile pathogens of the family Enterobacteriaceae that are primarily parasites of the digestive tracts of humans. These bacteria produce a diarrhea-inducing enterotoxin, are urease negative, and do not produce hydrogen sulfide gas. Some

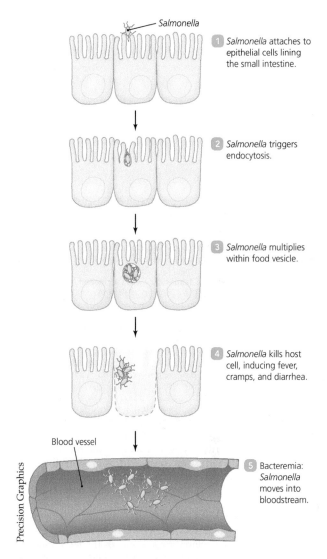

1 *Salmonella* attaches to epithelial cells lining the small intestine.

2 *Salmonella* triggers endocytosis.

3 *Salmonella* multiplies within food vesicle.

4 *Salmonella* kills host cell, inducing fever, cramps, and diarrhea.

5 Bacteremia: *Salmonella* moves into bloodstream.

▲ **Figure 13** **The events in salmonellosis.**

scientists suggest that *Shigella* may actually be a strain of *E. coli* that has become nonmotile and oxidase negative, while other researchers go so far as to consider *Shigella* an invasive, toxin-producing *E. coli* that is cloaked in *Shigella* antigens. Still other scientists contend the converse—that *E. coli* is really a disguised species of *Shigella* that has acquired genes for flagella!

In any case, taxonomists have historically identified four well-defined species of *Shigella: S. dysenteriae* (dis-en-te'rē-ī), *S. flexneri* (fleks'ner-ē), *S. boydii* (boy'dē-ē), and *S. sonnei* (sōn'ne-ē). *Shigella sonnei* is most commonly isolated in industrialized nations, whereas *S. flexneri* is the predominant species in developing countries. All four species cause a severe form of dysentery called **shigellosis** (shig-ĕ-lō'sis), which is characterized by abdominal cramps, fever, diarrhea, and purulent bloody stools.

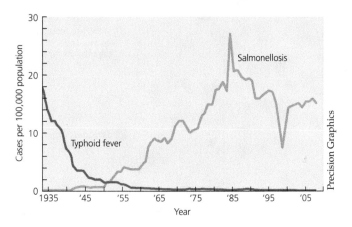

▲ **Figure 14 The incidences of diseases caused by *Salmonella* in the United States.** Whereas the incidence of typhoid fever has declined because of improved sewage treatment and personal hygiene, the incidence of reported cases of salmonellosis has increased. *What factors might explain the increase in the observed incidence of salmonellosis?*

*increase in the number of cases.*
*may be due to better diagnosis and reporting, rather than to an actual*
*number of cases of salmonellosis has declined. The observed increase*
*typhoid fever has decreased significantly, it is likely that the actual*
*by the same species and transmitted the same way, and the incidence of*
**Figure 14** *Since salmonellosis and typhoid fever are caused*

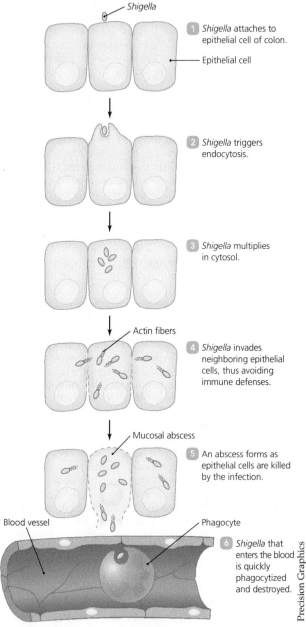

① *Shigella* attaches to epithelial cell of colon.

Epithelial cell

② *Shigella* triggers endocytosis.

③ *Shigella* multiplies in cytosol.

Actin fibers

④ *Shigella* invades neighboring epithelial cells, thus avoiding immune defenses.

Mucosal abscess

⑤ An abscess forms as epithelial cells are killed by the infection.

Blood vessel        Phagocyte

⑥ *Shigella* that enters the blood is quickly phagocytized and destroyed.

▲ **Figure 15 The events in shigellosis.**

Shigellosis is primarily associated with poor personal hygiene and ineffective sewage treatment. People become infected primarily by ingesting bacteria on their own contaminated hands and secondarily by consuming contaminated food. *Shigella* is little affected by stomach acid, so an infective dose may be as few as 200 cells; therefore, person-to-person spread is also possible, particularly among children and among homosexual men.

Initially, *Shigella* colonizes cells of the small intestine, causing an enterotoxin-mediated diarrhea; the main events in shigellosis, however, begin once bacteria invade cells of the large intestine (Figure 15). When *Shigella* attaches to a large intestine epithelial cell (①), the cell is stimulated to endocytize the bacterium (②), which then multiplies within the cell's cytosol (③). (Note that this differs from salmonellosis, in which bacteria multiply within endocytic vesicles. *Shigella* then polymerizes the host's actin fibers, which push the bacteria out of the host cell and into adjacent cells (④), in the process evading the host's immune system. As the bacteria kill host cells, abscesses form in the mucosa (⑤); any bacteria that enter the blood from a ruptured abscess are quickly phagocytized and destroyed (⑥), so bacteremia is rarely a part of shigellosis. About 20,000 cases of shigellosis are reported each year in the United States, but because mild cases are rarely reported, this figure may represent only 1% of the actual total.

*Shigella dysenteriae* secretes an exotoxin called **Shiga toxin,** which stops protein synthesis in its host's cells. Shiga toxin is similar to the Shiga-like toxin of *Escherichia coli* O157:H7. Shigellosis caused by *S. dysenteriae* is more serious than that caused by other species of *Shigella*, with a mortality rate as high as 20%.

Treatment of shigellosis involves replacement of fluids and electrolytes. The disease is usually self-limiting, but oral antimicrobial drugs such as ciprofloxacin, sulfonamides, penicillin, or cephalosporin can reduce the spread of *Shigella* to close contacts of the patient.

A recent live, attenuated vaccine against *S. flexneri* has been successful in preventing dysentery caused by this species, although the participants in the study experienced mild diarrhea

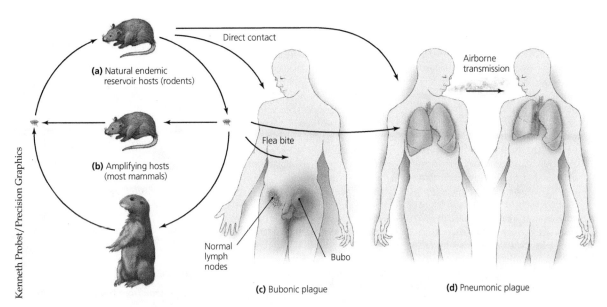

▲ **Figure 16 The natural history and transmission of *Yersinia pestis*.** This bacterium causes plague. **(a)** The natural endemic cycle of *Yersinia* among rodents. **(b)** The cycle involving amplifying mammalian hosts. **(c, d)** Humans develop one of two forms of plague as the result of the bite of infected fleas or direct contact with infected hosts. *Yersinia* can move from the bloodstream into the lungs to cause pneumonic plague, which can be spread between humans via the airborne transmission of the bacteria in aerosols. *Why is the plague so much less devastating today than it was in the Middle Ages?*

Figure 16 *Urban living has reduced contact between people and flea vectors living on wildlife and farm animals; improved hygiene and the use of insecticides have reduced contact with flea vectors living on pets; and antimicrobials are effective against Y. pestis.*

and fever as a result of immunization. Researchers are working to perfect a vaccine that will not cause symptoms.

## Yersinia

The genus *Yersinia* (yer-sin′ē-ă) contains three notable species— *Y. enterocolitica* (en′ter-ō-ko-lit′ĭ-kă), *Y. pseudotuberculosis* (soo-dō-too-ber-ky ū-lō′sis), and *Y. pestis* (pes′tis)—that are normally pathogens of animals. All three species contain virulence plasmids that code for adhesins and type III secretion systems. The adhesins allow *Yersinia* to attach to human cells, after which the type III system is used to inject proteins that trigger apoptosis in macrophages and neutrophils.

*Yersinia enterocolitica* and *Y. pseudotuberculosis* are enteric pathogens acquired via the consumption of food or water contaminated with animal feces. *Y. enterocolitica* is a common cause of painful inflammation of the intestinal tract; such inflammation is accompanied by diarrhea and fever that can last for weeks or months. Involvement of the terminal portion of the small intestine can result in painful inflammation of the mesenteric lymph nodes, which mimics appendicitis. *Y. pseudotuberculosis* produces a less severe inflammation of the intestines.

*Yersinia pestis* is an extremely virulent, nonenteric pathogen that has two clinical manifestations: **bubonic** (boo-bon′ik) **plague** and **pneumonic** (noo-mō′nik) **plague.** A major pandemic

of plague that lasted from the mid-500s A.D. to the late 700s is estimated to have claimed the lives of more than 40 million people. This devastation was surpassed during a second pandemic that killed about a third of the population of Europe (25 million people) in just five years during the 14th century. A third major pandemic spread from China across Asia, Africa, Europe, and the Americas in the 1860s. So great was the devastation of these three great pandemics that the word "plague" still provokes a sense of dread today.

Rats, mice, and voles are the hosts for the natural endemic cycle of *Yersinia pestis* (Figure 16a); they harbor the bacteria but do not develop disease. Among rodents, fleas are the vectors for the spread of the bacteria. As the bacteria multiply within a flea, they block the esophagus such that the flea can no longer ingest blood from a host. The starving flea jumps from host to host seeking a blood meal and infecting a new host with each bite. When other animals—including prairie dogs, rabbits, deer, camels, dogs, and cats—become infected via flea bites, they act as *amplifying hosts* (Figure 16b); that is, they support increases in the numbers of bacteria and infected fleas, even though the amplifying hosts die from bubonic plague. Humans become infected either when bitten by infected fleas that have left their normal animal hosts or through direct contact with infected animals (Figure 16c). Bubonic plague is not spread from person to person.

HIGHLIGHT

## THE TALE OF "TYPHOID MARY"

Mary Mallon is one of the most famous cooks in history—but not for the tastiness of her dishes. An asymptomatic carrier of typhoid, Mary is believed to have caused outbreaks of typhoid fever in at least seven New York families for whom she worked as a private cook during the early 1900s. She first came to attention in 1906, when George Soper, a sanitation engineer hired to investigate an outbreak of typhoid fever in a wealthy Long Island household, became suspicious upon learning that the family's cook—Mary—had mysteriously disappeared three weeks after the illnesses began. Subsequent investigations revealed that Mary had a history of working in households whose members fell ill with typhoid. Public health authorities ultimately tracked Mary down and confirmed the presence of *Salmonella enterica* serotype Typhi in her stool and gallbladder.

Uneducated and headstrong, Mary never quite believed that she could be the cause of so much sickness—perhaps because she never fell ill herself—and she refused to have her gallbladder removed, as authorities suggested. Deemed a public health hazard, Mary was quarantined in 1907 and not released until 1910, with the provision that she was never to work as a cook again. Within a few years, however, she was discovered in Manhattan, working as a food preparer, and still spreading typhoid. She was again detained and remained in quarantine until her death, from a stroke, in 1938.

▲ *A cook from the time of Typhoid Mary.*

Minnesota Historical Society / Corbis

Margaret Parsons and Karl F. Meyer, CDC

▲ **Figure 17 Bubo.** Such lymph nodes swollen by infection are a characteristic feature of bubonic plague.

Bubonic plague is characterized by high fever and swollen, painful lymph nodes called *buboes*[2] (Figure 17), which develop within a week of a flea bite. Untreated cases progress to bacteremia, which results in disseminated intravascular coag-ula-tion, subcutaneous hemorrhaging, and death of tissues, which may become infected with *Clostridium* (klos-trid′ē-ŭm) and de-velop gangrene. Because of the extensive darkening of dead skin, plague has been called the "Black Death." Untreated bubonic plague is fatal in 50% of cases. Even with treatment, up to 15% of patients die. In fatal infections, death usually occurs within a week of the onset of symptoms.

Pneumonic plague occurs when *Yersinia* in the bloodstream infects the lungs. Disease develops very rapidly—patients develop fever, malaise, and pulmonary distress within a day of infection. Pneumonic plague can spread from person to person through aerosols and sputum (Figure 16d), and if left untreated is fatal in nearly 100% of cases.

Because plague is so deadly and can progress so rapidly, di-agnosis and treatment must also be rapid. The characteristic symptoms, especially in patients that have traveled in areas where plague is endemic, are usually sufficient for diagnosis. Rodent control and better personal hygiene have almost elimi-nated plague in industrialized countries, although wild animals remain as reservoirs. Many antibacterial drugs, including strep-tomycin, gentamycin, tetracycline, and chloramphenicol, are ef-fective against *Yersinia*.

In summary, Figure 18 illustrates the general sites of infections by the more common members of the Enterobac teriaceae.

## The Pasteurellaceae

### Learning Objectives

✓ Describe two pathogenic genera in the family Pasteurellaceae.

✓ Identify and describe three diseases caused by species of *Haemophilus*.

In the previous sections we examined opportunistic and pathogenic Gram-negative, facultative anaerobes of the family

---

[2]From Greek *boubon*, meaning groin, referring to a swelling in the groin.

Central nervous system
*Escherichia*

Lower respiratory tract
*Klebsiella*
*Enterobacter*
*Escherichia*

Bloodstream
*Escherichia*
*Klebsiella*
*Enterobacter*

Gastrointestinal tract
*Salmonella*
*Shigella*
*Escherichia*
*Yersinia*

Urinary tract
*Escherichia*
*Proteus*
*Klebsiella*
*Morganella*

Kenneth Probst/Precision Graphics

▲ **Figure 18** **Sites of infection by some common members of the Enterobacteriaceae.** For each site, genera are listed in their relative order of prevalence.

Eye of Science/Photo Researchers

▲ **Figure 19** ***Haemophilus influenzae* is pleomorphic—it assumes many shapes.** *What simple lab test can be used to distinguish* Haemophilus *from* Escherichia?

Figure 19 *An oxidase test can distinguish Haemophilus, which is oxidase positive, from Escherichia, which is oxidase negative.*

## Haemophilus

*Haemophilus*[3] (hē-mof'i-lŭs) species are generally small, sometimes pleomorphic bacilli (Figure 19) that require heme and NAD⁺ for growth; as a result, they are obligate parasites, colonizing mucous membranes of humans and some animals. *Haemophilus influenzae* is the most notable pathogen in the genus, though *H. ducreyi* is an agent of a sexually transmitted disease. Other species in the genus primarily cause opportunistic infections.

**Haemophilus influenzae** Most strains of *Haemophilus influenzae* (in-flu-en'zī) have polysaccharide capsules that resist phagocytosis. Researchers distinguish among six strains by differences in the K antigens of the capsules. Type b usually causes 95% of *H. influenzae* diseases.

Belying its name, *H. influenzae* does not cause the flu; in fact, it is rarely found in the upper respiratory tract. Instead, *H. influenzae* b was the most common cause of meningitis in children 3–18 months of age before immunization brought it under control. The pathogen also causes inflammation of subcutaneous tissue, infantile arthritis, and life-threatening epiglottitis in children under four years old. In the latter disease, swelling of the epiglottis and surrounding tissues can completely block the pharynx.

Prompt treatment with antimicrobials is required for meningitis and epiglottitis. Over the past decade, the use of an effective vaccine—Hib, which is composed of capsular antigens conjugated to protein molecules—has virtually eliminated all

Enterobacteriaceae, all of which are oxidase negative. Now we consider another family of gammaproteobacteria—the **Pasteurellaceae** (pas-ter-el-ă'sē-ē), which contains species that are oxidase positive (see Figure 4). These microorganisms are mostly facultative anaerobes that are small, nonmotile, and fastidious in their growth requirements—they require heme or cytochromes. Two genera, *Pasteurella* and *Haemophilus*, contain most of this family's pathogens of humans.

## Pasteurella

*Pasteurella* (pas-ter-el'ă) is part of the normal microbiota in the oral and nasopharyngeal cavities of animals, including domestic cats and dogs. Humans are typically infected via animal bites and scratches or via inhalation of aerosols from animals. Most cases in humans are caused by *P. multocida* (mul-tŏ'si-da), which produces localized inflammation and swelling of lymph nodes at the site of infection. Patients with suppressed immunity are at risk of widespread infection and bacteremia.

Diagnosis of infection with *Pasteurella* depends on identification of the bacterium in cultures of specimens collected from patients. As noted, *Pasteurella* is fastidious in its growth requirements, so it must be cultured on blood or chocolate agar (autoclaved blood agar). A wide variety of antibacterial drugs are effective against *Pasteurella*, including penicillins, sulfonamides, trimethoprim, and fluoroquinolones.

[3]From Greek *haima*, meaning blood, and *philos*, meaning love.

337

▲ **Figure 20** **Chancroid (soft chancre).** This painful, soft, genital ulcer is caused by *Haemophilus ducreyi*.

disease caused by *H. influenzae* in the United States. Cuban scientists have produced a synthetic polysaccharide vaccine that is cheaper and purer, which may help poorer countries eliminate the disease as well.

The incidence of infections with strains other than type b has remained fairly constant in the United States. These strains of *H. influenzae* cause a variety of diseases, including conjunctivitis, sinusitis, dental abscesses, middle-ear infections, meningitis, bronchitis, and pneumonia. Strain *aegyptius* causes Brazilian purpuric fever, an extremely rapid pediatric disease characterized by conjunctivitis that within a few days is followed by fever, vomiting, abdominal pain, shock, and death. The pathogenesis of this disease is not understood, but fortunately it is rare in the United States.

## CRITICAL **THINKING**

*Haemophilus influenzae* was so named because researchers isolated the organism from flu patients. Specifically, how could a proper application of Koch's postulates have prevented this misnomer?

**Sexually Transmitted *Haemophilus*** Sexually transmitted *Haemophilus ducreyi* (doo-krā′ē) causes a genital ulcer, called *chancroid* (shang′ kroyd) or *soft chancre* (shang′ ker) (Figure 20), by producing a toxin that kills human epithelial cells. Chancroid is most often diagnosed in men because the ulceration is more visible and often painful in men, whereas the disease is often asymptomatic in women. Although prevalent in Africa and Asia, chancroid is rare in Europe and the Americas.

Thus far we have examined pathogenic Gram-negative cocci and the more commonly pathogenic, facultatively anaerobic, Gram-negative bacilli. Now we turn our attention to the pathogenic, Gram-negative, aerobic bacilli.

# Pathogenic, Gram-Negative, Aerobic Bacilli

Pathogenic, Gram-negative, aerobic bacilli are a diverse group of bacteria in several classes of the phylum Proteobacteria. The following sections examine some of the more common species in the order they are presented in *Bergey's Manual*: *Bartonella* and *Brucella* in the class Alphaproteobacteria; *Bordetella* and *Burkholderia* in the class Betaproteobacteria; and several members of the class Gammaproteobacteria, including the pseudomonads (*Pseudomonas*, *Moraxella*, and *Acinetobacter*), *Francisella*, *Legionella*, and *Coxiella*.

## *Bartonella*

### Learning Objective

✓ Distinguish among bartonellosis, trench fever, and cat scratch disease.

Members of *Bartonella* (bar-tō-nel′ä), a genus of aerobic bacilli in the class Alphaproteobacteria, are found in animals, but they are known to cause disease only in humans. They have fastidious growth requirements and must be cultured on special media such as blood agar. Many require prolonged incubation in a humid, 37°C atmosphere supplemented with carbon dioxide before they form visible colonies. Three species (formerly classified in the genus *Rochalimaea*) are pathogenic in humans.

*Bartonella bacilliformis* (ba-sil′li-for′mis) invades and weakens erythrocytes, causing **bartonellosis**—an often fatal disease characterized by fever, severe anemia, headache, muscle and joint pain, and chronic skin infections. Very small bloodsucking sand flies of the genus *Phlebotomus* (fle-bot′ō-mŭs) transmit the bacterium, so the disease is endemic only in Peru, Ecuador, and Colombia, where such flies live.

*Bartonella quintana* (kwin′ta-nä) causes **trench fever** (*five-day fever*), which was prevalent among soldiers during World War I. Human body lice transmit the bacterium from person to person. Many infections are asymptomatic, although in other patients severe headaches, fever, and pain in the long bones characterize the disease. The fever can be recurrent, returning every five days, giving the disease its alternative name. *B. quintana* also causes two newly described diseases in immunocompromised patients: *Bacillary angiomatosis* is characterized by fever, inflamed nodular skin lesions, and proliferation of blood vessels. *Bacillary peliosis hepatitis* is a disease in which patients develop blood-filled cavities in their livers.

*Bartonella henselae* (hen′sel-ī) causes **cat scratch disease** when the bacterium is introduced into humans through cat scratches and bites. Fleas may also transmit the bacterium from cats to people. Cat scratch disease has emerged as a relatively common and occasionally serious infection of children, affecting an estimated 22,000 children annually in the United States. This disease involves prolonged fever and malaise, plus localized swelling at the site of infection (Figure 21) and of local lymph nodes for several months. Serological testing of individuals who exhibit these characteristic signs and symptoms following exposure to cats confirms a diagnosis of cat scratch disease.

Gentamicin, erythromycin, azithromycin, or cephalosporin are used to treat most *Bartonella* infections, though there is a high rate of relapse.

## *Brucella*

### Learning Objective

✓ Describe brucellosis.

*Brucella* (broo-sel′lă) is a genus of small, nonmotile, aerobic coccobacilli that lack capsules but survive phagocytosis by preventing lysosomes from fusing with phagosomes containing the bacterium. Analysis of rRNA nucleotide base sequences reveals that *Brucella* is closely related to *Bartonella* in the class Alphaproteobacteria. Although *Brucella*-caused diseases in humans have been ascribed to four species, rRNA analysis has revealed the existence of only a single true species: *Brucella melitensis* (me-li-ten′sis); the other variants are strains of this one species. Because the classical specific epithets are so well known, they are mentioned here.

In animal hosts, the bacterium lives as an intracellular parasite in organs such as the uterus, placenta, and epididymis, but these organs are not infected in humans. Typically, infections in animals are either asymptomatic or cause a mild disease—**brucellosis** (broo-sel-ō′sis)—though they can cause sterility or abortion. Historically named *Brucella melitensis* infects goats and sheep; *B. abortus* (a-bort′us), cattle; *B. suis* (soo′is), swine; and *B. canis* (kā′nis), dogs, foxes, and coyotes.

▲ **Figure 21 Cat scratch disease.** The localized swelling at the site of cat scratches or bites is characteristic.

Humans become infected either by consuming unpasteurized contaminated dairy products or through contact with animal blood, urine, or placentas in workplaces such as slaughterhouses, veterinary clinics, and feedlots. The bacterium enters the body through breaks in mucous membranes of the digestive and respiratory tracts.

Brucellosis in humans is characterized by a fluctuating fever—which gives the disease one of its common names: *undulant fever*—and chills, sweating, headache, myalgia, and weight loss. The disease in humans has been given a variety of other names, including *Bang's disease,* after microbiologist

---

## BENEFICIAL MICROBES

### NEW VESSELS MADE FROM SCRATCH?

▲ **Bartonella.** LM  10 μm

*Bartonella henselae* causes cat scratch disease in part by being able to live inside human red blood cells as well as in cells lining blood vessels. Scientists at Beth Israel Deaconess Medical Center and the Harvard Medical School in Boston, Massachusetts, discovered recently that the bacterium triggers angiogenesis—the formation of new blood vessels—in infected tissues. Researchers speculate that the pathogen is increasing its food supply and habitat by stimulating the growth of new blood vessels.

How *Bartonella* manages to orchestrate angiogenesis is mysterious. We do know that the bacterium is more efficient in laboratory conditions than is vascular endothelial growth factor—the body's natural angiogenic cytokine. Perhaps it is more efficient in the body as well.

Scientists speculate that a full understanding of *Bartonella's* method could be harnessed to induce angiogenesis to circumvent blocked arteries in the heart, to prompt tissues to make new blood vessels in damaged limbs, or to speed up wound healing by increasing blood supply to damaged tissues. Investigators continue to probe the genetic basis of the intercellular communication between bacteria and host cells that allow this intriguing phenomenon. Perhaps in the future this pathogenic microbe will benefit patients with blood vessels grown from "scratch."

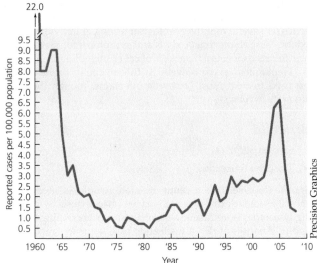

▲ **Figure 22** **The incidence of brucellosis in humans in the United States, 1971–2008.** The decline in cases is largely the result of improvements in livestock management.

▲ **Figure 23** Reported cases of pertussis in the United States, 1960–2008.

Bernhard Bang (1848–1932), who investigated the disease, and *Malta fever, rock fever of Gibraltar,* and *fever of Crete,* after localized epidemics in those locales.

Physicians treat brucellosis with doxycycline in combination with gentamycin, rifampin, or streptomycin. An attenuated vaccine for animals exists, but is not used in humans because the vaccine can cause disease. Through the vaccination of uninfected domesticated animals and the slaughter of infected ones, the threat of brucellosis has been reduced for U.S. residents (Figure 22).

### CRITICAL **THINKING**

Why do physicians substitute trimethoprim and sulfanilamide for tetracycline when treating children and pregnant women infected with *Brucella?*

## *Bordetella*

### Learning Objectives

✓ Describe five virulence factors of *Bordetella pertussis.*

✓ Identify the four phases of pertussis.

*Bordetella pertussis* (bōr-dĕ-tel′ă per-tus′is) is a small, aerobic, nonmotile, Gram-negative coccobacillus in the class Betaproteobacteria that is responsible for the disease **pertussis,**[4] commonly called *whooping cough. B. parapertussis* causes a milder form of pertussis.

### Pathogenesis, Epidemiology, and Disease

*Bordetella pertussis* causes disease by interfering with the action of ciliated epithelial cells of the trachea. Various adhesins and toxins mediate the disease.

The bacterium attaches to certain lipids in the cytoplasmic membranes of tracheal cells via two adhesins: *filamentous*

*hemagglutinin* and *pertussis toxin.* Filamentous hemagglutinin also binds to certain glycoproteins on the cytoplasmic membranes of neutrophils, initiating phagocytosis of the bacteria. *B. pertussis* survives within phagocytes, in the process evading the immune system. Pertussis toxin causes infected cells to produce more receptors for filamentous hemagglutinin, leading to further bacterial attachment and phagocytosis.

Four *B. pertussis* toxins are:

- *Pertussis toxin,* a portion of which interferes with the ciliated epithelial cell's metabolism, resulting in increased mucus production. (Note that pertussis toxin is both an adhesin and a toxin.)

- *Adenylate cyclase toxin,* which triggers increased mucus production and inhibits leukocyte movement, endocytosis, and killing. This function may provide protection for the bacterium early in an infection.

- *Dermonecrotic toxin,* which causes localized constriction and hemorrhage of blood vessels, resulting in cell death and tissue destruction.

- *Tracheal cytotoxin,* which at low concentrations inhibits the movement of cilia on ciliated respiratory cells, and at high concentrations causes the expulsion of the cells from the lining of the trachea.

Pertussis is considered a pediatric disease, as most cases are reported in children younger than five years old. More than 60 million children worldwide suffer from pertussis each year. There were over 10,000 reported cases in the United States in 2008 (Figure 23). However, these figures may considerably underestimate the actual number of cases, because patients with chronic coughs are not routinely tested for infection with *Bordetella,* and

---

[4]From Latin *per,* meaning intensive, and *tussis,* meaning cough.

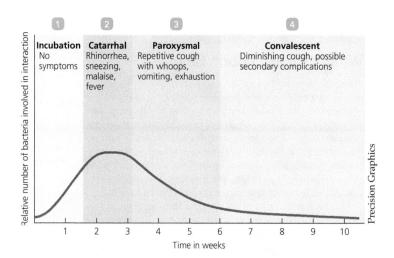

▲ **Figure 24** *Bordetella pertussis.* The bacteria attach to and infect ciliated epithelial cells, such as these of the trachea, eventually causing the death of the cells.

▲ **Figure 25** **The approximate time course for the progression of pertussis.**

because the disease in older children and adults is typically less severe and is frequently misdiagnosed as a cold or influenza.

Pertussis begins when bacteria, inhaled in aerosols, attach to and multiply in ciliated epithelial cells (Figure 24). Pertussis then progresses through four stages (Figure 25):

① During 7–10 days of **incubation** the bacteria multiply, but no symptoms are apparent.

② The **catarrhal**[5] (kă-tă′răl) **phase** is characterized by signs and symptoms that resemble a common cold. During this phase, which lasts one to two weeks, the bacteria are most abundant and the patient is most infectious.

③ The **paroxysmal**[6] (par-ok-siz′mal) **phase** begins as the ciliary action of the tracheal cells is impaired, even as copious mucus is secreted. The condition worsens as ciliated cells are expelled. To clear the accumulating mucus, the body initiates a series of deep coughs, each of which is followed by a characteristic "whoop" caused by the intake of air through the congested trachea. Each day a patient may experience 40–50 coughing spells that often end with vomiting and exhaustion. During this phase, which can last two to four weeks, coughing may be so severe that oxygen exchange is limited, such that the patient may turn blue or even die. Severe coughing breaks ribs of some patients.

④ During the **convalescent phase,** the number of bacteria present becomes quite small, the ciliated lining of the trachea grows back, and the severity and frequency of coughing diminishes. During this phase, which typically lasts three to four weeks or longer, secondary bacterial infections (such as with *Staphylococcus* or *Streptococcus*) in

the damaged epithelium may lead to bacteremia, pneumonia, seizures, and encephalopathy.

### Diagnosis, Treatment, and Prevention

The symptoms of pertussis are usually diagnostic, particularly when a patient is known to have been exposed to *Bordetella*. Even though health care workers can isolate *B. pertussis* from respiratory specimens, the bacterium is extremely sensitive to desiccation, so specimens must be inoculated at the patient's bedside onto *Bordet-Gengou* medium, which is specially designed to support the growth of this bacterium. If this is not practical, clinicians must use special transport media to get a specimen to a laboratory.

Treatment for pertussis is primarily supportive. By the time the disease is recognized, the immune system has often already "won the battle." Recovery depends on regeneration of the tracheal epithelium, not reduction of the number of bacteria; therefore, although antibacterial drugs reduce the number of bacteria and the patient's infectivity to others, they have little effect on the course of the disease.

Given that *B. pertussis* has no animal or environmental reservoir, and that effective vaccines (the P of DTaP and of Tdap) are available, whooping cough could be eradicated. Despite this possibility, over 10,000 cases occur each year in the United States. This is partly due to the refusal of parents to immunize their children and partly due to the fact that immunity, whether acquired artificially or naturally, lasts only about 10 years. The CDC urges parents to immunize their children and now recommends that all adults under age 65 receive one dose of acellular pertussis vaccine.

## *Burkholderia*

### Learning Objective

✓ Describe the advantageous metabolic features of *Burkholderia* as well as its pathogenicity.

---

[5]From Greek *katarrheo*, meaning to flow down.
[6]From Greek *paroxysmos*, meaning to irritate.

## When "Health Food" Isn't

In a single day, two 19-year-old women and one 20-year-old man sought treatment at a university health clinic, complaining of acute diarrhea, nausea, and vomiting. No blood was found in their stools. One of the women was found to have a urinary tract infection. All three had eaten lunch at a nearby health food store the previous day. The man had a turkey sandwich with tomato, sprouts, pickles, and sunflower seeds. One woman had a pocket sandwich with turkey, sprouts, and mandarin oranges; the other woman had the lunch special, described in the menu as a "delightful garden salad of fresh organic lettuces, sprouts, tomatoes, and cucumbers with zesty raspberry vinaigrette dressing." All had bottled water to drink.

1. Which of the foods is the most likely source of the infections?
2. What media would you use to culture and isolate enteric contaminants in the food?
3. Which enteric bacteria could cause these symptoms?
4. How did the woman likely acquire the urinary tract infection?
5. What is the likely treatment of choice?
6. What steps can the food store's manager and the students take to reduce the chance of subsequent infections?

*Burkholderia cepacia* (burk-hol-der'ē-ă se-pā'se-ă) is soil-dwelling, aerobic, flagellated betaproteobacterium. *Burkholderia* is noteworthy for its ability to decompose a broad range of organic molecules, making it a likely bacterium to assist in the cleanup of contaminated environmental sites. For example, *Burkholderia* is capable of digesting polychlorinated biphenyls (PCBs) and Agent Orange—an herbicide used extensively during the Vietnam War—which persist for long periods in the environment. Further, farmers can use *Burkholderia* to reduce the number of fungal infections of many plant crops, including peas, beans, alfalfa, canola, and cucumbers.

Unfortunately, *Burkholderia* can also grow in health care settings, metabolizing a variety of organic chemicals and resisting many antimicrobial drugs. The bacterium is one of the more important opportunistic pathogens of the lungs of cystic fibrosis patients, in whom it metabolizes the copious mucous secretions in the lungs. Evidence for patient-to-patient spread is clear, making it imperative that infected cystic fibrosis patients avoid contact with uninfected patients. Physicians treat *Burkholderia* infections with beta-lactams (penicillin, ceftriaxone, and aztreonam) and doxycycline.

Another soil-dwelling species, *Burkholderia pseudomallei* (soo-dō-mal'e-ē), causes *melioidosis* (mel'ē-oy-dō'sis), which is an Asian and Australian tropical disease that is emerging as a threat in other locales (see **Emerging Diseases: Melioidosis**). The CDC considers *B. pseudomallei* a potential agent of biological terrorism.

# Pseudomonads

## Learning Objectives

✓ Reconcile the apparent discrepancy between the ubiquitous distribution of pseudomonads with numerous virulence factors and the fact they cause so few diseases.

✓ Identify three genera of opportunistic pathogenic pseudomonads.

✓ Describe *Pseudomonas aeruginosa* as an opportunistic pathogen of burn victims and cystic fibrosis patients.

**Pseudomonads** (soo-dō-mō'nadz) are Gram-negative, aerobic bacilli in the class Gammaproteobacteria. Unlike the fastidious members of *Bartonella, Brucella,* and *Bordetella,* pseudomonads are not particular about their growth requirements. They are ubiquitous in soil, decaying organic matter, and almost every moist environment, including swimming pools, hot tubs, washcloths, and contact lens solutions. In hospitals they are frequently found growing in moist food, vases of cut flowers, sinks, sponges, toilets, floor mops, dialysis machines, respirators, humidifiers, and in disinfectant solutions. Some species can even grow using trace nutrients in distilled water. Pseudomonads utilize a wide range of organic carbon and nitrogen sources. The Entner-Doudoroff pathway is their major means of glucose catabolism rather than the more common Embden-Meyerhof pathway of glycolysis.

Here we examine three genera that are commonly isolated opportunistic pathogens—*Pseudomonas, Moraxella,* and *Acinetobacter*—beginning with the species of greatest medical importance: *Pseudomonas aeruginosa*.

### *Pseudomonas aeruginosa*

*Pseudomonas aeruginosa* (soo-dō-mō' nas ā-roo-ji-nō'să) is somewhat of a medical puzzle in that even though it expresses a wide range of virulence factors, it rarely causes disease. This is fortunate because its ubiquity and inherent resistance to a wide range of antimicrobial agents would render a more virulent *Pseudomonas* a formidable challenge to health care professionals. That *P. aeruginosa* is *only* an opportunistic pathogen is testimony to the vital importance of the body's protective tissues, cells, and chemical defenses.

*P. aeruginosa* has fimbriae and other adhesins that enable its attachment to host cells. The fimbriae are similar in structure to those of *N. gonorrhoeae*. The bacterial enzyme *neuraminidase* modifies the fimbriae receptors on a host cell in such a way that attachment of fimbriae is enhanced. A mucoid polysaccharide capsule also plays a role in attachment, particularly in the respiratory system of cystic fibrosis patients (as discussed shortly). The capsule also shields the bacterium from phagocytosis.

*P. aeruginosa* synthesizes other virulence factors, including toxins and enzymes. Lipid A (endotoxin) is prevalent in the cell wall of *Pseudomonas* and mediates fever, vasodilation, inflammation, shock, and other symptoms. Two toxins—*exotoxin A* and *exoenzyme S*—inhibit protein synthesis in eukaryotic cells, contributing to cell death and interfering with phagocytic killing. The enzyme *elastase* breaks down elastic fibers, degrades complement components, and cleaves IgA and IgG. The bacterium also produces a blue-green pigment, called *pyocyanin,* that triggers the formation of superoxide radical ($O_2^-$) and peroxide anion ($O_2^{2-}$), two reactive forms of oxygen that contribute to tissue damage in *Pseudomonas* infections.

Although a natural inhabitant of bodies of water and moist soil, *P. aeruginosa* is rarely part of the normal human microbiota. Nevertheless, because of its ubiquity and its virulence factors, this opportunistic pathogen colonizes immunocompromised patients and is involved in about 10% of nosocomial infections. Once it breaches the skin or mucous membranes, *P. aeruginosa* can successfully colonize almost any organ or system. It can be involved in urinary, ear, eye, central nervous system, gastrointestinal, muscle, skeletal, and cardiovascular infections. Infections in burn victims and cystic fibrosis patients are so common they deserve special mention.

*Pseudomonas* infections of severe burns are pervasive (Figure 26). The surface of a burned area provides a warm, moist environment, that is quickly colonized by this ubiquitous opportunist; almost two-thirds of burn victims develop environmental or nosocomial *Pseudomonas* infections.

*P. aeruginosa* also typically infects the lungs of cystic fibrosis patients, forming a biofilm that protects the bacteria from phagocytes. Such infections exacerbate the decline in pulmonary function in these patients by causing certain lung cells to synthesize large amounts of mucus. As the bacteria feed on the mucus, they signal host cells to secrete more of it, creating a positive feedback loop; the result of such *P. aeruginosa* infections

Leonard J. Morse

▲ **Figure 26** A *Pseudomonas aeruginosa* infection.
Bacteria growing under the bandages of this burn victim produce the green color. *What chemical is responsible for the blue-green appearance of this infection?*

**Figure 26** *Pyocyanin, a blue-green pigment secreted by P. aeruginosa, produces the color.*

is that cystic fibrosis patients are more likely to require hospitalization and more likely to die.

Diagnosis of *Pseudomonas* infection is not always easy because its presence in a culture may represent contamination acquired during collection, transport, or inoculation. Certainly,

Tetra Images/SuperStock

## EMERGING DISEASES

### MELIOIDOSIS

Isabella felt lucky. How many community college students had the opportunity to help a professor do research in northern Australia's Kakadu National Park for a month, get college credit for the experience, and not have to pay for the trip? Though she was the oldest person on the trip and often felt her 45 years as they hiked the trails, she didn't complain. Of course things would have been better if it didn't seem to rain all the time in Australia and if the thorns didn't tear at her legs quite so regularly; still, the trip was an adventure.

A week after her return to Houston, Texas, Isabella developed a high fever (39.2°C) and general weakness. All other signs, including the results of blood work, appeared normal. The doctors, suspecting flu, told her to get plenty of rest and sent her home. Two days later Isabella was intermittently drowsy and confused, her breathing was labored, and a small cut on her leg was an inflamed, pus-filled lesion. She was admitted to the hospital and died the next day.

She died of melioidosis, an emerging disease caused by a Gram-negative bacterium, *Burkholderia pseudomallei*, which is endemic to the tropics of Southeast Asia and which appears to be spreading into more moderate climes. Isabella had been infected either via inhalation or through a cut on her leg. Even with treatment, nearly 50% of melioidosis patients die, including Isabella.

Precision Graphics

**(MM)** Track melioidiosis online by going to the Study Area at www.masteringmicrobiology.com.

## BENEFICIAL MICROBES

### WHEN A BACTERIAL INFECTION IS A GOOD THING

▲ *Bdellovibrio* (pink) attacks *E. coli* (blue).

SEM · 2 µm

Gram-negative bacteria are common opportunistic and nosocomial pathogens of the cardiovascular system, producing bacteremia, toxemia, endocarditis, and other serious conditions. However, Gram-negative bacteria can themselves be the target of bacterial pathogens, specifically cells of *Bdellovibrio* (del-ō-vib'rē-ō) and *Micavibrio* (mī-kă-vib'rē-ō). These Gram-negative predators are voracious devourers of other Gram-negative bacteria; in fact, their Gram-negative cousins are their only diet!

*Bdellovibrio* latches onto a Gram-negative bacterium such as *Escherichia coli* or the hard-to-treat *Pseudomonas aeruginosa*, enters its prey's periplasm, digests its host, feasts, replicates, and lyses its victim. *Bdellovibrio* daughters quickly attack other cells, reducing the victim's population a hundredfold in short order.

*Micavibrio* also attaches to its victim's outer membrane, but it remains outside the cell, replicating by binary fission while literally sucking the life (and cytoplasm) from its target. The predators can attack both free-swimming and biofilm-associated Gram-negative bacteria.

Scientists hope to identify, isolate, and utilize the unusual enzymes that allow *Bdellovibrio* and *Micavibrio* to exclusively attach to and kill Gram-negative bacteria. Alternatively, researchers are considering using the bacterial predators as living antimicrobial poultices on skin or wound infections or as living, intravenous, antimicrobial treatments for cardiovascular infections—a patient would be infected to get rid of an infection.

---

pyocyanin discoloration of tissues is indicative of massive infection.

Treatment of *P. aeruginosa* is also frustrating. The bacterium is notoriously resistant to a wide range of antibacterial agents, including antimicrobial drugs, soaps, antibacterial dyes, and quaternary ammonium disinfectants. In fact, *Pseudomonas* has been reported to live in solutions of antibacterial drugs and disinfectants.

Resistance of the bacterium is due to the ability of *Pseudomonas* to metabolize many drugs, to the presence of non-specific proton/drug antiports that pump some types of drugs out of the bacterium, and to the ability of *Pseudomonas* to form biofilms, which resist the penetration of antibacterial drugs and detergents. Physicians treat infections with combinations of aminoglycoside, beta-lactam, and fluoroquinolone antimicrobials that have first proven efficacious against a particular isolate in a susceptibility test. Polymyxin, a drug that is also toxic to humans, is used sometimes as a last resort.

In summary, though *Pseudomonas aeruginosa* is ubiquitous and possesses a number of virulence factors, the bacterium rarely causes disease in healthy individuals because it cannot normally penetrate the skin and mucous membranes, nor ultimately evade the body's other defenses. Only in debilitated patients does this opportunist thrive.

### Moraxella and Acinetobacter

*Moraxella* (mōr'ak-sel'ă) and *Acinetobacter* (as-i-nē'tō-bak'ter) are aerobic, short, plump bacilli that formerly were classified in the same family as *Neisseria*. Analysis of rRNA has shown that they are more properly classified as pseudomonads.

*Moraxella catarrhalis* (kā-tah'răl-is, formerly *Branhamella catarrhalis*) is rarely pathogenic but can cause opportunistic infections of the sinuses, bronchi, ears, and lungs. The bacterium is susceptible to cephalosporins, erythromycin, tetracycline, and most other antibacterial drugs (with the exception of beta-lactams).

*Acinetobacter* grows in soil, water, and sewage and is only rarely associated with disease in humans, though it is often isolated from clinical specimens. It is an opportunistic pathogen that causes infections of the respiratory, urinary, and central nervous systems. Endocarditis and septicemia have also been reported in infections with *Acinetobacter*. It is often resistant to antimicrobial drugs, so susceptibility tests must guide the choice of an effective treatment.

### *Francisella*

#### Learning Objectives

✓ Describe the modes of transmission of *Francisella tularensis*.

✓ List practical measures that can be taken to prevent infection by *F. tularensis*.

*Francisella tularensis*[7] (fran'si-sel'lă too-lă-ren'sis) is a very small (0.2 µm × 0.2–0.7 µm), nonmotile, strictly aerobic, Gram-negative

---

[7]Named for Tulare County, California.

## THE MYSTERY ON MARTHA'S VINEYARD

Martha's Vineyard, an island near Cape Cod, Massachusetts, is well known as a vacation destination for wealthy New Englanders. But in recent years, it has also caught the attention of the CDC, owing to mysterious outbreaks of tularemia that occur on the island in the summer.

Of special interest to the CDC was the observation that landscape workers seemed to be especially susceptible to contracting the disease, leading to speculation that the use of lawn mowers

or other brush-cutting equipment may be releasing contaminated dust, soil, or grass into the air. Some wonder if mowing over grass that contains the contaminated feces of skunks or raccoons, or perhaps mowing over the bodies of dead infected rabbits, may be causing *F. tularensis* to become airborne. Others theorize that mosquitoes or another insect could be implicated in the spread of the disease. To date, no definitive answers have been found.

Russell Enscore, CDC

coccobacillus of the class Gammaproteobacteria that causes a zoonotic disease called **tularemia** (too-lă-rē′mē-ă). *F. tularensis* has a capsule that discourages (by unknown mechanisms) phagocytosis and intracellular digestion.

*F. tularensis* is found in temperate regions of the Northern Hemisphere living in water and as an intracellular parasite of animals and amoebae. Scientists do not know why it is not found below the equator. *Francisella* has an amazingly diverse assortment of hosts. It lives in mammals, birds, fish, bloodsucking ticks and insects, and amoebae. Indeed, one is hard pressed to find an animal that cannot be its host. The most common reservoirs in the United States are rabbits, muskrats, and ticks, which give the disease two of its common names—*rabbit fever* and *tick fever*.

*Francisella* is also incredibly varied in the ways it can be spread among hosts. Tularemia in humans is most often acquired either through the bite of an infected tick or via contact with an infected animal. The bacterium, by virtue of its small size, can pass through apparently unbroken skin or mucous membranes. Bloodsucking flies, mosquitoes, mites, and ticks also transmit *Francisella*, and humans can be infected by consuming infected meat, drinking contaminated water, or inhaling bacteria in aerosols produced during slaughter or in a laboratory. Fortunately, human-to-human spread does not occur.

*Francisella* is one of the more infectious of all bacteria: Infection requires as few as 10 organisms when transmitted by a biting arthropod or through unbroken skin or mucous membranes. For example, only about 10 cells must be inhaled to cause disease, although consumption of $10^8$ cells in food or drink is necessary to contract the disease via the digestive tract.

Infections from bites, scratches, or through breaks in the skin cause lesions at the site of infection as well as swollen regional lymph nodes (buboes). Inhalation may produce buboes in the chest that put pressure on lungs and induce dry cough, pain during breathing, and death.

Only 106 cases were reported in 2008, but the actual number of infections was probably much higher considering its virulence, prevalence in animals, and multiple modes of transmission. Tularemia frequently remains unsuspected because its symptoms— fever, chills, headache, sore throat, muscle aches, and nausea—are not notably different from those of many other bacterial and viral diseases, and because it is difficult to confirm tularemia by using laboratory tests. Though it is typically innocuous, respiratory tularemia is fatal to more than 30% of untreated patients. Tularemia was removed from the list of nationally notifiable diseases in 1994, but concern about the possible use of *Francisella* by bioterrorists led officials in 2000 to relist it.

The bacterium produces beta-lactamase, so penicillins and cephalosporins are ineffective, but other antimicrobial drugs have been used successfully. Currently, streptomycin is recommended for use against *Francisella*. A vaccine made from less virulent strains provides protection for people at risk of exposure. The vaccine is not entirely effective but can lessen the severity of the disease.

To prevent infection, people should avoid the major reservoirs of *Francisella* (rabbits, muskrats, and ticks), especially in endemic areas. They can protect themselves from tick bites by wearing long clothing with tight-fitting sleeves, cuffs, and collars, and by using repellent chemicals. Because *Francisella* is not present in tick saliva, but only in its feces, prompt removal of ticks can mitigate infection. Hikers and hunters should never handle ill-appearing wild animals or their carcasses, and should wear gloves and masks when field dressing game. **Highlight: The Mystery on Martha's Vineyard** discusses recent tularemia outbreaks in Massachusetts.

### CRITICAL **THINKING**

Most U.S. cases of tularemia occur in the late spring and summer months, and few cases occur in January. Why might this be so?

Jim Feeley, CDC

▲ **Figure 27** *Legionella pneumophila* **growing on buffered charcoal yeast extract agar.** This bacterium cannot be grown in culture without such special media.

## *Legionella*

### Learning Objectives

✓ Explain why *Legionella pneumophila* was unknown before 1976.

✓ Describe the symptoms and treatment of Legionnaires' disease.

In 1976, celebration of the 200th anniversary of the Declaration of Independence was curtailed in Philadelphia when hundreds of American Legion members attending a convention were stricken with severe pneumonia; 29 died. After extensive epidemiological research, this disease—dubbed **Legionnaires' disease** or **legionellosis**—was found to be caused by a previously unknown pathogen, which was subsequently named *Legionella* (lē-jŭ-nel′lă).

### Pathogenesis, Epidemiology, and Disease

To date, scientists have identified over 40 species of *Legionella*. These aerobic, slender, pleomorphic bacteria in the class Gammaproteobacteria are extremely fastidious in their nutrient requirements, and laboratory media must be enhanced with iron salts and the amino acid cysteine. **Figure 27** shows colonies growing on one commonly used medium—buffered charcoal yeast extract agar. *Legionella* species are almost universal inhabitants of water, but they had not been isolated previously because they stain poorly and cannot grow on common laboratory media. Nineteen species are known to cause disease in humans, but 85% of all infections in humans are caused by *L. pneumophila*[8] (noo-mō′fi-lă).

*Legionella pneumophila* presented a conundrum for early investigators: How can such a fastidious bacterium be nearly ubiquitous in moist environmental samples? In the original

---

[8]From Greek *pneuma*, meaning breath, and *philos*, meaning love.

epidemic, for example, *Legionella* was cultured from condensation in hotel air conditioning ducts, an environment that seems unsuitable for a microorganism with such demanding nutritional requirements. Investigations revealed that *Legionella* living in the environment invade freshwater protozoa, typically amoebae, and reproduce inside phagocytic vesicles. Thus the bacteria survive in the environment much as they survive in humans—as intracellular parasites.

Protozoa release bacteria-filled vesicles into the environment; alternatively, *Legionella* forms exit pores through a host cell's vesicular membrane and then through its cytoplasmic membrane. Humans acquire the disease by inhaling *Legionella* in aerosols produced by showers, vaporizers, spa whirlpools, hot tubs, air conditioning systems, cooling towers, and grocery store misters. *Legionella* was not a notable pathogen until such devices provided a suitable means of transmitting the bacterium to humans.

Legionnaires' disease is characterized by fever, chills, a dry nonproductive cough, headache, and pneumonia. Complications involving the gastrointestinal tract, central nervous system, liver, and kidneys are common. If not promptly treated, pulmonary function rapidly decreases, resulting in death in 20% of patients with normal immunity. Mortality is much higher in immunocompromised individuals, particularly kidney and heart transplant recipients.

*L. pneumophila* also causes a flulike illness called *Pontiac fever* (after the Michigan city where it was first described). This disease has symptoms similar to those of Legionnaires' disease, but it does not involve pneumonia and is not fatal.

### Diagnosis, Treatment, and Prevention

Diagnosis is made by fluorescent antibody staining or other serological tests that reveal the presence of *Legionella* in clinical samples. The bacterium can also be cultured on suitable commercially available selective media such as buffered charcoal yeast extract.

Physicians use doxycycline, macrolides, or fluoroquinolones to treat Legionnaires' disease. Pontiac fever is self-limiting and requires no treatment.

Completely eliminating *Legionella* from water supplies is not feasible, as chlorination and heating are only moderately successful. However, the bacterium is not highly virulent, so reducing their number is typically a successful control measure.

## *Coxiella*

### Learning Objectives

✓ Explain how *Coxiella burnetii* survives desiccation.

✓ Describe the mode of transmission of Q fever.

*Coxiella burnetii* (kok-sē-el′ă ber-ne′tē-ē) is an extremely small, aerobic, obligate intracellular parasite (**Figure 28**) that grows and reproduces in the acidic environment within phagolysosomes. Its small size and dependence on the cytoplasm of eukaryotes for growth led early investigators to think it was a virus. However, its bacterial nature is unquestionable: It has a typical Gram-negative cell wall (albeit with minimal peptidoglycan), RNA and DNA (viruses typically have one or the other), functional ribosomes, and Krebs cycle enzymes. *Coxiella*

Moredun Animal Health Ltd./SPL/Photo
Researchers

1 µm

▲ **Figure 28** *Coxiella burnetii.* This intracellular pathogen grows and reproduces within phagolysosomes, here within one placental cell. An infective body of *Coxiella* can persist in the environment for years.

was originally classified with other obligate intracellular bacteria called *rickettsias*, but rRNA analysis reveals that *Coxiella* is more properly classified with *Legionella* in the class Gammaproteobacteria.

*Coxiella* forms an internal, stable, resistant *infective body* (sometimes called a spore) that is similar in structure and function to the endospores of some Gram-positive species. The infective body enables the bacterium to survive harsh environmental conditions (such as desiccation and heat) for years.

*C. burnetii* infects a wide range of mammalian and avian hosts and is transmitted among them by feeding ticks. Farm animals and pets are the reservoirs most often associated with disease in humans. Transmission to humans does not occur via feeding ticks; instead, humans are most frequently infected by inhaling infective bodies that become airborne when released from dried tick feces or from the dried urine, feces, or placentas of host animals. Humans can also become infected by consuming contaminated unpasteurized milk.

Most *Coxiella* infections are asymptomatic, though this bacterium can cause **Q fever,** so named because its cause was *questionable* (unknown) for many years. Q fever occurs worldwide, particularly among ranchers, veterinarians, and food handlers, and it may be either an acute or a chronic condition. Acute Q fever follows an incubation period of 20 days or more; besides a high fever, it involves severe headache, chills, muscle pain, and mild pneumonia. In chronic Q fever, months to years may pass from the time of infection until life-threatening endocarditis develops. Inflammation of the lungs and liver may occur simultaneously.

Q fever is diagnosed via serological testing. Oral doxycycline is the preferred antimicrobial. The biggest problem in treating Q fever is getting antimicrobial drugs to work in the acidic environment of phagolysosomes, where the bacteria live. Researchers have developed an effective vaccine for Q fever, but it is not available in the United States. Prevention involves avoiding the inhalation of dust contaminated with barnyard and pet wastes.

# Pathogenic, Gram-Negative, Anaerobic Bacilli

## Learning Objective

✓ Compare and contrast *Bacteroides* and *Prevotella* with one another, and with other Gram-negative opportunists.

Over 50 species of strictly anaerobic Gram-negative bacteria are known to colonize the human body. Indeed, such anaerobic bacteria are the predominant microbiota of the gastrointestinal, urinary, reproductive, and lower respiratory tracts—they outnumber aerobic and facultatively anaerobic bacteria by a factor of 100 or more. The abundance of anaerobic bacteria in these locations is important for human health: they inhibit the growth of most pathogens, and in the intestinal tract they synthesize vitamins and vitamin precursors and assist in the digestion of food.

Relatively few of these anaerobic normal microbiota cause disease, and then only when they are introduced into other parts of the body by trauma or surgery. Almost all of the opportunistic species are aerotolerant anaerobes; they produce catalase or superoxide dismutase, which are enzymes that inactivate hydrogen peroxide and superoxide radicals. The more important anaerobic opportunists are *Bacteroides* and *Prevotella*.

## Bacteroides

Bacteria in the genus *Bacteroides* (bak-ter-oy′dēz) are anaerobes that live as part of the normal microbiota of the intestinal tract and the upper respiratory tract. Being Gram-negative, they have an outer wall membrane containing lipopolysaccharide. However, in contrast to the lipid A of other Gram-negative bacteria discussed in this chapter, the lipid A formed by members of this genus has little endotoxin activity.

The most important pathogen in this genus is *Bacteroides fragilis* (fra′ji-lis). It is associated with about 85% of gastrointestinal diseases, even though it accounts for only about 1% of the bacteria in the colon. *B. fragilis* is a pleomorphic bacillus that produces a number of virulence factors. It attaches to host cells via fimbriae and a polysaccharide capsule, the latter of which also inhibits phagocytosis. Should the bacteria become phagocytized, short-chain fatty acids produced during anaerobic metabolism inhibit the activity of lysosomes, enabling the bacteria to survive within phagocytes.

*B. fragilis* is frequently involved in a variety of conditions, including abdominal infections (for example, those following a ruptured appendix), genital infections in females (for example, pelvic abscesses), and wound infections of the skin (which can result in life-threatening necrosis of muscle tissue). It is also involved in about 5% of all cases of bacteremia.

If anaerobic bacteria are to be isolated from patients, clinicians must maintain anaerobic conditions while collecting specimens, transporting them to the laboratory, and culturing them. Selective media are often used to reveal the presence of these bacteria. For example, because *B. fragilis* grows well in the presence of bile, it can be cultured on bile-esculin agar in an anaerobic environment—conditions which inhibit aerobic and most

www.troybio.com, BD Microbiology

▲ **Figure 29 Bacteroides fragilis.** The bacterium produces a black color on bile-esculin agar. Bile suppresses the growth of most aerobes and facultative anaerobes.

anaerobic bacteria (Figure 29). Metronidazole is the antimicrobial of choice for treating *Bacteroides* infections.

### Prevotella

Members of the genus *Prevotella* (prev′ō-tel′ă) are also anaerobic, Gram-negative bacilli. They differ from *Bacteroides* in that they are sensitive to bile; as a result, they do not grow in the intestinal tract, but are instead found in the urinary, genital, and respiratory tracts as part of the normal microbiota. Their virulence factors, including adhesive and antiphagocytic capsules and proteases that destroy antibodies, make them potential pathogens.

*Prevotella* is involved with other Gram-negative bacteria in about half of all sinus and ear infections and in almost all periodontal infections. Additionally, these bacteria cause gynecological infections such as pelvic inflammatory disease, pelvic abscesses, and endometriosis; brain abscesses; and abdominal infections.

Treatment of *Prevotella* infections involves surgical removal of infected tissue and the use of antimicrobial drugs.

## Chapter Summary

1. Lipid A in the outer membranes of Gram-negative bacteria can stimulate symptoms of fever, vasodilation, and shock, as well as blood clots throughout the body, a condition known as **disseminated intravascular coagulation (DIC).**

### Pathogenic Gram-Negative Cocci: *Neisseria*

1. *Neisseria* is a pathogenic, Gram-negative, oxidase-positive coccus; its virulence results from the presence of fimbriae, polysaccharide capsules, and lipooligosaccharide (containing lipid A) in its cell walls.

2. *Neisseria gonorrhoeae* causes **gonorrhea,** a sexually transmitted disease of humans. In men it results in acute inflammation of the urethra, whereas in women it is generally asymptomatic. It can infect the uterus and uterine tubes to cause **pelvic inflammatory disease (PID).**

3. *Neisseria meningitidis* causes a type of meningitis; the bacterium is transmitted on respiratory droplets and is life threatening when it enters the bloodstream or central nervous system. Blebbing by the bacterium can release a dangerous level of lipid A.

### Pathogenic, Gram-Negative, Facultatively Anaerobic Bacilli

1. Members of the **Enterobacteriaceae,** the **enteric bacteria,** can be pathogenic, are oxidase negative, reduce nitrate to nitrite, and ferment glucose anaerobically. Their outer membranes contain a lipopolysaccharide, contributing to their virulence. Many produce **siderophores,** which capture iron and make it available to the bacteria.
   **ANIMATIONS:** *Virulence Factors: Enteric Pathogens*

2. Pathogenic enteric bacteria are grouped as coliform opportunists, noncoliform opportunists, and true pathogens. **Coliforms** are found in the intestinal tracts of animals and humans.

3. *Escherichia coli* is the most common and most widely studied coliform. It causes gastroenteritis, non-nosocomial urinary tract infections, fatal hemorrhagic colitis, and hemolytic uremic syndrome.

4. *Klebsiella, Serratia, Enterobacter, Hafnia,* and *Citrobacter* are genera of coliform bacteria. *K. pneumoniae* causes a type of pneumonia. All are involved in nosocomial infections.

5. Noncoliform opportunistic pathogens of the family Enterobacteriaceae include *Proteus* (urinary tract infections) and *Morganella, Providencia,* and *Edwardsiella,* which can cause nosocomial infections in immunocompromised patients.

6. Truly pathogenic enteric bacteria include *Salmonella enterica,* which causes **salmonellosis,** a serious form of diarrhea. *S. enterica* serotypes Typhi and Paratyphi cause **typhoid fever.**

7. Members of the genus *Shigella* cause **shigellosis,** a severe form of diarrhea. **Shiga toxin,** secreted by some *Shigella,* arrests protein synthesis in host cells.

8. Two enteric species, *Yersinia enterocolitica* and *Y. pseudotuberculosis,* cause different degrees of intestinal distress; the virulent, nonenteric *Y. pestis* causes **bubonic plague** and **pneumonic plague** and has had a major historical impact.

9. Two genera in the family *Pasteurellaceae—Pasteurella* and *Haemophilus*—are significant human pathogens. They differ from enteric bacteria by being oxidase positive.

10. *Haemophilus influenzae* causes infantile meningitis, epiglottitis, arthritis, and inflammation of the skin. Widespread immunization with Hib vaccine has almost eliminated disease caused by this pathogen in the United States. *H. ducreyi* is responsible for a sexually transmitted lesion called chancroid.

## Pathogenic, Gram-Negative, Aerobic Bacilli

1. *Bartonella* includes pathogenic aerobic bacilli. *B. bacilliformis,* transmitted by sand flies, causes **bartonellosis.** *B. quintana,* transmitted by lice, causes five-day fever, or **trench fever.** *B. henselae,* transmitted through cat scratches, bites, and fleas, causes **cat scratch disease.**

2. *Brucella,* transmitted in unpasteurized contaminated milk, causes **brucellosis,** also known as Bang's disease, undulant fever, Malta fever, and other names.

3. *Bordetella pertussis* is responsible for **pertussis** (whooping cough), a pediatric disease in which the ciliated epithelial cells of the trachea are damaged. After **incubation,** the disease progresses through three additional phases: the **catarrhal phase** resembles a cold; in the **paroxysmal stage** the patient coughs deeply to expel copious mucus from the trachea; and in the **convalescent phase** the disease subsides, but secondary bacterial infections may ensue.

4. *Burkholderia* can decompose numerous environmental pollutants and can assist farmers by inhibiting fungal pathogens of plants; however, the bacterium also grows in the lungs of cystic fibrosis patients.

5. Pseudomonads are ubiquitous opportunistic pathogens. *Pseudomonas aeruginosa* is involved in many nosocomial infections and is common in burn victims and cystic fibrosis patients. *Moraxella* and *Acinetobacter* are opportunistic pathogenic pseudomonads that rarely cause disease.

6. **Tularemia** (rabbit fever or tick fever) is a zoonotic disease caused by extremely virulent *Francisella tularensis,* which is so small that it can pass through apparently unbroken skin.

7. **Legionnaires' disease** (legionellosis) and Pontiac fever are caused by *Legionella,* a bacterium transmitted in aerosols such as those produced by air conditioning systems.

8. *Coxiella burnetii* live in phagolysosomes of mammal and bird cells; its infective bodies are transmitted via aerosolized dried feces and urine to cause **Q fever.**

## Pathogenic, Gram-Negative, Anaerobic Bacilli

1. Gram-negative anaerobes—*Bacteroides* and *Prevotella*—are part of the normal microbiota of the intestinal, urinary, genital, and respiratory tracts.

2. Gram-negative anaerobes may cause disease as a result of virulence factors such as capsules, fimbriae, and proteases that degrade antibodies, particularly when the bacteria are introduced into novel sites in the body.

# Questions for Review  *Answers to the Questions for Review (except Short Answer questions) appear at the end of this chapter.*

## Multiple Choice

1. The presence of lipid A in the outer membranes of Gram-negative bacteria
   a. affects the formation of blood clots in the host.
   b. causes these bacteria to be oxidase positive.
   c. triggers the secretion of a protease enzyme to cleave IgA in mucus.
   d. enables enteric bacteria to ferment glucose anaerobically.

2. The only genus of Gram-negative cocci that causes significant disease in humans is
   a. *Pasteurella.*      c. *Klebsiella.*
   b. *Salmonella.*      d. *Neisseria.*

3. Which of the following bacterial cells is most likely to be virulent?
   a. a cell with fimbriae and LOS
   b. a cell with a polysaccharide capsule and lipooligosaccharide
   c. a cell with fimbriae, lipooligosaccharide, and a polysaccharide capsule
   d. a cell with fimbriae but no capsule

4. Which of the following statements is true?
   a. PID is a severe type of diarrhea in which infection spreads from the intestines to the bloodstream.
   b. PID can result from *Neisseria* infection.
   c. PID is more common in men than women.
   d. Members of the family Enterobacteriaceae usually cause PID.

5. A coliform bacterium that contaminates dairy products is
   a. *Bartonella.*      c. *Enterobacter.*
   b. *Serratia.*      d. *Proteus.*

6. Capsules of pathogenic enteric bacteria are virulence factors because they
   a. capture iron from hemoglobin and store it in the bacteria.
   b. release hemolysins that destroy red blood cells.
   c. produce fimbriae that enable the bacteria to attach to human cells.
   d. protect the bacteria from phagocytosis and from antibodies.

7. Which of the following bacteria might be responsible for the formation of petechiae in a host?
   a. *Neisseria meningitidis*      c. *Klebsiella*
   b. *Escherichia coli* O157:H7      d. *Proteus mirabilis*

8. The pathogen *Haemophilus influenzae* b causes
   a. meningitis in children.      c. endocarditis.
   b. upper respiratory flu.      d. genital chancroid.

9. Which of the following diseases is typically mild?
   a. Brazilian purpuric fever      c. pediatric meningitis
   b. bartonellosis      d. cat scratch disease

10. Which bacterium causes infections in many burn victims?
    a. *Moraxella catarrhalis*      c. *Escherichia coli*
    b. *Pseudomonas aeruginosa*      d. *Bartonella bacilliformis*

11. Which of the following statements is true of Q fever?
    a. For many years its cause was questionable.
    b. It was first described in 1976 during an outbreak in Quincy, Massachusetts.
    c. Researchers found it could be effectively treated with quinine.
    d. The sharp spikes of fever on patients' temperature charts resemble porcupine quills.

12. Which of the following is a bile-tolerant anaerobe?
    a. *Bacteroides*      c. *Shigella*
    b. *Escherichia*      d. *Prevotella*

349

## Matching

Match the bacteria with the disease (or symptoms) it causes.

1. ____ *Escherichia coli*
2. ____ *Klebsiella pneumoniae*
3. ____ *Proteus mirabilis*
4. ____ *Salmonella enterica* serotype Typhi
5. ____ *Shigella flexneri*
6. ____ *Yersinia pestis*

A. Bubonic plague
B. Typhoid fever
C. Gastroenteritis
D. Kidney stones
E. Purulent bloody stools, cramps, fever, and diarrhea
F. Pneumonia

## Labeling

Label the drawing below using these words: adhesin, exotoxin, H antigens, hemolysin, iron-binding protein, K antigens, lipid A, O antigen, fimbria, plasmid virulence genes, type III secretion system.

Kenneth Probst/Precision Graphics

## Short Answer

1. A physician prescribes fluid replacement to treat a patient with diarrhea. Although tests showed that a pathogenic enteric bacterium was the cause of the intestinal distress, why was an antimicrobial drug not prescribed?

2. Distinguish among the pathogenicity of coliforms, noncoliforms, and truly pathogenic enteric bacteria.

3. Why do nurses place antimicrobial agents in babies' eyes at birth?

4. Statistics show that meningococcal diseases are more frequent in college dormitories and military barracks than in the population at large. Suggest an explanation of this observation.

5. Why might an alcoholic be susceptible to pulmonary disease?

6. Name six factors that facilitate the production of disease by *Bordetella pertussis*.

7. Given that pseudomonads are present in almost every moist environment, why do they cause less disease than other, less prevalent Gram-negative bacteria?

8. Although an effective vaccine is available to eradicate pertussis in the United States, why has the number of reported cases increased since the 1970s?

9. What two illnesses can be caused by *Legionella pneumophila*?

10. What attribute of *Coxiella burnetii* enables it to survive desiccation and heat for an extended time?

11. What virulence factors allow Gram-negative anaerobes to cause disease?

12. What single biochemical test result distinguishes gammaproteobacteria in the family Enterobacteriaceae from gammaproteobacteria in the family Pasteurellaceae?

13. Describe transovarian transmission of a pathogen.

## Concept Mapping

Using the following terms, draw a concept map that describes *E. coli*. Or, complete this concept map online by going to the Study Area at www.masteringmicrobiology.com.

Blood
Bloody diarrhea
Cystitis
Enterotoxin
Gastroenteritis
Gram negative bacilli
Hemolytic uremic syndrome

Hemorrhagic colitis
Indicators of fecal contamination
Kidneys
Meninges
Meningitis
Normal intestinal microbiota

O157:H7
Pyelonephritis
Septicemia
Shiga-like toxin
Undercooked ground beef

Unpasteurized fruit juices
Unpasteurized milk
Urinary bladder
Water supplies

# Critical Thinking

1. A three-year-old boy complains to his day care worker that his head hurts. The worker calls the child's mother, who arrives 30 minutes later to pick up her son. She is concerned that he is now listless and unresponsive, so she drives straight to the hospital emergency room. Though the medical staff immediately treats the boy with penicillin, he dies—only four hours after initially complaining of a headache. What caused the boy's death? Were the day care workers or the hospital staff to blame for his death? What steps should be taken to protect the other children at the day care facility?

2. An epidemiologist notices a statistical difference in the fatality rates between cases of Gram-positive bacteremia treated with antimicrobial drugs and treated cases of Gram-negative bacteremia—that is, patients with Gram-positive bacteremia are much more likely to respond to treatment and survive. Explain one reason why this might be so.

3. In one summer month, local physicians reported 11 cases of severe diarrhea in infants less than three years of age. All the children lived in the same neighborhood and played in the same park, which has a wading pool. Cultures of stool specimens from the children revealed a Gram-negative bacillus that gave negative results for the following biochemical tests: oxidase, lactose, urease, and hydrogen sulfide production. The organism was also nonmotile. What is the organism? How was it transmitted among the children? What could officials do to limit infections of other children?

4. Several years ago, epidemiologists noted that the number of cases of salmonellosis increased dramatically in the summer and was lower the rest of the year. In contrast, the number of cases of typhoid fever, caused by the same bacterium, was constant throughout the year. Explain these observations.

5. Most physicians maintain that the viral "stomach flu" is really a bacterial infection. Which genera of bacteria discussed in this chapter are good candidates for causing this disease?

6. A hunter reports to his physician that he has been suffering with fever, chills, malaise, and fatigue. What Gram-negative bacteria may be causing his symptoms? How can a laboratory scientist distinguish among these species?

7. Ear piercings resulted in a rash of infections in teenagers, all of whom reported having their ears pierced at a kiosk in a local mall. What bacterial species might be responsible? Investigators traced the infections to a bacterium living in a bottle of disinfectant and in a sink used by employees. What bacterium is the likely agent? Why was successful treatment difficult?

8. A 21-month-old child was admitted into the hospital with fever, severe abdominal cramps, and bloody diarrhea. The family revealed they had purchased an iguana one month previously and the child had helped clean the cage. What bacterium was the likely cause of diarrhea? What was the possible treatment? How could the family prevent a recurrence?

Access more review material online in the Study Area at **www.masteringmicrobiology.com.** There, you'll find
- **Animations**
- **Concept Mapping Activities**
- **Flashcards**
- **Quizzes**

and more to help you succeed.

# Answers

Answers to multiple-choice, fill-in-blank, labeling, matching, and true/false questions are listed here. Answers for Short Answer and Critical Thinking questions are available for instructors only in the Instructor's Manual that accompanies this text.

**Multiple Choice**
1. a; 2. d; 3. c; 4. b; 5. c; 6. d; 7. a; 8. a; 9. d; 10. b; 11. a; 12. a

**Matching**
1. C; 2. F; 3. D; 4. B; 5. E; 6. A

**Labeling**
See Figure 8.

# Rickettsias, Chlamydias, Spirochetes, and Vibrios

From Chapter 21 of *Microbiology with Diseases by Taxonomy*, Third Edition. Robert W. Bauman. Copyright © 2011 by Pearson Education, Inc. Published by Benjamin Cummings, Inc. All rights reserved.

# Rickettsias, Chlamydias, Spirochetes, and Vibrios

Two days after consuming raw oysters at a cocktail party, a 40-year-old man is admitted to the hospital with a 105°F fever, nausea, myalgia (muscle pain), and circular lesions on his right leg. As part of his medical history he reveals that he consumes more than six bottles of beer a day. The hospital's diagnosis is an infection with *Vibrio vulnificus*, a bacterium that can cause septicemia (blood poisoning), particularly in individuals who are immunocompromised or have liver disease. Within 24 hours of the diagnosis, the man goes into septic shock and dies. Investigations reveal that he had a preexisting alcohol-related liver disease, and that the source of his infection was contaminated oysters.

*V. vulnificus* is a Gram-negative bacterium, but in some ways an atypical one: It has a slightly curved shape and differs metabolically from other flagellated enteric bacteria. In this chapter we focus on pathogenic Gram-negative bacteria that differ in some way from most other Gram-negative bacteria: the rickettsias, chlamydias, spirochetes, and vibrios.

 **Take the pre-test for this chapter online. Visit the Study Area at www.masteringmicrobiology.com.**

▲ The slightly curved rods of *Vibrio vulnificus* can cause severe disease or death.

We explored the more important pathogenic Gram-negative cocci and bacilli. But a number of bacteria that stain pink in a Gram stain differ from typical Gram-negative organisms in morphology, growth habit, or reproductive strategy. We examined one such group, the wall-less mycoplasmas, which are low G + C, Gram-positive bacteria that stain pink. Other unusual pathogens include the obligate intracellular rickettsias and chlamydias, the spiral-shaped spirochetes, and the slightly curved vibrios. Because of their unique features, these bacteria have traditionally been discussed separately—a tradition we continue here, beginning with the rickettsias.

# Rickettsias

**Rickettsias** (ri-ket′sē-ăz) are tiny, Gram-negative, obligate intracellular parasites that synthesize only a small amount of peptidoglycan and thus appear almost wall-less. The group as a whole is named after the most common genus of them (*Rickettsia*), named for Howard Ricketts (1871–1910), who first identified rickettsias and described the transmission of one species via its tick vector. Rickettsias are extremely small (0.3 μm × 1.0 μm); in fact, they are not much bigger than a large virus. Because of their small size, rickettsias were originally considered viruses, but closer examination has revealed that they contain both DNA and RNA, functional ribosomes, and Krebs cycle enzymes, and that they reproduce via binary fission—all characteristics of cells, not viruses.

Researchers have proposed several hypotheses to explain why rickettsias are obligate parasites, even though they have functional genes for protein synthesis, ATP production, and reproduction. Primary among these hypotheses is that rickettsias have very "leaky" cytoplasmic membranes and lose small cofactors (such as NAD$^+$) unless they are in an environment that contains an equivalent amount of these cofactors—such as the cytosol of a host cell.

Scientists classify rickettsias in the class Alphaproteobacteria of the bacterial phylum Proteobacteria based on the sequence of nucleotides in their rRNA molecules. Four genera of rickettsias—*Rickettsia, Orientia, Ehrlichia,* and *Anaplasma*—cause diseases in humans. We begin our discussion with *Rickettsia.*

## *Rickettsia*

### Learning Objectives

✓ List three species of *Rickettsia* that are responsible for human infections and identify their vectors.

✓ Describe the rash and petechiae of Rocky Mountain spotted fever (RMSF).

✓ Explain the relationship between epidemic typhus and Brill-Zinsser disease.

*Rickettsia* is a genus of nonmotile, aerobic, intracellular parasites that live in the cytosol of their host cells. They possess minimal cell walls of peptidoglycan and an outer membrane of lipopolysaccharide, which has little endotoxin activity. A loosely organized slime layer surrounds each cell. Rickettsias do not react well to the Gram stain, coloring only lightly pink,

J. L. Carson/Custom Medical Stock Photo LM | 20 μm

▲ **Figure 1 H and E stained *Rickettsia rickettsii.*** Rickettsias are intracellular parasites, here stained bright pink in cells lining kidney blood vessels.

so scientists use special staining procedures such as *hematoxylin and eosin (H and E)* stain to visualize them (Figure 1). Most human infections are by three species: *Rickettsia rickettsii* (ri-ket′-sē-ē), *R. prowazekii* (prō-wă-ze′kē-ē), and *R. typhi* (tī′fē).

Arthropod vectors transmit all three species of *Rickettsia,* which enter host cells by stimulating endocytosis. Once inside a host cell, the microbes secrete an enzyme that digests the endosome membrane, releasing the bacteria into the cytosol. As a result, rickettsias avoid the lysis that would ensue if a lysosome had merged with the endosome.

The pathogens grow and reproduce slowly, producing daughter cells only every 8–12 hours. *R. rickettsii* and *R. typhi* are continually released via exocytosis from long cytoplasmic extensions of host cells. In contrast, *R. prowazekii* gradually fills the host cell until the host cell lyses, releasing the parasites.

Outside of its host's cells, *Rickettsia* is unstable and dies quickly; therefore, rickettsias require vectors for transmission from host to host. Each rickettsial species is transmitted by different vectors, which also act as hosts and reservoirs.

### *Rickettsia rickettsii*

*R. rickettsii* causes **Rocky Mountain spotted fever (RMSF),** the most severe and most reported rickettsial illness. Even though the earliest reports of RMSF came from the Rocky Mountain states, the disease is actually more prevalent in the Appalachian Mountains, Oklahoma, and the southeastern states (Figure 2). Hard ticks in the genus *Dermacentor* (der-mă-sen′ter) transmit *R. rickettsii* among humans and rodents. The latter act as reservoirs. Male ticks infect female ticks during mating. Female ticks transmit the bacteria to eggs forming in their ovaries—a process called *transovarian transmission.*

*R. rickettsii* is typically dormant in the salivary glands of the ticks, and only when the arachnids feed for several hours are

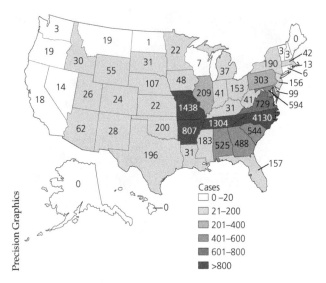

Cases
☐ 0–20
◻ 21–200
◻ 201–400
◻ 401–600
◼ 601–800
◼ >800

▲ **Figure 2** Incidence of Rocky Mountain spotted fever in the United States, 1999–2008.

Kenneth E. Greer/Visuals Unlimited

▲ **Figure 3**
The rash in a case of Rocky Mountain spotted fever.

the bacteria activated. Active bacteria are released from the tick's salivary glands into the mammalian host's circulatory system, where they infect endothelial cells lining small blood vessels. In rare cases, humans become infected following exposure to tissues and fluids from crushed ticks or to tick feces.

*R. rickettsii* secretes no toxins, and disease is not the product of the host's immune response. Apparently, damage to the blood vessels leads to leakage of plasma into the tissues, which may result in low blood pressure and insufficient nutrient and oxygen delivery to the body's organs.

About a week after infection, patients experience fever, headache, chills, muscle pain, nausea, and vomiting. In most cases (90%), a spotted, nonitchy rash develops on the trunk and appendages (Figure 3)—including the palms and soles, sites not involved in rashes caused by the chickenpox or measles viruses. In about 50% of patients, the rash develops into subcutaneous hemorrhages called *petechiae* (pe-tē'kē-ē). In severe cases, the respiratory, central nervous, gastrointestinal, and renal systems fail. Encephalitis may also occur, producing language disorders, delirium, convulsions, coma, and death. Even with treatment, almost 5% of patients die. Patients recovering from life-threatening acute Rocky Mountain spotted fever may experience paralysis of the legs, hearing loss, and gangrenous secondary infections with *Clostridium* (klos-trid'ē-ŭm) that necessitate the amputation of fingers, toes, arms, or legs.

Serological tests such as latex agglutination and fluorescent antibody stains are used to confirm an initial diagnosis based on sudden fever and headache following exposure to hard ticks, plus a rash on the soles or palms. Nucleic acid probes of specimens from rash lesions provide specific and accurate diagnosis, but such tests are expensive and typically are performed only by trained technicians in special laboratories. Early diagnosis is crucial because prompt treatment often makes the difference between recovery and death.

Physicians treat Rocky Mountain spotted fever by carefully removing the tick and prescribing doxycycline, tetracycline, or chloramphenicol. An effective vaccine is not available. Prevention of infection involves wearing tight-fitting clothing, using tick repellents, promptly removing attached ticks, and avoiding tick-infested areas, especially in spring and summer, when ticks are most voracious. It is impossible to eliminate the ticks in the wild, in part because they can survive without feeding for more than four years.

## CRITICAL **THINKING**

Why do most cases of Rocky Mountain spotted fever occur in May, June, and July?

### *Rickettsia prowazekii*

*Rickettsia prowazekii* causes **epidemic typhus,**[1] which is also called *louse-borne typhus* because it is vectored by the human body louse, *Pediculis humanus* (pĕ-dik'yu-lŭs hū-man'us). *R. prowazekii* kills lice within two to three weeks, which prevents transovarian transmission but allows sufficient time for lice to transmit the bacterium between humans. In contrast to other rickettsias, *R. prowazekii* has humans as its primary hosts.

Epidemic typhus occurs in crowded, unsanitary living conditions that favor the spread of body lice; it is endemic in Central and South America and in Africa. It can recur many years (even decades) following an initial episode. The recurrent disease (called *Brill-Zinsser*[2] *disease*) is mild, brief, and resembles murine typhus (discussed shortly).

Diagnosis is based on the observation of signs and symptoms—high fever, mental and physical depression, and a rash that lasts for about two weeks—following exposure to infected lice. Diagnosis must be confirmed by the demonstration of the bacterium in tissue samples using fluorescent antibody tests.

Epidemic typhus is treated with doxycycline, tetracycline, or chloramphenicol. Prevention involves controlling lice populations and maintaining good personal hygiene. An attenuated

[1]From Greek *typhos*, meaning stupor.
[2]After physician Nathan Brill and bacteriologist Hans Zinsser, who studied the condition.

vaccine against epidemic typhus is available for use in high-risk populations.

### Rickettsia typhi

*Rickettsia typhi* causes **murine**[3] (mū′rēn) **typhus,** which is so named because the major reservoir for the bacterium is rodents. The vectors for this disease, which is also known as *endemic typhus,* are fleas. The rat flea *Xenopsylla cheopis* (zen-op-sil′ă chē-op′is) and the cat flea *Ctenocephalides felis* (tē-nō-se-fal′idez fē′lis) (which also feeds on opossums, raccoons, and skunks) transmit the bacteria among the animal hosts and to humans. About 10 days following the bite of an infected flea, an abrupt fever, severe headache, chills, muscle pain, and nausea occur. A rash typically restricted to the chest and abdomen occurs in less than 50% of cases. The disease usually lasts about three weeks if left untreated and usually is not fatal.

Murine typhus is most often seen in the southern United States from Florida to California, and it is estimated that 50 cases occur annually, though the extent and incidence of the disease is not known because national notification requirements for murine typhus were discontinued in 1994. The disease is still endemic in every continent except Antarctica.

Diagnosis is initially based on signs and symptoms following exposure to fleas. An immunofluorescent antibody stain of a blood smear provides specific confirmation. Treatment is with tetracycline, doxycycline, or chloramphenicol. Prevention, as with other rickettsial diseases, involves avoiding bites by the arthropod vectors, wearing protective clothing, and using chemical repellents. No vaccine is available for murine typhus.

### Orientia tsutsugamushi

#### Learning Objective

✓ Identify the causative agent, vector, and reservoir of scrub typhus.

The rickettsial organism *Orientia tsutsugamushi* (ōr-ē-en′tē-ă tsoo-tsoo-gă-mū′shē) was formerly classified in the genus *Rickettsia,* but taxonomists now assign it to the new genus *Orientia.* It differs from *Rickettsia* by having significantly different rRNA nucleotide sequences, a thicker cell wall, and a minimal slime layer. Mites of the genus *Leptotrombidium* (lep′tō-trom-bid′-ē-ŭm), also known as red mites or chiggers, transmit *Orientia* among rodents and humans. Infected female mites transmit the bacterium to their offspring via transovarian transmission, and the offspring transmit it to a rodent or human while feeding. Because these arachnids feed on a host only once in their lives, an individual mite cannot transmit rickettsia directly from a rodent to a human. In addition to being the vector, mites are the only known reservoir of *Orientia.*

*O. tsutsugamushi* causes **scrub typhus,** a disease endemic to eastern Asia, Australia, and western Pacific islands, including Japan. It occurs in the United States among immigrants who arrived from endemic areas. Scrub typhus is characterized by

---

[3]From Latin *murinus,* meaning relating to mice.

fever, headache, and muscle pain, all of which develop about 11 days after a mite bite. Less than half of patients with scrub typhus also develop a spreading rash on their trunks and appendages. In a few cases, death results from failure of the heart and the central nervous system.

Scrub typhus is treated with tetracycline, doxycycline, or chloramphenicol. No vaccine is available. Prevention involves avoiding exposure to mites by wearing appropriate clothing and using repellent chemicals.

## Ehrlichia and Anaplasma

#### Learning Objectives

✓ Identify the diseases caused by *Ehrlichia* and *Anaplasma,* respectively.

✓ Identify the three developmental stages of *Ehrlichia* and *Anaplasma.*

✓ Discuss the difficulties in diagnosing ehrlichiosis and anaplasmosis.

*Ehrlichia chaffeensis* (er-lik′ē-ă chaf-ē-en′sis) and *Anaplasma phagocytophilum* (an-ă-plaz′mă fag-ō-sī-to′fil-ŭm, previously *E. equi,* ē′kwē) cause **human monocytic ehrlichiosis (HME)** and **anaplasmosis** (previously human granulocytic ehrlichiosis, HGE), respectively. These two diseases are considered *emerging diseases* in the United States because they were unknown before 1987, and the number of reported cases has increased from a few dozen per year in the 1980s to over 400 cases annually since 2005.

Ticks, including the Lone Star tick (*Amblyomma,* am-blē-ō′ma), the deer tick (*Ixodes,* ik-sō′dēz), and the dog tick (*Dermacentor),* transmit *Ehrlichia* and *Anaplasma* to humans. Once in the blood, each bacterium triggers its own phagocytosis by a white blood cell (either a monocyte or a neutrophil). Unlike *Rickettsia, Ehrlichia* and *Anaplasma* grow and reproduce within the host cell's phagosomes. Because the bacteria are killed if a phagosome fuses with a lysosome, the bacteria must somehow prevent fusion, but the mechanism is unknown. Inside a leukocyte the bacteria grow and reproduce through three developmental stages: an *elementary body,* an *initial body,* and a *morula* (Figure 4). The release of the cells from the morula and into the blood makes them available to feeding ticks.

HME and anaplasmosis resemble Rocky Mountain spotted fever but without the rash, which only rarely occurs in ehrlichiosis or anaplasmosis. *Leukopenia* (loo-kō-pē′nē-ă), which is an abnormally low leukocyte count, is also seen. Mortality of untreated HME is about 5%, and that of untreated anaplasmosis approaches 10%, especially in elderly patients.

Diagnosis of ehrlichiosis or anaplasmosis is difficult because the symptoms resemble those of other diseases. Physicians consider ehrlichiosis and anaplasmosis in any case of otherwise unexplained acute fever in patients exposed to ticks in endemic regions (Figure 5). Immunofluorescent antibodies against *Ehrlichia* or against *Anaplasma* can demonstrate the bacterium within blood cells, confirming the diagnosis.

Doxycycline and tetracycline are effective against both *Ehrlichia* and *Anaplasma* but chloramphenicol is not. Treatment

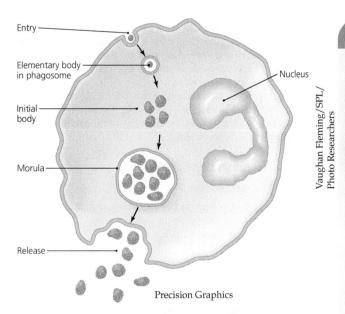

Entry

Elementary body
in phagosome

Initial
body

Morula

Release

Nucleus

Precision Graphics

▲ **Figure 4 The growth and reproduction cycle of *Ehrlichia* and *Anaplasma* in an infected leukocyte.** *If the rickettsia shown here is Ehrlichia chaffeensis, then what kind of leukocyte is it infecting?*

**Figure 4** *Ehrlichia chaffeensis infects human monocytes.*

should start immediately, even before the diagnosis is confirmed by serological testing, because the complications of infection and mortality rates increase when treatment is delayed. Prevention involves avoiding tick-infested areas, promptly removing ticks, wearing tight-fitting clothing, and using repellent chemicals. Vaccines against the two species are not available.

**Clinical Case Study: Blame It on the Chiggers?** describes an interesting human rickettsial infection, and Table 1 summarizes the rickettsial species, vectors, reservoirs, and diseases.

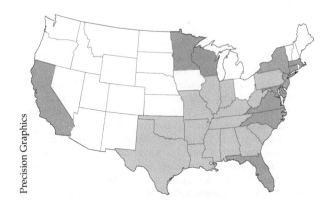

Precision Graphics

▲ **Figure 5 The geographical distribution of ehrlichiosis and anaplasmosis in the contiguous United States.** Blue indicates states where ehrlichiosis is endemic, orange where anaplasmosis is endemic, and purple where both diseases are endemic.

## Blame It on the Chiggers?

▲ *Chiggers (mites) embedded in feet.*

Vaughan Fleming/SPL/Photo Researchers

A 75-year-old man arrives one summer morning at the hospital with severe headache, chills, muscle pain, and nausea. He reports that the symptoms developed quite suddenly. He has had no rash. During the interview the man states that he is an immigrant from Poland, a survivor of a Nazi concentration camp, and an avid bird watcher who spends many hours in the woods near his home. He had not noticed any fleas, ticks, or lice on his body, but he had been "almost eaten alive by chiggers." He had not been out of the United States in 40 years.

1. What rickettsial diseases might the man have?
2. What are the vectors for these diseases?
3. What diagnostic test(s) might verify the initial diagnosis?
4. Is the man's life in danger?
5. What drug will the physician likely prescribe?

CRITICAL **THINKING**

Explain the derivation of the names of the diseases caused by *Ehrlichia*.

# Chlamydias

## Learning Objectives

✓ Describe the life cycle of chlamydias, including the two developmental forms.

✓ Discuss the term *energy parasite* as it relates to chlamydias.

**Chlamydias** are a group of bacteria that vie with rickettsias for the title "smallest bacterium." Like rickettsias, chlamydias are nonmotile and grow and multiply only within vesicles in host cells. Scientists once considered chlamydias to be viruses because of their small size, obligate intracellular lifestyle, and ability to pass through 0.45-μm pores in filters, which were thought to trap all cells. However, chlamydias are cellular and possess DNA, RNA, and functional 70S ribosomes. Each chlamydial cell is surrounded by two membranes, similar to a typical Gram-negative bacterium, but without peptidoglycan between the membranes—chlamydias lack cell walls. In contrast with rickettsias, chlamydias do not have arthropods as vectors or hosts. Because of their unusual features and unique rRNA nucleotide sequences, taxonomists now classify chlamydias in their own phylum: Chlamydiae.

▶ **Figure 6 Development of chlamydias. (a)** Elementary bodies and reticulate bodies, here of *Chlamydia*. **(b)** The life cycle of chlamydias. Times in parentheses refer to hours since infection.

(a)

Chlamydias have a unique developmental cycle involving two forms, both of which can occur within the endosome of a host cell (Figure 6a): tiny (0.2–0.4 μm) cocci called **elementary bodies (EBs)**, and larger (0.6–1.5 μm) pleomorphic **reticulate bodies (RBs)**. Elementary bodies are relatively dormant, resistant to environmental extremes, can survive outside cells, and are the infective forms. Reticulate bodies are noninfective, obligate intracellular forms that replicate via binary fission within phagosomes, where they survive by inhibiting the fusion of a lysosome with the phagosome. Chlamydias lack the metabolic enzymes needed to synthesize ATP, so they must depend on their host cells for the high-energy phosphate compounds they require; thus chlamydias have been called *energy parasites*.

In the life cycle of chlamydias (Figure 6b), once an EB attaches to a host cell (❶), it enters by triggering its own endocytosis (❷). Once inside the endosome, the EB converts into an RB (❸), which then divides rapidly into multiple RBs (❹). Once an infected endosome becomes filled with RBs, it is called an **inclusion body**. About 21 hours after infection, RBs within an inclusion body begin converting back to EBs (❺), and about 19 hours after that, the EBs are released from the host cell via exocytosis (❻), becoming available to infect new cells and completing the life cycle.

Three chlamydias cause disease in humans. In order of the prevalence with which they infect humans, they are *Chlamydia trachomatis*, *Chlamydophila pneumoniae*, and *Chlamydophila psittaci*. We begin our discussion with the most common species— *C. trachomatis*.

## *Chlamydia trachomatis*

### Learning Objectives

✓ List the types of cells in the human body that are most often infected by *Chlamydia*.

✓ Explain how sexually inactive children may become infected with *C. trachomatis*.

✓ Describe the cause and symptoms of lymphogranuloma venereum.

✓ Discuss the prevention of chlamydial infections.

*Chlamydia trachomatis* (kla-mid′ē-a tra-kō′ma-tis) has a very limited host range. One exceptional strain, which may eventually be classified as a separate species, causes pneumonia in mice, but all other strains are pathogens of humans.

### Pathogenesis and Epidemiology

*C. trachomatis* enters a human body through abrasions and lacerations and infects a limited array of cells—those that have receptors for elementary bodies, including cells of the conjunctiva and cells lining the mucous membranes of the trachea, bronchi, urethra, uterus, uterine (Fallopian) tubes, anus, and rectum. The clinical manifestations of chlamydial infection result from the

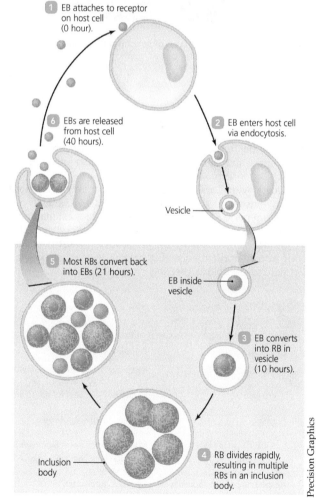

❶ EB attaches to receptor on host cell (0 hour).

❷ EB enters host cell via endocytosis.

❸ EB converts into RB in vesicle (10 hours).

❹ RB divides rapidly, resulting in multiple RBs in an inclusion body.

❺ Most RBs convert back into EBs (21 hours).

❻ EBs are released from host cell (40 hours).

Vesicle

EB inside vesicle

Inclusion body

(b)

359

M. A. Ansary/SPL/Photo Researchers

▲ **Figure 7  An advanced case of lymphogranuloma venereum in a man.** *Which microorganism causes lymphogranuloma venereum?*
**Figure 7** Chlamydia trachomatis.

destruction of infected cells at the site of infection, and from the inflammatory response this destruction stimulates. Reinfection in the same site by the same or a similar strain triggers a vigorous hypersensitive immune response that can result in blindness, sterility, or sexual dysfunction.

Infection with *C. trachomatis* is the most commonly reported sexually transmitted diseases in the United States; 1,093,514 cases were reported in 2008, but epidemiologists estimate that about 3.5 million asymptomatic cases go unreported annually. Sexually transmitted chlamydial infections are most prevalent among women under the age of 20 because they are physiologically more susceptible to infection.

Researchers further estimate that over 500 million people worldwide, particularly children, contract ocular infections with *C. trachomatis*. Children can be infected as they pass through the birth canal, and the pathogen can be transmitted from eye to eye via droplets, hands, contaminated fomites, or flies. Infected children also harbor the bacterium in their digestive and respiratory tracts, so the bacterium can be transmitted to other children or adults via fecal contamination and respiratory droplets. Chlamydial eye infections are endemic in crowded, poor communities where people have inadequate personal hygiene, inadequate sanitation, or inferior medical care, particularly in the Middle East, North Africa, and India.

### Diseases

The diseases caused by the various strains of *Chlamydia trachomatis* are of two main types: sexually transmitted diseases and an ocular disease called trachoma.

**Sexually Transmitted Diseases** A transient genital lesion and swollen, painfully inflamed, inguinal lymph nodes characterize **lymphogranuloma venereum**[4] (lim′fō-gran-ū-lō′mă ve-ne′rē-ŭm) (Figure 7), which is caused by the so-called *LGV strain* of *C. trachomatis*. The initial lesion of lymphogranuloma venereum occurs at the site of infection on the penis, urethra, scrotum, vulva, vagina, cervix, or rectum. This lesion is often overlooked because it is small, painless, and heals rapidly. Headache, muscle pain, and fever may also occur at this stage of the disease.

The second stage of the disease involves the development of buboes (swollen lymph nodes) associated with lymphatic vessels draining the site of infection. The buboes, which are accompanied by fever, chills, anorexia, and muscle pain, may enlarge to the point that they rupture, producing draining sores.

In a few cases, lymphogranuloma venereum proceeds to a third stage characterized by genital sores, constriction of the urethra, and genital elephantiasis. Arthritis may also occur during this third stage, particularly in young white males.

[4]From Latin *lympha*, meaning clear water; Latin *granulum*, meaning a small grain; Greek *oma*, meaning tumor (swelling); and Latin *Venus*, the goddess of sexual love.

**1**

## Characteristics of Rickettsias

| Organism | Primary Vectors | Reservoirs | Diseases |
|---|---|---|---|
| *R. rickettsii* | Hard ticks: wood tick (*Dermacentor andersoni*) and dog tick (*D. variabilis*) | Ticks, rodents | Rocky Mountain spotted fever (RMSF) |
| *R. prowazekii* | Human body louse (*Pediculus humanus*) | Humans, squirrels, squirrel fleas | Epidemic (louse-borne) typhus |
| *R. typhi* | Rat flea (*Xenopsylla cheopis*) and cat flea (*Ctenocephalides felis*) | Rodents | Murine (endemic) typhus |
| *Orientia tsutsugamushi* | Mite (chigger) (*Leptotrombidium* spp.) | Mites | Scrub typhus |
| *Ehrlichia* spp. | Hard tick: Lone Star tick (*Amblyomma americanum*) | Ticks | Human monocytic ehrlichiosis (HME) |
| *Anaplasma phagocytophilum* | Hard tick: *Ixodes* spp. | Ticks | Anaplasmosis |

TABLE

Western Ophthalmic Hospital/SPL/Photo Researchers

▲ **Figure 8** **An eyelid afflicted with trachoma.**

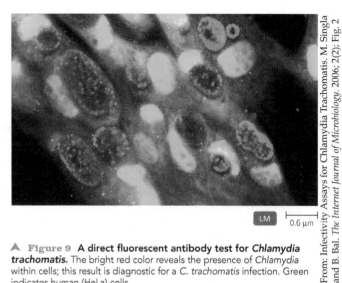

LM ⊢ 0.6 μm

From: Infectivity Assays for Chlamydia Trachomatis. M. Singla and B. Bal. *The Internet Journal of Microbiology.* 2006; 2(2); Fig. 2

▲ **Figure 9** **A direct fluorescent antibody test for *Chlamydia trachomatis.*** The bright red color reveals the presence of *Chlamydia* within cells; this result is diagnostic for a *C. trachomatis* infection. Green indicates human (HeLa) cells.

Although about 85% of genital tract infections in women are asymptomatic, more than 75% of infections in men have symptoms. Infected men also often have urethral inflammation, which cannot be distinguished from gonorrhea based on symptoms alone. Such chlamydial urethritis accounts for about 50% of cases of *nongonococcal urethritis.*

*Proctitis*[5] may occur in men and women as a result of lymphatic spread of the bacterium from the vagina, vulva, cervix, or urethra to the rectum. About 15% of the cases of proctitis in homosexual men result from the spread of *C. trachomatis* via anal intercourse.

An immune response against reinfections of *C. trachomatis* in women can have serious consequences, causing pelvic inflammatory disease. PID involves chronic pelvic pain; irreversible damage to the uterine tubes, uterus, and ovaries; and sterility.

**Trachoma** The so-called *trachoma strains* of *C. trachomatis* cause a disease of the eye called **trachoma** (trǎ-kō′mǎ; Figure 8), which is the leading cause of nontraumatic blindness in humans. The pathogen multiplies in cells of the conjunctiva and kills them, triggering a copious, purulent[6] (pus-filled) discharge that causes the conjunctiva to become scarred. Such scarring in turn causes the patient's eyelids to turn inward, such that the eyelashes abrade, irritate, and scar the cornea, triggering an invasion of blood vessels into this normally clear surface of the eye. A scarred cornea filled with blood vessels is no longer transparent, and the eventual result is blindness.

Trachoma is typically a disease of children who have been infected during birth. However, LGV strains of *C. trachomatis* may produce blindness by a similar process in adults when bacteria from the genitalia are introduced into the eyes via fomites or fingers.

[5]From Greek *proktos,* meaning rectum, and *itis,* meaning inflammation.
[6]From Latin *pur,* meaning pus.

## Diagnosis, Treatment, and Prevention

Diagnosis of chlamydial infection involves demonstration of bacteria inside cells from the site of infection. Specimens can be obtained from the urethra, vagina, or anus by inserting, rotating, and then removing a sterile swab. Giemsa-stained specimens may reveal bacteria or inclusion bodies within cells, but the most specific method of diagnosis involves amplifying the number of chlamydia by inoculating the specimen into a culture of susceptible cells. Laboratory technicians then demonstrate the presence of *Chlamydia* in the cell culture by means of specific fluorescent antibodies (Figure 9) or nucleic acid probes.

Physicians prescribe tetracycline or azithromycin for 21 days to eliminate genital infections of LGV strains of *C. trachomatis* in adults. Erythromycin or sulfonamides are recommended for treatment of pregnant women. Trachoma strains of *C. trachomatis* infecting the eyes of newborns are treated with erythromycin cream for 10–14 days, whereas ocular infections with LGV strains in adults are treated with doxycycline cream for 7 days. Surgical correction of eyelid deformities may prevent the abrasion, scarring, and blindness that typically result from ocular infections.

Prevention of sexually transmitted chlamydial infections is best achieved by abstinence or faithful mutual monogamy. Condoms may provide some protection, though some researchers warn that irritation by condoms and their lubricants actually increases the likelihood of infection. Blindness can be prevented only by prompt treatment with antibacterial agents and prevention of reinfection. Unfortunately, genital chlamydial infections are often asymptomatic and frequently occur among populations that have limited access to medical care.

### CRITICAL **THINKING**

Why is either erythromycin or sulfonamide substituted for doxycycline in treatment of chlamydial infections in children? Why are penicillins and cephalosporins useless against *Chlamydia*?

TABLE 2

## Characteristics of the Smallest Microbes

| Feature | Rickettsias | Chlamydias | Mycoplasmas | Viruses |
|---|---|---|---|---|
| Cellular structure | Small cells with little peptidoglycan in cell walls | Small, wall-less cells with two membranes | Small, wall-less, pleomorphic cells with sterol in cytoplasmic membranes | Acellular |
| Diameter | 0.3 μm | EBs: 0.2–0.4 μm<br>RBs: 0.6–1.5 μm | 0.1–0.3 μm | 0.01–0.3 μm |
| Lifestyle | Obligate intercellular parasites within cytosol | Obligate intercellular parasites within endosomes | Free-living | Obligate intercellular parasites within cytosol or nuclei |
| Replication | Binary fission | Binary fission of reticulate bodies | Binary fission | Chemical assembly |
| Nucleic acid(s) | Both DNA and RNA | Both DNA and RNA | Both DNA and RNA | DNA or RNA |
| Functional ribosomes | Present | Present | Present | Absent |
| Metabolism | Present | Present | Limited—lack Krebs cycle, electron transport chains, and enzymes for cell wall synthesis | Completely dependent on metabolic enzymes of host cell |
| ATP-generating system | Present | Absent | Present | Absent |
| Phylum | Proteobacteria | Chlamydiae | Firmicutes | None officially recognized |

## Chlamydophila pneumoniae

### Learning Objective

✓ Describe three diseases associated with *Chlamydophila pneumoniae*.

*Chlamydophila pneumoniae* (kla-mē-dof′ĭl-ă nū-mō′nē-ī) causes about 10% of U.S. cases of community-acquired pneumonia and 5% of the cases of bronchitis and sinusitis. Based primarily on circumstantial and epidemiological data, this chlamydia has also been implicated as a cause of some cases of atherosclerosis—lipid deposits on the walls of arteries, and the first stage of arteriosclerosis, or hardening of the arteries. Most infections with *Chlamydophila pneumoniae* are mild, producing only malaise and a chronic cough, and do not require hospitalization. Some cases, however, are characterized by the development of a severe pneumonia that cannot be distinguished from primary atypical pneumonia, which is caused by *Mycoplasma pneumoniae* (mī′kō-plaz-mă nū-mō′nē-ī).

Fluorescent antibodies demonstrate the intercellular presence of *C. pneumoniae,* which is diagnostic. Tetracycline or erythromycin for 14 days is used to treat infections of *C. pneumoniae,* but the drugs are not always effective, and infections may persist. Prevention of infection is difficult because the bacterium is ubiquitous and spreads via respiratory droplets.

## Chlamydophila psittaci

### Learning Objective

✓ Describe the diseases caused by *Chlamydophila psittaci.*

*Chlamydophila psittaci* (sit′ă-sē) causes **ornithosis**[7] (ōr-ni-thō′sis), a disease of birds that can be transmitted to humans, in whom it typically causes flulike symptoms. In some cases severe pneumonia occurs, and rarely nonrespiratory conditions such as endocarditis, hepatitis, arthritis, conjunctivitis, and encephalitis are observed. The disease is sometimes called *psittacosis* or *parrot fever* because it was first identified in parrots (*psitakos* means parrot in Greek). Several dozen cases of ornithosis are reported in the United States annually, often in adults. Most likely this disease is underreported because symptoms are often mild and diagnosis is difficult. Zookeepers, veterinarians, poultry farmers, pet shop workers, and owners of pet birds are at greatest risk of infection.

Elementary bodies of *Chlamydophila psittaci* may be inhaled in aerosolized bird feces or respiratory secretions, or ingested from fingers or fomites that have contacted infected birds. Pet birds may transmit the disease to humans via beak-to-mouth contact. Because very brief exposure to birds can be sufficient for the transmission of elementary bodies, some patients cannot recall having any contact with birds. Symptoms usually occur within 10 days of exposure to the chlamydias. Without treatment, the mortality rate of ornithosis is about 20%, but with treatment death is rare.

Because the symptoms of ornithosis are the same as those of many respiratory infections, diagnosis requires demonstration of *C. psittaci* by serological testing. Doxycycline for two weeks is the preferred treatment. Prevention involves wearing protective clothing when handling infected birds, 30-day quarantine of and tetracycline treatment for all imported birds, and preventive husbandry, in which bird cages are regularly cleaned and are positioned so as to prevent the transfer of feces, feathers, food, and other materials from cage to cage. No vaccine for either birds or humans is available.

**Table 2** compares and contrasts the features of the smallest microbes—rickettsias, chlamydias, mycoplasmas, and viruses. Next we turn our attention to the spirochetes.

---

[7]From Greek *ornith*, meaning bird.

# Spirochetes

## Learning Objective

✓ Describe the morphology and locomotion of spirochetes.

**Spirochetes** (spī′rō-kētz), which means *coiled hairs* in Greek, are thin (0.1–0.5 μm in diameter), tightly coiled, helically shaped, Gram-negative bacteria that share certain unique features—most notably axial filaments. Axial filaments are composed of endoflagella located in the periplasmic space between the cytoplasmic membrane and the outer (wall) membrane. As its axial filament rotates a spirochete corkscrews through its environment—a type of locomotion thought to enable pathogenic spirochetes to burrow through their hosts' tissues. Mutants lacking endoflagella are rod shaped rather than helical, indicating that the axial filaments play a role in maintaining cell shape.

Taxonomists place spirochetes in their own phylum—Spirochaetes. Three genera, *Treponema, Borrelia,* and *Leptospira,* cause diseases in humans; we begin by discussing *Treponema.*

## Treponema

### Learning Objectives

✓ Describe the disease caused by *Treponema pallidum.*

✓ Describe the four phases of untreated syphilis and the treatment for each.

✓ Describe the diseases caused by nonvenereal strains of *Treponema.*

*Treponema* (trep-ō-nē′mă) is a pathogen of humans only. Four types cause diseases, the most widespread of which is *Treponema pallidum pallidum* (i.e., subspecies, strain, or serotype *pallidum*). We will first examine this sexually transmitted pathogen and the venereal disease it causes, and then we will briefly consider the nonvenereal diseases caused by the other three strains—*T. pallidum endemicum, T. pallidum pertenue,* and *T. carateum.*

### Treponema pallidum pallidum

*Treponema pallidum pallidum* (pal′li-dŭm), which is usually simply called *T. pallidum,* causes **syphilis.** Its flattened helical cells are so narrow (0.1 μm) that they are difficult to see by regular light microscopy in Gram-stained specimens. Therefore, scientists use phase-contrast or dark-field microscopy, or they intensify the contrast of the cells with dye linked to antitreponemal antibodies or with special stains using silver atoms **(Figure 10).**

The bacterium lives naturally in humans only. It is destroyed by exposure to heat, disinfectants, soaps, drying, the concentration of oxygen in air, and pH changes, so it cannot survive in the environment. Scientists have not successfully cultured *T. pallidum* in cell-free media, though they have coaxed it to multiply in rabbits, monkeys, and rabbit epithelial cell cultures. Outside of humans it multiplies slowly (binary fission occurs once every 30 hours) and only for a few generations.

Edwin P. Ewing, Jr., CDC

LM · 3 μm

▲ **Figure 10** **Spirochetes of *Treponema pallidum pallidum.*** Here, stained with a silver stain.

**Pathogenicity and Epidemiology** Scientists have had difficulty identifying the virulence factors of *T. pallidum* because the pathogen cannot be cultured. Researchers have used recombinant DNA techniques to insert genes from *Treponema* into *Escherichia coli* (esh-ĕ-rik′ē-ă kō′lē) and have then isolated the proteins the genes coded. Apparently, some of these proteins enable *Treponema* to adhere to human cells. Virulent strains also produce hyaluronidase, which may enable *Treponema* to infiltrate intracellular spaces. The bacterium has a glycocalyx, which may protect it from phagocytosis by leukocytes.

Syphilis occurs worldwide. Europeans first recognized the disease in 1495, leading some epidemiologists to hypothesize that syphilis was brought to Europe from the Western Hemisphere by returning Spanish explorers. Another hypothesis is that *T. pallidum* evolved from a less pathogenic strain of *Treponema* endemic to North Africa, and that its spread throughout Europe was coincidental to Europeans' explorations of the New World. In any case, the discovery and development of antimicrobial drugs over four centuries later has greatly reduced the number of syphilis cases **(Figure 11a).** The disease remains prevalent among sex workers, men who have sex with men, and users of illegal drugs. It occurs throughout the United States, particularly in the Southeast **(Figure 11b).**

Because of its fastidiousness and sensitivity, *T. pallidum* is an obligate parasite of humans and is transmitted almost solely via sexual contact, usually during the early stage of infection, when the spirochetes are most numerous. The risk of infection from a single, unprotected sexual contact with an infected partner is 10–30%. *T. pallidum* can rarely spread through blood transfusion; it cannot spread by fomites such as toilet seats, eating utensils, or clothing.

**Disease** Untreated syphilis has four phases: primary, secondary, latent, and tertiary syphilis. In *primary syphilis,* a small,

363

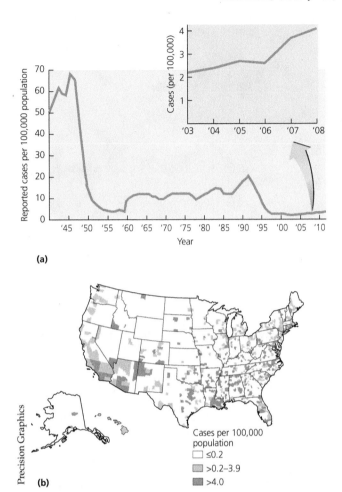

(a)

(b)

Precision Graphics

Cases per 100,000
population
☐ ≤0.2
▨ >0.2–3.9
▨ >4.0

▲ **Figure 11** **The incidence of adult syphilis in the United States. (a)** Nationwide incidence of syphilis, 1941–2008. **(b)** Reported cases of adult syphilis per 100,000 population, by county, 2006.

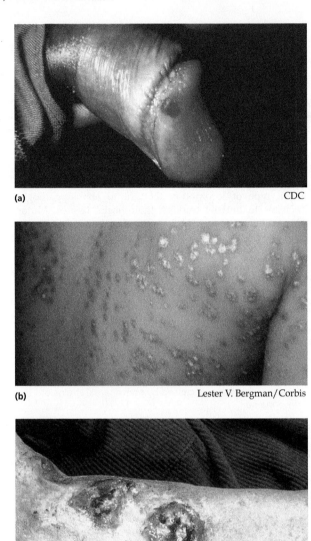

(a) CDC

(b) Lester V. Bergman/Corbis

(c) CDC

▲ **Figure 12** **The lesions of syphilis. (a)** A chancre, a hardened and painless lesion of primary syphilis that forms at the site of the infection. **(b)** A widespread rash characteristic of secondary syphilis. **(c)** A gumma, a painful rubbery lesion that often occurs on the skin or bones during tertiary syphilis.

painless, reddened lesion called a **chancre** (shan'ker) forms at the site of infection 10–21 days following exposure (Figure 12a). Although chancres typically form on the external genitalia, about 20% form in the mouth, around the anus, or on the fingers, lips, or nipples. Chancres are often unobserved, especially in women, in whom these lesions frequently form on the cervix. The center of a chancre fills with serum that is extremely infectious because of the presence of millions of spirochetes. Chancres remain for three to six weeks and then disappear without scarring.

In about a third of cases, the disappearance of the chancre is the end of the disease. However, in most infections *Treponema* has invaded the bloodstream and spreads throughout the body to cause the symptoms and signs of *secondary syphilis:* sore throat, headache, mild fever, malaise, myalgia (muscle pain), lymphadenopathy (diseased lymph nodes), and a widespread rash (Figure 12b) that can include the palms and the soles of the

feet. Although this rash does not itch or hurt, it can persist for months, and like the primary chancre, rash lesions are filled with spirochetes and are extremely contagious. People, including health care workers, can become infected when fluid from the lesions enters breaks in the skin, though such nonsexual transmission of syphilis is rare.

After several weeks or months the rash gradually disappears, and the patient enters a *latent (clinically inactive) phase* of the disease. The majority of cases do not advance beyond this point, especially in developed countries where antimicrobial drugs are in use.

Latency may last 30 or more years, after which perhaps a third of the originally infected patients proceed to *tertiary syphilis*. This phase is not associated with the direct effects of *Treponema*, but rather with severe complications resulting from inflammation and a hyperimmune response against the pathogen. Tertiary syphilis may affect virtually any tissue or organ and can cause dementia, blindness, paralysis, heart failure, and syphilitic lesions called **gummas** (gŭm′ăz), which are rubbery, painfully swollen lesions that can occur in bones, in nervous tissue, or on the skin (Figure 12c).

**Congenital syphilis** results when *Treponema* crosses the placenta from an infected mother to her fetus. Transmission to the fetus from a mother experiencing primary or secondary syphilis often results in the death of the fetus. If transmission occurs while the mother is in the latent phase of the disease, the result can be a latent infection in the fetus that causes mental retardation and malformation of many fetal organs. After birth, newborns with latent infections usually exhibit a widespread rash at some time during their first two years of life.

**Diagnosis, Treatment, and Prevention** The diagnosis of primary, secondary, and congenital syphilis is relatively easy and rapid using specific antibody tests against antigens of *Treponema pallidum pallidum*. Spirochetes can be observed in fresh discharge from lesions but only when microscopic observations of clinical samples are made immediately—*Treponema* usually does not survive transport to a laboratory. Nonpathogenic spirochetes, which are a normal part of the oral microbiota, can yield false positive results, so clinical specimens from the mouth cannot be tested for syphilis. Tertiary syphilis is extremely difficult to diagnose because it mimics many other diseases, because few (if any) spirochetes are present, and because the signs and symptoms may occur years apart and seem unrelated to one another.

Penicillin is the drug of choice for treating primary, secondary, latent, and congenital syphilis, but it is not efficacious for tertiary syphilis, because this phase is caused by a hyperimmune response, not an active infection. Doxycycline is used for patients with penicillin allergy.

The Centers for Disease Control and Prevention has established a national goal for control of syphilis: maintaining an incidence of fewer than 0.2 cases of syphilis per 100,000 population in every county in the United States. This measure should reduce the incidence of syphilis to the point that the disease will be eliminated in the United States. A vaccine against syphilis is not available, so abstinence, faithful mutual monogamy, and consistent and proper condom usage are the primary ways to avoid contracting syphilis. All sexual partners of syphilis patients must be treated with prophylactic penicillin to prevent spread of the disease.

### Nonvenereal Treponemal Diseases

Other members of *Treponema* cause three nonsexually transmitted diseases in humans: bejel, yaws, and pinta. These diseases

▲ **Figure 13** **Yaws.** The draining lesions are characteristic of the later stages of the disease.

are primarily seen in impoverished children in Africa, Asia, and South America who live in unsanitary conditions. The spirochetes that cause these diseases look like *Treponema pallidum pallidum*.

*T. pallidum endemicum* (en-de′mi-kŭm) causes **bejel** (be′jel), a disease seen in children in Africa, Asia, and Australia. In bejel, the spirochetes are spread by contaminated eating utensils, so it is not surprising that the initial lesion is an oral lesion, which typically is so small that it is rarely observed. As the disease progresses, larger and more numerous secondary lesions form around the lips and inside the mouth. In the later stages of the disease, gummas form on the skin, bones, or nasopharyngeal mucous membranes.

*T. pallidum pertenue*[8] (per-ten′ū-ē) causes **yaws** (yăz), a disease of tropical South America, central Africa, and Southeast Asia that is characterized initially by granular skin lesions that, although unsightly, are painless. Over time the lesions develop into large, destructive, draining lesions of the skin, bones, and lymph nodes (Figure 13). The disease is spread via contact with spirochetes in fluid draining from the lesions.

*T. carateum*[9] (kar-a′tē-ŭm) causes **pinta** (pēn′tă), a skin disease seen in children in Central and South America. The spirochetes are spread among the children by skin-to-skin contact. After one to three weeks of incubation, hard, pus-filled lesions

---

[8]Some taxonomists consider this organism to be a separate species: *T. pertenue.*
[9]Some taxonomists consider this organism to be a subspecies: *T. pallidum carateum.*

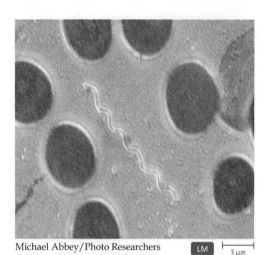

Michael Abbey/Photo Researchers    LM    3 μm

▲ **Figure 14** *Borrelia burgdorferi.* This Gram-negative spiral-shaped spirochete lives in the blood and causes Lyme disease.

called papules form at the site of infection; the papules enlarge and persist for months or years, resulting in scarring and disfigurement.

Physicians diagnose bejel, yaws, and pinta by their distinctive appearance in children from endemic areas. Clinicians can not detect spirochetes in specimens from the lesions of bejel, but they are present in patients with pinta and yaws.

Penicillin, tetracycline, and chloramphenicol are the most favored antimicrobial agents for treating these three tropical diseases. Prevention involves limiting the spread of the bacteria by preventing contact with the lesions.

## *Borrelia*

### Learning Objectives

✓ Describe Lyme disease, its vector, and its causative agent.

✓ Discuss the life cycle of the *Ixodes* tick as it relates to Lyme disease.

✓ Compare and contrast the two types of relapsing fever, including their causes and vectors.

Members of the genus *Borrelia* (bō-rē′lē-ă) are lightly staining, Gram-negative spirochetes that are larger than species of *Treponema*. These spirochetes cause two diseases in humans: Lyme disease and relapsing fever.

### Lyme Disease

In 1975, epidemiologists noted that the incidence of childhood rheumatoid arthritis in Lyme, Connecticut, was over 100 times higher than expected. Upon investigation, they discovered that ticks transmitted the spirochete *Borrelia burgdorferi*[10] (burg-dōr′-

---

[10]Named for the French bacteriologist Amedee Borrel and a specialist in tick-borne diseases, Willy Burgdorfer.

---

### MICROBE AT A GLANCE

#### *Treponema pallidum*

**Taxonomy:** Domain Bacteria, phylum Spirochaetes, class "Spirochaetes," order Spirochaetales, family Spirochaetaceae

**Cell morphology and arrangement:** Flattened spirochete

**Gram reaction:** Negative

**Virulence factors:** Adhesion proteins, corkscrew motility, glycocalyx, hyaluronidase

**Diseases caused:** Syphilis: primary syphilis is lesion at site of infection, secondary syphilis is body rash, tertiary syphilis can have widespread and varied signs and symptoms including gummas; strain *endemicum* causes bejel; strain *pertenue* causes yaws; strain *carateum* causes pinta

**Treatment for diseases:** Penicillin for primary and secondary syphilis; tertiary syphilis not treatable; penicillin, tetracycline, or chloramphenicol to treat bejel, yaws, and pinta

**Prevention of disease:** Abstinence, mutual monogamy, condom usage for syphilis; avoid contact with patients with other diseases

Endoflagella

Axial filament

Cytoplasmic membrane

Periplasmic space

Outer membrane

Kenneth Probst/Precision Graphics

(MM) Download the Microbe at a Glance flashcards from the Study Area at www.masteringmicrobiology.com.

fer-ē; Figure 14) to human hosts to cause what became known as Lyme disease. **Lyme disease** is characterized by dermatological, cardiac, and neurological abnormalities in addition to the observed arthritis. Infected children may have paralysis of one side of their face (Bell's palsy). Even though its discovery was relatively recent, retrospective epidemiological studies have shown that Lyme disease was present in the United States for decades before its discovery.

*B. burgdorferi* is an unusual bacterium in that it lacks iron-containing enzymes and iron-containing proteins in its electron

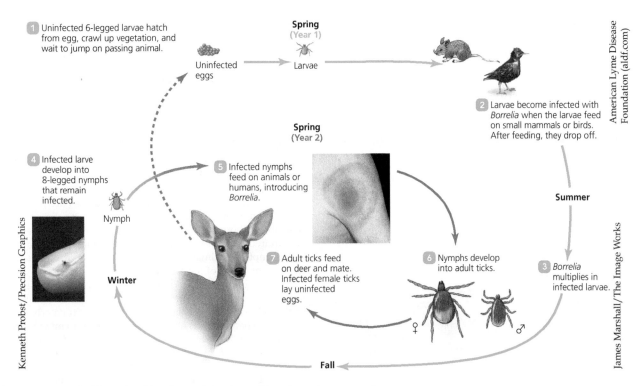

1 Uninfected 6-legged larvae hatch from egg, crawl up vegetation, and wait to jump on passing animal.

**Spring** (Year 1)

Uninfected eggs

Larvae

2 Larvae become infected with *Borrelia* when the larvae feed on small mammals or birds. After feeding, they drop off.

4 Infected larve develop into 8-legged nymphs that remain infected.

**Spring** (Year 2)

5 Infected nymphs feed on animals or humans, introducing *Borrelia*.

Nymph

**Summer**

7 Adult ticks feed on deer and mate. Infected female ticks lay uninfected eggs.

6 Nymphs develop into adult ticks.

3 *Borrelia* multiplies in infected larvae.

**Winter**

♀ ♂

**Fall**

American Lyme Disease Foundation (aldf.com)

Kenneth Probst/Precision Graphics

James Marshall/The Image Works

▲ **Figure 15** **The life cycle of the deer tick *Ixodes* and its role as the vector of Lyme disease.** *At what other stage, besides the nymph stage, can a tick infect a human with B. burgdorferi?*

**Figure 15** *Adult ticks infected with B. burgdorferi can also infect humans during a blood meal.*

transport chains. By utilizing manganese rather than iron, the spirochete circumvents one of the body's natural defense mechanisms: the lack of free iron in human tissues and fluids.

Hard ticks of the genus *Ixodes*—*I. scapularis* (scap-ū-lar'is) in the northeast and central United States, *I. pacificus* (pas-i′fi-kŭs) on the Pacific coast, *I. ricinus* (ri-ki′nŭs) in Europe, and *I. persulcatus* (per-sool-ka′tŭs) in eastern Europe and Asia—are the vectors of Lyme disease. An understanding of the life cycle of these ticks is essential to an understanding of Lyme disease.

An *Ixodes* tick lives for two years, during which it passes through three stages of development: a six-legged larva, an eight-legged nymph, and an eight-legged adult. During each stage it attaches to an animal host for a single blood meal. After each of its three feedings, the tick drops off its host and lives in leaf litter or on brush.

The different stages of each species of *Ixodes* typically feed on different hosts. For example, the larvae and nymphs of *I. scapularis* tend to feed on deer mice, whereas the adults most frequently feed on deer. In contrast, *I. pacificus* adults feed frequently on lizards, a host that does not support the growth of *Borrelia*. All stages of all species of *Ixodes* may feed on humans.

Transovarian transmission of *Borrelia* is rare, so ticks that hatch in the spring are uninfected (Figure 15) ( 1 ). Larvae become infected during their first blood meal ( 2 ). Over the winter,

larvae digest their blood meals while *Borrelia* replicates in the ticks' guts ( 3 ).

In the spring of their second year, the ticks molt into nymphs ( 4 ) and feed a second time, infecting the new hosts with *Borrelia* via saliva ( 5 ). Uninfected nymphs can become infected at this time if they feed on an infected host. Laboratory studies have shown that infected ticks must remain on a host for 48 hours in order to transmit enough spirochetes to establish a *Borrelia* infection in that host.

Nymphs drop off and undergo further development into adults ( 6 ). In the fall, adult ticks feed a final time, mate, lay eggs, and die ( 7 ). Adults infected with *Borrelia* infect their hosts as they feed. Adult ticks are much larger than nymphs, so humans usually see and remove adults before they can transmit *Borrelia*; thus, nymphs most often infect humans.

## CRITICAL **THINKING**

For what other pathogen discussed in this chapter is *Ixodes* also the vector?

Lyme disease mimics many other diseases, and its range of signs and symptoms is vast. The disease typically has three phases in untreated patients:

**(a)**

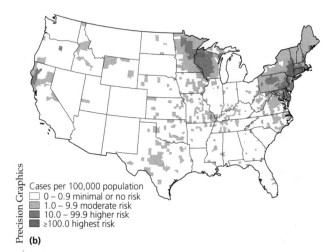

Cases per 100,000 population
☐ 0 – 0.9 minimal or no risk
1.0 – 9.9 moderate risk
10.0 – 99.9 higher risk
≥100.0 highest risk

Precision Graphics

**(b)**

▲ **Figure 16** **The occurrence of Lyme disease in the United States.** (a) Incidence of cases, 1982–2008. (b) The geographic distribution of the disease, 1992–2006.

1. An expanding red rash, which often resembles a bull's-eye, occurs at the site of infection within 30 days. About 75% of patients have such a rash, which lasts for several weeks. Other early signs and symptoms include malaise, headaches, dizziness, stiff neck, severe fatigue, fever, chills, muscle and joint pain, and lymphadenopathy.

2. Neurological symptoms (for example, meningitis, encephalitis, and peripheral nerve neuropathy) and cardiac dysfunction typify the second phase, which is seen in only 10% of patients.

3. The final phase is characterized by severe arthritis that can last for years.

The pathological conditions of the latter phases of Lyme disease are due in large part to the body's immunological response; rarely is *Borrelia* seen in the involved tissue or isolated in cultures of specimens from these sites.

Two major events have contributed to the increase in cases of Lyme disease in the United States over the past decades (Figure 16a): The human population has encroached on woodland areas, and the deer population has been protected and even encouraged to feed in suburban yards. Thus, humans have been brought into closer association with deer ticks infected with *Borrelia*.

A diagnosis of Lyme disease, which is typically indicated by observations of its usual signs and symptoms, is rarely confirmed by detecting *Borrelia* in blood smears; instead, the diagnosis is confirmed through the use of serological tests.

Treatment with antimicrobial drugs such as doxycycline or a penicillin effectively cures most cases of Lyme disease in the first phase, though prolonged treatment with large doses may be required. Treatment of later phases is more difficult because later symptoms primarily result from immune responses rather than the presence of the spirochetes.

People hiking, picnicking, and working outdoors in areas where Lyme disease is prevalent (Figure 16b) should take precautions to reduce the chances of infection, particularly during summer, when nymphs are feeding. People who must be in the woods should wear long-sleeved shirts and long, tight-fitting pants, and should tuck the cuffs of their pants into their socks to deny ticks access to skin. Repellents containing *DEET* (*N,N*-diethyl-*m*-toluamide), which is noxious to ticks, should be used. As soon as possible after leaving a tick-infected area, people should thoroughly examine their bodies for ticks or their bites. Though researchers have developed a vaccine against *B. burgdorferi*, it is not widely used because of the ready availability of other preventive measures, and because the vaccine may produce the symptoms of Lyme disease in some patients.

## CRITICAL **THINKING**

Health departments recommend that outdoor enthusiasts wear light-colored pants while hiking in areas where *Ixodes* is endemic. Why?

### Relapsing Fever

Other species of spirochetes in the genus *Borrelia* can cause two types of relapsing fever. A disease called **louse-borne relapsing fever** results when *Borrelia recurrentis* (re-kur-ren'tis) is transmitted between humans by the human body louse *Pediculus humanus*. A disease known as **tick-borne relapsing fever** occurs when any of several species of *Borrelia* are transmitted between humans by soft ticks in the genus *Ornithodoros* (or-ni-thod'ō-rŭs).

Lice become infected with *B. recurrentis* when they feed on infected humans, the only reservoir for this spirochete. When infected lice are crushed, spirochetes can infect bite wounds. Because lice live only a few months, maintenance of louse-borne relapsing fever in a population requires crowded, unsanitary conditions such as occur in poor neighborhoods and during wars and natural disasters. This relapsing fever occurs in central and eastern Africa and in South America.

**Figure 17 The time course of recurring episodes of fever in relapsing fevers.**

Ben Adler, Australian Research Council Centre of Excellence in Structural and Functional Microbial Genomics, Monash University VIC, Australia

▲ **Figure 18 *Leptospira interrogans.*** The spirochete has one end hooked like a question mark.

Prevention involves avoidance of ticks and lice, good personal hygiene, and the use of repellent chemicals. Effective rodent control is crucial to the control of endemic relapsing fever. Vaccines are not available.

## *Leptospira*

### Learning Objective

✓ Describe *Leptospira interrogans* and zoonotic leptospirosis.

The last of the three groups of spirochetes that infect humans is *Leptospira interrogans* (lep′tō-spī′ră in-ter′ră-ganz). The specific epithet *interrogans* alludes to the fact that one end of the spirochete is hooked in a manner reminiscent of a question mark (Figure 18). This thin, pathogenic spirochete is an obligate aerobe that is highly motile by means of two axial filaments, each of which is anchored at one end. Clinicians and researchers grow it on special media enriched with bovine serum albumin or rabbit serum.

*L. interrogans* normally occurs in many wild and domestic animals—in particular, rats, raccoons, foxes, dogs, horses, cattle, and pigs—in which it grows asymptomatically in the kidney tubules. Humans contract the zoonotic disease **leptospirosis** (lep′tō-spī-rō′sis) through direct contact with the urine of infected animals or indirectly via contact with the spirochetes in contaminated streams, lakes, or moist soil, environments in which the organisms can remain viable for six weeks or more. Person-to-person spread has not been observed.

After *Leptospira* gains initial access to the body through invisible cuts and abrasions in the skin or mucous membranes, it corkscrews its way through these tissues. It then travels via the bloodstream throughout the body, including the central nervous system, damaging cells lining the small blood vessels and triggering fever and intense pain. Infection may lead to hemorrhaging and to liver and kidney dysfunction. Eventually, the bacteremia resolves, and the spirochetes are found only in the kidneys. As the disease progresses, spirochetes are excreted in urine. Leptospirosis is usually not fatal.

Leptospirosis occurs throughout the world. National reporting in the United States has ceased in part because the disease is rare; a total of only 89 cases were reported in the last two years (1993–1994) that leptospirosis was listed as a nationally reportable disease.

In contrast to hard ticks, the soft ticks of the genus *Ornithodoros* that transmit tick-borne relapsing fever can live for years between feedings and pass spirochetes to their offspring via transovarian transmission. Soft ticks can also transmit *Borrelia* spp. (species) to animals, particularly mice and rats. Ticks and rodents are reservoirs of infection. This relapsing fever has a worldwide distribution; in the United States it is found primarily in the West.

Both types of relapsing fever are characterized by recurrent episodes of septicemia and fever separated by symptom-free intervals—a pattern that results from the body's repeated efforts to remove the spirochetes, which continually change their antigenic surface components (Figure 17). Within the first week of infection, the spirochetes induce a fever (❶), which is associated with chills, myalgia, and headache. In response to infection, the body produces antibodies that are directed against the spirochetes' surface molecules; once the antibodies have targeted the spirochetes, phagocytes clear most pathogens from the blood, and the body's temperature returns to normal (❷). However, some *Borrelia* evade the immune response by changing their antigenic surface molecules; when these spirochetes multiply, they induce a relapse of fever (❸). The body mounts a second immune response, this time against the new antigens, eventually again clearing the blood of most spirochetes and again returning body temperature to normal (❹). But a few spirochetes yet again change their antigenic components, leading to still another recurrence of fever, continuing the pattern (❺).

Because of their relatively large size and abundance in the blood, observation of spirochetes in blood smears taken during periods of recurrent fever is the primary method of diagnosis.

Physicians successfully treat the relapsing fevers with doxycycline or, in pregnant women and children, with erythromycin.

369

Because *Leptospira* is very thin and does not stain well with Gram, silver, or Giemsa stain, specific antibody tests revealing the presence of the spirochete in clinical specimens are the preferred method of diagnosis. Intravenous penicillin is used to treat infections. Rodent control is the most effective way to limit the spread of *Leptospira,* but eradication is impractical because of the spirochete's many animal reservoirs. An effective vaccine is available for livestock and pets.

## CRITICAL **THINKING**

We discussed the identification of microbes using dichotomous taxonomic keys. Design such a key for the spirochetes discussed in this chapter.

# Pathogenic Gram-Negative Vibrios

To this point, we have discussed a number of unrelated Gram-negative bacteria: rickettsias, chlamydias, and the spirochetes. We will now turn our attention to a final group—the slightly curved bacteria called *vibrios.* The more important pathogenic vibrios of humans are in the genera *Vibrio, Campylobacter,* and *Helicobacter.*

## *Vibrio*

### Learning Objectives

✓ Contrast *Vibrio* with enteric bacteria in terms of their flagella and biochemical properties.

✓ Describe the action of cholera toxin in causing cholera.

✓ Name two species of *Vibrio* and describe the resulting diseases.

Vibrio (vib'rē-ō) is a genus of Gram-negative, slightly curved bacilli in class Gammaproteobacteria, and phylum Proteobacteria (Figure 19). *Vibrio* shares many characteristics with enteric bacteria such as *Escherichia* and *Salmonella,* including O polysaccharide antigens that enable epidemiologists to distinguish among strains; however, *Vibrio* is oxidase positive and has a polar flagellum, unlike enteric bacteria, which are oxidase negative and have peritrichous flagella.

*Vibrio* lives naturally in estuarine and marine environments worldwide. It prefers warm, salty, and alkaline water, and most pathogenic species can multiply inside shellfish. Eleven of the 34 species of *Vibrio* cause diseases in humans; of these, only *V. cholerae* (kol'er-ī) can survive in freshwater, making it the most likely species to infect humans (via contaminated drinking water). In the following sections we examine *V. cholerae* and the serious disease it causes.

### Pathogenesis and Epidemiology of *Vibrio cholerae*

*Vibrio cholerae,* particularly strain O1 El Tor, causes **cholera** (kol'er-ă, sometimes called *epidemic cholera*), one of the world's more pernicious diseases. The science of epidemiology began

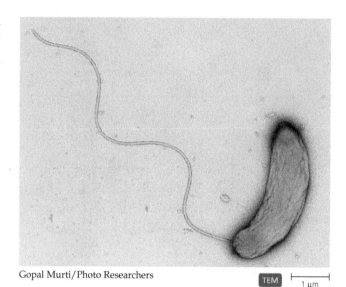

Gopal Murti/Photo Researchers

TEM | 1 μm

▲ **Figure 19** *Vibrio cholerae.* This bacterium causes cholera.

with Dr. John Snow's efforts to understand and limit the 1854 cholera epidemic in London.

Ships have introduced the pathogen into the harbors of every continent through their practice of taking on ballast water in one port and dumping it in another; two world wars have only exacerbated the situation. In the seven major pandemics that have occurred since 1800, millions of people have been sickened and thousands have died, causing significant socioeconomic upheaval.

The seventh pandemic of O1 El Tor began in 1961 in Asia, spread to Africa and Europe in the 1970s and 1980s, and reached Peru in January 1991. Figure 20 illustrates the progression of this cholera pandemic throughout Latin America in the first half of the 1990s. A new pandemic strain, *V. cholerae* O139 Bengal, arose in India in 1992 and is spreading across Asia; this strain is the first non-O1 strain capable of causing epidemic disease. Other strains of *V. cholerae* do not produce epidemic cholera, only milder gastroenteritis.

Humans become infected with *Vibrio cholerae* by ingesting contaminated food and water. Cholera is most frequent in communities with poor sewage and water treatment. After entering the digestive system, *Vibrio* is confronted with the inhospitable acidic environment of the stomach. Most cells die, which is why a high inoculum—at least $10^8$ cells—is typically required for the disease to develop. Fewer cells can achieve infection in people who use antacids.

Recent research indicates that only the environment within a human body activates *Vibrio* virulence genes. Thus, *Vibrio* shed in feces is more virulent than its counterparts in the environment. Scientists hypothesize that such gene activation may explain the rapid, almost explosive, nature of cholera epidemics.

Although cholera infections may be asymptomatic or cause mild diarrhea, some result in rapid, severe, and fatal fluid and

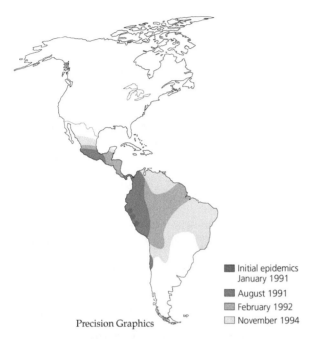

▲ **Figure 20** **The spread of cholera.** The Latin American epidemics were caused by *Vibrio cholerae* O1 El Tor in the first half of the 1990s.

Precision Graphics

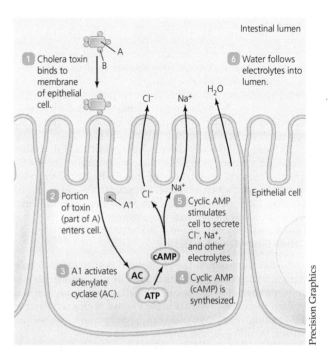

▲ **Figure 21** **The action of cholera toxin in intestinal epithelial cells.**

electrolyte loss. Symptoms usually begin two to three days following infection, with explosive watery diarrhea and vomiting. As the disease progresses, the colon is emptied and the stool becomes increasingly watery, colorless, and odorless. The stool, which is typically flecked with mucus, is called *rice-water stool* because it resembles water poured off a pan of boiled rice. Some patients lose 1 liter of fluid an hour, resulting in a 50% loss of body weight over the course of infection.

The most important virulence factor of *V. cholerae* is a potent exotoxin called **cholera toxin,** which is composed of five identical B subunits and a single A subunit. **Figure 21** illustrates the action of cholera toxin in producing the severe diarrhea that characterizes cholera. The process proceeds as follows:

1. One of the B subunits binds to a glycolipid receptor in the cytoplasmic membrane of an intestinal epithelial cell.

2. The A subunit is cleaved, and a portion (called A1) enters the cell's cytosol.

3. A1 acts as an enzyme that activates adenylate cyclase (AC).

4. Activated AC enzymatically converts ATP into cyclic AMP (cAMP).

5. cAMP stimulates the active secretion of excess amounts of electrolytes (sodium, chlorine, potassium, and bicarbonate ions) from the cell.

6. Water follows the movement of electrolytes from the cell and into the intestinal lumen via osmosis.

Severe fluid and electrolyte losses result in dehydration, metabolic acidosis (decreased pH of body fluids) due to loss of bicarbonate ions, hypokalemia,[11] and hypovolemic shock caused by reduced blood volume in the body. These conditions can produce muscle cramping, irregularities in heartbeat, kidney failure, coma, and death.

Cholera mortality is 60% in untreated patients infected by strain O1; death can occur less than 48 hours after infection. Disease produced by strain O139 is even more severe. In nonfatal cases, cholera ends spontaneously after a few days as the pathogens and toxins are flushed from the system by the severe diarrhea.

### Diagnosis, Treatment, and Prevention of Cholera

Rarely, an experienced observer may find the quick darting cells of *Vibrio* in the watery stool of a patient, but diagnosis is usually based on the characteristic diarrhea. *Vibrio* can be cultured on many laboratory media designed for stool cultures, but clinical specimens must be collected early in the disease (before the volume of stool dilutes the number of cells) and inoculated promptly because *Vibrio* is extremely sensitive to drying. Strains are distinguished by means of antibody tests specific for each antigenic variant.

Health care providers must promptly treat cholera patients with fluid and electrolyte replacement before hypovolemic shock

[11]From Greek *hypo*, meaning under; Latin *kalium*, meaning potassium; and Greek *haima*, meaning blood.

ensues. Antimicrobial drugs are not as important as with many other bacterial diseases, because they are lost in the watery stool; nevertheless, they may reduce the production of exotoxin and ameliorate the symptoms. Doxycycline is the drug of choice.

Because *Vibrio cholerae* can grow in estuarine and marine water, and because up to 20% of former patients still asymptomatically harbor the pathogen, it is unlikely that cholera will be eradicated worldwide. Nevertheless, adequate sewage and water treatment can limit the spread of *Vibrio* and prevent epidemics.

A new, oral vaccine developed against the O1 strains of *V. cholerae* appears promising; there is no vaccine for the O139 strain. Antibiotic prophylaxis of those who travel to endemic areas has not proven effective. Fortunately, because the infective dose for *V. cholerae* is high, proper hygiene generally makes vaccination and prophylaxis unnecessary.

### Other Diseases of *Vibrio*

*Vibrio parahaemolyticus* (pa-ră-hē-mō-li′ti-kŭs) causes cholera-like gastroenteritis following ingestion of shellfish harvested from contaminated estuaries; fortunately, only rarely is it severe enough to be fatal. Typically the disease is characterized by a self-limiting, explosive diarrhea accompanied by headache, nausea, vomiting, and cramping for 72 hours.

*V. vulnificus* (vul-nif′i-kŭs) is responsible for septicemia (blood poisoning) following consumption of contaminated shellfish, and for infections resulting from the washing of wounds with contaminated seawater. Wound infections are characterized by swelling and reddening at the site of infection and are accompanied by fever and chills. Infections with *V. vulnificus* are fatal for 50% of untreated patients; prompt treatment with doxycycline is effective.

## *Campylobacter jejuni*

### Learning Objectives

✓ List several possible reservoirs of *Campylobacter jejuni*.

✓ Describe gastroenteritis caused by *Campylobacter jejuni*.

*Campylobacter jejuni*[12] (kam′pi-lō-bak′ter jē-jū′nē) is likely the most common cause of bacterial gastroenteritis in the United States. Like *Vibrio*, it is Gram-negative, slightly curved, oxidase positive, and motile by means of polar flagella; however, genetic analysis has shown that this comma-shaped pathogen is properly classified in the class Deltaproteobacteria (and not in Gammaproteobacteria). *Campylobacter* also differs from *Vibrio* in being microaerophilic and capneic.

*Campylobacter* infections are zoonotic—many domesticated animals, including poultry, dogs, cats, rabbits, pigs, cattle, and minks, serve as reservoirs. Humans acquire the bacterium by consuming food, milk, or water contaminated with infected animal feces. The most common source of infection is contaminated poultry. One study found that of dozens of Thanksgiving turkeys tested, 100% were contaminated with *Campylobacter*.

[12]From Greek *kampylos*, meaning curved, and *jejunum*, the middle portion of the small intestine.

## The Case of the Lactovegetarians

Robert Weaver, CDC    LM    |—————| 10 μm

Two patients—a woman and her husband, ages 23 and 22, respectively—arrive at the health clinic one morning. They report having had severe abdominal cramps, grossly bloody diarrhea, nausea, and fever for 48 hours. Cultures of stool samples grown under microaerophilic, capneic conditions contain comma-shaped, Gram-negative bacilli. Both the patients are lactovegetarians and report being part of a "cow leasing" program at a local dairy in which patrons lease part of a cow's milk production so they can drink natural, whole, raw milk. The couple devised the program so that they and several neighbors could circumvent state regulations prohibiting the sale of unpasteurized milk. Investigators obtained and cultured a milk sample from the dairy's bulk milk tank: the cultures contained the bacterium pictured.

1. What is the pathogen?

2. How did the couple become infected?

3. Are the couple's colleagues at work at risk of acquiring an infection from the couple?

4. What other foods that are common sources of this bacterium can be ruled out in this case?

The pathogenicity of *C. jejuni* is not well understood, although the bacterium possesses adhesins, cytotoxins, and endotoxins that appear to enable colonization and invasion of the jejunum, ileum, and colon, producing bleeding lesions and triggering inflammation. Interestingly, nonmotile mutants are avirulent. *C. jejuni* infections commonly produce malaise, fever, abdominal pain, and bloody and frequent diarrhea—10 or more bowel movements per day are not uncommon. The disease is self-limiting; as bacteria are expelled from the intestinal tract, the symptoms abate, although a typical infection may last 7–10 days.

Scientists estimate that over 2 million cases of *Campylobacter* gastroenteritis occur each year in the United States—more than those caused by *Salmonella* and *Shigella* combined. However, *Campylobacter* gastroenteritis is not a reportable disease, so its actual incidence is unknown.

The number of infections can be reduced by proper food preparation, including thoroughly washing poultry carcasses, hands, and utensils that have contacted carcasses; cooking food sufficiently to kill bacteria; and pasteurizing cow's milk. Steps must also be taken to prevent contamination of the water supply with feces from stockyards, feedlots, and slaughterhouses.

## *Helicobacter pylori*

### Learning Objectives

✓ Discuss the major change in medical opinion concerning the cause of peptic ulcers.

✓ Describe the effect of *Helicobacter pylori* on the lining of the human stomach.

*Helicobacter pylori* (hel'ĭ-kō-bak'ter pī'lō-rē) is a slightly helical, highly motile bacterium that colonizes the stomachs of its hosts **(Figure 22)**. Based on rRNA nucleotide sequences, *Helicobacter* is classified in the class Deltaproteobacteria. It was originally placed in the genus *Campylobacter;* however, unlike *Campylobacter, Helicobacter* cannot reduce nitrate, has flagella, and is urease positive, a characteristic that is essential for colonizing the stomach.

Today, an idea that only a few years ago was very controversial—that *H. pylori* causes *gastritis*[13] and most **peptic ulcers,** which are erosions of the mucous membrane of the stomach or of the initial portion of the small intestine—is accepted as fact. What was once the prevailing view—that stress, alcohol consumption, spicy food, or excess stomach acid production caused ulcers—was discredited beginning in 1982, when Australian gastroenterologists Robin Warren

---

[13]From Greek *gaster*, meaning belly, and Greek *itis*, meaning inflammation.

Precision Graphics

SEM ┠─┨ 1 µm

▲ **Figure 22** *Helicobacter pylori.* The bacterium causes peptic ulcers.

---

Shutterstock

### *VIBRIO VULNIFICUS* INFECTION

Greg enjoyed Florida's beaches on the Gulf side; swimming in the warm water was his favorite pastime. Of course, the saltwater did sting his leg where he had cut himself on some coral, but it didn't sting enough to stop Greg from enjoying the beach. He spent the afternoon jogging in the pure sand, throwing a disc, watching the people, drinking a few beers, and of course spending more time in the water.

That evening he felt chilled, a condition he associated with too much sun during the day, but by midnight he thought he must have caught a rare summertime flu. He was definitely feverish, extremely weak and tired. His leg felt strangely tight, as if the underlying muscles were trying to burst through his skin.

The next morning he felt better, except for his leg. It was swollen, dark red, tremendously painful, and covered with fluid-filled blisters. The ugly sight motivated him to head straight for the hospital, a decision that likely saved his life.

Precision Graphics

Greg was the victim of an emerging pathogen, *Vibrio vulnificus*—a slightly curved, Gram-negative bacterium that is related to *V. cholerae* (cholera bacterium). *V. vulnificus* lives in salty, warm water around the globe and can live in marine organisms such as oysters. Unlike the cholera bacterium, *V. vulnificus* is able to infect a person by penetrating directly into a deep wound, a cut, or even a tiny scratch.

Greg's doctor cut away the dead tissue and prescribed doxycycline and cephalosporin for two weeks, and Greg survived and kept his leg. Half of the victims of *Vibrio vulnificus* are not so lucky; they lose a limb or die. Who knew that a beach could be so dangerous?

**(MM)** Track *Vibrio vulnificus* online by going to the Study Area at www.masteringmicrobiology.com.

## MICROBE AT A GLANCE

### *Helicobacter pylori*

**Taxonomy:** Domain Bacteria, phylum Proteobacteria, class Epsilonproteobacteria, order Campylobacterales, family Campylobacteraceae

**Cell morphology and arrangement:** Slightly helical bacillus

**Gram reaction:** Negative

**Virulence factors:** Protein that inhibits acid production, urease, flagella, adhesins, antiphagocytic enzymes

**Diseases caused:** Peptic ulcer

**Treatment for diseases:** Antibacterial drugs in conjunction with drugs that inhibit acid production in the stomach

**Prevention of disease:** Good personal hygiene, adequate sewage treatment, water purification, proper food handling

Flagellum

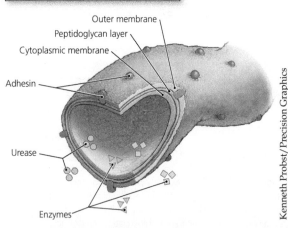

Outer membrane
Peptidoglycan layer
Cytoplasmic membrane

Adhesin

Urease

Enzymes

Kenneth Probst/Precision Graphics

(1937–) and Barry Marshall (1951–) detected *Helicobacter* colonizing the majority of their patients' stomachs. Following treatment with antibiotics, the bacteria and the ulcers disappeared. Dr. Marshall provided final proof of *H. pylori's* involvement by fulfilling Koch's postulates himself—he drank one of his cultures of *Helicobacter*! As he expected, he developed painful gastritis and was able to isolate *H. pylori* from his diseased stomach. His sacrifice was worth it: Marshall and Warren received the 2005 Nobel Prize in Physiology or Medicine for their discovery. Since then scientists have shown that long-term infection with *Helicobacter* is a significant risk factor for stomach cancer.

*H. pylori* possesses numerous virulence factors that enable it to colonize the human stomach: a protein that inhibits acid production by stomach cells; flagella that enable the pathogen to burrow through mucus lining the stomach; adhesins that facilitate binding to gastric cells; enzymes that inhibit phagocytic killing; and urease, an enzyme that degrades urea, which is present in gastric juice, to produce highly alkaline ammonia, which neutralizes stomach acid.

The portal of entry for *H. pylori* is the mouth. Studies have shown that *H. pylori* in feces on the hands, in well water, or on fomites may infect humans. In addition, cat feces may be a source of infection.

The formation of a peptic ulcer occurs as follows (Figure 23): The process begins when *H. pylori* (protected by urease) burrows through the stomach's protective layer of mucus to reach the underlying epithelial cells (1), where the bacteria attach to the cells' cytoplasmic membranes and multiply. A variety of factors—the triggering of inflammation by bacterial exotoxin and perhaps the destruction of mucus-producing cells by the bacteria—causes the layer of mucus to become thin (2), allowing acidic gastric juice to digest the stomach lining. Once the epithelial layer has been ulcerated by gastric juice, *H. pylori* gains access to the underlying muscle tissue and blood vessels (3). Those bacteria that are phagocytized survive in part through the actions of catalase and superoxide dismutase, enzymes that neutralize part of the phagocytes' killing mechanism.

The presence of *H. pylori* in specimens from the stomach can be demonstrated by a positive urease test within one to two hours of culturing; the bacterium can also be seen in Gram-stained specimens. Definitive identification is based on a series of biochemical tests.

Physicians treat ulcers with two or three antimicrobial drugs given in combination with drugs that inhibit acid production, allowing the stomach lining to regenerate. Prevention of infection involves good personal hygiene, adequate sewage treatment, water purification, and proper food handling.

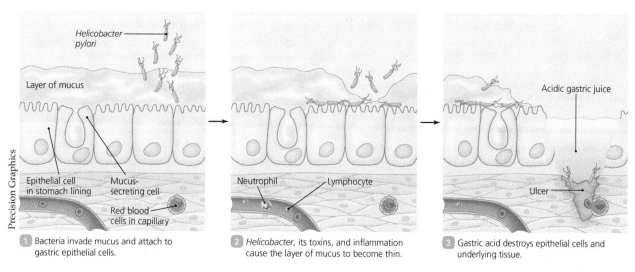

Precision Graphics

1 Bacteria invade mucus and attach to gastric epithelial cells.

2 *Helicobacter*, its toxins, and inflammation cause the layer of mucus to become thin.

3 Gastric acid destroys epithelial cells and underlying tissue.

▲ **Figure 23** The role of *Helicobacter pylori* in the formation of peptic ulcers.

# Chapter Summary

## Rickettsias

1. **Rickettsias** are extremely small, Gram-negative, obligate intracellular parasites.

2. *Rickettsia rickettsii* causes **Rocky Mountain spotted fever (RMSF),** a serious illness transmitted by ticks. Rash, malaise, petechiae, encephalitis, and death (in 5% of cases) characterize the disease.

3. *Rickettsia prowazekii* causes louse-borne or **epidemic typhus,** characterized by fever, depression, and rash. The disease may recur as Brill-Zinsser disease.

4. *Rickettsia typhi* causes endemic typhus, also called **murine typhus** because the major reservoir is rodents. Various fleas act as vectors to transmit the bacterium to humans.

5. Mites (chiggers) transmit *Orientia tsutsugamushi* to cause **scrub typhus,** which is characterized by a spreading rash.

6. *Ehrlichia chaffeensis* causes **human monocytic ehrlichiosis (HME),** and *Anaplasma phagocytophilum* causes **anaplasmosis.** These bacteria are transmitted to humans via the Lone Star tick, the deer tick, or the dog tick. The bacteria enter leukocytes and grow through three developmental stages: an elementary body, an initial body, and a morula.

## Chlamydias

1. Chlamydias are small, nonmotile obligate intracellular parasites; their developmental cycle includes infectious **elementary bodies (EBs)** and noninfectious **reticulate bodies (RBs).** An endosome full of RBs is called an **inclusion body.**

2. *Chlamydia trachomatis* enters the body through abrasions in mucous membranes of the genitalia, eyes, or respiratory tract.

*Chlamydia* causes the most-reported sexually transmitted disease in the United States.

3. *Chlamydia trachomatis* causes **lymphogranuloma venereum.** The majority of infections in women are asymptomatic, whereas the majority of infections in men result in buboes, fever, chills, anorexia, and muscle pain. Other symptoms and signs may include proctitis (in men and women), and pelvic inflammatory disease and sterility (in women). *Chlamydia* infections can be prevented by abstinence or faithful mutual monogamy.

4. **Trachoma** is a serious eye disease that is caused by *C. trachomatis* and may result in blindness.

5. *Chlamydophila pneumoniae* causes bronchitis, pneumonia, and sinusitis.

6. *Chlamydophila psittaci* causes **ornithosis** (also called psittacosis or parrot fever), a respiratory disease of birds that can be transmitted to humans.

## Spirochetes

1. **Spirochetes** are helical bacteria with axial filaments that cause the organism to corkscrew, enabling it to burrow into a host's tissues.

2. **Syphilis** is caused by *Treponema pallidum pallidum,* a sexually transmitted obligate parasite of humans.

3. Primary syphilis is characterized by a **chancre,** a red lesion at the infection site. If *Treponema* moves from the chancre to the bloodstream, secondary syphilis results, causing rash, aches, and pains. After a period of latency, progression may occur to tertiary syphilis, characterized by swollen **gummas,** dementia, blindness, paralysis, and heart failure.

4. **Congenital syphilis** results when an infected mother infects her fetus.

5. Penicillin is used to treat all except tertiary syphilis; no vaccine is available.

6. *Treponema pallidum endemicum* causes **bejel,** an oral disease observed in children in Africa, Asia, and Australia.

7. *Treponema pallidum pertenue* causes **yaws,** a skin disease observed in South America, central Africa, and Southeast Asia.

8. *Treponema carateum* (*T. pallidum carateum*) causes **pinta,** a disfiguring skin disease observed in children in Central and South America.

9. *Borrelia burgdorferi* causes **Lyme disease,** a disease transmitted by ticks of the genus *Ixodes* and characterized by a bull's-eye rash, neurological and cardiac dysfunction, and severe arthritis.

10. Human body lice transmit *Borrelia recurrentis*, which causes **louse-borne relapsing fever** in Africa and South America. In the western United States, soft ticks transmit several different species of *Borrelia* causing **tick-borne relapsing fever.**

11. *Leptospira interrogans* causes **leptospirosis,** a zoonotic disease in humans transmitted via animal urine and characterized by pain, headache, and liver and kidney dysfunction.

## Pathogenic Gram-Negative Vibrios

1. *Vibrio* is a genus of Gram-negative curved bacteria with polar flagella that naturally live in marine environments.

2. *Vibrio cholerae* causes **cholera,** a disease contracted via the ingestion of contaminated food and water. Cholera has been pandemic through the centuries.

3. Via a series of biochemical steps, **cholera toxin**—an exotoxin produced by *Vibrio cholerae*—causes the movement of water out of the intestinal epithelium, resulting in potentially fatal diarrhea.

4. *Vibrio parahaemolyticus* enters the body via ingestion of shellfish from contaminated waters; it causes a milder form of cholera-like gastroenteritis.

5. *Vibrio vulnificus,* contracted either by ingestion of contaminated shellfish or by contamination of wounds with seawater, causes a potentially fatal blood poisoning.

6. *Campylobacter jejuni,* which is found in domestic animal reservoirs, commonly causes gastroenteritis when ingested in contaminated food, water, or milk.

7. Once *Helicobacter pylori* reduces the amount of mucus produced in the stomach, acidic gastric juice eats away the stomach lining, causing **peptic ulcers.**

# Questions for Review
*Answers to the Questions for Review (except Short Answer questions) appear at the end of this chapter.*

## Multiple Choice

1. Most human infections caused by species of *Rickettsia*
   a. are acquired from fomites.
   b. could be prevented by handwashing.
   c. are transmitted via vectors.
   d. are sexually transmitted.

2. The bacterium that causes RMSF is more likely to infect a human
   a. if an infected tick feeds for several hours.
   b. when an infected tick initially penetrates the skin.
   c. when contaminated tick feces dry and become airborne.
   d. if the human is exposed to rodent feces containing the bacterium.

3. The most severe rickettsial illness is caused by
   a. *Rickettsia typhi.*          c. *Orientia tsutsugamushi.*
   b. *Rickettsia rickettsii.*      d. *Ehrlichia chaffeensis.*

4. The smallest cellular microbes are
   a. rickettsias.                  c. chlamydias.
   b. mycoplasmas.                  d. both a and c.

5. The most commonly reported sexually transmitted disease in the United States is caused by the bacterium
   a. *Mycoplasma genitalium.*      c. *Chlamyophila proctitis.*
   b. *Chlamydia trachomatis.*      d. *Ureaplasma urealyticum.*

6. Which of the following diseases would be *least* likely in rural areas of the United States?
   a. epidemic typhus
   b. Rocky Mountain spotted fever
   c. murine typhus
   d. lymphogranuloma venereum

7. Treatment of chlamydial infections involves
   a. erythromycin cream.
   b. doxycycline creams.
   c. surgical correction of eyelid deformities.
   d. all of the above

8. Which of the following organisms is transmitted via sexual contact?
   a. *Treponema pallidum endemicum*
   b. *Treponema pallidum pertenue*
   c. *Treponema pallidum pallidum*
   d. *Treponema carateum*

9. Which of the following is *not* true of cholera?
   a. The causative agent lives naturally in marine water.
   b. There is an effective vaccine for cholera.
   c. Strain O1 El Tor has been responsible for several pandemics.
   d. Rice-water stool is a symptom.

10. During which stage of syphilis is penicillin ineffective?
    a. primary syphilis              c. tertiary syphilis
    b. secondary syphilis            d. all of the above

11. Two weeks after a backpacking trip in Tennessee, a hiker experienced flulike symptoms and noticed a red rash on his thigh. What is the likely cause of his illness?
    a. *Treponema pallidum pertenue*  c. *Borrelia recurrentis*
    b. *Borrelia burgdorferi*         d. *Leptospira interrogans*

12. The most common cause of bacterial gastroenteritis in the United States is
    a. *Vibrio parahaemolyticus.*     c. *Helicobacter pylori.*
    b. *Campylobacter jejuni.*        d. *Vibrio cholerae.*

13. Historical journals have described gummas on patients. What disease most likely caused these lesions?
    a. ornithosis
    b. syphilis
    c. trachoma
    d. pneumonia

## Labeling

Label the following stages and structures of the chlamydia life cycle: *elementary body, endocytosis, vesicle, host cell, inclusion body, reticulate body.* Indicate how many hours typically transpire at each lettered step.

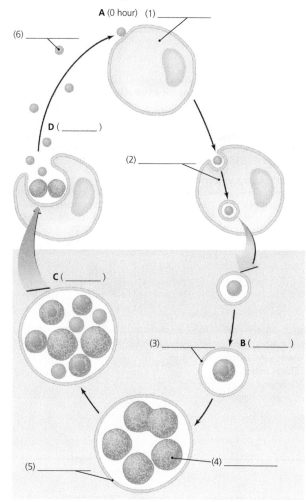

Precision Graphics

## Short Answer

1. Describe a hypothesis to explain why rickettsias are obligate parasites.

2. Describe the three developmental stages of the bacteria *Ehrlichia* and *Anaplasma*.

3. Why have scientists had problems identifying the virulence factors of *Treponema pallidum pallidum*?

4. Describe the phases of untreated syphilis.

5. Discuss the prospects for the eradication of leptospirosis.

6. Beginning with the ingestion of water contaminated with *V. cholerae* O1 El Tor, describe the course of the disease it causes.

## Matching

1. Match the disease with the causative pathogen.

    ____ Rocky Mountain spotted fever    A. *Rickettsia typhi*

    ____ Endemic typhus    B. *Rickettsia prowazekii*

    ____ Epidemic typhus    C. *Rickettsia rickettsii*

    ____ Scrub typhus    D. *Orientia tsutsugamushi*

    ____ HME    E. *Ehrlichia chaffeensis*

2. Match the pathogen with the vector responsible for transmitting it to humans.

    ____ *Rickettsia typhi*    A. Rat flea

    ____ *Rickettsia prowazekii*    B. Body louse

    ____ *Rickettsia rickettsii*    C. Hard tick

    ____ *Orientia tsutsugamushi*    D. Mite

    ____ *Ehrlichia chaffeensis*    E. Soft tick

    ____ *Borrelia burgdorferi*

    ____ *Borrelia recurrentis*

    ____ *Anaplasma phagocytophilum*

3. Match the pathogen with the disease(s) it causes.

    ____ *Chlamydophila psittaci*    A. Syphilis

    ____ *Chlamydophila pneumoniae*    B. Trachoma

    ____ *Chlamydia trachomatis*    C. Sinusitis

    ____ *Treponema pallidum pallidum*    D. Lymphogranuloma venereum

    ____ *Treponema pallidum pertenue*

    ____ *Treponema pallidum endemicum*    E. Proctitis

    ____ *Treponema carateum*    F. Pelvic inflammatory disease

    ____ *Borrelia burgdorferi*

       G. Ornithosis

       H. Yaws

       I. Bejel

       J. Pinta

       K. Lyme disease

4. Match the following diseases with the causative bacterium.

    ____ Peptic ulcers    A. *Vibrio cholerae*

    ____ Gastroenteritis (various forms)    B. *Vibrio parahaemolyticus*

    ____ Blood poisoning    C. *Vibrio vulnificus*

    ____ Cholera    D. *Campylobacter jejuni*

       E. *Helicobacter pylori*

# Concept Mapping

Using the following terms, draw a concept map that describes syphilis. Or, complete this concept map online by going to the Study Area at www.masteringmicrobiology.com.

Body-wide rash
Cardiovascular syphilis
Cell-free media
Chancre
Congenital syphilis

Darkfield microscopy
Gummas
Infect fetus in pregnant
    women
Last for years

Latent stage
Neurosyphilis
Never progress
Penicillin
Primary syphilis

Secondary syphilis
Serologic tests
Spirochete
Tertiary syphilis
*Treponema pallidum*

# Critical Thinking

1. Why is it more difficult to rid a community of a disease transmitted by arthropods (for example, Lyme disease or RMSF) than a disease transmitted via contaminated drinking water (for example, cholera)?

2. Some scientists think that syphilis is a New World disease brought to Europe by returning Spanish explorers; others think that syphilis traveled the opposite way. Design an experiment to test the two hypotheses.

3. A patient arrives at a medical emergency room in Austin, Texas, complaining of 48 hours of severe abdominal cramping and persistent diarrhea. While waiting, he falls into a coma. He is admitted into the hospital but never regains consciousness; a week later he dies. No one else in his family is ill. They report that the man has not been out of the country, but that they all dined at a seafood restaurant the night before the man became sick. He alone ate sea

urchins. Culture of the man's stool reveals the presence of curved bacilli. What bacterium might account for the man's death?

4. Scientists discover a mutant strain of *Helicobacter pylori* that is urease negative. The strain is found to cause ulcers only in patients that either consume large quantities of antacids and/or take drugs to block acid production. Explain why only these patients develop ulcers when infected by the mutant strain.

5. Thirty-nine members of an extended family sought medical treatment for headaches, myalgia, and recurring fevers, each lasting about three days. The outbreak occurred shortly after a one-day family gathering in a remote, seldom-used mountain cabin in New Mexico. What disease did they contract? What causes this disease? What is the appropriate treatment? How could this family have protected itself?

Access more review material online in the Study Area at **www.masteringmicrobiology.com.** There, you'll find
- **Concept Mapping Activities**
- **Flashcards**
- **Quizzes**

and more to help you succeed.

# Answers

Answers to multiple-choice, fill-in-blank, labeling, matching, and true/false questions are listed here. Answers for Short Answer and Critical Thinking questions are available for instructors only in the Instructor's Manual that accompanies this text.

**Multiple Choice**
1. c; 2. a; 3. b; 4. d; 5. b; 6. a; 7. d; 8. c; 9. b; 10. c; 11. b; 12. b; 13. b

**Labeling**
See Figure 6.

**Matching**
1. C Rocky Mountain spotted fever; A Endemic typhus; B Epidemic typhus; D Scrub typhus; E HME; 2. A *Rickettsia typhi*; B *Rickettsia prowazekii*; C *Rickettsia rickettsii*; D *Orientia tsutsugamushi*; C *Ehrlichia chaffeensis*; C *Borrelia burgdorferi*; B *Borrelia recurrentis*; C *Anaplasma phagocytophilum*; 3. G *Chlamydophila psittaci*; C *Chlamydophila pneumoniae*; B,D,E,F *Chlamydia trachomatis*; A *Treponema pallidum pallidum*; H *Treponema pallidum pertenue*; I *Treponema pallidum endemicum*; J *Treponema carateum*; K *Borrelia burgdorferi*; 4. E Peptic ulcers; A,B,D Gastroenteritis; C Blood poisoning; A Cholera

# Pathogenic Fungi

The fungus *Microsporum* is beautiful when observed on a microscope slide, but it is much less welcome when found between the toes and on the soles of the feet, where it is one cause of the condition called *tinea pedis*—commonly known as "athlete's foot." Despite its name, this surface fungal disease with symptoms of itching, peeling, and other irritation affects athletes and nonathletes alike; having warm, moist feet is a much more important factor than being physically active. Because fungal spores are constantly being shed from the feet and onto bedding and furniture—and onto moist bathroom floors—athlete's foot is common among college students living in dorms. The spores are hardy; most survive for a long time in the environment, resisting desiccation, heat, cold, salt, acid, and even some antimicrobial cleansers. The best way to deal with athlete's foot is to keep your feet dry, change your socks frequently, use an antifungal cream, and wear a pair of flip-flops in public bathrooms.

In this chapter we examine this and other fungi that cause human diseases.

(MM) Take the pre-test for this chapter online. Visit the Study Area at www.masteringmicrobiology.com.

E. Gueho/Photo Researchers

An ascomycete fungus, *Microsporum*, is one cause of athlete's foot among other fungal skin diseases.

From Chapter 22 of *Microbiology with Diseases by Taxonomy*, Third Edition. Robert W. Bauman. Copyright © 2011 by Pearson Education, Inc. Published by Benjamin Cummings, Inc. All rights reserved.

**Medical mycology** is the field of medicine that is concerned with the diagnosis, management, and prevention of fungal diseases, or **mycoses** (mī-kō'sēz). Most fungi exist as saprobes (absorbing nutrients from dead organisms) and function as the major decomposers of organic matter in the environment. More than 100,000 species of fungi have been classified in three divisions—Zygomycota, Ascomycota, and Basidiomycota—and of these, fewer than 200 have been demonstrated to cause diseases in humans.

This chapter is not arranged according to any taxonomic scheme, because the classification of fungi is difficult. For example, most fungi have both a sexual stage, known as a *teleomorph*, and an asexual stage, known as an *anamorph*. The taxonomic code allows scientists to give each stage its own unique name. For example, the anamorph *Aspergillus* (as-per-jil'ŭs) is the same fungus as the teleomorph *Neosartorya* (nē-ō-sar-tōr'ya).

To minimize confusion, this chapter considers mycoses using only a single name (usually the anamorph) and according to the site of disease, though this convention is imperfect, as some fungi can invade tissues where they are not typically found. We also consider mycoses based on whether the fungus is a true pathogen or merely an opportunist. First, however, we will briefly consider some of the basic topics in medical mycology.

# An Overview of Medical Mycology

## Learning Objective

✓ Summarize some of the complexities of identifying and treating fungal infections.

Human mycoses are among the more difficult diseases to diagnose and treat properly. Signs of mycoses are often missed or misinterpreted, and once identified, fungi often prove to be remarkably resistant to antimicrobial agents. Before we begin our discussion of fungal diseases, therefore, it will be helpful to consider some of the characteristics that set fungal infections apart from other microbial infections.

## The Epidemiology of Mycoses

### Learning Objectives

✓ State the most significant mode of transmission for mycoses.

✓ Explain why the actual prevalence of fungal infections is unknown.

Fungi and the spores they produce are almost everywhere in the environment—in soil, in water, and on or in most multicellular organisms, including plants and animals. They coat the surfaces of almost every object, whether made of wood, glass, metal, or plastic; thus, it is not surprising that most of us will experience a mycosis at some time.

Mycoses are typically acquired via inhalation, trauma, or ingestion; only very infrequently are fungi spread from person to person. Therefore, most mycoses are *not* contagious. Epidemics of mycoses can and do occur, but not as a result of person-to-person contact. Instead, they result from mass exposure to some environmental source of fungi. For example, the cleanup of bird droppings near a building's air conditioning intake vents stirs up fungal spores in the droppings. The airborne spores could then be drawn inside the building and distributed throughout its duct system, potentially infecting numerous people.

One group of fungi that *are* contagious are *dermatophytes* (der'mă-tō-fitz), which live on the dead layers of skin and which may be transmitted between people via fomites. Species of the genera *Candida* (kan'did-a) and *Pneumocystis* (nū-mō-sis'tis) also appear to be transmitted at least some of the time by contact among humans.

Because most mycoses are not contagious, they typically are not reportable; that is, neither local public health agencies nor the Centers for Disease Control and Prevention (CDC) must be notified when they are diagnosed. Again, there are a few exceptions: Pathogenic fungi are usually reported in geographic areas where they are endemic, and certain opportunistic fungal pathogens of AIDS patients are also tracked.

The fact that most mycoses are not reportable creates a problem for epidemiologists. Without reliable data, it is impossible to track the effects of mycoses on the population, to ascertain their risks, and to identify actions to prevent them.

## CRITICAL **THINKING**

Discuss the relationship between the following two facts: (1) A huge number of fungal spores are present in the environment, and (2) fungal diseases are not typically acquired via contact with infected individuals. How does not relying on a host for transmission benefit a fungus?

# Categories of Fungal Agents: True Fungal Pathogens and Opportunistic Fungi

## Learning Objectives

✓ Compare and contrast true fungal pathogens with opportunistic fungi.

✓ Identify factors that predispose people to opportunistic fungal infections.

Of all the fungi known to cause disease in humans, only four—*Blastomyces dermatitidis, Coccidioides immitis, Histoplasma capsulatum,* and *Paracoccidioides brasiliensis*—are considered true pathogens; that is, they can cause disease in otherwise healthy individuals. Other fungi, such as *Candida albicans,* are *opportunistic fungi,* which lack genes for proteins that aid in colonizing body tissues, though they can take advantage of some weakness in a host's defenses to become established and cause disease. Thus, whereas true fungal pathogens can infect anyone, regardless of immune status, opportunists infect only weakened individuals.

Four factors increase an individual's risk of experiencing opportunistic mycoses: invasive medical procedures, medical therapies, certain disease conditions, and specific lifestyle factors (Table 1). Surgical insertion of devices such as heart-valve implants can introduce fungal spores and provide a site for fungal colonization, while a variety of medical therapies leave patients with a weakened or dysfunctional immune system. AIDS, diabetes, other serious illnesses, and malnutrition also lessen immunity. Poor hygiene results in reduced skin defenses, and IV drug use can directly introduce fungi into the blood. Note that many of the factors that contribute to opportunistic fungal infections involve the actions of medical personnel in health care settings; thus correct antisepsis and medical procedures by health care providers play a crucial role in reducing the incidence of mycoses of opportunistic fungi.

In addition to differences in pathogenesis and matters related to host susceptibility, fungal pathogens and opportunists differ with respect to geographical distribution. Whereas the four pathogenic fungi are endemic to certain regions, primarily in the Americas, opportunistic fungi are distributed throughout the world.

**Dermatophytes**—fungi that normally live on the skin, nails, and hair—are the only fungi that do not fall comfortably into either the pathogenic or opportunistic groupings. They are considered by some researchers to be "emerging" pathogens. Dermatophytes can infect all individuals, not just the immunocompromised, which makes them similar to the pathogens. They are not, however, intrinsically invasive, being limited to body surfaces. They also have a tendency to occur in people with the same predisposing factors that allow access by opportunistic fungi. For these reasons, dermatophytes will be discussed as opportunists, rather than as pathogens.

### CRITICAL THINKING

Suggest a way in which each of the risk factors listed in Table 1 can be reduced or eliminated to limit opportunistic infections. What can a patient do? What can health care providers do?

## Clinical Manifestations of Fungal Diseases

### Learning Objective

✓ Describe three primary clinical manifestations of mycoses.

Fungal diseases are grouped into the following three categories of clinical manifestations:

- *Fungal infections,* which are the most common mycoses, are caused by the presence in the body of either true pathogens or opportunists. As previously noted, this chapter discusses mycoses according to general location within the body. Systemic mycoses are discussed first, followed by superficial, cutaneous, and subcutaneous mycoses.

- *Toxicoses* (poisonings) are acquired through ingestion, as occurs when poisonous mushrooms are eaten. Although relatively rare, toxicoses are discussed briefly near the end of the chapter.

**TABLE 1**

## Factors That Predispose Individuals to Opportunistic Mycoses

| Factors | Examples |
|---|---|
| Medical procedures | Surgery; insertion of medical implants (heart valves, artificial joints); catheterization |
| Medical therapies | Immunosuppressive therapies accompanying transplantation; radiation and other cancer therapies; steroid treatments; long-term use of antibacterial agents |
| Disease conditions | Inherited immune defects; leukemia and lymphomas; AIDS; diabetes and other metabolic disorders; severe burns; preexisting chronic illnesses |
| Lifestyle factors | Malnutrition; poor hygiene; IV drug abuse |

- *Allergies* (hypersensitivity reactions) most commonly result from the inhalation of fungal spores and are the subject of the chapter's final section.

## The Diagnosis of Fungal Infections

### Learning Objective

✓ Discuss why the diagnosis of opportunistic fungal infections can be difficult.

Most patients reporting to a hospital emergency room with a severe respiratory illness are routinely tested for influenza, bacterial pneumonia, and perhaps tuberculosis; without some concrete reason to suspect a fungal infection, physicians may not look for them. However, if an emergency-room patient with respiratory distress reveals that she breeds exotic birds, she is much more likely to also be tested for mycoses. Thus a patient's history—including occupation, hobbies, travel history, and the presence of preexisting medical conditions—is critical for diagnosis of most mycoses. Even when fungal infections are relatively obvious, as when distinctive mycelial growth is observed, definitive diagnosis requires isolation, laboratory culture, and morphological analysis of the fungus involved.

Microbiologists culture fungi collected from patients on *Sabouraud dextrose agar,* a medium that favors fungal growth over bacterial growth. The appearance of colonies, and the microscopic appearance of yeast cells, mycelia, or mold spores, are usually diagnostic.

Several techniques are commonly used in identifying fungi. *Potassium hydroxide (KOH) preparations* dissolve keratin in skin scrapings or biopsy specimens, leaving only fungal cells for examination. *Gomori methenamine silver (GMS) stain* is used on tissue sections to stain fungal cells black (other cells remain unstained) (Figure 1). *Direct immunofluorescence stain* can also be used to detect fungal cells in tissues; however, immunological tests, though very useful for other microbial infectious

Maxine Jalbert and Leo Kaufman, CDC

Libero Ajello, CDC

**(a)** LM 4 µm **(b)** LM 10 µm

▲ **Figure 1 Fungal stains. (a)** GMS (Gomori methenamine silver) stain. *Histoplasma capsulatum*, shown here, causes histoplasmosis. **(b)** Direct fluorescent stain of *Candida albicans*.

agents, are not always useful for fungi. Because fungi are so prevalent in the environment and many are part of the normal microbiota, it is often impossible to distinguish between actual infection and simple exposure.

Diagnosis of opportunistic fungal infections is especially challenging. When a fungal opportunist infects tissues in which it is normally not found, it may display abnormal morphology that complicates identification. In addition, the fungi that produce pulmonary infections—the true pathogens and a few opportunists—produce symptoms and imaging profiles (X-ray studies, CT scans) that strongly resemble those of tuberculosis. Fungal masses may also resemble tumors.

## Antifungal Therapies
### Learning Objective
✓ Discuss the advantages and disadvantages of fungicidal and fungistatic medications.

Mycoses are among the most difficult diseases to heal for two reasons. First, fungi generally possess the biochemical ability to resist T cells during cell-mediated immune responses. Second, fungi are biochemically similar to human cells, which means that most fungicides are toxic to human tissues. The majority of antifungal agents exploit one of the few differences between human and fungal cells—instead of cholesterol, the membranes of fungal cells contain a related molecule, *ergosterol*. Antifungal drugs target either ergosterol synthesis or its insertion into fungal membranes. However, cholesterol and ergosterol are not sufficiently different to prevent some damage to human tissues by such antifungal agents. Serious side effects associated with long-term use of almost all antifungal agents include anemia, headache, rashes, gastrointestinal upset, and serious liver and kidney damage.

The "gold standard" of antifungal agents is the fungicidal drug *amphotericin B*, considered the best drug for treating systemic mycoses and other fungal infections that do not respond to other drugs. Unfortunately, it is also one of the more toxic antifungal agents to humans. The major alternatives to amphotericin B are the azole drugs—*ketoconazole, itraconazole,* and

*fluconazole*—which are fungistatic (inhibitory) rather than fungicidal and less toxic to humans.

Two antifungal drugs that do not target ergosterol are *5-fluorocytosine*, which inhibits RNA and DNA synthesis and is given in conjunction with amphotericin B in the treatment of cryptococcal infections, and *griseofulvin*, which interferes with microtubule formation and chromosomal separation in mitosis. Griseofulvin accumulates in the outer epidermal layers of the skin, preventing fungal penetration and growth. Since these skin cells are scheduled to die as they move toward the surface, griseofulvin's toxicity does not permanently damage humans. Patients generally tolerate the drug for the duration of treatment. For example, griseofulvin is usually administered orally for up to a year to clear fungal infections of the nails without harming the patient.

Treatment of opportunistic fungal infections in immunocompromised patients involves two steps: a high-dose treatment to eliminate or reduce the number of fungal pathogens, followed by long-term (usually lifelong) maintenance therapy involving the administration of antifungal agents to control ongoing infections and prevent new infections.

With just a few antifungal drugs being used for long periods and treating more and more patients, scientists predict that the drugs should select drug-resistant strains from the fungal population. Fortunately, this is rarely the case; naturally occurring resistance, especially against amphotericin B, is extremely rare, though researchers cannot explain why resistance does not develop as it does in bacterial populations under similar conditions of long-term use. Nevertheless, strains of *Candida, Cryptococcus,* and *Aspergillus* in AIDS patients, many of whom must remain on antifungal drugs for life, have developed some resistance against 5-fluorocytosine and the azole drugs.

## Antifungal Vaccines
### Learning Objective
✓ Explain why antifungal vaccines are difficult to develop.

Prevention of fungal infections generally entails avoiding endemic areas and keeping one's immune system healthy. Vaccines against fungi have been difficult to develop because fungal metabolism is similar to our own.

Scientists have developed attenuated vaccines against *Coccidioides*, but there is concern that the weakened microbe could revert to a virulent form and cause disease in immunized individuals. Recently, researchers used recombinant DNA to create a live vaccine that protects mice against a blastomycosis and have conjugated fungal antigens with diphtheria toxoid to create a vaccine against *Candida*, which is the most common fungus infecting AIDS patients. These new vaccines are safer than live, attenuated vaccines and more effective than killed vaccines.

Now that we have considered some of the basics of medical mycology, we turn our attention to the first category of important mycoses: systemic mycoses caused by the four truly pathogenic fungi.

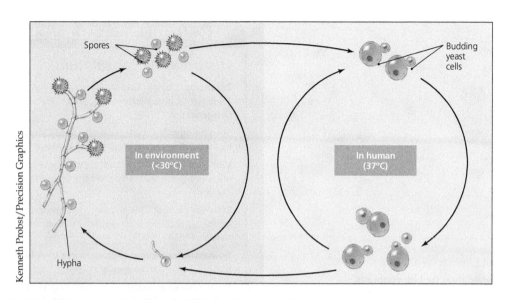

▲ **Figure 2** **The dimorphic nature of true fungal pathogens.** The mycelial form grows in the environment, and the yeast form grows within a human host. Shown here is *Histoplasma capsulatum*. *What are the other three genera of pathogenic, dimorphic fungi?*

**Figure 2** *In addition to Histoplasma, members of the genera Blastomyces, Coccidioides, and Paracoccidioides are pathogenic fungi.*

# Systemic Mycoses Caused by Pathogenic Fungi

## Learning Objectives

✓ Compare and contrast the endemic areas for the four genera of pathogenic fungi that cause systemic mycoses.

✓ Compare the clinical appearances of the diseases resulting from each of the four pathogenic fungi.

✓ Identify the laboratory techniques used to distinguish among the four pathogenic fungi.

**Systemic mycoses**—those fungal infections that spread throughout the body—result from infections by one of the four pathogenic fungi: *Blastomyces, Coccidioides, Histoplasma,* or *Paracoccidioides.* All are in the fungal division Ascomycota. These pathogenic fungi are uniformly acquired through inhalation, and all begin as a generalized pulmonary infection that then spreads, via the blood to the rest of the body.

All four are also **dimorphic**[1] (dī-mōr′fik); that is, they can have two forms. In the environment, where the temperature is typically below 30°C, they appear as mycelial thalli composed of hyphae, whereas within the body (37°C) they grow as spherical yeasts (Figure 2). The two forms differ not only structurally but also physiologically. Yeast forms are invasive because they express a variety of enzymes and other proteins that aid their growth and reproduction in the body. For example, they are

tolerant of higher temperatures and are relatively resistant to phagocytic killing.

Dimorphic fungi are extremely hazardous to laboratory personnel, who must take specific precautions to avoid exposure to spores, particularly when culturing the organisms. Biological safety cabinets with HEPA filters, protective clothing, and masks are required when working with these pathogens.

In the following sections we consider each of the systemic conditions caused by true fungal pathogens, beginning with histoplasmosis.

## Histoplasmosis

*Histoplasma capsulatum* (his-tō-plaz′mă kap-soo-lā′tŭm), the causative agent of **histoplasmosis** (his′tō-plaz-mō′sis), is an ascomycete and the most common fungal pathogen affecting humans. *H. capsulatum* is particularly prevalent in the eastern United States along the Ohio River Valley, but endemic areas also exist in Africa and South America (Figure 3). *H. capsulatum* is found in moist soils containing high levels of nitrogen such as from the droppings of bats and birds.

Two strains of *H. capsulatum* (a fungal strain referred to as a variety, or var.) are recognized: var. *capsulatum*, which is the most widely distributed, and var. *duboisii* (dū-bwa′sē-ē) which is limited to Africa. Spores of both may become airborne and inhaled when soil containing the fungus is disturbed by wind or by human activities. Cutaneous inoculation can also lead to disease, but such infections are extremely rare.

---

[1]Form Greek *di*, meaning two, and *morphe*, meaning shape.

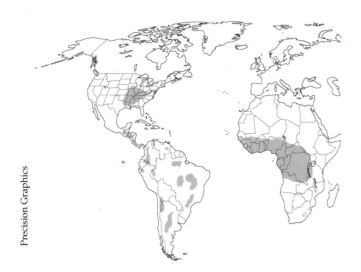

▲ **Figure 3** Endemic areas for histoplasmosis.

## CRITICAL **THINKING**

Statistically, men are more likely than women to contract histoplasmosis. What might explain this fact?

*H. capsulatum* is an intracellular parasite that survives inhalation and subsequent phagocytosis by macrophages in air sacs of the lungs. These macrophages then disperse the fungus beyond the lungs via the blood and lymph. Cell-mediated immunity eventually develops, clearing the organism from healthy patients.

About 95% of individuals infected with pulmonary *Histoplasma* are asymptomatic, and their subclinical cases resolve without damage. Some individuals may experience mild or nonspecific respiratory symptoms (for example, pains while breathing or mild coughing) that also disappear on their own. Slightly more pronounced symptoms—fever, night sweats, and weight loss—may occur in a few individuals. About 5% of patients develop clinical histoplasmosis, which manifests as one of four diseases:

- *Chronic pulmonary histoplasmosis* is characterized by severe coughing, blood-tinged sputum, night sweats, loss of appetite, and weight loss. It is often seen in individuals with preexisting lung disease. It can be mistaken for tuberculosis.

- *Chronic cutaneous histoplasmosis,* characterized by ulcerative skin lesions, can follow the spread of infection from the lungs.

- *Systemic histoplasmosis* can also follow if infection spreads from the lungs, but it is usually seen only in AIDS patients. This syndrome, characterized by enlargement of the spleen and liver, can be rapid, severe, and fatal.

- *Ocular histoplasmosis* is a type I hypersensitivity reaction against *Histoplasma* in the eye; it is characterized by inflammation and redness.

## MICROBE AT A GLANCE

### *Histoplasma capsulatum*

**Taxonomy:** Domain Eukarya, Kingdom Fungi, phylum Ascomycota, class Ascomycetes, order Onygenales, family Onygenaceae

**Morphology:** Thermally dimorphic: <30°C, it forms septate hyphae; 37°C, it forms single-celled yeasts

**Virulence factors:** Survives phagocytosis to live inside macrophages, which can deliver the fungus throughout the body

**Diseases caused:** Chronic pulmonary histoplasmosis, chronic cutaneous histoplasmosis, systematic histoplasmosis, ocular histoplasmosis

**Treatment for diseases:** ketoconazole for mild infections; amphotericin B for more severe cases

**Prevention of disease:** Ninety percent of people living in endemic areas (Ohio River Valley in North America, equatorial West Africa, and isolated areas of South America) are infected. A healthy immune system is necessary to avoid disease.

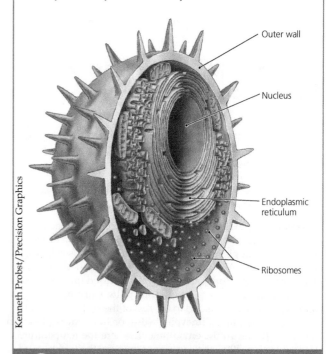

Outer wall

Nucleus

Endoplasmic reticulum

Ribosomes

(MM) Download the Microbe at a Glance flashcards from the Study Area at www.masteringmicrobiology.com.

Libero Ajello, CDC

LM | 25 μm

▲ **Figure 4** The characteristic spiny spores of mycelial *Histoplasma capsulatum.*

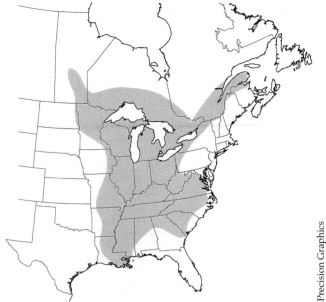

Precision Graphics

▲ **Figure 5** Geographic distribution of *Blastomyces.*

Diagnosis of histoplasmosis is based on the identification of the distinctive budding yeast in KOH- or GMS-prepared samples of skin scrapings, sputum, cerebrospinal fluid, or various tissues. The diagnosis is confirmed by the observation of dimorphism in cultures grown from such samples. Cultured *H. capsulatum* produces distinctively spiny spores that are also diagnostic (Figure 4). Antibody tests are not useful indicators of *Histoplasma* infection because many people have been ex-posed without contracting disease. In the endemic regions of the United States, close to 90% of the population tests positive for *H. capsulatum* exposure.

Infections in immunocompetent individuals typically resolve without treatment. When symptoms do not resolve, amphotericin B is prescribed. Ketoconazole can be used to treat mild infections. Maintenance therapy for AIDS patients is recommended.

## Blastomycosis

**Blastomycoses** (blas'tō-mī-kō'sēz) are caused by another as-comycete, *Blastomyces dermatitidis* (blas-tō-mī'sēz der-mă-tit'i-dis), which is endemic across the southeastern United States north to Canada (Figure 5). Outbreaks have also been reported in Latin America, Africa, Asia, and Europe. *B. dermatitidis* normally grows and sporulates in cool, damp soil rich in organic material such as decaying vegetation and animal wastes. In humans, both recreational and occupational exposure occurs when fungal spores in soil become airborne and are inhaled. A relatively small inoculum can produce disease. The incidence of human infection is increasing, in part, because of increases in the number of immunocompromised individuals in the population.

*Pulmonary blastomycosis* is the most common manifestation of *Blastomyces* infection. After spores enter the lungs, they convert to yeast forms and multiply. Initial pulmonary lesions are asymptomatic in most individuals. If symptoms do develop, they are vague and include muscle aches, cough, fever, chills,

malaise, and weight loss. Purulent (pus-filled) lesions develop and expand as the yeasts multiply, resulting in death of tissues and cavity formation. Rarely, a deep productive cough and chest pain accompany the generalized symptoms. In otherwise healthy people, pulmonary blastomycosis typically resolves successfully, although it may become chronic. Respiratory failure and death occur at a high frequency among AIDS patients.

The fungus can spread beyond the lungs. *Cutaneous blastomycosis* occurs in 60–70% of cases and consists of generally painless lesions on the face and upper body (Figure 6). The lesions can be raised and wartlike, or they may be craterlike if tissue death occurs. In roughly 30% of cases, the fungus spreads to the spine, pelvis, cranium, ribs, long bones, or subcutaneous tissues surrounding joints, a condition called *osteoarticular*[2] (os'tē-ō-ar-tik'ū-lar) *blastomycosis.* About 40% of AIDS patients experience meningitis resulting from dissemination of *Blastomyces* to the central nervous system. Abscesses may form in other tissue systems as well.

Diagnosis relies on identification of *B. dermatitidis* following culture, or direct examination of various samples such as sputum, bronchial washings, biopsies, cerebrospinal fluid, or skin scrapings. Observation of dimorphism in laboratory cultures coupled with microscopic examination is diagnostic.

Physicians treat blastomycoses with amphotericin B for 10 weeks or longer. Oral itraconazole may be used as an alternative but must be administered for a minimum of three to six months. Relapse is common in AIDS patients, and suppressive maintenance therapy with itraconazole is recommended.

[2]From Greek *osteon*, meaning bone, and *arthron*, meaning joint.

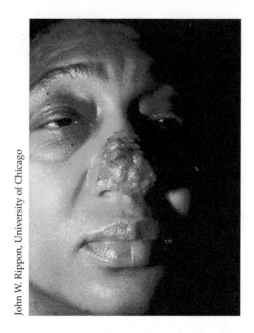

John W. Rippon, University of Chicago

▲ **Figure 6 Cutaneous blastomycosis in an American woman.** This condition typically results from the spread of *Blastomyces dermatitidis* from the lungs to the skin.

## CRITICAL **THINKING**

Outbreaks of blastomycoses have occurred in Latin America even though the pathogen normally is not found there. Based on what you have read, explain why a few cases of blastomycosis might appear outside of Northern Hemisphere endemic areas.

## Coccidioidomycosis

**Coccidioidomycosis** (kok-sid-ē-oy′dō-mī-kō-sis), caused by ascomycete *Coccidioides immitis* (kok-sid-ē-oy′dēz im′i-tis), is found almost exclusively in the southwestern United States (Arizona, California, Nevada, New Mexico, and Texas) and northern Mexico. Small, focally endemic areas also exist in semiarid parts of Central and South America (Figure 7). Fungi can be recovered from desert soil, rodent burrows, ar-cheologi-cal remains, and mines. Dust that coats materials from endemic areas, including Native American pots and blankets sold to tourists, can serve as a vehicle of infection. Infection rates in endemic areas have risen in recent years as a result of population expansion and increased recreational activities, such as the use of off-road vehicles in the desert. More ominous threats to human health, however, are windstorms and earthquakes, which can disturb large tracts of contaminated soil, spreading the fungal elements for miles downwind and exposing thousands of people.

In the warm and dry summer and fall months, particularly in drought cycles, *C. immitis* grows as a mycelium and produces sturdy chains of asexual spores called *arthroconidia*. When mature, arthroconidia germinate into new mycelia in the

Precision Graphics

▲ **Figure 7 Endemic areas of *Coccidioides*.**

environment, but if inhaled, arthroconidia germinate in the lungs to produce a parasitic form called a *spherule* (sfer′ool) (Figure 8). As each spherule matures, it enlarges and generates a large number of spores via multiple cleavages, until it ruptures and releases the spores into the surrounding tissue. Each spore then forms a new spherule to continue the cycle of division and release. This type of growth accounts for the seriousness of *Coccidioides* infection.

Spherule    Spores

E. C. Chan/Visuals Unlimited

LM    ⊢———⊣ 25 µm

▲ **Figure 8 Spherules of *Coccidioides immitis*.** Note the numerous spores within a spherule.

From: Dermatology Photo Quiz. M. Miller. *Resident & Staff Physician*. May 2006; (52)5; Fig. 1

▲ **Figure 9** **Coccidioidomycosis lesions in subcutaneous tissue.** Painless lesions result from the spread of *Coccidioides immitis* from the lungs.

Visuals Unlimited

LM | 5 µm

▲ **Figure 10** **The "steering wheel" formation of buds characteristic of *Paracoccidioides brasiliensis*.**

The major manifestation of coccidioidomycosis is pulmonary. About 60% of patients experience either no symptoms or mild, unremarkable symptoms that go unnoticed and typically resolve on their own. Other patients develop more severe infections characterized by fever, cough, chest pain, difficulty breathing, coughing up or spitting blood, headache, night sweats, weight loss, and pneumonia; in some individuals a diffuse rash may appear on the trunk. Occasionally the mild forms of the pulmonary disease become more chronic, in which cases the continued multiplication of spherules results in large, permanent cavities in the lungs similar to those seen in tuberculosis patients.

In a very small percentage of cases, generally in those who are severely immunocompromised, *C. immitis* spreads from the lungs to various other sites. Invasion of the central nervous system (CNS) may result in meningitis, headache, nausea, and emotional disturbance. Infection can also spread to the bones, joints, and painless subcutaneous tissues; subcutaneous lesions are inflamed masses of granular material (Figure 9).

The diagnosis of coccidioidomycosis can be based on the identification of spherules in KOH- or GMS-treated samples collected from patients. Health care workers administer a *coccidioidin skin test* to screen patients for contact with *Coccidioides*. In the test, antigens of *Coccidioides* are injected under the skin. If the body has antibodies against the fungus— that is, the patient has been or is infected—then the site will become inflamed. Diagnosis is confirmed by the isolation of the mycelial form of *C. immitis* in laboratory culture or isolation of encapsulated yeasts in the patients' tissues.

Although infections in otherwise healthy patients generally resolve on their own without damage, amphotericin B is the drug of choice. CNS involvement is fatal without treatment. In AIDS patients, maintenance therapy with itraconazole or fluconazole is recommended to prevent relapse or reinfection. The wearing of protective masks in endemic areas can prevent exposure to spores, but constant, daily wearing of masks may be impractical for all but those whose occupations put them at clear risk of infection.

## Paracoccidioidomycosis

Another ascomycete, *Paracoccidioides brasiliensis* (par'ă-kok-sid-ē-oy'dēz brǎ-sil-ē-en'sis) causes **paracoccidioidomycosis** (par'ă-kok-sid-ē-oy'dō-mī-kō'sis), a chronic fungal disease similar to blastomycosis and coccidioidomycosis. *P. brasiliensis* is found in cool, damp soil from southern Mexico to regions of South America, particularly in Brazil. Because this fungus is far more geographically limited than the other true fungal pathogens, paracoccidioidomycosis is not a common disease. Those most at risk include farm workers in endemic areas.

Infections range from asymptomatic to systemic, and disease first becomes apparent as a pulmonary form that is slow to develop but manifests as chronic cough, fever, night sweats, malaise, and weight loss. The fungus almost always spreads, producing a chronic inflammatory disease of mucous membranes. Painful ulcerated lesions of the gums, tongue, lips, and palate progressively worsen over the course of weeks to months.

KOH or GMS preparations of tissue samples reveal yeast cells with multiple buds in a "steering wheel" formation that is diagnostic for this organism (Figure 10). Laboratory culture at 25°C and at 37°C demonstrating dimorphism is confirmatory. Serological identification of antibodies also is useful. Treatment is with amphotericin B or ketoconazole.

### CRITICAL **THINKING**

All of the true fungal pathogens manifest initially as a pulmonary disease. Explain how you could ascertain which of the four pathogens a patient has.

## What's Ailing the Bird Enthusiast?

Alamy

A 64-year-old man arrives at a hospital emergency room with signs and symptoms of serious pulmonary infection. He complains of a deep cough, blood-tinged sputum, night sweats, and weight loss. His liver and spleen feel enlarged upon physical examination. X-ray studies of his chest suggest tuberculosis, but a tuberculin skin test is negative, as is an HIV test. The man, an Ohio native, has recently traveled to Africa and Asia. He is also an avid bird enthusiast who likes to watch birds from his balcony.

He keeps many bird feeders on the balcony, attracts numerous birds, and spends an hour a day cleaning up bird droppings.

Skin tests are positive for histoplasmosis but inconclusive for coccidioidomycosis and blastomycosis.

1. What is the most likely infecting agent? How do you suppose this individual acquired the disease?

2. Is this disease unusual in people who work with birds?

3. Given that some tests were inconclusive, what other tests or lab work would aid in arriving at a specific diagnosis?

4. What treatment would most likely be prescribed?

# Systemic Mycoses Caused by Opportunistic Fungi

### Learning Objective

✓ Discuss the difficulties in diagnosing opportunistic fungal infections.

Opportunistic mycoses do not typically affect healthy humans, because the fungi involved lack genes for virulence factors that make them actively invasive. Instead, opportunistic mycoses are limited to people with poor immunity. Because of the growing number of AIDS patients, opportunistic fungal infections have become one of the more significant causes of human disease and death. Even though any fungus can become an opportunist, five genera of fungi are routinely encountered: *Pneumocystis, Candida, Aspergillus, Cryptococcus,* and *Mucor.*

Opportunistic infections present a formidable challenge to clinicians. Because they appear only when their hosts are weakened, they often display "odd" clinical signatures; that is, their symptoms are often atypical, or they occur in individuals not residing in endemic areas for a particular fungus. Increased severity of symptoms is often a reflection of the poor immune status of the patient and frequently results in higher fatality rates, even if the fungus is normally nonthreatening.

In the following sections we consider some of the mycoses caused by the "classical" fungal opportunists, beginning with *Pneumocystis pneumonia.*

## *Pneumocystis* Pneumonia

### Learning Objective

✓ List the characteristics of *Pneumocystis* that distinguish it from other fungal opportunists.

*Pneumocystis jiroveci* (nū-mō-sis'tis jē-rō-vĕt'zē), an ascomycete of the normal respiratory microbiota formerly known as *P. carinii,* is one of the more common opportunistic fungal infections seen in AIDS patients. Prior to the AIDS epidemic, disease caused by *Pneumocystis* was extremely rare.

Even though the organism was first identified in 1909, little is known about it. Originally considered a protozoan, it has been reclassified as a fungus based on rRNA nucleotide sequences and biochemistry. Its morphological and developmental characteristics, however, still resemble those of protozoa more than those of fungi. Because *P. jiroveci* is an obligate parasite and cannot survive on its own in the environment, transmission most likely occurs through inhalation.

*P. jiroveci* is distributed worldwide in humans; based on serological confirmation of antibodies, the majority of healthy children (75%) have been exposed to the fungus by the age of five. In immunocompetent people, infection is asymptomatic, and generally clearance of the fungus from the body is followed by lasting immunity. However, some individuals may remain infected indefinitely; in such carriers the organism remains in the alveoli (air sacs of lungs) and can be passed in respiratory droplets.

Before the AIDS epidemic, the disease **Pneumocystis pneumonia** was observed only in malnourished, premature infants and debilitated elderly patients. Now, the disease is almost diagnostic for AIDS. *Pneumocystis* pneumonia is abbreviated *PCP,* which originally stood for *Pneumocystis carinii* pneumonia but now can be considered to stand for *Pneumocystis* pneumonia.

Once the fungus enters the lungs of an AIDS patient, it multiplies rapidly, extensively colonizing the lungs, because the patient's defenses are impaired. Widespread inflammation, fever, difficulty in breathing, and a nonproductive cough are characteristic. If left untreated, PCP involves more and more lung tissue until death occurs.

Diagnosis relies on clinical and microscopic findings. Chest X-ray studies usually reveal abnormal lung features. Stained smears of fluid from the lungs or from biopsies can reveal distinctive morphological forms of the fungus (Figure 11). The use of fluorescent antibody on samples taken from patients is more sensitive and provides a more specific diagnosis.

Because the fungus has many of the characteristics of protozoa, both primary treatment and maintenance therapy are with

Lois Norman, CDC

LM  10 μm

▲ **Figure 11 Cysts of *Pneumocystis jiroveci* in lung tissue.** Such microscopic findings are diagnostic.

the antiprotozoan drugs trimethoprim and sulfanilamide. Pentamidine, another antiprotozoan drug, is an alternative. The drugs may be aerosolized to allow for direct inhalation into the lungs.

## Candidiasis

### Learning Objective

✓ Explain how candidiasis can develop from a localized infection to a systemic mycosis.

**Candidiasis** (kan-di-dī′ă-sis) is any opportunistic fungal infection or disease caused by various species of the genus *Candida*—most commonly *Candida albicans* (al′bi-kanz). Fungi in this genus of dimorphic ascomycetes are common members of the microbiota of the skin and mucous membranes; for example, the digestive tracts of 40–80% of all healthy individuals harbor *Candida* species. *Candida* is one of a very few fungi that can be transmitted between individuals. From its site as a normal inhabitant of the female reproductive tract, for example, it can be passed to babies during childbirth and to men during sexual contact.

Although *Candida* species can infect tissues in essentially every body system, producing a wide range of disease manifestations in humans (Figure 12), in all cases the fungus is an opportunist. It is *Candida* that causes vaginal yeast infections, as the fungus grows prolifically when normal bacterial microbiota are inhibited due to changes in vaginal pH or use of antibacterial drugs. Localized, superficial infections are seen in individuals with impairment of the barrier function of the epithelial layers (generally newborns and the elderly).

Systemic disease is seen almost universally in immunocompromised individuals. Different segments of the population experience a given manifestation of candidiasis at different rates. For example, whereas oral candidiasis (thrush) is rare in

▶ **Figure 12 Four of the many manifestations of candidiasis.**
**(a)** Oropharyngeal candidiasis, or thrush. **(b)** Diaper rash. **(c)** Nail infection (onychomycosis). **(d)** Ocular candidiasis.

(a)  P. Marazzi/Photo Researchers

(b)  Phototake

(c)  Edward H. Gill/Custom Medical Stock Photo

(d)  Atlas of Ophthalmology (www.atlasophthalmology.com)

## TABLE 2

## The Clinical Manifestations of Candidiasis

| Type | Clinical Signs and Symptoms | Predisposing Factors |
|---|---|---|
| Oropharyngeal (thrush) | White plaques on the mucosa of the mouth, tongue, gums, palate, and/or pharynx | Diabetes, AIDS, cancers, various chemotherapeutic drug regimens |
| Cutaneous | Moist, macular red rash between skin folds | Moisture, heat, and friction of skin in skin folds and between digits, particularly in the obese |
| | Diaper rash: raised red rash, pustules in the gluteal region | Infrequently changed, soiled diapers |
| | Onychomycosis: painful red swelling around the nails, destruction of nail tissue, and loss of the nail | Immunocompromised individuals |
| Vulvovaginal | Creamy white, curdlike discharge, burning, redness, painful intercourse | Use of broad-spectrum antibiotics, pregnancy, diabetes, changes to the vaginal microbiota |
| Chronic mucocutaneous | Lesions associated with the skin, nails, and mucous membranes; severe forms may occur | Various metabolic problems relating to cell-mediated immunity (e.g., diabetes) in children |
| Neonatal and congenital | Meningitis, renal disorders, or generalized, bodywide, red, vesicular rash | Young age, low birth weight, use of antibiotics by the mother |
| Esophageal | White plaques along the esophagus, burning pain, nausea, and vomiting | AIDS, immunocompromised status |
| Gastrointestinal | Ulceration of the stomach and intestinal mucosa | Hematological cancers |
| Pulmonary | Generalized, nonspecific symptoms; often remains undiagnosed until autopsy | Infection spread from other types of candidiasis |
| Peritoneal | Fever, pain, tenderness | Indwelling catheters for dialysis or gastrointestinal perforation |
| Urinary tract | Urinary tract infection: painful urination, possible discharge | Chemotherapeutic drug regimens, catheterization, diabetes, preexisting bladder problems |
| | Renal: fever, pain, rigors, fungus ball | |
| Meningeal | Swelling of the meninges, fever, headache, stiffness of the neck | Spread of *Candida* during systemic infection |
| Hepatic and splenic | Fever, swelling of the liver and spleen, liver dysfunction, lesions and abscesses | Leukemia |
| Endocardial, myocardial pericardial | Fever, heart murmur, congestive heart failure, anemia | Preexisting heart valve disease, catheterization plus use, of antibiotics, IV drug abuse, valve prosthetics |
| Ocular | Cloudy vision, lesions within the eye | Spread of candidiasis, indwelling catheters, IV drug abuse, trauma |
| Osteoarticular | Pain when weight is placed on joint | Spread of candidiasis, prosthetic implants |
| Candidemia | Antibiotic-resistant fevers, tachycardia, hypotension, skin lesions, small abscesses in various organ systems | IV or urinary catheters, use of antibacterial drugs, surgery, severe burns, antibacterial therapy |

healthy individuals and occurs in only about 5% of newborns, it affects 10% of the elderly and nearly all those infected with HIV once they develop clinical AIDS. Table 2 summarizes the wide variety of clinical manifestations of candidiasis.

Physicians diagnose candidiasis on the basis of signs and demonstration of clusters of budding yeasts (see Figure 1b) and *pseudohyphae,* which are series of buds remaining attached to the parent cell and appearing as a filamentous hypha.

In immunocompetent patients, for whom excessive friction and body moisture in skin folds or preexisting diseases are the reasons for fungal colonization, resolution involves treating these underlying problems in addition to administering topical antifungal agents. Oral candidiasis in infants and children is treated with nystatin. Azole suppositories, creams, and/or oral administration of fluconazole are used for vaginal candidiasis.

The same infections in AIDS patients are much more difficult to treat because most superficial or mucous membrane infections in these patients do not respond well to topical antifungal treatments. Orally administered fluconazole is used for primary and maintenance therapy for candidiasis in AIDS patients. Invasive candidiasis requires treatment with amphotericin B, and often with 5-fluorocytosine; fluconazole may be substituted for either drug.

## CRITICAL **THINKING**

Even though *Candida* species are not as virulent as some microbial pathogens, the fungus can still invade every human tissue. Propose a possible explanation for this observation.

From: Aspergillus fumigatus keratitis after laser in situ keratomileusis: a case report and review of post-LASIK fungal keratitis. F. Rahimi, M. N. Hashemian and M. T. Rajabi. Eye. 2007 Jun; 21(6):843–5; Fig. 1c

▲ **Figure 13  An invasive aspergilloma in the eye.** *In what group of individuals is aspergillosis an emerging disease?*

**Figure 13** *Aspergillosis is an emerging disease of AIDS patients.*

## Aspergillosis

### Learning Objective

✓ Describe the clinical manifestations of aspergillosis.

**Aspergillosis** (as′per-ji-lō-sis) is not a single disease, but instead a term for several diseases resulting from the inhalation of spores of fungi in the genus *Aspergillus* (as-per-jil′ŭs) in the division Ascomycota. *Aspergillus* is found in soil, food, compost, agricultural buildings, and air vents of homes and offices worldwide. Although exposure to *Aspergillus* most commonly causes only allergies, more serious diseases can occur, and aspergillosis is a growing problem for AIDS patients. Because the fungi are so common in the environment, little can be done to prevent exposure to the spores.

Even though *Aspergillus* species can be opportunistic pathogens of almost all body tissues, these fungi are chiefly responsible for causing three clinical pulmonary diseases:

- *Hypersensitivity aspergillosis* manifests as asthma or other allergic symptoms and results most commonly from inhalation of *Aspergillus* spores. Symptoms may be mild and result in no damage, or they may become chronic, with recurrent episodes leading to permanent damage.

- *Noninvasive aspergillomas*—ball-like masses of fungal hyphae—can form in the cavities resulting from a previous case of pulmonary tuberculosis. Most cases are asymptomatic, though coughing of blood-tinged sputum may occur.

- *Acute invasive pulmonary aspergillosis* is more serious. Signs and symptoms, which include fever, cough, and pain, may present as pneumonia. Death of lung tissue can lead to significant respiratory impairment.

*Aspergillus* also causes nonpulmonary disease when aspergillomas form in paranasal sinuses, ear canals, eyelids (Figure 13), the conjunctivas, eye sockets, or brain. Rarely,

## MICROBE AT A GLANCE

### Aspergillus

**Taxonomy:** Domain Eukarya, Kingdom Fungi, phylum Ascomycota, class Ascomycetes, order Eurotiales, family Trichocomaceae; principally three species cause disease in humans: *A. fumigatus, A. niger,* and *A. flavus*

**Morphology:** Septate hyphae

**Virulence factors:** Allergenic surface molecules; opportunistic pathogen with little virulence except in immunocompromised patients

**Diseases caused:** Hypersensitivity aspergillosis (allergy), noninvasive aspergilloma, acute invasive pulmonary aspergillosis, cutaneous aspergillosis, systemic aspergillosis

**Treatment for diseases:** Allergy: anti-inflammatory drugs and desensitization to allergens; other disease: amphotericin B and surgical removal of aspergillomas

**Prevention of disease:** Maintain a healthy immune system.

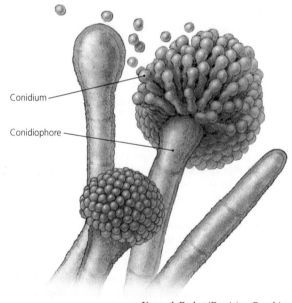

Kenneth Probst/Precision Graphics

Download the Microbe at a Glance flashcards from the Study Area at www.masteringmicrobiology.com.

*cutaneous aspergillosis* results when the fungus is either introduced into the skin by trauma or spreads from the lungs in AIDS patients. Lesions begin as raised, red papules that progressively die. *Systemic aspergillosis,* which involves invasion of the major organ systems, occurs in AIDS patients and IV drug abusers. The fungus produces abscesses in the brain, kidneys,

## EMERGING DISEASES

### PULMONARY BLASTOMYCOSIS

iStockPhoto

Phil was glad he had spent the summer fishing, hiking, and camping in western Ontario. Canada is beautiful, and he had needed time off from his two jobs and full schedule of nursing classes. Now he was back in college and remembrances of Canada were helping him cope with the stress.

However, Phil didn't feel well. He was probably coming down with the flu—fever and chills, shivering and coughing, muscle aches, tiredness, a general feeling of yuckiness, and no runny nose; yes, it must be the flu. Or was it? He knew from microbiology class that many diseases of bacteria, protozoa, and viruses have flulike symptoms. Phil had forgotten fungi.

Phil tried every over-the-counter remedy, to no avail. He tried the health clinic on campus, but the antibiotics he received made things worse, not better. He was losing weight, and pus-filled, raised sores had appeared on his face, neck, and legs. More alarming: his testes were swollen and aching. This was getting serious.

Precision Graphics

*Blastomyces*, an emergent, dimorphic fungus, was attacking Phil. Inhaled spores from hyphae growing on wet leaves primarily in Wisconsin and Ontario had germinated in Phil's lungs. The yeast phase was multiplying and spreading throughout his body, producing skin lesions that lasted for months, finally resolving into raised, wartlike scars.

Researchers don't know why blastomycosis is becoming more prevalent. Perhaps it has to do with better diagnosis and reporting; perhaps it has to do with a growing number of AIDS patients who are susceptible to infection; or perhaps it has to do with more people like Phil adventuring into the wilderness.

The good news is that with proper diagnosis, Phil got the treatment he needed—itraconazole for six months. He graduated, and now he is a nurse who knows that flulike symptoms can sometimes indicate serious fungal infection.

(MM) **Track pulmonary blastomycosis online by going to the Study Area at www.masteringmicrobiology.com.**

heart, bones, and gastrointestinal tract. Systemic aspergillosis is often fatal, especially when the brain is involved.

Clinical history and radiographs demonstrating abnormal lung structure are suggestive of aspergillosis, but diagnosis must be confirmed via laboratory techniques. The presence of septate hyphae and distinctive conidia in KOH- and GMS-prepared samples taken from a patient are diagnostic. Immunological tests to detect antigens in the blood are confirmatory.

Treatment of hypersensitivity involves either the use of various allergy medications or desensitization to the allergen. Invasive disease is treated by surgical removal of aspergillomas and surrounding tissues, plus high-dose, intravenous administration of amphotericin B. Systemic infections must be treated with amphotericin B in conjunction with other antifungal agents. Maintenance therapy with itraconazole is suggested for preventing relapse in AIDS patients.

## Cryptococcosis

### Learning Objective

✓ Discuss the characteristics of *Cryptococcus* that contribute to the severity of cryptococcoses in immunocompromised patients.

A basidiomycete, *Cryptococcus neoformans* (krip-tō-kok'ŭs nē-ō-for'manz), is the primary species causing **cryptococcoses** (krip'-tō-kok-ō'sēz). Two strains are known. *C. neoformans gattii* is

found in Australia, Papua New Guinea, parts of Africa, the Mediterranean, India, Southeast Asia, parts of Central and South America, and in southern California. It primarily infects immunocompetent individuals. *C. neoformans neoformans* is found worldwide and predominantly infects AIDS patients. Approximately 50% of all cryptococcal infections reported each year are due to strain *neoformans*.

Human infections follow the inhalation of spores or dried yeast in aerosols from the droppings of birds. People who work around buildings where birds roost are at increased risk of infection. Hospitals, convalescent homes, and other such facilities often place devices that deter the roosting of birds near air-intake vents in an effort to prevent *Cryptococcus*-contaminated air from entering a building.

The pathogenesis of *Cryptococcus* is enhanced by several characteristics of this fungus: the presence of a phagocytosis-resistant capsule surrounding the yeast form; the ability of the yeast to produce melanin, which further inhibits phagocytosis; and the organism's predilection for the central nervous system (CNS), which is isolated from the immune system by the so-called blood-brain barrier. Cryptococcal infections also tend to appear in terminal AIDS patients when little immune function remains.

*Primary pulmonary cryptococcosis* is asymptomatic in most individuals, although some individuals experience a low-grade fever, cough, and mild chest pain. In a few cases, *invasive pulmonary cryptococcosis* occurs, resulting in chronic pneumonia in which cough and pulmonary lesions progressively worsen over a period of years.

*Cryptococcal meningitis,* the most common clinical form of cryptococcal infection, follows dissemination of the fungus to the CNS. Symptoms develop slowly and include headache, dizziness, drowsiness, irritability, confusion, nausea, vomiting, and neck stiffness. In late stages of the disease, loss of vision and coma occur. Acute onset of rapidly fatal cryptococcal meningitis occurs in individuals with widespread infection.

*Cryptococcoma* (krip'tō-kok-ō'mă) is a very rare condition in which solid fungal masses form in the cerebral hemispheres, cerebellum, or (rarely) in the spinal cord. The symptoms of this condition, which can be mistaken for cerebral tumors, are similar to those of cryptococcal meningitis but also include motor and neurological impairment.

*Cutaneous cryptococcosis* may also develop. Primary infections manifest as ulcerated skin lesions or as inflammation of subcutaneous tissues. Infection may resolve on its own, but patients should be monitored for infection spreading to the CNS. Secondary cutaneous lesions occur following spread of *Cryptococcus* to other areas of the body. In AIDS patients, cutaneous cryptococcosis is the second most common manifestation of *Cryptococcus* infection (after meningitis). Lesions are common on the head and neck.

Diagnosis involves collecting specimen samples that correlate with the symptoms. GMS stains revealing the presence of encapsulated yeast in cerebrospinal fluid are highly suggestive of cryptococcal meningitis, even if no overt symptoms are present (Figure 14). Recovery of *Cryptococcus* from respiratory secretions is generally not diagnostic because of general environmental exposure, but any patient testing positive for *C. neoformans* should be monitored for systemic disease. The preferred method of confirming cryptococcal meningitis is detection of fungal antigens in cerebrospinal fluid. In AIDS patients, antigens can be detected in serum as well.

Treatment for cryptococcoses is with amphotericin B and 5-fluorocytosine administered together for 6–10 weeks. The synergistic action of the two drugs allows lower doses of amphotericin B to be used, but toxicity is not completely eliminated. Although AIDS patients may appear well following primary treatment, the fungus typically remains and must be actively suppressed by lifelong use of oral fluconazole.

### CRITICAL **THINKING**

Compare and contrast the clinical features of cryptococcosis and PCP. Why are both of these diseases so dangerous to AIDS patients?

## Zygomycoses

### Learning Objective

✓ Describe the clinical forms of zygomycoses.

**Zygomycoses** (zī'gō-mī-kō'sez) are opportunistic fungal infections caused by various genera of fungi classified in the division

Edwin P. Ewing, Jr., CDC

LM    10 μm

▲ **Figure 14  GMS stain of *Cryptococcus.*** Yeasts of this dimorphic fungus multiply in the lungs, as shown, and may spread to other parts of the body.

Zygomycota, especially *Mucor* [or sometimes *Rhizopus* (rī-zō'pŭs) or *Absidia* (ab-sid'ē-ă)]. All three have a worldwide distribution and are extremely common in soil, on decaying organic matter, or as contaminants that cause food spoilage (*Rhizopus* is the classic bread mold).

Zygomycoses are commonly seen in patients with uncontrolled diabetes, in people who inject illegal drugs, in some cancer patients, and in some patients receiving antimicrobial agents. Infections generally develop in the face and head area but can develop elsewhere and may spread throughout the bodies of severely immunocompromised individuals, resulting in the following conditions:

- *Rhinocerebral zygomycosis* begins with infection of the nasal sinuses following inhalation of spores. The fungus spreads to the mouth and nose, producing macroscopic cottonlike growths. *Mucor* can subsequently invade blood vessels, where it produces fibrous clots, causes tissue death, and subsequently invades the brain, which is fatal within days, even with treatment.

- *Pulmonary zygomycosis* follows inhalation of spores (as from moldy foods). The fungus kills lung tissue, resulting in the formation of cavities.

- *Gastrointestinal zygomycosis* involves ulcers in the intestinal tract.

- *Cutaneous zygomycosis* results from the introduction of fungi through the skin after trauma (such as burns or needle punctures). Lesions range from pustules and ulcers to abscesses and dead patches of skin.

Diagnosis usually involves microscopic findings of fungus. Samples may be obtained from scrapings of lesions, lung aspirates, or biopsies. KOH- or GMS-stained tissue sections reveal hyphae with irregular branching and few septate divisions.

Treatment, which should begin as soon as infection is suspected, involves physical removal of infected tissues and management of predisposing factors. Amphotericin B administered intravenously for 8–10 weeks is the drug of choice for all zygomycoses.

## The Emergence of Fungal Opportunists in AIDS Patients

### Learning Objectives

✓ Identify several emerging fungal opportunists seen among AIDS patients.

✓ Identify the factors that contribute to the emergence of new fungal opportunists.

Immunosuppression is not unique to AIDS patients, but because HIV systematically destroys functional immunity, AIDS patients are extremely vulnerable to opportunistic fungal infections. In otherwise healthy people, immunosuppressive episodes are transitory and result from surgery, chemotherapy, or an acute illness. With AIDS, by contrast, immune dysfunction is permanent. For this reason, once an opportunistic infection is established in an AIDS patient, it is not likely ever to be cured fully. In fact, mycoses account for most deaths associated with AIDS. *Pneumocystis jiroveci, Candida albicans, Aspergillus fumigatus,* and *Cryptococcus neoformans* are so common in HIV-positive individuals that their mycoses are part of what defines end-stage AIDS.

The emergence of new fungal opportunists results from a combination of factors. First, the number of immunocompromised individuals is increasing as a result of the AIDS epidemic. Then, the widespread use of antifungal drugs in this enlarging group of immunocompromised individuals selects fungi resistant to the drugs. Thus as the immunocompromised population grows, fungi can be expected to increasingly cause illness and death. An AIDS patient's lack of immunity allows a normally superficial fungus to gain access to internal systems, with significant, even fatal, results. Over the course of the past decade, several new fungal opportunists have been identified, including *Fusarium* spp. and *Penicillium marneffei,* which are ascomycetes, and *Trichosporon beigelii,* which is a basidiomycete.

*Fusarium* (fū-zā′rē-ŭm) species cause respiratory distress, disseminated infections, and *fungemia* (fungi in the bloodstream). These fungi also produce toxins that can accumulate to dangerous levels when ingested in food. *Fusarium* spp. are resistant to all antifungal agents, including amphotericin B.

*Penicillium marneffei* (pen-i-sil′ē-ŭm mar-nef-ē′ī) is a dimorphic, invasive fungus that causes pulmonary disease upon inhalation. It is the third most frequent illness seen in AIDS patients in Southeast Asia (behind tuberculosis and cryptococcosis).

When *Trichosporon beigelii* (trik-ō-spōr′on bā-gĕl-ē′ē) enters an AIDS patient through the lungs, the gastrointestinal tract, or catheters, it causes a drug-resistant systemic disease that is typically fatal.

To combat the threat posed by these opportunists, health care providers maintain rigorous hygiene during medical procedures. Researchers are developing new therapies that limit immunosuppression in all patients, including those with AIDS.

# Superficial, Cutaneous, and Subcutaneous Mycoses

### Learning Objective

✓ Describe the general manifestations of superficial, cutaneous, and subcutaneous mycoses.

All the mycoses we discuss in the following sections are localized at sites at or near the surface of the body. They are the most commonly reported fungal diseases. All are opportunistic infections, but unlike those we have just discussed, they can be acquired both through environmental exposure and more frequently via person-to-person contact. Most of these fungi are not life threatening, but they often cause chronic, recurring infections and diseases.

## Superficial Mycoses

### Learning Objective

✓ Compare and contrast the clinical and diagnostic features of dermatophytosis and *Malassezia* infections.

Superficial mycoses are the most common fungal infections. They are confined to the outer, dead layers of the skin, nails, or hair, all of which are composed of dead cells filled with a protein called *keratin*—the primary food of these fungi. In AIDS patients, superficial mycoses can spread to cover significant areas of skin or become systemic.

### Black Piedra and White Piedra

*Piedra*[3] (pē-ā′drǎ) is a superficial infection characterized by nodules on hair shafts. Transmission is usually by way of shared hair brushes and combs, and several members of a family are typically infected at the same time.

*Piedraia hortae* (pī-drā′ǎ hōr′tī), an ascomycete which causes **black piedra,** is distributed throughout Central and South America and Southeast Asia. It forms hard, black nodules **(Figure 15a). White piedra,** which is found worldwide in the tropics and subtropics, is caused by a basidiomycete, *Trichosporon beigelii,* which produces soft, gray to white nodules **(Figure 15b).** In both diseases, the clinical appearance of the hair is diagnostic for the disease.

Treatment for both types of piedra typically involves shaving to remove infected hair; one shave is usually sufficient. To treat difficult-to-cure cases or women in cultures where cutting the hair is socially devastating, physicians prescribe antifungal agents such as terbinafine.

### Dermatophytoses

**Dermatophytoses** (der′mǎ-tō-fi-tō′sēz) are infections caused by dermatophytes, which are fungi that grow only on skin, nails, and hair. In the past, such infections were called *ringworms,* because dermatophytes produce circular, scaly patches that resemble a worm lying just below the surface of the skin. Even though we

---

[3]Spanish, meaning a stone.

Dermatophytoses can have a variety of clinical manifestations, some of which are summarized in Table 3. Most such diseases are clinically distinctive and so common that they are readily recognized. KOH preparations of skin or nail scrapings or hair samples reveal hyphae and arthroconidia, which confirm a diagnosis. Determination of a specific dermatophyte requires laboratory culture, but is usually unnecessary because treatment is the same for all.

Limited infections are treated with topical antifungal agents, but more widespread infections of the scalp or skin, as well as nail infections, must be treated with oral agents. Terbinafine, administered for 6–12 weeks, is effective in most cases. Chronic or stubborn cases are treated with griseofulvin until cured. **Clinical Case Study: Is It Athlete's Foot?** explores some of the difficulties in dealing with dermatophyte infections.

### Malassezia Infections

*Malassezia furfur* (mal-ă-sē′zē-ă fur′fur) is a basidiomycete that is a normal member of the microbiota of the skin of humans worldwide. It feeds on the skin's oil and causes common, chronic superficial infections.

Infections with *M. furfur* result in **pityriasis** (pit-i-rī′ă-sis), characterized by depigmented or hyperpigmented patches of scaly skin resulting from fungal interference with melanin production (Figure 16). This condition typically occurs on the trunk, shoulders, and arms, and rarely on the face and neck. KOH preparations of clinical specimens reveal masses of budding yeast and short hyphal forms that are diagnostic for *M. furfur*.

Superficial *Malassezia* infections are treated topically with solutions of antifungal imidazoles, such as ketoconazole shampoos. Alternatively, topical applications of zinc pyrithione, selenium sulfide lotions, or propylene glycol solutions can be used. Oral therapy with ketoconazole may be required to treat extensive infections or infections that do not respond to topical treatments. Relapses of *Malassezia* infections are common, and prophylactic topical treatment may be necessary. The skin takes months to regain its normal pigmentation following successful treatment of pityriasis.

### CRITICAL **THINKING**

Explain why many superficial fungal infections are chronic, recurring problems.

## Cutaneous and Subcutaneous Mycoses

### Learning Objectives

✓ Explain why cutaneous and subcutaneous mycoses are not as common as superficial mycoses.

✓ State the specific difference between chromoblastomycosis and phaeohyphomycosis.

✓ Describe how the lesions of lymphocutaneous sporotrichosis correlate with its spread through the lymphatic system.

The fungi involved in cutaneous and subcutaneous mycoses are common soil saprobes (organisms that live on dead organisms),

(a)

(b)

▲ **Figure 15** **Two forms of piedra.** Piedra is a superficial fungal infection of the hair. **(a)** The hard nodules of black piedra, caused by *Piedraia hortae.* **(b)** The looser, light-colored nodules of white piedra, caused by *Trichosporon beigelii.*

know worms are not involved, the medical names for many dermatophytoses use the term *tinea* (tin′ē-a), which is Latin for worm. Dermatophytes use keratin as a nutrient source and thus colonize only dead tissue. The fungi may provoke cell-mediated immune responses, which can damage living tissues. Dermatophytes are among the few contagious fungi; that is, fungi that spread from person to person. Spores and bits of hyphae are constantly shed from infected individuals, making recurrent infections common.

Three genera of ascomycetes are responsible for most dermatophytoses: (1) *Trichophyton* (trĭk-ō-fī′ton) species, (2) *Microsporum* (mī-kros′po-rŭm) species, and (3) *Epidermophyton floccosum* (ep′i-der-mof′i-ton flŏk′ŏ-sŭm), which we discussed in the vignette at the beginning of the chapter. All three cause skin and nail infections, but *Trichophyton* species also infect hair. Rare subcutaneous infections occur in AIDS patients.

▲ **Figure 16 Pityriasis.** The variably pigmented skin patches are caused by *Malassezia furfur.*

## CLINICAL CASE STUDY

### Is it Athlete's Foot?

A 30-year-old man comes into a community clinic complaining of persistent redness, itching, and peeling skin on the soles of his feet and between his toes. He states that he works out daily and plays on several sports teams.

He concluded he has athlete's foot, but every over-the-counter antifungal agent he has tried has failed to cure his condition. He has finally come to the clinic because his toenails have begun to thicken, yellow, and detach from the nail bed. His condition is pictured.

1. Given the information here, can athlete's foot be diagnosed definitively? If not, what laboratory tests should be performed to identify the infecting organism?

2. What treatment is likely? Would the recommended treatment be different if two fungal species, and not just one fungal species, were present?

but the diseases they produce are not as common as superficial mycoses because infection requires traumatic introduction of fungi through the dead outer layers of skin into the deeper, living tissue. Most lesions remain localized just below the skin, though infections may rarely become systemic.

### Chromoblastomycosis and Phaeohyphomycosis

**Chromoblastomycosis** (krō'mō-blas'tō-mī-kō'sis) and **phaeohyphomycosis** (fē'ō-hī'fō-mī-kō'sis) are similar-appearing cutaneous and subcutaneous mycoses caused by dark-pigmented

## TABLE 3

### Common Dermatophytoses

| Disease | Agents | Common Signs | Source |
|---------|--------|--------------|--------|
| Tinea pedis ("athlete's foot") | *Trichophyton rubrum; T. mentagrophytes* var. *interdigitale; Epidermophyton floccosum* | Red, raised lesions on and around the toes and soles of the feet; webbing between the toes is heavily infected | Human reservoirs in toe webbing; carpeting holding infected skin cells |
| Tinea cruris ("jock itch") | *T. rubrum; T. mentagrophytes* var. *interdigitale; E. floccosum* | Red, raised lesions on and around the groin and buttocks | Usually spreads from the feet |
| Tinea unguium (onychomycosis) | *T. rubrum; T. mentagrophytes* var. *interdigitale* | *Superficial white onychomycosis:* patches or pits on the nail surface<br><br>*Invasive onychomycosis:* yellowing and thickening of the distal nail plate, often leading to loss of the nail | Humans |
| Tinea corporis | *T. rubrum; Microsporum gypseum; M. canis* | Red, raised, ringlike lesions occurring on various skin surfaces (tinea corporis on the trunk, tinea capitis on the scalp, tinea barbae of the beard) | Can spread from other body sites; can be acquired following contact with contaminated soil or animals |
| Tinea capitis | *M. canis; M. gypseum; T. equinum; T. verrucosum; T. tonsurans; T. violaceum; T. schoenleinii* | *Ectothrix invasion:* fungus develops arthroconidia on the outside of the hair shafts, destroying the cuticle<br><br>*Endothrix invasion:* fungus develops arthroconidia inside the hair shaft without destruction<br><br>*Favus:* crusts form on the scalp, with associated hair loss | Humans; can be acquired following contact with contaminated soil or animals |

Sclerotic body

Hypha

M. McGinnis/Doctor Fungus/Visuals Unlimited

Everett Benke/Visuals Unlimited

(a) LM 50 μm  (b) LM 10 μm

▲ **Figure 17 A leg with extensive lesions of chromoblastomycosis.** In this case they are caused by *Fonsecaea pedrosoi*.

▲ **Figure 18** **Microscopic differences between chromoblastomycosis and phaeohyphomycosis. (a)** Sclerotic bodies seen in chromoblastomycoses, here caused by *Fonsecaea pedrosoi*. **(b)** Hyphal forms found in tissues during phaeohyphomycosis, here caused by *Cladophialophora bantiana*.

ascomycetes. Table 4 lists some ascomycetes that commonly cause these mycoses.

Initially, chromoblastomycosis uniformly presents as small, scaly, itchy but painless lesions on the skin surface resulting from fungal growth in subcutaneous tissues near the site of inoculation. Over the course of several years, the lesions progressively worsen, becoming large, flat to thick, tough, and wartlike. They become tumorlike and extensive if not treated (Figure 17). Inflammation, fibrosis, and abscess formation occur in surrounding tissues. The fungus can spread throughout the body.

Phaeohyphomycoses are more variable in presentation, involving colonization of the nasal passages and sinuses in allergy sufferers and AIDS patients, or of the brains of AIDS patients. Fortunately, brain infection is the rarest form of phaeohyphomycosis and occurs only in the severely immunocompromised.

KOH preparations and GMS staining of skin scrapings, biopsy material, or cerebrospinal fluid reveal the key distinguishing feature between the two diseases: the microscopic morphology of the fungal cells within tissues. Tissue sections from chromoblastomycosis cases contain golden brown *sclerotic bodies* that are distinctive and distinguishable from budding yeast forms (Figure 18a), whereas tissues from phaeohyphomycosis cases contain brown-pigmented hyphae (Figure 18b). Determining the species of fungus causing these two diseases requires laboratory culture, macroscopic examination of colonies on agar, and microscopic examination of spores.

Both diseases are difficult to treat, especially in advanced cases. Some cases of phaeohyphomycosis can be treated with itraconazole, but the disease is permanently destructive to tissues. Chromoblastomycosis requires surgical removal of infected and surrounding tissues followed by antifungal therapy. Extensive lesions may require amputation. Thiabendazole and 5-fluorocytosine, given for 3–12 months, have been effective in some cases. The earlier treatment begins, the more likely it will be successful.

Despite the worldwide occurrence of the relevant fungi, the overall incidence of infection is relatively low. People who work daily in the soil with bare feet are at risk if they incur foot wounds. The simple act of wearing shoes would greatly reduce the number of infections.

## Mycetomas

Fungal **mycetomas** (mī-sē-tō′măs) are tumorlike infections of the skin, fascia (lining of muscles), and bones of the hands or feet caused by mycelial fungi of several genera in the division Ascomycota (see Table 4). These fungi are distributed worldwide, but infection is most prevalent in countries near the equator. The cases that occur in the United States are almost always caused by *Pseudallescheria* or *Exophiala*.

Mycetoma-producing fungi live in the soil and are introduced into humans via wounds caused by twigs, thorns, or leaves contaminated with fungi. As with chromoblastomycosis and phaeohyphomycosis, those who work barefoot in soil are most at risk, and wearing protective shoes or clothing can greatly reduce incidence.

Infection begins near the site of inoculation with the formation of small, hard, subsurface nodules that slowly worsen and spread as time passes. Local swelling occurs, and ulcerated lesions begin to produce pus. Infected areas release an oily fluid containing fungal "granules" (spores and fungal elements). The fungi spread to more tissues, destroying bone and causing permanent deformity (Figure 19).

A combination of the symptoms and microscopic demonstration of fungi in samples from the infected area is diagnostic for mycetomas. Laboratory culture of specimens produces macroscopic colonies that can be identified to species.

Treatment involves surgical removal of the mycetoma that may, in severe cases, involve amputation of an infected limb.

From: Prise en charge des mycétomes en Afrique de l'Ouest. M. Develoux, M. T. Dieng, A. Kane and B. Ndiaye. *Bull. Soc. Pathol. Exot.* 2003; 96(5):376–82

▲ **Figure 19  A mycetoma of the ankle.** Here it results from the invasion and destruction of bone and other tissues by the fungus *Madurella mycetomatis.*

Surgery is followed by one to three years of antifungal therapy with ketoconazole. Even combinations of surgery and antifungal agents are not always effective.

### Sporotrichosis

*Sporothrix schenckii* (spōr'ō-thriks shen'kē-ī) is a dimorphic ascomycete that causes **sporotrichosis** (spōr'ō-tri-kō'sis), or *rose-gardener's disease,* a subcutaneous infection usually limited to the arms or legs. *S. schenckii* resides in the soil and is most commonly introduced by thorn pricks or wood splinters. Avid gardeners, farmers, and artisans who work with natural plant materials

▲ **Figure 20  Lymphocutaneous sporotrichosis on the arm.** The locations of these secondary, subcutaneous lesions correspond to the course of lymphatic vessels leading from sites of primary, surface lesions. *How is sporotrichosis contracted?*

**Figure 20** *Sporotrichosis is contracted when the soilborne fungus is inoculated into the skin by thorn pricks and scratches.*

have the highest incidence of sporotrichosis. Though distributed throughout the tropics and subtropics, most cases occur in Latin America, Mexico, and Africa. The disease is also common in warm, moist areas of the United States.

*Cutaneous sporotrichosis* initially appears as painless, nodular lesions that form around the site of inoculation. With time, these lesions produce a pus-filled discharge, but they remain localized and do not spread. In *lymphocutaneous sporotrichosis,* however, the fungus enters the lymphatic system near the site of a primary lesion, giving rise to secondary lesions on the skin surface along the course of lymphatic vessels (Figure 20). The fungus remains restricted to subcutaneous tissues and does not enter the blood.

Microscopic observation of pus or biopsy tissue stained with GMS can reveal budding yeast forms in severe infections, but often the fungus is present at a low density, making direct examination of clinical samples a difficult method of diagnosis. The patient's history and clinical signs, plus the observation of the dimorphic nature of *S. schenckii* in laboratory culture, are considered diagnostic for sporotrichosis.

Cutaneous lesions can be treated successfully with topical applications of saturated potassium iodide for several months. Itraconazole and terbinafine are also useful treatments. Prevention requires the wearing of gloves, long clothing, and shoes to prevent inoculation.

### CRITICAL THINKING

Make a dichotomous key to distinguish among all the fungal mycoses covered in the previous sections.

## Fungal Intoxications and Allergies

### Learning Objectives

✓ Compare and contrast mycotoxicosis, mycetismus, and fungal allergies.

✓ Define *mycotoxin.*

Some fungi produce toxins or cause allergies. Fungal toxins, called, **mycotoxins** (mī'kō-tok-sinz), are low-molecular-weight

**TABLE 4**

| Some Ascomycete Genera of Cutaneous and Subcutaneous Mycoses |
| --- |
| **Chromoblastomycosis** |
| *Fonsecaea* |
| *Phialophora* |
| *Cladophialophora* |
| **Phaeohyphomycosis** |
| *Alternaria* |
| *Exophiala* |
| *Wangiella* |
| *Cladophialophora* |
| **Mycetoma** |
| *Madurella* |
| *Pseudallescheria* |
| *Exophiala* |
| *Acremonium* |
| **Sporotrichosis** |
| *Sporothrix* |

metabolites that can harm humans and animals that ingest them, causing *toxicosis* (poisoning). **Mycotoxicosis** (mī′kō-tok-si-kō-sis) is caused by eating mycotoxins; the fungus itself is not present. **Mycetismus** (mī′sē-tiz′mŭs) is mushroom poisoning resulting from eating the fungus. Fungal *allergens* are usually proteins or glycoproteins that elicit hypersensitivity reactions in sensitive people who contact them.

## Mycotoxicoses

### Learning Objective

✓ Identify the most common group of mycotoxins.

Fungi produce mycotoxins during their normal metabolic activities. People most commonly consume mycotoxins in grains or vegetables that have become contaminated with fungi. Some mycotoxins can also be ingested in milk from a cow that has ingested toxin-contaminated feed. Up to 25% of the world's food supply is contaminated with mycotoxins, but only 20 of the 300 or so known toxins are ever present at dangerous levels. Long-term ingestion of mycotoxins can cause liver and kidney damage, gastrointestinal or gynecological disturbances, or cancers; each mycotoxin produces a specific clinical manifestation.

**Aflatoxins** (af′lă-tok′sinz) produced by the ascomycete *Aspergillus* are the best-known mycotoxins. Aflatoxins are fatal to many vertebrates and are carcinogenic at low levels when consumed continually. Aflatoxins cause liver damage and liver cancer throughout the world, but *aflatoxicosis* is most prevalent in the tropics, where mycotoxins are more common because of subsistence farming, poor food-storage conditions, and warm, moist conditions that foster the growth of *Aspergillus* in harvested foods.

Some mycotoxins are considered useful. Among them are ergot alkaloids, produced by some strains of another ascomycete, *Claviceps purpurea* (klav′i-seps poor-poo′rē-ă). For example, *ergometrine* is used to stimulate labor contractions and is used to constrict the mother's blood vessels after birth (when she is at risk of bleeding excessively). Another mycotoxin, *ergotamine*, is used to treat migraine headaches.

## Mushroom Poisoning (Mycetismus)

### Learning Objective

✓ Describe at least two types of mushroom poisoning.

Most mushrooms (the spore-bearing structures of certain basidiomycetes) are not toxic, though some produce extremely dangerous poisons capable of causing neurological dysfunction or hallucinations, organ damage, or even death. *Mushroom poisoning (mycetismus)* typically occurs when untrained individuals pick and eat wild mushrooms. Young children are especially attracted to colorful mushrooms, which can be poisonous. Poisonous mushrooms are commonly called *toadstools*.

The deadliest mushroom toxin is produced by the "death cap" mushroom, *Amanita phalloides* (am-ă-nī′tă fal-ōy′dēz) **(Figure 21)**. The death cap contains two related polypeptide toxins: *phalloidin*, which irreversibly binds actin within cells, disrupting cell structure; and *alpha-amanitin*, which inhibits mRNA synthesis. Both toxins cause liver damage.

▶ **Figure 21**
*Amanita phalloides*, the "death cap" mushroom.

Peter Arnold

Other deadly mushrooms include the false morel, *Gyromitra esculenta* (gī-rō-mē′tră es-kū-len′tă), which causes bloody diarrhea, convulsions, and death within two days after ingestion, and *Cortinarius gentilis* (kōr′ti-nar-ē-us jen′til-is), which causes excessive thirst, nausea, and kidney failure between three days and three weeks after ingestion.

*Psilocybe cubensis* (sil-ō-sī′bē kū-ben′sis) produces hallucinogenic *psilocybin*, and *Amanita muscaria* (mus-ka′rē-ă) produces two hallucinogenic toxins—*ibotenic acid* and *muscimol*. These toxins may also cause convulsions in children.

Treatment involves inducing vomiting followed by oral administration of activated charcoal to absorb toxins. Severe mushroom poisoning may necessitate a liver transplant.

## Allergies to Fungi

### Learning Objective

✓ Identify the types of hypersensitivity reactions that fungal allergens produce.

Fungal allergens are common and can be found both indoors and out. Over 80 genera of fungi have been demonstrated to trigger fungal allergies. Epidemiologists estimate that 3–10% of humans worldwide are affected. However, determining the specific cause of allergies is often difficult—the presence of spores in an environment does not necessarily mean that they are responsible for allergies. Because skin sensitivity testing is not performed on most people, the true impact of fungal allergens remains undetermined, even though they continue to be blamed for a variety of illnesses (see **Highlight: Does "Killer Mold" Exist?**).

Fungal spores dispersed in the air are common allergens. The concentrations of such spores may peak in autumn or spring, although they are present year-round. Fungal allergens typically cause type I hypersensitivities in which immunoglobulin E binds the allergen, triggering responses such as asthma, eczema, hay fever, and watery eyes and nose.

Less frequently, type III hypersensitivities result from chronic inhalation of particular fungal allergens. In these cases, allergens that have penetrated deep into the lungs encounter

## DOES "KILLER MOLD" EXIST?

In 1994, eight infants in Cleveland were hospitalized with life-threatening pulmonary hemorrhage. One child died. Each of the infants had lived in water-damaged buildings, and initial epidemiological investigations pointed at the black mold *Stachybotrys chartarum* as the agent responsible. The cases were widely reported in the media, and *Stachybotrys* became known as "killer black mold." Since then, the mold has been blamed for everything from "sick building syndrome" to asthma to other occurrences of pulmonary hemorrhage in infants.

A subsequent review of the Cleveland cases by the CDC, however, found serious shortcomings in the initial investigations. Significantly, *Stachybotrys* could not be recovered from any of the infants, and in most of the cases the level of mold in the water-damaged homes was below detection limits or statistically no different from

levels in homes without water damage. In the numerous studies that have been conducted on *Stachybotrys* since 1994, none has established a direct causal relationship between the mold and infant deaths. Nor have researchers found any compelling relationship between *Stachybotrys* and any increased prevalence of asthma or other respiratory illnesses. Within the scientific community, "killer mold" remains an unproven moniker.

In approaching mold contamination of any kind, individuals should exercise their common sense. Some people are naturally sensitive to mold—*Stachybotrys* and others. Immunocompromised or allergy-prone individuals in particular may be at increased risk of experiencing adverse reactions to mold. Decisions regarding the more drastic methods of mold removal, such as burning down your

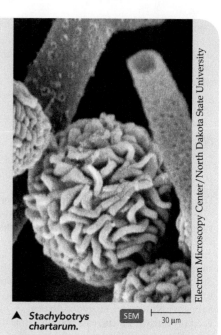

▲ *Stachybotrys chartarum.*  SEM  30 μm

Electron Microscopy Center/North Dakota State University

house, should be cautiously and reflectively considered.

complementary antibodies and form immune complexes in the alveoli that lead to inflammation, fibrosis, and, in some cases, death. Type III fungal hypersensitivities are associated with certain occupations, such as farming, in which workers are constantly exposed to fungal spores in moldy vegetation.

### CRITICAL **THINKING**

Despite the fact that fungi are everywhere, fungal allergies are still not as common as allergies to pollen or dust mites. Propose an explanation to explain this observation.

# Chapter Summary

## An Overview of Medical Mycology

1. **Medical mycology** is the study of the diagnosis, management, and prevention of **mycoses** (fungal diseases). Only a few fungi cause serious diseases in humans. The actual incidence of most mycoses is unknown because they are not reportable.

2. Most fungi are not considered contagious agents because they do not spread by human-to-human contact. The few exceptions include the **dermatophytes** and species of *Candida* and *Pneumocystis*.

3. True fungal pathogens are capable of actively invading the tissues of normal, healthy people. Opportunists infect only weakened patients.

4. Clinically, mycoses include infections, toxicoses, and hypersensitivity reactions. Infections can be **superficial, cutaneous, subcutaneous,** or **systemic mycoses.**

5. Diagnosis of mycoses usually correlates signs and symptoms with microscopic examination of tissues or laboratory cultures for identifying unique morphological features. Biochemical and immunological tests exist for some fungi.

6. Amphotericin B kills most fungi and can be used to treat most fungal infections, but because it is somewhat toxic to humans, long-term treatment with fungistatic drugs is often used instead.

## Systemic Mycoses Caused by Pathogenic Fungi

1. **Systemic mycoses**—fungal infections that spread throughout the body—are caused by one of four pathogenic, dimorphic fungi: *Blastomyces, Coccidioides, Histoplasma,* or *Paracoccidioides*. Whereas each is geographically limited, they all cause similar pulmonary diseases and can spread beyond the lungs.

2. *Histoplasma capsulatum*, which causes **histoplasmosis,** is associated primarily with bat and bird droppings in soil in the Ohio River Valley. Generally, histoplasmosis is an occupationally acquired disease, but recreational exposure does occur. *H. capsulatum* can be carried from the lungs inside macrophages.

3. **Blastomycosis** is found in the eastern United States and is caused by *Blastomyces dermatitidis*, which normally lives in soil rich in

organic material. *B. dermatitidis* almost always spreads beyond the lungs to produce cutaneous lesions.

4. *Coccidioides immitis,* which is limited to deserts, causes **coccidioidomycosis,** which is common in AIDS patients. Contaminated dust is a major source of transmission.

5. *Paracoccidioides brasiliensis* is found in Brazil and some other regions of South and Central America. It causes **paracoccidioidomycosis.** Following a pulmonary phase, the fungus spreads and creates permanently disfiguring lesions on the face and neck.

6. Pathogenic fungi are diagnosed by morphological analysis and by demonstration of dimorphism. Serological tests are also available. If treated promptly, they can be controlled.

7. Opportunistic infections are difficult to diagnose and treat successfully. AIDS patients require both primary treatment to curb infections and maintenance therapy to keep fungal pathogens and opportunists under control.

## Systemic Mycoses Caused by Opportunistic Fungi

1. *Pneumocystis jiroveci* causes ***Pneumocystis* pneumonia (PCP),** a leading cause of death in AIDS patients in the United States. The organism shows a blend of characteristics similar to those of both protozoans and fungi. PCP is debilitating because the fungus multiplies rapidly.

2. **Candidiasis,** caused by various species of *Candida,* is one of the most important pathogens of AIDS patients, but it can also cause infections in relatively healthy individuals. Disease ranges from superficial infections to systemic candidiasis.

3. **Aspergillosis** is a group of diseases caused by *Aspergillus* species, including noninvasive fungal balls in the lungs and invasive diseases that can be fatal. *Aspergillus* is very common in the environment, from which it is inhaled.

4. *Cryptococcus neoformans,* common in bird droppings and soil, causes **cryptococcoses,** which most frequently manifest as cryptococcal meningitis in AIDS patients. Other clinical manifestations are possible.

5. **Zygomycoses,** caused by *Mucor* and various other genera of zygomycetes, can involve the brain, resulting in death. Less severe infections also occur.

6. Diseases caused by *Pneumocystis, Candida, Aspergillus* spp., and *Cryptococcus* are defining illnesses of AIDS patients.

7. *Fusarium, Penicillium,* and *Trichosporon* are emerging opportunists. Factors contributing to their emergence include AIDS

and the selective pressure of antifungal agents, which select for resistant strains of fungi.

## Superficial, Cutaneous, and Subcutaneous Mycoses

1. Superficial, cutaneous, and subcutaneous mycoses are caused by opportunistic fungi.

2. **Black piedra** and **white piedra** are benign, superficial infections of the hair shafts that can be transmitted among family members through shared combs and brushes.

3. **Dermatophytoses** (tineas, ringworms) encompass superficial skin, nail, and hair infections caused by a variety of fungi transmitted from individual to individual. Three genera predominate: *Trichophyton, Microsporum,* and *Epidermophyton.*

4. *Malassezia furfur* is a fungus that infects the skin. Clinical manifestations include **pityriasis,** in which fungal growth disrupts melanin production to produce discolored patches.

5. Most superficial infections are diagnosed by simple clinical observation of symptoms; all can be treated successfully. Rarely are such infections severe or invasive, but they have a tendency to recur.

6. **Chromoblastomycosis** and **phaeohyphomycosis** are similar diseases resulting from infection with dark-pigmented fungi. Both are acquired by traumatic introduction of fungi into the skin. Lesions may be extensive and can spread internally. The two diseases are distinguished by differences in fungal morphology in tissue sections.

7. **Mycetomas** are invasive and destructive infections following introduction of soil fungi through scrapes or pricks from vegetation. Cutaneous lesions can spread to adjacent bone and can be permanently damaging. Surgery or amputation is required to remove infected tissues.

8. **Sporotrichosis** also is acquired from inoculation of soil fungi by thorn pricks. Lymphatic dispersal of the organisms results in multiple lesions along the course of lymphatic vessels.

## Fungal Intoxications and Allergies

1. Fungal metabolism may result in **mycotoxins,** which if eaten can cause neurological and physiological damage and lead to death. **Mycetismus** results from eating mycotoxic mushrooms. Other foods contaminated with mycotoxins cause **mycotoxicosis.**

2. **Aflatoxins,** produced by *Aspergillus,* are well-known mycotoxins.

3. Fungal allergens (spores or other fungal elements) cause type I hypersensitivities or, more rarely, type III hypersensitivities.

---

# Questions for Review  *Answers to the Questions for Review (except for Short Answer questions) appear at the end of this chapter.*

## Multiple Choice

1. A fungus that can infect both healthy and immunocompromised patients is called
   a. a true pathogen.
   b. an opportunistic pathogen.
   c. a commensal organism.
   d. a symbiotic organism.

2. Of the following fungi, which is usually transmitted from person to person?
   a. *Blastomyces dermatitidis*
   b. *Coccidioides immitis*
   c. *Tricophyton rubrum*
   d. *Aspergillus fumigatus*

3. Which of the following is not used to identify true fungal pathogens?
   a. growth at 25°C and 37°C to show dimorphism
   b. GMS staining of infected tissues
   c. serological testing
   d. clinical symptoms alone

4. Because amphotericin B is extremely toxic to humans, most clinicians prescribe it only for
   a. dermatophyte infections.
   b. *Malassezia* infections.
   c. systemic infections.
   d. black piedra.

5. Ringworm is caused by a
   a. helminth.
   b. dermatophyte.
   c. dimorphic fungus.
   d. commensal fungus.

6. Which of the following is considered a classical opportunistic fungus?
   a. *Piedraia hortae*
   b. *Histoplasma capsulatum*
   c. *Fonsecaea pedrosoi*
   d. *Aspergillus niger*

7. Subcutaneous infections tend to be acquired through
   a. inhalation and remain localized.
   b. inhalation and become systemic.
   c. trauma and remain localized.
   d. trauma and become systemic.

8. The term *dermatophyte* refers to
   a. pathogenicity.
   b. where a fungus grows.
   c. method of spread.
   d. pigmentation.

9. Which of the following subcutaneous mycoses may exhibit respiratory and cerebral forms?
   a. chromoblastomycosis
   b. mycetoma
   c. phaeohyphomycosis
   d. sporotrichosis

10. Which of the following systemic mycoses is endemic to the deserts of the southwestern United States?
    a. blastomycosis
    b. coccidioidomycosis
    c. histoplasmosis
    d. paracoccidioidomycosis

11. A spherule stage is seen in humans infected with what organism?
    a. *Blastomyces dermatitidis*
    b. *Coccidioides immitis*
    c. *Histoplasma capsulatum*
    d. *Paracoccidioides brasiliensis*

12. Of the following fungal diseases, which is found in almost all terminal AIDS patients?
    a. chromoblastomycosis
    b. blastomycosis
    c. candidiasis
    d. piedra

13. Which of the following predisposing factors would leave a patient with the greatest long-term risk of acquiring a fungal infection?
    a. invasive medical procedures
    b. AIDS
    c. chronic illness such as diabetes
    d. short-term treatment with antibacterial agents

14. Fungal allergens generally stimulate what type of reaction?
    a. type I hypersensitivity
    b. type II hypersensitivity
    c. type III hypersensitivity
    d. type IV hypersensitivity

15. A pathogenic feature of *Cryptococcus neoformans* is
    a. production of destructive enzymes.
    b. production of a capsule.
    c. infection of immune cells.
    d. variation of surface antigens to avoid immune system recognition.

16. The most common manifestation of *Cryptococcus* infection in AIDS patients is
    a. blindness.
    b. cutaneous infection.
    c. meningitis.
    d. pneumonia.

17. Bread mold can cause which disease?
    a. aspergillosis
    b. dermatophytosis
    c. mycetoma
    d. zygomycosis

18. Mycetismus is caused by
    a. inhalation of fungal allergens.
    b. ingestion of mushrooms.
    c. traumatic inoculation of fungi beneath the skin.
    d. close contact with infected individuals.

19. One of the more poisonous mycotoxins is produced by
    a. *Amanita phalloides*.
    b. *Amanita muscaria*.
    c. *Psilocybe cubensis*.
    d. *Claviceps purpurea*.

20. The number of mycoses worldwide is rising, in part, because
    a. the number of fungi in the environment is rising.
    b. the number of immunocompromised individuals in the population is rising.
    c. fungi have become more pathogenic.
    d. fungi are developing a tendency to be spread from person to person.

## Modified True/False

Indicate which of the following are true and which are false. Rewrite false statements to make them true by changing the nontaxonomic italicized word(s).

1. _____ Fungi are generally *not transmitted* from person to person.

2. _____ On the whole, fungal infections are relatively *easy* to treat.

3. _____ *Dermatophytes* are always contracted from the environment.

4. _____ Chromoblastomycosis and phaeohyphomycosis are both caused by *dark-pigmented* ascomycetes.

5. _____ *Sporotrichosis* is always caused by traumatic introduction of fungi beneath the skin.

6. _____ Coccidioidomycosis does not occur normally outside the *Western Hemisphere*.

7. _____ Treatment of individuals with broad-spectrum antibacterial agents is a predisposing factor for *opportunistic* fungal infections.

8. _____ *Candida albicans* generally causes localized opportunistic infections but can become systemic, particularly in the *immunocompetent*.

9. _____ Relapse of fungal diseases is common in *AIDS patients*.

10. _____ *Almost everyone has* allergies to fungal elements.

## Fill in the Blanks

1. Dimorphic fungi exist as _____ forms in the environment and as _____ forms in their hosts.

2. The true fungal pathogens are _____, _____, _____, and _____.

3. Many antifungal agents target the compound _____ in fungal cytoplasmic membranes.

4. _____ piedra is characterized by hard nodules on the hair shaft, whereas _____ piedra is characterized by soft nodules.

5. Sporotrichosis is caused by the traumatic introduction of _____ _____ into the skin (give genus and species).

6. Which systemic mycosis is associated with bird droppings? _____ _____ (give genus and species).

7. The five most common agents of opportunistic fungal infections are _____, _____, _____, _____, and _____.

8. Thrush is caused by _____ (genus name).

9. *Pneumocystis* was once classified as a _____, but now it is classified as a _____.

10. Ergot alkaloids are produced by some strains of the genus _____.

## Matching

Match each of the following diseases with the manner(s) in which fungi enter the body. Answers can be used more than once.

A. Inhalation     C. Trauma

B. Contact     D. Ingestion

____ Aspergillosis

____ Candidiasis

____ Chromoblastomycosis

____ Coccidioidomycosis

____ Cryptococcosis

____ Dermatophytosis

____ Histoplasmosis

____ Hypersensitivity reactions

____ Mushroom poisoning

____ Mycetoma

____ Sporotrichosis

## Short Answer

1. Amphotericin B is considered the "gold standard" of antifungal agents. Technically, its mode of action works against most fungal infections. Why, then, isn't it prescribed for most fungal infections?

2. Discuss why it is difficult in many cases to determine the source of superficial fungal infections (that is, from other humans, animals, or the environment).

3. Given that superficial fungal infections are only on the surface, why is it necessary to even try to identify the source of infection?

4. AIDS patients usually die of bacterial or fungal infections. Why do so many fungal infections appear in these individuals, and why are mycoses severe while fungi, for the most part, are benign residents of the environment?

5. How does mycotoxicosis differ from mycetismus?

6. Color each map below to show the general area where each disease is endemic.

Blastomycosis

Coccidioidomycosis

Histoplasmosis

# Concept Mapping

Using the following terms, draw a concept map that describes systemic mycoses. Or, complete this concept map online by going to the Study Area at www.masteringmicrobiology.com.

5-fluorocytosine
Amphotericin B **(4)**
*Aspergillus* species
*Blastomyces dermatitidis*
*Candida albicans*
*Coccidioides immitis*

Cryptococcal meningitis
*Cryptococcus neoformans*
Every body system
Fluconazole
*Histoplasma capsulatum*
Inhalation

Opportunistic fungi
Other organs
*Paracoccidioides*
  *brasiliensis*
Pathogenic fungi
*Pneumocystis jiroveci*

Pneumocystis pneumonia
Pulmonary disease
Respiratory infection
Trimethoprim/
  Sulfanilamide

# Critical Thinking

1. Correlate the observation that the majority of fungal infections are caused by opportunists with the fact that most infections are acquired from the environment. How does this make the control and diagnosis of fungal infections difficult?

2. The four pathogenic fungi (*Blastomyces, Coccidioides, Histoplasma,* and *Paracoccidioides*) are all dimorphic. Antifungal agents, like all antimicrobials, are generally designed to target something specific about the organism to avoid harming human tissues. Propose how you could use the idea of dimorphism to produce new antifungal agents.

3. What actions could be taken to limit the contamination of foods with fungal toxins? Would these actions differ depending on where in the world the food is grown? Explain.

4. Onychomycoses are nail infections that can be caused by several species of fungi. Explain why these mycoses are so difficult to treat, and why it is generally necessary to treat patients with oral antifungal agents for long periods of time.

5. What factors contribute to the pathogenicity of *Cryptococcus* infections?

6. Clinically, all fungi that cause subcutaneous mycoses produce lesions on the skin around the site of inoculation. What are some of the things you would look for when attempting to distinguish among them?

7. Given the various predisposing factors that make humans susceptible to opportunistic infections, how can health care providers curtail the rising incidence of such infections?

Access more review material online in the Study Area at **www.masteringmicrobiology.com.** There, you'll find
- **Concept Mapping Activities**
- **Flashcards**
- **Quizzes**

and more to help you succeed.

# Answers

Answers to multiple-choice, fill-in-blank, labeling, matching, and true/false questions are listed here. Answers for Short Answer and Critical Thinking questions are available for instructors only in the Instructor's Manual that accompanies this text.

**Multiple Choice**
1. a; 2. c; 3. d; 4. c; 5. b; 6. d; 7. c; 8. b; 9. c; 10. b; 11. b; 12. c; 13. b; 14. a; 15. b; 16. c; 17. d; 18. b; 19. a; 20. b

**Modified True/False**
1. True; 2. *difficult;* 3. *Systemic mycoses;* 4. True; 5. True; 6. True; 7. True; 8. *immunocompromised;* 9. True; 10. *3–10% of individuals have*

**Fill in the Blanks**
1. mycelial forms, yeast forms; 2. *Blastomyces dermatitidis, Coccidioides immitis, Histoplasma capsulatum, Paracoccidioides brasiliensis;* 3. ergosterol; 4. Black, white;

5. *Sporothrix schenckii;* 6. *Cryptococcus neoformans;* 7. *Aspergillus, Candida, Cryptococcus, Pneumocystis, Mucor;* 8. *Candida;* 9. protozoan, fungus; 10. *Claviceps*

**Matching**
A,C Aspergillosis; B Candidiasis; C Chromoblastomycosis; A Coccidioidomycosis; A Cryptococcosis; B Dermaphytosis; A,C Histoplasmosis; A Hypersensitivity reactions; D Mushroom poisoning; C Mycetoma; C Sporotrichosis

# Parasitic Protozoa, Helminths, and Arthropod Vectors

Andrew Syred/Photo Researchers

Suckers and hooklets attach *Taenia* to its human host's intestinal wall. The body of the helminth is composed of segments, giving the worm its common name—tapeworm.

The next time you sit down to a nice meal containing pork, it's probably a good idea to make sure the meat is properly cooked—if not well done. One reason is that the muscles of pigs can be infected with cysts that are the immature stage of *Taenia solium*, a parasitic tapeworm commonly called the pork tapeworm. The cysts remain viable in undercooked pork, and in the human small intestine they develop into mature tapeworms, which can grow as long as 800 cm (more than 26 feet). Cysts of a similar tapeworm, *Taenia saginata* (the beef tapeworm) also develop in the intestines of humans who eat insufficiently cooked infected beef.

This chapter provides a brief survey of parasitology, the study of eukaryotic parasites—in particular, various protozoa and helminths (tapeworms, other flatworms called flukes, and roundworms). Because parasitologists also study arthropod vectors (including mites, ticks, flies, mosquitoes, and fleas), which are important in the transmission of a variety of infectious organisms, we consider vectors in the final section of the chapter.

 Take the pre-test for this chapter online. Visit the Study Area at www.masteringmicrobiology.com.

From Chapter 23 of *Microbiology with Diseases by Taxonomy*, Third Edition. Robert W. Bauman. Copyright © 2011 by Pearson Education, Inc. Published by Benjamin Cummings, Inc. All rights reserved.

Parasites live, feed and grow in or on another organism at the expense of their host's metabolism. Sometimes no obvious damage is done to the host, but in other cases parasitism can lead to a host's death. Many protozoan and helminthic parasites exist worldwide, especially in the tropics and subtropics, and particularly among people living in rural, undeveloped, or overcrowded places. Parasitic diseases are also emerging as serious threats among developed nations in nontropical regions. This rise is due to many factors, but can most generally be attributed to human migration, poor regulation and inadequate inspection of food and water supplies, and a changing world climate that alters parasites' transmission patterns, particularly those transmitted by vectors. As a whole, parasites infect billions of humans each year, making parasitic infections medically, socially, and economically important.

Parasitic infections often involve several hosts—a **definitive host** in which mature (often sexual) forms of the parasite are present and usually reproducing, and with many parasites, one or more **intermediate hosts** in which immature parasites undergo various stages of maturation. In general, parasites infect human hosts in one of three major ways: by being ingested,

through vector-borne transmission, or via direct contact and penetration of the skin or mucous membranes (Figure 1).

We begin our consideration of parasitic infections by discussing the protozoan parasites of humans.

# Protozoan Parasites of Humans

## Learning Objective

✓ Describe the epidemiology of the more important protozoan parasites.

Protozoa are unicellular eukaryotes found in a wide range of habitats. Although the majority of protozoa are free-living and do not adversely affect humans or animals, some are parasites that can cause debilitating and deadly diseases.

Among the many protozoa that enter the body via ingestion, most have two morphological forms: A feeding and reproducing stage called a *trophozoite*, which lives within the host, and a dormant *cyst* stage, which can survive in the environment and is infective to new hosts. Once ingested by a host, cysts

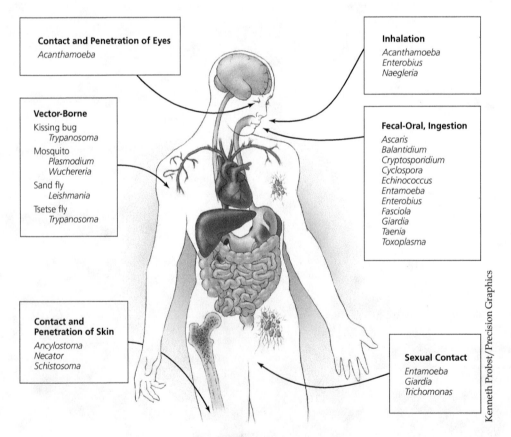

▲ **Figure 1  The major routes by which humans acquire parasitic infections.** They are: the fecal-oral route, the vector-borne route, and direct contact. Occasionally parasites are inhaled. Listed genera are discussed in the chapter.

undergo **excystment** and develop into new trophozoites, which resume feeding and reproducing. In most cases, trophozoites undergo **encystment** before leaving the host in the feces, becoming available to infect other hosts.

This chapter presents the protozoa in four groups. The scheme presented in this chapter reflects the largely obsolete, but clinically useful, classical groupings for these parasites, which were based primarily on mode of locomotion: the ciliates, the amoebae, the flagellates, and the typically nonmotile apicomplexans.

## Ciliates

### Learning Objective

✓ Describe the characteristics of *Balantidium coli*.

**Ciliates** (sil'ē-āts) are protozoa that in their trophozoite stages use cilia for locomotion, for acquiring food, or both. *Balantidium coli* (bal-an-tid'ē-ŭm kō'lē), a relatively large (50 μm × 100 μm) ciliate commonly found in animal intestinal tracts, is the only ciliate known to cause disease in humans. Pigs are its most common host, but it is also found in rodents and nonhuman primates. Humans become infected by consuming food or water contaminated with feces containing cysts.

Following ingestion, excystment occurs in the small intestine, releasing trophozoites that use their cilia to attach to (and then burrow through) the mucosal epithelium lining the intestine. Eventually, some trophozoites undergo encystment, and both cysts and trophozoites are shed in feces. Trophozoites die outside the body, but cysts are hardy and infective.

In healthy adults, *B. coli* infection is generally asymptomatic. For those in poor health, however, **balantidiasis** (bal'an-ti-dī'ă-sis) occurs. Persistent diarrhea, abdominal pain, and weight loss characterize the disease. Severe infections produce *dysentery* (frequent and painful diarrhea, often containing blood and mucus) and possibly ulceration and bleeding from the intestinal mucosa. *Balantidium* infection is rarely fatal.

Paradoxically, cysts are few and usually cannot be recovered from stool (fecal) samples, although they are the infective stage. Noninfective trophozoites, by contrast, can be detected, and their presence is diagnostic for the disease. Fresh stool samples must be used for diagnostic purposes because the trophozoites do not survive long outside the intestinal tract. The treatment of choice for balantidiasis is the antibacterial drug tetracycline, which does not kill *B. coli* directly but instead modifies the normal microbiota of the digestive tract such that the small intestine is unsuitable for infection by the ciliate.

Prevention of balantidiasis relies on good personal hygiene, especially for those who live around or work with pigs. Additionally, efficient water sanitation is necessary to kill cysts or remove them from drinking water.

### CRITICAL **THINKING**

Why are diseases such as balantidiasis generally more severe in those who are already in poor health?

## Amoebae

### Learning Objective

✓ Compare and contrast three amoebae that cause disease in humans.

**Amoebae** (ă-mē'bē, singular: *amoeba*, ă-mē'bă) are protozoa that have no truly defined shape and that move and acquire food through the use of pseudopodia. Although amoebae are abundant throughout the world in freshwater, seawater, and moist soil, few cause disease. The most important amoebic pathogen is *Entamoeba*.

### *Entamoeba*

*Entamoeba histolytica* (ent-ă-mē'bă his-tō-li'ti-kă) is carried asymptomatically in the digestive tracts of roughly 10% of the world's human population. When disease develops, it can be fatal, causing a worldwide annual mortality of over 100,000. Carriers predominate in less-developed countries, especially in rural areas, where human feces are used to fertilize food crops and where water sanitation is deficient. Travelers, immigrants, and institutionalized populations are at greatest risk within industrialized nations. No animal reservoirs exist, but human carriers are sufficiently numerous to ensure continued transmission of the parasite.

Infection occurs most commonly through the drinking of water contaminated with feces that contain cysts. The parasite can also be ingested following fecal contamination of hands or food or during oral-anal intercourse.

Excystment in the small intestine releases trophozoites that migrate to the large intestine and multiply. The organism uses pseudopodia to attach to the intestinal mucosa, where it feeds and reproduces via binary fission. Both trophozoites and cysts are shed into the environment in feces, but the trophozoites die quickly, leaving infective cysts.

Depending on the health of the host and the virulence of the particular infecting strain, three types of **amebiasis** (ă-mē-bī'ă-sis) can result. The least severe form, *luminal amebiasis,* occurs in otherwise healthy individuals. Infections are asymptomatic; trophozoites remain in the lumen of the intestine, where they do little tissue damage. Invasive *amebic dysentery* is a more serious and more common form of infection characterized by severe diarrhea, colitis (inflammation of the colon), appendicitis, and ulceration of the intestinal mucosa. Bloody, mucus-containing stools and pain are characteristic of amebic dysentery, which affects about 500 million people worldwide. In the most serious disease, *invasive extraintestinal amebiasis,* trophozoites invade the peritoneal cavity and the bloodstream, which carries them throughout the body. Lesions of dead cells formed by the trophozoites occur most commonly in the liver but can also be found in the lungs, spleen, kidneys, and brain. Amebic dysentery and invasive extraintestinal amebiasis can be fatal, especially without adequate treatment.

N. J. Wheeler, Jr., CDC

LM ⊢————⊣ 50 μm

▲ **Figure 2** **Trophozoite of *Entamoeba histolytica*.** This specimen has ingested erythrocytes (red blood cells).

Diagnosis is based on the identification of microscopic cysts or trophozoites (Figure 2) recovered from either fresh stool specimens or intestinal biopsies. Microscopic analysis is necessary to distinguish amebic dysentery from dysentery caused by bacteria. Serological identification using antibodies to detect antigens can aid in distinguishing *E. histolytica* from nonpathogenic amoebae.

For asymptomatic infections, the drug paromomycin is effective. Physicians prescribe iodoquinol for symptomatic amebiasis. They may also prescribe antibacterial agents at the same time to prevent secondary bacterial infections. The coupling of oral rehydration therapy with drug treatment is recommended, and vital in severe cases.

Several preventive measures interrupt the transmission of *Entamoeba*. Discontinuing the use of human wastes as fertilizer reduces the transmission of amebiasis. Normal methods of treating wastewater and drinking water are helpful but not completely effective because the infectious cysts are hardy. Effective processing of water requires extra chemical treatment, filtration, or extensive boiling to eliminate all cysts. Good personal hygiene can eliminate transmission via intimate contact.

### Acanthamoeba and Naegleria

Two other amoebae—*Acanthamoeba* (ă-kan-thă-mē′bă) and *Naegleria* (nā-glē′rē-ă)—cause rare and usually fatal infections of the brain. These amoebae are common free-living inhabitants of warm lakes, ponds, puddles, ditches, mud, and moist soil. They are also found in artificial water systems such as swimming pools, air conditioning units, humidifiers, and dialysis units. Contact lens wearers who use tap water (as opposed to sterile saline solution) to wash and store their lenses create an additional focal point for infection. *Naegleria* may assume a flagellated form in addition to its amoeboid and cyst stages.

*Acanthamoeba* usually enters a host through cuts or scrapes on the skin, through the conjunctiva via abrasions from contact lenses or trauma, or through inhalation of contaminated water while swimming. *Acanthamoeba keratitis,* in which trophozoites invade and perforate the eye, results from conjunctival inoculation. Damage can be extensive enough to require corneal replacement. The more common disease caused by infection with *Acanthamoeba* is **amebic encephalitis** (inflammation of the brain), characterized by headache, altered mental state, and neurological deficit. Symptoms progressively worsen over a period of weeks until the patient dies.

Infection with *Naegleria* occurs when swimmers inhale water contaminated with trophozoites, which then invade the nasal mucosa and replicate. The trophozoites migrate to the brain, where they cause an **amebic meningoencephalitis** (inflammation of the brain and its membranes). Severe headache, fever, vomiting, and neurological tissue destruction lead to hemorrhage, coma, and usually death within three to seven days after the onset of symptoms.

Physicians diagnose *Acanthamoeba* and *Naegleria* infections by detecting trophozoites in corneal scrapings, cerebrospinal fluid, or biopsy material. Keratitis can be treated topically with anti-inflammatory drugs. Physicians treat *Acanthamoeba* encephalitis with pentamidine and *Naegleria* infection with amphotericin B, but by the time they have diagnosed the disease, it is almost always too late to begin effective treatment.

As both these amoebae are environmentally hardy, control and prevention of infection can be difficult. Swimmers and bathers should avoid waterways in which the organisms are known to be endemic. Nonsterile solutions should never be used to clean or store contact lenses. Swimming pools should be properly chlorinated and tested periodically to ensure their safety. Air conditioning systems, dialysis units, and other devices that routinely use water should also be cleaned thoroughly and regularly to prevent amoebae from becoming resident.

## Flagellates

### Learning Objectives

✓ Contrast the life cycles of *Trypanosoma cruzi* and *Trypanosoma brucei*.

✓ Describe the life cycle of *Leishmania* and the clinical forms of leishmaniasis.

✓ Compare *Giardia* infections to those caused by *Entamoeba* and *Balantidium*.

✓ Identify the risk factors and preventive measures for *Trichomonas vaginalis* infection.

In 1832 Charles Darwin (1809–1882) explored South America as one of the naturalists sailing aboard HMS *Beagle*. His explorations were to impact him profoundly—intellectually and medically. During the voyage he began to formulate his ideas concerning the evolution of species, and he was bitten by a bloodsucking bug that may have infected him with *Trypanosoma cruzi*, a flagellated protozoan that afflicted him for the rest of his life. The following sections explore this and other parasitic flagellates that infect humans.

**Flagellates** (flaj′e-lātz) are protozoa that possess at least one long flagellum, which is used for movement. The number and arrangement of the flagella are important features for determining the species of flagellate present within a host.

Here we will examine some parasitic kinetoplastids (*Trypanosoma* and *Leishmania*), *Giardia* (a diplomonad), and *Trichomonas* (a parabasalid). We begin our discussion of the more important flagellate parasites with *Trypanosoma cruzi*.

### Trypanosoma cruzi

*Trypanosoma cruzi* (tri-pan′ō-sō-mă kroo′zē) causes **Chagas' disease.** This disease, named for Brazilian doctor Carlos Chagas (1879–1934), is endemic throughout Central and South America. Localized outbreaks have also occurred in California and Texas. Opossums and armadillos are the primary reservoirs for *T. cruzi*, but most mammals, including humans, can harbor the organism. Transmission occurs through the bite of true bugs—a type of insect—in the genus *Triatoma* (trī-ă-tō′mă). These blood-sucking bugs feed preferentially from blood vessels in the lips, which gives the bugs their common name—kissing bugs.

Figure 3 illustrates the basic life cycle of *T. cruzi*. Within the hindgut of the kissing bug, a stage called *epimastigotes*[1] develop into infective trypomastigotes ( 1 ), which are shed in the bug's feces while the bug feeds on a mammalian host ( 2 ). When the host scratches the itchy wounds created by the bug bites, the *trypomastigotes* in the feces enter the nearby wounds ( 3 ). The trypomastigotes are then carried in the bloodstream throughout the body and penetrate certain cells, especially macrophages and heart muscle cells, where they transform into small, nonflagellated forms called *amastigotes* ( 4 ). The multiplication of these intracellular amastigotes via binary fission eventually causes the cells to rupture ( 5 ), releasing amastigotes that either infect other cells ( 6 ) or revert to trypomastigotes that circulate in the bloodstream ( 7 ). The circulating trypomastigotes are subsequently ingested by a kissing bug when it takes a blood meal ( 8 ). Within the midgut of the kissing bug, binary fission of the trypomastigotes produces epimastigotes ( 9 ), completing the cycle.

Chagas' disease progresses over the course of several months through the following four stages:

1. An acute stage characterized by *chagomas*, which are swellings at the sites of the bites

2. A generalized stage characterized by fever, swollen lymph nodes, myocarditis (inflammation of the heart muscle), and enlargement of the spleen, esophagus, and colon

3. A chronic stage, which is asymptomatic and can last for years

4. A symptomatic stage characterized primarily by congestive heart failure following the formation of *pseudocysts,* which are clusters of amastigotes in heart muscle tissue

Parasite-induced heart disease is one of the leading causes of death in Latin America.

---

[1]From Greek *epi*, meaning on, and *mastix*, meaning whip. The flagellum of an epimastigote originates on the middle of the cell.

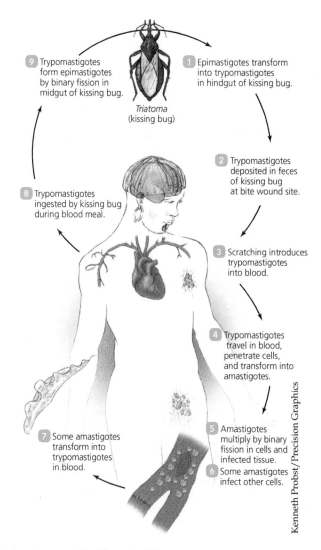

9 Trypomastigotes form epimastigotes by binary fission in midgut of kissing bug.

*Triatoma* (kissing bug)

1 Epimastigotes transform into trypomastigotes in hindgut of kissing bug.

8 Trypomastigotes ingested by kissing bug during blood meal.

2 Trypomastigotes deposited in feces of kissing bug at bite wound site.

3 Scratching introduces trypomastigotes into blood.

4 Trypomastigotes travel in blood, penetrate cells, and transform into amastigotes.

7 Some amastigotes transform into trypomastigotes in blood.

5 Amastigotes multiply by binary fission in cells and infected tissue.

6 Some amastigotes infect other cells.

Kenneth Probst/Precision Graphics

▲ **Figure 3** **The life cycle of *Trypanosoma cruzi.*** *Triatoma*, the vector, is shown life-size.

Microscopic identification of trypomastigotes or their antigens in blood, lymph, spinal fluid, or a tissue biopsy is diagnostic for *T. cruzi* (Figure 4). Another simple and practical diagnostic method is *xenodiagnosis*. In this procedure, uninfected kissing bugs are allowed to feed on a person suspected of having a *T. cruzi* infection. Four weeks later, the bugs are dissected. The presence of parasites within the hindgut of the bug indicates the person is infected.

In its earliest stages, Chagas' disease can be treated with benznidazole or nifurtimox; late stages cannot be treated. Prevention of Chagas' disease involves replacing thatch and mud building materials, which provide homes for the bugs, with concrete and brick. The use of insecticides, both personally and in the home, and sleeping under insecticide-impregnated

LM 　10 μm

▲ **Figure 4** Mature trypomastigotes of *T. cruzi* among erthyrocytes.

netting can prevent insect feeding. No vaccines exist for Chagas' disease.

### Trypanosoma brucei

*Trypanosoma brucei* (brūs'ē) causes **African sleeping sickness,** which afflicts more than 10,000 people annually in equatorial and subequatorial savanna, agricultural, and riverine areas of Africa. Its geographical range depends on the range of its insect vector, the tsetse (tset'sē) fly (*Glossina,* glo-sī'nǎ). There are two variants of *Trypanosoma brucei*—*T. brucei gambiense* (gam'bē-en'sē), which occurs primarily in western Africa, and *T. brucei rhodesiense* (rō-dē'zē-en'sē) in eastern and southern Africa.

Whereas cattle and sheep are the reservoirs for *T. brucei gambiense,* several species of wild animals apparently serve as reservoirs for *T. brucei rhodesiense.* Although humans usually become infected when bitten by tsetse flies previously infected while feeding on infected animals, flies may transmit both variants of *T. brucei* between humans.

The life cycle of *T. brucei* proceeds as follows (Figure 5): Within the salivary gland of a male or female tsetse fly, a form of the parasite called an epimastigote matures into an infective trypomastigote (1). During the course of taking a blood meal from an animal or human, tsetse flies inject trypomastigotes into the wounds (2). Trypomastigotes then travel throughout the lymphatic and circulatory systems to other sites (3), where they reproduce by binary fission (4). Eventually, some trypomastigotes enter the central nervous system (5), while others continue to circulate in the blood, where they can be picked up by feeding tsetse flies (6). In the midgut of the fly, trypomastigotes multiply by binary fission, producing immature epimastigotes that migrate to the salivary glands (7), where they mature and become trypomastigotes that are infective to new hosts when the fly feeds once again.

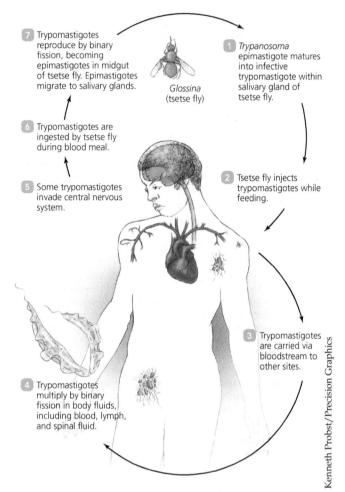

7 Trypomastigotes reproduce by binary fission, becoming epimastigotes in midgut of tsetse fly. Epimastigotes migrate to salivary glands.

1 *Trypanosoma* epimastigote matures into infective trypomastigote within salivary gland of tsetse fly.

*Glossina* (tsetse fly)

6 Trypomastigotes are ingested by tsetse fly during blood meal.

5 Some trypomastigotes invade central nervous system.

2 Tsetse fly injects trypomastigotes while feeding.

3 Trypomastigotes are carried via bloodstream to other sites.

4 Trypomastigotes multiply by binary fission in body fluids, including blood, lymph, and spinal fluid.

Kenneth Probst/Precision Graphics

▲ **Figure 5** The life cycle of *Trypanosoma brucei. Glossina* is shown life-size. *By which mode of transmission do trypanosomes infect humans?*

**Figure 5** *Trypanosomes are transmitted to humans by arthropod vectors.*

The life cycle of *T. brucei* differs from that of *T. cruzi* in several ways:

- *T. brucei* matures in the salivary gland of the tsetse fly, whereas *T. cruzi* matures in the hindgut of the kissing bug.
- Tsetse flies directly inject *T. brucei.* In contrast, the host rubs *T. cruzi* found in a kissing bug's feces into a wound.
- *T. brucei* remains outside its hosts' cells, whereas amastigotes of *T. cruzi* live inside host cells.

Untreated African sleeping sickness progresses through three clinical stages. First, the wound created at the site of each fly bite becomes a lesion containing dead tissue and rapidly dividing parasites. Next, the presence of parasites in the blood triggers fever, swelling of lymph nodes, and headaches. Finally, invasion of the central nervous system results in meningoencephalitis, characterized by headache, extreme drowsiness, abnormal neurological function, and coma. The patient will die perhaps within six months of onset of disease. Symptoms may take years to develop with *T. brucei rhodesiense*, but begin within three to six months with *T. brucei gambiense*.

All *T. brucei* infections are characterized by cyclical waves of *parasitemia* (parasites in the blood) that occur roughly every 7–10 days. Although the presence of parasites in the blood is in itself serious, these cycles are particularly dangerous because with each wave of replication, *T. brucei* changes its surface glycoproteins and thus its surface antigens. The result is that by the time the host's immune system has produced antibodies against a given set of glycoproteins, the parasite has already produced a new set, continually leaving the host's immune system one step behind the parasite. Once infected, a patient is incapable of clearing the infection and never becomes immune.

Microscopic observation of trypomastigotes in blood, lymph, spinal fluid, or a tissue biopsy is diagnostic for both strains of *T. brucei*. Trypomastigotes are long and thin with a single long flagellum running along the cell and extending past the posterior end. Trypomastigotes of *T. brucei* are less curled than those of *T. cruzi*.

African sleeping sickness is one of the few human diseases that is 100% fatal if not treated. Treatment must begin as soon as possible after infection. However, immediate treatment is rare because poor health care infrastructure in endemic areas often prevents identification of the disease at its earliest stages. Pentamidine or suramin is used to treat the early stages. Melarsoprol is used when the disease progresses to the central nervous system because this drug crosses the blood-brain barrier. Eflornithine, a newer and more expensive drug, is remarkably effective against *T. brucei gambiense* (but not against *T. brucei rhodesiense*). In 2001, private pharmaceutical companies guaranteed availability of this drug through the World Health Organization to those who need it.

Clearing of tsetse fly habitats and broad application of insecticides have reduced the occurrence of African sleeping sickness in some localities. However, large-scale spraying of insecticides is impractical, expensive, and may have disastrous long-term environmental consequences. Some countries release up to a million sterile male tsetse flies a week, outnumbering wild flies 10 to 1. Most female flies mate with sterile males and produce no offspring—some scientists call this birth control for tsetse flies. Some regions have eradicated tsetse flies using this method. Personal insecticide use is preferable, as is the use of insecticide-impregnated netting and long, loose-fitting clothing, which can prevent insect feeding. No vaccine currently exists for African sleeping sickness.

### Leishmania

*Leishmania* (lēsh-man'ē-ă) is a genus of kinetoplastid protozoa commonly hosted by wild and domestic dogs and small rodents. *Leishmania* is endemic in parts of the tropics and subtropics, including Central and South America, central and southern Asia, Africa, Europe, and the Middle East. **Leishmaniasis**

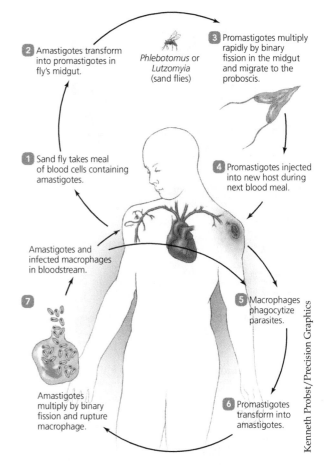

▲ **Figure 6** **The life cycle of *Leishmania*.** Sand fly is shown life-size. *What is the effect of amastigote replication on the host's immune system?*

(lēsh'mă-nī'ă-sis) is a **zoonosis**—a disease of animals transmitted to humans. Twenty-one of the 30 known species of *Leishmania* can infect humans.

*Leishmania* has two developmental stages: *amastigotes*, which lack flagella and multiply within a mammalian host's macrophages and monocytes (types of white blood cells), and *promastigotes*, each of which has a single anterior flagellum and develops extracellularly within a vector's gut. In the life cycle of *Leishmania* (Figure 6), a sand fly of the genera *Phlebotomus* (fle-bot'ō-mŭs) or *Lutzomyia* (lūts-ŏm'yē-a) ingests white blood cells containing amastigotes during a blood meal (1). The amastigotes are released from the phagocytes in the fly's midgut, where they transform into promastigotes (2). Rapidly dividing promastigotes fill the fly's digestive tract and migrate to the proboscis (3), so that each time the fly feeds, it injects promastigotes into a new host (4). Macrophages near the bite site

411

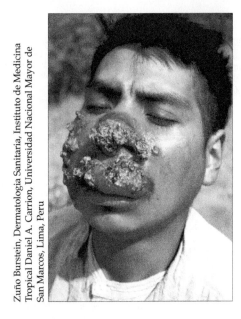

Figure 7 **Mucocutaneous leishmaniasis.** The large skin lesions are permanently disfiguring.

phagocytize the promastigotes (**5**), which then transform into amastigotes (**6**). The amastigotes reproduce via binary fission until the macrophage ruptures, releasing amastigotes that circulate in the bloodstream and/or infect other macrophages (**7**), within which they can be ingested by another sand fly.

The clinical manifestations of leishmaniasis depend on the species of *Leishmania* and the immune response of the infected host. Upon initial infection, macrophages become activated, but not sufficiently to kill the intracellular parasites. The macrophages stimulate inflammatory responses that continue to be propagated by the infection of new macrophages. Depletion of macrophage numbers due to the reproduction of amastigotes decreases the efficiency of the immune response. The severity of the resulting immune dysfunction depends on the overall number of macrophages infected. Of the more than 1.5 million cases of leishmaniasis reported each year, over 45,000 are fatal.

Three clinical forms of leishmaniasis are commonly observed. *Cutaneous leishmaniasis* involves large painless skin ulcers that form around the bite wounds. Such lesions often become secondarily infected with bacteria. Scars remain when the lesions heal. *Mucocutaneous leishmaniasis* results when skin lesions enlarge to encompass the mucous membranes of the mouth, nose, or soft palate. Damage is severe and permanently disfiguring (Figure 7). Neither of these forms of leishmaniasis is fatal. However, *visceral leishmaniasis* (also known as *kala-azar*) is fatal in 95% of untreated cases. In this disease, macrophages spread the parasite to the liver, spleen, bone marrow, and lymph nodes. Inflammation, fever, weight loss, and anemia increase in severity as the disease progresses. Visceral

leishmaniasis is becoming increasingly problematic as an opportunistic infection among AIDS patients.

Microscopic identification of amastigotes in samples from cutaneous lesions, the spleen, or bone marrow is diagnostic of *Leishmania* infection. Immunoassays using antibodies to detect antigen can be used to confirm the diagnosis and to identify the strain. Molecular techniques such as PCR are needed to determine the species.

Most cases of leishmaniasis heal without treatment (though scars may remain) and confer immunity upon the recovered patient. At one time, lesions were purposefully encouraged on the buttocks of small children to induce immunity and prevent lesions from leaving more visible scars. Treatment, which is required for more serious infections and for visceral leishmaniasis, generally involves administering sodium stibogluconate or meglumine antimonate. Pentamidine has been used with some success to treat resistant strains of *Leishmania*.

Prevention is essentially limited to reducing exposure by controlling reservoir host and sand fly populations. For example, rodent nesting sites and burrows can be destroyed around human habitations to reduce contact with potentially infected populations. In some areas, infected dogs are destroyed. Spraying insecticide around homes can reduce the number of sand flies. Personal use of insect repellents, protective clothing, and netting further limits exposure. A vaccine for leishmaniasis does not exist.

## CRITICAL **THINKING**

Given the regions of the world where *Leishmania* and HIV are endemic, would you expect the incidence of *Leishmania* to increase or decrease in the next decade? Explain your answer.

### *Giardia*

*Giardia intestinalis* (jē-ar′dē-ă in-tes′ti-năl′is; previously called *G. lamblia*) is the causative agent of **giardiasis** (jē-ar-dī′ă-sis), one of the more common waterborne gastrointestinal diseases in the United States. *Giardia* lives in the intestinal tracts of animals and humans worldwide. The organism is very hardy and can also be found in water, in soil, on food, and on surfaces that have been contaminated with feces. The organism can survive for months in the environment owing to the protective outer shell of its cyst.

Infection usually results from the ingestion of cysts in contaminated drinking water or accidental ingestion during swimming. Hikers, campers, and their pets are at particular risk because infected wild animals shed *Giardia* into mountain streams. Because beavers are common zoonotic sources of *Giardia*, giardiasis is sometimes referred to as "beaver fever." Even if humans avoid drinking stream water, they usually don't think twice about letting their dogs drink it. Unfortunately, it is often only a matter of time before the dog passes the protozoan to its owner. Alternatively, eating unwashed raw fruits or vegetables that have been contaminated by feces can lead to infection, as can contact with feces during sex. Giardiasis outbreaks in day care facilities are

## MICROBE AT A GLANCE

### *Giardia intestinalis*

**Taxonomy:** Nomenclature is in flux; one possibility, used in this book: domain Eukarya, kingdom Diplomonadida

**Other names:** Formerly called *Giardia lamblia*

**Morphology:** Single-celled protozoan with four pairs of flagella and a ventral adhesive disk

**Virulence factors:** Adhesive disk, resistant cyst

**Diseases caused:** Giardiasis (form of diarrhea)

**Treatment for disease:** Metronidazole, oral rehydration, and electrolyte replacement

**Prevention of disease:** Sterilize water either chemically or via filtration (boiling generally not sufficient because of cysts); good personal hygiene to prevent consumption of cysts

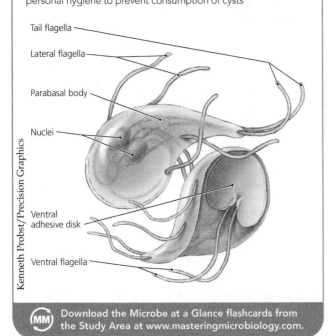

Tail flagella
Lateral flagella
Parabasal body
Nuclei
Ventral adhesive disk
Ventral flagella

Kenneth Probst/Precision Graphics

Download the Microbe at a Glance flashcards from the Study Area at www.masteringmicrobiology.com.

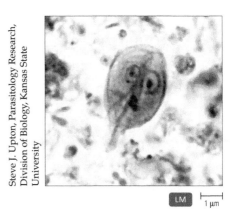

Steve J. Upton, Parasitology Research, Division of Biology, Kansas State University

LM | 1 μm

▲ **Figure 8 Trophozoite of *Giardia intestinalis*.** Two nuclei make this diplomonad resemble a face.

transmission. Cysts survive and remain infective for several months.

Giardiasis can range from an asymptomatic infection to significant gastrointestinal disease. Signs and symptoms, when they occur, include severe watery diarrhea, abdominal pain, bloating, nausea, vomiting, ineffective absorption of nutrients, and low-grade fever. Stools are foul smelling, usually with the "rotten-egg" smell of hydrogen sulfide. Incubation lasts roughly one to two weeks, and symptoms resolve after one to four weeks in normal, healthy adults. In extreme cases, the attachment of parasites to the intestinal mucosa causes superficial tissue damage, and fluid loss becomes life threatening. Chronic giardiasis can occur, often among animals.

Diagnosis of giardiasis, which involves direct microscopic examination of stool specimens, is based on the observation of flat, pear-shaped trophozoites that resemble a face when viewed from below (Figure 8). In addition to the "face," which results from the pair of nuclei that resemble eyes, four pairs of flagella extending from the ventral surface may also be visible. Clinicians may need to examine several stool samples as the parasites are shed only intermittently.

Metronidazole is the drug of choice for treatment of giardiasis. If diarrhea is not present, treatment is often waived. Oral rehydration therapy may be required for severe cases of giardiasis, or to treat very young children regardless of the severity of infection.

To prevent infection in regions where *Giardia* is endemic, filtering water is necessary. When hiking, neither humans nor their pets should drink unfiltered stream or river water. Most camping and hiking stores sell portable water filtration kits, making it unnecessary to carry bottled water. Filtered water should be used for cooking and cleaning eating utensils. In day care facilities, scrupulous hygiene practices and the separation of feeding and diaper-changing areas are essential to preventing transmission. Recovering patients should be extremely vigilant with their personal hygiene to avoid transmitting *Giardia* to family members and should avoid swimming for several weeks after recovery to ensure they do not shed parasites into the water.

usually the result of children putting contaminated toys or eating utensils into their mouths.

*Giardia* has a life cycle similar to that of *Entamoeba*. Following ingestion, each cyst is triggered by acid in the stomach to release a trophozoite into the small intestine that begins multiplying via binary fission. Trophozoites either remain free in the lumen of the small intestine or attach to the intestinal mucosa via a ventral adhesive disk; they do not invade the intestinal wall. As trophozoites pass into the colon, encystment occurs. Cysts are immediately infective upon release, leading to a significant incidence of person-to-person and self-to-self

J.L. Carson/Custom Medical Stock Photo

LM  ⊢ 15 μm ⊣

▲ **Figure 9** **Trophozoites of *Trichomonas vaginalis*.** Five anterior flagella, one associated with an undulating membrane, characterize this parabasalid.

### CRITICAL **THINKING**

How does the visually distinctive appearance of *Giardia* trophozoites improve the success of medical treatment of giardiasis as compared to that for amoebic infections?

### *Trichomonas*

*Trichomonas vaginalis* (trik-ō-mō′nas va-jin-al′is) is globally distributed and is the most common protozoan causing disease in people of industrialized nations. The parasite lives on the vulvas and in the vaginas of women and in the urethras and prostates of men. This obligate parasite, which is incapable of surviving long outside a human host, is transmitted almost exclusively via sex. *T. vaginalis* occurs most frequently in people with a preexisting sexually transmitted disease, such as chlamydial infection, and in people with multiple sex partners.

In women, infection results in **vaginosis** (vaj-i-nō′sis), which is accompanied by a purulent (pus-filled) odorous discharge, vaginal and cervical lesions, abdominal pain, painful urination, and painful intercourse. Since inflammation is not typically involved, it is "vaginosis" rather than "vaginitis." Trophozoites feed on vaginal tissue, leading to erosion of the epithelium. *T. vaginalis* infection may cause inflammation of the urethra or bladder of men, but more typically men are asymptomatic.

Microscopic observation of actively motile trophozoites in vaginal and urethral secretions is diagnostic. The trophozoites are flat and possess five flagella and a sail-like undulating membrane (**Figure 9**). An immunofluorescent assay can be performed when infection is suspected and microscopy is too

## CLINICAL CASE STUDY

### A Sick Soldier

A 20-year-old soldier serving in Iraq reports to his medic and complains of several large painless sores on his head and face. Some of the ulcers have healed, leaving scars. A sample taken from a lesion and examined microscopically shows the presence of flagellated protozoa.

1. Can a diagnosis be made from this information? If so, what is the diagnosis?

2. What treatment should the medic order?

3. How did the soldier become infected?

4. The soldier asks how he can prevent this disease in the future. How should the medic respond?

5. The soldier is a strong, healthy 20-year-old with a fully functioning immune system. Why was his body not able to sufficiently fight off the parasite?

Leslie E. Kossoff / Associated Press

insensitive. Patients and all their sexual partners must be treated to prevent reinfection. Metronidazole is the drug of choice, though some resistant strains of *T. vaginalis* exist. Prevention involves abstinence, mutual monogamy, or consistent and correct condom usage.

## Apicomplexans

### Learning Objectives

✓ Describe the life cycle of *Plasmodium* and relate malarial symptoms to stages in the life cycle.

✓ Describe the clinical manifestations of *Toxoplasma gondii* infections.

✓ Compare and contrast the intestinal diseases caused by *Cryptosporidium* and *Cyclospora*.

**Apicomplexans** (ap-i-kom-plek′sănz) are alveolate protozoa whose infective forms are characterized by an ornate complex of organelles at their apical ends, which gives the group its name. They have also been called *sporozoa* because during their life cycles they assume nonmotile, sporelike shapes, but this term is not accurate because the term *spores* correctly refers to reproductive structures of multicellular plants and fungi. All apicomplexans are parasites of animals, and all have complicated life cycles involving at least two types of hosts. A major feature of apicomplexan life cycles is *schizogony*—a form of

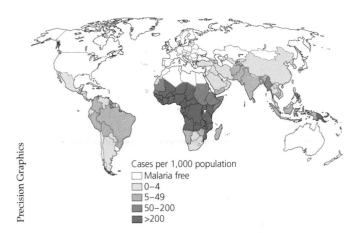

Cases per 1,000 population
☐ Malaria free
☐ 0–4
☐ 5–49
☐ 50–200
☐ >200

Precision Graphics

▲ **Figure 10 The geographical distribution and incidence of malaria.** The disease may be returning to areas from which it was once eradicated, including Europe and the United States.

asexual reproduction in which multinucleate *schizonts* form before the cells divide.

*Plasmodium, Toxoplasma, Cryptosporidium,* and *Cyclospora* are four important apicomplexan parasites. We begin our discussion with *Plasmodium,* the causative agent of malaria and the most infamous protozoan parasite in the world.

### Plasmodium

Four species of *Plasmodium* (plaz-mō′dē-ŭm) cause **malaria** in humans: *P. falciparum* (fal-sip′ar-ŭm), *P. vivax* (vī′vaks), *P. ovale* (ō-vă′lē), and *P. malariae* (mă-lār′ē-ī). Malaria is endemic in over 109 countries and territories throughout the tropics and subtropics, where the parasites′ mosquito vector breeds (Figure 10). The movement of infected individuals and mosquitoes continues to expand beyond these endemic areas, threatening to reintroduce *Plasmodium* into countries, including the United States, where mosquito eradication programs eliminated the disease decades ago. Over 240 million people are infected with *Plasmodium,* and 880,000 (usually children) die annually, making malaria among the deadlier killers. Females of 60 different species of the mosquito genus *Anopheles* (ă-nof′ĕ-lēz) serve as vectors of *Plasmodium.* (Male *Anopheles* do not feed on blood.)

The life cycle of *Plasmodium* has three prominent stages (Figure 11):

1. The **exoerythrocytic phase,** as its name indicates, occurs outside of red blood cells. During a blood meal on a human, an infected female mosquito injects a stage of *Plasmodium* called a *sporozoite* along with saliva containing an anticoagulant into the blood (1). Sporozoites reach the liver via the bloodstream and over the course of one to two weeks undergo schizogony within liver cells (2). Schizogony produces a *Plasmodium* stage called *merozoites* that proceed to rupture the liver cells and enter the blood (3). *P. ovale* and *P. vivax* are further capable of forming a resting

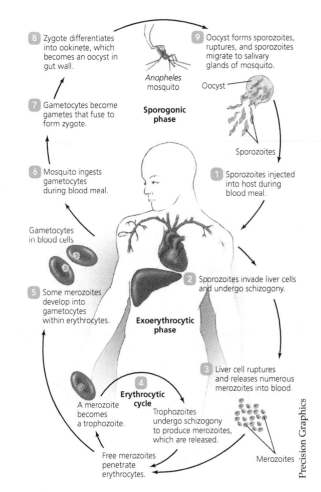

▲ **Figure 11 The life cycle of *Plasmodium.*** The exoerythrocytic phase and the erythrocytic cycle occur in humans, and the sporogonic phase in mosquitoes. *During which stage is malaria usually diagnosed in humans?*

*Figure 11 Malaria in humans is diagnosed during the parasite's erythrocytic cycle.*

stage called a *hypnozoite* (not shown), which can remain dormant in liver cells for years and be reactivated at any time, causing relapses of malaria.

2. The **erythrocytic cycle** (4) begins when free merozoites penetrate erythrocytes and become yet another stage, called *trophozoites,* that endocytize the erythrocytes′ hemoglobin protein. Presence of trophozoites inside blood cells is the diagnostic sign of malaria. Trophozoites undergo schizogony to produce more merozoites that lyse erythrocytes, and the cycle continues to repeat. Lysis of erythrocytes occurs nearly simultaneously and cyclically—every 48–72 hours, depending on the species of *Plasmodium* involved. Most merozoites infect new erythrocytes, but some remain in red blood cells, where they develop into male and female *gametocytes* (5).

415

Trophozoites

Erythrocyte
(red blood cell)

Steven Glenn, Laboratory and Consultation
Division/CDC

LM ├─────┤ 8 μm

▲ **Figure 12** **Trophozoites of *Plasmodium falciparum* inside
erythrocytes.** Trophozoites often appear as a ring of cytoplasm with a
dotlike nucleus.

3. The **sporogonic phase** begins when a female mosquito
   feeding on an infected human ingests gametocytes within
   erythrocytes ( 6 ). Freed from erythrocytes within the mosquito's digestive tract, gametocytes develop into *gametes*,
   and male gametes fertilize female gametes to produce *zygotes* ( 7 ). A zygote differentiates into an *ookinete*, which penetrates the mosquito's gut wall and becomes an *oocyst*, which
   undergoes meiosis ( 8 ). Some 10–20 days later, the oocyst
   ruptures, releasing thousands of sporozoites that migrate to
   the mosquito's salivary glands ( 9 ). The mosquito then
   transmits the sporozoites to a new host during a blood
   meal, completing the parasite's life cycle.

People living in endemic areas, and their descendants
throughout the world, have evolved to have one or more of the
following genetic traits that increase their resistance to malaria:

- *Sickle-cell trait.* Individuals with this gene produce an
  abnormal type of hemoglobin called hemoglobin S
  (hemoglobin A is normal). Hemoglobin S causes
  erythrocytes to become sickle-shaped, and somehow it
  also makes erythrocytes resist penetration by *Plasmodium*.

- *Hemoglobin C.* Humans with two genes for hemoglobin C
  are invulnerable to malaria. The mechanism by which this
  mutation provides protection is unknown.

- Genetic deficiency for the enzyme *glucose-6-phosphate dehy-
  drogenase.* Trophozoites must acquire this enzyme from a
  human host before the trophozoite can synthesize DNA;
  thus, humans without the enzyme are spared malaria.

- Lack of so-called *Duffy*[2] antigens on erythrocytes. Because
  *P. vivax* requires Duffy antigens to attach to and infect
  erythrocytes, Duffy-negative individuals are resistant to
  this species.

───────

[2]Named for the patient in which the antigen was discovered.

The severity of malaria caused by each species varies.
*P. ovale* generally causes mild disease; *P. vivax* usually results in
chronic malaria, with periodic recurrence of symptoms;
*P. malariae* and *P. falciparum* cause more serious malaria, with
*P. falciparum* infection possibly fatal.

The general symptoms of malaria are associated with syn-
chronous cycles of erythrocyte lysis. Two weeks after the erythrocytic cycle begins, sufficient numbers of parasites exist to cause
symptoms of fever, chills, diarrhea, headache, and (occasionally)
pulmonary or cardiac dysfunction. Fever correlates with erythrocyte lysis and most likely results from efforts of the immune system to remove cellular debris, toxins, and merozoites. Loss of
erythrocytes leads to anemia, weakness, and fatigue. The inability of the liver to process the inordinate amount of hemoglobin
released from dying erythrocytes results in *jaundice*.

*P. falciparum* causes a form of malaria called *blackwater fever*,
which is characterized by extreme fever, large-scale erythrocyte
lysis, renal failure, and dark urine discolored by excreted hemoglobin. Protozoan proteins inserted on the surfaces of infected
erythrocytes cause erythrocytes to become rigid and inelastic
such that they cannot squeeze through capillaries, blocking
blood flow and causing small hemorrhages in various tissues
(and ultimately tissue death). *Cerebral malaria* results when tissue death occurs in the brain. Falciparum malaria can be fatal
within 24 hours of the onset of symptoms.

If a victim survives the acute stages of malaria, immunity
gradually develops. Periodic episodes become less severe over
time—unless the victim becomes immunocompromised, in
which case episodes can return to original levels of severity.

Microscopy is most commonly used for diagnosing
malaria because *Plasmodium* species can be readily identified
and distinguished in blood smears. Ringlike trophozoites
within erythrocytes are often the diagnostic stage (**Figure 12**).
Demonstrating antibodies against *Plasmodium* in the serum can
also be used for differential diagnosis. However, because the
symptoms might be confused with those of less severe infections, diagnosis may be missed in nonendemic areas unless a
good case history, including travel history, is obtained.

Treatment varies by species and severity of symptoms.
Drug choices are constantly revised based on effectiveness and
the existence of resistant strains of *Plasmodium*. Standard antimalarial drugs include chloroquine, mefloquine, or atovaquone
in combination with proguanil. These are used for uncomplicated malarial infections in areas where drug resistance does
not exist. The World Health Organization recommends new
drugs based on a compound called artemisinin, which is derived from a shrub used in traditional Chinese treatment of
malaria. Antifever medication and blood transfusions may be
required as supportive measures.

Control of malaria involves limiting contact with mosquitoes carrying *Plasmodium*. Widespread use of insecticides,
drainage of wetlands, and removal of standing water can reduce
mosquito breeding rates. Personal use of insect repellents, netting, and protective clothing reduces mosquito bites. Travelers
to endemic areas can take preventive medication to avoid infection. Atovaquone and proguanil are drugs of choice and are usually taken several weeks before and after travel. Chloroquine is

## MICROBE AT A GLANCE

### *Plasmodium falciparum*

**Taxonomy:** Nomenclature is in flux; one possibility, used in this book: domain Eukarya, kingdom Alveolata, phylum Apicomplexa, class Sporozoea, order Eucoccidiida, family Plasmodiidae

**Morphology:** Sporozoite (slender, elongate single cell); merozoite (oval single cell); trophozoite (ring of cytoplasm with a dotlike nucleus; "ring form"); ookinete (motile wormlike form); oocyte (spherical)

**Virulence factors:** Lives intracellularly

**Diseases caused:** Malignant tertian malaria—a form of malaria called blackwater fever

**Treatment for disease:** Chloroquine, mefloquine, atovaquone, proguanil, artemisinin

**Prevention of disease:** Mosquito control, avoid mosquito bites

*Plasmodium falciparum* merozoite entering red blood cell

Red blood cell

Kenneth Probst/Precision Graphics

(MM) Download the Microbe at a Glance flashcards from the Study Area at www.masteringmicrobiology.com.

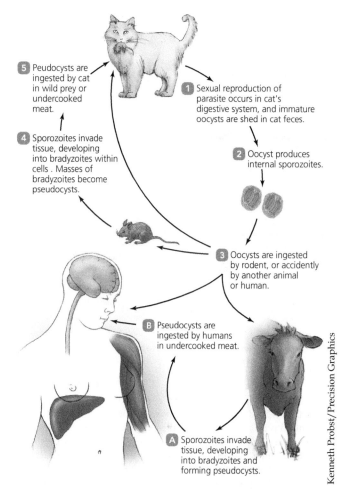

**5** Peudocysts are ingested by cat in wild prey or undercooked meat.

**1** Sexual reproduction of parasite occurs in cat's digestive system, and immature oocysts are shed in cat feces.

**4** Sporozoites invade tissue, developing into bradyzoites within cells . Masses of bradyzoites become pseudocysts.

**2** Oocyst produces internal sporozoites.

**3** Oocysts are ingested by rodent, or accidently by another animal or human.

**B** Pseudocysts are ingested by humans in undercooked meat.

**A** Sporozoites invade tissue, developing into bradyzoites and forming pseudocysts.

Kenneth Probst/Precision Graphics

▲ **Figure 13 The life cycle of *Toxoplasma gondii*.** *Which two groups of humans are most at risk from toxoplasmosis?*

**Figure 13** *AIDS patients and first-trimester fetuses are at greatest risk from toxoplasmosis.*

sometimes given prophylactically before travel to areas where *Plasmodium* is still susceptible to this drug. Several malaria vaccines are currently under development.

### *Toxoplasma*

*Toxoplasma gondii* (tok-sō-plaz′mă gon′dē-ē) is one of the world's most widely distributed protozoan parasites— 25% of the world's human population is infected. Wild and domestic mammals and birds are major reservoirs for *Toxoplasma,* and cats are the definitive host, in which the protozoan reproduces sexually.

Humans typically become infected by ingesting undercooked meat containing the parasite. People at greatest risk include butchers, hunters, and anyone who tastes food while preparing it. Ingestion or inhalation with contaminated soil can also be a source of infection. The protozoan can also cross a placenta to infect the fetus. Historically, contact with infected cats and their feces was proposed as a major risk for infection, but recent studies have shown that cats are not the major source of infection for humans because they shed *Toxoplasma* only briefly.

In the life cycle of *Toxoplasma* (Figure 13), male and female gametes in a cat's digestive tract fuse to form zygotes, which develop into immature *oocysts* that are shed in the feces (**1**). During the few days a cat sheds oocysts, it can excrete up to 10 million per day. Oocysts survive in moist soil for several months, contaminating vegetation grown in this soil. As each oocyst matures, it produces *sporozoites* internally (**2**). When rodents ingest mature oocysts on vegetation (**3**), digestion releases the sporozoites, which invade the rodent's muscles, lymph

Edwin P. Ewing Jr./CDC

▲ **Figure 14 Pseudocysts of *Toxoplasma gondii*.** Pseudocysts contain bradyzoites and are one infective stage of this protozoan.

nodes, digestive organs, and brain. Sporozoites proliferate asexually to produce *bradyzoites*. Thick walls form around masses of cells filled with bradyzoites to form *pseudocysts* (**4**).

*Toxoplasma* must return to a cat to reproduce, so pseudocysts preferentially form on and inhibit those parts of a rodent's brain that process cat odors and those that induce fear. With its fear of the smell of cats gone, the rodent is easily caught and eaten (**5**). Bradyzoites released from digested pseudocysts infect the cat's intestinal cells where the parasites become gametes, completing the life cycle.

Nonrodent animals (and occasionally people) become accidental hosts when they ingest oocysts containing sporozoites (**3**). These develop into pseudocysts containing bradyzoites (**A**). Humans most often are infected by eating pseudocysts in undercooked meat (**B**).

Although the majority of people infected with *T. gondii* have no symptoms, a small percentage develop **toxoplasmosis** (tok'sō-plaz-mō-sis), a fever-producing illness with headache, muscle pain, sore throat, and enlarged lymph nodes in the head and neck. Toxoplasmosis generally results in no permanent damage and is self-limiting, resolving spontaneously within a few months to a year. However, toxoplasmosis is more severe in two populations: AIDS patients and fetuses. In AIDS patients, symptoms are thought to result when tissue pseudocysts reactivate as the immune system fails. Spastic paralysis, blindness, myocarditis, encephalitis, and death result.

Transplacental transfer of *Toxoplasma* from mother to fetus is most dangerous in the first trimester of pregnancy; it can

## CLINICAL CASE STUDY

### A Protozoan Mystery

Mae Melvin, CDC

LM | 15 µm

A 20-year-old student was admitted to his college's student health center with headaches and fever shortly after beginning the fall semester. He had spent his summer working with an international aid organization in Nigeria and had returned to the United States only a week earlier. Gross examination revealed a diffuse rash and numerous insect bites. The young man had spent most of his summer outdoors in rural areas, had taken no prophylactic antimalarial medication, and had spent some time on African game reserves working with the families of local guides. The patient could not specifically remember receiving any of the bite wounds on his body, and he did not always use insect repellent in the field. The young man was admitted to the local hospital, where intermittent fever, nausea, and headache continued. Initial blood smears proved negative for malaria.

1. What are some possible protozoan diseases the patient could have contracted in Africa?
2. Can this disease be identified from the symptoms alone?
3. Based on the pictured blood smear, what would you conclude about the cause of the disease?
4. What would the treatment be if the patient had tested positive for malaria?
5. What treatment would you now recommend?
6. What prevention would you have suggested to this individual?
7. Is there a local threat of anyone else contracting this disease from the young man?

result in spontaneous abortion, stillbirth, or epilepsy, mental retardation, *microcephaly* (abnormally small head), inflammation of the retina, blindness, anemia, jaundice, and other conditions. Ocular infections may remain dormant for years, at which time blindness develops.

Physicians diagnose via microscopic identification of parasites in tissue biopsies (**Figure 14**), or via molecular identification of *T. gondii* genetic material or products in specimens using PCR, Southern blot, or DNA probes. Serology is the most common diagnostic method.

Asymptomatic patients do not need treatment for toxoplasmosis. For those with signs and symptoms, physicians prescribe one of the antimalarial drugs, which all act against

*Toxoplasma* as well. Treatment of infected pregnant women prevents most transplacental infections. More aggressive treatment may be needed for AIDS patients, including the addition of steroids to reduce tissue inflammation.

Controlling the incidence of *T. gondii* infection is difficult because so many hosts harbor the parasites. A vaccine for cats is currently under development to reduce the chance of pet-to-owner transmission. The best prevention is to thoroughly cook or deep-freeze meats and to avoid contact with contaminated soil.

### Cryptosporidium

*Cryptosporidium enteritis* (krip′tō-spō-rid′ē-ŭm en-ter-ī′tis), also known as *cryptosporidiosis* (krip′tō-spō-rid-ē-ō′sis), is a zoonosis; that is, it is a disease of animals that is transmitted to people. *Cryptosporidium parvum* (par-vŭm); an apicomplexan, causes the disease. Once thought to infect only livestock and poultry, *Cryptosporidium* is carried asymptomatically by about 30% of people living in developing nations. It is estimated that most natural waterways in the United States are contaminated with the oocysts of *Cryptosporidium* from livestock wastes.

Infection most commonly results from drinking water contaminated with oocysts, but direct fecal-oral transmission resulting from poor hygienic practices also occurs, particularly in day care facilities. In the intestine, oocysts release sporozoites, which invade the intestinal mucosa and become intracellular parasites. Eventually, new oocysts are produced, released into the lumen of the intestine, and shed in the feces.

Signs and symptoms of *Cryptosporidium* enteritis include severe diarrhea that lasts from one to two weeks accompanied by headache, muscular pain, cramping, and severe fluid and weight

Oocysts

LM | 5 μm

▲ **Figure 15  Oocysts of *Cryptosporidium parvum*.** Here they are in a stained fecal smear.

From: Three-step stool examination for cryptosporidiosis in 10 homosexual men with protracted watery diarrhea. P. Ma, R. Soave. *Journal of Infectious Diseases*. 1983 May; 137(5):824–28. Provided by the CDC

loss. In HIV-positive individuals, chronic *Cryptosporidium* enteritis is life threatening and is one of the indicator diseases revealing that a person has AIDS.

Most diagnostic techniques are not very sensitive for *Cryptosporidium,* but microscopic examination of concentrated fecal samples or biopsy material can reveal oocysts (Figure 15).

### EMERGING DISEASES

Rebecca Ash

Precision Graphics

## BABESIOSIS

Leslie hated being sick, but here she was on a fine summer day with a headache, muscle pains, and sore joints. It was just as well she didn't know that the worst was yet to come.

A small deer tick (*Ixodes scapularis*) had taken a blood meal from Leslie's leg six weeks before. The tick was so small and the bite so painless that Leslie was unaware of the attack. She was equally unaware that the tick had infected her with an apicomplexan parasite normally found in mice. *Babesia microti* was eating her red blood cells from the inside out.

Leslie became anemic, jaundiced, fatigued, and depressed, and she was losing weight. As she became weaker, she had trouble catching her breath, and within the week, her kidneys began to fail. Intermittent fever, shaking chills, drenching sweat, nausea, and anorexia came next. Leslie was utterly miserable, but with intensive medical care, including the use of the antimicrobials atovaquone, azithromycin, clindamycin, and quinine, she pulled through.

In the last decade, the number of reported cases of babesiosis has quadrupled. Perhaps this emerging disease is spreading because its tick vector has an expanded range due to global warming. Perhaps physicians are more aware of a disease whose incidence has been constant. Whatever the reason for our increased awareness of babesiosis, Leslie was grateful that she was diagnosed and treated effectively so her nightmare could finally end.

(MM) Track babesiosis online by going to the Study Area at www.masteringmicrobiology.com.

## TABLE 1

## Key Features of Protozoan Parasites of Humans

| Organism | Primary Diseases | Geographical Distribution | Mode of Transmission | Host Organisms |
|---|---|---|---|---|
| **Ciliates** | | | | |
| *Balantidium coli* | Balantidiasis, dysentery | Worldwide | Fecal-oral | Pigs, rodents, primates, humans |
| **Amoebae** | | | | |
| *Entamoeba histolytica* | Luminal amebiasis, amebic dysentery, invasive extraintestinal amebiasis | Worldwide | Fecal-oral | Humans |
| *Acanthamoeba* spp. | Ulcerative keratitis, amebic encephalitis | Worldwide | Contact | Humans |
| *Naegleria* | Primary amebic meningoencephalitis | Worldwide | Inhalation | Humans |
| **Flagellates** | | | | |
| *Trypanosoma brucei* | African sleeping sickness | African subcontinent | Tsetse fly (*Glossina*) | Wild game, pigs, humans |
| *Trypanosoma cruzi* | Chagas' disease | Central and South America | Kissing bug (*Triatoma*) | Opossums, armadillos, humans |
| *Leishmania* spp. | Cutaneous, mucocutaneous, or visceral leishmaniasis | Tropics, subtropics | Sand flies (*Phlebotomus, Lutzomyia*) | Canines, rodents, humans |
| *Giardia intestinalis (lamblia)* | Giardiasis | Developed nations, tropics | Fecal-oral | Humans, wild animals |
| *Trichomonas vaginalis* | Vaginitis | Developed nations | Sexual contact | Humans |
| **Apicomplexans** | | | | |
| *Plasmodium* spp. | Malaria | Tropics, subtropics | Mosquitoes (*Anopheles*) | Humans |
| *Toxoplasma gondii* | Toxoplasmosis | Worldwide | Fecal-oral | Cats, livestock, humans |
| *Cryptosporidium parvum* | *Cryptosporidium* enteritis (cryptosporidiosis) | Worldwide | Fecal-oral | Livestock, poultry, humans |
| *Cyclospora cayetanensis* | Cyclosporiasis, gastrointestinal disorders | North, Central, and South America | Fecal-oral | Humans |

Fluorescent-labeled antibodies reveal low concentrations of oocysts in appropriate specimens.

Treatment essentially consists of oral rehydration therapy, because few drugs are effective against *Cryptosporidium*. Drinking from rivers and streams should be avoided in areas where *Cryptosporidium* is found; filtration is required to remove oocysts from drinking water because they cannot be killed by chlorination. Good personal hygiene can eliminate fecal-oral transmission of the parasite.

### Cyclospora

*Cyclospora cayetanensis* (sī-klō-spōr′ă kī′ē-tan-en′sis) is a waterborne apicomplexan that has been responsible for an emerging disease, *cyclosporiasis,* that has affected hundreds in the United States since the early 1980s. The disease is not transmitted between individuals but acquired by eating or drinking oocysts in contaminated food or water. Outbreaks have been linked in particular to raspberries imported from Central and South America. The environmental reservoir for *Cyclospora* remains unknown.

Once *Cyclospora* enters the intestine, it invades the mucosal layer, causing symptoms, which develop after about a week. Manifestations include cramps, watery diarrhea, myalgia (muscle pain), and fever. Symptoms are more severe in AIDS patients, leading to severe dehydration and weight loss. The disease usually resolves in days or weeks in immunocompetent patients.

Microscopic examination of stool samples can sometimes reveal the presence of oocysts in extensive infections, but fluorescent DNA probes more reliably detect the presence of *Cyclospora*. *Cyclospora* infections are treated with trimethoprim and sulfamethoxazole given in combination for seven days.

Reliable food testing does not currently exist but would be an important tool in preventing contaminated food from reaching U.S. consumers. The only reliable methods for reducing risk of infection in the United States are thoroughly washing fruits and vegetables prior to eating them raw. Cooking or freezing also kills many oocysts.

Table 1 lists the general characteristics of the protozoan parasites discussed in this chapter.

▶ **Figure 16 Features of tapeworm morphology.** Each tapeworm consists of an organ of attachment called a scolex, a neck, and a long chain of segments called proglottids.

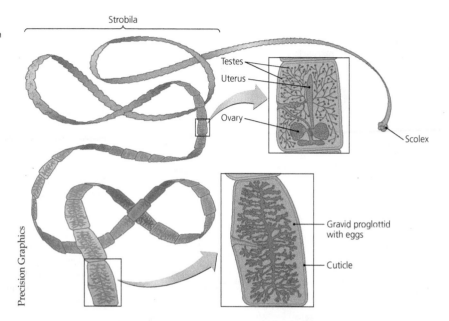

Strobila

Testes
Uterus
Ovary
Scolex

Gravid proglottid with eggs
Cuticle

Precision Graphics

# Helminthic Parasites of Humans

## Learning Objective

✓ Describe the general morphological and physiological features of parasitic worms.

**Helminths** are macroscopic, multicellular, eukaryotic worms found throughout the natural world, some in parasitic associations with other animals. They are not microorganisms, though microbiologists generally study them, in part because the diagnostic signs of infestation—eggs or larvae—are microscopic.

Taxonomists divide parasitic helminths into three groups: *cestodes* (ses'tōdz), *trematodes* (trem'a-tōdz), and *nematodes* (nēm'a-tōdz).

The life cycles of parasitic helminths are complex. For many, intermediate hosts are required to support larval (immature) stages needed for the worms to reach maturity. Adult worms are either *dioecious*,[3] meaning that the male and female sex organs are in separate worms, or *monoecious*,[4] meaning that each worm has both sex organs. Monoecious organisms either fertilize each other during copulation or are capable of self-fertilization, depending on the species. Because most parasitic helminths release large numbers of fertilized eggs into the environment, transmission to new hosts is likely to occur.

## Cestodes

### Learning Objectives

✓ Describe the common features of the life cycles of tapeworms that infect humans.

✓ List the predominant modes of infection for *Taenia* and *Echinococcus*, and suggest measures to prevent infection.

All **cestodes,** commonly called *tapeworms,* are flat, segmented, intestinal parasites that completely lack digestive systems. Though they differ in size when mature, all possess the same general body plan (**Figure 16**). The **scolex** (skō'leks) is a small attachment organ that possesses suckers and/or hooks used to attach the worm to host tissues (see the photo at the beginning of the chapter). Anchorage is the only role of a scolex; there is no mouth. Cestodes acquire nutrients by absorption through the worm's *cuticle* (outer "skin").

Behind the scolex is the neck region. Body segments, called **proglottids** (prō-glot'idz), grow from the neck continuously, so long as the worm remains attached to its host. New proglottids displace older ones, moving the older ones farther from the neck. Proglottids mature, producing both male and female reproductive organs. Thus a chain of proglottids, called a *strobila* (strō'bi-lă; plural: *strobilae,* strō'bi-lī), reflects a sequence of development: proglottids near the neck are immature, those in the middle are mature, and those near the end are *gravid*[5]—full of fertilized eggs. Each proglottid is monoecious and may fertilize other proglottids of the same or different tapeworm; a proglottid is not capable of fertilizing itself, although the tapeworm is self-fertile.

After fertilization occurs and the proglottids fill with eggs, gravid proglottids break off the strobila and pass out of the intestine along with feces. In a few cases, the proglottids rupture within the intestine, releasing eggs directly into the feces. Some tapeworms produce proglottids large enough to be obviously visible in stools.

[3]From Greek *di*, meaning two, and *oikos*, meaning house.
[4]From Greek *mono*, meaning one, *and oikos*, meaning house.
[5]From Latin *gravidus*, meaning heavy—that is, pregnant.

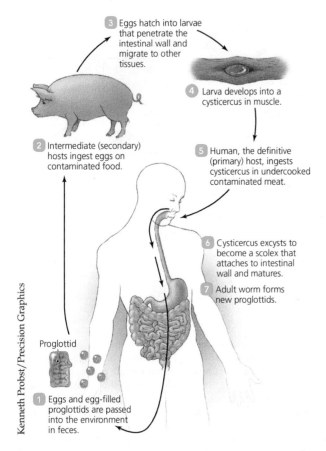

**3** Eggs hatch into larvae that penetrate the intestinal wall and migrate to other tissues.

**4** Larva develops into a cysticercus in muscle.

**2** Intermediate (secondary) hosts ingest eggs on contaminated food.

**5** Human, the definitive (primary) host, ingests cysticercus in undercooked contaminated meat.

**6** Cysticercus excysts to become a scolex that attaches to intestinal wall and matures.

**7** Adult worm forms new proglottids.

Proglottid

**1** Eggs and egg-filled proglottids are passed into the environment in feces.

Kenneth Probst/Precision Graphics

▲ **Figure 17** **A generalized life cycle of some tapeworms of humans.** *Which species of* Taenia *is shown in this representation?*

**Figure 17** *Taenia solium is illustrated, as indicated by the intermediate host being a pig.*

## Generalized Tapeworm Life Cycle

The generalized life cycle of most tapeworms of humans is depicted in **Figure 17**. Gravid proglottids and/or eggs enter the environment in feces from infested humans, who are the definitive (primary) hosts (**1**). Intermediate (secondary) hosts, which vary with the species of tapeworm, become infected by ingesting vegetation contaminated with gravid proglottids or eggs (**2**). Eggs hatch into larvae within the intermediate host's intestine, and the larvae penetrate the intestinal wall and migrate to other tissues, often muscle (**3**), where the larvae develop into immature forms called **cysticerci** (sis-ti-ser'sī) (**4**). Cysticerci are generally harmless to intermediate hosts. Humans become infected by consuming undercooked meat containing cysticerci (**5**). A cysticercus excysts in the human's intestine to become a scolex that attaches to the intestinal wall and matures (**6**), developing into a new adult tapeworm (**7**), which eventually sheds gravid proglottids, completing the cycle.

### *Taenia*

*Taenia saginata* (te'ne-a sa-ji-na'ta), the beef tapeworm, and *Taenia solium* (so'lī-um), the pork tapeworm, are so named because cattle and swine, respectively, serve as intermediate hosts. Both tapeworm species are distributed worldwide in areas where beef and pork are eaten. Poor, rural areas with inadequate sewage treatment and where humans and livestock live in close proximity have the highest incidence of human infection. Overall, *Taenia* infections in humans are rare in the United States.

Tapeworms attached to the intestinal epithelium can grow quite large. At maturity, *T. saginata* worms have 1000–2000 proglottids, each of which can contain 100,000 eggs. *T. solium* adults average 1000 proglottids, each of which contains about 50,000 eggs. An infested human passes strobilae of about six proglottids per day.

Rarely, humans become intermediate hosts of *T. solium* when they ingest eggs or gravid proglottids rather than cysticerci. Larvae released from the eggs become cysticerci in the human, who is thereby an accidental intermediate host. For the parasite this is a dead end. Humans are not intermediate hosts for *T. saginata*.

Most people actively shed strobilae without experiencing symptoms, though in some cases, nausea, abdominal pain, weight loss, and diarrhea accompany infestation. If the tapeworm is particularly large, blockage of the intestine is possible.

Diagnosis is achieved by microscopic identification of proglottids in fecal samples at least three months after infection. Examination of the scolex is required to differentiate between *T. saginata* and *T. solium*.

Normally, treatment is with praziquantel. Thoroughly cooking or freezing meat is the easiest method of prevention. Because cysticerci are readily visible in meat, giving it a "mealy" look, inspecting meat can reduce the chances of eating infected meat.

### *Echinococcus*

*Echinococcus granulosus* (ĕ-kī'nō-kok'ŭs gra-nū-lō'sŭs) is an unusual tapeworm of canines in that its body consists of only three proglottids—one immature, one sexually mature, and one gravid. A gravid proglottid is released each time the neck forms a new immature proglottid. Canines are infected by eating cysticerci in various herbivorous hosts such as cattle, sheep, and deer. Incidence is highest in areas wherever livestock are kept, including the western United States.

Humans become accidental intermediate hosts by consuming food or water contaminated with *Echinococcus* eggs shed in dogs' feces. The eggs release larvae into the intestine; the larvae invade the circulatory system and are carried throughout the

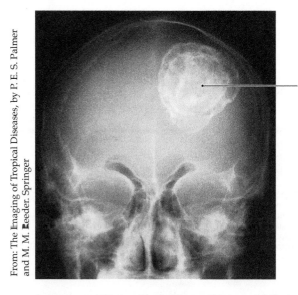

From: The Imaging of Tropical Diseases, by P. E. S. Palmer and M. M. Reeder. Springer

▲ **Figure 18 X ray of hydatid cyst.** This large, calcified cyst is in the cerebrum of a 20-year-old man.

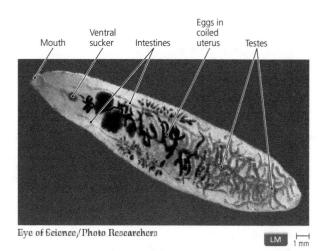

Mouth Ventral sucker Intestines Eggs in coiled uterus Testes

Eye of Science/Photo Researchers

LM ⊢——⊣ 1 mm

▲ **Figure 19 Some features of fluke morphology.** Note the sucker, which keeps the leaf-shaped flatworm attached to its host's tissues.

body, where they form **hydatid**[6] (hī′da-tid) cysts and cause **hydatid disease.** Hydatid cysts form in any organ but occur primarily in the liver.

Over several years, hydatid cysts can calcify and enlarge to the size of grapefruits (20 cm in diameter), filling with fluid and several million granular *protoscoleces*. Each protoscolex is the potential scolex of a new worm, but since dogs do not normally eat humans, the protoscoleces of hydatid cysts in humans are a dead end for *Echinococcus*.

Symptoms of hydatid disease follow the enlargement of cysts in infected tissue and result from tissue dysfunction. For example, hydatid cysts in the liver produce abdominal pain and obstruction of the bile ducts. If a hydatid cyst ruptures, protoscoleces spread throughout the body via the bloodstream, and each protoscolex grows into a new hydatid cyst. Hydatid cysts in the brain, lungs, bones, heart, or kidneys can be fatal.

Diagnosis involves visualization of cyst masses using ultrasound, CT scan, or radiography (Figure 18), followed by serological confirmation via immunoassays. Biopsies should be avoided as rupture of a cyst can lead to the spread of protoscoleces.

Treatment involves surgery to remove cysts, followed by the anthelmintic drug albendazole. Human infection is prevented by good hygiene practices to avoid fecal-oral transmission of eggs from infected dogs. It is also a good idea to avoid drinking untreated water from streams or other waterways in areas where foxes, coyotes, or wolves roam.

---

[6]From Greek *hydatis*, meaning a drop of water, presumably in reference to the fluid that accumulates within hydatid cysts.

## Trematodes

### Learning Objectives

✓ Explain how the life cycles of blood flukes differ from those of other flukes.

✓ Discuss the life cycles and disease manifestations of *Schistosoma* and *Fasciola*.

**Trematodes,** commonly known as *flukes* (flūks), are flat, leaf-shaped worms (Figure 19). A fluke has no anus and so has an incomplete digestive tract. A ventral sucker enables a parasite to attach to host tissues and obtain nutrients. The geographical distribution of flukes is extremely limited by the geographical distribution of the specific species of snails they require as intermediate hosts.

Researchers group flukes together according to the sites in the body they parasitize. The following sections examine some representative flukes, but first we consider common features of fluke life cycles.

### Common Features of the Fluke Life Cycle

Flukes that cause disease in humans share similar complex life cycles (Figure 20). Fluke eggs pass from the body in feces or urine, depending on the site of infestation (**1**). Eggs deposited in freshwater hatch to release free-swimming larvae called *miracidia* (mir-a-sid′ē-a) (**2**). Within 24 hours, miracidia actively seek out and burrow into a snail of a specific species (**3**). Two or three cycles of asexual reproduction within the snail produce larvae called *cercariae* (ser-kār′ē-ī) (**4**), which leave the snail as free-swimming forms. The next steps differ depending on whether the parasite is a blood, liver, lung, or intestinal fluke. In blood flukes, the cercariae aggressively seek out and penetrate the skin of humans (**5a**); in some intestinal and liver flukes,

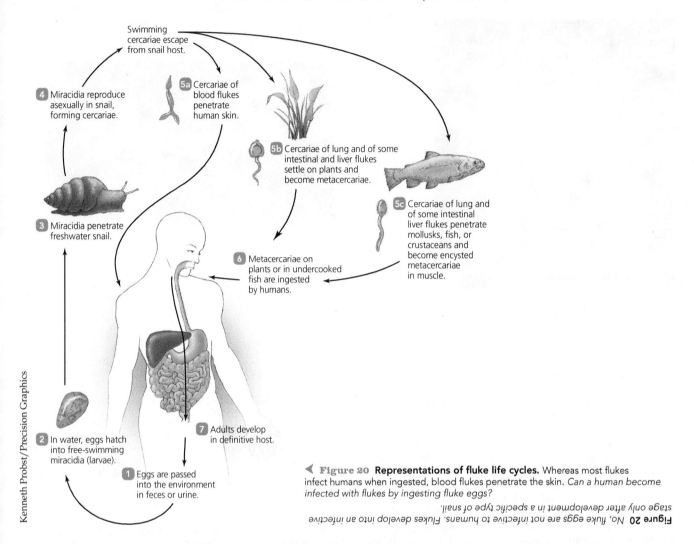

**4** Miracidia reproduce asexually in snail, forming cercariae.

Swimming cercariae escape from snail host.

**5a** Cercariae of blood flukes penetrate human skin.

**5b** Cercariae of lung and of some intestinal and liver flukes settle on plants and become metacercariae.

**5c** Cercariae of lung and of some intestinal liver flukes penetrate mollusks, fish, or crustaceans and become encysted metacercariae in muscle.

**3** Miracidia penetrate freshwater snail.

**6** Metacercariae on plants or in undercooked fish are ingested by humans.

**2** In water, eggs hatch into free-swimming miracidia (larvae).

**7** Adults develop in definitive host.

**1** Eggs are passed into the environment in feces or urine.

Kenneth Probst/Precision Graphics

◀ **Figure 20** **Representations of fluke life cycles.** Whereas most flukes infect humans when ingested, blood flukes penetrate the skin. *Can a human become infected with flukes by ingesting fluke eggs?*

**Figure 20** *No, fluke eggs are not infective to humans. Flukes develop into an infective stage only after development in a specific type of snail.*

cercariae encyst to become *metacercariae* on vegetation (**5b**); while in lung flukes and other intestinal and liver flukes, cercariae encyst to become metacercariae within a second intermediate host (**5c**). For liver, lung, and intestinal flukes, humans become infected by ingesting metacercariae (**6**). Once inside the definitive host, the parasites migrate to appropriate sites and develop into adults (**7**), which then produce perhaps 25,000 eggs per day that pass into the environment in feces or urine.

With the exception of one dioecious genus (*Schistosoma*), all flukes are monoecious. They are not self-fertile.

Now, we consider examples of specific species of flukes, beginning with *Fasciola*, a liver fluke.

## CRITICAL **THINKING**

Compare the general tapeworm life cycle to the general fluke life cycle. What is similar? What is different?

### Representative Liver Fluke: *Fasciola*

Two species of liver fluke—*Fasciola hepatica* (fa-sē'ō-lă he-pa'-ti-kă) and *F. gigantica* (ji-gan'ti-kă)—infect sheep and cattle worldwide. *Fasciola* also can infect humans, who become accidental definitive hosts when they ingest metacercariae encysted on aquatic vegetation such as watercress. Following excystment in the intestine, the larvae burrow through the intestinal wall, the peritoneal cavity, or the liver to reach the bile ducts, where they mature within three to four months.

Acute disease characterized by tissue death, abdominal pain, fever, nausea, vomiting, and diarrhea accompanies the migration of the parasite from the intestine to the liver; chronic infection begins when flukes take up residence in the bile ducts. Symptoms coincide with episodes of bile duct obstruction and inflammation, and heavy infections cause liver failure. Lesions can occur in other tissues as well.

Diagnosis involves the correlation of symptoms and patient history with microscopic identification of eggs in fecal matter, although *Fasciola* eggs are not always readily distinguishable from those of other intestinal and liver flukes, and symptoms alone mimic other liver disorders. However, liver failure following the consumption of watercress or other raw vegetables grown in endemic areas is suggestive.

Treatment is dependent on accurate diagnosis, as *F. hepatica* does not respond to praziquantel as other flukes do. Either triclabendazole or bithionol is effective.

## CRITICAL **THINKING**

Thoroughly cooking raw vegetables prior to consumption would kill the metacercariae of *Fasciola* and prevent infection. Why is this method of prevention not practical?

## Blood Flukes: *Schistosoma*

Blood flukes in the genus *Schistosoma* (skis-tō-sō′mă) are dioecious and cause **schistosomiasis** (skis′tō-sō-mī′ă-sis)—a potentially fatal disease and one of the major public health problems in the world. The World Health Organization estimates that over 200 million people are infected worldwide, of which 20 million suffer serious disease and about 20,000 die annually. Most cases of schistosomiasis occur in sub-Saharan Africa, but *Schistosoma* is endemic in 76 countries. (See **Highlight: Snail Fever Reemerges in China.**)

Three geographically limited species of *Schistosoma* infect humans:

- *S. mansoni* (man-sō′nē) is common to the Caribbean, Venezuela, Brazil, Arabia, and large areas of Africa.
- *S. haematobium* (hē′mă-tō′bē-ŭm) is found only in Africa and India.
- *S. japonicum* (jă-pon′i-kŭm) occurs in China, Taiwan, the Philippines, and Japan, although infections in Japan are relatively rare.

CDC

LM  100 µm

▲ **Figure 21**
**An egg of *Schistosoma mansoni*, from a stool sample.**
Distinctive spines characterize the eggs of blood flukes.

Humans are the principal definitive host for most species of *Schistosoma*. Cercariae burrow through the skin of humans who contact contaminated water while washing clothes and utensils, bathing, or swimming. The larvae enter the circulatory system, where they mature and mate. Females lay eggs, which have distinctive spines (Figure 21), in the walls of the blood vessels. The eggs work their way to the lumen of the intestine (*S. mansoni* and *S. japonicum*) or lumens of the urinary bladder and ureters (*S. haematobium*) to be eliminated into the environment.

## HIGHLIGHT

### SNAIL FEVER REEMERGES IN CHINA

In China, schistosomiasis is known mainly as "snail fever," since the blood fluke that causes the disease commonly breeds in snails there. The snails live in lakes all over China, and the parasite is transmitted to humans when skin comes into contact with infested water. The flukes travel through the bloodstream and attack the liver, pancreas, and stomach. People are often slow to realize they have the condition; chronic symptoms include lethargy, high fevers, swollen stomachs (as shown), and a lingering and painful death in some cases.

Many of the victims live in villages around lakes and are farmers and fishermen; thus, avoiding contact with infested water is almost impossible. Infection rates in some villages is as high as 80%. The disease was nearly eradicated in the 1950s, when the government regularly swept lakes of snails, but with the waning of such controls today—coupled with frequent floods—the disease is reemerging in rural areas and even extending into urban regions. Nearly 900,000 people now have the disease in China, and an estimated 30 million more are at risk. With proper medication, schistomosiasis can be kept under control; however, many Chinese cannot afford treatment, complicating the challenge China faces in curbing the spread of this disease.

A. Crump, W.H.O./Photo Researchers

A transient dermatitis called *swimmer's itch* may occur in the area where cercariae burrow into the skin. Migration through the circulatory system is generally asymptomatic.

*S. mansoni* and *S. japonicum* infections become chronic when eggs lodge in the liver, lungs, brain, or other organs. Trapped eggs die and calcify in the liver, leading to tissue damage that is generally fatal. In *S. haematobium* infections, movement of eggs into the bladder and ureters results in blood in the urine, blockage due to long-term fibrosis and calcification and, in some geographical regions, fatal bladder cancer.

The number of cases of schistosomiasis has increased over the past few decades as economic stability in endemic regions has allowed improved irrigation systems and water reservoirs that provide more habitat for intermediate host snails.

Diagnosis is most effectively made by microscopic identification of spiny eggs in either stool or urine samples. The species of blood fluke causing a given infection can be ascertained from the shape of the egg and the location of its spine. If eggs are not seen but infection is suspected, immunological assays can be used to identify antigen.

The drug of choice for treatment of schistosomiasis is praziquantel. Prevention of infection depends on improved sanitation, particularly sewage treatment, and avoiding contact with contaminated water. A recombinant vaccine for *S. mansoni* is currently in clinical trials.

### CRITICAL **THINKING**

Propose some additional methods that could be used to prevent transmission of *Schistosoma* infections to humans.

## Nematodes

### Learning Objectives

✓ Describe the common characteristics of nematodes.

✓ Compare and contrast the three most common nematode infections of humans.

✓ Discuss the life cycle of filarial nematodes, and contrast it with the life cycles of intestinal nematodes.

**Nematodes,** or roundworms, are long, cylindrical worms that taper at each end, possess complete digestive tracts, and have a protective outer layer called a *cuticle.*

### Features of the Life Cycle of Roundworms

Nematodes are highly successful parasites of almost all vertebrates, including humans. They have a number of reproductive strategies:

- Most intestinal nematodes shed their eggs into the lumen of the intestine, where they are eliminated with the feces. The eggs are then consumed by the definitive host either in contaminated food (particularly raw fruits and vegetables that grow close to the soil) or in contaminated drinking water.

- For a few intestinal nematodes, larvae hatch in the soil and actively penetrate the skin of new hosts. Once in the body, they travel a circuitous route (discussed in a later section) to the intestine.

- Other nematodes encyst in muscle tissue and are consumed in raw or undercooked meat.

- Mosquitoes transmit a few species of nematodes, called *filarial nematodes*, among hosts.

All nematodes are dioecious and develop through four larval stages either within eggs, in intermediate hosts, or in the environment before becoming adults. Adult, sexually mature stages are found only in definitive hosts. Copulation of male and female worms leads to the production of fertilized eggs and perpetuation of the cycle.

We examine representative intestinal and filarial nematodes in the following sections. We begin with the largest nematode parasite of humans, *Ascaris lumbricoides*.

### Ascaris

*Ascaris lumbricoides* (as'kă-ris lŭm'bri-koy'dez), the causative agent of **ascariasis** (as-kă-rī'ă-sis), is the most common nematode infection of humans worldwide, infecting approximately 1 billion people, primarily in tropical and subtropical regions. *Ascaris* is also the largest nematode to infect humans, growing as large as 30 cm in length. The nematode is endemic in rural areas of the southeastern United States.

Adult worms grow and reproduce in the small intestine, where females produce about 200,000 eggs every day. Eggs passed with feces can remain viable for years in moist, warm soil, where an embryo develops within each egg. After eggs are ingested in water or on vegetables, the larvae invade the intestinal wall to enter the circulatory or lymphatic systems. From there the larvae reach the lungs, where they develop through two more larval stages in approximately two weeks. The worms are then coughed up into the pharynx and swallowed. The parasites subsequently develop into adults in the intestine.

Most infections are asymptomatic, though if the worm burden (number of worms) is high, intestinal symptoms and signs can include abdominal pain, nausea, vomiting, and complete intestinal obstruction, which may be fatal. Transitory fever and pulmonary symptoms, including dry cough, difficulty in breathing, and bloody sputum, may occur during larval migration.

Diagnosis is made by the microscopic identification of eggs in the stool, larvae in sputum, or (rarely) by identification of adult worms passed in the stool or exiting via the nose or mouth—a distinctly unpleasant experience with larger worms (Figure 22). The treatment of *Ascaris* with albendazole, mebendazole, or pyrantel pamoate over one to three days is 90% effective. Surgery may be required to alleviate intestinal obstruction. Proper sanitation and hygiene, including treatment of sewage and drinking water, are important for prevention. Good personal hygiene and cooking practices are also important methods of preventing infection in endemic areas.

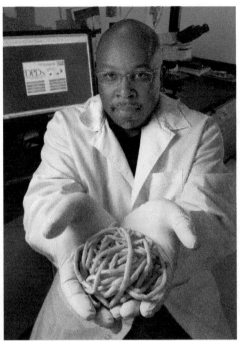

Henry Bishop, CDC

▲ **Figure 22** *Ascaris lumbricoides.* This mass of worms passed from a child in Kenya, Africa. Infestation also occurs in the southeastern United States.

### *Ancylostoma* and *Necator*

Hookworms—so called because adults resemble shepherd's hooks—are the second most common nematode infecting humans, responsible for more than 600 million infections worldwide, sucking the equivalent of all the blood from 1.5 million people per day. Two hookworms infect humans. *Ancylostoma duodenale* (an-si-los′tō-mă doo′ō-de-nā′lē) is distributed throughout Africa, Asia, the Americas, the Middle East, North Africa, and southern Europe. *Necator americanus* (nē-kā′tor ă-mer-i-ka′nŭs) predominates in the Americas and Australia but can be found in Asia and Africa as well.

Eggs passed in the stools of infected humans are deposited in soil, where they hatch in a couple of days if the soil is warm and moist. The initial larvae develop over a span of 5–10 days into infective larvae that can survive up to five weeks in soil. The larvae burrow through human skin and are carried by the circulatory system to the heart and the lungs. In the lungs, larvae burrow into the air cavity and migrate up the trachea to the esophagus, where they are swallowed. Larvae attach to the small intestine, mature into adults, and mate. Most adults survive in the intestine for one to two years or longer.

Adult worms have ghastly looking mouths (Figure 23) and suck the blood of their hosts, consuming as much as 150 μl of blood per day per worm. This results in chronic anemia, iron deficiency, and protein deficiency.

Dennis Kunkel/Visuals Unlimited/Getty Images  0.25 mm

▲ **Figure 23 Mouth of a hookworm.** The sharp teeth allow the parasite to attach to the intestinal wall and feed on blood.

Itching, rash, and inflammation that can persist for several weeks characterize *ground itch,* which occurs at the site of skin penetration by larvae. Ground itch is generally worse with successive infections. Pulmonary symptoms can also occur.

Microscopic identification of eggs in the stool along with anemia and blood in the feces is diagnostic.

Treatment is with albendazole, mebendazole, or pyrantel pamoate for several days. *N. americanus* is more difficult to treat effectively. Proper sanitation (sewage treatment) is essential for prevention. In areas where hookworm is endemic, going barefoot should be avoided to prevent exposure.

### *Enterobius*

*Enterobius vermicularis* (en-ter-ō′bī-ŭs ver-mi-kū-lar′is) infects about 500 million people worldwide, particularly in temperate climates, in school-age children, and in conditions of overcrowding. *Enterobius* is the most common parasitic worm found in the United States, affecting 40 million Americans. It is commonly known as the pinworm, after the shape of the female worm's tail. Humans are the only host for *Enterobius.*

After mating in the colon, female pinworms migrate at night to the anus, where they deposit eggs perianally. Scratching dislodges eggs onto clothes or bedding, where they dry out, become aerosolized, and settle in water or on food that is then ingested. Alternatively, scratching deposits eggs on the skin and under the fingernails, such that infected individuals can continually reinfect themselves by ingesting the eggs on their hands or in food. Adult worms mature in several weeks and live in the intestinal tract for approximately two months.

One-third of all *Enterobius* infections are asymptomatic. When symptoms do occur, intense perianal itching is the chief complaint. Scratching can lead to secondary bacterial infections.

427

CDC

LM ⊢——⊣ 50 μm

▲ **Figure 24** **Eggs of *Enterobius vermicularis*.** Note the characteristic flattening of one side of each egg.

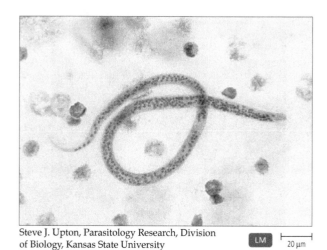

Steve J. Upton, Parasitology Research, Division of Biology, Kansas State University

LM ⊢——⊣ 20 μm

▲ **Figure 25** A microfilaria of *Wuchereria bancrofti* in blood.

Rarely, worms enter a female's genital tract, where they can cause inflammation of the vulva.

Microscopy is used for diagnosis. In the morning, before bathing or defecation, transparent sticky tape is applied to the perianal area to collect the readily identifiable microscopic eggs (Figure 24). Adult worms, if recovered, are also diagnostic.

Treatment is with an initial dose of pyrantel pamoate or mebendazole followed by a second treatment two weeks later to kill any newly acquired worms. Prevention of reinfection and spread to family members requires thorough laundering of all clothes and bedding of infected individuals. Further, infected individuals should not handle food to be consumed by others.

### *Wuchereria*

*Wuchereria bancrofti* (voo-ker-e′rē-ă ban-krof′tē) is a *filarial nematode*—a type of nematode that does not infect the intestinal tract of vertebrate hosts but rather the lymphatic system, causing **filariasis** (fil-ă-rī′ă-sis). *W. bancrofti* infects the lymphatic system of about 120 million people throughout the tropics of Africa, India, Southeast Asia, Indonesia, the Pacific Islands, South America, and the Caribbean. Female mosquitoes of the genera *Culex* (kyu′leks), *Aedes* (ā-ē′dēz), and *Anopheles* transmit the worm.

Mosquitoes ingest circulating larvae called *microfilariae* (mī′krō-fi-lar′ē-ī) while feeding on humans (Figure 25). The microfilariae develop as larvae in the mosquito and eventually migrate to the salivary glands. When the mosquito next feeds, parasites are injected into a new person.

Larvae migrate via the circulatory system to deeper tissues, where they mature. Adults live and reproduce for up to 17 years in lymphatic vessels. During the day, microfilariae stay in capillaries of internal organs; they swim freely in the bloodstream only at night, coinciding with the feeding habits of most mosquitoes.

Filariasis remains asymptomatic for years. As the disease progresses, lymphatic damage occurs—subcutaneous tissues swell grotesquely because blocked lymphatic vessels cannot drain properly. The end result is **elephantiasis** (el-ĕ-fan-tī′ă-sis), generally in the lower extremities, in which tissues enlarge and harden in areas where lymph has accumulated (Figure 26). Elephantiasis can be further associated with secondary bacterial infections in affected portions of the body.

Diagnosis is made by the microscopic identification of microfilariae in the blood. Blood samples are collected at night, when microfilariae circulate. In addition to microscopy, immunoassays using antibodies to detect *W. bancrofti* antigens in the blood can be used for diagnosis.

Treatment with diethylcarbamazine effectively kills microfilariae and adult worms.

Prevention relies on using insect repellents or mosquito netting, wearing loose, long, light-colored clothing, or remaining indoors when mosquitoes are most active. In endemic areas, particularly urban areas, eliminating standing water (a requirement of mosquitoes' life cycle) around human dwellings decreases mosquito numbers. Widespread spraying with insecticides to kill mosquitoes has reduced the prevalence of filariasis.

Table 2 summarizes the key features of the common helminthic parasites of humans.

Andy Crump, W.H.O./SPL/Photo Researchers

▲ **Figure 26 Elephantiasis in a leg.** This condition follows years of infection with *Wuchereria bancrofti*. Adult *Wuchereria* are found in what human body system?

Figure 26 *Adults of Wuchereria live in the lymphatic system.*

## 2 Key Features of Representative Helminthic Parasites of Humans

| Organism | Primary Infection or Disease | Geographical Distribution | Mode of Transmission | Length of Adult Worms |
|---|---|---|---|---|
| **Cestodes (Tapeworms)** | | | | |
| *Taenia saginata*; *Taenia solium* | Beef tapeworm infestation; pork tapeworm infestation | Worldwide with local endemic areas | Consumption of undercooked meat | *T. saginata*: 5–25 m; *T. solium*: 2–7 m |
| *Echinococcus granulosus* | Hydatid disease | Worldwide with local endemic areas | Consumption of eggs shed in dog feces | 3–6 mm |
| **Trematodes (Flukes)** | | | | |
| *Fasciola hepatica*; *F. gigantica* | Fascioliasis | *F. hepatica*: Europe, Middle East, Asia; *F. gigantica*: Asia, Africa, Hawaii | Consumption of watercress or lettuce | Up to 30 mm; up to 75 mm |
| *Schistosoma* spp. | Schistosomiasis | *S. mansoni*: Caribbean, S. America, Arabia, Africa; *S. haematobium*: Africa, India; *S. japonicum*: east Asia | Direct penetration of the skin | 7–20 mm |
| **Nematodes (Roundworms)** | | | | |
| *Ascaris lumbricoides* | Ascariasis | Tropics and subtropics worldwide | Fecal-oral | Females: 20–35 cm; males: 15–30 cm |
| *Ancylostoma duodenale*, *Necator americanus* | Hookworm disease | *Ancylostoma*: Africa, Asia, the Americas, Middle East, North Africa, southern Europe; *Necator*: the Americas, Australia, Asia, Africa | Direct penetration of the skin | *Ancylostoma* females: 10–13 mm, males: 8–11 mm; *Necator* females: 9–11 mm, males: 7–9 mm |
| *Enterobius vermicularis* | Pinworm | Worldwide | Anal-oral and fecal-oral, inhalation | Females: 8–13 mm; males: 2–5 mm |
| *Wuchereria bancrofti* | Filariasis, elephantiasis | Worldwide, tropics | Mosquitoes | Females: 80–100 mm; males: 40 mm |

Protozoan and helminthic diseases are found worldwide, and much of the world's population is at risk of infection. Many of the drugs used to treat parasitic diseases have been around for decades, and whereas most remain effective, resistant parasites are occurring with greater frequency. No effective vaccines have been produced for any of the diseases discussed in this chapter. The only way to protect oneself, therefore, is to avoid exposure.

# Arthropod Vectors

## Learning Objective

✓ List the principal arthropod vectors of human pathogens, and give one example of a pathogen transmitted by each.

Vectors are animals—usually *arthropods* (ar'thrō-podz)—that carry microbial pathogens. An **arthropod** is an animal with a segmented body, a hard exoskeleton (external skeleton), and jointed legs. Arthropods are extremely diverse and abundant—insects alone account for more than half of all the known species on Earth.

Some arthropods are *biological vectors,* meaning that they also serve as hosts for the pathogens they transmit. Given that arthropods are usually small organisms (so small that we don't notice them until they bite us), and given that they produce large numbers of offspring, controlling arthropod vectors to eliminate their role in the transmission of important human diseases is an almost insurmountable task.

Disease vectors belong to two classes of arthropods: *Arachnida* (ticks and mites) and the more common *Insecta* (fleas, lice, flies, and true bugs). Mosquitoes—a type of fly—are the most important vector of human diseases. Most arthropod vectors are found on a host only when they are actively feeding. Lice are the only vectors that may spend their entire lives in association with a single individual.

# Chapter Summary

1. **Parasitology** is the study of protozoan and helminthic parasites of animals and humans. All parasites have a **definitive host** in which adult or sexual stages reproduce, and many parasites also have one or more **intermediate hosts,** in which immature stages live.

## Protozoan Parasites of Humans

1. Many protozoa have two life stages: a trophozoite (feeding) stage and a dormant cyst stage. **Encystment** is the process of cyst formation; **excystment** refers to the process by which cysts become trophozoites.

2. *Balantidium coli* is the only **ciliate** to cause disease in humans. It is responsible for **balantidiasis,** usually a mild gastrointestinal illness.

3. **Amoebae** are protozoa that move and feed using pseudopodia. *Entamoeba histolytica* is a relatively common protozoan parasite that causes **amebiasis,** which can be mild luminal amebiasis, more severe amebic dysentery, or very severe invasive extraintestinal amebiasis, in which the parasite causes lesions in the liver, lungs, brain, and other organs.

4. *Acanthamoeba* and *Naegleria* are free-living amoebae that rarely infect humans. Both are acquired from water. *Acanthamoeba* causes keratitis and **amebic encephalitis,** which progresses slowly and is usually fatal. *Naegleria* causes a more rapid **amebic meningoencephalitis,** which is also fatal.

5. Parasitic **flagellates** include *Trypanosoma, Leishmania, Giardia,* and *Trichomonas.*

6. *Trypanosoma cruzi,* transmitted by the kissing bug *(Triatoma),* causes **Chagas' disease** in the Americas, where it is a frequent cause of heart disease. *T. brucei,* transmitted by the tsetse fly *(Glossina),* causes **African sleeping sickness.**

7. Both trypanosomes have similar life cycles. Epimastigotes in the insect gut develop into infective trypomastigotes introduced to the human host by the insect vector. *T. cruzi* trypomastigotes develop intracellularly in macrophages and heart muscle as amastigotes. *T. brucei* trypomastigotes remain in the blood, are antigenically variable, can spread to the CNS, and can be fatal.

8. Many species of *Leishmania* infect humans. Each parasite has two developmental stages: an intracellular amastigote in mammals and a promastigote form in sand flies, which transmit the disease. Three clinical forms of **leishmaniasis** are seen, each with increasing severity: cutaneous, mucocutaneous, and visceral. Leishmaniasis is a **zoonosis**—a disease of animals transmitted to humans.

9. *Giardia intestinalis* is a frequent cause of gastrointestinal disease **(giardiasis)** and is endemic worldwide. Giardiasis is rarely fatal.

10. *Trichomonas vaginalis* is the most common protozoan disease of humans. This sexually transmitted protozoan causes **vaginosis.** Prevention relies on abstinence, monogamy, and condom usage.

11. *Plasmodium* species, *Toxoplasma, Cryptosporidium,* and *Cyclospora* are all **apicomplexans,** in which sexual reproduction produces oocysts that undergo schizogony to produce various forms.

12. Four species of *Plasmodium* cause **malaria** and are transmitted by female *Anopheles* mosquitoes. The complex life cycle of *Plasmodium* has three stages: Sporozoites travel to the liver to initiate the **exoerythrocytic phase.** Rupture of liver cells releases merozoites from intracellular schizonts. Merozoites infect erythrocytes to initiate the **erythrocytic cycle.** The **sporogonic phase** in the mosquito has an oocyst that divides to form sporozoites, which are injected into humans when the mosquito feeds. Dormant hypnozoites are produced by *P. ovale* and *P. vivax. P. falciparum* produces the deadliest form of malaria. Several host traits influence whether or not an individual is susceptible to malaria.

13. *Toxoplasma gondii* causes **toxoplasmosis,** a disease of cats that can be acquired by other animals and humans, primarily via the consumption of meat containing the parasites. **Toxoplasmosis** is generally mild in humans, but *Toxoplasma* can cross the placenta to cause serious harm to fetuses.

14. *Cryptosporidium parvum* and *Cyclospora cayetanensis* both cause waterborne gastrointestinal disease in the United States. *Cryptosporidum*, which causes ***Cryptosporidium enteritis*** (cryptosporidiosis), is resistant to standard water treatment methods. Cyclosporiasis is an emerging disease in the U.S.

## Helminthic Parasites of Humans

1. **Helminths** are multicellular eukaryotic worms, some of which are parasitic.

2. **Cestodes** (tapeworms) all share similar morphologies and general life cycles. A **scolex** attaches the tapeworm to the intestine of its definitive host. From this extends a neck region from which **proglottids** grow. When fertilized eggs (sometimes within gravid proglottids) are eaten by an intermediate host, they hatch to release larval stages that invade tissues of the intermediate host and form **cysticerci**. When the cysticerci are eaten by a definitive host, they undergo development into adult tapeworms.

3. Humans are the definitive hosts of *Taenia saginata*, the beef tapeworm, and *Taenia solium*, the pork tapeworm. Humans become infected by eating cysticerci in undercooked beef or pork, respectively.

4. *Echinococcus granulosus* forms **hydatid** cysts to cause **hydatid disease** in humans who are accidental intermediate hosts when they ingest the helminth's eggs. The definitive host is a canine.

5. **Trematodes**, or flukes, are often divided into four groups: blood, intestinal, liver, and lung flukes. Eggs deposited in water hatch to release miracidia, which burrow into freshwater snails. Following asexual reproduction cercariae are released into the water. In intestinal, liver, and lung flukes, cercariae encyst on plants or in a second intermediate host as metacercariae, which are ingested by human hosts. Cercariae of blood flukes directly penetrate the skin of humans. After maturation occurs in the human, flukes release eggs back into the environment via the feces or urine.

6. *Fasciola* is a liver fluke. Humans acquire *Fasciola* by ingesting metacercariae on watercress or other vegetables.

7. Species of *Schistosoma* (blood flukes) affect millions of people worldwide, causing **schistosomiasis.** Three species infect humans: *S. mansoni, S. japonicum,* and *S. haematobium,* each of which is geographically limited. Extensive infections significantly damage the liver.

8. **Nematodes** are round, unsegmented worms with pointed ends.

9. *Ascaris lumbricoides,* the largest nematode to infect humans, causes **ascariasis,** which is the most common nematode disease of humans in the world. Eggs containing infective larvae are consumed with contaminated vegetables. The eggs hatch in the intestine, and larvae enter the lymphatic system. Worm migration through the body may be associated with various symptoms, but infections are usually not fatal.

10. *Ancylostoma duodenale* and *Necator americanus* are both hookworms, the second most common nematodes to infect humans worldwide. Eggs deposited in soil mature to form infective larvae that leave the egg and actively burrow through human skin to initiate infection. The circulatory system carries the worms through the lungs and heart. Eventually worms migrate up the respiratory tract to the pharynx, where they are swallowed. They become adults in the intestine, where they attach to the intestinal mucosa and feed on blood. Hookworm infection can lead to anemia and other blood-related dysfunction.

11. The pinworm *Enterobius vermicularis* is the most common parasitic worm infestation of humans in the United States and the third most common in the world. Eggs deposited in the perianal area are introduced into the mouth following scratching to reinfect the human host. Transmission among family members is also common.

12. *Wuchereria bancrofti* is a filarial (threadlike) nematode of humans, causing **filariasis.** It lives in the lymphatic system, where adult worms block lymph flow, causing **elephantiasis,** in which lymph accumulates, especially in the lower extremities. Bacterial infections may ensue, and subcutaneous tissues harden, producing permanent disfigurement. The parasite is transmitted when microfilariae, which circulate in the blood, are picked up by feeding mosquitoes.

## Arthropod Vectors

1. **Arthropods** are organisms with segmented bodies, jointed legs, and a hard exoskeleton. They are found worldwide in nearly all habitats, and some may serve as biological vectors for many organisms. Arthropod vectors are arachnids (adults having eight legs) or insects (adults having six legs).

2. Arachnid vectors include mites and ticks.

3. Insect vectors include fleas, lice, flies, and kissing bugs. Mosquitoes are the most important arthropod vectors of human diseases.

---

# Questions for Review
*Answers to the Questions for Review (except for Short Answer questions) appear at the end of this chapter.*

## Multiple Choice

1. Parasitology is the study of
   a. parasitic viruses.
   b. parasitic prokaryotes.
   c. parasitic fungi.
   d. parasitic eukaryotes.

2. The only ciliate to cause disease in humans is
   a. *Naegleria.*
   b. *Balantidium.*
   c. *Fasciola.*
   d. *Trypanosoma.*

3. Which of the following organisms is regularly transmitted sexually?
   a. *Trichomonas*
   b. *Entamoeba*
   c. *Trypanosoma*
   d. *Enterobius*

4. *Leishmania* species are transmitted by
   a. sand flies.
   b. tsetse flies.
   c. kissing bugs.
   d. mosquitoes.

5. Which of the following is the name of the intracellular infection stage of *Leishmania*?
   a. miracidia
   b. metacercaria
   c. bradyzoite
   d. amastigote

6. In malaria, which stage occurs in red blood cells?
   a. exoerythrocytic phase
   b. erythrocytic cycle
   c. sporogonic phase
   d. amastigote cycle

7. The definitive host for *Toxoplasma gondii* is
   a. humans.
   b. cats.
   c. birds.
   b. mosquitoes.

8. Tapeworms are generally transmitted via
   a. consumption of an intermediate host.
   b. consumption of the definitive host.
   c. vectors such as mosquitoes.
   d. consumption of adult tapeworms.

9. *Cryptosporidium* cannot be killed by routine boiling. Another parasite resistant to such boiling is
   a. *Giardia*.
   b. *Trypanosoma*.
   c. *Toxoplasma*.
   d. *Plasmodium*.

10. The immature fluke stages that infect snail intermediate hosts are called
    a. metacercariae.
    b. cercariae.
    c. cysticerci.
    d. miracidia.

11. The beef tapeworm is known by the scientific name
    a. *Taenia solium*.
    b. *Taenia saginata*.
    c. *Ancylostoma duodenale*.
    d. *Echinococcus granulosus*.

12. *Enterobius vermicularis* is commonly called
    a. hookworm.
    b. pinworm.
    c. whipworm.
    d. tapeworm.

13. The infective larvae of *Necator americanus* must pass through which human organ to mature?
    a. bladder
    b. brain
    c. lung
    d. liver

14. Both *Plasmodium* species and *Wuchereria bancrofti* can be carried by mosquitoes in the genus
    a. *Aedes*.
    b. *Anopheles*.
    c. *Culex*.
    d. *Ctenocephalides*.

15. Which of the following arthropods is responsible for transmitting the most parasitic diseases?
    a. fleas
    b. ticks
    c. mosquitoes
    d. true bugs

16. The majority of cestodes are transmitted via
    a. ingestion.
    b. vectors.
    c. direct contact.
    d. inhalation.

17. Which of the following is most effective in preventing infection by *Giardia*?
    a. sexual abstinence
    b. drinking only bottled water
    c. use of insect repellent
    d. cooking all food

18. The sporogonic phase of *Plasmodium* occurs in
    a. red blood cells.
    b. liver cells.
    c. schizonts.
    d. *Anopheles* mosquitoes.

19. The tapeworm attachment organ is a
    a. scolex.
    b. proglottid.
    c. strobila.
    d. cuticle.

20. Trophozoite-cyst conversion is vital to the life of
    a. *Balantidium*.
    b. *Entamoeba*.
    c. *Giardia*.
    d. all of the above

## Modified True/False

Mark each statement as true or false. Rewrite the false statements to make them true by changing the italicized word(s).

____ 1. *Sexual contact* is the most common method of transmitting parasites.

____ 2. Examination of *stool samples* can reveal the presence of *Naegleria* parasites.

____ 3. *Trichomonas vaginalis* is the most common parasitic protozoan of humans in the industrialized world.

____ 4. *Trypanosoma brucei* is transmitted by tsetse flies and *Trypanosoma cruzi* is transmitted by kissing bugs.

____ 5. *Plasmodium falciparum* causes the most serious form of malaria.

____ 6. Toxoplasmosis can be transmitted across a *placenta*.

____ 7. Humans can become intermediate hosts for *Taenia solium*.

____ 8. *Fasciola hepatica* can be acquired by eating infected *sheep*.

____ 9. The number of cases of schistosomiasis has *increased* worldwide owing to improved technology and economic stability in endemic areas.

____ 10. *Wuchereria bancrofti* is a filarial nematode that infects the *lymphatic system*.

## Fill in the Blanks

1. *Balantidium coli* can be distinguished from *Entamoeba histolytica* microscopically because *B. coli* has _____.

2. _____ may be transmitted to humans from cat litter boxes.

3. African sleeping sickness is caused by *Trypanosoma* _____ but not by *Trypanosoma* _____ .

4. The parasitic amoeba _____ can be acquired by ingestion.

5. *Plasmodium vivax* and *P. ovale* can both form dormant _____ .

6. Of the parasitic helminths discussed in this chapter, the only one transmitted by mosquitoes is _____ .

7. The following helminths can directly penetrate the skin of humans to establish infection: _____, _____ and _____ (give genera only).

8. A trematode that can be acquired by eating raw or undercooked vegetables is _____ .

9. Hookworm disease is caused by _____ in the Middle East.

10. Both of the following parasites demonstrate nocturnal movement, which is important during diagnosis: _____ and _____ .

## Matching

Match the terms with the correct organisms. Answers may be used more than once, and an organism may have more than one answer.

____ 1. *Balantidium coli*        A. Miracidia

____ 2. *Echinococcus granulosus*   B. Bradyzoites

____ 3. *Fasciola* spp.           C. Schizogony

____ 4. *Leishmania* spp.         D. Microfilaria

____ 5. *Plasmodium falciparum*   E. Hydatid cyst

____ 6. *Plasmodium vivax*        F. Cysticerci

____ 7. *Taenia* spp.             G. Trophozoites

____ 8. *Toxoplasma gondii*       H. Amastigotes

____ 9. *Trypanosoma*             I. Hypnozoites

____ 10. *Wuchereria bancrofti*    J. Trypomastigotes

## Labeling

Label the three stages of the *Plasmodium* life cycle, and label the forms of the parasite where indicated.

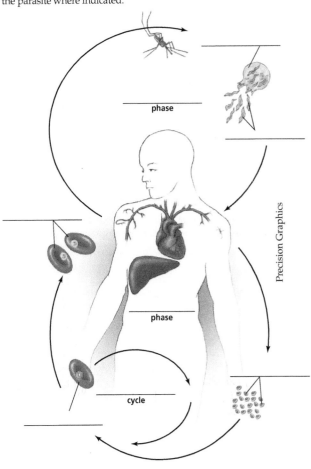

_____ phase

_____ phase

_____ cycle

## Short Answer

1. Why do insect vectors and animal reservoirs increase the difficulty of preventing and controlling parasitic infections in humans?

2. How is the transmission of the amoeba *Entamoeba* different from the transmission of the amoebae *Acanthamoeba* and *Naegleria*?

# Concept Mapping

Using the following terms, draw a concept map that describes intestinal protozoan parasites. Or, complete this concept map online by going to the Study Area at www.masteringmicrobiology.com.

| | | | |
|---|---|---|---|
| Amoebae | Cysts | Flagellates | Reproducing/feeding stage |
| Apicomplexans | Diarrhea | *Giardia intestinalis* | Trophozoites |
| *Balantidium coli* | Dormant stage | Livestock wastes | Two morphological forms |
| Ciliates | *Entamoeba histolytica* | New host | Unknown |
| *Cryptosporidium parvum* | Environment | Oocyst | Water |
| *Cyclospora cayetanensis* | Fecal-oral route | People with AIDS | |

# Critical Thinking

1. Compare *Entamoeba*, *Acanthamoeba*, and *Naegleria*. Based on incidence, which of these parasites is a threat to more people? Clinically, which is the most serious? Explain why your answer is not the same for both questions.

2. Explain how each of the following could lead to the reemergence of malaria in the United States: (a) global warming, (b) increased travel of individuals from endemic regions to the United States, (c) increased immigration of individuals from endemic regions to the United States, (d) regulations against the use of insecticides, and (e) laws protecting wetlands.

3. People who suffer from AIDS are severely immunocompromised because HIV destroys immune cells; thus, all the diseases in this chapter could be a threat to an AIDS patient. Which diseases, however, would specifically exacerbate the immune dysfunction of AIDS? Why?

4. Discuss why sickle-cell trait is advantageous to people living in areas where malaria is endemic but not advantageous in malaria-free areas.

5. Present a logical argument to explain the differences between the clinical manifestations of *Trypanosoma brucei* and *T. cruzi*. Relate your argument to the respective life cycles.

6. What feature of the life cycle of *T. brucei* makes it difficult to create a successful vaccine?

7. On July 10, a man in Palm Beach, Florida, was admitted to the hospital with a month-long history of fever, chills, headache, and vomiting. A parasite was observed in a blood smear. What parasite causes these signs and symptoms? What is the treatment? Is this a rare disease in Florida?

8. In March 2009, a Peace Corps volunteer was evacuated from Malawi in Africa because of a two-week history of headaches, vision loss, and an episode of unconsciousness. Doctors discovered a granular swelling in his brain and eggs with peripheral spines in his urine. What is the diagnosis? What species is involved? What is the treatment?

9. Humans can accidentally become intermediate hosts of *Taenia solium*. Why is this is a dead end for the parasite?

Access more review material online in the Study Area at **www.masteringmicrobiology.com.** There, you'll find

- **Concept Mapping Activities**
- **Flashcards**
- **Quizzes**

and more to help you succeed.

# Answers

Answers to multiple-choice, fill-in-blank, labeling, matching, and true/false questions are listed here. Answers for Short Answer and Critical Thinking questions are available for instructors only in the Instructor's Manual that accompanies this text.

### Multiple Choice
1. d; 2. b; 3. a; 4. a; 5. d; 6. b; 7. b; 8. a; 9. a; 10. d; 11. b; 12. b; 13. c; 14. b; 15. c; 16. a; 17. b; 18. d; 19. a; 20. d

### Modified True/False
1. *Ingestion*; 2. *corneal scrapings, cerebrospinal fluid, or biopsy material*; 3. True; 4. True; 5. True; 6. True; 7. True; 8. *water plants*; 9. True; 10. True

### Fill in the Blanks
1. cilia; 2. *Toxoplasma gondii*; 3. *brucei, cruzi*; 4. *Entamoeba*; 5. hypnozoites; 6. *Wuchereria*; 7. *Ancylostoma, Necator, Schistosoma*; 8. *Fasciola*; 9. *Ancylostoma*; 10. *Enterobius vermicularis* and *Wuchereria bancrofti*

### Matching
1. G; 2. E; 3. A; 4. H; 5. C, G; 6. C, G, I; 7. F; 8. B; 9. J; 10. D

### Labeling
See Figure 11.

# Characterizing and Classifying Viruses, Viroids, and Prions

From Chapter 13 of *Microbiology with Diseases by Taxonomy*, Third Edition. Robert W. Bauman. Copyright © 2011 by Pearson Education, Inc. Published by Benjamin Cummings, Inc. All rights reserved.

# Characterizing and Classifying Viruses, Viroids, and Prions

In April 2007, the chief of a village in the Democratic Republic of the Congo (DRC) developed a severe fever, and then he bled to death over a few days. Over a hundred people who attended his funeral also contracted the same disease. Eight months later in a neighboring village, a mother delivered her baby but then both died of bloody diarrhea, and the nurse who cared for them was showing the same signs. Deadly Ebola hemorrhagic fever was on the prowl once again in the DRC.

Hemorrhagic fevers, smallpox, AIDS, SARS, influenza, common colds—many of the world's deadliest and most feared, as well as many common diseases are caused by viruses. However, not all viruses are harmful to humans. Some, such as bacteriophages, attack pathogens and have clinical use. This chapter is an introduction to viruses and other pathogenic particles called viroids and prions: how they infect cells, how they multiply, and how they differ from cellular pathogens.

 Take the pre-test for this chapter online. Visit the Study Area at www.masteringmicrobiology.com.

Ebola virus, one of several hemorrhagic fever viruses, is one of the world's deadlier pathogens.

Not all pathogens are cellular. Many infections of humans, animals, and plants, and even of bacteria, are caused by **acellular** (noncellular) agents, including viruses and other pathogenic particles called viroids and prions. Although these agents are like some eukaryotic and prokaryotic microbes in that they cause disease when they invade susceptible cells, they are simple compared to a cell—lacking cell membranes and composed of only a few organic molecules. In addition to lacking a cellular structure, they lack most of the characteristics of life. They cannot carry out any metabolic pathway, they can neither grow nor respond to the environment, and they cannot reproduce independently but instead must utilize the chemical and structural components of the cells they infect. They must recruit the cell's metabolic pathways in order to increase their numbers.

In this chapter we first examine a range of topics concerning viruses: what their characteristics are, how they are classified, how they replicate, what role they play in some kinds of cancers, how they are maintained in the laboratory, and whether or not viruses are alive. Then we consider the nature of viroids and prions.

# Characteristics of Viruses

Viruses cause most of the diseases that still plague the industrialized world: the common cold, influenza, herpes, SARS, and AIDS, to name a few. Although we have immunizations against many viral diseases and are adept at treating the symptoms of others, the characteristics of viruses and the means by which they attack their hosts make cures for viral diseases elusive. Throughout this section, consider the clinical implications of viral characteristics.

We begin by looking at the characteristics viruses have in common. A **virus** is a minuscule, acellular, infectious agent having one or several pieces of nucleic acid—either DNA or RNA. The nucleic acid is the genetic material (genome) of the virus. Being acellular, viruses have no cytoplasmic membrane (though, as we will see, some viruses possess a membrane-like *envelope*). Viruses also lack cytosol and functional organelles. They are not capable of metabolic activity on their own; instead, once viruses have invaded a cell, they take control of the cell's metabolic machinery to produce more molecules of viral nucleic acid and viral proteins, which then assemble into new viruses via a process we will examine shortly.

Viruses have an extracellular and an intracellular state. Outside of a cell, in the extracellular state, a virus is called a **virion** (vir′ē-on). Basically, a virion consists of a protein coat, called a **capsid,** surrounding a nucleic acid core (Figure 1a). Together the nucleic acid and its capsid are also called a *nucleocapsid,* which in many cases can crystallize like crystalline chemicals (Figure 1b). Some virions have a phospholipid membrane called an **envelope** surrounding the nucleocapsid. The outermost layer of a virion (capsid or envelope) provides the virus both protection and recognition sites that bind to complementary chemicals on the surfaces of their specific host cells. Once a virus is inside, the intracellular state is initiated, and the

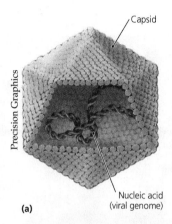

Capsid

Nucleic acid
(viral genome)

**(a)**

Precision Graphics

Yu. G. Kuznetsov and A. McPherson,
University of California, Irvine

**(b)**    AFM    200 nm

▲ **Figure 1 Virions, complete virus particles, include a nucleic acid, a capsid, and in some cases an envelope. (a)** A drawing of a nonenveloped polyhedral virus containing DNA. **(b)** An atomic force microscope image of crystallized tobacco mosaic virus. Like many chemicals and unlike cells, some viruses can form crystals.

capsid is removed. A virus without its capsid exists solely as nucleic acid, but is still referred to as a virus.

Now that we have examined ways in which viruses are alike, we will consider the characteristics that are used to distinguish different viral groups. Viruses differ in the type of genetic material they contain, the kinds of cells they attack, their size, the nature of their capsid coat, their shapes, and the presence or absence of an envelope.

## Genetic Material of Viruses

### Learning Objective

✓ Discuss viral genomes in terms of dsDNA, ssDNA, ssRNA, dsRNA, and number of segments of nucleic acid.

Viruses show more variety in the nature of their genomes than do cells. Whereas the genome of every cell is double-stranded DNA, the genome of a virus may be either DNA or RNA. The primary

Partial genome of *E. coli*

Viral genome

TEM | 400 nm

▲ **Figure 2** **The relative sizes of genomes.** *Escherichia coli* was ruptured to release the DNA.

way in which scientists categorize and classify viruses is based on the type of genetic material that makes up the viral genome.

Some viral genomes, such as those of herpesvirus and chickenpox virus, are double-stranded DNA (dsDNA), like the genomes of cells. Other viruses use either single-stranded RNA (ssRNA), single-stranded DNA (ssDNA), or double-stranded RNA (dsRNA) as their genomes. These molecules never function as a genome in any cell—in fact, ssDNA and dsRNA are almost nonexistent in cells. Further, the genome of any particular virus may be either linear and composed of several molecules of nucleic acid, as in eukaryotic cells, or circular and singular, as in most prokaryotic cells. For example, the genome of an influenzavirus is composed of eight linear segments of single-stranded RNA, whereas the genome of poliovirus is one molecule of single-stranded RNA.

Viral genomes are usually much smaller than the genomes of cells. For example, the genome of the smallest chlamydial bacterium has almost 1000 genes, whereas the genome of virus MS2 has only three genes. Figure 2 compares the genome of a virus with the genome of the bacterium *Escherichia coli* (esh-ĕ-rik′ē-ă kō′lē), which contains over 4000 genes.

### CRITICAL **THINKING**

Some viral genomes, composed of single-stranded RNA, act as mRNA. What advantage might these viruses have over other kinds of viruses?

## Hosts of Viruses

### Learning Objectives

✓ Explain the mechanism by which viruses are specific for their host cells.

✓ Compare and contrast viruses of fungi, plants, animals, and bacteria.

Most viruses infect only a particular host's cells. This specificity is due to the precise affinity of viral surface proteins or glycoproteins for complementary proteins or glycoproteins on the surface of the host cell. Viruses may be so specific they infect not only a particular host, but a particular kind of cell in that host. For example, HIV (human immunodeficiency virus, the agent that causes AIDS) specifically attacks helper T lymphocytes (a type of white blood cell) in humans and has no effect on, say, human muscle or bone cells. By contrast, some viruses are *generalists;* they infect many kinds of cells in many different hosts. An example of a generalist virus is West Nile virus, which can infect most species of birds, several mammalian species, and some reptiles.

All types of organisms are susceptible to some sort of viral attack. There are viruses that infect archaeal, bacterial, plant, protozoan, fungal, and animal cells (Figure 3). There is even a tiny virus that attacks a large virus. Most viral research and scientific study has focused on bacterial and animal viruses. A virus that infects bacteria is referred to as a **bacteriophage** (bak-tēr′ē-ō-fāj), or simply a **phage** (fāj). Scientists have determined that bacteriophages outnumber all bacteria, archaea, and eukaryotes put together. We will return our attention to bacteriophages and animal viruses later in this chapter.

Viruses of plants are less well known than bacterial and animal viruses, even though viruses were first identified and isolated from tobacco plants. Plant viruses infect many food crops, including corn, beans, sugar cane, tobacco, and potatoes, resulting in billions of dollars in losses each year. Viruses of plants are introduced into plant cells either through abrasions of the cell wall or by plant parasites such as nematodes and aphids. After entry, plant viruses follow the replication cycle discussed below for animal viruses.

Fungal viruses have been little studied. We do know that fungal viruses are different from animal and bacterial viruses in that fungal viruses exist only within cells; that is, they seemingly have no extracellular state. Presumably, fungal viruses cannot penetrate a thick fungal cell wall. However, because fusion of cells is typically a part of a fungal life cycle, viral infections can easily be propagated by the fusion of an infected fungal cell with an uninfected one.

Not all viruses are deleterious. The box, **Beneficial Microbes: Good Viruses? Who Knew?**, illustrates some useful aspects of viruses in the environment.

## Sizes of Viruses

In the late 1800s, scientists hypothesized that the cause of many diseases, including polio and smallpox, was an agent smaller than a bacterium. They named these tiny agents "viruses," from

▶ **Figure 3 Some examples of plant, bacterial, and human hosts of viral infections. (a)** Left, a tobacco leaf infected with tobacco mosaic virus, the first virus discovered. **(b)** A bacterial cell under attack by bacteriophages (pink). **(c)** A human white blood cell's cytoplasmic membrane, to which HIV (blue) is attached.

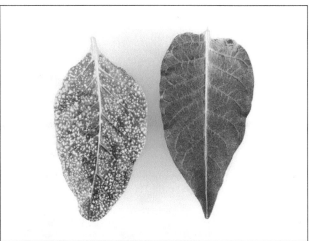

(a) From: Programmed cell death, mitochondria and the plant hypersensitive response. E. Lam, N. Kato, M. Lawton. *Nature.* 2001 June; 411:848–53, Fig.1. Reprinted with permission from Nature Publishing Group (www.nature.com)

(b) Kevin M. Rosso, Ph.D

(c) Eye of Science/Photo Researchers

the Latin word for "poison." Viruses are so small that only a few can be seen by light microscopy. One hundred million polioviruses could fit side by side on the period at the end of this sentence. The smallest viruses have a diameter of 10 nm, whereas the largest are approximately 400 nm in diameter, which is about the size of the smallest bacterial cells. Figure 4 compares the sizes of selected viruses to *E. coli* and a human red blood cell.

In 1892, Russian microbiologist Dmitri Ivanowski (1864–1920) first demonstrated that viruses are acellular with an experiment designed to elucidate the cause of tobacco mosaic disease. He filtered the sap of infected tobacco plants through a porcelain filter fine enough to trap even the smallest of bacterial cells. Viruses, however, were not trapped but instead passed through the filter with the liquid, which remained infectious to tobacco plants. This experiment proved the existence of an acellular disease-causing entity smaller than a bacterium. Tobacco mosaic virus (TMV) was isolated and characterized in 1935 by an American chemist, Wendell Stanley (1904–1971). The invention of electron microscopy allowed scientists to finally see TMV and other viruses.

## Capsid Morphology

### Learning Objective

✓ Discuss the structure and function of the viral capsid.

As we have seen, viruses have capsids—protein coats that provide both protection for viral nucleic acid and a means by which many viruses attach to their hosts' cells. The capsid of a virus is composed of proteinaceous subunits called **capsomeres** (or *capsomers*). Some capsomeres are composed of only a single type of protein, whereas others are composed of several different kinds of proteins. Recall that viral nucleic acid surrounded by its capsid is termed a *nucleocapsid*.

### CRITICAL **THINKING**

In some viruses, the capsomeres act enzymatically as well as structurally. What advantage might this provide the virus?

## Viral Shapes

The shapes of virions are also used to classify viruses. There are three basic types of viral shapes: helical, polyhedral, and complex (Figure 5). The capsid of a helical virus is composed of capsomeres that bond together in a spiral fashion to form a tube around the nucleic acid. The capsid of a polyhedral virus is roughly spherical, with a shape similar to a geodesic dome. The most common type of polyhedral capsid is an icosahedron, which has 20 sides.

▲ **Figure 4** **Sizes of selected virions.** Selected viruses are compared in size to a bacterium, *Escherichia coli*, and a human red blood cell. *How can viruses be so small and yet still be pathogenic?*

**Figure 4** *Viruses utilize a host cell's enzymes, organelles, and membranes to complete their replication cycle.*

---

MICROBES

### GOOD VIRUSES? WHO KNEW?

▲ **An algal bloom off the coast of Seattle, Washington.**

Viruses, though normally pathogenic to their host cells, do have positive influences, including what appear to be extensive roles in the environment. Recent discoveries by the United Kingdom's Marine and Freshwater Microbial Biodiversity program demonstrate important ways viruses impact our world.

First: Scientists found that a previously unknown virus attacks a tiny marine alga that multiplies to form algal blooms consisting of hundreds of thousands to millions of algal cells per milliliter of water (see photo). Algal blooms like these can deplete the water of oxygen at night, potentially harming fish and other marine life. The newly discovered virus stops blooms by killing the algae, a result which is good for animal life.

Second: When the algae die by this means, they release an airborne sulfate compound that acts to seed clouds. The resulting increased cloudiness noticeably shades the ocean, measurably lowering water temperature. Thus, a marine virus helps to reduce global warming!

Third: The researchers discovered a bacteriophage of oceanic cyanobacteria that transfers genes for photosynthetic machinery into its hosts' cells, so that the cells' photosynthetic rate increases. There are up to 10 million of these viruses in a single milliliter of seawater, so researchers estimate that much of the oxygen we breathe may be attributable to the action of these viruses on the blue-green bacteria.

▶ **Figure 5** **The shapes of virions. (a)** A helical virus, tobacco mosaic virus. The tubular shape of the capsid results from the tight arrangement of several rows of helical capsomeres. **(b)** Polyhedral virions of a virus that causes common colds. **(c)** Complex virions of smallpox virus. **(d)** The complex shape of rabies virus, which results from the shapes of the capsid and bullet-shaped envelope.

Complex viruses have capsids of many different shapes that do not readily fit into either of the other two categories. An example of a complex virus is smallpox virus, which has several covering layers (including lipid) and no easily identifiable capsid. The complex shapes of many bacteriophages include icosahedral heads, which contain the genome, attached to helical tails with tail fibers. The complex capsids of such bacteriophages somewhat resemble NASA's lunar lander (Figure 6).

## The Viral Envelope

Learning Objective

✓ Discuss the origin, structure, and function of the viral envelope.

All viruses lack cell membranes (after all, they are not cells), but some, particularly animal viruses, have an envelope similar in composition to a cell membrane surrounding their capsids. Other viral proteins called *matrix proteins* fill the region between capsid and envelope. A virus with a membrane is an *enveloped virion* (Figure 7); a virion without an envelope is called a *nonenveloped* or *naked virion.*

An enveloped virus acquires its envelope from its host cell during viral replication or release (discussed shortly). Indeed, the envelope of a virus is a portion of the membrane system of a host cell. Like a cytoplasmic membrane, a viral envelope is composed of a phospholipid bilayer and proteins. Some of the proteins are virally coded glycoproteins, which appear as spikes protruding outward from the envelope's surface (see Figure 7). Host DNA carries the genetic code required for the assembly of the phospholipids and some of the proteins in the envelope, while the viral genome specifies the other membrane proteins.

An envelope's proteins and glycoproteins often play a role in the recognition of host cells. A viral envelope does not perform other physiological roles of a cytoplasmic membrane such as endocytosis or active transport.

Table 1 summarizes the novel properties of viruses, and how those properties differ from the corresponding characteristics of cells. Next we turn our attention to the criteria by which virologists classify viruses.

## Classification of Viruses

Learning Objective

✓ List the characteristics by which viruses are classified.

The International Committee on Taxonomy of Viruses (ICTV) was established in 1966 to provide a single taxonomic scheme for viral classification and identification. Virologists classify

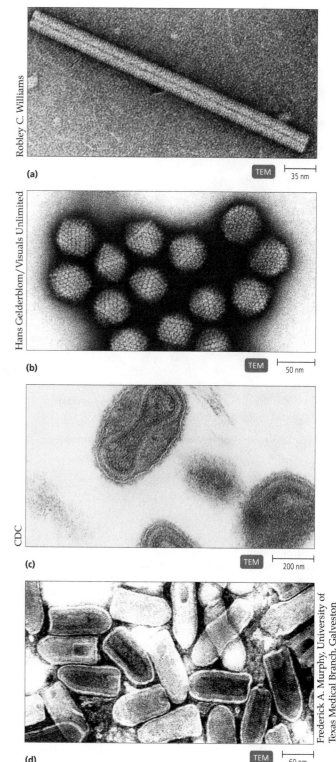

Robley C. Williams

**(a)** TEM 35 nm

Hans Gelderblom/Visuals Unlimited

**(b)** TEM 50 nm

CDC

**(c)** TEM 200 nm

Frederick A. Murphy, University of Texas Medical Branch, Galveston

**(d)** TEM 60 nm

▲ **Figure 6 The complex shape of bacteriophage T4.** It includes an icosahedral head and an ornate tail that enables viral attachment and penetration.

Head

Tail fibers

Base plate

Tail

(a)  SEM  70 nm  (b)

Kenneth Probst/Precision Graphics

Harold Fisher/Visuals Unlimited

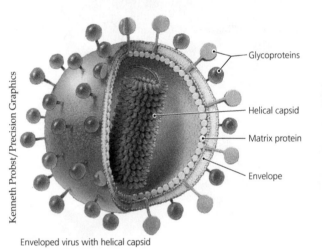

Glycoproteins

Helical capsid

Matrix protein

Envelope

Enveloped virus with helical capsid

Kenneth Probst/Precision Graphics

▲ **Figure 7 Enveloped virion.** Artist's rendition and electron micrograph of severe acute respiratory syndrome (SARS) virus, an enveloped virus with a helical capsid.

TEM  50 nm

Klaus Boller/Photo Researchers

viruses by their type of nucleic acid, presence of an envelope, shape, and size. So far, they have established families for all viral genera, but only three viral orders are described. Kingdoms, divisions, and classes have not been determined for viruses because the relationships among viruses are not well understood.

Family names are typically derived either from special characteristics of viruses within the family or from the name of an important member of the family. For example, family *Picornaviridae* contains very small[1] RNA viruses, and *Hepadnaviridae* contains a DNA virus that causes hepatitis B. Family *Herpesviridae* is named for herpes simplex, a virus that can cause genital herpes. Table 2 lists the major families of human viruses, grouped according to the type of nucleic acid each contains.

[1]Pico means one-trillionth, $10^{-12}$.

Specific epithets for viruses are their common English designations written in italics. Accordingly, the nomenclature for two important viral pathogens, HIV and rabies virus, is as follows:

|  | HIV | Rabies virus |
|---|---|---|
| **Order** | Not yet established | Mononegavirales |
| **Family** | *Retroviridae* | *Rhabdoviridae* |
| **Genus** | *Lentivirus* (len'ti-vī-rŭs) | *Lyssavirus* (lis'ă-vī-rŭs) |
| **Specific epithet** | *human immunodeficiency virus* | *rabies virus* |

## CRITICAL **THINKING**

Why has it been difficult to develop a complete taxonomy for viruses?

**1**

## The Novel Properties of Viruses

| Viruses | Cells |
|---|---|
| Inert macromolecules outside of a cell, but become active inside a cell | Metabolize on their own |
| Do not divide or grow | Divide and grow |
| Acellular | Cellular |
| Obligate intracellular parasites | Most are free-living |
| Contain either DNA or RNA, except *Cytomegalovirus* and *Minivirus* contain both | Contain both DNA and RNA |
| Genome can be dsDNA, ssDNA, dsRNA, or ssRNA | Genome is dsDNA |
| Ultramicroscopic in size, ranging from 10 nm to 400 nm | 200 nm to 12 cm in diameter |
| Have a proteinaceous capsid around genome; some have an envelope around the capsid | Surrounded by a phospholipid membrane and often a cell wall |
| Replicate in an assembly-line manner using the enzymes and organelles of a host cell | Self-replicating by asexual and/or sexual means |

**2**

## Families of Human Viruses

| Family | Strand Type | Representative Genera (Diseases) |
|---|---|---|
| **DNA Viruses** | | |
| *Poxviridae* | Double | *Orthopoxvirus* (smallpox) |
| *Herpesviridae* | Double | *Simplexvirus*, Herpes type 1 (fever blisters, respiratory infections), Herpes type 2 (genital infections); *Varicellovirus* (chickenpox); *Lymphocryptovirus*, Epstein-Barr virus (infectious mononucleosis, Burkitt's lymphoma); *Cytomegalovirus* (birth defects); *Roseolavirus* (roseola) |
| *Papillomaviridae* | Double | *Papillomavirus* (benign tumors, warts, cervical and penile cancers) |
| *Polyomaviridae* | Double | *Polyomavirus* (progressive multifocal leukoencephalopathy) |
| *Adenoviridae* | Double | *Mastadenovirus* (conjunctivitis, respiratory infections) |
| *Hepadnaviridae* | Partial single and partial double | *Orthohepadnavirus* (hepatitis B) |
| *Parvoviridae* | Single | *Erythrovirus* (erythema infectiosum) |
| **RNA Viruses** | | |
| *Picornaviridae* | Single, +[a] | *Enterovirus* (polio); *Hepatovirus* (hepatitis A); *Rhinovirus* (common cold) |
| *Caliciviridae* | Single, + | *Norovirus* (gastroenteritis) |
| *Astroviridae* | Single, + | *Astrovirus* (gastroenteritis) |
| *Hepeviridae* | Single, + | *Hepevirus* (hepatitis E) |
| *Togaviridae* | Single, + | *Alphavirus* (encephalitis); *Rubivirus* (rubella) |
| *Flaviviridae* | Single, + | *Flavivirus* (yellow fever); Japanese encephalitis virus (encephalitis); *Hepacivirus* (hepatitis C) |
| *Coronaviridae* | Single, + | *Coronavirus* (common cold, severe acute respiratory syndrome) |
| *Retroviridae* | Single, +, segmented | Human T cell leukemia virus (leukemia); *Lentivirus* (AIDS) |
| *Orthomyxoviridae* | Single, −[b], segmented | *Influenzavirus* (flu) |
| *Paramyxoviridae* | Single, − | *Paramyxovirus* (common cold, respiratory infections); *Pneumovirus* (pneumonia, common cold); *Morbillivirus* (measles); *Rubulavirus* (mumps) |
| *Rhabdoviridae* | Single, − | *Lyssavirus* (rabies) |
| *Bunyaviridae* | Single, −, segmented | *Bunyavirus* (California encephalitis virus); *Hantavirus* (pneumonia) |
| *Filoviridae* | Single, − | *Filovirus* (Ebola hemorrhagic fever); Marburg virus (hemorrhagic fever) |
| *Arenaviridae* | Single, −, segmented | *Lassavirus* (hemorrhagic fever) |
| *Reoviridae* | Double, segmented | *Orbivirus* (encephalitis); *Rotavirus* (diarrhea); *Coltivirus* (Colorado tick fever) |

[a]Positive-sense (+RNA) is equivalent to mRNA; i.e., it instructs ribosomes in protein translations.
[b]Negative-sense (−RNA) is complementary to mRNA; it cannot be directly translated.

### PRESCRIPTION BACTERIOPHAGES?

In 1917, Canadian biologist Felix d'Herelle published a paper announcing the discovery of the *bacteriophage*, a virus that preyed on bacteria. In fact, half the bacteria on Earth succumb to phages every two days! D'Herelle felt that phages can be natural weapons against bacterial pathogens.

Phage therapy was used in the early 1900s to combat dysentery, typhus, and cholera, but was largely abandoned in the 1940s in the United States, eclipsed by the development of antibiotics such as penicillin. Phage

▲ *Escherichia coli* infected with bacteriophages.

SEM  0.5 μm

therapy continued in the USSR and Eastern Europe, where research is still centered. Today, motivated by the growing problem of antibiotic-resistant bacteria, scientists in the U.S. and Western Europe have renewed interest in investigating phage therapy.

A phage reproduces by inserting genetic material into a bacterium, causing the bacterium to build copies of the virus that burst out of the cell to infect other bacteria. A single phage can become 10 trillion phages within two hours, killing 99.9% of its host bacteria. Each type of phage attacks a specific strain of bacteria. This means that phage treatment is effective only if the phages are carefully matched to the disease-causing bacterium. It also means that phage treatment, unlike the use of antibiotics, can be effective without killing the body's helpful bacteria.

Introducing an active microbe into a patient does present some dangers, however. Phages can kill bacteria, but they can also make bacteria more lethal. A strain of *Escherichia coli* that is responsible for a deadly form of food poisoning, for example, has been observed to gain the ability to produce a toxic chemical from a phage genome that integrates itself into the bacterium's DNA. If a phage being used in therapy picked up a toxin-coding gene, the attempted cure could become lethal.

## Viral Replication

As previously noted, viruses cannot reproduce themselves because they lack the genes for all the enzymes necessary for replication, nor do they possess functional ribosomes for protein synthesis. Instead, viruses are dependent on their hosts' enzymes and organelles to produce new virions. Once a host cell falls under control of a viral genome, it is forced to replicate viral genetic material and translate viral proteins, including viral capsomeres and viral enzymes.

The replication cycle of a virus usually results in the death and lysis of the host cell. Because the cell undergoes lysis near the end of the cycle, this type of replication is termed **lytic replication.** In general, a lytic replication cycle consists of the following five stages:

- **Attachment** of the virion to the host cell
- **Entry** of the virion or its genome into the host cell
- **Synthesis** of new nucleic acids and viral proteins by the host cell's enzymes and ribosomes
- **Assembly** of new virions within the host cell
- **Release** of the new virions from the host cell
  **ANIMATIONS:** *Viral Replication: Overview*

In the following sections we examine the events that occur in the replication of bacteriophages and animal viruses. We begin with lytic replication in bacteriophages, turn to a modification of

replication (called lysogenic replication), and then consider the replication of animal viruses.

## Lytic Replication of Bacteriophages

### Learning Objective

✓ Sketch and describe the five stages of the lytic replication cycle as it typically occurs in bacteriophages.

Studies of phages revealed the basics of viral biology. Indeed, bacteriophages make excellent tools for the general study of viruses because they are easier and less expensive to culture than animal or human viruses. **Beneficial Microbes: Prescription Bacteriophages?** is an interesting side note on the potential use of bacteriophages as an alternative to antibiotics.

Here we examine the replication of a much-studied dsDNA phage of *E. coli* called *type 4 (T4)*. T4 virions are complex, having the polyhedral heads and helical tails seen in many bacteriophages. We begin with attachment, the first stage of replication (Figure 8).

### Attachment ①

Because phages, like all virions, are nonmotile, contact with a bacterium occurs by purely random collision, brought about as molecular bombardment and currents move virions through the environment. The structures responsible for the attachment of T4

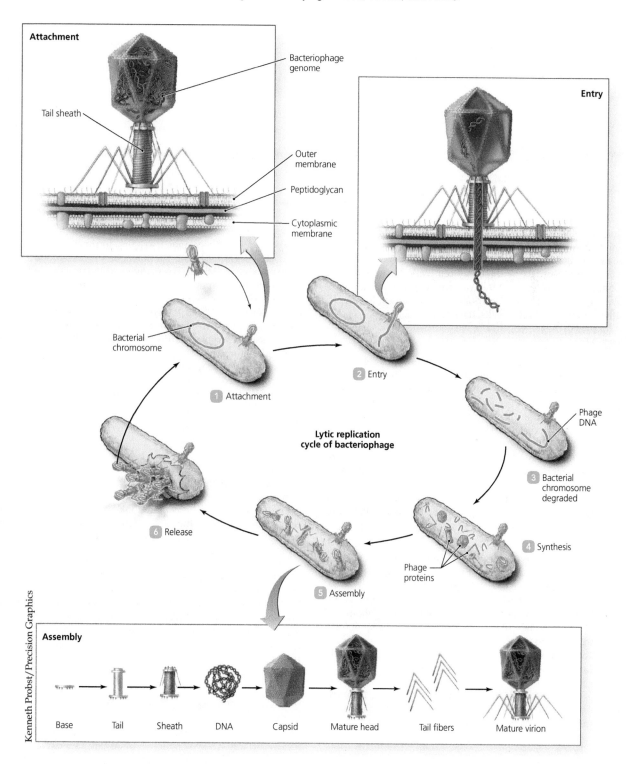

**Attachment**

Bacteriophage genome

Tail sheath

Outer membrane

Peptidoglycan

Cytoplasmic membrane

**Entry**

Bacterial chromosome

1 Attachment

2 Entry

**Lytic replication cycle of bacteriophage**

Phage DNA

3 Bacterial chromosome degraded

4 Synthesis

Phage proteins

5 Assembly

6 Release

**Assembly**

Base → Tail → Sheath → DNA → Capsid → Mature head → Tail fibers → Mature virion

Kenneth Probst / Precision Graphics

▲ **Figure 8  The lytic replication cycle in bacteriophages.** The phage shown in this illustration is T4, and the bacterium shown is *E. coli*. The circular bacterial chromosome is represented diagrammatically; in reality it would be much longer.

Precision Graphics

**◀ Figure 9 Pattern of virion abundance in lytic cycle.** Virion abundance over time for single lytic replication cycle. New virions are not observed in the culture medium until synthesis, assembly, and release (lysis) are complete, at which time (the burst time) the new virions are released all at once. Burst size is the number of new virions released per lysed host cell.

to its host bacterium are its tail fibers. Attachment is dependent on the chemical attraction and precise fit between attachment proteins on the phage's tail fibers and complementary receptor proteins on the surface of the host's cell wall. The specificity of the attachment proteins for the receptors ensures that the virus will attach only to *E. coli.* Bacteriophages may attach to receptor proteins on bacterial cells' walls, flagella, or pili.

### Entry ②

Now that phage T4 has attached to the bacterium's cell wall, it must still overcome the formidable barrier posed by the cell wall and cytoplasmic membrane if it is to enter the cell. T4 overcomes this obstacle in an elegant way. Upon contact with *E. coli,* T4 releases *lysozyme* (lī′sō-zīm), a protein enzyme carried within the capsid that weakens the peptidoglycan of the cell wall. The phage's tail sheath then contracts, which forces an internal hollow tube within the tail through the cell wall and membrane, much as a hypodermic needle penetrates the skin. The phage injects the genome through the tube and into the bacterium. The empty capsid, having performed its task, is left on the outside of the cell looking like an abandoned spacecraft.

### Synthesis ③ – ④

After entry, viral enzymes (either carried within the capsid or coded by viral genes and made by the bacterium) degrade the bacterial DNA into its constituent nucleotides. As a result, the bacterium stops synthesizing its own molecules and begins synthesizing new viruses under control of the viral genome.

For dsDNA viruses like T4, protein synthesis is straightforward and similar to cellular transcription and translation, except that mRNA is transcribed from viral DNA instead of cellular DNA. Translation by the host cell's ribosomes results in viral proteins, including head capsomeres, components of the tail, viral DNA polymerase (which replicates viral DNA), and lysozyme (which weakens the bacterial cell wall from within, enabling the virions to leave the cell once they have been assembled).

### Assembly ⑤

Scientists do not understand completely how phages are assembled inside a host cell, but it appears that as capsomeres accumulate within the cell, they spontaneously attach to one another

to form new capsid heads. Likewise, tails assemble and attach to heads, and tail fibers attach to tails, forming mature virions. Such capsid assembly is a spontaneous process, requiring little or no enzymatic activity. For many years it was assumed that all capsids formed around a genome in just such a spontaneous manner. However, recent research has shown that for some viruses, enzymes pump the genome into the assembled capsid under high pressure—five times that used in a paintball gun. This process resembles stuffing a strand of cooked spaghetti into a matchbox through a single small hole.

Sometimes a capsid assembles around leftover pieces of host DNA instead of viral DNA. A virion formed in this manner is still able to attach to a new host by means of its tail fibers, but instead of inserting phage DNA it transfers DNA from the first host into a new host.

### Release ⑥

Newly assembled virions are released from the cell as lysozyme completes its work on the cell wall and the bacterium disintegrates. Areas of disintegrating bacterial cells in a lawn of bacteria in a Petri plate look as if the lawn were being eaten, and it was the appearance of these *plaques* that prompted early scientists to give the name *bacteriophage,* "bacterial eater," to these viruses.

For phage T4, the process of lytic replication takes about 25 minutes and can produce as many as 100–200 new virions for each bacterial cell lysed (Figure 9). For any phage undergoing lytic replication, the period of time required to complete the entire process, from attachment to release, is called the *burst time,* and the number of new virions released from each lysed bacterial cell is called the *burst size.* **ANIMATIONS:** *Viral Replication: Virulent Bacteriophages*

CRITICAL **THINKING**

If a colony of 1.5 billion *E. coli* cells were infected with a single phage T4, and each lytic replication cycle of the phage produced 200 new phages, how many replication cycles would it take for T4 phages to overwhelm the entire bacterial colony? (Assume for the sake of simplicity that every phage completes its replication cycle in a different cell and that the bacteria themselves do not reproduce.)

# Lysogeny

## Learning Objective

✓ Compare and contrast the lysogenic replication cycle of viruses with the lytic cycle.

Not all viruses follow the lytic pattern of phage T4 we just examined. Some bacteriophages have a modified replication cycle in which infected host cells grow and reproduce normally for many generations before they lyse. Such a replication cycle is called a **lysogenic replication cycle** or **lysogeny** (lī-soj′ĕ-nē), and the phages are called **temperate phages** or *lysogenic phages.*

Here we examine lysogenic replication as it occurs in a much-studied temperate phage, *lambda phage,* which is another parasite of *E. coli.* A lambda phage has a linear molecule of dsDNA in a complex capsid consisting of an icosahedral head attached to a tail that lacks tail fibers (Figure 10).

Figure 11 illustrates lysogeny with lambda phage. First, the virion randomly contacts an *E. coli* cell and attaches via its tail (1). The viral DNA enters the cell, just as occurs with phage T4, but the host cell's DNA is not destroyed, and the phage's genome does not immediately assume control of the cell. Instead, the virus remains inactive. Such an inactive bacteriophage is called a **prophage** (prō′ fāj) (2). A prophage remains inactive

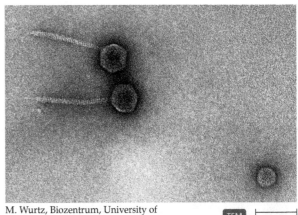

M. Wurtz, Biozentrum, University of Basil/SPL/Photo Researchers

TEM | 100 nm

▲ **Figure 10 Bacteriophage lambda.** Note the absence of tail fibers. *Phage T4 attaches by means of molecules on its tail fibers. How does lambda phage, which lacks fibers, attach?*

**Figure 10** *Lambda has attachment molecules at the end of its tail rather than on its tail fibers.*

▲ **Figure 11 The lysogenic replication cycle in bacteriophages.** The phage shown in this illustration is phage lambda, and the bacterium shown is *E. coli.* The circular bacterial chromosome is represented diagrammatically; in reality it would be much longer. *How is a lysogenic cycle different from a lytic cycle?*

**Figure 11** *In a lysogenic cycle, the virus is inserted into the bacterial chromosome, and it is replicated and passed on to all daughter cells until it is induced to leave the chromosome; a lytic cycle is a replication cycle that results in cell death.*

1 Attachment

Lambda phage

2 Entry

3 Prophage in chromosome

Lytic cycle

Lysogeny

6 Synthesis

8 Release

7 Assembly

4 Replication of chromosome and virus; cell division

5 Induction

Further replications and cell divisions

Kenneth Probst/Precision Graphics

HIGHLIGHT

## THE THREAT OF AVIAN INFLUENZA

In 1997, 18 people in Hong Kong contracted avian influenza, caused by the H5N1 strain of influenzavirus that spreads easily among chickens and other birds. At least half of these people caught the disease directly from birds, something that scientists had previously thought improbable. Human cases have had a 60% death rate. When people began dying of the illness, Hong Kong officials slaughtered all 1.5 million chickens within three days. That stopped a potential epidemic in Hong Kong, but it didn't stop the spread of the avian flu.

Avian flu virus very rarely spreads from one person to another. However, the possibility that this may change is of great concern to health officials worldwide. Avian flu viruses mutate quickly and can pick up genes from other flu viruses. If an avian flu virus picks up genes from a human flu virus, it could become a strain that spreads easily from person to person. In a worst-case scenario such a strain of avian/human flu, in this age of jet travel, could cause a pandemic killing 2–50 million people worldwide, according to the World Health Organization.

What should be done? In Asia, domesticated fowl have been slaughtered to prevent the virus from spreading. But while governments concentrated on culling domestic poultry, the virus spread to wild birds, such as geese, gray herons, and feral pigeons, and via wild birds it has spread throughout Asia, Europe, and central Africa.

Scientists have developed a vaccine that they believe could protect against the

AP Images

H5N1 strain of the virus. Unfortunately, a government could stockpile vaccine for one strain of flu only to have the virus mutate into a new form against which the vaccine is ineffective.

by coding for a protein that suppresses prophage genes. A side effect of this repressor protein is that it renders the bacterium resistant to additional infection by other viruses of the same type.

Another difference between a lysogenic cycle and a lytic cycle is that the prophage is inserted into the DNA of the bacterium, becoming a physical part of the bacterial chromosome (**3**). For DNA viruses like lambda phage, this is a simple process of fusing two pieces of DNA: one piece of DNA, the virus, is fused to another piece of DNA, the chromosome of the cell. Every time the cell replicates its infected chromosome, the prophage is also replicated (**4**). All daughter cells of a lysogenic cell are thus infected with the quiescent virus. A prophage and its descendants may remain a part of bacterial chromosomes for generations, or forever.

Lysogenic phages can change the phenotype of a bacterium, for example from a harmless form into a pathogen—a process called **lysogenic conversion.** Bacteriophage genes are responsible for toxins and other disease-evoking proteins found in the bacterial agents of diphtheria, cholera, rheumatic fever, and certain severe cases of diarrhea caused by *E. coli.*

At some later time a prophage might be excised from the chromosome by recombination or some other genetic event; it then reenters the lytic phase. The process whereby a prophage is excised from the host chromosome is called **induction** (**5**). Inductive agents are typically the same physical and chemical agents that damage DNA molecules, including ultraviolet light, X rays, and carcinogenic chemicals.

After induction, the lytic steps of synthesis (**6**), assembly (**7**), and release (**8**) resume from the point at which they stopped. The cell becomes filled with virions and breaks open.

Bacteriophages T4 and lambda demonstrate two replication strategies that are typical for many DNA viruses. RNA viruses and enveloped viruses present variations on the lytic and lysogenic cycles we have examined. We will next examine some of these variations as they occur with animal viruses.
**ANIMATIONS:** *Viral Replication: Temperate Bacteriophages*

## CRITICAL **THINKING**

What differences would you expect in the replication cycles of RNA phages from those of DNA phages? (Hints: Think about the processes of transcription, translation, and replication of nucleic acids. Also, note that RNA is not normally inserted into a DNA molecule.)

## Replication of Animal Viruses

### Learning Objectives

✓ Explain the differences between bacteriophage replication and animal viral replication.

✓ Compare and contrast the replication and synthesis of DNA, −RNA, and +RNA viruses.

✓ Compare and contrast the release of viral particles by lysis and budding.

✓ Compare and contrast latency in animal viruses with phage lysogeny.

Animal viruses have the same five basic steps in their replication pathways as bacteriophages—that is, attachment, entry, synthesis, assembly, and release. However, there are significant differences in the replication of animal viruses that result in part from the presence of envelopes around some of the viruses, and in part from the eukaryotic nature of animal cells as well as their lack of a cell wall. **Highlight: The Threat of Avian Influenza** highlights an animal virus that is of great concern to health officials worldwide.

In this section we examine the replication processes that are shared by DNA and RNA animal viruses, compare these processes with those of bacteriophages, and discuss how the synthesis of DNA and RNA viruses differ.

## Attachment of Animal Viruses

As with bacteriophages, attachment of an animal virus is dependent on the chemical attraction and exact fit between proteins or glycoproteins on the virion and complementary protein or glycoprotein receptors on the animal cell's cytoplasmic membrane. Unlike the bacteriophages we have examined, animal viruses lack both tails and tail fibers. Instead, animal viruses typically have glycoprotein spikes or other attachment molecules on their capsids or envelopes.

## Entry and Uncoating of Animal Viruses

Animal viruses enter a host cell shortly after attachment. Even though entry of animal viruses is not as well understood as entry of bacteriophages, there appear to be at least three different mechanisms: direct penetration, membrane fusion, and endocytosis.

Some naked viruses enter their hosts' cells by *direct penetration*—a process in which the viral capsid attaches and sinks into the cytoplasmic membrane, creating a pore through which the genome alone enters the cell (Figure 12a). Poliovirus infects host cells via direct penetration.

With other animal viruses, by contrast, the entire capsid and its contents (including the genome) enter the host cell by membrane fusion or endocytosis. With viruses using *membrane fusion*, including the measles and AIDS viruses, the viral envelope and the host cell membrane fuse, releasing the capsid into the cell's cytoplasm and leaving the envelope glycoproteins as part of the cell membrane (Figure 12b).

Most enveloped viruses and some naked viruses enter host cells by triggering *endocytosis*. Attachment of the virus to receptor molecules on the cell's surface stimulates the cell to endocytize the entire virus (Figure 12c). Adenoviruses (naked) and herpesviruses (enveloped) enter human host cells via endocytosis.

For those viruses that penetrate a host cell with their capsids intact, the capsids must be removed to release their genomes before the viruses can continue to replicate. The removal of a viral capsid within a host cell is called **uncoating**, a process that remains poorly understood. It apparently occurs via different means in different viruses; some viruses are uncoated within vesicles by cellular enzymes, whereas others are uncoated by enzymes within the cell's cytosol.

## Synthesis of Animal Viruses

Synthesis of animal viruses also differs from synthesis of bacteriophages. Each type of animal virus requires a different strategy for synthesis that depends on the kind of nucleic acid involved—whether it is DNA or RNA, and whether it is double stranded or single stranded. DNA viruses typically enter the nucleus, whereas most RNA viruses are replicated in the cytoplasm. As we discuss the synthesis and assembly of each type of animal virus, consider the following two questions:

**(a)** Direct penetration

**(b)** Membrane fusion

**(c)** Endocytosis

▲ **Figure 12  Three mechanisms of entry of animal viruses.**
**(a)** Direct penetration, a process whereby naked virions inject their genomes into their animal cell hosts. **(b)** Membrane fusion, in which fusion of the viral envelope and cell membrane dumps the capsid into the cell. **(c)** Endocytosis, in which attachment of a naked or an enveloped virus stimulates the host cell to engulf the entire virus. *After penetration, many animal viruses must be uncoated, but bacteriophages need not be. Why is this so?*

*Figure 12 Generally bacteriophages inject their DNA during penetration, so the capsid does not enter the cell.*

- How is mRNA—needed for the translation of viral proteins—synthesized?
- What molecule serves as a template for nucleic acid replication?

**dsDNA Viruses** Synthesis of new double-stranded DNA (dsDNA) virions is similar to the normal replication of cellular DNA and translation of proteins. The genomes of most dsDNA viruses enter the nucleus of the cell, where cellular enzymes replicate the viral genome in the same manner as they replicate host dsDNA—using each strand of viral DNA as a template for its complement. After messenger RNA is transcribed from viral DNA in the nucleus and capsomere proteins are made in the cytoplasm by host ribosomes, capsomeres enter the nucleus, where new virions spontaneously assemble. This method of replication is seen with herpes and papilloma (wart) viruses.

There are two well-known exceptions to this regimen of dsDNA viruses:

- Every part of a poxvirus is synthesized and assembled in the cytoplasm of the host's cell; the nucleus is not involved.
- The genome of hepatitis B viruses is replicated using an RNA intermediary instead of replicating DNA from a DNA template. In other words, the genome of hepatitis B virus is transcribed into RNA, which is then used as a template to make multiple copies of viral DNA genome. The latter process, which is the reverse of normal transcription, is mediated by a viral enzyme, *reverse transcriptase.*

**ssDNA Viruses** A human virus with a genome composed of single-stranded DNA (ssDNA) is a parvovirus (see Table 2). When a parvovirus enters the nucleus of a host cell, host enzymes produce a new strand of DNA complementary to the viral genome. This complementary strand binds to the ssDNA of the virus to form a dsDNA molecule. Transcription of mRNA, replication of new ssDNA, and viral assembly then follow the DNA virus pattern just described.

As previously noted, RNA is not used as genetic material in cells, so it follows that the synthesis of RNA viruses must differ significantly from typical cellular processes, and from the replication of DNA viruses as well. There are four types of RNA viruses: positive-sense, single-stranded RNA (designated +ssRNA); retroviruses (a kind of +ssRNA virus); negative-sense, single-stranded RNA (−ssRNA); and double-stranded RNA (dsRNA). The synthesis process for these RNA viruses is varied and rather complex. We start with the synthesis of +ssRNA viruses.

**Positive-Sense ssRNA Viruses** Single-stranded viral RNA that can act directly as mRNA is called **positive-strand RNA (+RNA).** Ribosomes translate polypeptides using the codons of such RNA. An example of a +ssRNA virus is poliovirus. In many +ssRNA viruses, a complementary **negative-strand RNA (−RNA)** is transcribed from the +ssRNA genome by viral RNA polymerase; −RNA then serves as the template for the transcription of multiple +ssRNA genomes. Such transcription of RNA from RNA is unique to viruses; no cell transcribes RNA from RNA.

**Retroviruses** Unlike other +ssRNA viruses, the +ssRNA viruses called **retroviruses** do not use their genome as mRNA. Instead, retroviruses use a DNA intermediary that is transcribed from +RNA by reverse transcriptase carried within the capsid. This DNA intermediary then serves as the template for the synthesis of additional +RNA molecules, which act both as mRNA for protein synthesis and as genomes for new virions. Human immunodeficiency virus (HIV) is a prominent retrovirus.

**Negative-Sense ssRNA Viruses** Other single-stranded RNA virions are −ssRNA viruses, which must overcome a unique problem. In order to synthesize a protein, a ribosome can use only mRNA (i.e., +RNA), because −RNA is not recognized by ribosomes. The virus overcomes this problem by carrying within its capsid an enzyme, *RNA-dependent RNA transcriptase,* which is released into the host cell's cytoplasm during uncoating and then transcribes +RNA molecules from the virus's −RNA genome. Translation of proteins can then occur as usual. The newly transcribed +RNA also serves as a template for transcription of additional copies of −RNA. Diseases caused by −ssRNA viruses include rabies and flu.

**dsRNA Viruses** Viruses that have double-stranded RNA use yet another method of synthesis. The positive strand of the molecule serves as mRNA for the translation of proteins, one of which is an RNA polymerase that transcribes dsRNA. Each strand of RNA acts as a template for transcription of its opposite, which is reminiscent of DNA replication in cells. Double-stranded RNA rotaviruses cause most cases of diarrhea in infants.

Figure 13 illustrates and Table 3 summarizes the various strategies by which animal viruses are synthesized.

## CRITICAL **THINKING**

Although many +ssRNA viruses use their genome directly as messenger RNA, +ssRNA retroviruses do not. Instead, their +RNA is transcribed into DNA by reverse transcriptase. What advantage do retroviruses gain by using reverse transcriptase?

## Assembly and Release of Animal Viruses

As with bacteriophages, once the components of animal viruses are synthesized, they assemble into virions that are then released from the host cell. Most DNA viruses assemble in and are released from the nucleus into the cytosol, whereas most RNA viruses develop solely in the cytoplasm. The number of viruses produced and released depends on both the type of virus and the size and initial health of the host cell.

Replication of animal viruses takes more time than replication of bacteriophages. Herpesviruses, for example, require almost 24 hours to replicate, as compared to 25 minutes for hundreds of copies of bacteriophage T4.

Enveloped animal viruses are often released via a process called **budding** (Figure 14). As virions are assembled, they are extruded through one of the cell's membranes—the nuclear,

**(a)** Positive-sense ssRNA virus

**(b)** Negative-sense ssRNA virus

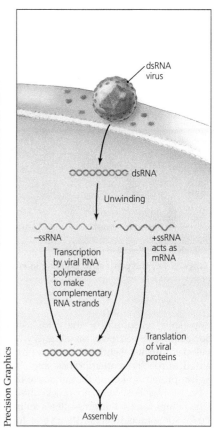

**(c)** Double-stranded RNA virus

▲ **Figure 13** **Synthesis of proteins and genomes in animal RNA viruses.**
**(a)** Positive-sense ssRNA virus, in which +ssRNA acts as mRNA and −ssRNA is the genome template.
**(b)** Negative-sense ssRNA virus: transcription forms +ssRNA to serve both as mRNA and template.
**(c)** dsRNA virus genome unwinds so that the positive-sense strand serves as mRNA, and each strand serves as a template for its complement.

**3**

## Synthesis Strategies of Animal Viruses

| Genome | How Is mRNA Synthesized? | What Molecule Is the Template for Genome Replication? |
|---|---|---|
| dsDNA | By RNA polymerase (in nucleus or cytoplasm of cell) | Each strand of DNA serves as template for its complement (except for hepatitis B, which synthesizes RNA to act as the template for new DNA) |
| ssDNA | By RNA polymerase (in nucleus of cell) | Complementary strand of DNA is synthesized to act as template |
| +ssRNA | Genome acts as mRNA | −RNA complementary to the genome is synthesized to act as template |
| +ssRNA (*Retroviridae*) | DNA is synthesized from RNA by reverse transcriptase; mRNA is transcribed from DNA by RNA polymerase | DNA |
| −ssRNA | By RNA-dependent RNA transcriptase | +RNA (mRNA) complementary to the genome |
| dsRNA | Positive strand of genome acts as mRNA | Each strand of genome acts as template for its complement |

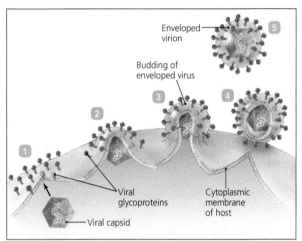

Kenneth Probst/Precision Graphics

▲ **Figure 14** **The process of budding in enveloped viruses.** *What term describes a nonenveloped virus?*

**Figure 14** *Naked.*

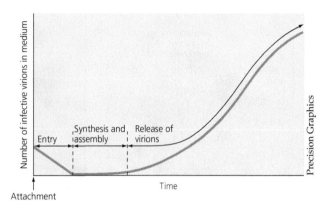

Precision Graphics

▲ **Figure 15** **Pattern of virion abundance in persistent infections.** A generalized curve of virion abundance for persistent infections by budding enveloped viruses. Because the curve does not represent any actual infection, units for the graph's axes are omitted.

endoplasmic reticulum, or the cytoplasmic membrane. Each virion acquires a portion of membrane, which becomes the viral envelope. During synthesis, some viral glycoproteins are inserted into cellular membranes, and these proteins become the glycoprotein spikes on the surface of the viral envelope.

Because the host cell is not quickly lysed, as occurs in bacteriophage replication, budding allows an infected cell to remain alive for some time. Infections with enveloped viruses in which host cells shed viruses slowly and relatively steadily are called *persistent infections;* a curve showing virus abundance over time during a persistent infection lacks the burst of new virions seen in lytic replication cycles (Figure 15) (compare to Figure 9).

Naked animal viruses may be released in one of two ways: They may either be extruded from the cell by exocytosis, in a manner similar to budding, but without the acquisition of an envelope, or they may cause lysis and death of the cell, reminiscent of bacteriophage release. **ANIMATIONS:** *Viral Replication: Animal Viruses*

---

**EMERGING** DISEASES

## CHIKUNGUNYA

Precision Graphics

An old man arrived at the doctor's office in Ravenna, Italy, with a combination of symptoms the physician had never heard of: a widespread, severe rash; difficulty in breathing; high fever; nausea; and extreme joint pain. Chikungunya (chik-en-gun' ya) had arrived in Europe.

Though scientists had known of chikungunya virus, which is related to equine encephalitis viruses, for over 50 years, most considered the tropical disease benign—a limited, mild irritation, not a catastrophe. Therefore, few researchers studied chikungunya virus or its disease. Now, they know better.

Over the past decade, chikungunya virus has spread throughout the nations of the Indian Ocean. In 2006, officials on the French-owned island of La Réunion in the Indian Ocean reported 47,000 cases of chikungunya in a single week! The same year it reemerged in India for the first time in four decades with more than 1.5 million reported cases. Why?

*Aedes albopictus* (Asian tiger mosquito), which carries the virus, has moved into temperate climates, including Europe and the United States, as the climate has warmed. With the mosquito comes the possibility of viral proliferation—the insects have spread the tropical disease as far north as Italy.

And our Italian patient? His crippling pain lasted for months, but he survived. Now that he knows about mosquito-borne chikungunya, he insists that his family and friends use mosquito repellant liberally. Officials in the rest of Europe and in the United States join in his concern: With the coming of *Ae. albopictus,* is incurable chikungunya far behind?

James Gathany, CDC

**MM** Track chikungunya online by going to the Study Area at www.masteringmicrobiology.com.

## TABLE 4 · A Comparison of Bacteriophage and Animal Virus Replication

| | Bacteriophage | Animal Virus |
|---|---|---|
| Attachment | Proteins on tails attach to proteins on cell wall | Spikes, capsids, or envelope proteins attach to proteins or glycoproteins on cell membrane |
| Penetration | Genome is injected into cell or diffuses into cell | Capsid enters cell by direct penetration, fusion, or endocytosis |
| Uncoating | None | Removal of capsid by cell enzymes |
| Site of synthesis | In cytoplasm | RNA viruses in cytoplasm; most DNA viruses in nucleus |
| Site of assembly | In cytoplasm | RNA viruses in cytoplasm; most DNA viruses in nucleus |
| Mechanism of release | Lysis | Naked virions: exocytosis or lysis; enveloped virions: budding |
| Nature of chronic infection | Lysogeny, always incorporated into host chromosome, may leave host chromosome | Latency, with or without incorporation into host DNA; incorporation is permanent |

### CRITICAL **THINKING**

If an enveloped virus were somehow released from a cell without budding, it would not have an envelope. What effect would this have on the virulence of the virus? Why?

Because viral replication uses cellular structures and pathways involved in the growth and maintenance of healthy cells, any strategy for the treatment of viral diseases that involves disrupting viral replication may disrupt normal cellular processes as well. This is one reason it is difficult to treat viral diseases.

### Latency of Animal Viruses

Some animal viruses, including chickenpox and herpes viruses, may remain dormant in cells in a process known as **latency;** the viruses involved in latency are called **latent viruses** or **proviruses.** Latency may be prolonged for years with no viral activity, signs, or symptoms. Though latency is similar to lysogeny as seen with bacteriophages, there are differences. Some latent viruses do not become incor porated into the chromosomes of their host cells, whereas lysogenic phages always do.

On the other hand, some animal viruses (e.g., HIV) are more like lysogenic phages in that they do become integrated into a host chromosome as a provirus. However, when a provirus is incorporated into its host DNA, the condition is permanent; induction does not occur in eukaryotes. Thus an incorporated provirus becomes a permanent, physical part of the host's chromosome, and all descendants of the infected cell will carry the provirus.

Given that RNA cannot be incorporated directly into a chromosome molecule, how does the ssRNA of HIV become a provirus incorporated into the DNA of its host cell? HIV can become a permanent part of a host's chromosome because it, like all retroviruses, carries reverse transcriptase, which transcribes the genetic information of the +RNA molecule to a DNA molecule—which *can* become incorporated into the host cell's genome.

### CRITICAL **THINKING**

A latent virus that is incorporated into a host cell's chromosome is never induced; that is, it never emerges from the host cell's chromosome to become a free virus. Given that it cannot emerge from the host cell's chromosome, can such a latent virus be considered "safe"? Why or why not?

Table 4 compares the features of the replication of bacteriophages and animal viruses. Next we turn our attention to the part viruses can play in cancer, beginning with a brief consideration of the terminology needed to understand the basic nature of cancer.

# The Role of Viruses in Cancer

### Learning Objectives

✓ Define the terms *neoplasia, tumor, benign, malignant, cancer,* and *metastasis.*

✓ Explain in simple terms how a cell may become cancerous, with special reference to the role of viruses.

Under normal conditions, the division of cells in a mature multicellular animal is under strict genetic control; that is, the animal's genes dictate that some types of cells can no longer divide at all, and that those that can divide are prevented from unlimited division. In this genetic control, either genes for cell division are "turned off," or genes that inhibit division are "turned on," or some combination of both these genetic events occur.

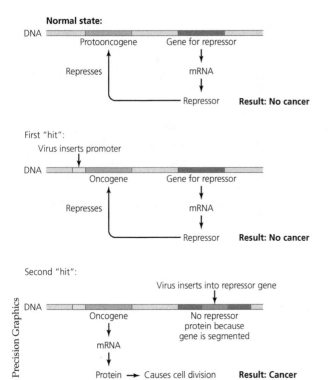

**▲ Figure 16 The oncogene theory of the induction of cancer in humans.** The theory suggests that more than one "hit" to the DNA (that is, any change or mutation), whether caused by a virus (as shown here) or various physical or chemical agents, is required to induce cancer.

However, if something upsets the genetic control, cells begin to divide uncontrollably. This phenomenon of uncontrolled cell division in a multicellular animal is called **neoplasia**[2] (nē-ō-plā′zē-ă). Cells undergoing neoplasia are said to be neoplastic, and a mass of neoplastic cells is a **tumor.**

Some tumors are **benign;** that is, they remain in one place and are not generally harmful, although occasionally such noninvasive tumors are painful and rob adjacent normal cells of space and nutrients. Other tumors are **malignant,** invading neighboring tissues and even traveling throughout the body to invade other organs and tissues to produce new tumors—a process called **metastasis** (mě-tas′tă-sis). Malignant tumors are also called **cancers.** Cancers rob normal cells of space and nutrients and cause pain; in some kinds of cancer, malignant cells derange the function of the affected tissues, until eventually the body can no longer withstand the loss of normal function and dies.

Several theories have been proposed to explain the role viruses play in the development of cancers. These theories revolve around the presence of *protooncogenes* (prō-tō-ong′kō-jēnz)—genes that play a role in cell division. So long as protooncogenes are repressed, no cancer results. However, activity of oncogenes (their name when they are active) or inactivation of

[2]From Greek *neo,* meaning new, and *plassein,* meaning to mold.

oncogene repressors can cause cancer to develop. In most cases, several genetic changes must occur before cancer develops. Put another way, "multiple hits" to the genome must occur for cancer to result (Figure 16).

A variety of environmental factors contribute to the inhibition of oncogene repressors and the activation of oncogenes. Ultraviolet light, radiation, certain chemicals called *carcinogens* (kar-si′nō-jenz), and viruses have all been implicated in the development of cancer.

Viruses cause 20–25% of human cancers in several ways. Some viruses carry copies of oncogenes as part of their genomes; other viruses promote oncogenes already present in the host; still other viruses interfere with normal tumor repression when they insert (as proviruses) into repressor genes.

That viruses cause some animal cancers is well established. In the first decade of the 1900s, virologist F. Peyton Rous (1879–1970) proved that viruses induce cancer in chickens. Though several DNA and RNA viruses are known to cause about 15% of human cancers, the link between viruses and most human cancers has been difficult to document. Among the virally induced cancers in humans are Burkitt's lymphoma, Hodgkin's disease, Kaposi's sarcoma, and cervical cancer. DNA viruses in the families *Adenoviridae, Herpesviridae, Hepadnaviridae, Papillomaviridae,* and *Polyomaviridae,* and two RNA viruses in the family *Retroviridae,* cause these and other human cancers.

### CRITICAL **THINKING**

Why are DNA viruses more likely to cause neoplasias than are RNA viruses?

# Culturing Viruses in the Laboratory

### Learning Objectives

✓ Describe some ethical and practical difficulties to overcome in culturing viruses.

✓ Describe three types of media used for culturing viruses.

Scientists must culture viruses in order to conduct research and develop vaccines and treatments, but because viruses cannot metabolize or replicate by themselves, they cannot be grown in standard microbiological broths or on agar plates. Instead, they must be cultured inside suitable host cells, a requirement that complicates the detection, identification, and characterization of viruses. Virologists have developed three types of media for culturing viruses: media consisting of mature organisms (bacteria, plants, or animals), embryonated (fertilized) eggs, and cell cultures. We begin by considering the culture of viruses in organisms.

## Culturing Viruses in Mature Organisms

### Learning Objectives

✓ Explain the use of a plaque assay in culturing viruses in bacteria.

✓ List three problems with growing viruses in animals.

▲ **Figure 17** **Viral plaques in a lawn of bacterial growth on the surface of an agar plate.** *What is the cause of viral plaques?*

Figure 17 *Each plaque is an area in a bacterial lawn where bacteria have succumbed to phage infections.*

In the following sections we consider the use of bacterial cells as a virus culture medium before considering the issues involved in growing viruses in living animals.

### Culturing Viruses in Bacteria

Most of our knowledge of viral replication has been derived from research on bacteriophages, which are relatively easy to culture because some bacteria are easily grown and maintained. Phages can be grown in bacteria maintained in either liquid cultures or on agar plates. In the latter case, bacteria and phages are mixed with warm (liquid) nutrient agar and poured in a thin layer across the surface of an agar plate. During incubation, bacteria infected by phages lyse and release new phages that infect nearby bacteria, while uninfected bacteria grow and reproduce normally. After incubation, the appearance of the plate includes a uniform bacterial lawn interrupted by clear zones called **plaques,** which are areas where phages have lysed the bacteria (Figure 17). Such plates enable the estimation of phage numbers via a technique called plaque assay, in which virologists assume that each plaque corresponds to a single phage in the original bacterium-virus mixture.

### Culturing Viruses in Plants and Animals

Plant and animal viruses can be grown in laboratory plants and animals. Recall that the first discovery and isolation of a virus was the discovery of tobacco mosaic virus in tobacco plants. Rats, mice, guinea pigs, rabbits, pigs, and primates have been used to culture and study animal viruses.

However, maintaining laboratory animals can be difficult and expensive, and this practice raises ethical issues for some. Growing viruses that infect only humans raises additional ethical complications. Therefore, scientists have developed alternative

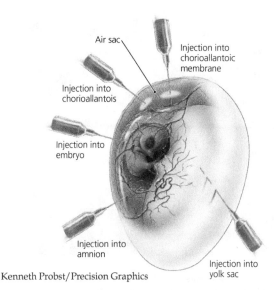

Kenneth Probst/Precision Graphics

▲ **Figure 18** **Inoculation sites for the culture of viruses in embryonated chicken eggs.** *Why are eggs often used to grow animal viruses?*

Figure 18 *Eggs are large, sterile, self-sufficient cells that contain a number of different sites suitable for viral replication.*

ways of culturing animal and human viruses using fertilized chicken eggs or cell cultures.

## Culturing Viruses in Embryonated Chicken Eggs

Chicken eggs are a useful culture medium for viruses because they are inexpensive, are among the largest of cells, are free of contaminating microbes, and contain a nourishing yolk (which makes them self-sufficient). Most suitable for culturing viruses are chicken eggs that have been fertilized and thus contain a developing embryo, the tissues of which (called membranes, which should not be confused with cellular membranes) provide ideal inoculation sites for growing viruses (Figure 18). Researchers inject samples of virus into embryonated eggs at the sites that are best suited for the particular virus's replication.

Vaccines against some viruses can also be prepared in egg cultures. You may have been asked if you are allergic to eggs before you received such a vaccine, because egg protein may remain as a contaminant in the vaccine.

## Culturing Viruses in Cell (Tissue) Culture

### Learning Objective

✓ Compare and contrast diploid cell culture and continuous cell culture.

Viruses can also be grown in **cell culture,** which consists of cells isolated from an organism and grown on the surface of a

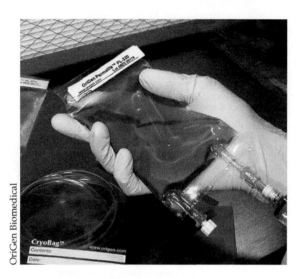

▲ **Figure 19  An example of cell culture.** The bag contains a colored nutrient medium for growing cells in which viruses can be cultured.

OriGen Biomedical

medium or in broth (Figure 19). Such cultures became practical when antibiotics provided a way to limit the growth of contaminating bacteria. Cell culture can be less expensive than maintaining research animals, plants, or eggs, and it avoids some of the moral problems associated with experiments performed on animals and humans. Cell cultures are sometimes called *tissue cultures,* but the term *cell culture* is more accurate because only a single type of cell is used in the culture. (By definition, a tissue is composed of at least two kinds of cells.)

Cell cultures are of two types. The first type, **diploid cell cultures,** are created from embryonic animal, plant, or human cells that have been isolated and provided appropriate growth conditions. The cells in diploid cell culture generally last no more than about 100 generations (cell divisions) before they die.

The second type of culture, **continuous cell cultures,** are longer lasting because they are derived from tumor cells. Recall that a characteristic of neoplastic cells is that they divide relentlessly, providing a never-ending supply of new cells. One of the more famous continuous cell cultures is of HeLa cells, derived from a woman named *He*nrietta *La*cks who died of cervical cancer in 1951. Though she is dead, Mrs. Lacks's cells live on in laboratories throughout the world.

It is interesting that HeLa cells have lost some of their original characteristics. For example, they are no longer diploid because they have lost many chromosomes. HeLa cells provide a semistandard[3] human tissue culture medium for studies on cell metabolism, aging, and (of course) viral infection.

---

[3]HeLa cells are "semistandard" because different strains have lost different chromosomes, and mutations have occurred over the years. Thus, HeLa cells in one laboratory may be slightly different from HeLa cells in another laboratory.

# Are Viruses Alive?

Learning Objective

✓ Discuss aspects of viral replication that are life-like and non-life-like.

Now that we have studied the characteristics and replication processes of viruses, let's return to a question: Are viruses alive?

To be able to wrestle with the answer, we must first recall the characteristics of life: growth, self-reproduction, responsiveness, and the ability to metabolize, all within structures called cells. According to these criteria, viruses seem to lack the qualities of living things, prompting some scientists to consider them nothing more than complex pathogenic chemicals. For other scientists, however, at least three observations—that viruses use sophisticated methods to invade cells, have the means of taking control of their host cells, and possess genomes containing instructions for replicating themselves—indicate that viruses are the ultimate parasites, because they use cells to make more viruses. According to this viewpoint, viruses are the least complex living entities.

In any case, viruses are right on the threshold of life—outside of cells they do not appear to be alive, but within cells they direct the synthesis and assembly required to make copies of themselves.

What do you think? Are viruses alive?

# Other Parasitic Particles: Viroids and Prions

Viruses are not the only submicroscopic entities capable of causing disorders within cells. In this section we will consider the characteristics of two molecular particles that infect cells: viroids and prions.

## Characteristics of Viroids

Learning Objectives

✓ Define and describe viroids.

✓ Compare and contrast viroids and viruses.

**Viroids** are extremely small, circular pieces of RNA that are infectious and pathogenic in plants (Figure 20). Viroids are similar to RNA viruses except that they lack capsids. Even though they are circular, viroids may appear linear because of hydrogen bonding within the molecule. Several plant diseases, including some of coconut palm, chrysanthemum, potato, cucumber, and avocado, are caused by viroids, including the stunting shown in Figure 21.

Genome of bacteriophage T7       PSTV

Theodor O. Diener, Agricultural Research
Service, USDA

TEM   500 nm

▲ **Figure 20** **The RNA strand of the small potato spindle tuber viroid (PSTV).** Also shown for comparison is the longer DNA genome of bacteriophage T7. *Compare both to the size of a bacterial genome in Figure 2. How are viroids similar to and different from viruses?*

*they lack a proteinaceous capsid.*
*and contain a single strand of RNA; they are different from viruses in that*
**Figure 20** *Viroids are similar to certain viruses in that they are infectious*

*Viroidlike agents*—infectious, pathogenic RNA particles that lack capsids but do not infect plants—affect some fungi. (They are not called viroids because they do not infect plants.) No animal diseases are known to be caused by viroidlike molecules, though the possibility exists that infectious RNA may be responsible for some diseases in humans.

## Characteristics of Prions

### Learning Objectives

✓ Define and describe prions, including their replication process.

✓ Compare and contrast prions and viruses.

✓ List four diseases caused by prions.

In 1982, Stanley Prusiner (1942–) described a proteinaceous infectious agent that was different from any other known infectious agent in that it lacked nucleic acid. Prusiner named such agents of disease **prions** (prē'onz), for *pro*teinaceous *in*fective particles. Before his discovery, the diseases now known to be caused by prions were thought to be caused by what were known as "slow viruses," which were so named because of the long delay between infection and the onset of signs and symptoms. Through experiments, Prusiner and his colleagues showed that prions are not viruses because they lack any nucleic acid.
**ANIMATIONS:** *Prions: Overview*

Some scientists resisted the concept of prions because particles that lack any nucleic acid violate the "universal" rule of protein synthesis—that proteins are translated from a molecule

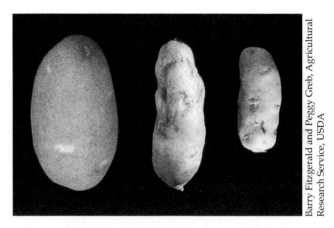

▲ **Figure 21** **One effect of viroids on plants.** The potatoes at right are stunted as the result of infection with PSTV viroids.

of mRNA. Since "infectious proteins" lack nucleic acid, how can they carry the information required to replicate themselves?

All mammals make a cytoplasmic membrane protein called *PrP*, which plays a role in the normal activity of the brain, though the exact function of PrP is unknown. The amino acid sequence in PrP is such that the protein can fold into two stable tertiary structures: the normal, functional structure of *cellular PrP* has several prominent α-helices, while a disease-causing form—*prion PrP*—is characterized by β-pleated sheets (Figure 22).

**(a)** Cellular PrP       **(b)** Prion PrP

▲ **Figure 22** **The two stable, three-dimensional forms of prion protein (PrP). (a)** Cellular prion protein found in normal functional cells has a preponderance of alpha-helices. **(b)** Prion PrP, which has the same amino acid sequence, is folded to produce a preponderance of beta-pleated sheets.

457

Vacuole

James King-Holmes/SPL/Photo Researchers

LM ├──────┤ 25 nm

▲ **Figure 23** **A brain showing the large vacuoles and spongy appearance typical in prion-induced diseases.** Shown here is the brain of a sheep with the prion disease called scrapie.

Prusiner determined that prion PrP acts enzymatically to convert cellular PrP into prion PrP by inducing a conformational change in the shape of cellular PrP. In other words, prion PrP refolds cellular PrP into a prion shape. As cellular ribosomes synthesize more cellular PrP, prions already present cause these new molecules to refold, becoming more prions. Thus, the rule of protein synthesis is maintained, because prions do not code for new prions but instead convert extant cellular PrP into prions. For his work, Prusiner was awarded a Nobel Prize in 1997. **ANIMATIONS:** *Prions: Characteristics*

Why don't prions develop in all mammals, given that all mammals have PrP? Under normal circumstances, it appears that other nearby proteins and polysaccharides in lipid rafts force PrP into the correct (cellular) shape. Only excess PrP production or mutations in the PrP gene result in the initial formation of prion PrP. For instance, it has been determined that human cellular PrP can misfold only if it contains methionine as the 129th amino acid. About 40% of humans have this type of PrP and are thus susceptible to prion disease.

All known prion diseases involve fatal neurological degeneration, the deposition of fibrils in the brain, and the loss of brain matter such that eventually large vacuoles form. The latter process results in a characteristic spongy appearance (Figure 23), which is why as a group, prion diseases are called *spongiform encephalopathies* (spŭn'ji-form en-sef'ă-lop'ă-thēz). The way in which prion PrP causes these changes in the brain is not totally understood, but it appears prions interupt signaling events that cellular PrP controls.

Prions are associated with several spongiform encephalopathies of animals and of humans, including *bovine spongiform encephalitis* (*BSE,* so-called mad cow disease), *scrapie* in sheep, *kuru* (a disease that afflicted Papua New Guinea in the 1950s but has since been eliminated), *chronic wasting disease* (*CWD*) in deer and elk, and *variant Creutzfeldt-Jakob disease*[4] (*vCJD*) in humans. All these diseases are transmitted through either the

### Invasion from Within or Without?

A 32-year-old husband and father of two small children lived in the midwestern United States. An avid hunter and hearty meat eater since childhood, the man visited annually with family and friends in Colorado for elk hunting. His job required frequent international travel (including Europe) where he enjoyed exotic foods.

Early in the spring of 1988, his wife recalls that he began having problems. Frequently he forgot to pick up things from the store or even that his wife had called him. Later that summer, he was unable to complete his paperwork at his business and had great difficulty performing even basic math. In England on business, he had forgotten his home phone number in the U.S. and couldn't remember how to spell his last name to ask for directory assistance.

By September he could not perform his job and his wife insisted he seek medical care. All the standard blood tests came back normal. A psychologist diagnosed depression, but after a brain biopsy, the man was found to have spongiform changes in his brain. He was given 6–8 weeks to live as there is no treatment for this condition.

1. What is the likely diagnosis?

2. The man's wife was concerned for her children's welfare and asked, "Can we catch this disease from my husband?" How would you respond?

3. Where and how was the man probably infected?

ingestion of infected tissue, including brain, spinal cord, eyes, and, in some cases, skeletal muscle tissue; transplants of infected tissue, including nervous tissue and blood; or contact between infected tissue and mucous membranes or skin abrasions. **ANIMATIONS:** *Prions: Diseases*

Normal cooking or sterilization procedures do not deactivate prions, though they are destroyed by incineration or autoclaving in 1 normal NaOH. The European Union recently approved the use of special enzymes developed using biotechnology to remove infectious prions from medical equipment.

There is no treatment for any prion disease, though scientists have determined that the antimalarial drug quinacrine and the antipsychotic drug chlorpromazine forestall spongiform encephalopathy in prion-infected mice. Human trials of these drugs are ongoing.

PrP proteins of different species are slightly different in primary structure, and at one time it was thought unlikely that prions of one species could cross over into another species to cause disease. However, an epidemic of BSE in Great Britain in the late 1980s and in France in the 2000s resulted in the spread of

---

[4]"Variant" because it is derived from BSE prions in cattle, as opposed to the regular form of CJD, which is a genetic disease.

## TABLE 5 Comparison of Viruses, Viroids, and Prions to Bacterial Cells

|  | Bacteria | Viruses | Viroids | Prions |
|---|---|---|---|---|
| Width | 200–2000 nm | 10–400 nm | 2 nm | 5 nm |
| Length | 200–550,000 nm | 20–800 nm | 40–130 nm | 5 nm |
| Nucleic acid? | Both DNA and RNA | Either DNA or RNA, never both | RNA only | None |
| Protein? | Present | Present | Absent | Present (PrP) |
| Cellular? | Yes | No | No | No |
| Cytoplasmic membrane? | Present | Absent (though some viruses do have a membranous envelope) | Absent | Absent |
| Functional ribosomes? | Present | Absent | Absent | Absent |
| Growth? | Present | Absent | Absent | Absent |
| Self-replicating? | Yes | No | No | Yes; transform PrP protein already present in cell |
| Responsiveness? | Present | Some bacteriophages respond to a host cell by injecting their genomes | Absent | Absent |
| Metabolism? | Present | Absent | Absent | Absent |

prions not only to other cattle, but also to humans who ate infected beef. To prevent further infection, most countries ban the use of animal-derived protein supplements in animal feed. Unfortunately, this step was too late to prevent the spread of bovine prions to more than 150 Europeans who have developed fatal vCJD. (See **Clinical Case Study: Invasion from Within or Without?**)

Prions composed of different proteins may lie behind other muscular and neuronal degenerative diseases, such as Alzheimer's disease, Parkinson's disease, and amyotrophic lateral sclerosis (ALS, or "Lou Gehrig's disease").

CRITICAL **THINKING**

Why did most scientists initially resist the idea of an infectious, replicating protein?

In this chapter we have seen that humans, animals, plants, fungi, bacteria, and archaea are susceptible to infection by acel lular pathogens: viruses, viroids, and prions. Table 5 summarizes the differences and similarities between these pathogenic agents and bacterial pathogens.

# Chapter Summary

1. Viruses, viroids, and prions are **acellular** disease-causing agents that lack cell structure and cannot metabolize, grow, self-reproduce, or respond to their environment.

## Characteristics of Viruses

1. A **virus** is a tiny infectious agent with nucleic acid surrounded by proteinaceous **capsomeres** that form a coat called a **capsid.** A virus exists in an extracellular state and an intracellular state. A **virion** is a complete viral particle, including a nucleic acid and a capsid, outside of a cell.

2. The genomes of viruses include either DNA or RNA. Viral genomes may be dsDNA, ssDNA, dsRNA, or ssRNA. They may exist as linear or circular and singular or multiple molecules of nucleic acid, depending on the type of virus.

3. A **bacteriophage** (or **phage**) is a virus that infects a bacterial cell.

4. Virions can have a membranous **envelope** or be naked—that is, without an envelope.

## Classification of Viruses

1. Viruses are classified based on type of nucleic acid, presence of an envelope, shape, and size.

2. The International Committee on Taxonomy of Viruses (ICTV) has recognized viral family and genus names. With the exception of three orders, higher taxa are not established.

## Viral Replication

1. Viruses depend on random contact with a specific host cell type for replication. Typically a virus in a cell proceeds with a lytic replication cycle with five stages: **attachment, entry, synthesis, assembly,** and **release.**
   ANIMATIONS: *Viral Replication: Overview*

2. Once attachment has been made between virion and host cell, the nucleic acid enters the cell. With phages, only the nucleic acid enters the host cell. With animal viruses, the entire virion often enters the cell, where the capsid is then removed in a process called **uncoating.**
   ANIMATIONS: *Viral Replication: Animal Viruses*

3. Within the host cell, the viral nucleic acid directs synthesis of more viruses using metabolic enzymes and ribosomes of the host cell.

4. Assembly of synthesized virions occurs in the host cell, typically as capsomeres surround replicated or transcribed nucleic acids to form new virions.

5. Virions are released from the host cell either by lysis of the host cell (seen with phages and animal viruses) or by the extrusion of enveloped virions through the host's cytoplasmic membrane (called **budding**), a process seen only with certain animal viruses. If budding continues over time, the infection is persistent. An envelope is derived from a cell membrane.
   **ANIMATIONS:** *Viral Replication: Virulent Bacteriophages*

6. **Temperate** (lysogenic) **phages** enter a bacterial cell and remain inactive, in a process called **lysogeny** or a **lysogenic replication cycle.** Such inactive phages are called **prophages** and are inserted into the chromosome of the cell and passed to its daughter cells. **Lysogenic conversion** results when phages carry genes that alter the phenotype of a bacterium. At some point in the generations that follow, a prophage may be excised from the chromosome in a process known as **induction.** At that point the prophage again becomes a lytic virus.
   **ANIMATIONS:** *Viral Replication: Temperate Bacteriophages*

7. In **latency,** a process similar to lysogeny, an animal virus remains inactive in a cell, possibly for years, as part of a chromosome or in the cytosol. A **latent** virus is also known as a **provirus.** A provirus that has become incorporated into a host's chromosome remains there.

8. With the exception of hepatitis B virus, dsDNA viruses act like cellular DNA in transcription and replication.

9. Some ssRNA viruses have **positive-strand RNA (+RNA),** which can be directly translated by ribosomes to synthesize protein. From the +RNA, complementary **negative-strand RNA (−RNA)** is transcribed to serve as a template for more +RNA.

10. **Retroviruses,** such as HIV, are +ssRNA viruses that carry reverse transcriptase, which transcribes DNA from RNA. This reverse process (DNA transcribed from RNA) is reflected in the name retrovirus.

11. −ssRNA viruses carry an RNA-dependent RNA transcriptase for transcribing mRNA from the −RNA genome so that protein can then be translated. Transcription of RNA from RNA is not found in cells.

12. In dsRNA viruses, one strand of RNA functions as a genome, and the other strand functions as a template for RNA replication.

## The Role of Viruses in Cancer

1. **Neoplasia** is uncontrolled cellular reproduction in a multicellular animal. A mass of neoplastic cells, called a **tumor,** may be relatively harmless **(benign)** or invasive **(malignant).** Malignant tumors are also called **cancer. Metastasis** describes the spreading of malignant tumors. Environmental factors or oncogenic viruses may cause neoplasia.

## Culturing Viruses in the Laboratory

1. In the laboratory, viruses must be cultured inside mature organisms, in embryonated chicken eggs, or in cell cultures because viruses cannot metabolize or replicate alone.

2. When a mixture of bacteria and phages is grown on an agar plate, bacteria infected with phages lyse, producing clear areas called **plaques** on the bacterial lawn. A technique called **plaque assay** enables the estimation of phage numbers.

3. Viruses can be grown in two types of **cell cultures.** Whereas **diploid cell cultures** last about 100 generations, **continuous cell cultures,** derived from cancer cells, last longer.

## Are Viruses Alive?

1. Outside of cells, viruses do not appear to be alive, but within cells, they exhibit lifelike qualities such as the ability to replicate themselves.

## Other Parasitic Particles: Viroids and Prions

1. **Viroids** are small circular pieces of RNA with no capsid that infect and cause disease in plants. Similar pathogenic RNA molecules have been found in fungi.

2. **Prions** are infectious protein particles that lack nucleic acids and replicate by converting similar, normal proteins into new prions. Diseases caused by prions are spongiform encephalopathies, which involve fatal neurological degeneration.
   **ANIMATIONS:** *Prions: Overview, Characteristics, and Diseases*

# Questions for Review
Answers to the Questions for Review (except Short Answer questions) appear at the end of this chapter.

## Multiple Choice

1. Which of the following is *not* an acellular agent?
   a. viroid
   b. virus
   c. rickettsia
   d. prion

2. Which of the following statements is true?
   a. Viruses move toward their host cells.
   b. Viruses are capable of metabolism.
   c. Viruses lack a cell membrane.
   d. Viruses grow in response to their environmental conditions.

3. A virus that is specific for a bacterial host is called a
   a. phage.
   b. prion.
   c. virion.
   d. viroid.

4. A naked virus
   a. has no membranous envelope.
   b. has injected its DNA or RNA into a host cell.
   c. is devoid of capsomeres.
   d. is one that is unattached to a host cell.

5. Which of the following statements is *false*?
   a. Viruses may have circular DNA.
   b. dsRNA is found in bacteria more often than in viruses.
   c. Viral DNA may be linear.
   d. Typically, viruses have DNA or RNA, but not both.

6. When a eukaryotic cell is infected with an enveloped virus and sheds viruses slowly over time, this infection is
   a. called a lytic infection.
   b. a prophage cycle.
   c. called a persistent infection.
   d. caused by a quiescent virus.

7. Another name for a complete virus is
   a. virion.          c. prion.
   b. viroid.          d. capsid.

8. Which of the following viruses can be latent?
   a. HIV              c. herpesviruses
   b. chickenpox virus  d. all of the above

9. Which of the following is *not* a criterion for specific family classification of viruses?
   a. the type of nucleic acid present
   b. envelope structure
   c. capsid type
   d. lipid composition

10. A clear zone of phage infection in a bacterial lawn is
    a. a prophage.     c. naked.
    b. a plaque.       d. a capsomere.

## Matching

Match each numbered term with its description.

1. ____ uncoating       A. dormant virus in a eukaryotic cell
2. ____ prophage        B. a virus that infects a bacterium
3. ____ retrovirus      C. transcribes DNA from RNA
4. ____ bacteriophage   D. protein coat of virus
5. ____ capsid          E. a membrane on the outside of a virus
6. ____ envelope        F. complete viral particle
7. ____ virion          G. inactive virus within bacterial cell
8. ____ provirus        H. removal of capsomeres from a virion
9. ____ benign tumor    I. invasive neoplastic cells
10. ____ cancer         J. harmless neoplastic cells

## Labeling

Label each step in the bacterioplage replication cycle below.

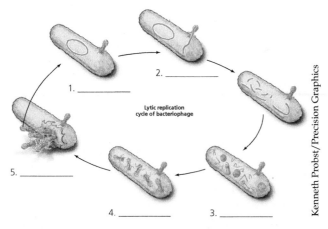

Lytic replication cycle of bacteriophage

1. _____
2. _____
3. _____
4. _____
5. _____

Kenneth Probst/Precision Graphics

## Short Answer

1. Compare and contrast a bacterium and a virus by writing either "Present" or "Absent" for each of the following structures.

| Structure | Bacterium | Virus |
|---|---|---|
| Cell membrane | | |
| Functional ribosome | | |
| Cytoplasm | | |
| Nucleic acid | | |
| Nuclear membrane | | |

2. Describe the five phases of a generalized lytic replication cycle.

3. Why is it difficult to treat viral infections?

4. Describe four different ways that viral nucleic acid can enter a host cell.

5. Contrast lysis and budding as means of release of virions from a host cell.

6. What is the difference between a virion and a virus particle?

7. How is a provirus like a prophage? How is it different?

8. Describe lysogeny.

9. How are viruses specific for their host's cells?

10. Compare and contrast diploid cell culture and continuous cell culture.

# Concept Mapping

Using the following terms, draw a concept map that describes the replication of animal viruses.
Or, complete this concept map online by going to the Study Area at www.masteringmicrobiology.com.

+ssRNA
−ssRNA
Assembly
Attachment
Budding
dsDNA

dsRNA
Endocytosis
Entry
Exocytosis
Fusion
Host cells

Lysis
New virions
Release
ssDNA
Synthesis
Uncoating

Viral genome
Viral nucleic acid
Viral proteins

# Critical Thinking

1. Small viruses typically have a single-stranded genome, while larger viruses usually have a double-stranded genome. What reasonable explanation can you offer for this observation?

2. What are the advantages and disadvantages to bacteriophages of the lytic and lysogenic reproductive strategies?

3. How are computer viruses similar to biological viruses? Are computer viruses alive? Why or why not?

4. Compare and contrast lysogeny by a prophage and latency by a provirus.

5. An agricultural microbiologist wants to stop the spread of a viral infection of a crop. Is stopping viral attachment a viable option? Why or why not?

 Mastering MICROBIOLOGY™

Access more review material online in the Study Area at **www.masteringmicrobiology.com.** There, you'll find
- **Animations**
- **MP3 Tutor Sessions**
- **Concept Mapping Activities**
- **Flashcards**
- **Quizzes**

and more to help you succeed.

# Answers

Answers to multiple-choice, fill-in-blank, labeling, matching, and true/false questions are listed here. Answers for Short Answer and Critical Thinking questions are available for instructors only in the Instructor's Manual that accompanies this text.

**Multiple Choice**
1. c; 2. c; 3. a; 4. a; 5. b; 6. c; 7. a; 8. d; 9. d; 10. b

**Matching**
1. H; 2. G; 3. C; 4. B; 5. D; 6. E; 7. F; 8. A; 9. J; 10. I

**Labeling**
See Figure 8.

# Pathogenic DNA Viruses

Everyone reading this textbook has been infected by DNA viruses at one time or another. Fever blisters (cold sores), warts, chickenpox, infectious mononucleosis, and many types of colds are all caused by viruses that have DNA genomes. DNA viruses are also the cause of smallpox, hepatitis B, shingles, and genital herpes, and they are associated with some cancers. Fortunately, many of the more severe diseases caused by DNA viruses, including hepatitis B and hepatic cancer, are relatively rare. However, smallpox—a disease that has been successfully eradicated in nature—is once again a public health concern because of its potential as an agent of bioterrorism.

In this chapter we focus on a selection of medically important DNA viruses—the differences among them, the diseases they cause, and the ways they may be transmitted, treated, and prevented.

 Take the pre-test for this chapter online. Visit the Study Area at www.masteringmicrobiology.com.

Linda M. Stannard, University of Cape Town/Photo Researchers

▲ Hepatitis B virus is a DNA virus that causes hepatitis and lung cancer.

From Chapter 24 of *Microbiology with Diseases by Taxonomy*, Third Edition. Robert W. Bauman. Copyright © 2011 by Pearson Education, Inc. Published by Benjamin Cummings, Inc. All rights reserved.

DNA viruses that cause human diseases are grouped into seven families based on several factors, including the type of DNA they contain, the presence or absence of an envelope, size, and the host cells they attack. DNA viruses have either double-stranded DNA (dsDNA) or single-stranded DNA (ssDNA) for their genomes, and that none of them contains functional RNA. Double-stranded DNA viruses belong to the families *Poxviridae, Herpesviridae, Papillomaviridae, Polyomaviridae,* and *Adenoviridae.* The family *Parvoviridae* contains viruses with ssDNA genomes. Viruses in the family *Hepadnaviridae* are unusual because they have a genome that is partly dsDNA and partly ssDNA. In the following sections we examine the infections and diseases caused by the viruses in each of these families.

# *Poxviridae*

## Learning Objectives

✓ Name two diseases caused by poxviruses and discuss their signs and symptoms.

✓ Describe the progression of disease in poxvirus infections.

✓ Discuss the historical importance of poxviruses in immunization and their use in disease eradication.

Poxviruses are double-stranded DNA viruses with complex capsids and envelopes (Figure 1). They are the second largest of viruses, being up to 300 nm in diameter, which is just visible with high-quality, optical, ultraviolet light microscopes. Their large size allows them to be potential vectors for the introduction of genetic material in vaccinations and gene therapy.

Specific poxviruses infect many mammals, including mice, camels, elephants, cattle, and monkeys. (Note that chickenpox, discussed later in this chapter, is caused neither by a poxvirus nor occurs in chickens; instead, it is caused by a herpesvirus that affects people.) Most animal poxviruses are species specific; they are unable to infect humans because they cannot attach to human cells, though a few poxviruses of monkeys, sheep, goats, and cattle can infect some humans because these people have surface proteins similar to proteins of those animals.

All poxviruses produce lesions that progress through a series of stages (Figure 2). The lesions begin as flat, reddened **macules**[1] (mak'ūlz), which then become raised sores called **papules**[2] (pap'ūlz); when the lesions fill with clear fluid, they are called **vesicles,** which then progress to pus-filled **pustules**[3] (pŭs'choolz), which are also known as **pocks** or **pox.** These terms for the stages of poxvirus lesions are also used to describe the lesions of other skin infections. Poxvirus pustules dry up to form a crust, and because these lesions penetrate the dermis, they result in characteristic scars.

---

[1]From Latin *maculatus,* meaning spotted.
[2]From Latin *papula,* meaning pimple.
[3]From Latin *pustula,* meaning blister.

TEM | 200 nm

▲ **Figure 1 Poxviruses.** Variola, the causative agent of smallpox, and vaccinia, the agent of cowpox, are in the genus *Orthopoxvirus.*

Infection with poxviruses occurs primarily through inhalation of viruses in droplets or dried crusts. Because the envelopes of poxviruses are relatively unstable outside a host's body, close contact is necessary for infection. The two main poxvirus diseases of humans are *smallpox* and *molluscum contagiosum.* Three diseases of animals—*orf* (sheep and goat pox), *cowpox,* and *monkeypox*—may be transmitted to humans as well.

## Smallpox

**Smallpox** has played important roles in the history of microbiology, immunization, epidemiology, and medicine. During the Middle Ages, 80% of the European population contracted smallpox. Later, European colonists introduced smallpox into susceptible Native Americans, resulting in the death of as many as 3.5 million people. Edward Jenner first demonstrated immunization using the relatively mild cowpox virus to protect against smallpox. He was successful because the antigens of cowpox virus are chemically similar to those of smallpox virus, so that exposure to cowpox results in immunological memory and subsequent resistance against both cowpox and smallpox.

Smallpox virus is in the genus *Orthopoxvirus.* Commonly known as **variola** (vă-rī'ō-lă), it exists in two forms, or strains. **Variola major** causes severe disease with a mortality rate of 20% or higher, depending upon the age and general health of the host; **variola minor** causes a less severe disease with a mortality rate of less than 1%. Both types of variola infect internal organs and produce fever—42°C (107°F) has been recorded—malaise, delirium, and prostration before moving via the bloodstream to the skin, where they produce the recognizable pox (Figure 3). Both strains also leave severe scars on the skin of survivors, especially on the face.

1 Macule

Epidermis

Dermis

2 Papule

3 Vesicle

Fluid

1 cm

4 Pustule

Pus

5 Crust

6 Scar

Kenneth Probst/Precision Graphics

◀ **Figure 2  The stages of the lesions in poxvirus infections.** Red macules become hard papules, then fluid-filled vesicles that become pus-filled pustules (pox), which then crust over and leave characteristic scars. *Are the dried viruses in the crusts of smallpox and cowpox lesions infective?*

**Figure 2** *Yes, the dried crusts of poxvirus lesions may contain active viruses. The Chinese used the viruses in crusts for variolation, an early attempt at vaccination.*

CDC

▲ **Figure 3  Smallpox lesions.** Facial scarring was often especially severe in smallpox.

Smallpox is the first human disease to be eradicated globally in nature. In 1967, the World Health Organization (WHO) began an extensive campaign of identification and isolation of smallpox victims, as well as vaccination of their contacts, with the goal of completely eliminating the disease. The efforts of WHO were successful, and in 1980 smallpox was declared to be eradicated—one of the great accomplishments of 20th-century medicine. The factors that made it possible for smallpox to be eliminated included the following:

- An inexpensive, stable, and effective vaccine (vaccinia, cowpox virus) is available.
- Smallpox is specific to humans; there are no animal reservoirs.
- The severe, obvious signs and symptoms of smallpox enable quick and accurate diagnosis and quarantine.
- There are no asymptomatic cases.
- The virus is spread only via close contact.

▲ **Figure 4** **Lesions of molluscum contagiosum.** *Molluscipoxvirus,* a poxvirus, causes the pearly white to light pink, tumorlike lesions.

Stocks of the virus are still maintained in laboratories in the United States and Russia as research tools for investigations concerning virulence, pathogenicity, protection against bioterrorism, vaccination, and recombinant DNA technology.

Routine vaccination against smallpox has ceased in the United States, though some health care workers and military personnel were vaccinated following the 2001 bioterrorism attack. Studies have shown that older citizens, who were vaccinated as children, still retain some immunity. One-tenth the regular vaccine dose is effective for revaccination of these adults.

Now that smallpox vaccination has been discontinued in many countries, experts are concerned that the world's population is once again susceptible to smallpox epidemics if the virus were accidentally released from storage or used as a biological weapon. For this reason, many scientists advocate the destruction of all smallpox virus stocks; other scientists insist that we must maintain the virus in secure laboratories so that it is available for the development of more effective vaccines and treatments if the virus is disseminated in a bioterrorism attack.

### CRITICAL **THINKING**

The United States and Russia have repeatedly agreed to destroy their stocks of the smallpox virus, but the deadline for destruction has been postponed numerous times. In the meantime, the entire genome of variola major has been sequenced. What reasons can governments cite for maintaining smallpox viruses? Should all laboratory stores of smallpox viruses be destroyed? Given that the genome of the virus has been sequenced, and that DNA can be synthesized, would elimination of all laboratory stocks really be the extinction of the smallpox virus?

## Molluscum Contagiosum

Another poxvirus, *Molluscipoxvirus,* causes **molluscum contagiosum** (mo-lŭs′kŭm kon-taj-ē-ō′sum), a skin disease characterized by smooth, waxy papules that frequently occur in lines where the patient has spread the virus by scratching (Figure 4). Lesions may occur anywhere but typically appear on the face, trunk, and external genitalia.

Molluscum contagiosum occurs worldwide and is typically spread by contact among infected children, sexually active individuals (particularly adolescents), and AIDS patients. Treatment involves removing the infected nodules by chemicals or freezing, though people with normal immune systems heal within months without treatment. Sexual abstinence prevents the genital form of the disease. Condoms do not afford protection, as the virus can spread from and to areas not covered by the condom.

## Other Poxvirus Infections

Poxvirus infections also occur in animals. Infections of humans with these animal viruses are usually relatively mild, resulting in pox and scars but little other damage. In the case of cowpox, the advent of milking machines has reduced the number of cases to near zero in the industrialized world. Other poxvirus infections, including those in sheep, goats, and monkeys, are less easily contracted by humans.

Transmission of these poxviruses to humans requires close contact with infected animals, similar to the contact Edward Jenner observed for milkmaids and cowpox. Still, an upsurge in the number of monkeypox cases in humans has been seen in the past decade. (See **Emerging Diseases: Monkeypox.**) This may be the result of human encroachment into monkey habitats or changes in viral antigens. Some researchers speculate that the cessation of smallpox vaccination may also be involved, because evidence suggests that smallpox vaccination also protects against monkeypox. Thus, the elimination of smallpox and the cessation of smallpox vaccination may have led to increased human susceptibility to monkeypox. Some scientists have recommended that smallpox vaccination be reinstated in areas where monkeypox is endemic.

## *Herpesviridae*

The family *Herpesviridae* contains a large group of viruses with enveloped polyhedral capsids containing linear dsDNA. A herpesvirus attaches to a host cell's receptor and enters the cell through the fusion of its envelope with the cytoplasmic membrane. After the viral genome is replicated and assembled in the cell's nucleus, the virion acquires its envelope from the nuclear membrane and exits the cell via exocytosis or cell lysis.

Many types of herpesviruses infect humans, and their high infection rates make them the most prevalent of DNA viruses. Indeed, three types of herpesvirus—herpes simplex, varicella-zoster, and Epstein-Barr (discussed shortly)—infect 90% of the adult population in the United States, and several other herpesviruses have infection rates over 50%.

Herpesviruses are often *latent;* that is, they may remain inactive inside infected cells, often for years. Such latent viruses may reactivate as a result of aging, chemotherapy,

## EMERGING DISEASES

### MONKEYPOX

Jamal was excited about the pet he got for his birthday; he was the only boy at school who had a prairie dog! Common dogs were boring; his prairie dog could climb up the drapes, run through plastic tube mazes, and sit on Jamal's shoulder to eat. Doggie was the best. In fact, everything would be just about perfect if only Jamal weren't sick in bed.

Two weeks after his birthday Jamal was exhausted and felt terrible. He had fever accompanied by headache and muscle aches, so his mother had kept him home from school. Then the lymph nodes in his neck and armpits had swollen, and he had gotten frightening, large, raised lesions all over his face and hands. He was really sick.

For the next three weeks, the lesions had become crusty and then fallen off, only to be replaced by new lesions. Jamal felt awful and missed playing with Doggie, who had been confined to his cage, while Jamal stayed in bed. Jamal's doctor had been unable to diagnose the disease, but an infectious disease specialist had finally confirmed monkeypox—a disease named for monkeys who can get the disease. In reality, monkeypox is a disease of rodents, including prairie dogs. Final investigation revealed that the pet wholesaler who had supplied Doggie to Jamal's pet store in Illinois had also supplied African monkeys to stores in Texas. At least one of those monkeys had been infected with monkeypox virus—a virus closely related to smallpox virus. The monkey had infected Doggie who had infected Jamal.

Jamal was sick for four weeks, but monkeypox is not as virulent as smallpox, so Jamal recovered with only some scars as a reminder that not all unusual pets are a blessing.

**Track monkeypox online by going to the Study Area at www.masteringmicrobiology.com.**

## MICROBE AT A GLANCE

### *Orthopoxvirus variola* (Smallpox Virus)

**Taxonomy:** Family *Poxviridae*

**Genome and morphology:** Single molecule of double-stranded DNA; enveloped, brick-shaped or pleomorphic, complex capsid, 250 nm × 250–300 nm × 150–300 nm

**Host:** Humans

**Virulence factors:** Remains very stable in aerosol form; highly contagious between people; can remain viable for as long as 24 hours

**Disease caused:** Smallpox

**Treatment for disease:** Administration of vaccine within four days of infection prevents disease in most patients; anticowpox immunoglobulins may be efficacious

**Prevention of disease:** Smallpox has been eliminated in nature and presumably could reappear only if released from secure storage facilities; if it were released, vaccination of exposed individuals and quarantine of patients would need to be implemented immediately

Outer membrane • Inner membrane • Core (DNA and proteins) • Surface proteins • Envelope • up to 300 nm

Kenneth Probst/Precision Graphics

**Download the Microbe at a Glance flashcards from the Study Area at www.masteringmicrobiology.com.**

immunosuppression, or physical and emotional stress, causing a recurrence of the manifestations of the diseases. Additionally, some latent herpesviruses insert into a host's chromosomes, where they may cause genetic changes and potentially induce cancer.

Besides causing the diseases for which the group is named (oral herpes and genital herpes), herpesviruses cause a variety of other diseases, including chickenpox, shingles, mononucleosis, and some cancers. **Human herpesviruses** have been assigned species names combining "HHV" (for "human herpesvirus")

467

Trigeminal (V)
nerve ganglion
Site of viral latency

Ophthalmic branch

Ocular herpes

Maxillary branch
Mandibular branch

Brachial ganglia
Site of viral latency

Fever blisters

Sacral ganglia
Site of viral latency

Genital herpes

Whitlow

Kenneth Probst/Precision Graphics

▲ **Figure 5 Sites of events in herpesvirus infections.** Infections typically occur when viruses invade the mucous membranes of either the lips (for the fever blisters of oral herpes) or the genitalia (for genital herpes), or through broken skin of a finger (for a whitlow). Viruses may remain latent for years in the trigeminal, brachial, or sacral ganglia before traveling down nerve cells to cause recurrent symptoms in the lips, genitalia, fingers, or eyes. *What factors may trigger the reactivation of latent herpesviruses and the recurrence of symptoms?*

*Figure 5 Stress, fever, trauma, sunlight, menstruation, or diseases such as AIDS may cause recurrent symptoms as a result of immune suppression.*

with numbers corresponding to the order in which they were discovered. Thus the genus *Simplexvirus* contains two species (as discussed in the next section) known as HHV-1 and HHV-2. *Varicellovirus* (which causes chickenpox and shingles) is HHV-3; *Lymphocryptovirus*, also known as Epstein-Barr virus, is HHV-4; *Cytomegalovirus* is HHV-5; *Roseolovirus* is HHV-6; and *Rhadinovirus*—HHV-8—is associated with a particular type of cancer in AIDS patients. All these viruses share similar capsids and genes but can be distinguished by genetic variations among them.

What about HHV-7? Scientists isolated this species of *Roseolovirus* in the 1980s from the T cells of an AIDS patient and

identified it as HHV-7 on the basis of its genome, envelope, capsid, and antigens. At this time, no disease has been attributed to this herpesvirus. It is an *orphan virus*—a virus without a known disease.

## Infections of *Human Herpesvirus 1* and *2*

### Learning Objectives

✓ Describe the diseases caused by *human herpesvirus 1* and *2*, including their signs, symptoms, treatment, and prevention.

✓ List conditions that may reactivate latent herpesviruses.

The name "herpes," which is derived from a Greek word meaning "to creep," is descriptive of the slowly spreading skin lesions that are seen with *human herpesvirus 1* (HHV-1) and *human herpesvirus 2* (HHV-2), which are in the genus *Simplexvirus*. They were known formerly as herpes simplex viruses (HSV-1 and HSV-2).

### Latency and Recurrent Lesions

One of the more distressing aspects of herpes infections is the recurrence of lesions. About two-thirds of patients with HHV-1 or HHV-2 will experience recurrences during their lives as a result of the activation of latent viruses. After a primary infection, these herpesviruses often enter sensory nerve cells and are carried by cytoplasmic flow to the base of the nerve, where they remain latent in the trigeminal, sacral, or other ganglia[4] (Figure 5). Such latent viruses may reactivate later in life as a result of immune suppression caused by stress, fever, trauma, sunlight, menstruation, or disease and travel down the nerve to produce recurrent lesions as often as every two weeks. Fortunately, the lesions of recurrent infections are rarely as severe as those of initial infections because of immunological memory.

### Types of HHV-1 and HHV-2 Infections

Historically, HHV-1 has also been known as "above the waist herpes," whereas HHV-2 has been known as "below the waist herpes." In the following subsections we consider the variety of infections caused by these two species.

**Oral Herpes** *Human herpesvirus 1* was the first human herpesvirus to be discovered. About two weeks after infection, the virions of HHV-1 produce painful, itchy skin lesions on the lips, called **fever blisters** or **cold sores** (Figure 6), which last 7–10 days; initial infections may also be accompanied by flulike signs and symptoms, including malaise, fever, and muscle pain. Severe infections in which the lesions extend into the oral cavity, called *herpetic gingivostomatitis*,[5] are most often seen in young patients and in patients with lowered immune function due to disease, chemotherapy, or radiation treatment. Young adults with sore throats resulting from other viral infections may also develop *herpetic pharyngitis*.

---

[4]A ganglion is a collection of nerve cell bodies containing the nuclei of the cells.
[5]From Latin *gingival*, meaning gum, Greek *stoma*, meaning mouth, and Greek *itis*, meaning inflammation.

▲ **Figure 6** **Oral herpes lesions.** *Which is the more likely cause of these lesions, HHV-1 or HHV-2?*

**Figure 6** *Approximately 90% of oral herpes lesions are caused by human herpesvirus 1.*

▲ **Figure 7** **Genital herpes lesions.** *Are these lesions caused by herpes type 1, or type 2?*

**Figure 7** *Either type of herpes can cause genital lesions, but "below the waist" lesions are usually caused by HHV-2.*

**Genital Herpes** HHV-1 can infect the genitalia. The virus causes about 15% of genital herpes lesions. The remainder are caused by *human herpesvirus 2.* HHV-2 differs slightly from HHV-1 in its surface antigens, primary location of infection, and mode of transmission. Type 2 herpes is usually associated with painful lesions on the genitalia (Figure 7) because the virions are typically transmitted sexually. However, HHV-2 can cause oral lesions when it infects the mouth. Thus, about 10% of oral cold sores result from HHV-2. The presence of HHV-2 in the oral region and of HHV-1 in the genital area is presumed to be the result of oral sex.

**Ocular Herpes** Ocular (ok′yū-lăr) or *ophthalmic* **herpes** is an infection caused by latent herpesviruses (Figure 8a). In ocular herpes, latent HHV-1 in the trigeminal ganglion travels down the ophthalmic branch of the trigeminal nerve instead of the mandibular or maxillary branches (see Figure 5). Symptoms and signs usually occur in only one eye and include a gritty feeling, conjunctivitis, pain, and sensitivity to light. The viruses may also cause corneal lesions. Recurrent ocular infections can lead to blindness as a result of corneal damage.

**Whitlow** An inflamed blister called a **whitlow**[6] (hwit′lō) may result if either HHV-1 or HHV-2 enters a cut or break in the skin of a finger (Figure 8b). A whitlow usually occurs on only one finger. Whitlow is a hazard for children who suck their thumbs and for health care workers in the fields of obstetrics, respiratory care, gynecology, and dentistry who come into contact with lesions. Such workers should always wear gloves when treating patients with herpes lesions. Since a whitlow is also a potential source of infection, symptomatic personnel should

[6]From Scandinavian *whick,* meaning nail, and *flaw,* meaning crack.

not work with patients until the worker's whitlow has healed. The viruses involved in whitlow may become latent in brachial ganglia and cause recurrent lesions.

**Neonatal Herpes** Although most herpes simplex infections in adults are painful and unpleasant, they are not life threatening. This is not the case for herpes infections in newborns. HHV-2 is usually the species involved in neonatal herpes. Neonatal herpes infections can be severe, with a mortality rate of 30% if the infection is cutaneous or oral, and of 80% if the central nervous system is infected.

A fetus can be infected *in utero* if the virus crosses the placental barrier, but it is more likely for a baby to be infected at birth through contact with lesions in the mother's reproductive tract. Also, mothers with oral lesions can infect their babies if they kiss them on the mouth. Pregnant women with herpes infections, even if asymptomatic, should inform their doctors. To protect the baby, delivery should be by cesarean section if genital lesions are present at the time of birth.

**Other Herpes Simplex Infections** Athletes may develop herpes lesions almost anywhere on their skin as a result of contact with herpes lesions during wrestling. *Herpes gladiatorum,* as this condition is called, is most often caused by HHV-1.

*Human herpesviruses 1* and 2 may also cause other diseases, including encephalitis, meningitis, and pneumonia. Patients with severe immune suppression, such as those with AIDS, are most likely to develop these rare disorders.

Table 1 compares infections caused by herpes viruses.

### Epidemiology and Pathogenesis of HHV-1 and HHV-2 Infections

HHV-1 and HHV-2 occur worldwide and are transmitted through close body contact. Active lesions are the usual source of infection, though asymptomatic carriers shed HHV-2 genitally. After entering the body through cracks or cuts in mucous membranes, viruses reproduce in epithelial cells near the site of

**(a)**                    **(b)**

▲ **Figure 8** **Two manifestations of herpesvirus infections.** **(a)** Ophthalmic or ocular herpes, the result of the reactivation of latent viruses in the trigeminal ganglion. **(b)** A whitlow on a health provider's finger, resulting from the entry of herpesviruses through a break in the skin of the finger. *How can health care workers protect themselves from a whitlow?*

*Figure 8  Health providers should always wear gloves when treating patients who have herpes lesions on any part of their bodies.*

infection and produce inflammation and cell death, resulting in painful, localized lesions on the skin. By causing infected cells to fuse with uninfected neighboring cells to form a structure called a *syncytium,* herpes virions spread from cell to cell, in the process avoiding the host's antibodies.

Initial infections with herpes simplex viruses are usually age specific. Primary HHV-1 infections typically occur via casual contact during childhood and usually produce no signs or symptoms; in fact, by age 2, about 80% of children have been asymptomatically infected with HHV-1. Most HHV-2 infections, by contrast, are acquired between the ages of 15 and 29 as a result of sexual activity, making genital herpes one of the more common sexually transmitted infection in the United States.

Approximately 60% of adult Americans have been exposed to HHV-1. HHV-2 infects about 17% of Americans over age 12.

## Diagnosis, Treatment, and Prevention of HHV-1 and HHV-2 Infections

Physicians often diagnose herpes infections by the presence of their characteristic, recurring lesions, especially in the genital region and on the lips. Microscopic examination of infected tissue reveals syncytia. Positive diagnosis is achieved by immunoassay that demonstrates the presence of viral antigen.

Infections with HHV-1 or HHV-2 are among the few viral diseases that can be controlled with chemotherapeutic agents, notably valaciclovir for both cold sores and genital herpes, and other nucleoside analogs such as iododeoxyuridine or trifluridine for ocular herpes. Topical applications of the drugs limit the duration of the lesions and reduce viral shedding, though none of these drugs cures the diseases or frees nerve cells of latent viral infections. Evidence suggests that a daily oral dose of acyclovir over a period of 6–12 months can be

**TABLE 1**

## Comparative Epidemiology and Pathology of *Human Herpesvirus 1* and *2* Infections

|  | **HHV-1 (HSV-1)** | **HHV-2 (HSV-2)** |
|---|---|---|
| Usual diseases | 90% of cold sores/fever blisters; whitlow | 85% of genital herpes cases |
| Mode of transmission | Close contact | Sexual intercourse |
| Site of latency | Trigeminal and brachial ganglia | Sacral ganglia |
| Locations of lesions | Face, mouth, and rarely trunk | External genitalia, and less commonly thighs, buttocks, and anus |
| Other complications | 15% of genital herpes cases; pharyngitis; gingivostomatitis; ocular/ophthalmic herpes; herpes gladiatorum; 30% of neonatal herpes cases | 10% of oral herpes cases; 70% of neonatal herpes cases |

effective in preventing recurrent genital herpes and in reducing the spread of herpes infections to sexual partners. Many obstetricians prescribe acyclovir during the final weeks of pregnancy for women with a history of genital herpes.

Health care workers can reduce their exposure to infection with herpes simplex by wearing latex gloves. Health providers with whitlows should not have contact with patients, especially newborns.

Sexual abstinence or faithful monogamy between uninfected partners is the only sure way of preventing genital infections. People with active lesions should abstain from sexual activity until the crusts have disappeared, and either male or female condoms should be used even in the absence of lesions because asymptomatic individuals still shed viruses. Herpes lesions in women are usually on the external genitalia, so use of a condom during sexual intercourse provides little protection for their partners. Some studies indicate that circumcision reduces by 25% the chance of getting genital herpes.

## CRITICAL **THINKING**

After a patient complains that his eyes are extremely sensitive to light and feel gritty, his doctor informs him that he has ocular herpes. What causes ocular herpes? Which human herpesvirus, type 1 or type 2, is more likely to cause ocular herpes? Why?

## *Human Herpesvirus 3* (Varicella-Zoster Virus) Infections

### Learning Objective

✓ Compare and contrast chickenpox in children with shingles in adults.

*Human herpesvirus 3,* commonly called **varicella-zoster virus (VZV),** takes its name from the two diseases it causes: *varicella,* which is typically a disease of children, and *herpes zoster,* which usually occurs in adults. Taxonomically, VZV is in the genus *Varicellovirus.* Note that the viral name is spelled differently than the disease.

### Epidemiology and Pathogenesis of HHV-3 (VZV) Infections

**Varicella** (var-i-sel'ă), commonly known as **chickenpox,** is a highly infectious disease most often seen in children. Viruses enter the body through the respiratory tract or eyes, replicate in cells at the site of infection, and then travel via the blood throughout the body, triggering fever, malaise, and skin lesions. Viruses are shed before and during the symptoms. Usually the disease is mild, though it is rarely fatal, especially if associated with secondary bacterial infections. Chickenpox is typically more severe in adults than in children, presumably because much of the tissue damage results from the patient's immune response, and adults have a more developed immune system than children do.

Custom Medical Stock Photo

▲ **Figure 9** **Characteristic chickenpox lesions.** *Varicellovirus* causes these thin-walled, fluid-filled vesicles on red bases.

About two to three weeks after infection, characteristic skin lesions first appear on the back and trunk and then spread to the face, neck, and limbs (Figure 9). In severe cases, the rash may spread into the mouth, pharynx, and vagina. Chickenpox lesions begin as macules, progress in one to two days to papules, and finally become thin-walled, fluid-filled vesicles on red bases, which have been called "dewdrops on rose petals." The vesicles turn cloudy, dry up, and crust over in a few days. Successive crops of lesions appear over a period of three to five days, so that at any given time all stages can be seen. Viruses are shed through respiratory droplets and the fluid in lesions; dry crusts are not infective.

Like many herpesviruses, VZV can become latent within sensory nerves and may remain dormant for years. In about 15% of individuals who have had chickenpox, conditions such as stress, aging, or immune suppression cause the viruses to reactivate, travel down the nerve they inhabit, and produce an extremely painful skin rash near the distal end of the nerve (Figure 10). This rash is known as **shingles** or **herpes zoster** (Figure 11).

*Zoster,* a Greek word that means belt, refers to the characteristic localization of shingle lesions along a band of skin, called a *dermatome,* which is innervated by a single sensory nerve (Figure 12). Shingles lesions form only in the dermatome associated with an infected nerve, and thus the lesions are localized and on the same side of the body as the infected nerve cell. Occasionally, lesions from latent infections of cranial nerves form in the eye, ear, or other part of the head. In some patients, the pain associated with shingles remains for months or years after the lesions have healed.

▶ **Figure 10 Latency and reactivation of varicella-zoster virus.** After initial infection, VZV can move up the spinal nerve and become latent in nerve cell bodies in spinal root ganglia. After subsequent reactivation (often years later), the viruses move down the spinal nerve to the skin, causing a rash known as shingles.

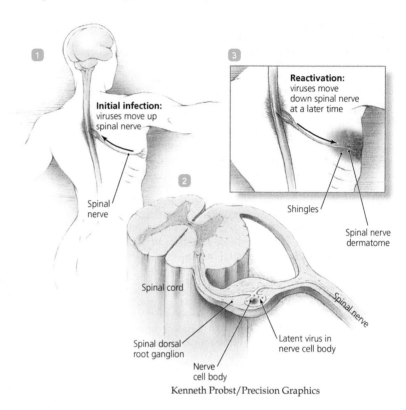

Kenneth Probst/Precision Graphics

▼ **Figure 11 Shingles, the rash caused by *Varicellovirus*.** These painful lesions occur on the dermatome innervated by an infected nerve.

Dr. P. Marazzi/Photo Researchers

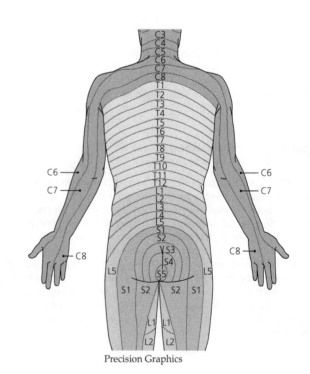

▶ **Figure 12 Dermatomes, the bands of skin innervated by a single sensory nerve.** The letters and numbers refer to the spinal nerve that innervates a given dermatome. Dermatomes are generally bilaterally symmetrical.

Precision Graphics

## Grandfather's Shingles

The Davises were excited about their newborn twin boys and couldn't wait to take them to see Mr. Davis's father. Grandfather Davis was excited to see his first grandsons as well and thought their visit might help take his mind off the pain of his shingles, which had suddenly appeared only days before.

1. What virus is responsible for Grandfather Davis's shingles?

2. What likely triggered his case of shingles?

3. Are the new parents at risk of catching shingles from Grandfather Davis?

4. Are the newborns at risk of contracting shingles from their grandfather? If Mrs. Davis asked your advice about visiting her father-in-law with the twins, what would you recommend?

5. Could the twins be vaccinated against shingles before the visit?

Kenneth Probst

**HIGHLIGHT**

## REYE'S SYNDROME: CAN ASPIRIN HARM CHILDREN WITH VIRAL DISEASES?

In the 1900s, Dr. Ralph Reye, an Australian pathologist, observed an unusual syndrome that often followed viral infections of patients under 18 years of age. The syndrome's features include acute encephalopathy (a brain disorder), fatty infiltration of internal organs, rash, and vomiting. Confusion, coma, seizures, respiratory arrest, and death often occur in later stages of the syndrome. Reye's syndrome, as it has come to be known, has followed infections of DNA viruses such as varicella (chickenpox) and Epstein-Barr viruses, as well as those of RNA viruses such as influenzavirus. The cause of the syndrome is unknown, but it is often associated with the use of aspirin to treat symptoms of these viral infections. Consequently, it is recommended that aspirin not be used to treat fever or pain in children or adolescents, particularly when a viral cause is suspected.

Unlike the multiple recurrences of herpes simplex lesions, shingles only occurs once or twice in an individual's life, usually after age 45. Before vaccination became routine, the majority of children developed chickenpox, but only a small percentage of adults developed shingles, presumably because most individuals develop complete immunity to VZV following chickenpox and therefore never acquire shingles. The observation that VZV from the lesions of shingles can cause chickenpox in individuals who have not had chickenpox revealed that VZV causes both shingles and chickenpox.

### Diagnosis, Treatment, and Prevention of HHV-3 (VZV) Infections

Chickenpox is usually diagnosed from the characteristic appearance of the lesions. In contrast, it is sometimes difficult to distinguish shingles from other herpesvirus lesions, though the localization within a dermatome is characteristic. Antibody tests are available to verify diagnosis of VZV infection.

Uncomplicated chickenpox is typically self-limiting and requires no treatment other than relief of the symptoms with acetaminophen and antihistamines. Aspirin should not be given to children or adolescents with symptoms of chickenpox because of the risk of contracting Reye's syndrome, a condition associated with several viral diseases and aspirin usage (see **Highlight: Reye's Syndrome**).

Treatment of shingles involves management of the symptoms and bed rest. Nonadherent dressings and loose-fitting clothing may help prevent irritation of the lesions. Acyclovir provides relief from the painful rash for some patients, but it is not a cure.

It is difficult to prevent exposure to VZV because viruses are shed from patients before obvious signs appear. The U.S. Food and Drug Administration (FDA) has approved an attenuated vaccine, though the vaccine has caused some cases of shingles in Japan, and immunocompromised individuals are at risk of developing disease from the vaccine. Nevertheless, the benefits of vaccination appear to outweigh the risks, and the Centers for Disease Control and Prevention (CDC) recommends two doses of chickenpox vaccine for all children who are least one year old and for adults up to age 50 who do not have evidence of immunity to chickenpox. A single dose of shingles vaccine is recommended for all adults over age 60.

## Human Herpesvirus 4 (Epstein-Barr Virus) Infections

### Learning Objective

✓ Describe the diseases associated with Epstein-Barr virus.

A fourth human herpesvirus is *Epstein-Barr virus (EBV)*, which is in the genus *Lymphocryptovirus*. EBV is named after its codiscoverers. The official name for the species is *human herpesvirus 4*, or HHV-4.

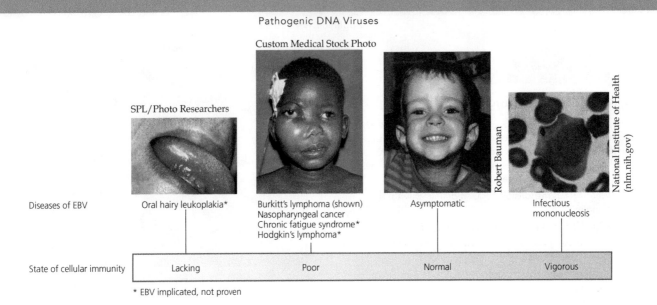

Diseases of EBV

SPL/Photo Researchers · Oral hairy leukoplakia*

Custom Medical Stock Photo · Burkitt's lymphoma (shown) Nasopharyngeal cancer Chronic fatigue syndrome* Hodgkin's lymphoma*

Asymptomatic

Robert Bauman

Infectious mononucleosis · National Institute of Health (nlm.nih.gov)

| State of cellular immunity | Lacking | Poor | Normal | Vigorous |
|---|---|---|---|---|

* EBV implicated, not proven

▲ **Figure 13 Diseases associated with Epstein-Barr virus.** Which disease results from infection with EBV appears to depend on the relative vigor of the host's cellular immune response, which itself can be related to age. Oral hairy leukoplakia, a precancerous change in the mucous membrane of the tongue, occurs in EBV-infected hosts with severely depressed cellular immunity (for example, AIDS patients). Burkitt's lymphoma, a cancer of the jaw, occurs primarily in African boys whose immune systems have been suppressed by the malaria parasite. Nasopharyngeal cancer is most common in China. EBV is implicated in Hodgkin's lymphoma and chronic fatigue syndrome, which also are associated with impaired immune function. Asymptomatic EBV infections are typical for children exposed at a young age, before the immune response has become vigorous. Infectious mononucleosis, which is characterized by enlarged B lymphocytes with lobed nuclei, results from infection with EBV during adulthood, when the cellular immune response is vigorous.

## Diseases Associated with HHV-4 (EBV) Infection

Like other herpesviruses, HHV-4 (EBV) is associated with a variety of diseases. First we consider two diseases EBV is known to cause—Burkitt's lymphoma and infectious mononucleosis—before discussing several other diseases for which EBV is implicated as a cause. As you read about the diseases with which EBV is associated, bear in mind that they are in part the result of the patient's immune status, which itself can be related to the patient's age.

In the 1950s, Denis Burkitt (1911–1993) described a malignant neoplasm of the jaw, primarily in African boys (Figure 13), that appeared to be infectious. This cancer is now known as **Burkitt's lymphoma.** Intrigued by the idea of an infectious cancer, Michael Epstein (1921–) and Yvonne Barr (1932–) cultured samples of the tumors and isolated Epstein-Barr virus, the first virus shown to be responsible for a human cancer.

Epstein-Barr virus also causes **infectious mononucleosis** (mon′ō-noo-klē-ō′sis) **(mono).** Discovery of the connection between EBV and mono was accidental. A laboratory technician who worked with EBV and Burkitt's lymphoma contracted mononucleosis while on vacation. Upon her return to work, her serum was found to contain antibodies against EBV antigens. Serological studies of large numbers of college students have provided statistical verification that EBV causes mono.

EBV is an etiological agent of *nasopharyngeal cancer* in patients from southern China and is implicated as a cause of *chronic fatigue syndrome* in the U.S. population, *oral hairy leukoplakia* in AIDS patients, and *Hodgkin's lymphoma.* Chronic fatigue syndrome is associated with debilitating fatigue, memory loss, and enlarged lymph nodes. Hairy leukoplakia is a precancerous change in the mucous membrane of the tongue. Hodgkin's lymphoma is a treatable cancer of B lymphocytes that spreads from one lymph node to another.

### CRITICAL **THINKING**

Whereas many doctors are convinced that Epstein-Barr virus causes chronic fatigue syndrome, others deny the association between EBV and the syndrome. Why is the etiology of chronic fatigue syndrome debated even though Epstein-Barr virus is present?

### Epidemiology and Pathogenesis of HHV-4 (EBV) Infections

Transmission of Epstein-Barr viruses usually occurs via saliva, often during the sharing of drinking glasses or while kissing. ("Kissing disease" is a common name for infectious mononucleosis.) After initially infecting the epithelial cells of the pharynx and parotid salivary glands, EBV virions enter the blood. In general, having viruses in the blood is called **viremia** (vī-rē′mē-ă).

EBV invades B lymphocytes,[7] becomes latent, and immortalizes the B cells by suppressing *apoptosis* (programmed cell death). Infected B cells are one source of lymphomas, including Burkitt's and Hodgkin's lymphomas.

Infectious mononucleosis results from a "civil war" between the humoral and cellular branches of specific immunity: cytotoxic T lymphocytes of the cell-mediated branch kill infected B lymphocytes. This "civil war" is responsible for the symptoms and signs of mono, including sore throat, fever, enlargement of the spleen and liver, and fatigue.

Seventy percent of Americans over the age of 30 have antibodies against EBV. As with other herpesviruses, the age of the host at the time of infection is a determining factor in the seriousness of the disease, in this case because the competence of cytotoxic T cells is in part related to age (see Figure 13). Infection during childhood, which is more likely to occur in countries with poor sanitation and inadequate standards of hygiene, is usually asymptomatic because a child's cellular immune system is immature and cannot cause severe tissue damage. Where living standards are higher, childhood infection is less likely, and the postponement of infection until adolescence or later results in a more vigorous cellular immune response that produces the signs and symptoms of mononucleosis.

Cofactors appear to play a role in the development of cancers by EBV. For example, Burkitt's lymphoma is almost exclusively limited to young males exposed to malaria parasites, and the restriction of EBV-induced nasopharyngeal cancer to certain geographical regions is suggestive of cofactors in food, environment, or the genes of regional populations.

Extreme disease, such as oral hairy leukoplakia, arises in individuals with a T cell deficiency, as occurs in malnourished children, the elderly, AIDS patients, and transplant recipients. These individuals are more susceptible to EBV because infected cells are not removed by cytotoxic T lymphocytes and therefore remain a site of virus proliferation.

### Diagnosis, Treatment, and Prevention of HHV-4 (EBV) Infections

Large, lobed, B lymphocytes with atypical nuclei and neutropenia are characteristic of EBV infection. Some diseases associated with EBV, such as hairy leukoplakia and Burkitt's lymphoma, are easily diagnosed by their characteristic signs. Other EBV infections, such as infectious mononucleosis, have symptoms common to many pathogens. Fluorescent antibodies directed against anti-EBV immunoglobulins or ELISA tests provide specific diagnosis.

Burkitt's lymphoma responds well to chemotherapy, and tumors can be removed from affected jaws of patients in geographic areas where surgery is available. Care of mono patients involves relief of the symptoms. Radiation or chemotherapy often successfully treats Hodgkin's lymphoma. There is no effective treatment for other EBV-induced conditions.

Prevention of EBV infection is almost impossible because the virus is widespread and transmitted readily in saliva. However, only a small proportion of EBV infections result in disease because the immune system is either too immature to cause cellular damage (in children) or cellular immunity is efficient enough to kill infected B lymphocytes.

## Human Herpesvirus 5 (Cytomegalovirus) Infections

### Learning Objective

✓ Describe the epidemiology of cytomegalovirus infection.

A fifth herpesvirus that affects humans is *Cytomegalovirus* (sī-tō-meg′ă-lō-vī′rŭs) (CMV), so called because cells infected with this virus become enlarged. *Cytomegalovirus* infection is one of the more common infections of humans. Studies have shown that 50% of the adult population of the United States is infected with CMV; in some other countries, 100% of the population tests positive for antibodies against CMV. Like other herpesviruses we have studied, HHV-5 becomes latent in various cells, and infection by CMV lasts for life.

### Epidemiology and Pathogenesis of HHV-5 (CMV) Infections

CMV is transmitted in bodily secretions, including saliva, mucus, milk, urine, feces, semen, and cervical secretions. Individual viruses are not highly contagious, so transmission requires intimate contact involving a large exchange of secretion. Transmission usually occurs via sexual intercourse, but can result from *in utero* exposure, vaginal birth, blood transfusions, and organ transplants. CMV infects 7.5% of all neonates, making it the most prevalent viral infection in this age group.

Most people infected with CMV are asymptomatic, but fetuses, newborns, and immunodeficient patients are susceptible to severe complications of CMV infection. About 10% of congenitally infected newborns develop signs of infection, including enlarged liver and spleen, jaundice, microcephaly, and anemia. CMV may also be **teratogenic**[8] (ter′ă-tō-jen′ik)—that is, cause birth defects—when the virus infects *stem cells*[9] in an embryo or fetus. In the worst cases, mental retardation, hearing and visual damage, or death may result.

AIDS patients and other immunosuppressed adults may develop pneumonia, blindness (if the virus targets the retina), or *cytomegalovirus mononucleosis*, which is similar to infectious mononucleosis caused by Epstein-Barr virus. CMV diseases result from initial infections or from latent viruses.

### Diagnosis, Treatment, and Prevention of HHV-5 (CMV) Infections

Diagnosis of CMV-induced diseases is dependent on laboratory procedures that reveal the presence of abnormally enlarged cells and inclusions within the nuclei of infected cells (Figure 14). Viruses and antibodies against them can be detected by ELISA

---

[7]These lymphocytes are also known as mononuclear leukocytes, from which the name mononucleosis is derived.
[8]From Greek *teratos*, meaning monster.
[9]Formative cells, the daughter cells of which develop into several different types of mature cells.

"Owls eye" cell

CDC

LM   |—100 µm|

▲ **Figure 14** **An owl's eye cell.** The cell is diagnostic for cytomegalovirus infection. Such abnormally enlarged cells have enlarged nuclei and contain inclusion bodies that are sites of viral assembly.

tests and DNA probes. Treatment for fetuses and newborns with complications of CMV infection is difficult because in most cases damage is done before an infection is discovered.

Treatment of adults can also be frustrating. Interferon and gammaglobulin treatment can slow the release of CMV from adults but does not affect the course of disease. Physicians inject fomivirsen into an infected eye to inhibit CMV replication in retinal cells. Fomivirsen is an RNA molecule complementary to CMV mRNA. It works by binding to the mRNA, preventing translation of polypeptides critical for CMV replication. This stops progression of disease but does not eliminate the infection. There is no vaccine for preventing infection.

Abstinence, mutual monogamy, and use of condoms can reduce the chances of infection. Organs harvested for transplantation can be made safe by treatment with monoclonal antibodies against CMV, which passively reduces the CMV load before the organs are transplanted.

## Other Herpesvirus Infections

### Learning Objective

✓ Describe the diseases that are associated with HHV-6 and HHV-8.

*Human herpesvirus 6* (HHV-6), in the genus *Roseolovirus,* causes **roseola** (rō-zē'ō'lă). Roseola is an endemic illness of children characterized by an abrupt fever, sore throat, enlarged lymph nodes, and a faint pink rash on the face, neck, trunk, and thighs (Figure 15). The name of the disease is derived from the rose-colored rash.

Some researchers have linked HHV-6 to multiple sclerosis (MS). These investigators point to the fact that over 75% of MS

Scott Camazine/Photo Researchers

▲ **Figure 15** **Roseola.** This rose-colored rash on the body results from infection with *human herpesvirus 6.*

patients have antibodies against the virus, that patients with higher antibody levels are more likely to develop MS later in life, and that the brain lesions of MS patients typically contain HHV-6. Further, MS patients respond well to treatment with interferon. This evidence is not proof of causation, but it provides tantalizing ideas for further research.

HHV-6 may also cause mononucleosis-like symptoms and signs, including enlargement of lymph nodes. There is some evidence that *human herpesvirus 6* may also be a cofactor in the pathogenesis of AIDS; that is, infection with HHV-6 may make individuals more susceptible to AIDS.

*Human herpesvirus 8 (HHV-8, Rhadinovirus)* causes Kaposi's sarcoma, a cancer often seen in AIDS patients (Figure 16). The virus is not found in cancer-free patients or in normal tissues of victims and has been shown to make cells lining blood vessels cancerous.

## *Papillomaviridae* and *Polyomaviridae*

Papillomaviruses and polyomaviruses each have a single molecule of double-stranded DNA contained in a small, naked, icosahedral capsid. They were previously classified in a single family, *Papovaviridae,* but have recently been separated into two families, *Papillomaviridae* and *Polyomaviridae,* based in part on the different diseases they cause.

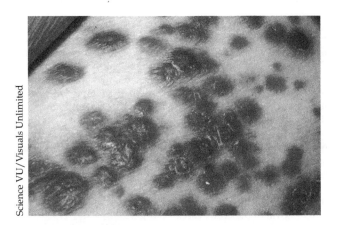

Science VU/Visuals Unlimited

▲ **Figure 16 Kaposi's sarcoma.** A rare and malignant neoplasia of blood and blood vessels, this cancer is most often seen in AIDS patients. *What observations support the hypothesis that Kaposi's sarcoma is caused by HHV-8?*

*cancerous.*
*in Kaposi tumor cells. The virus also causes some cells to become*
*HHV-8 is not found in healthy patients, but it is found* **Figure 16**

## Papillomavirus Infections

### Learning Objectives

✓ Describe four kinds of warts associated with papillomavirus infections.

✓ Describe the pathogenesis, treatment, and prevention of genital warts.

Papillomaviruses cause **papillomas** (pap-i-lō′măz), which are benign growths of the epithelium of the skin or mucous membranes commonly known as **warts.** Papillomas form on many body surfaces, but are most often found on the fingers or toes *(seed warts);* deep in the soles of the feet *(plantar warts);* on the trunk, face, elbow, or knees *(flat warts);* or on the external genitalia *(genital warts)* (Figure 17). Genital warts range in size from almost undetectable small bumps to giant, cauliflower-like growths called **condylomata acuminata**[10] (kon-di-lō′mah-tă ă-kyū-mi-nah′tă). Over 40 varieties of papillomaviruses cause warts in humans.

Although warts are often painful and unsightly, genital warts are even more distressing because of their association with an increased risk of cancer. Papillomaviruses of genital warts precipitate anal, vaginal, penile, and oral cancers, as well as nearly all cervical cancer. Papillomavirus infections appear to

---

[10]From Greek *kondyloma*, meaning knob, and Latin *acuminatus*, meaning pointed.

▶ **Figure 17 The various kinds of warts, the lesions caused by infections with papillomaviruses. (a)** Seed warts of the fingers. **(b)** Plantar warts on the sole of a foot. **(c)** Flat warts, which occur on the trunk, face, elbows, or knees. **(d)** Condylomata acuminata on a vulva. Such genital warts are considered precancerous.

(a)

Science VU/Visuals Unlimited

(b)

Hercules Robinson/Alamy

(c)

Photo Researchers

(d)

Biophoto Associates/Photo Researchers

## A Child with Warts

Ten-year-old Rudy has several large warts on the fingers of his right hand. They do not hurt, but their unsightly appearance causes him to shy away from people. He is afraid to shake hands, or to play with other children, out of fear that he may transfer the warts to them. Initially, his mother tells him not to worry about them, but Rudy cannot help feeling self-conscious. Furthermore, Rudy fears that the warts may somehow spread on his own body. After consulting with a physician, Rudy and his mother decide to have the warts surgically removed.

1. Is it possible that Rudy's warts will spread to other parts of his body?

2. Is it possible for someone else to "catch" Rudy's warts by shaking his hand?

3. If Rudy's warts disappear without treatment, are they likely to return to the same sites on his hand?

4. Are Rudy's warts likely to become cancerous?

5. Following surgical removal of the warts, is there a chance that Rudy will develop warts again?

double the risk of developing head and neck cancer and increase the risk of cancer in the tonsils fourteenfold.

### Epidemiology and Pathogenesis of Papillomavirus Infections

Papillomaviruses are transmitted via direct contact and, because they are stable outside the body, via fomites. They can also be spread from one location to another on a given person by a process called *autoinoculation.*

Viruses that cause genital warts invade the skin and mucous membranes of the penis (particularly when it is uncircumcised), vagina, and anus during sexual intercourse. The incubation time from infection to the development of the wart usually is three to four months. Genital warts are among the more common sexually transmitted diseases. Over 500,000 new cases are reported each year in the United States, most among young adults.

### Diagnosis, Treatment, and Prevention of Papillomavirus Infections

Diagnosis of warts is usually a simple matter of observation, though only DNA probes can elucidate the exact strain of papillomavirus involved. Warts usually regress over time as the cellular immune system recognizes and attacks virally infected cells. Cosmetic concerns and the pain associated with some warts may necessitate removing infected tissue via surgery, freezing, cauterization (burning), laser, or the use of caustic chemicals. These techniques are not entirely satisfactory because viruses may remain latent in neighboring tissue and produce new warts at a

later time. Laser surgery has the added risk of causing viruses to become airborne; some physicians have developed warts in their noses after inhaling airborne viruses during laser treatment. Over-the-counter remedies containing salicylic acid often reduce and remove warts. One of the stranger treatments is also one of the more effective—cover a wart with duct tape for several weeks, and it will likely disappear. Scientists do not know why this method works.

Effective treatment of cancers caused by papillomaviruses often depends on early diagnosis resulting from thorough inspection of the genitalia in both sexes, and in women by a Papanicolaou (Pap) smear to screen for cervical cancer. Treatment involves radiation or chemical therapy directed against reproducing tumor cells. Advanced cases of genital cancer necessitate removal of the entire diseased organ.

Prevention of most types of warts is difficult, but prevention of genital warts is possible by abstinence or mutual monogamy. Using recombinant DNA techniques, scientists have created a vaccine (Gardasil) that successfully prevents infection by the most common strains of sexually transmitted papillomaviruses, including the strains that cause most penile and cervical cancers. The CDC recommends three doses of HPV vaccine for all females 11–26 years of age.

The evidence for the effectiveness of condoms in preventing the spread of genital wart viruses is equivocal—one study suggests that condoms reduce the risk of acquiring genital warts by 25–50%, whereas other studies have revealed no decrease in the acquisition of warts by condom users or their partners. Researchers have found that circumcised men and their female sexual partners have about 35% less chance of getting genital cancer than do uncircumcised men or their partners. This research suggests that if all men were circumcised, the worldwide incidence of cervical cancer would be reduced at least 43%.

**Clinical Case Study: A Child with Warts** concerns a young patient with papillomas.

## Polyomavirus Infections

### Learning Objective

✓ Describe two diseases caused by polyomavirus infection in humans.

The search for cancer-causing viruses led scientists to the discovery of a group of viruses capable of causing several different tumors in animals and humans. Researchers named these viruses **polyomaviruses** by combining *poly* (meaning "many") and *oma* (meaning "tumor").

Polyomaviruses cause other diseases as well. Two human polyomaviruses, the *BK* and *JC* viruses, are endemic worldwide. The initials are derived from the names of the patients from which the viruses were first isolated. Most everyone appears to be infected with BK and JC by age 15, probably via the respiratory route. The viruses initially infect lymphocytes, and what happens subsequently depends at least in part on the state of an individual's immune system. If the immune response is normal, latent infections are typically prevented; if the immune

Spike

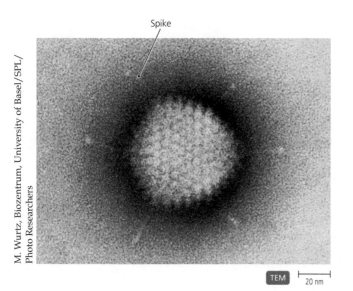

TEM    20 nm

▲ **Figure 18** **Adenovirus.** Notice the distinctive spikes.

M. Wurtz, Biozentrum, University of Basel/SPL/Photo Researchers

Dr. P. Marazzi/Photo Researchers

▲ **Figure 19** **Adenoviral conjunctivitis (pinkeye).** *What signs and symptoms can result from infections with various adenoviruses?*

**Figure 19** Respiratory adenoviruses cause sore throat, cough, fever, headache, and malaise; intestinal adenoviruses cause mild diarrhea in children; still other adenoviruses cause conjunctivitis (pinkeye).

system is compromised, however, then latent infections can become established in the kidneys, where reactivation of the viruses leads to the release of new virions. In the case of BK virus, the new virions can cause potentially severe urinary tract infections.

In individuals with latent infections of JC virus, reactivated virions are shed from kidney cells into the blood, spreading the virions throughout the body. Virions that reach the brain of an immunosuppressed individual cause a rare and fatal disease called **progressive multifocal leukoencephalopathy (PML),** in which the viruses infect and kill cells called oligodendrocytes in the white matter of the central nervous system. Oligodendrocytes produce myelin, a white lipid that surrounds and insulates some nerve cells. As myelin in multiple sites is lost, PML patients progressively lose various brain functions, as the name of the disease implies, because the conduction of nerve impulses becomes increasingly impaired. Vision, speech, coordination, and cognitive skills are affected. Eventually paralysis and death result.

Beta interferon treatments can prevent kidney damage by BK. The receptor for JC virus is a serotonin receptor, so researchers hope that serotonin receptor inhibitors will block JC virus. Unfortunately, by the time a diagnosis can be made, damage to the brain is often severe and irreversible.

## *Adenoviridae*

Learning Objective

✓ Discuss the epidemiology and pathogenicity of diseases caused by adenoviruses.

The last family of double-stranded DNA viruses we will discuss is *Adenoviridae.* Adenoviruses have a single, linear dsDNA

genome contained in a naked polyhedral capsid with spikes (Figure 18). Adenoviruses are so named because they were first discovered infecting cultures of human adenoid[11] cells.

Adenoviruses are but one of the many causative agents of "common colds." Even though colds typically have a common set of signs and symptoms, their causes are quite varied. At least 30 different respiratory adenoviruses (DNA viruses) and over 100 RNA viruses cause colds.

Adenoviruses, which are spread via respiratory droplets, are very stable outside the body and can survive on fomites and in improperly chlorinated drinking water. Respiratory adenovirus infections become established when adenoviruses are taken into cells lining the respiratory tract via endocytosis. The resulting infections have a variety of manifestations, including sneezing, sore throat, cough, headache, and malaise. For some reason, epidemics of respiratory adenoviruses occur on military bases but rarely under the similar conditions found in college dormitories.

Adenoviruses can also cause infections in other systems of the body. After entering cells lining the intestinal tract, intestinal adenoviruses can cause mild diarrhea in children. Still other adenoviruses infect the conjunctiva, resulting in conjunctivitis, which is also called *pinkeye* (Figure 19). Human adenovirus 36 is suspected of being a cause of obesity in humans. **Highlight: Catch a Cold and Catch Obesity** examines this interesting hypothesis.

Adenoviruses often produce semi-crystallized viral masses within the nuclei of infected cells (see Highlight box), a feature that is diagnostic for adenoviral infections. Although this feature

---

[11]Adenoids are swollen pharyngeal tonsils, which are masses of lymphatic tissue located in the pharynx, posterior to the nose.

## CATCH A COLD AND CATCH OBESITY?

Your roommate sneezes, and you get infected with obesity. Sound far-fetched? If researchers at Louisiana State University in Baton Rouge are correct, many cases of obesity may be blamed on adenoviruses—a family of DNA viruses more usually associated with common colds.

Researchers have shown that human adenovirus 36 (Ad-36) (and to a lesser extent its relatives Ad-37 and Ad-5) directly affects adipocytes (fat cells) in animals and humans. Ad-36 is present in about 30% of obese people but in only about 11% of the non-obese, and infected laboratory animals gain more weight than their identical siblings eating the same amount of food.

In identical human twins where one sibling is infected with Ad-36 and the other is not, the infected twins are heavier and fatter than their uninfected cotwins. At the cellular level, stem cells infected with Ad-36 more frequently become adipocytes than do uninfected stem cells, and infected adipocytes make and store more fat than uninfected fat cells.

Even more exciting than this circumstantial evidence, the researchers have shown that Ad-36 regulates a single gene in humans, a gene that is necessary and solely sufficient for fat production. Moreover, Ad-36 enhances a cell's ability to take up glucose, which can then be anabolized into fat and stored.

Perhaps someday soon, more effective anti-cold remedies may also help you lose weight.

▲ *Semi-crystalline masses of adenoviruses replicating in the nucleus of an infected cell.* TEM 800 nm

Frederick A. Murphy, University of Texas Medical Branch, Galveston

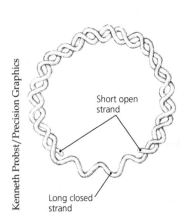

Kenneth Probst/Precision Graphics

Short open strand

Long closed strand

▲ **Figure 20  The genome of a hepadnavirus.** This unusual genome is composed of incompletely double-stranded DNA resulting from incomplete DNA replication.

is similar in appearance to the nuclear inclusions seen in cytomegalovirus infections, adenoviruses do not cause infected cells to enlarge.

Adenovirus infection can be treated during the early stages with gamma interferon, and a live, attenuated vaccine is available. The vaccine is used only for military recruits, because some adenoviruses of animals are known to be oncogenic, and there is concern about widespread use of a potentially oncogenic vaccine.

## Hepadnaviridae

Viruses of the family *Hepadnaviridae*[12] are enveloped DNA viruses with icosahedral capsids that invade and replicate in liver cells. From these characteristics, human **hepatitis B virus (HBV)** acquires the name of its genus, *Orthohepadnavirus*. Its scientific species name, *hepatitis B virus,* is also its common name.

The genome of a hepadnavirus is unique in that it is partly double-stranded DNA and partly single-stranded DNA (Figure 20). The amount of ssDNA in a hepadnaviral genome varies. Some virions are almost entirely dsDNA, whereas others have a significant amount of ssDNA. How does this variation in genomic structure occur?

HBV replicates through an RNA intermediary, a phenomenon that is unique among DNA viruses. During replication, one strand of the DNA genome of hepatitis B virus is transcribed into RNA by an enzyme called *reverse transcriptase*. This process is the opposite of normal transcription, thus the name of the enzyme. The RNA molecule then serves as a template for a new DNA strand. The result is an RNA-DNA hybrid molecule. Next, the RNA is removed and a DNA complement of the DNA strand is synthesized, forming dsDNA. Incomplete dsDNA results when virions are assembled before the complementary DNA strand is completely copied. Thus the earlier that assembly occurs, the more ssDNA will remain in the genome; the later that assembly occurs, the more complete replication will be, and the more dsDNA will be in the genome.

[12]From Greek *hepar,* meaning liver, and DNA.

▲ **Figure 21 Jaundice.** This condition is characterized by yellow skin and eyes. One cause of jaundice is liver damage by hepatitis B virus.

## Hepatitis B Infections

### Learning Objective

✓ Describe the epidemiology, treatment, and prevention of hepatitis B infections.

*Hepatitis* (hep-ă-tī′tis) is an inflammatory condition of the liver. The liver has many functions, including making blood-clotting factors, storing sugar and other nutrients, assisting in the digestion of lipids, and removing wastes from the blood. When a patient's liver is severely damaged by viral infection, all these functions are disturbed. **Jaundice** (jawn′dis), a yellowing of the skin and eyes, occurs when a greenish-yellow waste product called *bilirubin* accumulates in the blood (Figure 21). Hepatitis is also characterized by enlargement of the liver, abdominal distress, and bleeding into the skin and internal organs. The patient becomes stuporous and eventually goes into a coma as a result of the accumulation of nitrogenous wastes in the blood.

Hepatitis B virus is the only DNA virus that causes hepatitis; all other cases of viral hepatitis result from RNA viruses. Hepatitis B is also called *serum hepatitis.* HBV infection results in serious liver damage in less than 10% of cases, but co-infection with hepatitis D virus (an RNA virus also called *delta agent*) increases the risk of permanent liver damage.

### Epidemiology and Pathogenesis of HBV Infections

Hepatitis B viruses replicate in liver cells and are released by exocytosis rather than cell lysis. Infected liver cells thus serve as a source for the continual release of virions into the blood, resulting in billions of virions per milliliter of blood. Virions in the blood are shed into saliva, semen, and vaginal secretions.

HBV is transmitted when infected bodily fluids, particularly blood, come into contact with breaks in the skin or mucous membranes. The viral load is typically so high and the infective dose so low that infection can result from sharing a razor or toothbrush, making it difficult to determine the source

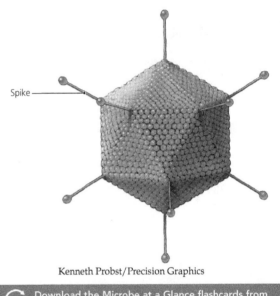
of infection. Improperly sterilized needles used in acupuncture, ear piercing, tattooing, intravenous drug usage, and blood transfusion have spread the virions, which can remain infective for at least a week outside the body. They may also be spread by sexual intercourse, especially anal intercourse, which can cause tearing of the rectal lining. Babies can become infected during childbirth.

Many infected individuals are asymptomatic, and most manifest only mild jaundice, low-grade fever, and malaise. Severe liver damage is most likely to result from such asymptomatic, chronic infections after 20–40 years. The CDC estimates that approximately 350 million people worldwide have chronic

Precision Graphics

▲ **Figure 22** **Estimated incidence of acute hepatitis B in the United States.**

infections. The carrier state is age related: newborns are much more likely to remain chronically infected than are individuals infected as adults.

Today, fewer cases of hepatitis B are seen in the United States as a result of vaccination programs and safer sexual practices (Figure 22). Still, approximately 3000 people die each year from hepatitis B infection.

## Diagnosis, Treatment, and Prevention of HBV Infections

Laboratory diagnosis of hepatitis B infection involves the use of labeled antibodies to detect the presence of viral antigens released from HBV-infected cells. The bodily fluids of infected individuals contain copious amounts of viral protein of three forms: so-called *Dane particles, spherical particles,* and *filamentous particles* (Figure 23). Dane particles are complete and infective virions, whereas spherical and filamentous particles are merely capsids composed of surface antigens without genomes. Within infected individuals, the release of so much excess viral surface antigen in the form of spherical and filamentous particles in effect serves as a decoy: the binding of antibody to empty capsids reduces the effective antibody response against infective Dane particles. The large amount of viral antigen released provides one benefit to a patient: it ensures a plentiful substrate for binding labeled antibodies in diagnostic tests.

There is no universally effective treatment for hepatitis B, though alpha interferon, lamivudine, or entecavir help in 40% of cases. Liver transplant is the only treatment for end-stage chronic hepatitis B.

Prevention is possible because an effective vaccine is available. Three doses of HBV vaccine result in protection against the virus in 95% of individuals. Several studies indicate that immunity against HBV lasts for at least 23 years, and probably for life. Vaccination is recommended for high-risk groups, including health care workers, illegal drug users, people receiving blood or blood products, and the sexually promiscuous, especially those who engage in anal intercourse. The CDC recommends HBV immunization for all children because children are at a greater risk of chronic infection, life-threatening liver damage, and (as we will see shortly) liver cancer.

To prevent the spread of HBV, special care should be taken with needles and other sharp instruments, especially in health care settings. Unlike most enveloped viruses, HBV is resistant to detergents, ether, freezing, acid, and moderate heat, but contaminated materials can be disinfected with 10% bleach solutions.

Linda Stanard/UCT/Photo Researchers

(a)

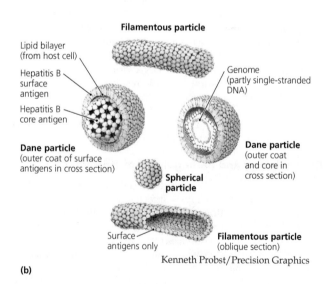

Kenneth Probst/Precision Graphics

(b)

▲ **Figure 23** **The three types of viral particles produced by hepatitis B viruses.** Dane bodies are complete virions, whereas filamentous particles and spherical particles are capsomeres that have assembled without genomes. **(a)** Micrograph. **(b)** Artist's rendition.

Abstinence or mutually faithful monogamy is the only sure way to prevent sexually transmitted infection.

## The Role of Hepatitis B Virus in Hepatic Cancer

### Learning Objective

✓ Describe evidence that hepatitis B virus causes hepatic cancer.

HBV has been shown to be associated with hepatic cancer based on the following evidence:

- Epidemiological studies reveal large numbers of hepatic cancer cases in geographic areas that also have a high prevalence of HBV.
- The HBV genome has been found integrated into hepatic cancer cells.
- Hepatic cancer cells typically express HBV antigen.
- Chronic carriers of HBV are 200 times more likely to develop hepatic cancer than are noncarriers.

How does HBV produce cancer? Perhaps the gap in the double strand of DNA allows HBV to easily integrate into the DNA of a liver cell, in the process possibly activating oncogenes or suppressing oncogene repressor genes. Another theory is that repair and cell growth in response to liver damage proceeds out of control, resulting in cancer. In any case, because of its association with HBV, hepatic cancer may become the first cancer eliminated as a result of vaccination.

## *Parvoviridae*

### Learning Objective

✓ Describe the pathogenesis of erythema infectiosum.

**Parvoviruses** are the only pathogens of humans with a single-stranded DNA (ssDNA) genome. They are also the smallest of the DNA viruses and have an icosahedral capsid. They cause a number of endemic diseases of animals, including a potentially fatal disease of puppies.

H. C. Robinson/Photo Researchers

▲ **Figure 24** **A case of erythema infectiosum (fifth disease).** Distinct reddening of facial skin that resembles the result of a slap is characteristic of this parvovirus-caused disease.

The primary parvovirus of humans is *B19 virus* in the genus *Erythrovirus,* which is the cause of **erythema infectiosum** (er-ĭ-thē′mă in-fek-shē-ō′sŭm), also known as **fifth disease** because it was the fifth childhood rash[13] on a 1905 list. Erythema infectiosum, as the name implies, is an infectious reddening of the skin, beginning on the cheeks (Figure 24) and appearing later on the arms, thighs, buttocks, and trunk. The rash is distinctive in appearance and usually sufficient for diagnosis. As the rash progresses, earlier lesions fade, though they can reappear if the patient is exposed to sunlight. Sunlight aggravates the eruptions at all stages. No treatment is available.

Table 2 summarizes features of DNA viruses of humans.

---

[13]The other four rashes are those of scarlet fever, rubella (German measles), roseola, and measles.

---

### COCAINE NO BRAINER

Cocaine addiction is a major health and societal problem in America. The drug allows the accumulation of a neurotransmitter that stimulates an intense sense of joy and feelings of increased confidence. Simply understood, addiction results when people sense a physical or mental need for the effect. Chemical agents have proved disappointing for treating cocaine addiction, but a microbe may change this state of affairs.

Scientists at the Scripps Research Institute in La Jolla, California, have engineered a filamentous bacteriophage that displays cocaine-binding antibodies on its surface. In the central nervous system, the phage absorbs cocaine, preventing the drug from interacting with neurons and mitigating the cocaine's effect. The scientists chose a bacteriophage to deliver the antibodies because bacteriophages can enter directly into the brain through the nose. Perhaps soon addicts can snort a treatment.

## TABLE 2 — Taxonomy and Characteristics of DNA Viruses of Humans

| Family | Strand Type | Enveloped or Naked | Capsid Symmetry | Size (diameter, nm) | Representative Genera (disease) |
|---|---|---|---|---|---|
| Poxviridae | Double | Enveloped | Complex | 200–300 | Orthopoxvirus (smallpox, cowpox), Molluscipoxvirus (molluscum contagiosum) |
| Herpesviridae | Double | Enveloped | Icosahedral | 150–200 | Simplexvirus—herpes, type 1 (fever blisters, respiratory infections, encephalitis), type 2 (genital infections), Varicellovirus (chickenpox), Lymphocryptovirus Epstein-Barr virus (infectious mononucleosis, Burkitt's lymphoma), Cytomegalovirus (birth defect), Roseolovirus (roseola) |
| Papillomaviridae | Double | Naked | Icosahedral | 45–55 | Papillomavirus (benign tumors, warts, cervical and penile cancers) |
| Polyomaviridae | Double | Naked | Icosahedral | 45–55 | Polyomavirus (progressive multifocal leukoencephalopathy) |
| Adenoviridae | Double | Naked | Icosahedral | 60–90 | Mastadenovirus (conjunctivitis, respiratory infections) |
| Hepadnaviridae | Partial single and partial double | Enveloped | Icosahedral | 42 | Orthohepadnavirus (hepatitis B) |
| Parvoviridae | Single | Naked | Icosahedral | 18–26 | Erythrovirus (fifth disease) |

# Chapter Summary

## Poxviridae

1. Poxviruses, among the largest of viruses, cause skin lesions that begin as flat, red **macules,** enlarge into **papules,** fill with clear fluid to become **vesicles,** and then become pus-filled **pustules,** also called **pocks** or **pox.** These crust over and may scar.

2. **Smallpox,** eradicated in nature by 1980, was caused by a poxvirus **(variola).** The smallpox virus strain commonly known as **variola minor** caused less-severe cases of smallpox than **variola major.** Governments maintain smallpox viruses in secure laboratories as research tools for studies in pathogenicity, vaccination and recombinant DNA technology, and as material for developing protection against bioterrorism attacks.

3. The poxvirus *Molluscipoxvirus* causes **molluscum contagiosum,** which results in tumorlike growths on the skin.

4. Although monkeypox and cowpox can infect humans, such infections are rare.

## Herpesviridae

1. Herpesviruses include viruses that cause fever blisters, genital herpes, chickenpox, shingles, mononucleosis, and cancer. Individual species are named **human herpesviruses 1** through **8 (HHV-1 through HHV-8).**

2. *Human herpesvirus 1* (HHV-1), which was known previously as herpes simplex type 1 (HSV-1), and *human herpesvirus 2* (HHV-2) (previously HSV-2) typically produce painful skin lesions on lips and genitalia, respectively. Oral herpes lesions are called **fever blisters** or **cold sores.**

3. HHV-1 and HHV-2 enter sensory nerve cells, where they may remain latent for years. Lesions recur in about two-thirds of patients in response to emotional stress, sunlight, immune suppression, or other factors that stimulate the latent viruses to reactivate.

4. **Ocular herpes** usually affects one eye to various degrees, from recurring discomfort and light sensitivity to blindness.

5. A **whitlow** is an inflamed blister resulting from infection of HHV-1 and HHV-2 via a cut or break in the skin.

6. Infections of HHV-1 and HHV-2 are usually treatable and are often preventable.

7. **Varicella (chickenpox)** in children and **herpes zoster (shingles)** in adults are both caused by *human herpesvirus 3,* which is also known as **varicella-zoster virus (VZV),** in the genus *Varicellovirus.* Skin lesions progress from macules to papules to vesicles to crusts. Latent viruses in the sensory nerves can be activated in adults by stress, age, or immune suppression.

8. **Burkitt's lymphoma** is an infectious cancer caused by *human herpesvirus 4,* which is also known as Epstein-Barr virus (EBV). This herpesvirus also causes **infectious mononucleosis (mono).** EBV is also implicated in chronic fatigue syndrome, Hodgkin's lymphoma, nasopharyngeal cancer, and in hairy leukoplakia seen in AIDS patients.

9. The *human herpesvirus 5,* cytomegalovirus (CMV), causes infected cells to enlarge. This virus is widespread, transmitted by bodily secretions, and often asymptomatic, though infections in immunosuppressed adults and congenitally infected newborns can be severe and may be fatal.

10. *Human herpesvirus 6 (HHV-6)* causes **roseola,** a rose-colored rash on the face of children.

11. HHV-7 is an orphan virus; that is, it causes no known disease.

12. *Human herpesvirus 8 (HHV-8)* causes Kaposi's sarcoma, a cancer often seen in AIDS patients.

## Papillomaviridae and Polyomaviridae

1. A **wart,** also known as a **papilloma,** is a benign growth of epithelium or mucous membrane caused by a papillomavirus. Seed warts are most often found on fingers or toes; plantar warts on the soles of the feet; flat warts on the trunk, face, elbow, or knees; and genital warts on the external genitalia. **Condylomata acuminata** are large, cauliflower-like genital warts.

2. **Polyomaviruses,** such as BK and JC viruses, infect the kidneys of most people, but cause disease only in immunosuppressed patients. In these cases, BK viruses compromise kidney function, and JC viruses cause **progressive multifocal leukoencephalopathy (PML),** which results in severe, irreversible brain damage.

## Adenoviridae

1. Adenoviruses are one cause of the "common cold" and a cause of one form of conjunctivitis (pinkeye).

## Hepadnaviridae

1. Hepadnaviruses are unique in being partially dsDNA and partially ssDNA—a condition resulting from incomplete DNA replication involving an RNA intermediary.

2. **Hepatitis B virus (HBV)** infects the liver, is transmitted in blood and other bodily fluids, and is the only DNA virus that causes **hepatitis.** A vaccine against HBV is available, but no treatment is universally acceptable.

3. HBV is implicated as a cause of liver cancer.

## Parvoviridae

1. **Parvoviruses,** the only genus of human pathogens with ssDNA genomes, include a virus that causes a fatal disease in puppies, and *B19 virus,* which causes **erythema infectiosum (fifth disease),** a harmless red rash occurring in children.

# Questions for Review

Answers to the Questions for Review (except Short Answer questions) appear at the end of this chapter.

## Multiple Choice

1. DNA viruses in which of the following families are relatively large and thus potentially well suited for vaccinations and the introduction of genetic material in gene therapy?
   a. *Herpesviridae*
   b. *Poxviridae*
   c. *Papillomaviridae*
   d. *Hepadnaviridae*

2. For which of the following reasons are most animal poxviruses unable to infect humans?
   a. Affected animals are not in frequent contact with humans.
   b. The human immune system makes it impossible for the foreign viral particles to reproduce effectively.
   c. Attachment to human cells is unlikely.
   d. Human cells lack the necessary enzymes for infection.

3. The initial flat, red skin lesions of poxviruses are called
   a. macules.
   b. papules.
   c. pustules.
   d. pocks.

4. Which of the following statements is true concerning variola major?
   a. It carries a mortality rate of less than 1%.
   b. It affects internal organs before appearing on the skin.
   c. It has been totally eradicated from the Earth.
   d. The skin lesions it causes are smooth, waxy, tumorlike nodules on the face.

5. Which of the following herpesvirus infections would be potentially most serious?
   a. a whitlow
   b. ocular herpes
   c. shingles
   d. cytomegalovirus in fetuses

6. A man experienced a laboratory accident in which he was infected with adenovirus. What signs or symptoms might he exhibit?
   a. fever
   b. headache
   c. cough
   d. pinkeye
   e. all of the above

7. Which of the following is an inflammatory condition of the liver?
   a. fifth disease
   b. PML
   c. seed warts
   d. hepatitis

8. Which of the following statements is *false?*
   a. B19 virus is the primary parvovirus of humans.
   b. Erythema infectiosum is caused by a parvovirus.
   c. In children, parvovirus infections are accompanied by a high mortality rate.
   d. Parvovirus infection in humans results in infectious reddening of the skin.

9. A distinguishing feature of poxvirus is
   a. its large size.
   b. a polyhedral capsid.
   c. the type of RNA it contains.
   d. the production of several types of warts.

10. Monkeypox has been diagnosed in several humans in Zaire. What might be recommended to prevent further risk of infection?
    a. Catch the monkeys for inoculation with monkeypox vaccine and then release them.
    b. Remove infected tissues from humans with chemicals, by surgery, or by freezing.
    c. Reinstate smallpox vaccinations for the population of Zaire.
    d. The diagnosis must have been incorrect, because humans are unaffected by monkeypox.

11. Which of the following viral families is most likely to contain viruses that exist in a latent state in humans?
    a. *Herpesviridae*
    b. *Poxviridae*
    c. *Adenoviridae*
    d. *Parvoviridae*

12. If the envelope of a particular virus were unstable outside the host's body, which of the following statements would you expect to be true concerning this virus?
    a. It would be a dsRNA virus.
    b. It would be transmitted by intimate contact.
    c. Touching a doorknob would easily transmit it.
    d. That virus would eventually cease to be a threat to the population.

13. Being habitually careful not to touch or rub your eyes with unwashed hands would reduce your risk of contracting
    a. chickenpox.
    b. infectious mononucleosis.
    c. seed warts.
    d. a cold.

14. *Human herpesvirus 2*
    a. can cause genital herpes.
    b. may infect a baby at birth.
    c. causes about 10% of cold sores.
    d. all of the above

15. Which of the following viruses is latent and can reactivate to cause further disease?
    a. herpesvirus
    b. papillomavirus
    c. adenovirus
    d. parvovirus

## Labeling

Label the successive stages of skin lesions as exemplified by smallpox.

1. _____

2. _____

3. _____

4. _____

5. _____

6. _____

Kenneth Probst/Precision Graphics

## Short Answer

1. The Smith family seems to get fever blisters regularly. Suggest an explanation for this observation.

2. You have been given a large grant to do postgraduate research on live smallpox viruses. Where in the world would you find samples?

3. What was the difference in the effects of variola major and variola minor?

4. What observation led scientists to understand the relationship between shingles and chickenpox?

5. Most of the world's population has been infected with EBV by age 1 and shows no ill effects, even where medical care is poor. In contrast, individuals in industrialized countries are ordinarily infected after puberty, and these older patients tend to have more severe reactions to infection despite better overall health and access to medical care. Explain this apparent paradox.

## Matching

In each of the blanks beside the diseases in the left column, write the letter of the viral family to which that disease's causative agent belongs. Answers may be used more than once.

____ Chickenpox

____ Smallpox

____ Cowpox

____ Molluscum contagiosum

____ HHV-1 infection

____ Whitlow

____ Shingles

____ Burkitt's lymphoma

____ Infectious mononucleosis

____ Chronic fatigue syndrome

____ Cytomegalovirus infection

____ Genital warts

____ Roseola

____ Plantar warts

____ Progressive multifocal leukoencephalopathy

____ Common cold

____ Hepatitis B

____ Fifth disease

A. *Poxviridae*

B. *Herpesviridae*

C. *Papillomaviridae*

D. *Adenoviridae*

E. *Hepadnaviridae*

F. *Parvoviridae*

G. *Polyomaviridae*

# Concept Mapping

Using the following terms, draw a concept map that describes herpesvirus.
Or, complete this concept map online by going to the Study Area at www.masteringmicrobiology.com.

Acyclovir
Cold sores
dsDNA
Envelope
Fever blisters

Finger infection
Genital herpes
Gingivostomatitis
Herpetic whitlow
Human herpesvirus-1

Human herpesvirus-2
Latency
Life-threatening
Neonatal herpes
Ocular herpes

Oral herpes
Polyhedral capsid
Primary infection
Recurrences
*Simplexvirus*

# Critical Thinking

1. Most DNA viruses replicate within nuclei of host cells, using host enzymes to replicate their DNA. In contrast, poxviruses replicate in the cytoplasm. What problem does this create for poxvirus replication? How could the virus overcome this problem?

2. Mrs. Rathbone called the pediatrician concerning her young daughter Rene, who had a rosy facial rash and coldlike sniffles for two weeks. What is the most likely cause of Rene's problem?

3. Certain features of smallpox viruses allowed them to be eradicated in nature. Which other DNA viruses are suitable candidates for eradication, and what features of their biology make them suitable candidates?

4. A 10-year-old girl at summer camp complains of fever, runny nose, cough, sore throat, and tiredness. Within several hours, 36 other girls report to the infirmary with the same signs and symptoms. Although the girls were assigned to several different cabins and ate in two different dining halls, all of them had participated in outdoor archery, had gone horseback riding, and had been swimming in the camp pool. Infection with what DNA virus could account for their symptoms? The facts point to a common source of infection; what is it? What could the camp management do to limit such an outbreak in the future?

5. A week after spending their vacation rafting down the Colorado River, all five members of the Chen family developed cold sores on their lips. Their doctor told them that the lesions were caused by a herpesvirus. Mr. and Mrs. Chen were stunned: Isn't herpes a sexually transmitted disease? How could it have affected their young children?

 **Mastering MICROBIOLOGY**™

Access more review material online in the Study Area at **www.masteringmicrobiology.com.** There, you'll find
- **Concept Mapping Activities**
- **Flashcards**
- **Quizzes**

and more to help you succeed.

# Answers

Answers to multiple-choice, fill-in-blank, labeling, matching, and true/false questions are listed here. Answers for Short Answer and Critical Thinking questions are available for instructors only in the Instructor's Manual that accompanies this text.

**Multiple Choice**
1. b; 2. c; 3. a; 4. b; 5. d; 6. e; 7. d; 8. c; 9. a; 10. c; 11. a; 12. b; 13. d; 14. d; 15. a

**Labeling**
See Figure 2.

**Matching**
B Chickenpox; A Smallpox; A Cowpox; A Molluscum contagiosum; B HHV-1; B Whitlow; B Shingles; B Burkitt's lymphoma; B Infectious mononucleosis; B Chronic fatigue syndrome; B Cytomegalovirus; C Genital warts; B Roseola; C Plantar warts; G Progressive multifocal leukoencephalopathy; D Common cold; E Hepatitis B; F Fifth disease

# Pathogenic RNA Viruses

From Chapter 25 of *Microbiology with Diseases by Taxonomy*, Third Edition. Robert W. Bauman. Copyright © 2011 by Pearson Education, Inc. Published by Benjamin Cummings, Inc. All rights reserved.

# Pathogenic RNA Viruses

A patient lies delirious and near death in an African hospital, **bleeding** from his eyes and gums and into his digestive tract as a result of Marburg hemorrhagic fever. An AIDS patient in Europe continues his expensive daily "cocktail" of antiviral drugs. Passengers on a cruise ship suffering from severe diarrhea wish they had never eaten food infected with **noroviruses**. Thousands of people around the world go to bed with fever, sore throat, cough, and malaise, hoping to survive the flu season.

What do these diseases have in common? They are all caused by viruses that use RNA as their genetic material. The manifestations of RNA viral infection are widely variable and pose great challenges in diagnosis, treatment, and prevention. Although RNA viruses can also cause diseases in animals and plants, in this chapter we will focus on RNA viruses that cause human diseases.

 **Take the pre-test for this chapter online. Visit the Study Area at www.masteringmicrobiology.com.**

Scott Camazine / Alamy

The filamentous Marburg virus, which is native to Africa, causes usually fatal hemorrhaging (bleeding).

Recall from previous chapters that all cells and all DNA viruses use DNA as their genetic material. In contrast, RNA viruses and viroids are the only agents that use RNA molecules to store their genetic information.

There are four basic types of RNA viruses:

- Positive single-stranded RNA (+ssRNA) viruses
- Retroviruses (which are +ssRNA viruses that convert their genome to DNA once they are inside a cell)
- Negative single-stranded RNA (−ssRNA) viruses
- Double-stranded RNA (dsRNA) viruses

Recall that positive RNA is RNA that can be used by a ribosome to translate protein; it is essentially mRNA. Negative RNA cannot be processed by a ribosome; it must first be transcribed as mRNA. In addition to grouping RNA viruses by the kind of RNA they contain, scientists also note that many RNA viruses have more than one molecule of RNA—in other words, their genomes are *segmented*.

RNA viruses of humans are categorized into 15 families on the basis of:

- Their genomic structure
- The presence of an envelope
- The size and shape of their capsid

Positive single-stranded RNA viruses of humans are classified into eight families: *Picornaviridae, Caliciviridae, Astroviridae, Hepeviridae, Togaviridae, Flaviviridae, Coronaviridae,* and *Retroviridae.* Negative single-stranded RNA viruses are in six families: *Paramyxoviridae, Rhabdoviridae, Filoviridae, Orthomyxoviridae, Bunyaviridae,* and *Arenaviridae.* The only family containing double-stranded RNA viruses is *Reoviridae.* We begin our discussion of pathogenic RNA viruses by considering four families of positive ssRNA viruses that lack envelopes.

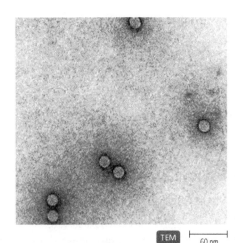

▲ **Figure 1 Rhinoviruses, the most common cause of colds.** The viruses are able to infect microvilli of nasal cells despite the layer of mucus. *What other types of viruses cause common colds?*

*Figure 1 Besides rhinoviruses (in the family Picornaviridae), adenoviruses, coronaviruses, reoviruses, and paramyxoviruses cause colds.*

Caliciviruses, astroviruses, and hepeviruses are generally larger than picornaviruses (27–40 nm in diameter) and have a six-pointed star shape; they cause gastrointestinal diseases.

In the following sections we will consider in turn three diseases caused by picornaviruses—common cold, polio, and hepatitis A—before examining diseases caused by caliciviruses, astroviruses, and hepeviruses.

## Common Colds Caused by Rhinoviruses

### Learning Objective

✓ Discuss treatment of the common cold.

Many Americans sniffle and sneeze their way through at least two colds each year. Though the symptoms of all colds are similar—sneezing, *rhinorrhea* (runny nose), congestion, mild sore throat, headache, malaise, and cough for 7–10 days—there is no single common cause of the "common cold." Rather, many different viruses, including picornaviruses, adenoviruses, coronaviruses, reoviruses, and paramyxoviruses, cause colds. However, the over 100 *serotypes* (varieties) of picornaviruses in the genus *Rhinovirus*, commonly known as **rhinoviruses**[2] (rī'nō-vī'rŭs-ĕz), cause most colds (Figure 1). Table 1 compares the symptoms of colds and other respiratory infections.

# Naked, Positive ssRNA Viruses: *Picornaviridae, Caliciviridae, Astroviridae,* and *Hepeviridae*

The families *Picornaviridae, Caliciviridae, Astroviridae,* and *Hepeviridae* contain positive single-stranded RNA viruses with naked polyhedral capsids. The family *Picornaviridae* is a large viral family containing many human pathogens, including viruses that cause common colds, poliomyelitis, and hepatitis A. Picornaviruses range in size from 22–30 nm in diameter, making them the smallest of animal viruses. Five hundred million picornaviruses could sit side by side on the head of a pin. Their small size and RNA genome is reflected in the name, **picornavirus**[1] (pi-kōr-nă-vī'rus). Representative picornaviruses that cause human diseases are in the genera *Rhinovirus, Enterovirus,* and *Hepatovirus.*

[1]From Latin *pico*, meaning small, and RNA virus.
[2]From Greek *rhinos*, meaning nose.

## TABLE 1 — Manifestations of Respiratory Infections

| Ailment | Manifestations |
| --- | --- |
| Common cold (viral) | Sneezing, rhinorrhea, congestion, sore throat, headache, malaise, cough |
| Influenza (viral) | Fever, rhinorrhea, headache, body aches, fatigue, dry cough, pharyngitis, congestion |
| "Strep" throat (bacterial) | Fever, red and sore throat, swollen lymph nodes in neck |
| Viral pneumonia | Fever, chills, mucus-producing cough, headache, body aches, fatigue |
| Bacterial pneumonia | Fever, chills, congestion, cough, chest pain, rapid breathing, and possible nausea and vomiting |
| Bronchitis (viral or bacterial) | Mucus-producing cough, wheezing |
| Inhalation anthrax (bacterial) | Fever, malaise, cough, chest discomfort, vomiting |
| Severe acute respiratory syndrome (SARS) | High fever (>38°C), chills, shaking, headache, malaise, myalgia |

## Epidemiology of *Rhinovirus* Infections

Rhinoviruses are limited to infecting the upper respiratory tract. They replicate best at a temperature of 33°C, which is the temperature of the nasal cavity.

Rhinoviruses are extremely infective—entry of a single virus into a person is sufficient to cause a cold in 50% of individuals. Symptomatic or not, an infected person can spread viruses by releasing them into the surrounding environment, where they are transmitted in aerosols produced by coughing or sneezing, via fomites (nonliving carriers of pathogens), or via hand-to-hand contact. Direct person-to-person contact is the most common means of transmitting these infections.

When cold symptoms are most severe, over 100,000 virions may be present in each milliliter of nasal mucus. They remain viable for hours outside the body. Infection often results from inoculation by hand into the mucous membranes of the eyes, where the viruses are washed by tears into the nasal cavity and readily infect nasal cells.

Although people of all ages are susceptible to rhinoviruses, people acquire some immunity against serotypes that have infected them in the past. For this reason, children typically have six to eight colds per year, younger adults have two to four, and adults over age 60 have one or fewer. An isolated population may acquire a certain amount of *herd immunity* to specific varieties of rhinoviruses; however, new serotypes introduced into the population by outsiders or by mutations in the RNA of the viruses ensure that no group is free of all colds.

## Diagnosis, Treatment, and Prevention of *Rhinovirus* Infections

The manifestations of rhinoviruses are usually diagnostic (see Table 1), and laboratory tests are required only if the serotype is to be identified.

While many home remedies and over-the-counter medicines exist to treat the common cold, none prevents colds or provides a cure. Studies of one "cure"—large amounts of vitamin C—have yielded conflicting results: some studies indicate no benefit, whereas others suggest a slight benefit for patients who are treated with vitamin C. A prescription remedy, pleconaril, taken at the onset of symptoms, reduces the seriousness and duration of colds caused by rhinoviruses. Antihistamines, decongestants, and pain relievers relieve the symptoms but do not reduce the duration of the disease. Rest and fluids allow the body to mount an effective immune response.

Because rhinoviruses do not share any common antigens that are accessible to the immune system, an effective vaccine for the common cold would have to immunize against hundreds of serotypes, which is impractical. Antisepsis is probably the most important preventive measure, especially if you have touched the hands of an infected person. Disinfection of fomites is also effective in limiting the spread of colds.

### CRITICAL THINKING

As you have probably noticed, colds occur more frequently in the fall and winter. One explanation for this observation is that more people are crowded together in buildings when school starts and the weather cools. Design an experiment or epidemiological survey to test the hypothesis that crowded conditions explain the prevalence of colds in the fall and winter.

## Diseases of Enteroviruses

### Learning Objectives

✓ Describe the effects of polioviruses on humans.

✓ Describe the contributions of Jonas Salk and Albert Sabin toward eliminating polio.

✓ Compare and contrast the diseases caused by coxsackieviruses and echoviruses.

A second genus of picornaviruses is *Enterovirus*. Contrary to their name, *enteroviruses* do not usually cause diseases of the digestive system. They infect the pharynx and intestine, where they multiply in the mucosa and lymphatic tissue without causing symptoms. Instead, enteroviruses are so named because they are transmitted via the fecal-oral route. Enteroviruses spread from their initial sites of infection through the blood (viremia) and infect different target cells, depending on the particular virus. Enteroviruses are cytolytic,[3] killing their host cells. The clinical manifestations of enteroviruses depend on the viral serotype, the size of the infecting dose, the target organ, and the

---

[3]From Greek *cytos*, meaning cell, and *lysis*, meaning dissolution.

Corbis

▲ **Figure 2** **A hospital ward full of mechanical respirators.** These "iron lungs" assisted the paralyzed respiratory muscles of polio patients and were common before 1955.

patient's health, gender, and age. There are three main types of enteroviruses: polioviruses, coxsackieviruses, and echoviruses.

## Poliomyelitis

Many Americans still remember the dreaded **poliomyelitis** (pō'lē-ō-mī'ĕ-lī'tis), or **polio,** epidemics of the past, when the floors of hospitals were filled with iron lungs (Figure 2) and schoolchildren donated their change to the March of Dimes to develop a polio vaccine. Because polioviruses are stable for prolonged periods in swimming pools and lakes and can be acquired by swallowing contaminated water, parents in the 1930s and 1940s often feared to let their children swim. Thankfully, those days appear to be over. The last case of wild-type poliomyelitis in the Americas occurred in 1979 (though vaccine-induced polio occurred as recently as 2001). The World Health Organization (WHO) has worked for years to eradicate polio worldwide (Figure 3). Then, like smallpox virus, poliovirus will exist only in laboratories.

There are three serotypes of poliovirus. After being ingested and infecting pharyngeal and intestinal cells, any of these serotypes could cause one of the following four conditions:

- *Asymptomatic* infections. Most infections (almost 90%) are asymptomatic.
- *Minor polio,* which includes nonspecific symptoms such as temporary fever, headache, malaise, and sore throat. Approximately 5% of cases are minor polio.
- *Nonparalytic polio,* resulting from polioviruses invading the meninges and central nervous system, producing muscle spasms and back pain in addition to the general symptoms of minor polio. Nonparalytic polio occurs in about 2% of cases.
- *Paralytic polio,* in which the viruses invade cells of the spinal cord and motor cortex of the brain, producing paralysis by limiting nerve impulse conduction. The degree of paralysis varies with the type of poliovirus involved, the infective dose, and the health and age of the patient. In **bulbar poliomyelitis,** the brain stem and medulla are infected, resulting in paralysis of muscles in the limbs or of respiratory muscles, in which case iron lungs were used to assist in respiration. In most paralytic cases, complete recovery resulted after 6–24 months, but in some cases paralysis was lifelong. Paralytic polio occurs in less than 2% of infections. Famous victims of paralytic polio include novelist Sir Walter Scott, President Franklin Delano Roosevelt, and violinist Itzhak Perlman (Figure 4).

*Postpolio syndrome* is a crippling deterioration in the function of polio-affected muscles that occurs in up to 80% of recovered polio patients some 30–40 years after their original bout with poliomyelitis. This condition is not caused by a reemergence of polioviruses, as viruses are not present. Instead, the effects appear to stem from an aging-related aggravation of nerve damage that occurred during the original infection.

The near elimination of polio stands as one of the great achievements of 20th-century medicine. It was made possible by the development of two effective vaccines. Jonas Salk (1914–1995) developed an **inactivated polio vaccine (IPV)** in 1955. Six years later, it was replaced in the United States by a live, attenuated, **oral polio vaccine (OPV)** developed by Albert Sabin (1906–1993). Both vaccines are effective in providing immunity against all three strains of poliovirus, though OPV occasionally

▶ **Figure 3** **Reports of naturally occurring polio in the first quarter of 2009.** The goal of global eradication of polio is within reach.

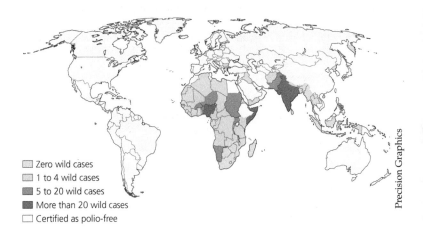

☐ Zero wild cases
☐ 1 to 4 wild cases
☐ 5 to 20 wild cases
■ More than 20 wild cases
☐ Certified as polio-free

Precision Graphics

493

Kathy Willnes/AP Images

P. Marazzi/SPL/Photo Researchers

(a)

(b)

P. Marazzi/SPL/Photo Researchers

mutates into a virulent form and causes polio. Table 2 compares the advantages and disadvantages of the two vaccines.

## CRITICAL **THINKING**

Smallpox is the only disease that has been eradicated worldwide, though scientists are close to eradicating polio. What features do the smallpox and polio viruses share that has allowed medical science to rid the world of these diseases? Compare these features to those of rhinoviruses in discussing the likelihood of eliminating colds caused by rhinoviruses.

## Other Diseases of Enteroviruses

The other enteroviruses that cause human disease are **coxsack-ieviruses**[4] and **echoviruses.** As with all enteroviruses, infection is by the fecal-oral route. Most infections are subclinical or result in mild fever, muscle aches, and malaise. There are two types of coxsackieviruses (type A and type B), each with several serotypes, as well as numerous serotypes of echoviruses, which cause a variety of human diseases.

**Coxsackieviruses** Coxsackie **A** viruses are associated with lesions and fever that last for a few days to weeks and are self-limiting. Several serotypes cause lesions of the mouth and pharynx called *herpangina* because of their resemblance to herpes lesions. Sore throat, pain in swallowing, and vomiting accompany herpangina.

▲ **Figure 5** **Lesions characteristic of hand-foot-and-mouth disease.** The malady is caused by a coxsackie A virus. **(a)** Lesions on the hard palate (roof of the mouth). **(b)** Lesions on a hand. *Why are coxsackieviruses considered enteroviruses when they do not cause infections of the gastrointestinal tract?*

**Figure 5** *All enteroviruses, including coxsackievirus, are infective through the gastrointestinal tract, though they may affect other organ systems.*

Another serotype of coxsackie A virus causes *hand-foot-and-mouth disease,* an apt name because it involves lesions on the extremities and in the mouth (Figure 5). Yet another coxsackie A virus causes an extremely contagious *acute hemorrhagic conjunctivitis.* Coxsackie A viruses also cause some colds.

**Coxsackie B** viruses are associated with *myocarditis* (inflammation of the heart muscle) and *pericardial*[5] *infections.* The symptoms in young adults may resemble myocardial infarction (heart

---

[4]From Coxsackie, New York, where the virus was first isolated.
[5]The pericardium is the membrane that surrounds and protects the heart.

## TABLE 2

## Comparison of Polio Vaccines

| | Advantages | Disadvantages |
|---|---|---|
| **Salk vaccine:** **Inactivated polio vaccine (IPV)** | Is effective and inexpensive; is stable during transport and storage; poses no risk of vaccine-related disease | Requires booster to achieve lifelong immunity; is injected and can be painful; requires higher community vaccination rate than does OPV |
| **Sabin vaccine:** **Oral polio vaccine (OPV)** | Induces secretory antibody response similar to natural infection; is easy to administer; can result in herd immunity | Requires boosters to achieve immunity; is more expensive than IPV; is less stable than IPV; can mutate to disease-causing form; poses risk of polio developing in immunocompromised patients |

**3**

## Comparison of Hepatitis Viruses

| Feature | Hepatitis A | Hepatitis B | Hepatitis C | Hepatitis D | Hepatitis E |
|---|---|---|---|---|---|
| Common names of disease | Infectious hepatitis | Serum hepatitis | Non-A, non-B hepatitis; chronic hepatitis | Delta agent hepatitis | Hepatitis E, enteric hepatitis |
| Virus family | *Picornaviridae* | *Hepadnaviridae* | *Flaviviridae* | *Arenaviridae* | *Hepeviridae* |
| Genome | +ssRNA | dsDNA | +ssRNA | −ssRNA | +ssRNA |
| Envelope? | Naked | Enveloped | Enveloped | Enveloped | Naked |
| Transmission | Fecal-oral | Needles; sex | Needles; sex | Needles; sex | Fecal-oral |
| Severity (mortality rate) | Mild (<0.5%) | Occasionally severe (1–2%) | Usually subclinical (0.5–4%) | Requires coinfection with hepatitis B virus; may be severe (high) | Mild (1–2%) except in pregnant women (20%) |
| Chronic carrier state? | No | Yes | Yes | No | No |
| Other disease associations | — | Hepatic cancer | Hepatic cancer | Cirrhosis | — |

attack), though fever is associated with a coxsackie infection. Newborns are particularly susceptible to coxsackie B myocarditis resulting in a rapid onset of heart failure with a high mortality rate.

One type of coxsackie B virus causes *pleurodynia* (ploor-ō-din′ē-ă), also known as *devil's grip*. This disease involves the sudden onset of fever and unilateral, severe, low thoracic pain, which may be excruciating. Coxsackie B virus can be transmitted across a placenta to produce severe and sometimes fatal disseminated disease of the brain, pancreas, and liver in the fetus. Infection of the pancreas by coxsackie B is suspected to be a cause of *diabetes mellitus* because the viruses destroy cells in the islets of Langerhans that produce insulin.

Both coxsackie A and B viruses can cause *viral meningitis*, an acute disease accompanied by headache and, with type A infections, a skin rash. Coxsackievirus meningitis is usually self-limiting and uneventful unless the patient is less than one year old.

**Echoviruses** The name *echovirus* is derived from *enteric cytopathic human orphan* virus, because these viruses are acquired intestinally and were not initially associated with any disease—they were *orphan viruses*. It is now known that echoviruses cause viral meningitis and some colds.

### Epidemiology of *Enterovirus* Infections

Enteroviruses have a worldwide distribution and occur particularly in areas with inadequate sewage treatment. Transmission is by the fecal-oral route involving ingestion of contaminated food or water or oral contact with infected hands or fomites. For some reason, enterovirus diseases are more common in summer.

As we have seen, enteroviruses pose the greatest risk to fetuses and newborns, with the exception of poliovirus, which results in more serious symptoms in older children and young adults.

### Diagnosis, Treatment, and Prevention of *Enterovirus* Infections

Enterovirus infections are usually benign and have mild symptoms, so they are not often diagnosed except in severe cases such as paralytic polio and viral meningitis. The cerebrospinal fluid (CSF) of viral meningitis patients has a normal glucose level, in contrast to that seen with bacterial meningitis. Viruses are rarely found in the CSF, so their presence there is diagnostic for viral meningitis; serological testing can confirm enterovirus infection.

No antiviral therapy is effective against enterovirus infection. Treatment involves support and limitation of pain and fever. Good hygiene and adequate sewage treatment can prevent infection with enteroviruses. No vaccines exist for coxsackievirus and echovirus infections, but effective vaccines do exist for polio.

## Hepatitis A

### Learning Objectives

✓ Describe the signs and symptoms of hepatitis.

✓ Compare and contrast the five viruses that cause hepatitis.

Like enteroviruses, **hepatitis A virus** (genus *Hepatovirus*), is transmitted through the fecal-oral route, but unlike enteroviruses it is not cytolytic. Hepatitis A virus can survive on surfaces such as countertops and cutting boards for days and resists common household disinfectants such as chlorine bleach.

Hepatitis A has an incubation period of about one month before fever, fatigue, nausea, anorexia, and jaundice abruptly start. As with hepatitis B (caused by a DNA virus), the patient's own cellular immune system kills infected liver cells, resulting in the signs and symptoms. Children are less likely than adults to develop symptoms, because their cellular immune responses are still immature. Hepatitis A virus does not cause chronic liver disease, and complete recovery occurs 99% of the time. Patients release virions in their feces and are infective even without developing symptoms. To prevent hepatitis A, two doses of hepatitis A vaccine are recommended for all children and adults.

Table 3 compares five viruses known to cause viral hepatitis. Four of them (hepatitis A, C, D, and E) are RNA viruses discussed in this chapter. The fifth is hepatitis B virus.

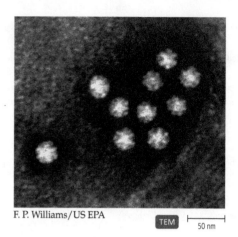

F. P. Williams/US EPA

TEM | 50 nm

▲ **Figure 6** Viruses of the families *Caliciviridae* and *Astroviridae* have naked, star-shaped capsids.

## Acute Gastroenteritis

### Learning Objective

✓ Compare and contrast caliciviruses and astroviruses.

Two groups of small (about 30–40 nm in diameter), round viruses that cause acute gastroenteritis are **caliciviruses** (kă-lis′i-vī′rŭs-ĕz) and **astroviruses** (as′trō-vī′rŭs-ĕz), which are slightly larger than picornaviruses and have naked, star-shaped, polyhedral capsids (Figure 6). Like enteroviruses, caliciviruses and astroviruses enter the body through the digestive system, but in contrast to enteroviruses they cause gastrointestinal disease. The capsids of caliciviruses have indentations, whereas those of astroviruses do not. Antigens of viruses in the two groups can be distinguished through serological tests. The incubation period for these two types of viruses is about 24 hours. Both caliciviruses and astroviruses have caused outbreaks of gastroenteritis in day care centers, schools, hospitals, nursing homes, restaurants, and on cruise ships. The symptoms resolve within 12–60 hours.

Caliciviruses cause diarrhea, nausea, and vomiting, though the symptoms of any given serotype vary from patient to patient. The best studied of the caliciviruses are **noroviruses,** first discovered in the stools of victims during an epidemic of diarrhea in Norwalk, Ohio. Noroviruses cause 90% of viral cases of gastroenteritis.

Astroviruses also cause diarrhea, but no vomiting, and they are less likely to infect adults. In the United States, about three-fourths of children have antibodies against astroviruses by age seven.

There is no specific treatment for caliciviral or astroviral gastroenteritis except support and replacement of lost fluid and electrolytes. Prevention of infection involves adequate sewage treatment, purification of water supplies, frequent handwashing, and disinfection of contaminated surfaces and fomites.

Marion Sourisseau, Marie-Christine PrÇvost, Olivier Schwartz, Institut Pasteur Paris

TEM | 30 nm

▲ **Figure 7** **Togaviruses.** Each virus has a closely appressed envelope around its capsid.

## Hepatitis E

### Learning Objective

✓ Describe the prevention of hepatitis E viral infection.

**Hepatitis E virus** (genus *Hepevirus*) was formerly considered a calicivirus based on structure and size (27–34 nm), but now it is placed in its own family, *Hepeviridae*. Hepatitis E virus infects the liver and causes **hepatitis E,** also known as *enteric hepatitis.* Hepatitis E is fatal to 20% of infected pregnant women. There is no treatment for hepatitis E. Prevention involves interrupting the fecal-oral route of infection with good personal hygiene, water purification, and sewage treatment.

So far we have considered naked, positive ssRNA viruses in the families *Picornaviridae, Caliciviridae, Astroviridae,* and *Hepeviridae.* Now we turn our attention to enveloped, positive ssRNA viruses.

## Enveloped, Positive ssRNA Viruses: *Togaviridae, Flaviviridae,* and *Coronaviridae*

Members of the *Togaviridae* and *Flaviviridae* are enveloped, icosahedral, positive, single-stranded RNA viruses. Flaviviruses are smaller and have a protein matrix between the capsid and envelope. Both flaviviruses and togaviruses differ from the viruses we examined previously in being enveloped (*toga* is Latin for "cloak"); however, the envelopes of togaviruses and flaviviruses are often tightly appressed to the capsids (like shrink wrapping), which allows individual capsomeres to be visualized (Figure 7). Because most togaviruses and flaviviruses are transmitted by arthropods (including mosquitoes, ticks, flies, mites, and lice), these viruses are designated **arboviruses**[6] (ar'bō-vī'rŭs-ĕz), and this shared characteristic is the reason taxonomists originally included the flaviviruses in family *Togaviridae*. However, differences in antigens, replication strategy, and RNA sequence indicate that flaviviruses belong in their own family. Thus, the term arbovirus has no taxonomic significance; some arboviruses are +ssRNA, some are −ssRNA, and some are dsRNA.

Viruses of the family *Coronaviridae* are also enveloped, positive, single-stranded RNA viruses. However, in contrast to togaviruses and flaviviruses, they have helical capsids (Figure 8), and none are arthropod borne.

In this section we consider diseases of the arboviruses from the families *Togaviridae* and *Flaviviridae,* discuss the togaviruses and flaviviruses that are not transmitted via arthropods, and finally discuss the coronaviruses.

## Diseases of +RNA Arboviruses

### Learning Objectives

✓ Define *zoonosis* and *arbovirus*.

✓ Compare and contrast EEE, WEE, and VEE.

✓ Describe the transmission and spread of West Nile virus encephalitis.

✓ Contrast the two types of dengue fever.

✓ Discuss the signs, symptoms, and prevention of yellow fever.

Specific genera of mosquitoes and ticks transmit arboviruses among animal hosts, usually small mammals or birds, and into humans. Animal diseases that spread to humans are called **zoonoses,**[7] so these diseases are both arboviral and zoonotic. Arthropod vectors remain infected with arboviruses and are a continual source of new infections when they bite vertebrate hosts. In animals, virions are released from infected cells into the blood (viremia), but persistent viremia does not occur as readily in humans. Thus, humans are dead-end hosts for these zoonotic viruses.

Arboviruses enter target cells through endocytosis and replicate within them. Most cause mild, flulike symptoms in humans within three to seven days of infection. Arboviral disease does not usually proceed beyond this initial manifestation. Occasionally, however, arboviruses in the blood infect the brain, liver, skin, or blood vessels. Diseases associated with such second-stage infections include several kinds of encephalitis, dengue fever, and yellow fever.

### Encephalitis

Different togaviruses cause **Eastern equine encephalitis (EEE), Western equine encephalitis (WEE),** and **Venezuelan equine encephalitis (VEE).** As the names indicate, viral replication occurs in the brains of horses as well as in humans. The normal host for these viruses is either a bird (EEE, WEE, VEE) or a rodent (VEE) (Figure 9). Of the three, EEE causes the most severe

---
[6]From arthropod borne.
[7]Plural of Greek *zoos*, meaning animal, and *nosis*, meaning disease.

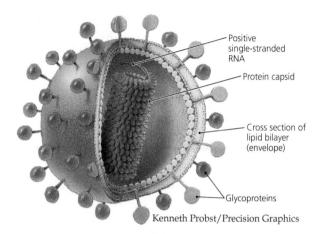

Positive single-stranded RNA

Protein capsid

Cross section of lipid bilayer (envelope)

Glycoproteins

Kenneth Probst/Precision Graphics

▲ **Figure 8 Enveloped +ssRNA coronavirus.** Viruses in the family *Coronaviridae* have helical capsids; whereas, viruses in the families *Togaviridae* and *Flaviviridae* have icosahedral capsids.

disease in humans, though any of them may produce fatal brain infections.

In 1999, hundreds of birds—mostly crows—suddenly began dying in the New York City area. At the same time, there were reports of people feeling ill with flulike symptoms after being bitten by mosquitoes. Seven of these patients developed viral encephalitis and died. As it turned out, all these events were related.

The culprit was West Nile virus. An arbovirus in the family *Flaviviridae* and endemic to Africa and Israel, West Nile virus had never before been seen in the Americas. After the initial outbreak, infected migratory birds carried the virus across the lower 48 United States. Mosquitoes further spread West Nile virus among bird populations, between birds and horses, and between birds and humans. Animals feeding on dead birds also become infected. Significant viremia with West Nile virus does not develop in humans, so humans are dead-end hosts except in cases of blood transfusion or organ transplant.

Eighty percent of infected humans have no symptoms; 20% have fever, headache, fatigue, and body aches. In the most severe cases—about 1 of 750 human infections—West Nile virus invades the nervous system to cause encephalitis, which may be fatal. Figure 10 illustrates the number of human cases and deaths due to West Nile virus.

Other flaviviruses also cause usually benign viral encephalitis. These viruses include *St. Louis, Japanese,* and *Russian spring-summer* viruses.

### Dengue Fever

A flavivirus transmitted by *Aedes* mosquitoes causes **dengue** (den'gā) **fever.** It afflicts approximately 100 million people in tropical and subtropical areas of the world (Figure 11). The disease usually occurs in two phases separated by 24 hours of remission. First, the patient suffers from fever, weakness, edema (swelling) of the extremities, and severe pain in the

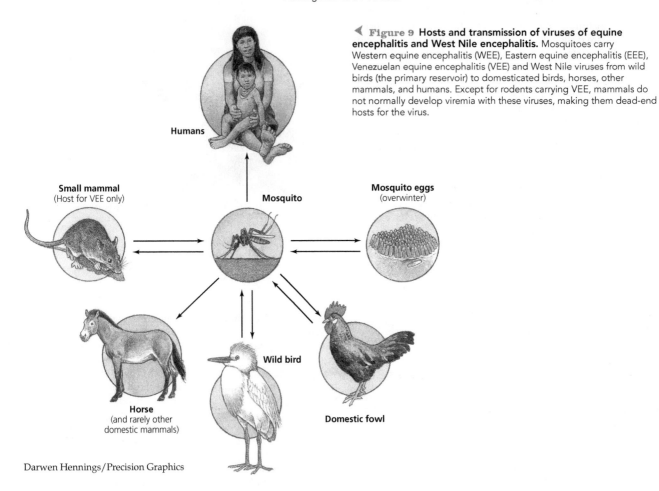

◄ **Figure 9 Hosts and transmission of viruses of equine encephalitis and West Nile encephalitis.** Mosquitoes carry Western equine encephalitis (WEE), Eastern equine encephalitis (EEE), Venezuelan equine encephalitis (VEE) and West Nile viruses from wild birds (the primary reservoir) to domesticated birds, horses, other mammals, and humans. Except for rodents carrying VEE, mammals do not normally develop viremia with these viruses, making them dead-end hosts for the virus.

**Humans**

**Small mammal**
(Host for VEE only)

**Mosquito**

**Mosquito eggs**
(overwinter)

**Horse**
(and rarely other
domestic mammals)

**Wild bird**

**Domestic fowl**

Darwen Hennings/Precision Graphics

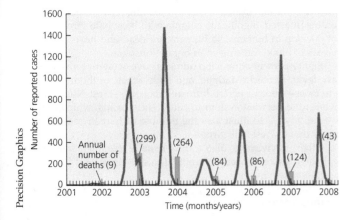

Precision Graphics

▲ **Figure 10 Human West Nile virus infections in the United States.** Note the seasonal nature of the disease.

head, back, and muscles. The severity of the pain is indicated by the common name for the disease, *breakbone fever*. The second phase involves a return of the fever and a bright red rash. Dengue fever is self-limiting and lasts six or seven days.

**Dengue hemorrhagic fever** is a more serious disease caused by reinfection with the dengue virus, and it involves a hyperimmune response (Figure 12). Inflammatory cytokines released by activated memory T cells cause rupture of blood vessels, internal bleeding, shock, and possibly death.

Dengue and dengue hemorrhagic fever are epidemic in South America. Given that *Aedes* mosquitoes already live in the southern United States, dengue could potentially become established there if the virus were introduced into the United States by immigrants or returning travelers.

## Yellow Fever

Another flavivirus causes **yellow fever,** a disease involving degeneration of the liver, kidneys, and heart, as well as massive hemorrhaging. Hemorrhaging in the intestines may result in "black vomit." Liver damage causes jaundice, from which the

USDA/Science Source/Photo Researchers

**(a)**

▲ **Figure 11 Dengue fever. (a)** *Aedes aegypti* mosquito. **(b)** Global distribution of dengue fever in 2009. The U.S. population is susceptible to this disease, which afflicts millions of people worldwide, because of the presence of the disease's vectors, mosquitoes in the genus *Aedes*.

▨ Areas of dengue
▨ Range of *Aedes*

Precision Graphics

**(b)**

disease acquires its name and its nickname, "Yellow Jack." The mortality rate of yellow fever can approach 20%. Before the 1900s, yellow fever epidemics ravaged the Americas, killing thousands. In 1793, it killed over 4000 people in Philadelphia (then the capital of the United States), and during the Spanish American War of 1898, it killed more American soldiers than bullets did. With mosquito control and the development of a vaccine in the 1900s, however, yellow fever has since been eliminated from the United States.

Yellow fever remains a significant disease, with 200,000 estimated cases and 30,000 deaths annually worldwide. A single dose of yellow fever vaccine provides protection to 95% of individuals, probably for their lifetimes.

Table 4 summarizes the arboviruses and their diseases, including additional viruses in families *Bunyaviridae* and *Reoviridae*.

### Diagnosis, Treatment, and Prevention of Arbovirus Infections

Serological tests, such as ELISA and agglutination of latex beads to which arbovirus antigens are affixed, are used for the diagnosis of arboviral infections. The only treatment for arboviral diseases is to provide supportive care. Only acetaminophen is recommended for managing pain and fever associated with dengue infections, as the anticoagulant properties of aspirin could aggravate the hemorrhagic properties of dengue virus infections.

Prevention of infection involves control of the vectors, which has resulted in elimination of many arboviral diseases in certain geographic areas. Insect repellents and netting reduce infections with arboviruses.

Vaccination is recommended for people traveling to areas where arboviral diseases are prevalent. Vaccines for humans are available against yellow fever, Japanese encephalitis, and Russian spring-summer encephalitis viruses. Animal vaccines against VEE, EEE, and West Nile encephalitis are also available. No vaccine is available for dengue.

CRITICAL **THINKING**

Suppose a vaccine for dengue that induced the production of memory T cells could be developed. After reviewing the characteristics of infection and reinfection, would you argue for or against the use of such a vaccine? Why or why not?

## Other Diseases of Enveloped +ssRNA Viruses

### Learning Objectives

✓ Describe the signs, effects, and prevention of rubella.

✓ Compare and contrast hepatitis C with the other types of viral hepatitis.

✓ Describe the structure of coronaviruses and the diseases they cause.

### Rubella

Rubella (rū-bel'ă) virus *(Rubivirus)* shares the structure and reproductive strategy of other togaviruses, but unlike them it is transmitted by the respiratory route and not by arthropod vectors. **Rubella** is one of five childhood viral diseases that produce skin lesions. (The other four are measles, caused by a −ssRNA virus and discussed later in this chapter; and chickenpox, roseola, and fifth disease.) Rubella, first distinguished as a separate disease by German physicians, is commonly known as "German measles" or "three-day measles."

Rubella only infects humans, entering the respiratory system and infecting cells of the upper respiratory tract. It spreads from there to lymph nodes and into the blood, and then throughout the body. Afterward, the characteristic rash of flat, pink to red spots (macules) develops (Figure 13) and lasts about three days. Rubella in children is usually not serious, but adults may develop arthritis or encephalitis. Patients shed virions in respiratory droplets for approximately two weeks before and two weeks after the rash.

**Initial infection**

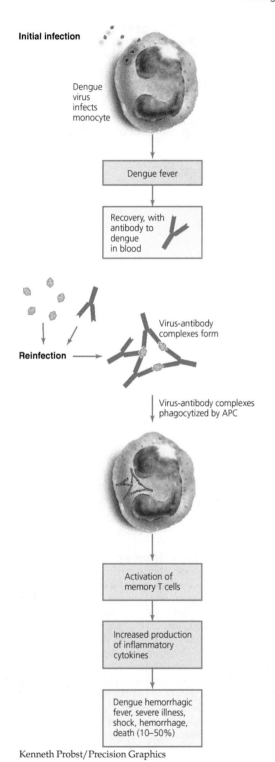

Dengue virus infects monocyte

Dengue fever

Recovery, with antibody to dengue in blood

Virus-antibody complexes form

**Reinfection**

Virus-antibody complexes phagocytized by APC

Activation of memory T cells

Increased production of inflammatory cytokines

Dengue hemorrhagic fever, severe illness, shock, hemorrhage, death (10–50%)

Kenneth Probst/Precision Graphics

◀ **Figure 12  Pathogenesis of dengue hemorrhagic fever.** The condition is a severe hyperimmune response to a second infection with dengue virus. Antigen-presenting cells phagocytize complexes of virus and antibodies (formed during the initial infection), which activates T memory cells. These release an abundance of lymphokines that induce hemorrhaging and shock.

Rubella was not seen as a serious disease until 1941, when Norman Gregg (1892–1966) an Australian ophthalmologist, recognized that rubella infections of pregnant women resulted in severe congenital defects in their babies. These effects include cardiac abnormalities, deafness, blindness, mental retardation, microcephaly,[8] and growth retardation. Death of the fetus is also common. It is now known that a mother is able to transmit the virus across the placenta even if she is asymptomatic.

Diagnosis of rubella is usually made by observation and by serological testing for IgM against rubella. No treatment is available, but immunization has proven effective at reducing the incidence of rubella in industrialized countries (Figure 14). The rubella vaccine is made from a live, attenuated virus, and therefore should never be given to pregnant women or immunocompromised patients. Immunization is aimed at reducing the number of rubella cases that might serve to introduce rubella to pregnant women.

## Hepatitis C

A flavivirus called **hepatitis C virus (HCV)** accounts for 90% of the cases of so-called non-A, non-B hepatitis in the United States (Table 3). About 3.2 million Americans are chronically infected by HCV, which is spread via needles, organ transplants, and sexual activity, but not by arthropod vectors. In the past, blood transfusions accounted for many cases of hepatitis C, but testing blood for HCV has considerably reduced the risk of infection by this means.

Hepatitis C is a chronic disease, often lasting for 20 years or longer, with few if any symptoms. Severe liver damage (20% of

---

[8]From Greek *mikro*, meaning small, and *kephalos*, meaning head.

Custom Medical Stock Photo, Inc.

▲ **Figure 13  The rash of rubella.** The disease, also known as German measles or three-day measles, is characterized by flattened red spots (macules).

Precision Graphics

▲ **Figure 14 The efficacy of vaccination against rubella.** The use of a live, attenuated virus vaccine has practically eliminated rubella in the United States.

Kjell-Olof Hedlund/Smittskyddsinstitutet (SMI)

TEM ⊢———⊣ 40 nm

▲ **Figure 15 Coronaviruses.** These +ssRNA viruses have distinctive envelopes with glycoprotein spikes that resemble flares from the corona of the sun.

cases) and liver failure (5% of cases) occur over time. Hepatic cancer can also result from HCV infection.

Alpha interferon and ribavirin provide some relief for hepatitis C but are not cures. There is no other treatment or vaccine for hepatitis C.

## Diseases of Coronaviruses

**Coronaviruses** (kō-rō′nă-vī′rŭs-ĕz) are enveloped, positive, single-stranded RNA viruses with helical capsids. Their envelopes form corona-like halos around the capsids, giving these viruses their name (Figure 15). Two coronaviruses cause colds and are the second most common cause of colds after picornavirus rhinoviruses. Coronaviruses are transmitted from epithelial cells of the upper respiratory tract in large droplets (sneezes and coughs) and, like rhinoviruses, replicate best at 33°C, which is the temperature of the nasal cavity.

In the winter of 2002–2003, a newly emerging disease of a previously unknown coronavirus made headlines worldwide (**Highlight: Sequencing the SARS Virus**). **Severe acute respiratory syndrome (SARS)** was first identified in China's Guangdong province. SARS initially taxed health care systems in several Asian countries, but unprecedented worldwide cooperation allowed epidemiologists to identify the virus, track its spread, sequence its genome, and investigate effective quarantine procedures faster than with any previous disease. SARS is characterized by symptoms of fever above 100.4°F (38°C), headache, general discomfort, and respiratory distress. By spring of 2003, the disease had spread to Singapore, Vietnam, Taiwan, Canada, and other parts of the world. Amazingly, epidemiologists were able to trace the disease's global spread back to a single individual: an infected physician who had traveled from China to Hong Kong in order to attend his nephew's wedding and unwittingly spread the disease to other travelers.

SARS created widespread alarm because of its sudden emergence, highly infectious nature (it is spread by close person-to-person contact), initially unknown origin, and 10% mortality rate. SARS remains a potential problem in China.

No antiviral treatment or vaccine is available against coronaviral infections. Symptoms of colds can be alleviated with antihistamines and analgesics. Some physicians prescribe antiviral drugs such as ribavirin or interferon for SARS. Prevention of SARS involves reducing the spread of the SARS virus by quarantining patients and using face masks (Figure 16).

Now we examine a unique type of +ssRNA—the retroviruses.

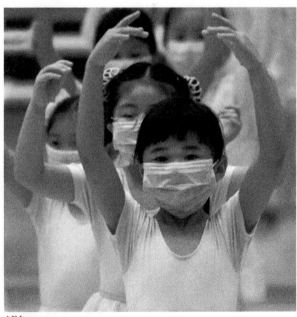

AP Images

▲ **Figure 16 Prevention of SARS.** Ballet students in Hong Kong in 2003 donned face masks to slow the spread of SARS virus.

**TABLE 4**

## Diseases Caused by Arboviruses, by Viral Family

| Disease | Vector | Natural Host(s) | Distribution | Symptoms |
|---|---|---|---|---|
| *Togaviridae* (enveloped, icosahedral, +ssRNA) | | | | |
| Eastern equine encephalitis (EEE) | *Aedes, Culex,* and *Culiseta* mosquitoes | Birds | Americas | Flulike symptoms and encephalitis |
| Western equine encephalitis (WEE) | *Aedes* and *Culex* mosquitoes | Birds | Americas | Flulike symptoms and encephalitis |
| Venezuelan equine encephalitis (VEE) | *Aedes* and *Culex* mosquitoes | Rodents, horses | Americas | Flulike symptoms and encephalitis |
| *Flaviviridae* (enveloped, icosahedral, +ssRNA) | | | | |
| Japanese encephalitis | *Culex* mosquitoes | Birds, pigs | Asia | Flulike symptoms and encephalitis |
| West Nile encephalitis | *Aedes, Anopheles,* and *Culex* mosquitoes | Birds | Africa, Europe, Asia, North America | Flulike symptoms and potentially fatal encephalitis |
| St. Louis encephalitis | *Culex* mosquitoes | Birds | North America | Flulike symptoms and encephalitis |
| Russian spring-summer encephalitis | *Ixodes* and *Dermacentor* ticks | Birds | Russia | Flulike symptoms and encephalitis |
| Dengue and dengue hemorrhagic fever | *Aedes* mosquitoes | Monkeys, humans | Worldwide, especially tropics | Severe pain, hemorrhaging, hepatitis, shock |
| Yellow fever | *Aedes* mosquitoes | Monkeys, humans | Africa, South America | Hepatitis, hemorrhagic fever, shock |
| Chikungunya | *Aedes* mosquitoes | Monkeys | Africa, Asia | Rash, nausea, joint pain |
| *Bunyaviridae* (enveloped, filamentous segmented, −ssRNA) | | | | |
| LaCrosse encephalitis | *Aedes* mosquitoes | Rodents, small mammals, birds | North America | Fever, rash, encephalitis |
| Rift Valley fever | *Aedes* mosquitoes | Sheep, goats, cattle | Africa, Asia | Hemorrhagic fever, encephalitis |
| Sand fly fever | *Phlebotomus* flies | Sheep, cattle | Africa | Hemorrhagic fever, encephalitis |
| Crimean-Congo hemorrhagic fever | *Hyalomma* ticks | Horses, cattle, goats, seabirds | Africa, Crimea | Hemorrhagic fever |
| *Reoviridae* (naked, dsRNA) | | | | |
| Colorado tick fever | *Dermacentor* ticks | Small mammals, deer | Western North America | Fever, chills, headache, photophobia, rash, and, in children, hemorrhage |

## HIGHLIGHT

### SEQUENCING THE SARS VIRUS

When SARS came to the world's attention in late 2002, the virus that causes it was unknown. To combat the growing epidemic, scientists needed to rapidly isolate the virus.

Scientists generated small slides spotted with numerous tiny DNA pieces from various viruses. This DNA microarray acted as a library that the scientists could use to compare with gene sequences from known and unknown viruses. The key to this comparison was that the DNA pieces on the array were all highly conserved—that is, the same sequence existed among many members of a taxon of viruses. So, if an unknown virus contained one of these gene pieces, it could be placed in the same group as the virus with which it shared a common DNA segment.

Once the array was generated, researchers purified a viral sample from a SARS patient. The resulting RNA was coated onto the array. The idea: any SARS RNA pieces that matched the DNA pieces on the array would stick to the slide; all other nonspecific segments would wash off. These common pieces were easily identified because they lit up via fluorescence imaging. Using this technique, the team quickly found out that SARS virus is a member of the coronavirus family. There are three types

▲ **SARS virus, a coronavirus.**

TEM | 500 nm

John Nicholls/Visuals Unlimited

of coronaviruses, but SARS didn't fit into any of these three: it was unique. Researchers have since learned much more about the SARS virus and are more prepared to face new outbreaks.

**Figure 17 The process by which reverse transcriptase transcribes dsDNA from ssRNA.** Three distinct steps occur rapidly and nearly simultaneously: **1 (a)** A complementary −ssDNA molecule is transcribed to form a DNA-RNA hybrid. Virion tRNA is used as a primer for this synthesis. **2 (b)** The RNA portion of the hybrid is degraded, leaving −ssDNA. **3 (c)** A complementary +DNA strand is synthesized to form dsDNA.

ssRNA-ssDNA hybrid

ssRNA

tRNA primer

Reverse transcriptase

**(a)**

RNA degrades

**(b)**

dsDNA

**(c)**

Kenneth Probst/Precision Graphics

# Enveloped, Positive ssRNA Viruses with Reverse Transcriptase: *Retroviridae*

## Learning Objectives

✓ Explain how retroviruses do not conform to the central dogma of molecular biology.

✓ Describe the steps of reverse transcription.

✓ List two types of retroviruses.

Scientists have studied **retroviruses** (re′trō-vī′rŭs-ĕz) more than any other group of viruses because of their unique features and the diseases they cause. These viruses have polyhedral capsids with spiked envelopes 80–146 nm in diameter and genomes composed of two molecules of positive, single-stranded RNA. Each virion also contains two tRNA molecules and 10–50 copies of the enzymes *reverse transcriptase, protease,* and *integrase,* whose function will be described shortly. The box on the following pages illustrates these features as exemplified by HIV, the most studied of the retroviruses.

The unique characteristic of retroviruses is that they do not conform to what is considered the *central dogma* of molecular biology; that is, that genetic information flows from DNA to RNA to translated proteins. Retroviruses[9] reverse this flow of information; that is, they transcribe DNA from RNA.

Retroviruses accomplish this amazing feat by means of a complex enzyme, **reverse transcriptase,** which transcribes double-stranded DNA from single-stranded RNA. Transcription occurs as the enzyme moves along an RNA molecule and can best be understood as occurring in three steps, though in reality the events occur simultaneously (Figure 17):

An RNA-DNA hybrid is made from the +RNA genome using tRNA carried by the virion as a primer for DNA synthesis. The DNA portion of the hybrid molecule is negative DNA.

The RNA portion of the hybrid molecule is degraded by reverse transcriptase, leaving −ssDNA.

The reverse transcriptase transcribes a complementary +DNA strand to form dsDNA, and the tRNA primer is removed.

The discovery of reverse transcriptase was a momentous event in biology, and it made possible an ongoing revolution in recombinant DNA technology and biotechnology. For example, it is much easier to isolate mRNA for a particular protein (e.g., human insulin) and then use reverse transcriptase to make a gene than it is to find the gene itself amid the DNA of 23 pairs of human chromosomes.

In the following sections we consider two types of retroviruses, both of which infect humans: those that are primarily oncogenic (genus *Deltaretrovirus*), and those that are primarily immunosuppressive (genus *Lentivirus*).

## Oncogenic Retroviruses

### Learning Objective

✓ Describe how oncogenic viruses may induce cancer.

Retroviruses have been linked with cancer ever since they were first isolated from chicken neoplasias. In 1981, Robert Gallo (1937–) and his associates isolated the first human retrovirus, **human T-lymphotropic virus 1 (HTLV-1),** from a patient with *adult acute T-cell lymphocytic leukemia,* a cancer of humans. Since then, two other human retroviruses of this type have been discovered: HTLV-2, which causes a rare cancer called *hairy cell leukemia* because of distinctive extensions of the cytoplasmic membrane of infected cells (Figure 18), and HTLV-5, which has not been linked to cancer or any other disease.

Professor Aaron Polliack/Photo Researchers

▲ **Figure 18 The characteristic extensions of the cytoplasmic membrane in hairy cell leukemia.**

[9]From Latin *retro*, meaning reverse.

HTLV-1 and HTLV-2 infect lymphocytes and are transmitted within these cells to other people via sexual intercourse, blood transfusion, and contaminated needles. HTLV-1 is primarily found in populations in Japan and the Caribbean and among African Americans. HTLV-2 is not as well studied as HTLV-1. An ELISA can reveal infection with an HTLV. As with many viral diseases, there is no specific antiviral treatment. Infections are chronic, and the long-term prognosis of patients is poor. Prevention involves the same changes in behavior needed to prevent HIV infection.

Oncogenic retroviruses cause cancer in various ways. For example, HTLV-1 codes for a protein, called *Tax*, that activates cell growth and division genes in helper T lymphocytes.

## Acquired Immunodeficiency Syndrome

### Learning Objectives

✓ Differentiate between a disease and a syndrome, using AIDS as an example.

✓ Describe the virions that cause AIDS.

✓ Explain the roles of gp41 and gp120 in HIV infection.

✓ Describe the relationship of helper T cells to the course of AIDS.

✓ List four measures that can be effective in preventing AIDS.

From the time of its discovery in 1981 among homosexual males in the United States to its emergence as a worldwide pandemic, no affliction has affected modern life as much as **acquired immunodeficiency syndrome (AIDS).** AIDS is not a disease but a **syndrome;** that is, a complex of signs, symptoms, and diseases associated with a common cause. AID syndrome is several opportunistic or rare infections, listed in Table 5, in the presence of antibodies against the **human immunodeficiency virus (HIV)** and a CD4 white blood cell count below 200 cells per microliter of blood.

HIV is restricted to replicating in humans and, as its name indicates, this pathogen destroys the human immune system. Its many characteristics that make it particularly difficult to combat are summarized in Table 6.

There are two major types of HIV. **HIV-1,** which is more prevalent in the United States and Europe, was discovered by Luc Montagnier (1932–) and his colleagues at the Pasteur Institute in 1983. **HIV-2,** the prevalent strain in West Africa, reproduces more slowly than HIV-1; therefore, HIV-1 will be the major focus of our discussion.

### Structure of HIV

HIV is a typical retrovirus in size and shape. Its envelope is characterized by two antigenic glycoproteins. The larger of these, named **gp120,**[10] is the primary attachment molecule of HIV and when shed into the blood triggers inflammation. Its antigenicity can change during the course of prolonged infection, making an effective antibody response against it very difficult. The smaller glycoprotein, **gp41,** promotes fusion of the

---

[10]gp120 is short for glycoprotein with a molecular weight of 120,000 daltons.

## TABLE 5 · Opportunistic Infections and Tumors of AIDS Patients

| Type | Manifestations |
|---|---|
| Bacterial infections | Tuberculosis, especially extrapulmonary (*Mycobacterium*) |
| | Rectal gonorrhea (*Neisseria*) |
| | Recurrent fever and septicemia due to *Salmonella*, *Haemophilus*, or *Streptococcus* |
| Fungal infections | *Pneumocystis* pneumonia |
| | Thrush, disseminated in trachea, lungs, esophagus (*Candida*) |
| | Histoplasmosis (*Histoplasma*) |
| Protozoal infections | Toxoplasmosis (*Toxoplasma*) |
| | Chronic diarrhea (*Cryptosporidium*, *Isospora*) |
| Viral-induced tumors | Kaposi's sarcoma (especially when associated with HHV-8) |
| | Lymphoma (induced by Epstein-Barr virus) |
| Viral infections | Cytomegalovirus disseminated in brain, lungs, retina, etc. |
| | *Human herpesvirus 1* and *2* disseminated in lungs, GI tract, etc. |
| | Progressive multifocal leukoencephalopathy (PML) (JC virus) |
| | Oral hairy leukoplakia (Epstein-Barr virus) |
| Others | Wasting disease; called *slim* in Africa (cause unknown) |
| | Dementia |

viral envelope to a target cell. The effects of these structural characteristics—antigenic variability and the ability to fuse with host cells—impede immune clearance of HIV from a patient.

### Origin of HIV

Evidence suggests that human immunodeficiency viruses arose from mutations of a similar virus, *simian immunodeficiency virus (SIV)*, found in African primates. The nucleotide sequence of SIV is similar to that of AIDS viruses. Antibodies against HIV have been found in human blood stored since 1959, though the first cases of AIDS were not documented until 1981. Based on mutation rates and the rate of antigenic change in HIV, it is estimated that HIV emerged in the human population in Africa about 1930.

The relationship between the two types of HIV is not clear. HIV-1 and HIV-2 are likely derived from different strains of SIV. We may never know the exact temporal relationships among the immunodeficiency viruses.

### Replication of HIV

The replication cycle of HIV is shown in Figure 19.

> **Figure 19  The replication cycle of HIV.**
The artist's rendition depicts the steps involved in the replication of the virus within a helper T cell: **1** attachment and penetration, **2** uncoating, **3** synthesis of dsDNA and entry into nucleus, **4** latency, **5** synthesis, **6** assembly and budding, and **7** maturation of the virion. Photos **(a)**, **(b)**, and **(c)** show attachment and penetration; photos **(d)**, **(e)**, and **(f)** show the budding and release of a virion.

(a)   TEM  ├─ 85 nm ─┤   (b)   (c)

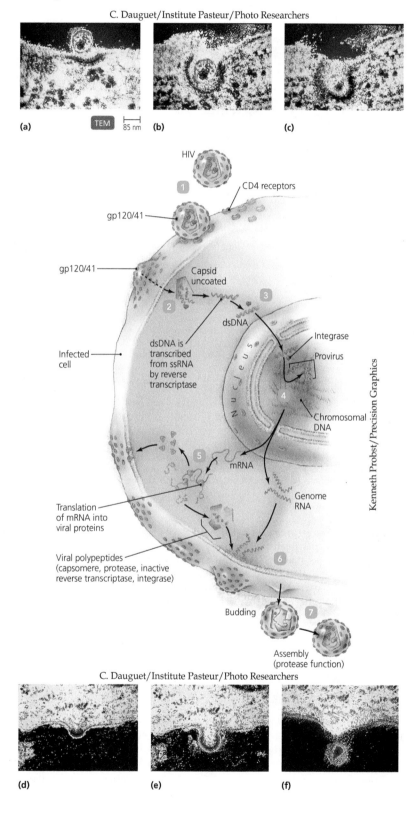

HIV

**1**

CD4 receptors

gp120/41

gp120/41

Capsid uncoated

**2**   **3**

dsDNA

Integrase

Provirus

Infected cell

dsDNA is transcribed from ssRNA by reverse transcriptase

Nucleus

**4**

Chromosomal DNA

**5**

mRNA

Translation of mRNA into viral proteins

Genome RNA

Viral polypeptides (capsomere, protease, inactive reverse transcriptase, integrase)

**6**

Budding   **7**

Assembly (protease function)

Kenneth Probst/Precision Graphics

(d)   (e)   (f)

Kenneth Probst/Precision Graphics

▲ **Figure 20** **The process by which HIV attaches to and enters a CD4 cell. (a)** Binding of gp120 to a CD4 receptor on the cell membrane. **(b)** Removal of the CD4-gp120 complex, allowing gp41 to attach to the cytoplasmic membrane. **(c)** Fusion of the lipid bilayers, introducing the capsid into the cytoplasm.

**Attachment, Penetration, and Uncoating** HIV infects four kinds of cells: helper T cells; cells of the macrophage lineage, including monocytes, macrophages, and *microglia* (special phagocytic cells of the central nervous system); smooth muscle cells, such as those in arterial walls; and *dendritic cells,* which are antigen-presenting cells of the skin, mucous membranes, and lymph nodes. B cells do not themselves become infected with

HIV, but they adhere to HIV that has been covered with complement proteins. They then deliver HIV to the lymphoid tissues, where T cells mature.

Attachment of HIV and entry into T cells and macrophages involves three steps **(Figure 20)**. First, gp120 binds to CD4 receptor molecules on a host cell. Second, the gp120-CD4 complex binds to another receptor, called a *chemokine receptor,* which removes gp120 from the virion. Different chemokine receptors exist on T cells and on macrophage derivatives—*CCR5*[11] on most cells and *CXCR4* on T cells. Finally, once a virion binds to a cell, its envelope contacts the cytoplasmic membrane via gp41 and fuses with it. The HIV capsid is introduced into the cytoplasm while its envelope remains behind as part of the cell's cytoplasmic membrane. Glycoprotein 41 remaining on the cytoplasmic membrane induces the cell to fuse to as many as 500 neighboring cells to form a **syncytium** (sin-sish'ē-ŭm), a giant multinucleate cell. Cellular fusion allows HIV to move from cell to cell without being exposed to antibodies in the blood.

In contrast, dendritic cells are infected in a single step, when the gp120 of HIV attaches to a receptor (DC-SIGN) found on their cytoplasmic membranes. HIV fuses with the target cell and introduces its capsid into the cytoplasm. Infected dendritic cells deliver HIV into T cells during antigen presentation.

**Latency and Synthesis** In the cytoplasm, reverse transcriptase uses cellular tRNA (packaged in the virion when it was assembled) as a primer to transcribe dsDNA. Reverse transcriptase is very error prone, making about five errors per genome, and this generates many new antigenic variations of HIV during the course of infection. As many as 100 variants may develop in a single patient over the course of the syndrome.

HIV is a latent virus. The dsDNA made by reverse transcriptase, which is known as a **provirus,** enters the nucleus and is inserted into a human chromosome by the virion-carried enzyme **integrase.** Once integrated, the provirus remains a part of the cellular DNA for life. Integrated HIV is transcribed and replicated in the same way as any cellular gene. It may remain dormant for years or be activated immediately, depending on its location in the human genome and the availability of enhancer and promoter sequences. Macrophages and monocytes are major reservoirs as well as means of distribution of HIV.

[11]Membrane proteins are often designated by letter-number combinations.

**6**

## Characteristics of HIV That Challenge the Immune System

| Characteristic | Effect(s) |
|---|---|
| Retroviral genome consists of two copies of +ssRNA | Reassortment of viral genes possible; virus is highly mutable, reverse transcription produces much genetic variation; genome can integrate into host's chromosomes |
| Targets helper T lymphocytes especially, but also macrophages, dendritic cells, smooth muscle cells | Infects key cells of host's immune system |
| Antigenic variability | Large amount of antigenic drift due to mutations helps virus evade host's immune response |
| Induces formation of syncytia | Increases routes of infection; intracellular site helps virus evade immune detection |

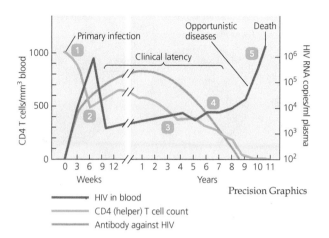

▲ **Figure 21 The course of AIDS.** The course follows helper T cell destruction. The circled numbers correspond to the steps described in the text.

(a)

**Assembly and Release** RNA transcribed from a provirus may be used in either of two ways:

- A molecule of RNA may be used as mRNA by ribosomes for the translation of viral proteins, including capsomeres, gp120, and reverse transcriptase.

- Two molecules of RNA are incorporated into a new virion along with copies of reverse transcriptase, integrase, and two molecules of tRNA (the latter are coded by the host's genome).

Virions subsequently bud from the cytoplasmic membrane (see Figure 19, step 6). At this point in its replication cycle, a virion is nonvirulent because its capsid is not assembled and reverse transcriptase is inactive. **Protease** (prō′tē-ās), a viral protein packaged in the virion, releases reverse transcriptase and capsomeres after the virion buds from the cell. This action of protease allows final assembly, rendering HIV virulent.

## Pathogenesis of AIDS

The course of AIDS is directly related to the destruction of helper T cells in a patient (Figure 21).

1. Initially, there is a burst of virion production and release from infected cells. This primary infection is accompanied by fever, fatigue, weight loss, diarrhea, and body aches.

2. The immune system responds by producing antibodies, and the number of free virions plummets. The body and HIV are waging an invisible war with few signs or symptoms. During this period, almost a billion virions are destroyed each day, while about 100 million CD4 helper T cells are killed by viruses and by cytotoxic T cells. No specific symptoms accompany this stage, and the patient is often unaware of the infection.

3. As latent viruses continue to replicate and virions are released into the blood, the body cannot adequately replenish helper T cells. Over the course of 5–10 years, the number of

(b)

▲ **Figure 22 Diseases associated with AIDS. (a)** Disseminated herpes. **(b)** Kaposi's sarcoma. *Which viruses cause herpes?*

**Figure 22** *Herpes is caused by human herpesvirus 1 and 2.*

helper T cells declines to a level that severely impairs the immune response.

4. The rate of antibody formation falls precipitously as helper T function is lost.

5. HIV production climbs, and the patient dies from infections the body can no longer resist.

Many of the diseases associated with the loss of immune function in AIDS (see Table 5) are nonlethal infections in other patients, but AIDS patients cannot effectively resist them. Diseases such as disseminated herpes and Kaposi's sarcoma (a cancer of blood vessels) (Figure 22), as well as toxoplasmosis and *Pneumocystis* pneumonia, are typical in AIDS patients. AIDS often results in dementia during the final stages.

507

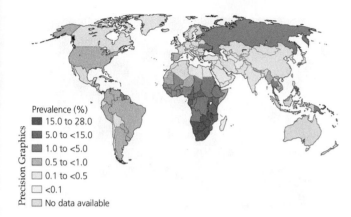

Prevalence (%)
- 15.0 to 28.0
- 5.0 to <15.0
- 1.0 to <5.0
- 0.5 to <1.0
- 0.1 to <0.5
- <0.1
- No data available

Precision Graphics

▲ **Figure 23** **The global prevalence of HIV (2007).**
Over 33 million were HIV positive. Note the alarming epidemic in sub-Saharan Africa.

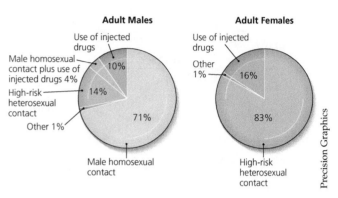

**Adult Males**

Use of injected drugs 10%
Male homosexual contact plus use of injected drugs 4%
High-risk heterosexual contact 14%
Other 1%
Male homosexual contact 71%

**Adult Females**

Use of injected drugs
Other 1% 16%
High-risk heterosexual contact 83%

Precision Graphics

▲ **Figure 24** **Modes of HIV transmission in Americans over 12 years of age during 2007.** Percentages represent the estimated proportions of HIV infections that result from each type of transmission. High-risk heterosexual behavior is sexual contact with a person known to have, or to be at high risk for, HIV infection.

## Epidemiology of AIDS

Epidemiologists first recognized AIDS in young male homosexuals in the United States, but it is now found throughout the world's population. The United Nations Program on AIDS estimates that there are about 33 million HIV-infected individuals worldwide. Approximately 7400 new infections occur every day. It is disturbing that although the rate of new infections declined throughout most of the 1990s, it is now rising again, presumably because of a false sense of security in richer nations with better access to availability of drugs that slow the progress of the disease, and because of a relaxation of precautions to prevent infection.

About a third of those infected have already developed AIDS; it is presumed that most of the rest will eventually succumb to the syndrome. The spread of AIDS in sub-Saharan Africa is particularly horrific (Figure 23).

HIV is found in all secretions of infected individuals; however, it typically exists in sufficient concentration to cause infection only in blood, semen, saliva, vaginal secretions, and breast milk. Virions are found both free and inside infected white blood cells. Sufficient numbers of virions must be transmitted to target cells to establish an infection, though the exact number of virions needed to establish an infection is unknown and probably varies with the strain of HIV and the overall health of the person's immune system. Infected blood contains 1000–100,000 virions per milliliter, and semen has 10–50 virions per milliliter. Other secretions have lower concentrations and are less infective than blood or semen.

Infected fluid must come in contact with a tear or lesion in the skin or mucous membranes, or it must be injected into the body. Because HIV is small—about 90 nm in diameter—a break in the protective membranes of the body large enough to allow entry of HIV may be too small to see or feel.

HIV is transmitted primarily via sexual contact (including vaginal, anal, and oral sex, either homosexual or heterosexual) and intravenous drug abuse (Figure 24). The risk of infection from a needlestick injury involving an HIV-infected patient is less than 1%. HIV can also be transmitted from mother to baby across the placenta and in breast milk. Approximately one-third of babies born to HIV-positive women are infected with HIV at birth. HIV is rarely acquired from blood transfusions, organ transplants, hemophiliac therapy, and tattooing. Behaviors that increase the risk of infection include the following:

- Sexual promiscuity; that is, sex with more than one partner
- Anal intercourse, especially receptive anal intercourse
- Intravenous drug use
- Sexual intercourse with anyone who engages in the previous three behaviors

The mode of infection is unknown for about 1% of AIDS patients. These patients are often unable or unwilling to answer questions about their sexual and drug abuse history. The Centers for Disease Control and Prevention (CDC) has documented a few cases of casual spread of HIV, including infections from sharing razors and toothbrushes and from mouth-to-mouth kissing. In all cases of casual spread, it is suspected that small amounts of the donor's blood may have entered abrasions in the recipient's mouth.

## Diagnosis, Treatment, and Prevention of AIDS

The signs and symptoms of AIDS vary according to the diseases present. The syndrome indicates that patients have one or more rare diseases, antibodies against HIV, and fewer than 200 CD4 lymphocytes per microliter of blood.[12] Patients also typically have unexplained weight loss, fatigue, and fever.

HIV itself is difficult to locate in patient's secretions and blood because it becomes a provirus inserted into the patient's chromosomes, and because for years HIV is kept in check by the immune system. Polymerase chain reaction (PCR) can be used to reveal the presence of HIV, and serological diagnosis can reveal antibodies against HIV. The latter involves detecting antibodies against HIV using ELISA, agglutination, or western blot

---

[12]The normal value for CD4 cells is 800–1200 cells/μl.

## HIGHLIGHT

# AIDS AND TUBERCULOSIS

In the early 1900s, millions of people suffered from tuberculosis (TB). Patients were treated with months of bed rest in a sanatorium. In the 1940s and 1950s, the introduction of effective antibiotic treatments brought about a dramatic decline in the disease. In recent years, however, tuberculosis has been on the rise once again. The World Health Organization (WHO) estimates that TB killed 1.8 million people worldwide in 2007. This resurgence of tuberculosis is linked to the spread of AIDS.

WHO estimates that one-third of the world's population is infected with *Mycobacterium tuberculosis*, the bacterium that causes tuberculosis. In most infected individuals, the immune system fights the infection and stops the bacterium from reproducing. The person doesn't feel sick, has no symptoms, and can't spread the disease. Among people with healthy immune systems, only 5–10% of those infected develop TB symptoms. But because HIV weakens the immune system, HIV-positive individuals are much more susceptible to developing the disease.

An HIV patient who contracts tuberculosis and is not treated has a 90–95% chance of dying in a few months. The leading cause of death among the HIV-infected population, tuberculosis accounts for 13% of AIDS deaths worldwide.

▲ *Mycobacterium tuberculosis.* TEM 1 µm

The good news is that tuberculosis can be treated successfully and inexpensively with a course of antibiotics taken faithfully for two to six months. Proper treatment and cure of tuberculosis can give an HIV patient years of additional life.

From: Critical Role of Bcr1-Dependent Adhesins in C. albicans Biofilm Formation In Vitro and In Vivo. C. J. Nobile, D. R. Andes, J. E. Nett, F. J. Smith Jr., F. Yue, et al. *PLoS Pathog.* 2006; 2(7):e63

testing. Definitive diagnosis of infection is by polymerase chain reaction assay. Most individuals develop antibodies within six months of infection, though some remain without detectable antibodies for three years or more. A positive test for antibodies does not mean that the patient is contagious, that HIV is currently present, or that the patient has or will develop AIDS; it merely indicates that the patient has been exposed to HIV.

A small percentage of infected individuals, called *long-term nonprogressors*, have not yet developed AIDS. It appears that these individuals are either infected with defective virions, lack effective coreceptors (CXCR4 and CCR5) needed to maintain an infection, or have unusually well-developed immune systems.

Discovering more effective treatment for AIDS is an area of intense research and development. Currently physicians prescribe **highly active antiretroviral therapy (HAART)**—a cocktail of antiviral drugs, including nucleoside analogs, protease inhibitors, and reverse transcriptase inhibitors—to reduce viral replication. HAART is expensive and must be taken on a fairly strict schedule. Studies indicate that HAART can stop the replication of HIV because strains of HIV are not likely to develop resistance to all the drugs simultaneously. As long as treatment continues, the patient can live a relatively normal life; however, treatment is not a cure, because the infection remains. Individual diseases associated with AIDS must be managed and treated on a case-by-case basis.

Progress in developing a vaccine against HIV has been disappointing. Among the problems that must be overcome in developing an effective vaccine are the following:

- A vaccine must generate both secretory IgA to prevent sexual transmission and infection, and cytotoxic T lymphocytes to eliminate infected cells.
- IgG induction, while a necessary part of a vaccine, can actually be detrimental to a patient. Because IgG-viral

complexes remain infective inside phagocytic cells, a vaccine must stimulate cellular immunity more than humoral immunity so that infected cells can be killed.

- HIV is highly mutable, generating antigenic variants that enable it to evade the immune response. Indeed, every nucleotide site of AIDS RNA is mutated with every incorrect nucleotide every day in an AIDS patient.
- HIV can spread through syncytia (formed by gp41) and thus can evade immune surveillance.
- HIV infects and inactivates macrophages, dendritic cells, and helper T cells—cells that combat infections and the very cells a vaccine would stimulate.
- Testing a vaccine presents ethical and medical problems because HIV is a pathogen of humans only. Scientists cannot ethically challenge vaccinated patients with active HIV.

Notwithstanding the challenges, scientists have developed a vaccine that protects monkeys from SIV disease and are hopeful that an effective vaccine for humans will become available. In the meantime, the principal way the AIDS epidemic can be slowed and eventually stopped is by effecting changes in behavior:

- Abstinence or faithful monogamy between uninfected individuals are the only truly safe behaviors. Studies have shown that although condoms reduce a heterosexual individual's risk of acquiring HIV by about 69%, the benefit of condom usage to a population can be offset by an overall increase in sexual activity. This finding presumably is due to a false sense of security that condoms provide.
- Use of new, clean needles and syringes for all injections, as well as caution in dealing with sharp, potentially contaminated objects, can reduce HIV infection rates. If clean supplies are not available, undiluted bleach or other antiviral agents can deactivate HIV.

### *Lentivirus human immunodeficiency virus* (HIV)

**Taxonomy:** Family *Retroviridae*

**Genome and morphology:** Two molecules of positive single-stranded RNA; polyhedral capsid with spiked envelope, about 110 to 145 nm in diameter

**Host:** Human

**Virulence factors:** Attaches to CD4 of helper T lymphocytes, vigorous mutation rate due to transcription errors of reverse transcriptase, latency

**Syndrome caused:** Acquired immunodeficiency syndrome

**Treatment for disease:** Highly active antiretroviral therapy (HAART), the so-called AIDS cocktail, composed of a variety of antiviral drugs such as nucleoside analogs, protease inhibitors, and inhibitors of reverse transcriptase

**Prevention of disease:** Sexual abstinence; monogamy. Refrain from sharing intravenous needles. Correct, consistent condom usage can reduce but not eliminate risk of infection. Male circumcision reduces risk of infection.

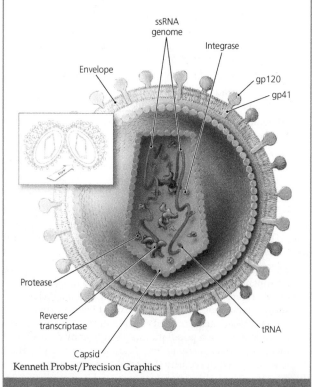

Kenneth Probst/Precision Graphics

- AZT given to pregnant women has reduced transplacental transfer of HIV, but infants can still be infected via breast milk. HIV-infected mothers should not breast-feed their infants.

- Screening of blood, blood products, and organ transplants for HIV and anti-HIV antibodies has virtually eliminated the risk of HIV infection from these sources.

- The CDC is considering recommending voluntary circumcision as a way to reduce the HIV transmission rate.

We have considered positive single-stranded RNA viruses, including retroviruses. Now we turn our attention to negative single-stranded RNA viruses.

# Enveloped, Unsegmented, Negative ssRNA Viruses: *Paramyxoviridae, Rhabdoviridae,* and *Filoviridae*

Viruses of the families *Paramyxoviridae, Rhabdoviridae,* and *Filoviridae* are enveloped, helical, negative, single-stranded RNA viruses. Recall that a negative RNA genome cannot be directly translated because its information is nonsensical to a ribosome; however, it is the complement of a readable sequence of nucleotides. Therefore, a −ssRNA virus must make a positive copy of its genome. The +ssRNA copy serves as mRNA for protein translation. The positive copy also serves as a template for transcription of more −ssRNA to be incorporated into new virions.

Viruses in the family *Paramyxoviridae* have similar morphologies and antigens. They also share the ability to cause infected cells to fuse with their neighbors, forming giant, multinucleate syncytia (Figure 25), which enable virions to pass from an infected cell into neighboring cells and to evade immune surveillance and antibodies. The family *Paramyxoviridae* contains four genera that infect humans: *Morbillivirus* (measles virus), *Respirovirus* (two species of parainfluenza viruses), *Rubulavirus* (mumps virus and two other species of parainfluenza viruses), and *Pneumovirus* (respiratory syncytial virus). **Highlight: Nipah Virus From Pigs to Humans** describes an emerging fatal disease caused by a newly identified genus in the *Paramyxoviridae.*

Rhabdoviruses *(Rhabdoviridae)* have bullet-shaped envelopes and include a variety of plant and animal pathogens. Rabies is the most significant pathogen among the rhabdoviruses.

Filoviruses *(Filoviridae)* are particularly significant because they are pathogens that cause a number of emerging and frightening diseases, including Ebola and Marburg hemorrhagic fevers.

## Measles

### Learning Objective

✓ Describe the signs and symptoms of rubeola and SSPE, and some ways of preventing them.

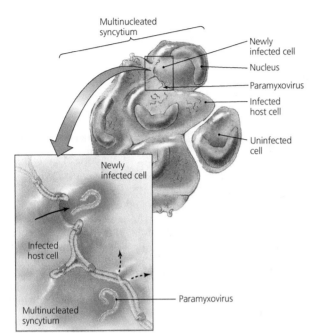

Kenneth Probst/Precision Graphics

▲ **Figure 25** **Syncytium formation.** Paramyxoviruses trigger infected cells to fuse with uninfected neighboring cells. Virions moving through these large multinucleate cells infect new cells, all the while evading the host's immune system.

P. Marazzi/Photo Researchers

Ulrich Niehoff

(a)

(b)

▲ **Figure 26** **Signs of measles. (a)** White Koplik's spots on the oral mucous membrane. **(b)** Raised lesions begin on the face and spread across the body. They may grow and fuse into large reddish patches.

Measles virus causes one of five classical childhood diseases. **Measles,** also known in the United States as *rubeola*[13] or *red measles,* is one of the more contagious and serious childhood diseases, and it should not be confused with the generally milder rubella (German measles). Table 7 compares and contrasts measles and rubella.

## Epidemiology of Measles Infections

Coughing, sneezing, and talking spread measles virus in the air via respiratory droplets. The virus infects cells of the respiratory tract before spreading via lymph and blood throughout the body. In addition to the respiratory tract, the conjunctiva, urinary tract, small blood vessels, lymphatics, and central nervous system become infected.

Humans are the only host for measles virus, and a large, dense population of susceptible individuals must be present for the virus to spread. In the United States before vaccination was instituted, measles outbreaks occurred in one- to three-year epidemic cycles as the critical number of susceptible individuals increased in the population. More than 80% of susceptible patients exposed to the virus developed symptoms 7–13 days after exposure.

Signs and symptoms include fever, sore throat, headache, dry cough, and conjunctivitis. After two days of illness, lesions

[13]Unfortunately, rubeola is the name given to rubella (German measles) in some other countries.

called **Koplik's spots** appear on the mucous membrane of the mouth (Figure 26a). These lesions, which have been described as grains of salt surrounded by a red halo, last one to two days and provide a definitive diagnosis of measles. Red, raised (maculopapular) lesions then appear on the head and spread over the body (Figure 26b). These lesions are extensive and often fuse to form red patches, which gradually turn brown as the disease progresses. Death may result.

Rare complications of measles include pneumonia, encephalitis, and the extremely serious **subacute sclerosing panencephalitis (SSPE).** SSPE is a slow, progressive disease of the central nervous system that involves personality changes, loss of memory, muscle spasms, and blindness. The disease begins 1–10 years after infection with measles virus and lasts a few years before resulting in death. A defective measles virus, which cannot make a capsid, causes SSPE. The virus replicates and moves from brain cell to brain cell via syncytia formation, limiting the functioning of infected cells and resulting in the symptoms. SSPE afflicts fewer than 7 measles patients in 1 million and is becoming much rarer as a result of vaccination of children.

An effective, live, attenuated vaccine for measles introduced in 1963 has eliminated measles as an endemic disease in the United States (Figure 27); however, measles remains a cause of death in other countries.

## Diagnosis, Treatment, and Prevention of Measles

The signs of measles, particularly Koplik's spots, are sufficient for diagnosis, but serological testing can confirm the presence of measles antigen in respiratory and blood specimens. No antiviral treatment is available.

Measles vaccine, in combination with vaccines against mumps and rubella (MMR vaccine), is given to children in the

Cases

150
120
90
60
30

1999 '00 '01 '02 '03 '04 '05 '06 '07 '08

Cases (thousands)

800

600

400

200

Attenuated
vaccine licensed

0

1950 '56 '62 '68 '74 '80 '86 '92 '98 '04 '10

Year

Precision Graphics

▲ **Figure 27** **Measles cases in the United States since 1950.** The number of cases has declined dramatically since vaccination began in 1963. *Why does the measles vaccine pose risks for immunocompromised contacts of vaccinated children?*

Figure 27 Measles vaccine is a live attenuated vaccine and can cause disease in the immunocompromised.

United States who are less than 15 months old. The measles portion of the vaccine is effective 95% of the time but is boosted before grade school to ensure protection against measles introduced from outside the country. Eradication of measles worldwide is possible, but there is no consensus among politicians and scientists that eradication would be worth the cost.

## Diseases of Parainfluenza Virus

### Learning Objective

✔ Identify the specific cause of croup.

Four strains of **parainfluenza viruses** (*Respirovirus*: human parainfluenza virus 1 and HPIV-3; and *Rubulavirus*: HPIV-2 and HPIV-4) cause respiratory tract disease, particularly in young children. Respiratory droplets and person-to-person contact transmit the virions. HPIV-1, 2, and 3 are associated with lower respiratory infections, whereas HPIV-4 is limited to mild, upper respiratory tract infections. **Croup** (kroop), a severe condition characterized by inflammation and swelling of the larynx, trachea, and bronchi and a "seal bark" cough, is a childhood disease of HPIV-1 and 2 and rarely of other respiratory viruses.

Most patients recover from parainfluenza infections within two days. There is no specific antiviral treatment beyond support and careful monitoring to check that airways do not become completely occluded. If they do, *intubation*, insertion of a tube into the airways, is necessary. Vaccination with deactivated virus is not effective, possibly because it fails to produce significant secretory antibody. Researchers have not developed a live attenuated vaccine against parainfluenza.

## Mumps

The **mumps** virus (*Rubulavirus*) is another −ssRNA virus. Mumps virions are spread in respiratory secretions and infect cells of the upper respiratory system. As virions are released from these areas, viremia develops, and a number of other organs are infected, resulting in fever and pain in swallowing. The parotid salivary glands, located just in front of the ears under

---

**HIGHLIGHT**

## NIPAH VIRUS: FROM PIGS TO HUMANS

Many diseases become known to science either when people encroach on a pathogen's home territory and come into contact with natural hosts, or when pathogens are introduced into geographical areas outside their historical range. Diseases resulting under such conditions are called *emerging diseases*. One example of an emerging disease is a new form of encephalitis that has appeared in Malaysia. The culprit: a never-before-identified virus now known as Nipah virus (genus *Henipavirus*) after the region in Malaysia in which it was discovered.

The victims of Nipah encephalitis experience high fever, severe headache, muscle pain, drowsiness, disorientation, convulsions, and coma. Forty percent of

them die. Serological investigations and RNA sequencing of the genome revealed that *Henipavirus* belongs to the family *Paramyxoviridae*. Victims contract Nipah virus from infected animals: 93% of Malaysian victims report occupational exposure to pigs.

How, then, do pigs become infected with Nipah virus? The prevailing theory involves human encroachment on bat habitats. Certain species of fruit bats are the natural hosts of Nipah virus. Highway workers pushing into these bats' rainforest habitats have disturbed their roosts, driving the bats into proximity with pig farms. The virus then "jumped" species and infected the pigs. Individuals working on pig farms or in slaughterhouses were subsequently infected either via the respiratory route

Andy Wong/ AP Images

▲ *Removing pigs to prevent the spread of Nipah virus.*

or through breaks in their skin and mucous membranes.

There is no cure for Nipah encephalitis, but scientists have inserted genes for *Henipavirus* proteins into cowpox virus, which thereby becomes an effective recombinant vaccine that protects against infection.

Barbara Rice, NIP/CDC

▲ **Figure 28 Parotitis.** This inflammation of the parotid salivary glands is a common sign of mumps.

Parotid salivary gland

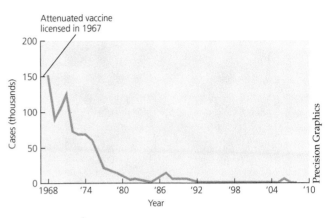

▲ **Figure 29 Incidence of mumps in the United States.** Mumps cases have declined since vaccination began in 1967. *With which other vaccines is mumps vaccine administered?*

Figure 29 *The mumps vaccine is administered with the measles and rubella vaccines.*

the skin covering the lower jaw, are particularly susceptible to the virus and become painfully enlarged, a condition known as *parotitis* (Figure 28). In some patients, the mumps virus causes inflammation of the testes (orchitis), meningitis, pancreatitis, or permanent deafness in one ear. In many other patients, infection is asymptomatic. Recovery from mumps is typically complete, and the patient has effective lifelong immunity.

There is no specific treatment for mumps. However, because an effective attenuated vaccine (MMR) is available and humans are the only natural host for the virus, mumps has almost been eradicated in the industrialized world (Figure 29). Epidemics of mumps in the late winter and early spring still occur in countries without vaccination programs, especially in densely populated areas.

## Disease of Respiratory Syncytial Virus

### Learning Objective

✓ Compare the effects of RSV infection in infants and adults.

**Respiratory syncytial virus (RSV)** in the genus *Pneumovirus* of the family *Paramyxoviridae* causes a disease of the lower respiratory tract, particularly in young children. As its name indicates, the virus causes formation of syncytia in the lungs. Additionally,

plugs of mucus, fibrin, and dead cells fill the smaller air passages, resulting in *dyspnea* (disp-nē′ă)—difficulty in breathing—and sometimes croup. RSV is the leading cause of fatal respiratory disease in infants and young children worldwide, especially those who are premature, immune impaired, or otherwise weakened. The disease in older children and adults is manifested as a cold or is asymptomatic. Most otherwise healthy people fully recover in one to two weeks.

Damage to the lungs is increased by the action of cytotoxic T cells and other specific immune responses to infection. Attempts at developing a vaccine with deactivated RSV have proven difficult because the vaccine enhances the severity of the cellular immune response and lung damage.

### Epidemiology of RSV Infection

RSV is prevalent in the United States: epidemiological studies reveal that 65–98% of children in day care centers are infected by age three. Approximately 125,000 infants require hospitalization each year, and about 2000 die. The virus is transmitted on fomites, hands, and less frequently via respiratory droplets. Because the virus is also extremely contagious, its introduction

**7**

| A Comparison of Measles and Rubella | | | | | |
|---|---|---|---|---|---|
| **Disease** | **Causative Agent** | **Primary Patient(s)** | **Complications** | **Skin Rash** | **Koplik's Spots** |
| **Measles** (also known as rubeola and red measles) | *Paramyxoviridae: Morbillivirus measles virus* | Child | Pneumonia, encephalitis, subacute sclerosing panencephalitis | Extensive | Present |
| **Rubella** (also known as German measles, rubeola, and three-day measles) | *Togaviridae: Rubivirus rubella virus* | Child, fetus | Birth defects | Mild | Absent |

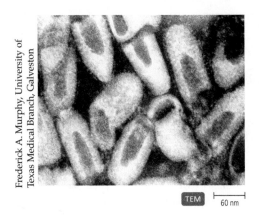

▲ **Figure 30  A rabies virus.** Note the bullet-shaped envelope.

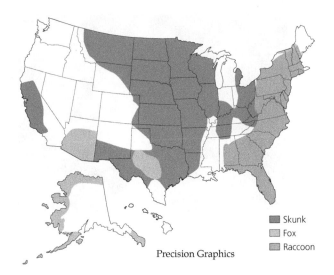

Skunk
Fox
Raccoon

Precision Graphics

▲ **Figure 31  Predominant wildlife reservoirs for rabies by area.** Absence of a color does not indicate the absence of rabies in that region, only that no wildlife reservoir is predominant. Bats, for instance, harbor rabies throughout the country but are rarely the predominant reservoir in an area. Nevertheless, bats are the major source of human infection.

into a nursery can be devastating; therefore, good aseptic technique by health care workers, and good hygiene by day care center employees, is essential. Handwashing and the use of gowns, goggles, masks, and gloves are important measures to reduce nosocomial infections.

### Diagnosis, Treatment, and Prevention of RSV Infection

Prompt diagnosis is essential if infected infants are to get the care they need. The signs of respiratory distress provide some diagnostic clues, but verification of RSV infection is made by immunoassay. Specimens of respiratory fluid may be tested by immunofluorescence, ELISA, or complementary DNA probes.

Supportive treatment involves administration of oxygen. Antisense RNA has shown promise in reducing the spread of RSV infection.

Control of RSV is limited to attempts to prevent the spread of RSV by frequent handwashing.

## Rabies

### Learning Objective

✓  Describe the effects, treatment, and prevention of rabies.

Although the cry "Mad dog! Mad dog!" may not make you apprehensive, in the 19th century—before Pasteur developed a rabies vaccine and treatment—a bite from a rabid dog was a death sentence, and the cry "Mad dog!" often spawned panic. Few people survived rabies before Pasteur's pivotal work.

**Rabies**[14] virus is a negative, single-stranded RNA (−ssRNA) virus in the genus *Lyssavirus,* family *Rhabdoviridae.* Like viruses in the family *Paramyxoviridae,* all of the rhabdoviruses have helical capsids, but those of rhabdoviruses are supercoiled into cylinders, which gives them a striated appearance, and are surrounded by bullet-shaped envelopes (Figure 30).

Glycoprotein spikes on the surface of the envelope serve as attachment proteins. Attachment to nerve cells triggers endocytosis, and rabies viruses then replicate in the cytoplasm of these cells. The virus is carried to the central nervous system via cytoplasmic flow within the neurons. The spinal cord and brain degenerate as a result of infection, though infected cells show little damage when examined microscopically. Viruses travel back to the periphery, including the salivary glands, through nerve cells. Viruses secreted in the saliva of infected mammals are typically the infective agents.

Initial signs and symptoms of rabies include pain or itching at the site of infection, fever, headache, malaise, and anorexia. Once viruses reach the central nervous system, neurological manifestations characteristic of rabies develop: **hydrophobia**[15] (triggered by the pain involved in attempts to swallow water), seizures, disorientation, hallucinations, and paralysis. Death results from respiratory paralysis and other neurological complications.

### Epidemiology of Rabies

Rabies is a classical zoonosis of mammals, though not all mammals are reservoirs. Rodents, for instance, rarely get rabies. The distribution of rabies in humans follows the distribution in animals. The primary animals involved differ from locale to locale and change over time as a result of dynamics of animal populations and interactions among animals and humans. The main reservoir of rabies in urban areas is the dog. In the wild, rabies can be found in foxes, badgers, raccoons, skunks, cats, bats, coyotes, and feral dogs (Figure 31). Bats are the source of most human cases of rabies in the United States, causing about 75% of cases between 1990 and 2008.

[14]From Latin *rabere,* meaning rage or madness.
[15]From Greek *hydro,* meaning water, and *phobos,* meaning fear.

Transmission of rabies viruses in the saliva of infected animals usually occurs via a bite. Infection is also possible via the introduction of viruses into breaks in the skin or mucous membranes or rarely through inhalation.

### Diagnosis, Treatment, and Prevention of Rabies

The neurological symptoms of rabies are unique and generally sufficient for diagnosis. Serological tests for antibodies can confirm a diagnosis. Postmortem laboratory tests are often conducted to determine whether a suspected animal in fact carries rabies virus. These tests include antigen detection by immunofluorescence and the identification of aggregates of virions (called **Negri bodies**) in the brain (Figure 32). Unfortunately, by the time symptoms and antibody production occur, it is too late to intervene, and the disease will follow its natural course **(Highlight: Rabies: A Threat from the Wild).**

The rabies vaccine—*human diploid cell vaccine (HDCV)*—is prepared from deactivated rabies viruses cultured in human diploid cells. It is administered intramuscularly on days 0, 3, 7, and 14 after exposure. The vaccine can also be administered prophylactically to workers who regularly come into contact with animals (veterinarians, zookeepers, and animal control workers) and to people traveling to areas of the world where rabies is prevalent.

Treatment of rabies begins with treatment of the site of infection. The wound should be thoroughly cleansed with water and soap or another substance that deactivates viruses. The World Health Organization recommends anointing the wound with antirabies serum. Initial treatment also involves injection

Biophoto Associates/Photo Researchers

▲ **Figure 32** **Negri bodies, a characteristic of rabies infection.** Here the viruses are in human cerebellum brain cells. *What are Negri bodies?*

*Figure 32 Negri bodies are stained aggregates of rabies virions.*

of *human rabies immune globulin (HRIG)*. Subsequent treatment involves five vaccine injections. Rabies is one of the few infections that can be treated with active immunization, because the progress of viral replication and movement to the brain is slow enough to allow effective immunity to develop before disease develops.

## HIGHLIGHT

### RABIES: A THREAT FROM THE WILD

Vaccination of cats and dogs has sharply reduced the number of cases of human rabies in the United States; however, infections from wild animals still result in a few cases of rabies each year.

In one case, a man entered the hospital with neurological disorders that produced uncontrolled facial twitching, anxiety, and feelings of fear. He also had a sore throat, difficulty in swallowing, and complained of itching all over his body. Though the symptoms were typical of rabies, it was not diagnosed because there was no history of an animal bite.

The patient remained alive for several days, but became increasingly agitated and refused to drink because of the pain involved in swallowing. He vomited repeatedly and his temperature rose to 106°F. He died one week after being admitted to the hospital.

An autopsy revealed circulating antibodies against rabies virus as well as Negri bodies in the victim's brain. Epidemiologists determined from interviews with the man's neighbors that a bat had landed on his face about a month before the symptoms began, though the bat had not bitten him. Possibly the bat scratched the man during the encounter and transmitted the virus. This story reinforces the recommendation of the Centers for Disease Control and Prevention (CDC) that all contacts with wild animals (particularly bats, skunks, foxes, and feral dogs) be taken seriously and rabies prophylaxis administered.

Not all cases of rabies exposure are so tragic. In 1885, a rabid dog savagely mauled a young boy, Joseph Meister. His distraught mother brought the boy

to Louis Pasteur, who was in the process of perfecting the rabies vaccine. The vaccine had never been tested on humans, but with assurance from doctors that the boy would surely die without treatment, Pasteur injected the 14 doses of attenuated virus that made up the vaccine at that time. Joseph survived and Pasteur's fame and fortune were further secured.

USGS Biological Resources Division, Western Ecological Research Center

Science Source/Photo Researchers

TEM | 250 nm

▲ **Figure 33** **Filamentous Ebola viruses.** Filoviruses can be up to 14,000 nm long.

Precision Graphics

■ Marburg
△ Ebola

▲ **Figure 34** **Sites in which localized human disease cases of Marburg and Ebola viruses are known to have occurred.**

Ultimately, control of rabies involves immunization of domestic dogs and cats and the removal of unwanted strays from urban areas. Little can be done to completely eliminate rabies in wild animals because rabies virus can infect so many species, though in the late 1990s an epidemic of rabies was stopped in southern Texas by the successful vaccination of the wild coyote population. This was accomplished by lacing meat with an oral vaccine and dropping it from airplanes into the coyotes' range.

## Hemorrhagic Fevers

### Learning Objective

✓ Describe the effects of filoviruses on the human body.

Filamentous viruses that cause **hemorrhagic fever** were originally placed in the *Rhabdoviridae* but have now been assigned to their own family, *Filoviridae,* primarily on the basis of the symptoms they cause. These enveloped viruses form long filaments, sometimes up to 14,000 nm long, that sometimes curve back upon themselves (Figure 33).

There are two known filoviruses: Marburg virus and Ebola virus. **Marburg virus** was first isolated from laboratory workers in Marburg, Germany, and it has also been found in Zimbabwe, Kenya, Uganda, Angola, and in the Democratic Republic of the Congo (DRC). Outbreaks of **Ebola virus** hemorrhagic fever were first recorded in the DRC in 1976 near the Ebola River. Ebola cases have also occurred in humans in Sudan, Ivory Coast, Gabon, Uganda, South Africa, Congo, and in a single laboratory worker in England via an accidental needlestick (Figure 34).

The natural reservoirs of filoviruses appear to be fruit bats, but the initial method of transmission to humans is unknown. The virions attack many cells of the body, especially macrophages and liver cells. One predominant manifestation is uncontrolled bleeding under the skin and from every body

opening as the internal organs are reduced to a jelly-like consistency. Hemorrhaging appears to be due to the synthesis of a virally coded glycoprotein that is expressed on the surface of infected cells lining blood vessels. The glycoprotein prevents neighboring cells from adhering to one another, allowing blood to leak out of the vessels. Headache and severe fever accompany this "meltdown." Up to 90% of human victims of Ebola die, and

## CLINICAL CASE STUDY

### The Sick Addict

▲ *Thrush.*

CDC

A 25-year-old male was admitted to the hospital with thrush, diarrhea, unexplained weight loss, and difficulty in breathing. Cultures of pulmonary fluid revealed the presence of *Pneumocystis jiroveci.* The man admitted to being a heroin addict and to sharing needles in a "shooting gallery."

1. What laboratory tests could confirm a diagnosis in this case?

2. How did the man most likely acquire the infection?

3. What changes to the man's immune system allowed the opportunistic infections of *Candida* (thrush) and *Pneumocystis* to arise?

4. What precautions should be taken with the patient's blood?

James Gathany, CDC

▲ **Figure 35 Working in a Biosafety Level 4 lab.** The "space suit," which is designed to completely prevent contact with pathogens, constitutes more than a physical barrier; should the material of the suit be breached, positive air pressure within the suit ensures that pathogens present will be blown back from the opening.

about 25% of Marburg victims die. Epidemics sometimes cease only when there are not enough living humans to sustain viral transmission.

Marburg and Ebola viruses spread from person to person via contaminated bodily fluids, primarily blood, and through the use of contaminated syringes. Even a small amount of infected blood contacting a mucous membrane or conjunctiva can induce disease. Ebola virus can also spread among monkeys through the air, but aerosol transmission from monkeys to humans or among humans has not been observed.

The symptoms of filovirus infection are diagnostic. Additionally, the typical curved virus filaments are found in the victim's blood. Investigators detect antigens and antibodies using immunofluorescence, ELISA, or radioactive immunoassay. Extreme caution must be exercised in dealing with Ebola and Marburg patients and their bodily fluids. In fact, Biosafety Level 4—which involve the use of complete "space suits" to protect laboratory workers from contact with blood, vomit, or any other bodily fluids that might be contaminated with virus (Figure 35)—is mandatory. The only treatment for Ebola and Marburg fevers involves fluid replacement.

In 2003, scientists developed a vaccine that protects monkeys from Ebola in as little as 28 days. Immunization involves injecting pieces of viral nucleic acid (both by themselves and inserted into adenovirus capsids) into the monkeys. It is not known whether the vaccine will protect humans.

### CRITICAL **THINKING**

Ebola hemorrhagic fever belongs to a group of diseases called "emerging diseases"—diseases that were previously unidentified or had never been identified in human populations. Emerging diseases are often first seen in less-developed countries such as the DRC. What factors may explain the emergence of new diseases in these countries?

Iowa State University Library, University Archives

▲ **Figure 36 A scene from the influenza pandemic of 1918–19.** Flu afflicted so many people in the United States that gymnasiums were used as hospital wards.

# Enveloped, Segmented, Negative ssRNA Viruses: *Orthomyxoviridae, Bunyaviridae,* and *Arenaviridae*

A second group of negative, enveloped, single-stranded RNA viruses differ from those in the previous section in having a **segmented genome;** that is, their capsids contain more than one molecule of nucleic acid. These viruses include the flu viruses of the family *Orthomyxoviridae* and hundreds of viruses in the families *Bunyaviridae* and *Arenaviridae* that normally infect animals but can be transmitted to humans.

## Influenza

### Learning Objective

✓ Describe the roles of hemagglutinin and neuraminidase in the replication cycle of influenzaviruses.

Imagine being the only elementary schoolchild of your sex in your mid-sized town because all of your peers died six winters ago. Or imagine returning to college after a break, only to learn that half of your fraternity brothers had died during the previous two months. These vignettes are not fictional; they happened to relatives of this author during the great flu pandemic in the winter of 1918–19 (Figure 36). During that winter, half the world's 1.9 billion people were infected with a new, extremely virulent strain of influenza virus, and an estimated 50 million died during that one flu season. In some U.S. cities, 10,000 people died each week for several months. Could it happen again? In this section we will learn about the characteristics of influenzaviruses that enable flu—a common infection, second only to common colds—to produce such devastating epidemics, and some ways to protect ourselves from the flu.

NIBSC/Photo Researchers

TEM | 100 nm

▲ **Figure 37** **Influenzaviruses budding from an infected cell.** *What are the types of glycoprotein spikes on influenzaviruses, and what is their relationship to viral strain?*

*Figure 37 Glycoprotein spikes on influenzaviruses are neuraminidase (NA) and hemagglutinin (HA); variations in these glycoproteins determine the strain of the virus.*

The causes of **influenza**[16] (in-flū-en′zǎ), or **flu,** are two species of orthomyxoviruses, designated types A and B. An influenza virion contains a genome consisting of eight different −ssRNA molecules surrounded by a pleomorphic (many-shaped) lipid envelope studded with prominent glycoprotein spikes composed of either **hemagglutinin**[17] (hě′mǎ-glū′ti-nin) **(HA)** or **neuraminidase** (nūr-ǎ-min′i-dāz) **(NA)** (Figure 37). Both HA and NA play roles in the attachment (and thus the virulence) of the viruses: NA spikes provide the virus access to cell surfaces by hydrolyzing mucus in the lungs, whereas HA spikes attach to pulmonary epithelial cells and trigger endocytosis. Because influenzaviruses rarely attack cells outside the lungs, so-called stomach flu is probably caused by enteroviruses and not by orthomyxoviruses.

The genomes of flu viruses are extremely variable, especially with respect to the genes that code for HA and NA. Mutations are responsible for the production of new strains of influenzavirus, via processes known as antigenic drift and antigenic shift. **Antigenic** (an-ti-gen′ik) **drift** (Figure 38a) refers to the accumulation of HA and NA mutations within a single strain of virus in a given geographic area. Such mutations produce relatively minor variations in spike glycoproteins. As a result of these minor changes in the virus's antigenicity, localized increases in the number of flu infections occur about every two years. **Antigenic shift** (Figure 38b) is a major antigenic change in influenza A resulting from the reassortment of genomes from different influenzavirus strains infecting the same host cells (ei-

[16]*Influenza,* which is Italian for "influence," derives from the mistaken idea that the alignment of celestial objects caused or "influenced" the disease.
[17]The word *hemagglutinin* refers to these spikes' ability to attach to and clump (agglutinate) red blood cells.

ther human hosts or animal hosts, including birds and pigs). On average, antigenic shift occurs in influenza A every 10 years. Asia is a major site of antigenic shift, and the source of most pandemic strains, because the very high population densities of humans, domesticated birds and pigs there; however, the 2009 H1N1 pandemic strain resulted from genetic reassortment of four influenza A viruses in animals and humans, most likely in Mexico.

In 2005, researchers determined the genetic sequence of the 1918–19 pandemic strain by analyzing preserved tissue from flu victims. They discovered that a combination of genes from influenza A viruses from birds, pigs, and humans caused the pandemic. The 2009 H1N1 strain contains many of the same genetic sequences as the 1918–19 strain, leading epidemiologists to estimate that one third of the world's population could be infected in this new pandemic. The outcome of the pandemic could be as severe as the 1918–19 outbreak, despite vaccines, antiviral drugs, and modern health care facilities, because there are so many more people today, we live closer together in urban areas, and international air travel make it easier for influenzaviruses to spread. WHO officials consider 2 million deaths worldwide a "best-case" scenario, though some epidemiologists estimated that over 360 million people could die from H1N1. **Emerging Diseases: H1N1 Influenza** illustrates one patient's story.

Once virions are taken into epithelial cells lining the lung, the viral envelopes fuse with the membranes of cellular vesicles. Viruses multiply using positive-sense RNA molecules both for translation of viral proteins and as templates for transcription of new −ssRNA genomes.

During the process by which virions bud from the cytoplasmic membrane of infected cells (see Figure 37), NA keeps viral proteins from clumping. During budding, genomic segments are enveloped in a random manner, such that each virion ends up with about 11 RNA molecules. However, to be functional, a virion must have at least one copy of each of the eight genomic segments. Numerous defective particles are released for every functional virion formed.

Deaths of epithelial cells infected with influenzaviruses eliminate the lungs' first line of defense against infection, its epithelial lining. As a result, flu patients are more susceptible to secondary bacterial infection. One common infecting bacterium is *Haemophilus influenzae* (hē-mof′i-lǔs in-flu-en′zī), which was mistakenly named because it was found in so many flu victims.

The signs and symptoms of flu—fever, malaise, headache, and myalgia (body aches)—are induced by cytokines released as part of the immune response. Rarely, flu viruses cause croup. The symptoms of influenza are compared to those of other respiratory infections in Table 1.

### Epidemiology of Influenza

The changing antigens of orthomyxoviruses guarantee that there will be susceptible people, especially children, each flu season. Infection occurs primarily through inhalation of airborne viruses but can also occur via fomites.

Strains of influenza are named by type (A or B), location and date of original identification, and antigen (HA and NA). For example, A/Singapore/1/09 (H1N2) is influenza type A,

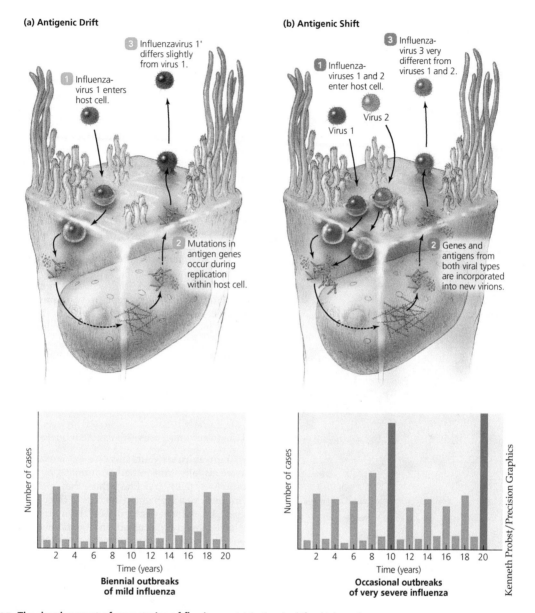

**(a) Antigenic Drift**

1 Influenza-virus 1 enters host cell.

3 Influenzavirus 1' differs slightly from virus 1.

2 Mutations in antigen genes occur during replication within host cell.

Number of cases

Time (years)
**Biennial outbreaks of mild influenza**

**(b) Antigenic Shift**

1 Influenza-viruses 1 and 2 enter host cell.

Virus 1  Virus 2

3 Influenza-virus 3 very different from viruses 1 and 2.

2 Genes and antigens from both viral types are incorporated into new virions.

Number of cases

Time (years)
**Occasional outbreaks of very severe influenza**

Kenneth Probst/Precision Graphics

▲ **Figure 38  The development of new strains of flu viruses. (a)** Antigenic drift, which results from variation in the NA and HA spikes of a single strain of influenzavirus. **(b)** Antigenic shift, which occurs when RNA molecules from two or more influenzaviruses infecting a single cell are incorporated into a single virion. Because antigenic shift produces significantly greater antigenic variability than occurs in antigenic drift, antigenic shifts can result in major epidemics or pandemics.

isolated in Singapore in January 2009, that contains HA and NA antigens of type 1 and type 2, respectively. If the virus is isolated from an animal, the animal name is appended to the location. From these names, common names such as "Hong Kong flu" or "swine flu" arise. The number of different flu strains is almost infinite.

Every year millions of Americans are infected, and an estimated 64,000 Americans die annually of flu-related illness. Pa-

tients with weak immune systems, including the very young, the elderly, and those immunocompromised as a result of cancer therapy or disease, are particularly vulnerable.

**Diagnosis, Treatment, and Prevention of Influenza**

The manifestation of flu signs and symptoms during a community-wide outbreak of the flu is often sufficient for

## MICROBE AT A GLANCE

### *Influenzavirus A* and *Influenzavirus B*

**Taxonomy:** Family *Orthomyxoviridae*

**Genome and morphology:** Eight molecules of negative single-stranded RNA in helical capsids, surrounded by an envelope

**Hosts:** Vertebrates, including humans, pigs, birds, horses, sea mammals

**Virulence factors:** Hemagglutinin and neuraminidase glycoproteins allow attachment to pulmonary cells where viruses induce their own endocytosis

**Syndrome caused:** Influenza (flu)

**Treatment for disease:** Amantadine, oseltamivir, zanamivir

**Prevention of disease:** Annual vaccine provides protection against some strains

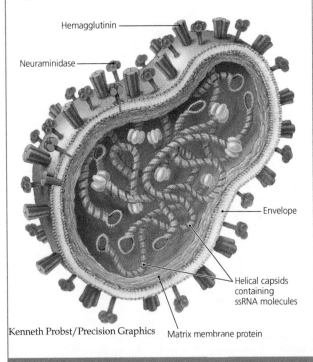

Hemagglutinin

Neuraminidase

Envelope

Helical capsids containing ssRNA molecules

Kenneth Probst/Precision Graphics   Matrix membrane protein

 Download the Microbe at a Glance flashcards from the Study Area at www.masteringmicrobiology.com.

diagnosis of influenza. Laboratory tests such as immunofluorescence or ELISA can distinguish strains of flu virus.

Hundreds of millions of dollars are spent each year in the United States on antihistamines and pain relievers to alleviate flu symptoms. Aspirin and aspirin-like products should not be used to treat the symptoms of flu in children and teenagers because of increased risk of *Reye's syndrome*.

Oseltamivir pills or inhaled zanamivir mist are neuraminidase inhibitors that block the release of virions from infected cells. These prescription drugs must be taken during the first 48 hours of infection because they cannot prevent the later immunopathogenic manifestations of the disease. Scientists using computer modeling of epidemics estimate that if a flu patient passes the virus to only one or two other people, then an epidemic can be stopped with antiviral drugs. However, health care workers and drug manufacturers would be overwhelmed if each sick person infected three or more contacts.

The greatest success in controlling flu epidemics has come from culling infected birds and from immunization by injection or inhalation with multivalent vaccines, that is, vaccines that contain several antigens at once. The WHO has personnel in Asia who track changes in the HA and NA antigens of emerging flu viruses. Newly discovered antigens are then used to create flu vaccine in advance of the next flu season in the United States. The vaccines are at least 70% effective but only against the viral antigens they contain.

Flu vaccines are made of deactivated viruses; therefore, contrary to many people's perception, you cannot get flu from the vaccine. However, you may get flu from strains of influenzavirus not included in the vaccine. Flu vaccine usually provides protection for no more than three years. Natural active immunity as a result of infection lasts much longer but is probably not lifelong.

## Diseases of Bunyaviruses

### Learning Objective

✓ Contrast hantaviruses with the other bunyaviruses.

Most **bunyaviruses** (bun'ya-vī'rŭs-ĕz) are zoonotic pathogens that are usually transmitted to humans by biting arthropods (mosquitoes, ticks, and flies); thus, they are arboviruses. Bunyaviruses have a segmented genome of three −ssRNA molecules (Figure 39), which distinguishes them from the arboviruses we have already discussed in the families *Togaviridae* and *Flaviviridae,* which have unsegmented +ssRNA.

### Epidemiology of Bunyavirus Infections

Four genera of *Bunyaviridae* contain human pathogens. The viruses of *Rift Valley fever, California encephalitis,* and *hemorrhagic fevers* are arboviruses and thus enter the blood through the bite of an arthropod, which establishes an initial viremia. The blood carries viruses to target organs, such as the brain, kidney, liver, or blood vessels. Each bunyavirus has a specific target, and different viruses cause encephalitis, fever, or rash. Most patients have mild symptoms, but symptomatic cases can be severe and fatal.

**Hantaviruses** are an exceptional type of bunyaviruses: they are not arboviruses, but are transmitted to humans via inhalation of virions in dried mouse urine or feces. Two American strains[18] of hantaviruses infect the lungs only, causing a rapid, severe, and often fatal pneumonia called *Hantavirus* (han'tā-vī'rŭs) **pulmonary syndrome (HPS).** This syndrome was first

[18]Sin Nombre and Convict Creek strains.

recognized during an epidemic in the Four Corners[19] area of the United States in May 1993.

Bunyaviruses cause human diseases around the world. Each virus is typically found only in certain geographic areas. However, with modern travel patterns, viruses can be introduced into new areas relatively easily.

### Diagnosis, Treatment, and Prevention of Bunyavirus Infections

Diseases caused by bunyavirus infections are indistinguishable from illnesses caused by several other viruses, so laboratory tests must be employed for diagnosis. ELISAs are used to detect viral antigens associated with Rift Valley fever, the LaCrosse strain of California encephalitis, and hemorrhagic fevers. Hantaviruses in the United States were first identified in patients' tissue using the *reverse transcriptase polymerase chain reaction*: viral RNA was transcribed to DNA using retroviral reverse transcriptase, multiple copies of the DNA were generated through polymerase chain reaction, and the resulting strands were compared to known hantavirus sequences.

No specific treatment exists for most bunyavirus infections. Human disease caused by arboviruses is prevented by limiting

[19]Four Corners is the geographic area where Arizona, Utah, New Mexico, and Colorado meet.

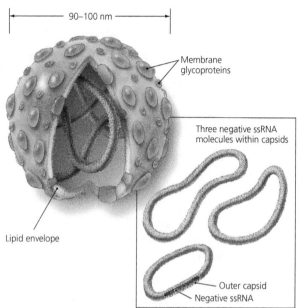

90–100 nm

Membrane glycoproteins

Three negative ssRNA molecules within capsids

Lipid envelope

Outer capsid
Negative ssRNA

Kenneth Probst / Precision Graphics

▲ **Figure 39** **A bunyavirus is an enveloped helical virion.** The genome consists of three −ssRNA molecules.

---

DISEASES

iStockPhoto

Precision Graphics

## H1N1 INFLUENZA

Middle school is supposed to be a time of exploration, learning, and fun, but Maria was too sick to enjoy it right now. Her 104°F fever had lasted two very unpleasant days, but at last it had gone. For another two days she ached all over and was dizzy; her head felt as if it could explode at any moment; and the nausea, frequent vomiting, and extreme tiredness were unrelenting. For over a week her tired red eyes stared listlessly as she struggled to cope with a constantly running nose, severe sore throat, and a dry hacking cough. Would this onslaught never end? A newly emerging strain of influenza type A had a victim in its grasp.

Flu viruses infect birds, pigs, horses, and humans. These viruses normally mutate, producing slightly different strains every year—a process called antigenic drift. About once a decade, however, different strains of influenzaviruses infect a single cell and within it they exchange major pieces of RNA, producing a new, quite different strain of virus—a process called antigenic shift. The virus attacking Maria was such a newly emerged influenzavirus, a strain that contained RNA from influenzaviruses of humans, birds, and swine in a novel combination. The virus, commonly called swine flu virus, is officially 2009A(H1N1).

This new strain can have devastating and sometimes fatal effects on hosts because it has antigenic combinations that the adaptive immune system has never seen before, necessitating a prolonged defensive response before the body can conquer the infection. When H1N1 flu cases reached epidemic levels on multiple continents by June 2009, the World Health Organization declared a pandemic—the first flu pandemic since 1968. During this period, the well-known signs and symptoms of flu play out.

Maria was exhausted and weak for another two weeks, but she survived the flu, though many other patients were not so fortunate.

 **(MM)** Track H1N1 influenza online by going to the Study Area at www.masteringmicrobiology.com.

Charles Humphrey/CDC

▲ **Figure 40** **The sandy appearance of arenaviruses.** The graininess results from the presence of numerous ribosomes within the capsid. Although the ribosomes are functional, the virions apparently do not use them.

contact with the vectors (the use of netting and insect repellents) and by reducing arthropod abundance (elimination of breeding sites and the use of insecticides). Rodent control is necessary to prevent *Hantavirus* pulmonary syndrome. A vaccine has been developed to protect humans and animals against Rift Valley fever, and ribavirin has proved effective in treating Crimean-Congo hemorrhagic fever.

## Diseases of Arenaviruses

### Learning Objectives

✓ Identify the distinguishing characteristics of arenaviruses.

✓ Describe the unique feature of satellite viruses such as hepatitis D virus.

**Arenaviruses**[20] (ă-rē′nă-vī′rŭs-ĕz) are the final group of segmented, negative ssRNA viruses we will consider. Their segmented genomes are each composed of two RNA molecules. Most arenaviruses contain ribosomes, which gives them a sandy appearance in electron micrographs (Figure 40). The ribosomes are functional *in vitro*,[21] but there is no evidence that the viruses utilize them in nature.

### Zoonoses

Arenaviruses cause zoonoses that include hemorrhagic fevers named for locales where they occur (**Lassa** in Africa, **Junin** in Argentina, **Sabiá** in Brazil, and **Machupo** in Bolivia) and **lymphocytic choriomeningitis** (lim-fō-sit′ik kō-rē-ō-men-in-jī′ tis) **(LCM).** Hemorrhagic fever viruses in the family *Arenaviridae*

[20]From Greek *arenosa*, meaning sandy.
[21]From Latin *in*, meaning within, and *vitreus*, meaning glassware; in other words "in the laboratory."

are endemic in rodent populations in Africa and South America. They cause severe bleeding under the skin and into internal organs. LCM virus has been found infecting pet hamsters in the United States. Contrary to its name, LCM is rarely associated with meningitis but more typically manifests with flulike symptoms.

Humans become infected through the inhalation of aerosols or consumption of contaminated food or from fomites. Lassa fever virus can be spread from human to human through contact with bodily fluids.

Diagnosis of arenaviral diseases is based on a combination of symptoms and immunoassay. Fluid samples from hemorrhagic patients are too dangerous for normal laboratories and instead must be processed in maximum biocontainment facilities. LCM samples can be handled with Biosafety Level 3 procedures (gown, mask, gloves, and labs with laminar flow hoods).

Supportive care is usually all that can be done for patients with arenavirus zoonoses, though ribavirin has shown some benefit in treating Lassa fever. Prevention of arenavirus disease involves rodent control and limiting contact with rodents, their droppings, and their dried urine.

### Hepatitis D

**Hepatitis D virus** *(Deltavirus),* which is also known as *delta agent,* is an arenavirus that causes hepatitis D and plays a role along with hepatitis B virus in triggering liver cancer. Delta agent is unusual in that it does not possess genes for the glycoproteins it requires to attach to liver cells. To become infective, it "steals" the necessary glycoprotein molecules from hepatitis B viruses that are simultaneously infecting the same liver cell. For this reason, hepatitis D virus is called a **satellite virus** because its replication cycle "revolves around" a helper virus.

Like hepatitis B virus, hepatitis D virus is spread in bodily fluids via sexual activity and the use of contaminated needles. Prevention involves the same precautions used to prevent infection with hepatitis B virus—abstinence, monogamy, condom usage, the use of sterile needles, and avoidance of accidental needlesticks. Since hepatitis D virus requires hepatitis B virus to become virulent, hepatitis B vaccine limits the spread of hepatitis D viruses.

## Naked, Segmented dsRNA Viruses: *Reoviridae*

### Learning Objective

✓ Discuss the meaning of the name "reovirus."

**Reoviruses** (rē′ō-vī′rŭs-ĕz) are respiratory and enteric viruses with naked icosahedral capsids. They are unique in being the only microbes, viral or cellular, with genomes composed of double-stranded RNA (dsRNA). Each virus contains 10–12 segments of dsRNA.

Reoviruses were originally orphan viruses—not initially associated with any diseases—though now many have been linked to specific conditions. The acronym *reo* is derived from *respiratory, enteric, orphan.* Reoviruses include *Rotavirus* and *Coltivirus.*

Linda Stanard/Photo Researchers

TEM  50 nm

▲ **Figure 41 Rotaviruses.** The wheel-like appearance of rotaviruses, from which they get their name.

## Rotaviruses

### Learning Objective

✓ Describe the effects of rotavirus infections.

*Rotavirus*[22] (rō′tă-vī′rŭs) is an almost spherical reovirus with prominent glycoprotein spikes **(Figure 41)**. During replication, rotaviruses acquire and then lose an envelope. Even without envelopes, they function like enveloped viruses because glycoprotein spikes on their capsids act as attachment molecules that trigger endocytosis, a process common to enveloped viruses. Rotaviruses infect almost all children everywhere in the first few years of life via the fecal-oral route.

Rotaviruses are the most common cause of infantile gastroenteritis and account annually in the U.S. for about 55,000 cases of diarrhea in children requiring hospitalization as a result of fluid and electrolyte loss. In developing countries, rotaviruses account for an estimated 600,000 deaths annually from uncontrolled diarrhea **(Figure 42)**. Infected children may pass as many as 100 trillion virions per gram of stool.

---

[22]From Latin *rota*, meaning wheel.

Rotavirus infection is self-limiting, and treatment involves supportive care such as replacement of lost water and electrolytes. Prevention of infection involves good personal hygiene, proper sewage treatment, and vaccination. The vaccine approved for use in the U.S. prevents 75% of rotavirus cases and reduces hospitalizations and deaths by more than 96%.

## Coltiviruses

### Learning Objective

✓ Discuss the most common disease caused by a coltivirus.

*Coltivirus* (kol′tē-vī′rŭs) is an arbovirus that causes a zoonosis, **Colorado tick fever** (see Table 4), for which these viruses are named. Colorado tick fever is usually a mild disease involving fever and chills, though severe cases can manifest as headache, photophobia, myalgia, conjunctivitis, rash, and, in children, hemorrhaging. Colorado tick fever should not be confused with Rocky Mountain spotted fever, a tick-borne bacterial disease. Colorado tick fever is self-limiting, but red blood cells in all stages of development retain the virus for some time. Patients should not donate blood for several months after recovery.

Health care providers diagnose Colorado tick fever by detecting antigens in the blood using ELISA or other immunoassays. As with many viral diseases, there is no specific treatment. Prevention involves limiting contact with infected ticks.

RNA viruses are a heterogeneous group of virions capable of causing diseases of varying severity, including several life-threatening ones. Table 8 summarizes the physical characteristics of most RNA viruses of humans, as well as the diseases they cause. As we have seen, RNA viruses pose significant problems for health care personnel with respect to diagnosis, treatment, and prevention, and some of these viruses also pose threats to health care workers who must handle them. Emerging RNA viruses are of particular concern as people move deeper into rainforests and come into contact with new viral agents, but such viruses have also provided the impetus for expanded research into the fields of immunization and treatment of viral diseases.

▶ **Figure 42 Deaths from rotaviral diarrhea (2008).** Mortality is most common in developing countries.

• = 1000 deaths

Precision Graphics

## 8

## TABLE

## Taxonomy and Characteristics of Human RNA Viruses

| Family | Strand Type | Enveloped or Naked | Capsid Symmetry | Size (nm) | Representative Genera (Diseases) |
|---|---|---|---|---|---|
| *Picornaviridae* | Single, positive | Naked | Icosahedral | 22–30 | *Enterovirus* (polio) <br> *Rhinovirus* (common cold) <br> *Hepatovirus* (hepatitis A) |
| *Caliciviridae* | Single, positive | Naked | Icosahedral | 35–40 | *Norovirus* (acute gastroenteritis) |
| *Hepeviridae* | Single, positive | Naked | Icosahedral | 27–34 | *Hepevirus* (hepatitis E) |
| *Astroviridae* | Single, positive | Naked | Icosahedral | 30 | *Astrovirus* (gastroenteritis) |
| *Togaviridae* | Single, positive | Enveloped | Icosahedral | 40–75 | *Alphavirus* (encephalitis) <br> *Rubivirus* (rubella) |
| *Flaviviridae* | Single, positive | Enveloped | Icosahedral | 37–50 | *Flavivirus* (yellow fever) <br> *Hepacivirus* (hepatitis C) |
| *Coronaviridae* | Single, positive | Enveloped | Helical | 80–160 | *Coronavirus* (common cold, severe acute respiratory syndrome) |
| *Retroviridae* | Single, positive, segmented | Enveloped | Icosahedral | 80–146 | *Deltaretrovirus* (leukemia) <br> *Lentivirus* (AIDS) |
| *Paramyxoviridae* | Single, negative | Enveloped | Helical | 125–250 | *Paramyxovirus* (colds, respiratory infections) <br> *Pneumovirus* (respiratory syncytial disease, rarely croup or common cold) <br> *Morbillivirus* (measles) <br> *Rubulavirus* (mumps) |
| *Rhabdoviridae* | Single, negative | Enveloped | Helical | $75 \times 130$–240 | *Lyssavirus* (rabies) |
| *Filoviridae* | Single, negative | Enveloped | Helical | 790–970 | *Ebolavirus* (Ebola hemorrhagic fever) <br> *Marburgvirus* (Marburg hemorrhagic fever) |
| *Orthomyxoviridae* | Single, negative, segmented | Enveloped | Helical | 80–120 | *Influenzavirus* (flu, rarely croup) |
| *Bunyaviridae* | Single, negative, segmented | Enveloped | Helical | 90–100 | *Bunyavirus* (encephalitis) <br> *Hantavirus* (pneumonia) |
| *Arenaviridae* | Single, negative, segmented | Enveloped | Helical | 50–300 | *Lassavirus* (hemorrhagic fever) <br> *Deltavirus* (hepatitis D) |
| *Reoviridae* | Double, segmented | Naked | Icosahedral | 78–80 | *Rotavirus* (diarrhea) <br> *Coltivirus* (Colorado tick fever) |

# Chapter Summary

## Naked, Positive ssRNA Viruses: *Picornaviridae*, *Caliciviridae*, *Astroviridae*, and *Hepeviridae*

1. RNA viruses and viroids are the only infective agents that use RNA molecules as their genetic material.

2. **Picornaviruses** are the smallest of animal viruses and include the **rhinoviruses** and **enteroviruses.** Rhinoviruses are extremely infective in the upper respiratory tract and cause most "common" colds. Enteroviruses, which are mostly cytolytic picornaviruses that infect via the fecal-oral route, include poliovirus, coxsackievirus, and echovirus.

3. **Poliomyelitis,** or **polio,** is a disease of varied degrees of severity from asymptomatic infections to **bulbar poliomyelitis** (requiring an iron lung to assist in breathing), and postpolio syndrome occurring 30–40 years after infection. Eradication of polio, due to effective vaccination, is imminent.

4. Jonas Salk developed **inactivated polio vaccine (IPV)** in 1955. It was replaced by live **oral polio vaccine (OPV),** which was developed by Albert Sabin in 1961. Now, health professionals in many countries have switched back to IPV because OPV, which is a live, attenuated vaccine, can revert to a disease-causing form.

5. **Coxsackie A virus** causes lesions in the mouth and throat, respiratory infections, hand-foot-and-mouth disease, viral meningitis, and acute hemorrhagic conjunctivitis. **Coxsackie B virus** causes myocarditis and pericardial infections, which may be fatal in newborns. In addition, coxsackie B viruses cause pleurodynia and viral meningitis, and may be a cause of diabetes mellitus.

6. So-called orphan viruses are initially unassociated with a specific disease.

7. **Echoviruses** (enteric cytopathic human orphan viruses) cause viral meningitis and colds.

8. **Hepatitis A virus** is a noncytolytic picornavirus that infects liver cells but is rarely fatal.

9. **Caliciviruses** and **astroviruses** are small viruses that enter through the digestive system, multiply in the cells of the intestinal tract, and cause gastroenteritis and diarrhea. **Noroviruses** are representative caliciviruses.

10. **Hepatitis E virus** causes **hepatitis E,** which is fatal to about 20% of infected, pregnant women.

## Enveloped, Positive ssRNA Viruses: *Togaviridae, Flaviviridae,* and *Coronaviridae*

1. Flaviviruses and most togaviruses are **arboviruses** (viruses transmitted by arthropods) and are enveloped, icosahedral, positive, ssRNA viruses that cause flulike symptoms, encephalitis, dengue, and yellow fever.

2. Various viruses, most transmitted via mosquito vectors, cause zoonoses—diseases of animals that are spread to humans. Those caused by togaviruses are **Eastern equine encephalitis (EEE), Western equine encephalitis (WEE),** and **Venezuelan equine encephalitis (VEE).** A flavivirus causes West Nile encephalitis. All these may be fatal in humans.

3. **Dengue** and **dengue hemorrhagic fever** are endemic diseases in South America caused by flaviviruses and carried by the *Aedes* mosquito.

4. **Yellow fever,** which is contracted through the bite of a mosquito carrying a flavivirus, results in internal hemorrhaging and damage to liver, kidneys, and heart.

5. *Rubivirus,* a togavirus that is not transmitted by an arthropod vector, causes **rubella,** commonly known as "German measles" or "three-day measles." It can cause serious birth defects if the virus crosses the placenta into a fetus.

6. **Hepatitis C virus (HCV),** caused by a flavivirus and transmitted via the fecal-oral route, is a disease that often results in serious liver damage.

7. **Coronaviruses** have a corona-like envelope and cause colds as well as gastroenteritis in children. A newly discovered coronavirus causes **severe acute respiratory syndrome (SARS).**

## Enveloped, Positive ssRNA Viruses with Reverse Transcriptase: *Retroviridae*

1. **Retroviruses** have **reverse transcriptase** and **integrase** enzymes. The first allows retroviruses to make dsDNA from RNA templates; the latter allows them to integrate into a host cell's chromosomes.

2. **Human T-lymphotropic viruses** are oncogenic retroviruses associated with cancer of lymphocytes. HTLV-1 causes adult acute T-cell lymphocytic leukemia; HTLV-2 causes hairy cell leukemia. Sexual intercourse, blood transfusion, and contaminated needles transmit them.

3. **Acquired immunodeficiency syndrome (AIDS)** is a condition marked by the presence of antibodies against **HIV** in conjunction with certain opportunistic infections. A **syndrome** is a complex of signs and symptoms with a common cause.

4. **Human immunodeficiency viruses (HIV-1** or **HIV-2)** destroy the immune system. HIV is characterized by glycoproteins such as **gp120** and **gp41,** which enable attachment, antigenic variability,

and formation of **syncytia** (fused cells). The destruction of the immune system results in vulnerability to any infection.

5. HIV affects helper T cells, macrophages, and dendritic cells. Using gp120, HIV fuses to a cell, uncoats, enters the cell, and transcribes dsDNA to become a **provirus,** which inserts into a cellular chromosome. After HIV is replicated and released, an internal viral enzyme, **protease,** makes HIV virulent. HIV is spread primarily through contact with an infected individual's secretions or blood.

6. **Highly active antiretroviral therapy (HAART)** is a combination of antiviral drugs for the treatment of AIDS.

## Enveloped, Unsegmented, Negative ssRNA Viruses: *Paramyxoviridae, Rhabdoviridae,* and *Filoviridae*

1. Paramyxoviruses can cause infected cells to fuse together into giant, multinucleate syncytia. One virus causes **measles** ("rubeola" or "red measles"), recognized by **Koplik's spots** in the mouth followed by lesions on the head and trunk. Complications of measles include **subacute sclerosing panencephalitis (SSPE),** a progressive fatal disease of the central nervous system. Vaccination is effective and eradication is possible.

2. **Parainfluenza** viruses usually cause mild coldlike diseases, including **croup.** There is no effective vaccine.

3. **Mumps** virus is a paramyxovirus that causes painfully enlarged parotid glands. Mumps vaccine is very effective, and eradication is possible.

4. **Respiratory syncytial virus (RSV)** is a paramyxovirus that affects the lungs and can be fatal in infants and young children, while in older children and adults the symptoms are similar to those of a cold.

5. **Rabies** is caused by a rhabdovirus—a bullet-shaped virus with glycoprotein spikes—that attaches to muscle cells, replicates, moves into nerve cells and eventually causes brain degeneration. Infection usually results from bites by infected mammals. Symptoms include pain in swallowing (which results in **hydrophobia**), seizures, paralysis, and death. Rabies may be identified by aggregates of virions called **Negri bodies** in the brain of an affected mammal. Human and animal vaccines are effective.

6. **Marburg virus** and **Ebola virus** are filamentous viruses that cause hemorrhagic fever. There is no known treatment or prevention for hemorrhagic fever, though a vaccine has been effective in preventing disease in monkeys.

## Enveloped, Segmented, Negative ssRNA Viruses: *Orthomyxoviridae, Bunyaviridae,* and *Arenaviridae*

1. A **segmented genome** consists of more than one molecule of nucleic acid. The term usually refers to viruses, as the genomes of most of the known viral families are not segmented.

2. **Influenza (flu)** is caused by type A or B orthomyxoviruses, which enter lung cells by means of **hemagglutinin (HA)** and **neuraminidase (NA)** glycoprotein spikes. Gene mutations for HA and NA account for continual formation of new variants of flu viruses. **Antigenic drift** occurs every 2 or 3 years when a single

strain mutates within a local population. **Antigenic shift** of influenza A virus occurs about every 10 years and results in reassortment of genomes from different strains of animal and human viruses infecting a common cell. Vaccines for the flu in any given flu season are prepared against newly identified variants.

3. **Bunyaviruses,** with three −ssRNA molecules as a genome, are zoonotic pathogens. They are usually arboviruses. Each bunyavirus has a specific target and may cause encephalitis, fever, rash, or death.

4. **Hantaviruses** are bunyaviruses that are transmitted to humans via inhalation of virions in dried mouse urine. They cause *Hantavirus* **pulmonary syndrome.**

5. **Arenaviruses** are segmented −ssRNA viruses with apparently nonfunctional ribosomes. They cause **Lassa, Junin,** and **Machupo**

hemorrhagic fevers; **lymphocytic choriomeningitis (LCM);** and hepatitis D.

6. **Hepatitis D virus,** also known as delta agent, is a **satellite virus;** that is, it requires proteins coded by another virus (in this case hepatitis B virus) to complete its replication cycle.

## Naked, Segmented, dsRNA Viruses: *Reoviridae*

1. The **reoviruses** are unique in having double-stranded RNA as a genome. They include *Rotavirus,* which has glycoprotein spikes for attachment and causes potentially fatal infantile gastroenteritis, and *Coltivirus,* which causes **Colorado tick fever.**

# Questions for Review
*Answers to the Questions for Review (except for Short Answer questions) appear at the end of this chapter.*

## Multiple Choice

1. A segmented genome is one that
   a. has more than one strand of nucleic acid.
   b. has double-stranded RNA.
   c. has both RNA and DNA strands.
   d. has both +ssRNA and −ssRNA molecules.

2. What do viruses in the families *Picornaviridae, Caliciviridae, Astroviridae, Coronaviridae, Togaviridae, Flaviviridae,* and *Retroviridae* have in common?
   a. They are arboviruses.
   b. They are nonpathogenic.
   c. They have positive single-stranded RNA genomes.
   d. They have negative single-stranded RNA genomes.

3. The smallest animal viruses are in the family
   a. *Caliciviridae.*          c. *Togaviridae.*
   b. *Astroviridae.*          d. *Picornaviridae.*

4. Which of the following viruses cause most colds?
   a. rhinoviruses          c. pneumoviruses
   b. parainfluenza viruses          d. bunyaviruses

5. Arboviruses are
   a. zoonotic pathogens.
   b. deactivated viruses used in vaccines.
   c. viruses that are transmitted to humans via the bite of an arthropod.
   d. found in arbors.

6. Negri bodies are associated with which of the following?
   a. Marburg virus          c. coltivirus
   b. hantavirus          d. rabies virus

7. If mosquitoes were eradicated from an area, which of the following diseases would be most affected?
   a. mumps
   b. hantavirus pulmonary syndrome
   c. hepatitis E
   d. breakbone fever

8. Koplik's spots are oral lesions associated with
   a. mumps.          c. flu.
   b. measles.          d. colds.

9. Which of the following is an accurate statement concerning zoonoses?
   a. They are animal diseases that spread to humans.
   b. They are diseases specifically transmitted by mosquitoes and ticks.
   c. They are mucus-borne viruses, which are transmitted in the droplets of moisture in a sneeze or cough.
   d. They are diseases that can be transmitted from humans to an animal population.

10. A horror movie portrays victims of biological warfare with uncontrolled bleeding from the eyes, mouth, nose, ears, and anus. What actual virus causes these symptoms?
    a. Ebola virus          c. hantavirus
    b. bunyavirus          d. human immunodeficiency virus

11. Reoviruses, such as rotaviruses and coltiviruses, are unique in
    a. being naked.
    b. having double-stranded RNA.
    c. being both arboviruses and zoonotic.
    d. having protein spikes.

## Matching

Match the diseases on the left with the infecting virus on the right.

____ Myocarditis          A. Rhabdoviridae

____ Colorado tick fever          B. Paramyxoviridae

____ Rabies          C. Reoviridae

____ Influenza          D. Coronaviridae

____ Dengue fever          E. Togaviridae

____ German measles          F. Flaviviridae

____ Acute gastroenteritis          G. Orthomyxoviridae

____ Ebola virus          H. Orphan virus

____ RSV          I. Caliciviridae

____ Western equine encephalitis          J. Filoviridae

____ No known disease          K. Picornaviridae

## True/False

1. ____ A single virion is sufficient to cause a cold.

2. ____ All infections of polio are crippling.

3. ____ Postpolio syndrome is due to latent polioviruses that become active 30–40 years after the initial infection.

4. ____ Because the oral polio vaccine contains live attenuated viruses, mutations of these viruses can cause polio.

5. ____ A typical host for a togavirus is a horse.

## Labeling

Label the steps in retroviral replication shown for HIV.

Kenneth Probst/Precision Graphics

## Short Answer

1. Why are humans considered "dead-end" hosts for many arboviruses?

2. Young Luis has skin lesions. His mother knows from microbiology class that five childhood diseases can produce spots. Name those five diseases and the viruses that cause each. List some questions to ask to determine which of these viruses Luis has.

3. The patient in room 519 exhibits yellowing skin and eyes, and it is suspected among the nursing staff that the diagnosis will be some kind of viral hepatitis. Make a chart of five kinds of hepatitis mentioned in this chapter, the infecting pathogen, how the patient might have become infected, and the relative degree of seriousness.

4. Why is AIDS more accurately termed a "syndrome" instead of a "disease"?

5. Consider the viruses you studied in this chapter. Which three would you rank as the deadliest?

6. Support or refute the following statement: "Rubeola is common and of little concern as a childhood disease."

7. Translate the following identification label on a vial of influenza virus: B/Kuwait/6/10 (H1N3).

8. Polio and smallpox have been eliminated as natural threats to human health in the United States. (Some risk from bioterrorism remains.) You have considered the features of these diseases that allowed them to be eliminated. From your studies of other viruses, what other viral diseases are candidates for elimination? Why hasn't AIDS been eliminated?

9. Several laboratory tests are used to identify viruses. From your study of this chapter alone, which tests would you surmise are the most common?

10. Why are there more cases of West Nile virus encephalitis in summer than in winter of every year?

11. Compare influenzavirus A 2009 (H1N1) to the 1918–1919 pandemic influenzavirus.

# Concept Mapping

Using the following terms, draw a concept map that describes polioviruses. Or, complete this concept map online by going to the Study Area at www.masteringmicrobiology.com.

<2% of cases
2% of cases
5% of cases
90% of cases
Asymptomatic infection
Bulbar poliomyelitis

Central nervous system
Enteroviruses
Fecal-oral route
Inactivated polio vaccine
  (IPV)
Intestine

Limb paralysis
Minor polio
Nonparalytic polio
Oral polio vaccine (OPV)
Paralytic polio
Pharynx

Respiratory paralysis
Sabin vaccine
Salk vaccine
Three serotypes

# Critical Thinking

1. Early presented the use of dichotomous keys to identify microorganisms. Design a key for the RNA viruses discussed in this chapter.

2. A 20-year-old man is brought to a South Carolina hospital's emergency room suffering from seizures, disorientation, hallucinations, and an inordinate fear of water. His family members report that he had suffered with fever and headache for several days. The patient had been bitten by a dog approximately 12 days before admission. What disease does the patient have? Will a vaccine be an effective treatment? If the dog is found to be disease free, what wild animals are the likely source of infection in South Carolina? What treatment should the patient's family, coworkers, friends, and caregivers receive?

3. How did coltiviruses get their name?

4. Retroviruses such as HIV use RNA as a primer for DNA synthesis. Why is a primer necessary?

5. In 2003, alligator farms reported significant loss of animals to West Nile virus. Since alligator hide is generally too thick for mosquitoes to feed, how can you explain the alligators' infections?

Access more review material online in the Study Area at **www.masteringmicrobiology.com.** There, you'll find
- **Concept Mapping Activities**
- **Flashcards**
- **Quizzes**

and more to help you succeed.

# Answers

Answers to multiple-choice, fill-in-blank, labeling, matching, and true/false questions are listed here. Answers for Short Answer and Critical Thinking questions are available for instructors only in the Instructor's Manual that accompanies this text.

**Multiple Choice**
1. a; 2. c; 3. d; 4. a; 5. c; 6. d; 7. d; 8. b; 9. a; 10. a; 11.b

**Matching**
K Myocarditis; C Colorado tick fever; A Rabies; G Influenza; F Dengue fever; D German measles; I Acute gastroenteritis; J Ebola virus; B RSV; E Western equine encephalitis; H No known disease

**True/False**
1. True; 2. False; 3. False; 4. True; 5. True

**Labeling**
See Figure 19.

# Index

548

Methylprednisolone, 247-248
Metrifonate, 110
metronidazole, 99, 107, 112, 300, 348, 413-414
  toxicity of, 99
Metronidazole (flagyl), 99
Mexico, 22, 138, 141, 321, 378, 386-387, 398, 518, 521
MfpA protein, 102
MHC proteins, 192-193, 206, 246
  class I, 192-193, 206, 246
  class II, 192-193, 206, 246
mice, 122, 207, 223, 300-301, 319, 332, 335, 357, 359, 367, 369, 382, 419, 455, 458, 464
Microbes, 3, 11, 14, 21-22, 46, 66, 80, 83, 88-89, 97, 99-102, 112-113, 118-124, 127, 129, 132, 146-147, 151, 153-154, 156, 158, 160-161, 171, 173, 178-179, 181-182, 185, 212-213, 215, 229, 257, 261-268, 270-272, 274, 279, 282, 294-295, 298, 306, 318, 320, 339, 344, 355, 362, 370, 376, 437-438, 440, 444, 455, 481, 483, 522
  classification of, 147, 264-265, 294
  indigenous, 120
  structure of, 14, 99, 154, 182, 294
Microbial antagonism, 96-97, 100, 120, 146, 155, 171, 268
  in innate immunity, 155
  normal microbiota and, 100, 155, 171
Microbial competition, 120
Microbial growth, 85-115
  control of, 86, 93
  defined, 93
Microbial metabolism, 43-84
  amino acid biosynthesis, 75
  carbohydrate biosynthesis, 74
  carbohydrate catabolism, 53, 57, 66, 80, 82-83
  chemical reactions underlying, 45, 79
  enzymes in, 45, 47, 51, 63, 81
  lipid biosynthesis, 75
  lipid catabolism, 68
  nucleotide biosynthesis, 77
  photosynthesis and, 73
  protein catabolism, 68-69
Microbiology, 1, 3-4, 40, 43, 66, 85, 117, 135, 151, 177, 209, 233, 255, 282, 285, 321, 353, 379, 392, 405, 435, 463-464, 489, 527
  chemistry of, 4
  clinical, 135, 392
  definition, 3
  environmental, 3-4
  food, 117, 135
  general, 151, 285, 392, 464
  history, 321, 392, 464
  history of, 464
  hospital, 117, 135, 321
  medical, 3
  public health, 463
  soil, 282
Microcephaly, 125, 418, 475, 500
Micrococcus, 121, 259
Micrococcus luteus, 259
Microfilament, 30
Microfilaments, 30, 38
  plant cell, 38
Microglia, 158, 172-173, 192, 506
Micrographs, 9, 522
Micromonospora, 88, 105
Micromonospora purpurea, 88
Microorganisms, 2, 4, 22, 28, 44-46, 51, 59, 66-68, 74, 80, 83, 86-88, 101, 112-113, 117-118, 120, 125, 127, 130, 135, 137, 144, 146, 148, 152-157, 160-161, 171-172, 174, 177, 181, 201, 204, 230, 248, 252, 256, 262, 278, 282, 294, 296-297, 326, 337, 421, 528
  agriculture, 146
  beneficial, 22, 46, 101, 118, 153
  fastidious, 296, 337
  importance, 45, 230, 278
  in nature, 46, 282
  nutritional requirements, 296
Microscope, 10, 158, 169, 178, 223-224, 228, 280-281, 307, 379, 437
  fluorescence, 223-224
  light, 10, 158, 223, 280-281
Microscopes, 464
Microscopy, 4, 11, 158, 363, 378, 414, 416, 428-429, 439
  electron, 4, 158, 439
  light, 158, 363, 429, 439

Microsporidia, 202
Microsporidiosis, 202
Microsporidium, 202
Microsporum, 122, 379, 395-396, 401
Microsporum gypseum, 396
Microtubule, 30, 110-111, 382
Microtubules, 28-31, 36, 38-40
  of centrioles, 30
  plant cell, 38
  structure and function of, 28
  triplets of, 28, 30-31, 38
  tubulin, 28, 30, 39-40
Microvilli, 491
Middle ear, 294-295, 317
  infections, 294-295, 317
  otitis media, 295, 317
Migration, 167-168, 171, 295, 310, 406, 424, 426, 431
Milk, 76, 83, 101, 123, 133-135, 146, 187-188, 203-206, 253, 268, 276, 293, 306, 312, 330, 333, 347, 349-350, 372, 376, 399, 475, 508, 510
  pasteurization, 146
  pasteurization of, 146
  safety of, 146
Mimicry, 248, 252
  molecular, 248, 252
MinD, 45, 59, 118, 144, 165, 197, 473-474
MinE, 274
Minerals, 47
Minimum bactericidal concentration (MBC) test, 97-98, 113
Minimum inhibitory concentration (MIC), 97-98, 113
Minimum inhibitory concentration (MIC) test, 97-98
Minor polio, 493, 528
Miscarriage, 241, 306
Mites, 119, 136, 140, 153, 234, 236-237, 254, 345, 357-358, 360, 375, 400, 405, 430-431, 497
  dust, 140, 153, 234, 236-237, 254, 345, 400
Mitochondria, 30, 32-33, 35-36, 38-39, 57, 59-61, 63, 68, 83, 90, 110, 439
  chemiosmosis in, 57
  cristae, 32, 35, 39, 59
  DNA, 32-33, 35-36, 38-39, 63, 110
  enzymes in, 32, 63, 90
  features of, 36
  fungal cell, 38, 90
  plant cell, 38
  proteins, 30, 33, 36, 38-39, 59, 68, 90, 110, 439
  ribosomes, 32-33, 35-36, 38-39, 90
  structure, 30, 32-33, 35-36, 38-39, 90, 110, 439
Mitochondrial DNA, 161
Mitochondrial matrix, 73
Mitochondrial membranes, 59, 63
Mitochondrial ribosomes, 33
Mitochondrion, 6, 30, 32-34, 40, 42, 61, 73
Mitosis, 30-31, 35, 38, 109, 115, 247, 382
  fungal, 30, 38, 109, 382
  in animal cells, 31, 35
  term, 382
Mitosis (nuclear division), 30-31
MMR vaccine, 511
Models, 50, 243
Modified live vaccines, 212
Modified Thayer-Martin medium, 322
Mold, 87, 236, 238, 242, 253, 267, 381, 393, 399-400, 402, 454
Molds, 109, 234
Molecular biology, 503
  central dogma of, 503
Molecular formula, 48
Molecular mass, 181
Molecular mimicry, 248, 252
molecular weight, 22, 504
Molecule, 3, 15, 20, 22-23, 25, 32, 37-38, 40, 46-50, 53-57, 59-61, 63, 65-68, 71, 73-74, 76, 79-84, 91, 102-103, 107-108, 113, 125, 162-163, 181-185, 187, 192-193, 196, 198, 204, 206, 218-220, 235, 241, 257, 295, 308, 382, 438, 447-448, 450-451, 453, 456-457, 467, 476, 480-481, 491, 503-504, 507, 517, 525
Molecules, 4, 8, 12, 14-17, 19-20, 22-24, 26, 28, 31-32, 37-38, 40, 45-48, 50, 52-57, 59-63, 65-71, 73-76, 79-84, 87-88, 90, 92-93, 95, 102-106, 109, 112, 125, 130, 156, 162-163, 165-168, 172, 179-182, 184-185, 187-189, 192-194, 196, 199, 201, 203-207, 212-214, 217, 219-220, 222-225, 234-236, 239-243, 246-247, 249, 251, 257-258, 274, 287, 301,

305, 309, 322, 337, 342, 355, 369, 391, 437-438, 446-450, 457-460, 491, 503, 506-507, 510, 518-524, 526
  chemical bonds and, 47, 68
  diffusion, 16-17, 19-20, 26, 37, 40, 62, 225
  hydrogen bonds, 184
  hydrogen bonds and, 184
  inorganic, 19, 47-48, 56, 59-60, 66, 70, 73, 80-82
  macromolecules, 45-46, 48, 53, 74, 79, 181
  organic, 45, 47-48, 53, 55, 59-60, 65-67, 69, 73, 75, 79-82, 88, 274, 342, 437
  organic molecules, 48, 66-67, 69, 73, 75, 82, 88, 342, 437
  polar, 37
Mollicutes, 269, 306
Molluscipoxvirus, 466, 484
Molluscum contagiosum, 464, 466, 484, 486-487
Monkeypox, 217, 464, 466-467, 484-485
Monkeys, 122, 241, 251, 363, 464, 466-467, 485, 502, 509, 517, 525
Monobactam, 91, 104
Monobactams, 90, 104, 112
Monoclonal antibodies, 218, 224, 228-229, 247-248, 476
  production of, 218, 247-248
Monoclonal antibody, 218, 247
  hybridomas, 218
  production, 218, 247
Monocytes, 158-159, 163, 168, 172-175, 411, 506
Monomer, 187-188
Monomers, 68
Mononucleosis, 136, 228, 250, 443, 463, 467, 474-476, 484, 486-487
  cytomegalovirus, 443, 475-476, 484, 486-487
Monosaccharides, 14
Montagnier, Luc, 504
Montagu, Mary, 211
Moraxella, 121, 322, 338, 342, 344, 349
Moraxella catarrhalis, 344, 349
Morbidity, 126, 140, 142, 147, 149, 211, 293
Morbidity and Mortality Weekly Report (MMWR), 140
Morbillivirus, 443, 510, 513, 524
Morbillivirus (measles virus), 510
Morganella, 327, 331-332, 337, 348
Morphine, 237
Morphology, 159, 257, 260, 264, 277, 295, 302, 324, 332, 355, 363, 366, 374, 382, 384, 391, 397, 401, 413, 417, 421, 423, 439, 467, 481, 510, 520
  fungal, 382, 391, 397, 401
  of prokaryotic cells, 257
Mortality, 140, 143, 211, 293-294, 296, 299-300, 303, 325, 334, 346, 357-358, 362, 371, 407, 464, 469, 485, 495, 499, 501, 523
  AIDS, 143, 211, 296, 469
mortality rate, 296, 303, 334, 362, 464, 469, 485, 495, 499, 501
Mortality rates, 293, 299, 358
Morula, 357-358, 375
Mosquito, 122, 136, 148-149, 406, 415-417, 428-430, 452, 498-499, 525
  vector, 136, 148-149, 406, 415, 430, 525
Mosquito control, 417, 499
Mosquitoes, 119, 136-137, 140, 146, 345, 405, 415-416, 420, 426, 428-433, 497-499, 502, 520, 526, 528
motility, 7, 9, 25, 36-37, 40, 266, 306, 327, 366
  cyanobacteria, 266
  eukaryotic, 25, 36-37, 40
  gliding, 25, 266
  Listeria, 266, 306
  of spirochetes, 9, 40
  prokaryotes, 7, 25, 36-37, 266, 306
  prokaryotic, 25, 36-37
  protozoa, 37
  spirochetes, 9, 37, 40, 366
Motor cortex, 493
Motor neuron, 300, 303
Motor neurons, 304
Mountains, 355
Mouse, 145, 218, 301, 520, 526
Mouth, 62, 87, 100, 119-121, 124, 134, 147-148, 268, 279, 288, 294, 301-302, 317, 331, 362, 364-365, 374, 390, 393, 412, 421, 423, 426-427, 431, 468-471, 494, 508, 511, 524-526
  normal microbiota of, 120
Movement, 7, 10-11, 14, 16-18, 26-28, 30, 37-39, 47, 66, 81, 92, 104, 114, 122-123, 133, 146-147,

160, 220, 227, 258, 291, 331, 340, 371, 376, 409, 415, 426, 433, 515
  of bacteria, 11, 14, 18, 26, 37-39, 104, 291, 331
  prokaryotic, 26-28, 30, 37-39, 92, 258
  proteins and, 14, 81
Moxifloxacin, 107
mRNA, 90, 92, 105, 109, 163-164, 305, 399, 438, 443, 446, 450-451, 454, 457, 460, 476, 491, 503, 505, 507, 510
MRSA, 100-102, 105, 290, 317, 320
Mucinase, 130
Mucocutaneous leishmaniasis, 412
Mucor, 388, 393, 401, 404
Mucosa, 180-181, 334, 390, 407-408, 413, 419, 431, 492
Mucosa-associated lymphatic tissue (MALT), 180
Mucous membrane, 11, 87, 125, 135, 151, 154, 173, 188, 199, 204, 291, 373, 390, 474, 485, 511, 517
Mucous membranes, 97, 120, 123-124, 134-135, 146, 152-156, 159, 169, 171, 173-174, 178, 187, 192-193, 234, 267, 270, 274, 286, 303, 307, 316-317, 322-323, 337, 339, 343-345, 359, 365, 369, 375, 387, 389-390, 406, 412, 458, 468-469, 477-478, 481, 492, 506, 508, 512, 515
  as portals of entry, 134
  pathogens and, 135, 146, 152, 178
  structure of, 154
Mucus, 87, 130, 134, 147, 151, 153-155, 171-173, 188, 235-236, 295, 307, 319, 323, 340-341, 343, 349, 371, 374-376, 407, 475, 491-492, 513, 518, 526
  cell surface, 188
Multicellular organisms, 4, 26, 380
Multiple resistance, 102
Multiple sclerosis, 129, 249, 252, 476
Multiple sclerosis (MS), 476
  HHV-6 and, 476
Mumps, 143, 145, 210-211, 213, 216-217, 223, 228, 443, 510-513, 524-526
  vaccine against, 211, 213, 512
Mumps vaccine, 513, 525
Mumps virus, 217, 510, 512-513, 525
mumps virus (Rubulavirus), 512
Mupirocin, 88, 92, 106, 112
  mechanism of action of, 92
Murine (endemic) typhus, 360
Murine typhus, 356-357, 375-376
Muscimol, 399
Muscle, 66, 99, 106, 121, 132, 145, 150, 163, 169-170, 173, 190, 235-238, 244, 248, 254, 267-268, 287, 292, 299-301, 303-304, 314, 333, 338, 343, 345, 347, 354, 356-358, 360, 364, 368, 371, 374-375, 385, 392, 409, 418-420, 422, 424, 426, 430, 438, 458, 467-468, 493-494, 506, 511-512, 525
Muscle cells, 244, 267, 314, 409, 506, 525
  animal, 267, 525
Muscle contraction, 235-236, 254, 301, 304
Muscle tissue, 66, 99, 238, 299, 347, 374, 409, 426, 458
Muscles, 192, 202, 235-236, 267, 292, 301, 303-304, 373, 397, 405, 417, 493, 498
Mushroom, 242, 399, 403-404
Mushroom poisoning, 399, 403-404
Mushrooms, 242, 381, 399, 401-402
  poisonous, 381, 399, 402
Mutant, 101, 130, 310, 378
Mutants, 363, 372
Mutation, 49, 107-110, 113-114, 125, 416, 454, 504, 510
  rate, 107, 504, 510
mutation rate, 510
Mutations, 100, 102, 104-109, 111, 162, 186, 212, 252, 456, 458, 492, 504, 506, 518-519, 525, 527
  acquired, 252, 504, 525
  beneficial, 100
  causes of, 518
  effects of, 492, 504
  HIV and, 504, 506
  point, 102, 106, 186
  random, 104-105, 186, 518
  rate of, 100, 504
  types, 102, 212, 456, 504, 518-519
  types of, 102, 212, 456, 504, 518
Mutualism, 118-119, 146, 148
  bacterial, 119, 148
Mycelium, 386

mycetoma, 316, 318, 397-398, 402-404
Mycetomas, 397, 401
  fungal, 397, 401
Mycobacteria, 90, 96, 104-105, 107, 112, 213, 269, 309-310, 313-314, 319
  characteristics, 96, 269, 309
Mycobacterium, 12, 75, 90, 95, 102, 106, 121, 127-128, 135, 195, 217, 219, 223, 244-245, 252-253, 261, 268-269, 280-281, 286, 309-315, 318-320, 325, 504, 509
  M. avium-intracellulare, 309
  M. bovis, 312
  M. leprae, 217, 309, 313
  M. tuberculosis, 95, 102, 245, 252, 309-314
Mycobacterium avium, 314, 318-319
Mycobacterium avium-intracellulare, 314, 318-319
Mycobacterium bovis, 135
Mycobacterium leprae, 95, 128, 269, 313, 318
Mycobacterium tuberculosis, 75, 102, 106, 127, 195, 217, 219, 223, 244-245, 252, 269, 309-310, 312, 318-319, 325, 509
  genome, 75
  resistant strains of, 102
Mycolactone, 314
Mycolic acid, 14, 75, 90, 104-105, 112, 269, 281, 309, 313, 318-319
Mycology, 380, 382, 400
Mycophenolate mofetil, 247-248
Mycoplasma, 14, 106, 228, 267-269, 306-307, 318, 362, 376
Mycoplasma genitalium, 318, 376
Mycoplasma hominis, 318
Mycoplasma pneumoniae, 14, 307, 318, 362
Mycoplasmas, 18, 261, 266-267, 269, 280-281, 286, 305-308, 318-319, 355, 362, 376
  characteristics of, 266, 269, 286, 306, 355, 362
  Mycoplasma genitalium, 318, 376
  Mycoplasma hominis, 318
  Mycoplasma pneumoniae, 307, 318, 362
  other types of, 307
Mycoses, 380-383, 388, 394-398, 400-404
  clinical manifestations of, 381
  diagnosis of, 381-382, 400, 404
  epidemiology of, 380
  infections, 380-383, 388, 394-398, 400-404
  opportunistic, 380-382, 388, 394, 401-404
  pathogenic, 380-383, 388, 394-398, 400-404
  respiratory, 381, 388, 394, 400, 402, 404
  superficial, 381, 394-396, 400-401, 403
  systemic, 381-383, 388, 394, 396, 400-404
  treatment of, 382, 395, 402
Mycoses (fungal diseases), 400
  superficial, 400
  systemic, 400
Mycosis, 380, 389, 403
  superficial, 389, 403
  systemic, 389, 403
Mycotoxicosis, 398-399, 401, 403
Mycotoxin, 398-399
Mycotoxins, 398-399, 401-402
Myelin, 249, 479
Myelomas, 218, 228
Myocarditis, 409, 418, 494-495, 524, 526, 528
Myxobacteria, 261, 273, 277-281
  life cycle, 277-278
Myxospores, 277-278, 280

**N**

N-acetylglucosamine, 12, 37, 41, 90, 274
N-Acetylglucosamine (NAG), 12, 37, 90
N-acetylmuramic acid, 12, 37, 90
N-Acetylmuramic acid (NAM), 12, 37, 90
NADH, 47, 55-63, 65-68, 79-80, 82-84
  in beta-oxidation, 68
  in chemiosmosis, 80
  in glycolysis, 57, 62, 66, 68, 80, 82
  in photosynthesis, 59
  molecule, 47, 55-57, 59-61, 63, 65-68, 79-80, 82-84
NADPH, 47, 63-65, 71-74, 78-79, 81
  in noncyclic photophosphorylation, 72-73, 81
  in photosynthesis, 71
  pentose phosphate pathway, 63-65, 73-74, 78-79, 81
Naegleria, 406, 408, 420, 430-434
Nails, 130, 270, 303, 381-382, 390, 394
Naked virus, 460
Nanoarchaeum, 262
Narrow-spectrum drugs, 96, 113

Nasal, 120, 124, 133, 151, 154-155, 227, 234, 236, 295, 307, 313, 317, 393, 397, 408, 491-492, 501
  bone, 234, 397
  cavity, 120, 124, 154, 492, 501
Nasal cavity, 120, 124, 154, 492, 501
  normal microbiota of, 120
Nasal mucus, 151, 154-155, 492
nasolacrimal ducts, 155
Nasopharyngeal cancer, 474-475, 484
Natural active immunity, 520
Natural killer cells, 161
Natural killer lymphocytes (NK cells), 185
Natural killer (NK) lymphocytes, 158, 172
Natural penicillin, 290
natural penicillins, 104
Naturally acquired active immunity, 202-203, 205-207
Naturally acquired immunity, 202
  active, 202
  passive, 202
Naturally acquired passive immunity, 203, 205-207
Nature, 4, 10-12, 15, 39, 46, 62, 118, 126, 132-133, 147-148, 192, 264, 274, 282, 314, 346, 370, 383, 398, 437, 439, 448, 453, 463, 465, 467, 484, 487, 498, 501, 522
Necator americanus, 427, 429, 431-432
necrosis, 66, 192, 198, 204, 300, 310-311, 347
necrotizing fasciitis, 292-293, 297, 317
Negative control, 226
Negative feedback, 53, 80, 82
Negative taxis, 11
Negative-strand RNA, 450, 460
Negri bodies, 515, 525-526
Neisseria, 11, 42, 60, 121, 125, 157, 160, 217, 224, 259, 273-274, 280, 308, 322-325, 344, 348-349, 504
  diplococci of, 259, 322
  N. gonorrhoeae, 322-325
  N. meningitidis, 322, 324-325
  structure and physiology of, 322
Neisseria gonorrhoeae, 11, 42, 125, 160, 224, 259, 308, 322, 324, 348
  identification, 224
Neisseria meningitidis, 157, 324, 348-349
Nematodes, 110, 119, 421, 426, 429, 431, 438
  key features, 429
  life cycle of, 426
nematodes (roundworms), 429
  Ascaris, 429
  hookworm, 429
Neomycin, 88, 105
  production, 88, 105
  resistance, 105
Neonatal herpes, 469-470, 487
Neonatal meningitis, 329, 332
Neoplasia, 453-454, 460, 477
Nephrons, 292-293
Nerve, 124, 130, 152, 168, 170-171, 212, 235-236, 249, 300-304, 309, 313, 368, 468-472, 479, 484, 493, 514, 525
Nerve cells, 212, 301, 309, 313, 468, 470, 479, 484, 514, 525
Nerve impulse, 301, 304, 493
Nerve impulses, 170-171, 249, 303-304, 479
Nerves, 99, 105, 471, 484
Nervous system, 104, 108, 158, 172-173, 251, 300-301, 303, 316, 325, 337, 343, 346, 348, 357, 369, 385, 387, 392, 410-411, 469, 479, 483, 493, 497, 506, 511, 514, 525, 528
  components of, 158
Nervous systems, 344
Nervous tissue, 248-249, 365, 458
Neuraminidase, 108, 342, 517-518, 520, 525
  influenzavirus, 108, 518, 520
  Pseudomonas aeruginosa, 342
Neuraminidase inhibitors, 108, 520
Neuraminidase (NA), 525
neurological disorders, 515
Neuromuscular junction, 300-301
Neuromuscular junctions, 303
Neuron, 300-301, 303-304
Neurons, 249, 300, 302-304, 483, 514
neurosyphilis, 378
Neurotoxin, 132, 300, 303
Neurotoxins, 130, 299, 301
  clostridial, 299
Neurotransmitter, 110, 267, 301, 303-304, 483
Neurotransmitters, 110, 300, 303
  and disease, 300